ELEMENTS OF GAS TU

McGraw-Hill Series in Aeronautical and Aerospace Engineering

Consulting Editor

***John D. Anderson, Jr.**, University of Maryland*

Anderson: *Computational Fluid Dynamics: The Basics with Applications*
Anderson: *Fundamentals of Aerodynamics*
Anderson: *Hypersonic and High Temperature Gas Dynamics*
Anderson: *Introduction to Flight*
Anderson: *Modern Compressible Flow: With Historical Perspective*
Burton: *Introduction to Dynamic Systems Analysis*
D'Azzo and Houpis: *Linear Control System Analysis and Design*
Donaldson: *Analysis of Aircraft Structures: An Introduction*
Gibson: *Principles of Composite Material Mechanics*
Kane, Likins, and Levinson: *Spacecraft Dynamics*
Katz and Plotkin: *Low-Speed Aerodynamics: From Wing Theory to Panel Methods*
Mattingly: *Elements of Gas Turbine Propulsion*
Nelson: *Flight Stability and Automatic Control*
Peery and Azar: *Aircraft Structures*
Rivello: *Theory and Analysis of Flight Structures*
Schlichting: *Boundary Layer Theory*
White: *Viscous Fluid Flow*
Wiesel: *Spaceflight Dynamics*

McGraw-Hill Series in Mechanical Engineering

Consulting Editors

***Jack P. Holman**, Southern Methodist University*
***John R. Lloyd**, Michigan State University*

Anderson: *Computational Fluid Dynamics: The Basics with Applications*
Anderson: *Modern Compressible Flow: With Historical Perspective*
Arora: *Introduction to Optimum Design*
Bray and Stanley: *Nondestructive Evaluation: A Tool for Design, Manufacturing, and Service*
Burton: *Introduction to Dynamic Systems Analysis*
Culp: *Principles of Energy Conversion*
Dally: *Packaging of Electronic Systems: A Mechanical Engineering Approach*
Dieter: *Engineering Design: A Materials and Processing Approach*
Doebelin: *Engineering Experimentation: Planning, Execution, Reporting*
Driels: *Linear Control Systems Engineering*
Eckert and Drake: *Analysis of Heat and Mass Transfer*
Edwards and McKee: *Fundamentals of Mechanical Component Design*
Gebhart: *Heat Conduction and Mass Diffusion*
Gibson: *Principles of Composite Material Mechanics*
Hamrock: *Fundamentals of Fluid Film Lubrication*
Heywood: *Internal Combustion Engine Fundamentals*
Hinze: *Turbulence*
Holman: *Experimental Methods for Engineers*
Howell and Buckius: *Fundamentals of Engineering Thermodynamics*
Hutton: *Applied Mechanical Vibrations*
Juvinall: *Engineering Considerations of Stress, Strain, and Strength*
Kane and Levinson: *Dynamics: Theory and Applications*
Kays and Crawford: *Convective Heat and Mass Transfer*
Kelly: *Fundamentals of Mechanical Vibrations*
Kimbrell: *Kinematics Analysis and Synthesis*
Kreider and Rabl: *Heating and Cooling of Buildings*
Martin: *Kinematics and Dynamics of Machines*
Mattingly: *Elements of Gas Turbine Propulsion*
Modest: *Radiative Heat Transfer*
Norton: *Design of Machinery*
Phelan: *Fundamentals of Mechanical Design*
Raven: *Automatic Control Engineering*
Reddy: *An Introduction to the Finite Element Method*
Rosenberg and Karnopp: *Introduction to Physical Systems Dynamics*
Schlichting: *Boundary-Layer Theory*
Shames: *Mechanics of Fluids*
Sherman: *Viscous Flow*
Shigley: *Kinematic Analysis of Mechanisms*
Shigley and Mischke: *Mechanical Engineering Design*
Shigley and Uicker: *Theory of Machines and Mechanisms*
Stiffler: *Design with Microprocessors for Mechanical Engineers*
Stoecker and Jones: *Refrigeration and Air Conditioning*
Turns: *An Introduction to Combustion: Concepts and Applications*
Ullman: *The Mechanical Design Process*
Vanderplaats: *Numerical Optimization: Techniques for Engineering Design, with Applications*
Wark: *Advanced Thermodynamics for Engineers*
White: *Viscous Fluid Flow*
Zeid: *CAD/CAM Theory and Practice*

ELEMENTS OF GAS TURBINE PROPULSION

Jack D. Mattingly

Department of Mechanical and Manufacturing Engineering
Seattle University

With a Foreword By
Hans von Ohain

McGraw-Hill, Inc.

New York St. Louis San Francisco Auckland Bogotá Caracas
Lisbon London Madrid Mexico City Milan Montreal
New Delhi San Juan Singapore Sydney Tokyo Toronto

Diskette to accompany this text is available separately from your nearest McGraw-Hill office or write to:

McGraw-Hill Book Co
60 Tuas Basin Link
Singapore 638775

or fax (65) 862 3354

When ordering, please quote part number **0-07-114521-D**

ELEMENTS OF GAS TURBINE PROPULSION
International Editions 1996

2 3 4 5 6 7 8 9 0 BJE FC 9 8 7

This book was set in Times Roman.
The editors were John J. Corrigan and James W. Bradley;
the production supervisor was Leroy A. Young.
The cover was designed by Merrill Haber.
Drawings were done by ECL Art.

Library of Congress Cataloging-in-Publication Data

Mattingly, Jack D.
Elements of gas turbine propulsion / Jack D. Mattingly; with a foreword by Hans von Ohain.
p. cm. – (McGraw-Hill series in mechanical engineering)
(McGraw-Hill series in aeronautical and aerospace engineering)
Includes bibliographical references and index.
ISBN 0-07-912196-9 (set)
1. Airplanes–Jet propulsion. I. Title. II. Series.
III. Series: McGraw-Hill series in aeronautical and aerospace engineering.
TL709.M38 1996
629.134'353–dc20 95-897

When ordering this title, use ISBN 0-07-114521-4

Printed in Singapore

ABOUT THE AUTHOR

Jack D. Mattingly received his B.S. and M.S. in Mechanical Engineering from the University of Notre Dame, and his Ph.D. in Aeronautics and Astronautics at the University of Washington. While studying for his doctorate under Gordon C. Oates, he pioneered research in the mixing of coannular swirling flows and developed a major new test facility. During his 28 years of experience in analysis and design of propulsion and thermodynamic systems, he has developed aerothermodynamic cycle analysis models and created engineering software for air-breathing propulsion systems. Dr. Mattingly has more than 23 years of experience in Engineering Education, previously as a senior member of the Department of Aeronautics at the United States Air Force Academy, where he established a top undergraduate propulsion program. He retired from active duty with the U.S. Air Force in 1989 and joined the faculty of Seattle University. In addition, he has taught and done research in propulsion and thermal energy systems at the Aeropropulsion and Power Laboratory, Air Force Institute of Technology, University of Washington, University of Notre Dame, University of Wisconsin, and IBM Corp. He was also founder of the AIAA/Air Breathing Propulsion Team Aircraft Engine Design Competition for undergraduate students. Among his many distinguished teaching awards is Outstanding Educator for 1992 from Seattle University. Having published more than 20 technical papers, articles, and textbooks in his field, Dr. Mattingly was the principal author of *Aircraft Engine Design* (1987), an unprecedented conceptual design textbook for air breathing engines. He is currently Chair, Department of Mechanical and Manufacturing Engineering at Seattle University.

I have been blessed to share my life with Sheila, my best friend and wife. She has been my inspiration and helper, and the one who sacrificed the most to make this work possible. I dedicate this book and accompanying software to Sheila.

I would like to share with all the following passage I received from a very close friend over 18 years ago. This passage provides guidance and focus to my life. I hope it can be as much help to you.

FABRIC OF LIFE

I want to say something to all of you
Who have become a part
Of the fabric of my life
The color and texture
Which you have brought into
My being
Have become a song
And I want to sing it forever.
There is an energy in us
Which makes things happen
When the paths of other persons
Touch ours
And we have to be there
And let it happen.
When the time of our particular sunset comes
Our thing, our accomplishment
Won't really matter
A great deal.
But the clarity and care
With which we have loved others
Will speak with vitality
Of the great gift of life
We have been for each other.

Anonymous

CONTENTS

FOREWORD

BACKGROUND

The first flight of the Wright brothers in December 1903 marked the beginning of the magnificent evolution of *human-controlled, powered flight.* The driving forces of this evolution are the ever-growing demands for improvements in

- Flight performance (i.e., greater flight speed, altitude, and range and better maneuverability)
- Cost (i.e., better fuel economy, lower cost of production and maintenance, increased lifetime)
- Adverse environmental effects (i.e., noise and harmful exhaust gas effects)
- Safety, reliability, and endurance
- Controls and navigation

These strong demands continuously furthered the efforts of advancing the aircraft system.

The tight interdependency between the performance characteristics of aerovehicle and aeropropulsion systems plays a very important role in this evolution. Therefore, to gain better insight into the evolution of the aeropropulsion system, one has to be aware of the challenges and advancements of aerovehicle technology.

The Aerovehicle

A brief review of the evolution of the aerovehicle will be given first. One can observe a continuous trend toward stronger and lighter airframe designs, structures, and materials—from wood and fabric to all-metal structures; to lighter, stronger, and more heat-resistant materials; and finally to a growing use of strong and light composite materials. At the same time, the aerodynamic quality of the aerovehicle is being continuously improved. To see this development in proper historical perspective, let us keep in mind the following information.

In the early years of the 20th century, the science of aerodynamics was in its infancy. Specifically, the aerodynamic lift was not scientifically well understood. Joukowski and Kutta's model of lift by circulation around the wing and Prandtl's boundary-layer and turbulence theories were in their incipient stages. Therefore, the early pioneers could not benefit from existent scientific knowledge in aerodynamics and had to conduct their own fundamental investigations.

The most desirable major aerodynamic characteristics of the aerovehicle are a low *drag coefficient* as well as a high *lift/drag ratio* L/D for cruise conditions, and a high *maximum lift coefficient* for landing. In Fig. 1, one can see that the world's first successful glider vehicle by Lilienthal, in the early 1890s, had an L/D of about 5. In comparison, birds have an L/D ranging from about 5 to 20. The Wright brothers' first human-controlled, powered aircraft had an L/D of about 7.5. As the L/D values increased over the years, sailplanes advanced most rapidly and now are attaining the enormously high values of about 50 and greater. This was achieved by employing ultrahigh wing aspect ratios and aerodynamic profiles especially tailored for the low operational Reynolds and Mach numbers. In the late 1940s, subsonic transport aircraft advanced to L/D values of about 20 by continuously improving the

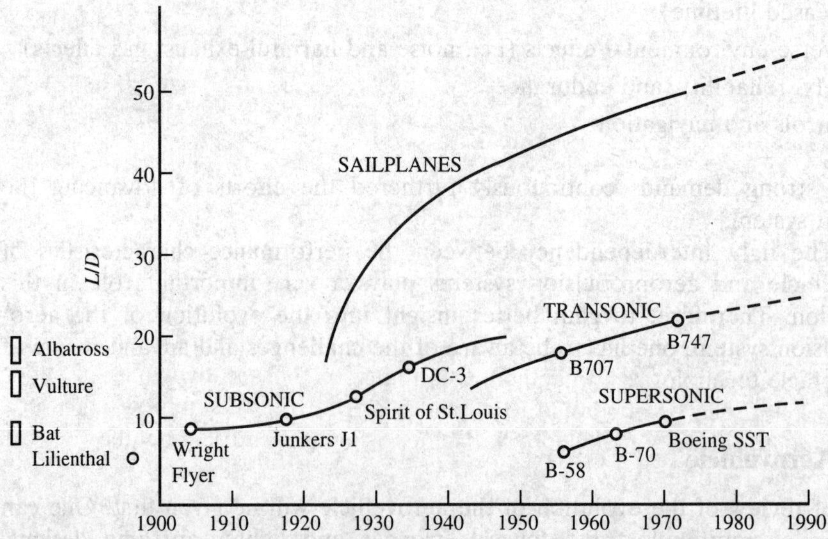

FIGURE 1
Progress in lift/drag ratio L/D.

aerodynamic shapes, employing advanced profiles, achieving extremely smooth and accurate surfaces, and incorporating inventions such as the engine cowl and the retractable landing gear.

The continuous increase in flight speed required a corresponding reduction of the *landing speed/cruise speed* ratio. This was accomplished by innovative wing structures incorporating wingslots and wing flaps which, during the landing process, enlarged the wing area and increased significantly the lift coefficient. Today, the arrowhead-shaped wing contributes to a high lift for landing (vortex lift). Also, in the 1940s, work began to extend the high L/D value from the subsonic to the transonic flight speed regime by employing the swept-back wing and later, in 1952, the area rule of Whitcomb to reduce *transonic drag rise.* Dr Theodore von Karman describes in his memoirs, *The Wind and Beyond* (Ref. 1 at the end of the Foreword), how the *swept-back wing* or simply *swept wing* for transonic and supersonic flight came into existence:

> The fifth Volta Congress in Rome, 1935, was the first serious international scientific congress devoted to the possibilities of supersonic flight. I was one of those who had received a formal invitation to give a paper at the conference from Italy's great Gugliemo Marconi, inventor of the wireless telegraph. All of the world's leading aerodynamicists were invited.
>
> This meeting was historic because it marked the beginning of the supersonic age. It was the beginning in the sense that the conference opened the door to supersonics as a meaningful study in connection with supersonic flight, and, secondly, because most developments in supersonics occurred rapidly from then on, culminating in 1946—a mere 11 years later—in Captain Charles Yeager's piercing the sound barrier with the X-1 plane in level flight. In terms of future aircraft development, the most significant paper at the conference proved to be one given by a young man, Dr. Adolf Busemann of Germany, by first publicly suggesting the swept-back wing and showing how its properties might solve many aerodynamic problems at speeds just below and above the speed of sound.

Through these investigations, the myth that sonic speed is the fundamental limit of aircraft flight velocity, the *sound barrier,* was overcome.

In the late 1960s, the Boeing 747 with swept-back wings had, in transonic cruise speed, an L/D value of nearly 20. In the supersonic flight speed regime, L/D values improved from 5 in the mid-1950s (such as L/D values of the B-58 Hustler and later of the Concorde) to a possible L/D value of 10 and greater in the 1990s. This great improvement possibility in the aerodynamics of supersonic aircraft can be attributed to applications of artificial stability, to the area rule, and to advanced wing profile shapes which extend laminar flow over a larger wing portion.

The hypersonic speed regime is not fully explored. First, emphasis was placed on winged reentry vehicles and lifting bodies where a high L/D value was not of greatest importance. Later investigations have shown that the L/D values can be greatly improved. For example, the maximum L/D for a "wave rider" is about 6 (Ref. 2). Such investigations are of importance for hypersonic programs.

The Aeropropulsion System

At the beginning of this century, steam and internal combustion engines were in existence but were far too heavy for flight application. The Wright brothers recognized the great future potential of the internal combustion engine and developed both a relatively lightweight engine suitable for flight application and an efficient propeller. Fig. 2 shows the progress of the propulsion systems over the years. The Wright brothers' first aeropropulsion system had a shaft power of 12 hp, and its power/weight ratio (ratio of power output to total propulsion system weight, including propeller and transmission) was about 0.05 hp/lb. Through the subsequent four decades of evolution, the overall efficiency and the power/weight ratio improved substantially, the latter by more than one order magnitude to about 0.8 hp/lb. This great improvement was achieved by engine design structures and materials, advanced fuel injection, advanced aerodynamic shapes of the propeller blades, variable-pitch propellers, and engine superchargers. The overall efficiency (engine and propeller) reached about 28 percent. The power output of the largest engine amounted to about 5000 hp.

In the late 1930s and early 1940s, the turbojet engine came into existence. This new propulsion system was immediately superior to the reciprocating engine with respect to the power/weight ratio (by about a factor of 3);

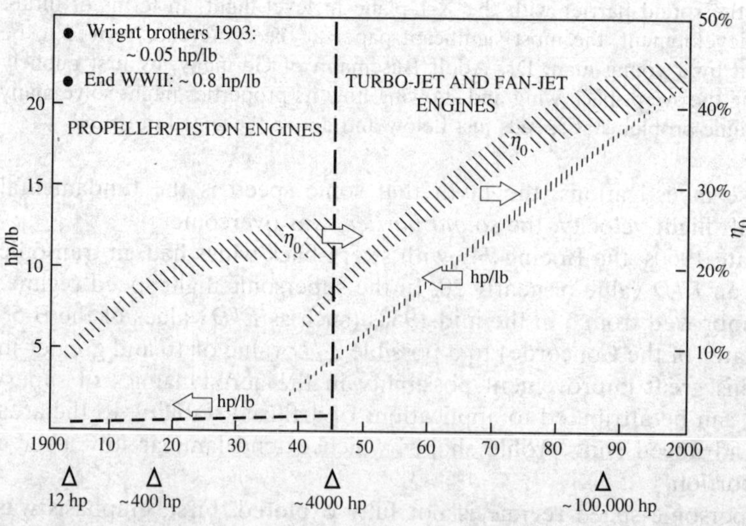

FIGURE 2
Trends of power per weight (hp/lb) and overall efficiency (η_O) of aeropropulsion systems from 1900 to 2000.

however, its overall efficiency was initially much lower than that of the reciprocating engine. As can be seen from Fig. 2, progress was rapid. In less than four decades, the power/weight ratio increased more than 10-fold, and the overall efficiency exceeded that of a diesel propulsion system. The power output of today's largest gas turbine engines reaches nearly 100,000 equivalent hp.

Impact Upon the Total Aircraft Performance

The previously-described truly gigantic advancements of stronger and lighter structures and greater aerodynamic quality in aerovehicles and greatly advanced overall efficiency and enormously increased power output/weight ratios in aeropropulsion systems had a tremendous impact upon flight performance, such as on flight range, economy, maneuverability, flight speed, and altitude. The increase in flight speed over the years is shown in Fig. 3. The Wright brothers began with the first human-controlled, powered flight in 1903; they continued to improve their aircraft system and, in 1906, conducted longer flights with safe takeoff, landing, and curved flight maneuvers. While the flight speed was only about 35 mi/hr, the consequences of these first flights were enormous:

- Worldwide interest in powered flight was stimulated.
- The science of aerodynamics received a strong motivation.

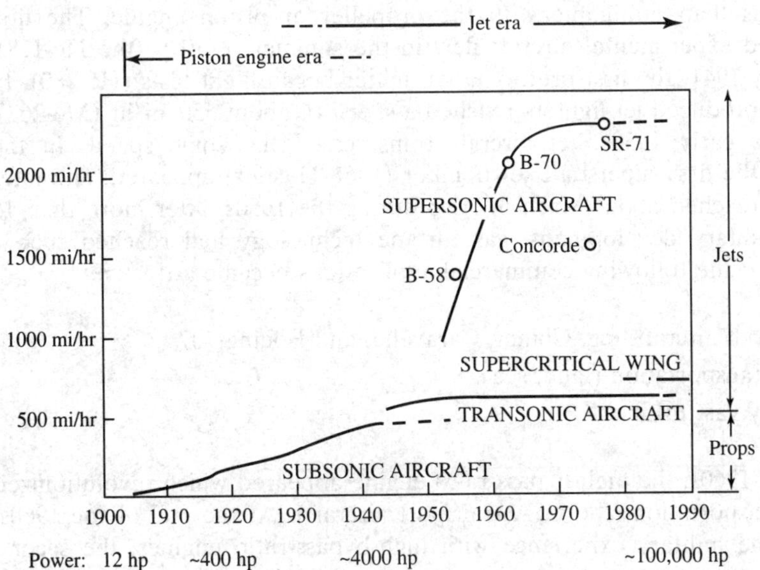

FIGURE 3
Aircraft speed trends.

- The U.S. government became interested in power flight for potential defense applications, specifically reconnaissance missions.

In 1909, the Wright brothers built the first military aircraft under government contract. During World War I, aircraft technology progressed rapidly. The flight speed reached about 150 mi/hr, and the engine power attained 400 hp. After World War I, military interest in aircraft systems dropped, but aircraft technology had reached such a degree of maturity that two nonmilitary application fields could emerge, namely:

- Commercial aviation, mail and passenger transport (first all-metal monoplane for passenger and mail transport, the Junkers F13, in 1919, sold worldwide)
- Stunt flying leading to general aviation (sport and private transportation)

In the period from 1920 to 1940, the speed increased from about 150 to 350 mi/hr through evolutionary improvements in vehicle aerodynamics and engine technology, as discussed previously. At the end of World War II, the flight speed of propeller aircraft reached about 400 to 450 mi/hr, and the power output of the largest reciprocating engines was about 5000 hp. This constituted almost the performance limit of the *propeller/reciprocating engine propulsion system.* Today, the propeller/reciprocating engine survives only in smaller, lower-speed aircraft used in general aviation.

In the late 1930s, jet propulsion emerged which promised far greater flight speeds than attainable with the propeller or piston engine. The first jet-propelled experimental aircraft flew in the summer of 1939 (the He-178), and in early 1941, the first prototype jet fighter began flight tests (He-280). In 1944, mass-produced jet fighters reached a speed of about 550 mi/hr (Me-262).

In the early 1950s, jet aircraft transgressed the sonic speed. In the mid-1950s, the first supersonic jet bomber (B-58 Hustler) appeared, and later the XB-70 reached about Mach 3. Also during the 1950s, after more than 15 years of military development, gas turbine technology had reached such a maturity that the following commercial applications became attractive:

- Commercial aircraft, e.g. Comet, Caravelle, and Boeing 707
- Surface transportation (land, sea)
- Stationary gas turbines

In the 1960s, the high-bypass-ratio engine appeared which revolutionized military transportation (the C5A transport aircraft). At the end of the 1960s, based on the military experience with high-bypass-ratio engines, the second generation of commercial jet aircraft came into existence, the *widebody* aircraft. An example is the Boeing 747 with a large passenger capacity of nearly 400. Somewhat later came the Lockheed L-1011 and Douglas DC10. By that time, the entire commercial airline fleet used turbine engines exclusively. Advantages for the airlines were:

- Very high overall efficiency and, consequently, a long flight range with economical operation
- Overhaul at about 5 million miles
- Short turnaround time
- Passenger enjoyment of the very quiet and vibration-free flight, short travel time, and comfort of smooth stratospheric flight
- Community enjoyment of quiet, pollution-free aircraft

By the end of the 1960s, the entire business of passenger transportation was essentially diverted from ships and railroads to aircraft. In the 1970s, the supersonic Concorde with a flight speed of 1500 mi/hr (the third generation of commercial transport) appeared with an equivalent output of about 100,000 hp.

Summary

In hindsight, the evolution of aerovehicle and aeropropulsion systems looks like the result of a master plan. The evolution began with the piston engine and propeller which constituted the best propulsion system for the initially low flight speeds, and had an outstanding growth potential up to about 450 mi/hr. In the early 1940s, when flight technology reached the ability to enter into the transonic flight speed regime, the jet engine had just demonstrated its suitability for this speed regime. A vigorous jet engine development program was launched. Soon the jet engine proved to be not only an excellent transonic but also a supersonic propulsion system. This resulted in the truly exploding growth in flight speed, as shown in Fig. 3.

It is interesting to note that military development preceded commercial applications by 15 to 20 years for both the propeller engine and the gas turbine engine. The reason was that costly, high-risk, long-term developments conducted by the military sector were necessary before a useful commercial application could be envisioned. After about 75 years of powered flight, the aircraft has outranked all other modes of passenger transportation and has become a very important export article of the United States.

The evolutions of both aerovehicle and aeropropulsion systems have in no way reached a technological level which is close to the ultimate potential! The evolution will go on for many decades toward capabilities far beyond current feasibility and, perhaps, imagination.

HOW JET PROPULSION CAME INTO EXISTENCE

The idea of air-breathing jet propulsion originated at the beginning of the 20th century. Several patents regarding air-breathing jet engines had been applied for by various inventors of different nationalities who worked independently of each other.

From a technical standpoint, *air-breathing jet propulsion* can be defined as a special type of internal combustion engine which produces its net output power as the rate of change in the kinetic energy of the engine's working fluid. The working fluid enters as environmental air which is ducted through an inlet diffuser into the engine; the engine exhaust gas consists partly of combustion gas and partly of air. The exhaust gas is expanded through a thrust nozzle or nozzles to ambient pressure. A few examples of early air-breathing jet propulsion patents are as follows:

1. In 1908, Lorin patented a jet engine which was based upon piston machinery (Fig. 4*a*).
2. In 1913, Lorin patented a jet engine based on ram compression in supersonic flight (Fig. 4*b*), the *ramjet.*
3. In 1921, M. Guillaume patented a jet engine based on turbomachinery; the intake air was compressed by an axial-flow compressor followed by a combustor and an axial-flow turbine driving the compressor (Fig. 4*c*).

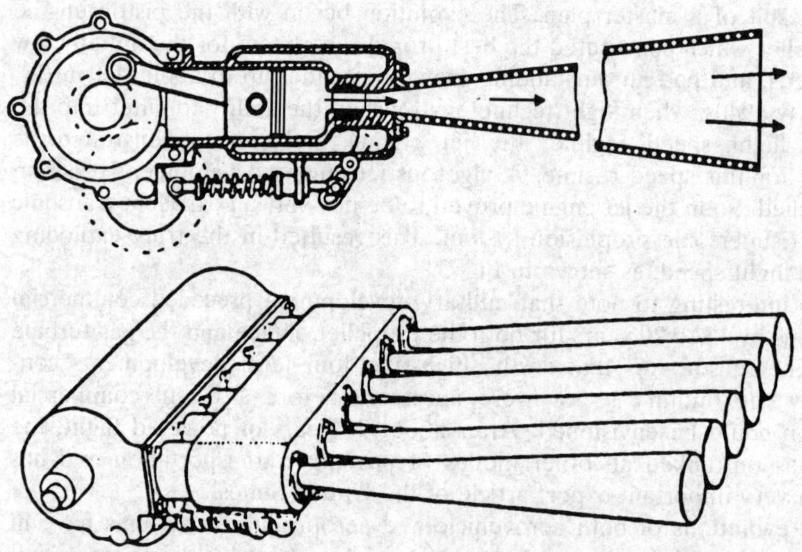

FIGURE 4*a*
Lorin's 1908 patent.

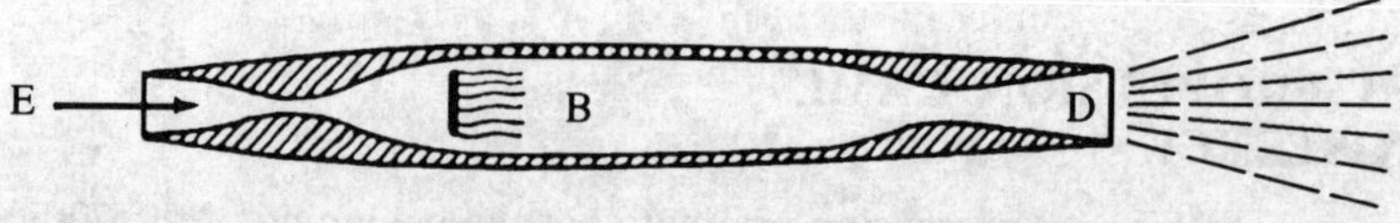

FIGURE 4*b*
Lorin's 1913 patent.

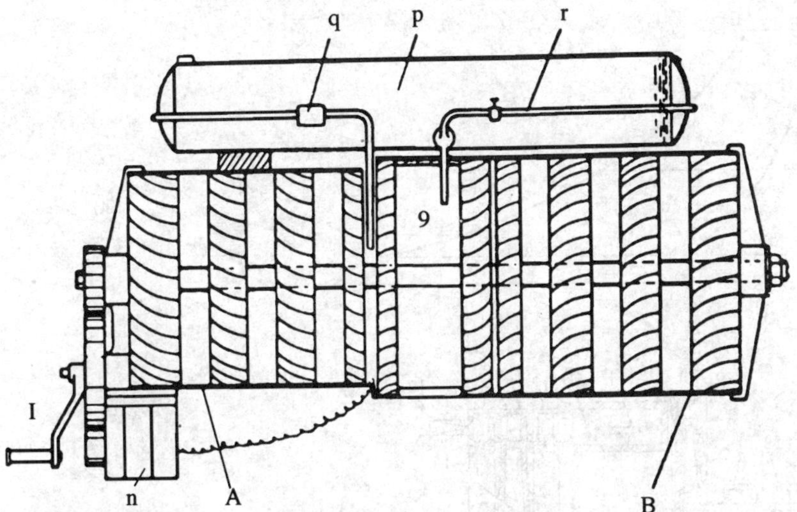

FIGURE 4c
1921 Guillaume patent.

These patents clearly described the air-breathing jet principle but were not executed in practice. The reason lies mainly in the previously-mentioned strong interdependency between aerovehicle and aeropropulsion systems. The jet engine has, in comparison with the propeller engine, a high exhaust speed (for example, 600 mi/hr and more). In the early 1920s, the aerovehicle had a flight speed capability which could not exceed about 200 mi/hr. Hence, at that time, the so-called propulsive efficiency of the jet engine was very low (about 30 to 40 percent) in comparison to the propeller which could reach more than 80 percent. So, in the early 1920s, the jet engine was not compatible with the too-slow aerovehicle. Also, in the early 1920s, an excellent theoretical study about the possibilities of enjoying jet propulsion had been conducted by Buckingham of the Bureau of Standards under contract with NACA. The result of this study was clear—the jet engine could not be efficiently employed if the aerovehicle could not greatly exceed the flight speed of 200 mi/hr; a flight speed beyond 400 mi/hr seemed to be necessary. The consequences of the results of this study were that the aircraft engine industry and the scientific and engineering community had no interest in the various jet engine inventions. So the early jet engine concepts were forgotten for a long time. They were unknown to Sir Frank Whittle, to me, and to the British and German patent offices. In 1939, however, the retired patent examiner Gohlke found out about the early jet patents and published them in a synoptic review.

The first patent of a turbojet engine, which was later developed and produced, was that of Frank Whittle, now Sir Frank (see Fig. 5). His patent was applied for in January 1930. This patent shows a multistage, axial-flow compressor followed by a radial compressor stage, a combustor, an axial-flow turbine driving the compressor, and an exhaust nozzle. Such configurations are

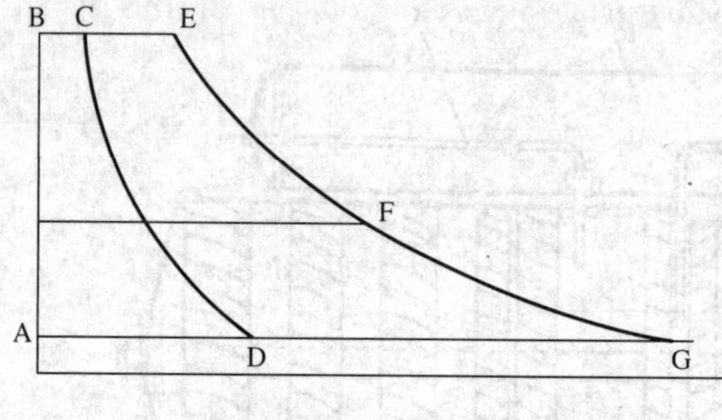

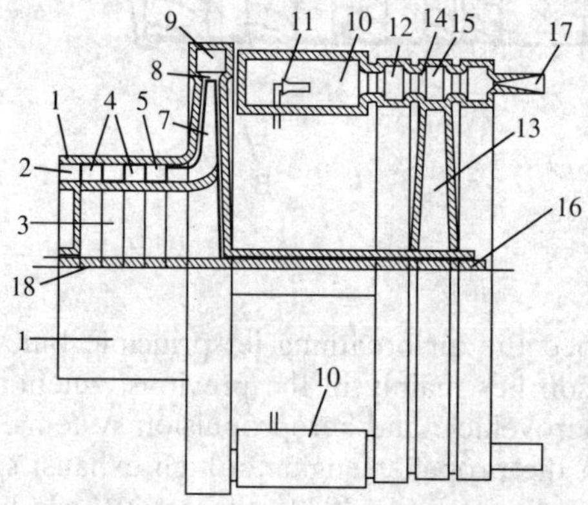

FIGURE 5
Whittle's turbojet patent drawing. (*National Air and Space Museum.*)

still used today for small- and medium-power output engines, specifically for remote-controlled vehicles.

The Turbojet Development of Sir Frank Whittle

Frank Whittle (Ref. 3) was a cadet of the Royal Air Force. In 1928, when he was 21 years old, he became interested in the possibilities of rocket propulsion and propeller gas turbines for aircraft, and he treated these subjects in his thesis. He graduated and became a pilot officer, continuously thinking about air-breathing jet propulsion. In 1929, he investigated the possibilities of a ducted fan driven by a reciprocating engine and employing a kind of afterburner prior to expansion of the fan gas. He finally rejected this idea on the basis of his performance investigations. The same idea was conceived later in Italy and built by Caproni Campini. The vehicle flew on August 28, 1940, but had a low performance, as predicted by Sir Frank in 1929.

Suddenly, in December 1929, Frank Whittle was struck by the idea of increasing the fan pressure ratio and substituting a turbine for the reciprocating engine. This clearly constituted a compact, lightweight turbojet engine. He applied for a patent for the turbojet (Fig. 5) in January 1930.

Frank Whittle discussed this idea with fellow officers and his superior officer. They were very impressed, and a meeting was arranged between him and officials of the British Air Ministry, Department of Engine Development. This department, in turn, sought advice from Dr. A. A. Griffith, who was interested in the development of a propeller gas turbine. Dr. Griffith expressed doubts about the feasibility of Whittle's turbojet concept from a standpoint of too-high fuel consumption. Actually, *in high-speed flight,* the turbojet has great advantages over a propeller gas turbine due to the fact that the turbojet is much lighter than the propeller gas turbine and can fly faster because of the absence of the propeller. Whittle rightfully considered the turbojet as a fortunate synthesis or hybrid of the "propeller gas turbine" and "rocket" principles. As Sir Frank recalls, the department wrote a letter which, in essence, stated that any form of a gas turbine would be impractical in view of the long history of failure and the lack of turbine materials capable of withstanding the high stresses at high temperatures. Whittle's outstanding and very important views were that the flying gas turbine had great advantages over a stationary gas turbine power plant due to the efficient ram pressure recovery, low environmental temperature in high altitude, and high efficiency of the jet nozzle. Unfortunately, these views were ignored by the department.

Frank Whittle (Fig. 6) tried to interest the turbine industry in his concept of jet propulsion, but he did not succeed. Lacking financial support, Whittle allowed his patent to lapse. A long, dormant period was ahead for Frank Whittle's jet propulsion ideas.

After 5 years, in mid-1935, two former Royal Air Force (RAF) officers tried to revive Whittle's turbojet concept. Whittle was enthused and wrote, "the jet engine had, like the Phoenix, risen from its ashes." (Ref. 3). At that time, Whittle was under enormous pressure. He was preparing for the examination in mechanical sciences (Tripos); his goal was to graduate with "First-Class Honors." Now, in addition, he had to design his first experimental jet engine in late 1935. In March 1936, a small company, Power Jets Ltd., was formed to build and test Whittle's engine, the W. U. (Whittle Unit). In spite of all the additional work, Whittle passed his exam in June 1936 with First-Class Honors.

In April 1937, Whittle had his bench-test jet engine ready for the first test run. It ran excellently; however, it ran out of control because liquid fuel had collected inside the engine and started to vaporize as the engine became hot, thereby adding uncontrolled fuel quantities to the combustion process. The problem was easily overcome. This first test run was the world's first run of a bench-test jet engine operating with liquid fuel (Fig. 7). In June 1939, the testing and development had progressed to a point that the Air Ministry's Director of Scientific Research (D.S.R.) promised Frank Whittle a contract for building a flight engine and an experimental aircraft, the Gloster E28/29 (Gloster/Whittle). On May 15, 1941, the first flight of the Gloster/Whittle took place (Fig. 8).

Senior ministry officials initially showed little interest, and a request for filming was ignored; however, during further flight demonstrations, interest in

FIGURE 6
Frank Whittle using slide rule to perform calculations. (*Bettman.*)

jet propulsion increased. Of particular interest was a performance demonstration given to Sir Winston Churchill. At that occasion, the Gloster/Whittle accelerated away from the three escorting fighters, one Tempest and two Spitfires.

Several British aircraft engine corporations adapted the work of Frank Whittle. Specifically, Rolls-Royce, due to the efforts of Sir Stanley G. Hooker (Ref. 4), developed the first operational and the first production engine for the two-engine Gloster Meteor, Britain's first jet fighter. In March 1943, the Gloster Meteor prototype made its first flight, powered by two de Haviland (H-1) radial jet engines. In July 1944, the Meteor I, powered with two Rolls-Royce Welland engines became operational. Its only combat action (in World War II) was in August 1944 in a successful attack against the German V1 flying bomb; it was the only fighter with sufficient level speed for the purpose. Mass production began with the Meteor III powered by two Rolls-Royce Dervents in 1945. The Meteor remained the RAF's first-line jet fighter until 1955.

From the beginning of his jet propulsion activities, Frank Whittle had been seeking means for improving the propulsive efficiency of turbojet engines

FIGURE 7
Whittle's test engine. (*National Air and Space Museum.*)

(Ref. 4). He conceived novel ideas for which he filed a patent application in 1936, which can be called a *bypass engine* or *turbofan.* To avoid a complete new design, Whittle sought an interim solution which could be merely "tacked on" to a jet engine. This configuration was later known as the *aft fan.* Whittle's work on *fan jets* or *bypass engines* and *aft fans* was way ahead of his time. It was of greatest importance for the future of turbopropulsion.

FIGURE 8
Gloster E28/29. (*National Air and Space Museum.*)

Whittle's Impact on U.S. Jet Development

In the summer of 1941, U.S. Army Air Corp General Henry H. Arnold was invited to observe flight demonstrations of the Gloster/Whittle. He was very impressed and decided this technology should be brought over to the United States. In September 1941, an agreement was signed between U.S. Secretary of War Stimson and Sir Henry Self of the British Air Commission. The United States could have the engine W1X and a set of drawings of the Whittle W2B jet engine, provided that close secrecy was maintained and the number of people involved were held to a minimum. Under these conditions, open bids for the jet engine development were not possible. General Arnold chose General Electric for jet engine development because of the great experience this company had in the development of aircraft engine turbosuperchargers. The W2B engine was built and tested on March 18, 1942, under the name *GE 1-A*. This engine had a static thrust of 1250 lb and weighed 1000 lb (Ref. 3). In the meantime, the Bell Aircomet (XP-59A) was being designed and built. On October 3, 1942, the Aircomet with two GE 1-A engines flew up to 10,000 ft. This aircraft, while in the first tests seemed to have good performance characteristics, had an incurable "snaking" instability and so provided a poor gun platform for a fighter pilot. Also, another serious shortcoming was that the top speed was not sufficiently above that of an advanced propeller fighter. For these reasons, the Bell XP-59A with two GE 1-A engines (W2B) did not become a production fighter. From these experiences, it appeared that an engine of more than 4000-lb thrust was required for a single-engine fighter which would be capable of more than 500 mi/hr operational speed. Lockheed was chosen to design a new jet fighter because when the project was discussed with the engineering staff, Lockheed's Kelly Johnson assured them a single-engine jet fighter in the "500 plus" mi/hr class could be built on the basis of a 4000-lb thrust engine.

General Electric developed the 4000-lb thrust engine, the I40 (an advanced version of Whittle's W2B engine), and Lockheed built the P80A Shooting Star, which flew on June 11, 1944. Although it did not enter combat during World War II, the Shooting Star became the United States' front-line fighter and outranked the Gloster Meteor with an international speed record (above 620 mi/hr near the ground).

By about 1945, Frank Whittle had successfully completed, with greatest tenacity under the most adverse conditions, the enormous task of leading Great Britain and the United States into the jet age.

Other Early Turbojet Developments in the United States

Independent of European influence, several turbojet and propeller gas turbine projects had been initiated in the United States in 1939 and 1940. Although these projects had been terminated or prematurely canceled, they had contributed significantly to the know-how and technology of aircraft gas turbines, specifically their combustor and turbomachinery components.

One of these projects was the 2500-hp Northrop propeller gas turbine (Turbodyne) and a high-pressure-ratio turbojet under the excellent project leadership of Vladimir Pavelecka. Although the development goal of the large aircraft gas turbine engine was essentially met in late 1940, the project was canceled because the Air Force had lost interest in propeller gas turbines in view of the enormous advancement of the competitive jet engines.

Westinghouse had developed outstanding axial turbojet engines. The first very successful test runs of the Westinghouse X19A took place in March 1943. In the beginning of the 1950s, the Navy canceled the development contract, and top management of Westinghouse decided to discontinue work on turbojet engines.

The Lockheed Corporation began to work on a very advanced turbojet conceived by an outstanding engineer, Nathan C. Price. This engine was so far ahead of its time that it would have needed a far longer development time than that provided by the contract. The development contract was canceled in 1941.

Pratt & Whitney had started to work on its own jet propulsion ideas in the early 1940s but could not pursue these concepts because of the too-stringent obligations during wartime for the development and production of advanced aircraft piston engines. After World War II, Pratt & Whitney decided to go completely into turbojet development using axial-flow turbomachinery. The company began with the construction of a gigantic Test and Research facility. The government gave Pratt & Whitney a contract to build a large number of 5000-lb thrust Rolls-Royce Nene engines with a radial compressor of the basic Whittle design. Subsequently, Pratt & Whitney developed its own large axial-flow, dual-rotor turbojet and later a fan-jet with a small bypass ratio for the advanced B52.

Turbojet Development of Hans von Ohain

My interest in aircraft propulsion began in the fall of 1933 while I was a student at the Georgia Augusta University of Gottingen in physics under Prof. R. Pohl with a minor in applied mechanics under Prof. Ludwig Prandtl. I was 21 years old and beginning my Ph.D. thesis in physics which was not related to jet propulsion.

The strong vibrations and noise of the propeller piston engine triggered my interest in aircraft propulsion. I felt the natural smoothness and elegance of flying was greatly spoiled by the reciprocating engine with propellers. It appeared to me that a steady, thermodynamic flow process was needed. Such a process would not produce vibrations. Also, an engine based upon such a process could probably be lighter and more powerful than a reciprocating engine with a propeller because the steady flow conditions would allow a much greater mass flow of working medium per cross section. These characteristics appeared to me to be most important for achieving higher flight speeds. I made performance estimates for several steady flow engine types and finally chose a special gas turbine configuration which appeared to me as a lightweight, simple propulsion system with low development risks. The rotor consisted of a straight-vane radial outflow compressor back-to-back with a straight vane radial inflow turbine. Both compressor and turbine rotors had nearly equal outer diameters which corresponds to a good match between them.

In early 1935, I worked out a patent for the various features of a gas turbine consisting of radial outflow compressor rotor, combustor, radial inflow turbine, and a central exhaust thrust nozzle. With the help of my patent attorney, Dr. E. Wiegand, a thorough patent search was made. A number of interesting aeropropulsion systems without a propeller were found, but we did not come across the earlier patents of Lorin, Guillaume, and Frank Whittle. (I learned for the first time about one of Frank Whittle's patents in early 1937 when the German Patent Office held one of his patents and one patent of the Swedish corporation Milo, against some of my patent claims.)

My main problem was finding support for my turbojet ideas. A good approach, it seemed to me, was to first build a model. This model should be able to demonstrate the aerodynamic functions at very low-performance runs. The tip speed of this model was a little over 500 ft/sec. Of course, I never considered high-power demonstration runs for two reasons. The cost for building such an apparatus could easily be a factor of 10 or 20 times greater than that for building a low-speed model. Also, a test facility would be required for high-performance test or demonstration runs. I knew a head machinist in an automobile repair shop, Max Hahn, to whom I showed the sketches of my model. He made many changes to simplify the construction which greatly reduced the cost. The model was built at my expense by Hahn in 1935 (Fig. 9).

In mid-1935, I had completed my doctoral thesis and oral examination and had received my diploma in November 1935. I continued working in Prof. Pohl's institute and discussed with him my project "aircraft propulsion." He was interested in my theoretical write-up. Although my project did not fit Pohl's institute, he was extremely helpful to me. He let me test the model engine in the backyard of his institute and gave me instrumentation and an electric starting motor. Because the combustors did not work, the model did not run without power from the starting motor. Long, yellow flames leaked out of the turbine. It looked more like a flame thrower than an aircraft gas turbine.

I asked Prof. Pohl to write me a letter of introduction to Ernst Heinkel, the famous pioneer of high-speed aircraft and sole owner of his company. Professor Pohl actually wrote a very nice letter of recommendation. I had chosen Heinkel because he had the reputation of being an unconventional thinker obsessed with the idea of high-speed aircraft. Intuitively, I also felt that an aircraft engine company would not accept my turbine project. I learned later that my intuition was absolutely right. Today, I am convinced no one except Heinkel (see Fig. 10) would have supported my jet ideas at that time. Heinkel invited me to his home on the evening of March 17, 1936, to explain

FIGURE 9
Max Hahn with model engine. (*National Air and Space Museum.*)

the jet principle to him. He, in turn, gave me a view of his plan. He wanted the jet development to be apart from the airplane factory. For this purpose, he intended to construct a small, temporary building near the Warnow River. I was very enthusiastic about this idea since it gave me a feeling of freedom and independence from the other part of the company and an assurance of Heinkel's confidence in me. Also, he strongly emphasized that he himself wanted to finance the entire jet development without involvement of the German Air Ministry. Finally, he explained to me that he had arranged a meeting between me and his top engineers for the next morning.

On March 18, 1936, I met with a group of 8 to 10 Heinkel engineers and explained my jet propulsion thoughts. Although they saw many problems, specifically with the combustion, they were not completely negative. Heinkel called me to a conference at the end of March. He pointed out that several uncertainties, specifically the combustion problems, should be solved before the gas turbine development could be started. He wanted me to work on this problem and to report to him all the difficulties I might encounter. He offered me a kind of consulting contract which stated that the preliminary work (combustor development) could probably be completed in about 2 months. If successful, the turbojet development would then be started, and I would

FIGURE 10
Ernst Heinkel (left) and Hans von Ohain (right). (*National Air and Space Museum.*)

receive a regular employment contract. I signed this contract on April 3, 1936, and would start working in the Heinkel Company on April 15.

The first experiments with the model in early 1936 had convinced me that the volume of the combustion chambers was far too small for achieving a stable combustion. This was later substantiated in a discussion with combustion engineers at an industrial exhibit. I found a simple way to correct this condition. Cycle analysis of my model clearly showed that for high turbine inlet temperatures, such as 700°C and higher, a centrifugal compressor with a radial inflow turbine was most suitable as a basis for combustor development. My greatest problem was how to develop a functioning combustor in a few months. In my judgment, such a development would need at least 6 months, more likely 1 year, while Heinkel's estimate was 2 months. I had grave doubts whether Heinkel would endure such a long development time without seeing any visible progress, such as an experimental jet engine in operation. However, to avoid any combustor difficulties, I was considering a hydrogen combustor system with a nearly uniform turbine inlet temperature distribution. This hydrogen combustor system should be designed so that it could be built without any risk or need for preliminary testing.

My idea was to separate the compressor and turbine on the rotor by a shaft and to employ an annular connecting duct from the exit of the compressor diffuser to the inlet of the turbine. Within this annular duct, I wanted to place a row of hollow vanes (about 60). These hollow vanes would

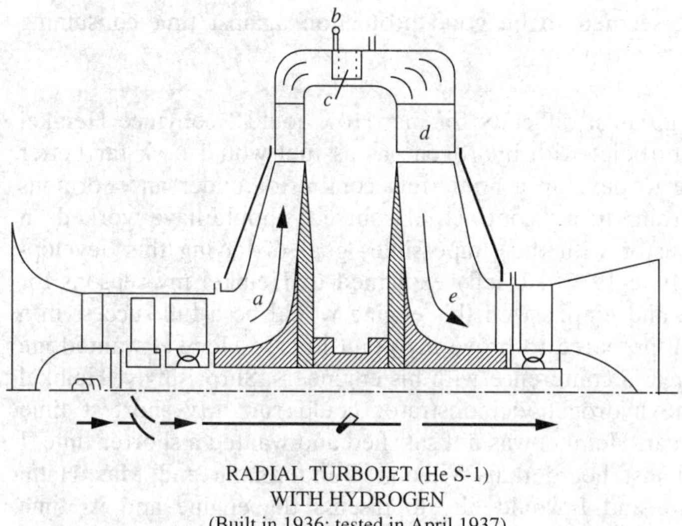

FIGURE 11
Von Ohain's hydrogen demonstrator engine.

have blunt trailing edges with many small holes through which hydrogen gas jets would be discharged into the air wakes behind the blunt trailing edges. In this way, the hydrogen combustion would be anchored at the blunt trailing edges of the hollow vanes. I was absolutely certain this combustor system would successfully function without any development or preliminary testing. I was also certain that no pretesting or development was necessary for the simple radial-flow turbomachinery. Testing of the hydrogen demonstrator engine (Fig. 11) showed that my judgment was correct on both points.

By mid-May 1936 I had nearly completed the layout of the hydrogen demonstrator engine. To build this engine was, for me, most important, not only for quick achievement of an impressive demonstration of the jet principle, but also for very significant technical reasons:

1. One reason was to obtain a solid basis for the design of the flight engine and the development of the liquid-fuel combustor, which should be started as a parallel development as soon as possible.
2. To achieve this solid basis, the hydrogen engine was the surest and quickest way when one does not have compressor and turbine test stands.
3. The anticipated step-by-step development approach: First testing the compressor-turbine unit with the "no-risk" hydrogen combustor and then using the tested turbomachine for exploring its interaction with the liquid-fuel

combustor system seemed to be good protection against time-consuming setbacks.

Now came the greatest difficulty for me: How could I convince Heinkel that first building a turbojet with hydrogen gas as fuel would be a far better approach than trying to develop a liquid-fuel combustor under an enormous time pressure? According to my contract, of course, I should have worked on the liquid-fuel combustor with the (impossible) goal of having this development completed by June 1936. I briefly explained to Heinkel my reasons for the hydrogen engine and emphasized this engine would be a full success in a short time. I was well prepared to prove my point in case Heinkel wanted me to discuss this matter in a conference with his engineers. Surprisingly, Heinkel asked only when the hydrogen demonstrator could run. My shortest time estimate was half a year. Heinkel was not satisfied and wanted a shorter time. I told him that I had just heard that Wilhelm Gundermann and Max Hahn would work with me, and I would like to discuss the engine and its time schedule with them. So, Heinkel had agreed with my reasons to build the hydrogen jet demonstrator first.

About a week after my discussion with Heinkel, I joined Gundermann and Hahn in their large office. I showed them the layout of the hydrogen engine. Gundermann told me he had attended my presentation to the group of Heinkel's leading engineers in March 1936. He was surprised that I departed from the liquid-fueled turbojet program. I explained my reasons and also told about Heinkel's strong desire to have the hydrogen engine built in less than half a year. After studying my layout, both men came to the conclusion that it would not be possible to build this engine in less than 6 months, perhaps even longer. Gundermann, Hahn, and I began to work as an excellent team.

The engine was completed at the end of February 1937, and the start of our demonstration program was in the first half of March, according to Gundermann's and my recollections. The first run is clearly engraved in my memory: Hahn had just attached the last connections between engine and test stand; it was after midnight, and we asked ourselves if we should make a short run. We decided to do it! The engine had a 2-hp electric starting motor. Hahn wanted to throw off the belt-connecting starter motor and hydrogen engine if self-supporting operation was indicated. Gundermann observed the exhaust side to detect possible hot spots—none were visible. I was in the test room. The motor brought the engine to somewhat above 2000 rpm. The ignition was on, and I opened the hydrogen valve carefully. The ignition of the engine sounded very similar to the ignition of a home gas heating system. I gave more gas, Hahn waved, the belt was off, and the engine now ran self-supporting and accelerated very well. The reason for the good acceleration probably was twofold: the relatively low moment of inertia of the rotor and the enormously wide operational range of the hydrogen combustion system. We all experienced a great joy which is difficult to describe. Hahn called Heinkel, and he came to our test stand about 20 minutes later, shortly before 1:00 a.m. We made a second demonstration run. Heinkel was enthused—he congratulated us and emphasized that we should now begin to build the liquid-fuel engine for flying.

The next day and until the end of March, Heinkel began to show further demonstration runs to some of his leading engineers and important friends. The next day following our "night show," Heinkel visited us with Walter and Siegfried Guenther (his two top aerodynamic designers) for a demonstration run. They were very impressed and asked me about the equivalent horsepower per square meter. I replied, "A little less than 1000," but hastened to add that the flight engine would have more than 2500 hp/m^2 because of the much greater tip speed and greater relative flow cross sections. During April, we conducted a systematic testing program.

After the first run of the hydrogen engine, Heinkel ordered his patent office to apply for patents of the hydrogen engine. Because of earlier patents, the only patentable item was my hydrogen combustion system.

I became employed as division chief, reporting directly to Heinkel, and received an independent royalty contract, as I had desired. An enormous amount of pressure was now exerted by Heinkel to build the flight engine.

During the last months of 1937, Walter and Siegfried Guenther began with predesign studies of the first jet-propelled aircraft (He-178) and specified a static thrust of 1100 lb for the flight engine (He.S3). The aircraft was essentially an experimental aircraft with some provisions for armament.

In late 1937, while I was working on different layouts of the flight engine, Max Hahn showed me his idea of arranging the combustor in the large unused space in front of the radial-flow compressor. He pointed out that this would greatly reduce the rotor length and total weight. Hahn's suggestion was incorporated into the layout of the flight engine (see Fig. 12). In early 1938, we had a well-functioning annular combustor for gasoline. The design of the flight engine was frozen in the summer of 1938 to complete construction and testing by early 1939.

In spring 1939, aircraft and engine were completed, but the engine performance was too low: about 800-lb thrust, while a thrust of 1000 to 1100 lb was desirable to start the aircraft from Heinkel's relatively short company airfield. We made several improvements, mostly optimizing the easily exchangeable radial cascades of the compressor-diffuser and turbine stator. In early August, we had reached 1000 lb of thrust. We made only several 1-hr test runs with the flight engine. However, upon suggestion of the Air Ministry, we completed a continuous 10-hr test run with a rotor which was not used for flight tests.

On August 27, 1939, the first flight of the He-178 with jet engine He.S3B was made with Erich Warsitz as pilot (Fig. 13). This was the first flight of a turbojet aircraft in the world. It demonstrated not only the feasibility of jet propulsion, but also several characteristics that had been doubted by many

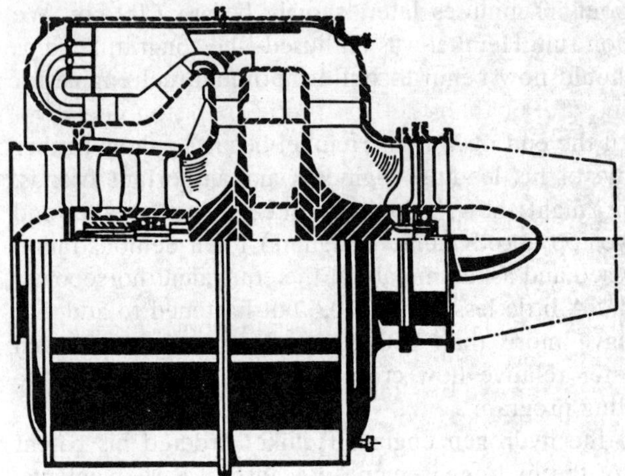

FIGURE 12
1937 Design of the He.S3 turbojet engine.

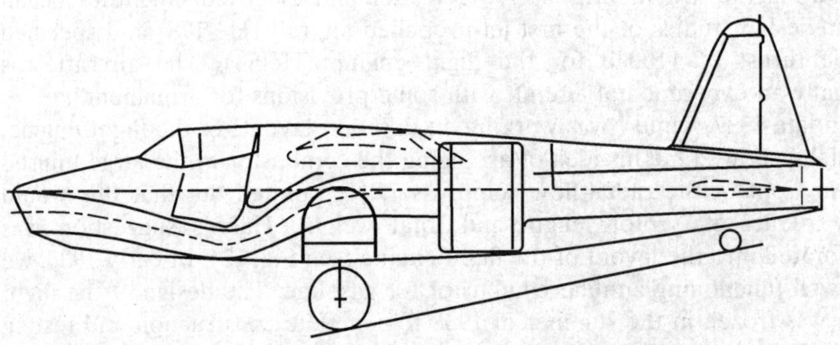

FIGURE 13
The world's first jet-powered aircraft, the Heinkel He-178, was powered by the von Ohain–designed He.S3B turbojet engine. (*National Air and Space Museum.*)

opponents of turbojet propulsion:

- The flying engine had a very favorable ratio of net power output to engine weight—about 2 to 3 times better than the best propeller/piston engines of equal thrust power.
- The combustion chambers could be made small enough to fit in the engine envelope and could have a wide operational range from start to high altitude and from low to high flight speed.

The advantages of developing a flight demonstration turbojet in Heinkel's aircraft company were unique. Among the advantages were complete technical freedom, lack of importance attached to financial aspects, no government requirements, and no time delays; the aircraft was, so to speak, waiting for the engine. These great advantages were true only for the initial phases of jet engine development up to the first flight demonstrator. For making a production engine, however, enormous disadvantages included complete lack of experts in fabrication (turbomachinery, etc.), materials, research (turbines), accessory drives, control systems, no machine tools or component test stands, etc. Heinkel was very aware of this situation. His plan was to hire engineers from the aircraft engine field and to purchase an aircraft engine company.

Other Early Turbojet Development in Germany

The following events developed at the same time, which was of great importance for the early phases of the turbojet evolution:

1. Professor Herbert Wagner privately started an aircraft gas turbine development project.
2. The Air Ministry became aware of Heinkel's turbojet project in 1938 and exerted a strong influence upon the engine industry to start turbo development projects.
3. Heinkel purchased an aircraft engine corporation and received a contract for development and production of a high-performance turbojet engine.

In 1934, Wagner conceived the idea of an axial-flow propeller gas turbine while he was a professor of aeronautics in Berlin and formed a corporation to pursue these ideas. (I heard about Wagner's project for the first time in spring of 1939.) By introducing a design parameter that was the ratio of propeller power input to total net power output, he had conceived a gas turbine engine that was a cross between a turbojet and a propeller gas turbine.

Wagner first explored what would happen if the propeller power input was 50 percent of the total power output. This condition was favorable for long-range transport. Then in 1936, he investigated the "limiting case" of zero propeller power input, which constituted a turbojet. This engine was of great interest for high-speed aircraft because of its light weight.

The unique feature of Wagner's design was the utilization of 50 percent reaction turbomachinery (or *symmetric blading*). A compressor with 50 percent reaction blading has the greatest pressure ratio and efficiency for a given blade approach Mach number; but the design is difficult because of the inherently strong three-dimensional flow phenomena. This problem was solved by one of Wagner's coworkers, Rudolf Friedrich.

At the time Wagner was working on the turbojet engine, in about 1936, he became technical director of the Junkers Airframe Corporation in Dessau. The jet engine work was conducted in the Junkers machine factory, which was located in Magdeburg. The head of his turbojet development was Max A. Mueller, his former "first assistant."

In late fall, 1938, Wagner had decided to leave the Junkers Corporation, but he wanted to obtain funds from the Air Ministry for the continuation of his turbojet development work. The Air Ministry agreed to Wagner's request under the condition that the jet development be continued at the Junkers Aircraft Engine Company in Dessau. This seemed to be acceptable to Herbert Wagner. However, his team of about 12 very outstanding scientists and engineers (among them the team leader, Max A. Mueller, and the highly regarded Dr. R. Friedrich) refused to join the Junkers Aircraft Engine Company under the proposed working conditions. Heinkel made them very attractive work offers which convinced Wagner's former team to join the Heinkel Company. Heinkel added Wagner's axial turbojet to his development efforts (designated as the He.S30). So, in early 1939, Heinkel had achieved one goal—to attract excellent engineers for his turbojet development.

In early 1938, the Air Ministry had become aware of Heinkel's private jet propulsion development. The Engine Development Division of the Air Ministry had a small section for special propulsion systems which did not use propellers and piston engines, but rather used special rockets for short-time performance boost or takeoff assistance. Head of this section was Hans Mauch. He asked Heinkel to see his turbojet development in early summer 1938, more than one year before the first flight of the He-178. After he saw Heinkel's hydrogen turbojet demonstrator in operation and the plans for the flight engine, he was very impressed. He thanked Heinkel for the demonstration and pointed out that turbojet propulsion was, for him, a completely *unknown* and new concept. He soon became convinced that the turbojet was the key to high-speed flight. He came, however, to the conclusion that Heinkel, as an airframe company, would never be capable of developing a production engine because the company lacked engine test and manufacturing facilities and, most of all, it lacked engineers experienced in engine development and testing techniques. He wanted the Heinkel team to join an aircraft engine company (Daimler-Benz) and serve as a nucleus for turbojet propulsion development. Furthermore, he stated that Ernst Heinkel should receive full reimbursement and recognition for his great pioneering achievements. Heinkel refused.

In the summer of 1938, Mauch met with Helmut Schelp, who was in charge of jet propulsion in the Research Division of the Air Ministry. Mauch invited Schelp to join him in the Engine Development Division. Schelp accepted the transfer because he saw far greater opportunities for action than in his Research Division. In contrast to Mauch, Schelp was very well aware of turbojet propulsion and was convinced about its feasibility. He was well versed in axial and radial turbomachinery and with the aerothermodynamic performance calculation methods of turbojet, ramjet, and pulse jet. Like Mauch, he was convinced of the necessity that the aircraft engine companies should work on the development of turbojet engines. However, Schelp did not see a necessity for Heinkel to discontinue his jet engine development. He saw in Heinkel's progress a most helpful contribution for convincing the engine industry to also engage in the development of turbojets, and for proving to the higher echelons of the Air Ministry the necessity of launching a turbojet development program throughout the aircraft engine companies.

Schelp worked out the plans and programs for jet propulsion systems, decided on their most suitable missions, and selected associated aircraft types. Schelp's goal was to establish a complete jet propulsion program for the German aircraft engine industry. He also talked with Hans Antz of the Airframe Development Division of the Air Ministry to launch a turbojet fighter aircraft development as soon as possible. This became the Me-262. To implement the program, Mauch and Schelp decided to visit aircraft engine manufacturers—Junkers Motoren (Jumo), Daimler-Benz, BMW Flugmotorenbau, and Bradenburgische Motorenweke (Bramo). Mauch and Schelp offered each company a research contract to determine the best type of jet engine and its most suitable mission. After each study was completed and evaluated, a major engine development contract might be awarded.

The industry's response to these proposals has been summed up by R. Schlaifer in *Development of Aircraft Engines, and Fuels* (Ref. 4): "The reaction of the engine companies to Mauch's proposals was far from enthusiastic, but it was not completely hostile."

Anselm Franz and Hermann Oestrich were clearly in favor of developing a gas turbine engine. Otto Mader, head of engine development at Jumo, made two counter arguments against taking on turbojet propulsion developments. He said, first, that the highest priority of Jumo was to upgrade the performance of its current and future piston engines, and that this effort was already underpowered; and, second, Jumo did not have workers with the necessary expertise in turbomachine engine development! After several meetings between Mader and Schelp, however, Mader accepted the jet engine development contract and put Franz in charge of the turbojet project. At that time, Dr. Anselm Franz was head of the supercharger group. Daimler-Benz completely rejected any work on gas turbine engines at that time. Meanwhile, BMW and Bramo began a merger, and after it was finalized, Hermann Oestrich became the head of the gas turbine project for BMW.

These developments show that the aircraft engine industries in Germany

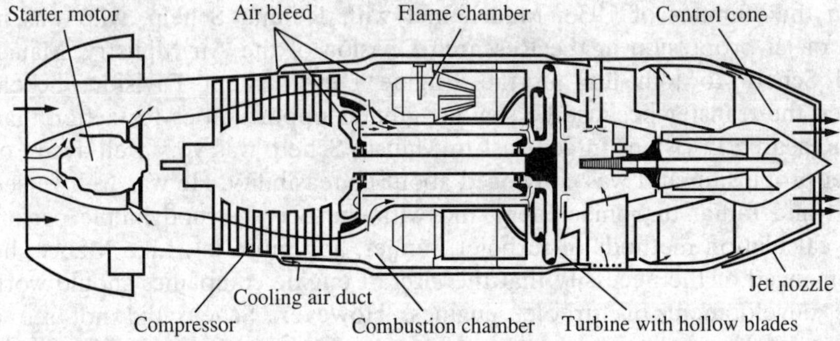

FIGURE 14
Drawing of Jumo 004B turbojet engine showing air cooling system [thrust = 2000 lb, airflow = 46.6 lb/sec, pressure ratio = 3.14, turbine inlet temperature = 1427°F, fuel consumption = 1.4 (lb/hr)/hr, engine weight = 1650 lb, diameter = 30 in, length = 152 in, efficiencies: 78% compressor, 95% combustor, 79.5% turbine].

did not begin to develop jet engines on their own initiative, but rather on the initiative and leadership of Mauch, and specifically of Helmut Schelp of the technical section of the German Air Ministry. Without their actions, the engine companies in Germany would not have begun development work on turbojet propulsion. The net result of Schelp's planning efforts was that two important turbojet engine developments were undertaken by the German aircraft engine industry, the Junkers Engine Division and BMW.

The Jumo 004 (shown in Fig. 14), developed under the leadership of Anselm Franz, was perhaps one of the truly unique achievements in the history of early jet propulsion development leading to mass production, for the following reasons:

- It employed axial-flow turbomachinery and straight throughflow combustors.
- It overcame the nonavailability of nickel by air-cooled hollow turbine blades made out of sheet metal.
- The manufacturing cost of the engine amounted to about one-fifth that of a propeller/piston engine having the equivalent power output.
- The total time from the start of development to the beginning of large-scale production was a little over 4 years (see Table 1).
- It incorporated a variable-area nozzle governed by the control system of the engine, and model 004E incorporated afterburning.

The above points reflect the design philosophy of Dr. A. Franz for the Jumo 004, which was lowest possible development risk, shortest development time, dealing with a complete lack of heat-resistant materials, and minimizing manufacturing cost. From this design philosophy, it is understandable that the Jumo 004 engine, while fully meeting the requirements, did not have the

TABLE 1
Jumo 004 development and production schedule

Start of development	Fall 1939
First test run	Oct. 11, 1940
First flight in Me-262	July 18, 1942
Preproduction	1943
Beginning of production	Early 1944
Introduction of hollow blades	Late 1944
About 6000 engines delivered	May 1945

highest overall performance compared to some contemporary experimental axial-flow engines, such as the He.S30 and others. If it had been possible for the Jumo 004 to employ heat resistant materials, then the engine thrust, the thrust/weight ratio, and the efficiency would have been increased substantially. Also the engine life could have been drastically increased from about 25 hr to well over 100 hr. However, since the combat life of a German fighter was well below 25 hr, the economical optimum could tolerate a short engine life and the avoidance of nickel. Furthermore, to avoid any development risk or time delay, the compressor type chosen for the Jumo 004 was one where essentially all the static pressure increase occurs in the rotor and none in the stator (a free-vortex type of compressor having constant axial velocity over the blade span). Although such a compressor type does not have the best performance, at that time it was best understood. The above-described points show that the Jumo 004 represented an outstanding compromise between engine performance, the existent design constraints due to materials shortage, the need for short development time, and earliest possible production.

The BMW 003 turbojet engine, which was developed under the leadership of Hermann Oestrich, was also a resounding success. Since its thrust was smaller than that of the Jumo 004, it was ideally suited for the He-162. After World War II, Oestrich and a group of prominent scientists and engineers from Germany went to France and helped lay the foundation for France's turbojet industry.

Now I would like to go back to the end of 1939, when Heinkel began to make plans for buying an engine company. After the first flight of the He-178 on August 27, 1939, Heinkel invited high officials of the Air Ministry to see a flight demonstration of the He-178. This demonstration took place on November 1, 1939. At that occasion, Heinkel offered the development of a jet fighter, the He-280, which had two outboard engines under the wing. Heinkel received a contract for this aircraft in early 1940. In addition, I believe Udet and Heinkel had made an agreement that Heinkel would get official permission to buy the Hirth Engine Company, if the first flight of the He-280 could be demonstrated by April 1941.

The He-280 had severe restrictions with respect to distance of the engine nacelle from the ground. It actually was designed for the axial engine He.S30 (the Wagner turbojet engine). It appeared, however, unlikely that the He.S30 would be ready in time. On the other hand, it was impossible to use an engine of the He.S3B type, which had powered the He-178, because the diameter of this engine type would have been far too large. Under these conditions, I could see only one possible solution for succeeding in time, and this solution had extreme high risk. I employed a radial rotor similar to that of the He.S3B and combined it with an axial (adjustable) vane diffuser and a straight throughflow annular combustor.

The company designation of this engine was He.S8A. We had only about 14 months for this development, but we were lucky—it worked surprisingly well, and Heinkel could demonstrate the first flight of the He-280 on April 2, 1941. The government pilot was Engineer Bade. Earlier flights in late March were done by Heinkel's test pilot, Fritz Schaefer.

A few days after this demonstration, Heinkel obtained permission to buy the Hirth Motoren Company in Stuttgart, which was known for its excellent small aircraft engines. This company had outstanding engineers, scientists, machinists, precision machine tools, and test stands. Heinkel relocated the development of the He.S30 to his new Heinkel-Hirth engine company in order to make use of the excellent test and manufacturing facilities. In the summer of 1942, the He.S30 was ready for testing. It performed outstandingly well. The continuous thrust was about 1650 lb. From a technical standpoint, this engine had by far the best ratio of thrust to weight in comparison to all other contemporary engines. The superiority of the He.S30 was, in large part, the result of its advanced 50 percent reaction degree axial-flow compressor, designed by Dr. R. Friedrich. However, the success of the He.S30 came too late. The He-280 had been thoroughly tested. While it was clearly superior to the best contemporary propeller/piston fighter aircraft, the He-280 had considerably lower flight performance than the Me-262 with respect to speed, altitude, and range. Also, the armament of the He-280 was not as strong as that of the Me-262. For these reasons, the He.S8 and the He.S30 were canceled in the fall of 1942; the He-280 was officially canceled in early 1943. The Me-262 (Fig. 15) went on to become the first operational jet fighter powered by two Jumo 004B turbojet engines. The Air Ministry did give full recognition to the excellence of the 50 percent reaction degree compressor type as most suitable for future turbojet developments.

Thus, in the fall of 1942, Heinkel had lost his initial leadership in jet aircraft and turbojet engines. Ironically, this happened when he had just reached his goal of owning an aircraft engine company with an outstanding team of scientists and engineers. It was the combined team of the original Hirth team, the Heinkel team, and Wagner's team. These conditions made Heinkel fully competitive with the existent aircraft engine industry. The Air Ministry had recognized the excellence of Heinkel's new team and facilities. Helmut Schelp, who in the meantime had become the successor of Hans Mauch, was in favor of the Heinkel-Hirth Company's receiving a new turbojet

FIGURE 15
Messerschmitt Me-262 jet fighter. (*National Air and Space Museum.*)

engine development contract. He clearly foresaw the need for a strong engine for the advanced Me-262, the Arado-234, the Junkers-287, and others. This new engine was supposed to have a thrust of nearly 3000 lb with a growth potential to 4000 lb as well as a high pressure ratio for improving the fuel economy. We began working on the He.S011 engine in the fall of 1942. The He.S011 was an axial-flow design with 50 percent reaction degree compressor blading, similar to that designed by Dr. Friedrich, and a two-stage, axial-flow, air-cooled turbine. Note that Helmut Schelp not only had established the performance specifications, but also had contributed to the overall design with excellent technical input and suggestions pertaining to the advanced diagonal inducer stage, the two-stage air-cooled turbine, and the variable exhaust nozzle system.

I was in charge of the He.S011 development, while the local director of the Heinkel-Hirth plant, Curt Schif, was in charge of He.S011 production. The top engineer of the Hirth Corporation was Dr. Max Bentele. He was well known for his outstanding knowledge in dealing with blade vibration problems. Upon special request of the Air Ministry, he had solved the serious turbine blade vibration problems of the Jumo 004 in the summer of 1943.

Dr. Bentele was responsible for the component development of the He.S011. After considerable initial difficulties, he achieved excellent performance characteristics of compressor and turbine which made it possible, by the end of 1944, for the performance requirements of the 011 to be met or surpassed. He also contributed to the preparation for production of the 011, which was planned to start in June 1945. The end of World War II, of course, terminated the production plan before it had started. Only a few He.S011 engines are in existence today, and they are exhibited in several museums in the United States and Great Britain.

In other countries, such as Russia and Japan, interesting developments in the field of propeller gas turbines and turbojets had also been undertaken. It is, however, not sufficiently known to what extent these developments were interrelated with, or influenced by, the previously described jet developments and what their development schedules had been.

In summary, at the end of the 1930s and in the first half of the 1940s, turbojet propulsion had come into existence in Europe and the United States. It had been demonstrated that the turbojet is, for high-speed flight, uniquely superior to the propeller/piston engines because of the following two major characteristics:

1. The ratio of power output to weight of the early turbojets was at least 2 or 3 times greater than that of the best propeller/piston engines. This is one necessary condition of propulsion systems for high-speed flight and good maneuverability.
2. Since, in the turbojet, the propeller is replaced by ducted turbomachinery, the turbojet is inherently capable as a propulsion system of high subsonic and supersonic flight speeds.

In the following, it will be discussed how the turbojet engine progressed to the performance capabilities of today.

EVOLUTION OF AIR-BREATHING TURBOPROPULSION SYSTEMS TO THE TECHNOLOGY LEVEL OF TODAY

The early turbojets were used as propulsion systems for high-speed fighter and reconnaissance aircraft. For these applications, the early turbojets (because of their superior power/weight ratios) were far more suitable propulsion systems than the traditional propeller/piston engines. However, the early turbojets were not suitable for those application areas where greatest fuel economy, highest reliability, and a very long endurance and service life were required. For making air-breathing turbojet propulsion systems applicable for all types of aircraft, ranging from helicopters to high-speed, long-range transports, the following development goals were, and still are, being pursued:

- Higher overall efficiency (i.e., the product of thermodynamic and propulsion efficiencies)
- Larger-power-output engines
- Larger ratios of power output to engine weight, volume, and frontal area
- Greater service life, endurance, and reliability
- Strong reduction of adverse environmental exhaust gases
- Reduced noise

To achieve these goals, parallel research and development efforts were undertaken in areas such as

- Fundamental research in combustion processes, development, and technology efforts for increasing specific mass flow through combustors and reducing the total pressure drop; and for achieving nearly 100 percent combustion efficiency with a more uniform temperature profile at combustor exit.
- Minimizing the excitation of vibrations (including aeroelastic effects) and associated fatigue phenomena.
- Continuous improvement of the structural design and structural materials, such as composite materials, heat- and oxidation-resistant alloys and ceramics.
- Increasing the turbine temperature capability by improving air cooling effectiveness. Also increasing the polytropic turbine efficiency.
- Improvement of the compressor with respect to greater specific mass flow, greater stage pressure ratio, greater overall pressure ratio, and greater polytropic efficiency.
- Advanced controllable-thrust nozzles and their interactions with the aircraft.
- Advanced control systems to improve operation of existing and new engines.

All the above research and development areas were, and still are, of great importance for the progress in turbopropulsion systems; however, the compressor can perhaps be singled out as the key component because its advancement was a major determining factor of the rate of progress in turbo engine development. This will become apparent from the following brief description of the evolution of the turbopropulsion systems.

Development of High-Pressure-Ratio Turbojets

The first step to improve the early turbojets was to increase their overall efficiency. To do this, it was necessary to increase the thermodynamic cycle efficiency by increasing the compressor pressure ratio. The trend of compressor pressure ratio over the calendar years is shown in Table 2.

TABLE 2
Trend in compressor pressure ratios

Calendar years	Compressor pressure ratio
Late 1930 to mid-1940	3:1 to about 5:1
Second half of 1940s	5:1 and 6:1
Early 1950	About 10:1
Middle to late 1960s	20:1 to about 25:1
End of century (2000)	30:1 to about 40:1

In the early 1940s, it was well understood that a high-pressure-ratio (above 6:1), single-spool, fixed-geometry compressor can operate with good efficiency only at the design point, or very close to it. The reason is that at the design point, all compressor stages are matched on the basis of the compressibility effects. Consequently, under off-design conditions where the compressibility effects are changed, the stages of a high-pressure-ratio compressor are severely mismatched, resulting in a very low off-design efficiency. For example, at an operational compressor rpm (which would be substantially below the design rpm), the compressibility effects are small. Under such off-design conditions, the front stages tend to operate under *stalled* conditions, while the last stages tend to work under *turbining* conditions. Such compressor characteristics are unacceptable for the following reasons:

- Enormous difficulties in starting such an engine
- Very poor overall efficiency (or poor fuel economy) under part-load operation
- Very low overall efficiency at high supersonic flight speed (because the corrected rpm is very low as a result of the high stagnation temperature of the air at the compressor inlet)

By the end of the 1940s and early 1950s, excellent approaches emerged for the elimination of the above shortcomings of simple high-pressure-ratio compressors. Pratt & Whitney, under the leadership of Perry Pratt, designed a high-pressure-ratio jet engine (the J57) with a *dual-rotor* configuration. (In later years, triple-rotor configurations were also employed.) The ratio of rpm values of the low- and high-pressure spools varies with the overall pressure ratio and, in this way, alleviates the mismatching effects caused by the changes in compressibility. At approximately the same time, Gerhard Neumann of General Electric conceived a high-pressure-ratio, single-spool compressor having automatically controlled *variable stator blades*. This compressor configuration was also capable of producing very high pressure ratios because it alleviated the mismatching phenomena under off-design operation by stator blade adjustment. In addition, the controlled variable-stator-compressor offers the possibility of a quick reaction against compressor stall. The variable-stator concept became the basis for a new, highly successful turbojet engine, the J79, which was selected as the powerplant for many important supersonic Air Force and Navy aircraft. A third possibility to minimize mismatching phenomena was *variable front-stage bleeding,* which was employed in several engines.

Before I continue with the evolution of the turbo engines toward higher overall efficiencies, a brief discussion about the research and development efforts on compressor bladings and individual stages is in order. Such efforts existed to a small degree even before the advent of the turbojet (in Switzerland, Germany, England, and other countries). However, in the mid-1940s, those research efforts began to greatly intensify after the turbojet appeared. It was recognized that basic research and technology efforts were needed in order to continuously increase

- Stage pressure ratio and efficiency
- Mass throughflow capability

Very significant contributions had been made by universities, research institutes, and government laboratories (NACA, later NASA; Aero Propulsion Laboratory, and others), and industry laboratories. Many outstanding research results were obtained from universities in areas of rotating stall, three-dimensional and nonsteady flow phenomena and transonic flow effects, novel flow visualization techniques for diagnostics (which identified flow regions having improvement possibilities), understanding of noise origination, and many others.

Two examples where government laboratories had achieved very crucial advancements which were later adapted by industry were the following: In the early 1950s, the NACA Lewis Research Center, under the leadership of Abe Silverstein, advanced compressor aerodynamics to transonic and supersonic flow, critical contributions for increasing the compressor-stage pressure ratio. He initiated a large transonic and supersonic compressor research program. Many in-depth studies furnished information for utilizing this new compressor concept. Later, the Air Force Propulsion Laboratory, under the leadership of Arthur Wennerstrom, conducted advanced compressor research and introduced a very important supersonic compressor concept, which was particularly applicable for front stages because it solved the most difficult combined requirements of high mass flow ratio, high pressure ratio, high efficiency, and broad characteristics.

The continuous flow of research and technological contributions extended over the last four decades and is still going on. The total cost may have been several hundred million dollars. Some of the results can be summarized as follows: The polytropic compressor efficiency, which was slightly below 80 percent in 1943, is now about 92 percent; the average stage pressure ratio, which was about 1.15:1 in 1943, is now about 1.4:1 and greater; the corrected mass flow rate per unit area capability grew over the same time period by more than 50 percent.

The improvement in compressor efficiency had an enormous impact on engine performance, specifically on the overall engine efficiency. The substantially increased stage pressure ratio and the increased corrected mass flow rate per unit area capability resulted in a substantial reduction of engine length, frontal area, and weight-per-power output.

Let us now return to the 1950s. As previously stated, the new turbojets employing a dual-rotor configuration or controlled variable-stator blades were capable of substantially higher pressure ratios than the fixed-geometry, single-spool engines of the 1940s. Engine cycle analysis showed that the high power-per-unit mass flow rate needed for the advanced engines required higher turbine inlet temperatures. This requirement led to continuous major research efforts to achieve high-efficiency combustion with low pollution, to increase the effectiveness of turbine blade-cooling methods, and to improve the temperature capabilities of materials. So the turbojets of the 1950s had made substantial progress in thermodynamic efficiency and propulsive thrust per pound of inlet air per second. The latter characteristic means that the velocity of the exhaust gas jet had increased.

Development of High-Bypass-Ratio Turbofans

For supersonic flight speeds, the overall efficiency of these turbojets was outstanding. However, for high subsonic and transonic flight speeds (around 500 to 600 mi/hr), the velocity of the exhaust gas jet was too high to obtain a good propulsive efficiency. Under these conditions, the *bypass engine* (also called *turbofan* or *fan-jet*) became a very attractive approach for improving the propulsive efficiency. The first fan-jets had a relatively small bypass ratio of about 2:1. (*Bypass ratio* is the ratio of mass flow bypassing the turbine to mass flow passing through the turbine.) In the early 1960s, the U.S. Air Force had established requirements for military transports capable of an extremely long range at high subsonic cruise speeds. Such requirements could be met only by employing propulsion systems of highest possible thermodynamic and propulsive efficiencies, which led to the following engine characteristics:

- Very high compressor pressure ratios between 20:1 and 30:1 which could be achieved by combining the concepts of variable stator and dual rotor
- Very high turbine inlet temperatures
- Very high bypass ratios, around 8:1

The first engine of this type was the TF39 (Fig. 16), a military transport engine developed by General Electric under the leadership of Gerhard Neumann. Four of the TF39 turbofan engines powered the Lockheed C5A.

The Air Force Propulsion Laboratory, under the leadership of Cliff Simpson, had played a key role in the establishment of these requirements. Simpson also succeeded in convincing the highest Air Force and Department of Defense echelons of the significance of this new type of air-breathing propulsion system, which he considered a technological breakthrough. (At that time, it was difficult to generate interest in advanced air-breathing propulsion system concepts, since the nation's attention was focused on rocket propulsion for space exploration.)

The advantages of the high-bypass-ratio turbofan engines can be summarized as follows:

- High overall efficiency, resulting in a long flight range

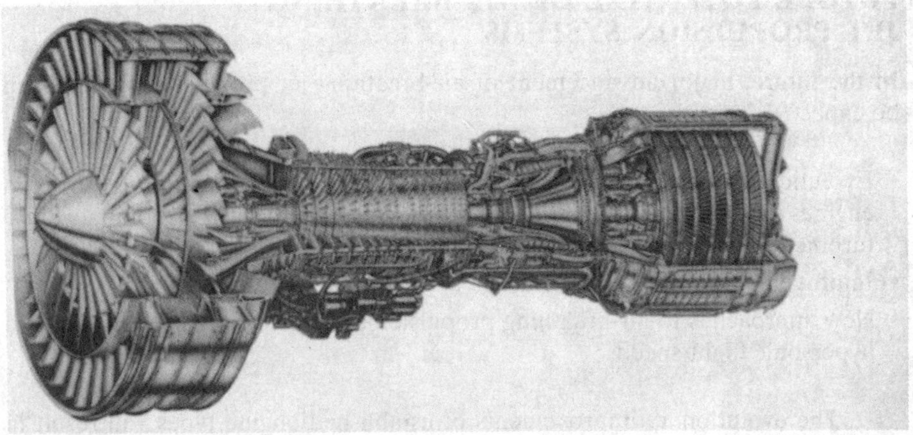

FIGURE 16
The TF39 high-bypass-ratio turbofan engine used on the Lockheed C5 transport. (*Courtesy of General Electric Aircraft Engines.*)

- Strong increase in propulsive thrust at low flight speeds, which is important for takeoff, climbing, and efficient part-load operation
- Lower jet velocity, which leads to great noise reduction
- Low fuel consumption, which reduces chemical emissions

These characteristics had been demonstrated in the late 1960s and early 1970s. They also became of great interest for commercial aircraft and led to the development of the *widebody* passenger aircraft.

During the 1980s, the continuous flow of advanced technology of turbo engine components had brought a high degree of maturity to the various aircraft gas turbine engine types, such as the following:

- The above-discussed high-bypass-ratio engines
- The low-bypass-ratio engines with afterburning for supersonic flight
- The pure turbojet for high supersonic flight Mach numbers of approximately 3

The small and medium aircraft shaft-power gas turbines also benefited enormously from the continuous improvement of turbomachinery technology. These small gas turbines are used in helicopters and subsonic propeller aircraft. The high power/weight ratio and the high thermodynamic efficiency of the advanced shaft-power gas turbine engines played a key role in the advancement of helicopters.

FUTURE POTENTIAL OF AIR-BREATHING JET PROPULSION SYSTEMS

In the future, major advancement of air-breathing jet propulsion systems can be expected from

- Evolutionary improvements of the established large-bypass-ratio turbofan engines for transonic flight speeds and the low-bypass-ratio turbofan, or pure turbojet engines, for supersonic flight speeds
- Improvements and new approaches to engine-airplane integration
- New approaches to air-breathing propulsion systems for high supersonic and hypersonic flight speeds

The evolutionary improvements of established engine types will result in greater fuel economy and better performance characteristics. By the end of the century, one can expect polytropic efficiencies of turbine and compressor of nearly 95 percent. Furthermore, one will see considerably increased single-stage pressure ratios; significantly higher turbine inlet temperatures resulting from better heat- and oxidation-resistant materials, and more effective blade-cooling methods; and much lighter structural designs and materials (composite materials). This technological progress may result in an overall engine efficiency increase of about 20 percent and in a weight reduction for given horsepower output by probably a factor of 2 and higher.

For the evolution of high-bypass-ratio engines at cruise speeds between 500 and 600 mi/hr, the following trend is important; the greater the turbine inlet temperature and the higher the polytropic efficiencies of the compressor and the turbine, the higher the optimum pressure ratio of the gas turbine engine and the bypass ratio of the fan. In the future, this trend will lead to larger bypass ratios; hence, the fan shroud will become relatively large in diameter and will contribute substantially to the weight and external drag of the propulsion system. Several solutions are conceivable to alleviate this problem, but at this time it is not possible to predict the most promising approach.

One way is to eliminate the fan shroud by using an unshrouded fan (having a multiplicity of swept-back fan blades, see Fig. 17), also called a *prop-fan.* This configuration is currently in an experimental state and may become very important in the future for improving fuel economy. Another possibility may lie in the development of a transonic airframe configuration in which the large fan shrouds have a dual function: They contribute, in part, to the stability of the aircraft (horizontal and vertical stabilizer surfaces) while serving at the same time as a shroud for the fan. Finally, it may be conceivable that, in the future, a practical airframe and wing configuration can be developed which will be capable of extending a high lift/drag ratio to a flight speed regime which is very close to the speed of sound (a kind of well-known "supercritical" airframe configuration proposed by Whitcomb of NASA). If

FIGURE 17
PW-Allison 578DX propulsion system. (*Courtesy of Allison Gas Turbine Division.*)

such an airframe configuration could be developed, the bypass ratio at these relatively high flight speeds would be substantially lower than that for flight speeds around 500 mi/hr and, therefore, a shrouded fan would be most applicable.

Perhaps a most interesting question is: Can one expect a future supersonic passenger transport which is economically feasible in view of the progress of future transonic passenger transports? The general trend of the airplane lift/drag ratio is decreasing with increasing flight Mach number, while the overall efficiency of aeropropulsion systems increases with increasing flight Mach number. Currently, the lift/drag ratio of the Boeing 747 compared to that of the supersonic Concorde is about 3:1. In the future, the corresponding ratio may decrease to about 2:1, and the structural weight of the supersonic aircraft will greatly be improved. Such improvements may be the result of advancements in the aerodynamic shape, the structure, the structural airframe materials, and the best use of artificial stability. The overall efficiency of the supersonic flight engine can also be improved, including its capability of cruising subsonically with only one engine. This is important in case one of the two engines fails. Under this condition, the mission must be completed at subsonic speed without requiring an additional fuel reserve. It appears that advanced supersonic-cruise aircraft systems have the potential to achieve these conditions and, thus, become economically acceptable in the future.

New Approaches to Engine-Airplane Integration

In general, the investigations of engine-airplane integration have the goal to avoid or minimize losses due to adverse interface phenomena between the engine exhaust inlet stream or jet and the air vehicle. However, many favorable effects can be achieved by properly integrating functions of the propulsion system with functions of the airplane. Historically, Prof. Ackeret (University of Zurich, Switzerland) had first suggested, in 1921, reaccelerating the boundary-layer air near the trailing edge of the wing. He showed that this method of producing the propulsive thrust can result in substantial gains in overall efficiency of the propulsion system. In the 1970s, various investigations had shown that similar results can be obtained by using momentum exchange of the high-pressure bypass air with the boundary-layer air.

Other uses of bypass air are to energize the boundary layer at proper locations of the wing in order to prevent boundary-layer separation and to increase the circulation around the wing (often called *supercirculation*). This method may become important for advanced short-takeoff-and-landing (STOL) applications. For future V/STOL applications, new methods of thrust vectoring and thrust augmentation may have very attractive possibilities. Also, bypass air may be used for boundary-layer suction and ejection in advanced laminar systems.

Air-Breathing Propulsion Systems for High Supersonic and Hypersonic Speeds

In air-breathing propulsion systems, the combined compression by ram and turbo compressor is of great benefit to the thermodynamic propulsion process up to flight Mach numbers approaching 3. When the flight Mach number increases further, the benefits of the turbo compressor begin to decrease and the engine begins to operate essentially as a ramjet. When the flight Mach number exceeds about 3.5, any additional compression by a turbo compressor would be a disadvantage. Thus, if the engine operates best as a pure subsonic combustion ramjet, it fits in a flight Mach number regime from about 3.5 to 5. Beyond flight Mach numbers of about 6, the pressure and temperature ratios would be unfavorably high if the engine continued to operate as a subsonic combustion ramjet. The reasons are as follows:

- High degree of dissociation of the combustor exhaust flow, reducing the energy available for exhaust velocity
- Pressures far too high for Brayton cycle operations or for the structure to withstand

For these reasons, the cycle will be changed from a subsonic to a supersonic combustion ramjet, and hydrogen will be used as fuel because hydrogen has the greatest

- Combustion heat and fuel-air concentration range
- Diffusion speed and reaction speed
- Heat-sink capabilities

This supersonic combustion ramjet cycle is characterized by a reduction of the undisturbed hypersonic flight Mach number to a somewhat lower hypersonic Mach number with an increase in entropy, which should be as low as possible. The deceleration process must be chosen in such a manner that the increases in static pressure and entropy correspond to a high-performance Brayton cycle. The internal thrust generated by the exhaust gas must be larger than the external drag forces acting on the vehicle.

To minimize the parasitic drag of the ramjet vehicle systems, various external ramjet vehicle configurations have been suggested. However, theoretical and experimental investigations will be necessary to explore their associated aerothermochemical problems.

For the experimental research, one may consider investigations using free-flight models or hypersonic wind tunnels with true temperature simulation. Historically, it may be of interest that many suggestions and investigations had been made as to how to achieve clean hypersonic airflows with true stagnation temperatures. I remember much work and many discussions with Dr. R. Mills, E. Johnson, Dr. Frank Wattendorf, and Dr. Toni Ferri about "air accelerator" concepts, which aimed to avoid flow stagnation and the generation of ultrahigh static temperatures and chemical dissociation.

Since the Wright brothers, enormous achievements have been made in both low-speed and high-speed air-breathing propulsion systems. The coming of the jet age opened up the new frontiers of transonic and supersonic flight (see Fig. 3). While substantial accomplishments have been made during the past several decades in the field of high supersonic and hypersonic flight (see Ref. 2), it appears that even greater challenges lie ahead.

For me, being a part of the growth in air-breathing propulsion over the past 60 years has been both an exciting adventure and a privilege. This foreword has given you a view of its history and future challenges. The following book presents an excellent foundation in air-breathing propulsion and can prepare you for these challenges. My wish is that you will have as much fun in propulsion as I have.

Hans von Ohain
German inventor of the jet engine

REFERENCES

1. von Karman, Theodore, *The Wind and Beyond,* Little, Brown, and Company, Boston, 1967.
2. Heiser, William H., and Pratt, David T., *Hypersonic Airbreathing Propulsion,* AIAA Education Series, AIAA, Washington, 1994.

3. Boyne, Walter J., and Lopez, Donald S., *The Jet Age, Forty Years of Jet Aviation,* Smithsonian Institution Press, Washington, 1979.
4. Schlaifer, Robert, and Heron, S. D., *Development of Aircraft Engines, and Fuels,* Pergamon Press, New York, 1970 (reprint of 1950 ed.).

PREFACE

This undergraduate text provides an introduction to the fundamentals of gas turbine engines and jet propulsion. These basic elements determine the behavior, design, and operation of the jet engines and chemical rocket motors used for propulsion. The text contains sufficient material for two sequential courses in propulsion: an introductory course in jet propulsion and a gas turbine engine components course. It is based on one- and two-course sequences taught at several different universities over the past 15 years. The author has also used this text for a course on turbomachinery.

The outstanding historical foreword by Hans von Ohain (the German inventor of the jet engine) gives a unique perspective on the first 50 years of jet propulsion. His account of past development work is highlighted by his early experiences. He concludes with predictions of future developments.

The text gives examples of existing designs and typical values of design parameters. Many example problems are included in this text to help the student see the application of a concept after it is introduced. Problems are included at the end of each chapter that emphasize those particular principles. Two extensive design problems for the preliminary selection and design of a gas turbine engine cycle are included. Several turbomachinery design problems are also included.

The text material is divided into four parts:

- Introduction to aircraft and rocket propulsion (Chap. 1)
- Basic concepts and one-dimensional gas dynamics (Chaps. 2 and 3)

- Analysis and performance of air-breathing propulsion systems (Chaps. 4 through 8)
- Analysis and design of gas turbine engine components (Chaps. 9 and 10)

Chapter 1 introduces the types of air-breathing and rocket propulsion systems and their basic performance parameters. Also included is an introduction to aircraft and rocket systems which reveals the influence that propulsion system performance has on the overall system. This material facilitates incorporation of a basic propulsion design problem into a course, such as new engines for an existing aircraft.

The fundamental laws of mass conservation, momentum, and thermodynamics for a control volume (open system) and the properties of perfect gases are reviewed in Chap. 2. For some students, the material on one-dimensional gas dynamics in Chap. 3 will be a review of material they have already had. For other students, this chapter may be their first exposure to this information and may require greater effort to understand.

The analysis of gas turbine engines begins in Chap. 4 with the definitions of installed thrust, uninstalled thrust, and installation losses. This chapter also reviews the ideal Brayton cycle which limits gas turbine engine performance.

Two types of analysis are developed and applied to gas turbine engines in Chaps. 5 through 8: parametric cycle analysis (thermodynamic design point) and performance analysis. The text uses the cycle analysis methods introduced by Professor Frank E. Marble of the California Institute of Technology and further developed by Gordon C. Oates (deceased) of the University of Washington and Jack L. Kerrebrock of the Massachusetts Institute of Technology. The steps of parametric cycle analysis are identified in Chap. 5 and then used to model engine cycles from the simple ramjet to the complex, mixed-flow, afterburning turbofan engine. Families of engine designs are analyzed in the *parametric analysis* of Chaps. 5 and 7 for ideal engines and engines with losses, respectively. Chapter 6 develops the overall relationships for engine components with losses. The *performance analysis* of Chap. 8 models the actual behavior of an engine and shows why its performance changes with flight conditions and throttle settings. The results of the engine performance analysis can be used to establish component performance requirements.

Chapter 9 covers both axial-flow and centrifugal-flow turbomachinery. Included are basic theory and mean-line design of axial-flow compressors and turbines, quick design tools (e.g., repeating-row, repeating-stage design of axial-flow compressors), example multistage compressor designs, flow path and blade shapes, turbomachinery stresses, and turbine cooling. Example output from the COMPR and TURBN programs is included in several example problems.

Inlets, exhaust nozzles, and combustion systems are modeled and analyzed in Chap. 10. The special operation and performance characteristics of supersonic inlets are examined and an example of an external compression inlet is designed. The principles of physics that control the operation and design of main burners and afterburners are also covered.

The extensive appendixes contain tables for compressible flow functions, normal and oblique shocks, Rayleigh line flow, Fanno line flow, and properties of standard atmosphere. There is also material on turbomachinery stresses as well as useful data on existing gas turbine engines and liquid-propellant rocket engines.

Five computer programs are provided for use with this textbook:

- AFPROP—properties of combustion products for air and $(CH_2)_n$
- COMPR—axial-flow compressor mean-line design analysis
- PARA—parametric engine cycle analysis
- PERF—engine performance analysis
- TURBN—axial-flow turbine mean-line design analysis

The AFPROP program can be used to help solve problems of perfect gases with variable specific heats. The PARA and PERF programs support the material in Chaps. 5 through 8. PARA is very useful in determining variations in engine performance with design parameters and in limiting the useful range of design values. PERF can predict the variation of an engine's performance with flight condition and throttle. Both are very useful in evaluating alternative engine designs and can be used in design problems that require selection of an engine for an existing airframe and specified mission. The COMPR and TURBN programs permit preliminary design of axial-flow turbomachinery.

Introductory Course:

- Chapters 1 and 2, all
- Chapter 3, Secs. 3-1 through 3-7
- Chapter 4, all
- Chapter 5, Secs. 5-1 through 5-9 and other engine cycles of interest
- Chapter 6, Secs. 6-1 through 6-8
- Chapter 7, Secs. 7-1 through 7-4 and other engine cycles of interest
- Chapter 8, Secs. 8-1 through 8-4 and one of Secs. 8-5, 8-6, and 8-7

Gas Turbine Engine Components Course:

- Chapter 2, all
- Chapter 3, all
- Chapter 8, Secs. 8-1 through 8-7
- Chapter 9 and App. J, all
- Chapter 10, all

The material in Chaps. 2, 3, and 9 and App. J of this text have also been used to teach the major portion of an undergraduate turbomachinery course.

ACKNOWLEDGMENTS

I am deeply indebted to Professor Gordon C. Oates (deceased) and Dr. William H. Heiser. Professor Oates taught me the basics of engine cycle analysis during my doctoral studies at the University of Washington and later until his untimely death in 1986. While Dr. Heiser was a Distinguished Visiting Professor at the U.S. Air Force Academy from 1983 to 1985, we developed an outstanding engine design course and wrote the textbook *Aircraft Engine Design.* He has been my friend and mentor over the years.

Special thanks to Brigadier General Daniel H. Daley (USAF, retired, and former Head, Department of Aeronautics, U.S. Air Force Academy), who sponsored my studies under Prof. Oates and guided me during the compilation of the teaching notes "Elements of Propulsion." These notes have been used in the Academy's propulsion courses and are the basis for this textbook.

I also thank all the students who have been in my propulsion courses and my coworkers at the Department of Aeronautics, U.S. Air Force Academy, CO; the Air Force Aero Propulsion and Power Laboratory, Wright-Patterson Air Force Base, OH; and Seattle University. Many of these students and coworkers provided insight and guidance in developing this material.

I acknowledge the hard work and determination of Scott Henderson who worked all the problems and design problems and checked my solutions. He made significant improvements to the quality and clarity of these problems.

McGraw-Hill and I would like to thank the following reviewers for their many helpful comments and suggestions: John Anderson, University of Maryland; Patrick Dunn, University of Notre Dame; Saeed Farokhi, The University of Kansas; Afshin Ghajar, Oklahoma State University; John Lloyd, Michigan State University; Frank Redd, Utah State University; and Susan Ying, Florida State University.

Jack D. Mattingly

LIST OF SYMBOLS

A	area; constant
a	speed of sound; constant
b	constant [Eq. (5-90)]
C	effective exhaust velocity [Eq. (1-53)]; circumference; work output coefficient
C_A	angularity coefficient
C_C	work output coefficient of core
C_D	coefficient of drag; discharge coefficient
C_F	thrust coefficient
C_{fg}	gross thrust coefficient
C_L	coefficient of lift
C_P	pressure coefficient
C_{prop}	work output coefficient of propeller
C_{tot}	total work output coefficient
C_V	velocity coefficient
C^*	characteristic velocity
c	chord
c_f	frictional coefficient
c_p	specific heat at constant pressure
c_v	specific heat at constant volume
c_x	axial chord
D	drag
d	differential (infinitesimal increase in); diameter
E	energy; modulus of elasticity
e	energy per unit mass; polytropic efficiency; exponential (=2.7183)
EF	endurance factor [Eq. (1-38)]
F	force; uninstalled thrust; thrust
F_g	gross thrust

f	fuel/air ratio; function
FR	thrust ratio [Eq. (5-56)]
g	acceleration of gravity
g_c	Newton's constant
g_0	acceleration of gravity at sea level
H	enthalpy
h	enthalpy per unit mass; height
h_{PR}	low heating value of fuel
I	impulse function [$= PA(1 + \gamma M^2)$]
I_{sp}	specific impulse [Eq. (1-55)]
K	constant
L	length
M	Mach number; momentum
$\dot{M}$	time rate of change of momentum
m	mass
$\dot{m}$	mass flow rate
$\mathcal{M}$	molecular weight
MFP	mass flow parameter
MR	vehicle mass ratio
N	revolutions per minute
n	load factor; burning rate exponent
n_b	number of blades
P	pressure
P_f	profile factor
P_s	weight specific excess power
P_t	total pressure
PF	pattern factor
Q	heat interaction
$\dot{Q}$	rate of heat interaction
q	heat interaction per unit mass; dynamic pressure [$=\rho V^2/(2g_c)$]
R	gas constant; extensive property; radius; additional drag
R_u	universal gas constant
r	radius; burning rate
RF	range factor [Eq. (1-43)]
$°R$	degree of reaction
S	uninstalled thrust specific fuel consumption; entropy
$\dot{S}$	time rate of change of entropy
S_w	wing planform area
s	entropy per unit mass; blade spacing
T	temperature; installed thrust
T_t	total temperature
t	time; airfoil thickness
TR	throttle ratio [Eq. (8-34)]
TSFC	installed thrust specific fuel consumption

U	internal energy; blade tangential or rotor velocity
u	internal energy per unit mass; velocity
V	absolute velocity; volume
v	volume per unit mass; velocity
W	weight; width
$\dot{W}$	power
w	work interaction per unit mass; velocity
$\dot{w}$	weight flow rate
x, y, z	coordinate system
z_e	energy height [Eq. (1-25)]
Z	Zweifel tangential force coefficient [Eq. (9-97)]

Greek

α	bypass ratio; angle; coefficient of linear thermal expansion
β	angle
Γ	$=\sqrt{\gamma\left(\frac{2}{\gamma+1}\right)^{(\gamma+1)/(\gamma-1)}}$; constant
γ	ratio of specific heats; angle
Δ	change
δ	change; dimensionless pressure ($=P/P_{\text{ref}}$); deviation
∂	partial differential
ε	nozzle area ratio; rotor turning angle
η	efficiency
θ	angle; dimensionless temperature ($=T/T_{\text{ref}}$)
μ	Mach angle
Π	product
π	pressure ratio defined by Eq. (5-3)
ρ	density ($=1/v$)
Σ	sum
σ	control volume boundary; dimensionless density ($=\rho/\rho_{\text{ref}}$); tensile stress
τ	temperature ratio defined by Eq. (5-4); shear stress; torque
τ_λ	enthalpy ratio defined by Eq. (5-7)
ϕ	installation loss coefficient; fuel equivalence ratio; function; total pressure loss coefficient
Φ	function; cooling effectiveness; flow coefficient
ω	angular speed

Subscripts

A	air mass
a	air; atmosphere

AB	afterburner
add	additive
b	burner or combustor; boattail or afterbody; blade; burning
C	core stream
c	compressor; corrected; centrifugal; chamber
DB	duct burner
d	diffuser or inlet; disk
dr	disk/rim interface
dry	afterburner not operating
e	exit; exhaust; earth
ext	external
F	fan stream
f	fan; fuel; final
fn	fan nozzle
g	gearing; gas
H	high-pressure
HP	horsepower
h	hub
i	initial; inside; ideal
int	internal
j	jet
L	low-pressure
M	mixer
m	mechanical; mean; middle
max	corresponding to maximum
N	new
n	nozzle
nac	nacelle
O	overall; output
o	overall; outer
opt	optimum
P	propulsive; products
p	propellant
pl	payload
prop	propeller
R	reference; relative; reactants
r	ram; reduced; rim; rotor
ref	reference condition
s	stage; separation; solid; stator
SL	sea-level
SLS	sea-level static
T	thermal
t	total; turbine; throat; tip; thermal
vac	vacuum
w	forebody; wing

wet	afterburner operating
x, y, z	directional component
σ	control volume
$0, 1, 2, \ldots, 19$	different locations in space

Superscripts

*	state corresponding to $M = 1$; corresponding to optimum state
—	average

CHAPTER 1

INTRODUCTION

1-1 PROPULSION

The *Random House College Dictionary* (Ref. 1) defines *propulsion* as "the act of propelling, the state of being propelled, a propelling force or impulse" and defines the verb *propel* as "to drive, or cause to move, forward or onward." From these definitions, we can conclude that the study of propulsion includes the study of the propelling force, the motion caused, and the bodies involved. Propulsion involves an object to be propelled plus one or more additional bodies, called *propellant.*

The study of propulsion is concerned with vehicles such as automobiles, trains, ships, aircraft, and spacecraft. The focus of this textbook is on the propulsion of aircraft and spacecraft. Methods devised to produce a thrust force for the propulsion of a vehicle in flight are based on the principle of jet propulsion (the momentum change of a fluid by the propulsion system). The fluid may be the gas used by the engine itself (e.g., turbojet), it may be a fluid available in the surrounding environment (e.g., air used by a propeller), or it may be stored in the vehicle and carried by it during the flight (e.g., rocket).

Jet propulsion systems can be subdivided into two broad categories: air-breathing and non-air-breathing. Air-breathing propulsion systems include the reciprocating, turbojet, turbofan, ramjet, turboprop, and turboshaft engines. Non-air-breathing engines include rocket motors, nuclear propulsion systems, and electric propulsion systems. We focus on gas turbine propulsion systems (turbojet, turbofan, turboprop, and turboshaft engines) in this textbook.

The material in this textbook is divided into three parts:

- Basic concepts and one-dimensional gas dynamics
- Analysis and performance of air-breathing propulsion systems
- Analysis of gas turbine engine components

This chapter introduces the types of air-breathing and rocket propulsion systems and the basic propulsion performance parameters. Also included is an introduction to aircraft and rocket performance. The material on aircraft performance shows the influence of the gas turbine engine performance on the performance of the aircraft system. This material also permits incorporation of a gas turbine engine design problem such as new engines for an existing aircraft.

Numerous examples are included throughout this book to help students see the application of a concept after it is introduced. For some students, the material on basic concepts and gas dynamics will be a review of material covered in other courses they have already taken. For other students, this may be their first exposure to this material, and it may require more effort to understand.

1-2 UNITS AND DIMENSIONS

Since the engineering world uses both the metric SI and English unit system, both will be used in this textbook. One singular distinction exists between the English system and SI—the unit of force is defined in the former but derived in the latter. Newton's second law of motion relates force to mass, length, and time. It states that the sum of the forces is proportional to the rate of change of the momentum ($\mathbf{M} = m\mathbf{V}$). The constant of proportionality is $1/g_c$.

$$\sum \mathbf{F} = \frac{1}{g_c}\frac{d(m\mathbf{V})}{dt} = \frac{1}{g_c}\frac{d\mathbf{M}}{dt} \tag{1-1}$$

The units for each term in the above equation are listed in Table 1-1 for both SI and English units. In any unit system, only four of the five items in the table can be specified, and the latter is derived from Eq. (1-1).

As a result of selecting $g_c = 1$ and defining the units of mass, length, and time in SI units, the unit of force is derived from Eq. (1-1) as

TABLE 1-1
Units and dimensions

Unit system	Force	g_c	Mass	Length	Time
SI	Derived	1	Kilogram (kg)	Meter (m)	Second (sec)
English	Pound-force (lbf)	Derived	Pound-mass (lbm)	Foot (ft)	Second (sec)

kilogram-meters per square second ($kg \cdot m/sec^2$), which is called the *newton* (N). In English units, the value of g_c is derived from Eq. (1-1) as

$$\boxed{g_c = 32.174 \text{ ft} \cdot \text{lbm}/(\text{lbf} \cdot \text{sec}^2)}$$

Rather than adopt the convention used in many recent textbooks of developing material or use with *only* SI metric units ($g_c = 1$), we will maintain g_c in all our equations. Thus g_c will also show up in the equations for *potential energy* (PE) and *kinetic energy* (KE):

$$\text{PE} = \frac{mgz}{g_c}$$

$$\text{KE} = \frac{mV^2}{2g_c}$$

The total energy per unit mass e is the sum of the specific internal energy u, specific kinetic energy ke, and specific potential energy pe.

$$e \equiv u + \text{ke} + \text{pe} = u + \frac{V^2}{2g_c} + \frac{gz}{g_c}$$

There are a multitude of engineering units for the quantities of interest in propulsion. For example, energy can be expressed in the SI unit of *joule* ($1 \text{ J} = 1 \text{ N} \cdot \text{m}$), in British thermal units (Btu's), or in foot-pound force ($\text{ft} \cdot \text{lbf}$). One must be able to use the available data in the units provided and convert the units when required. Table 1-2 is a unit conversion table provided to help you in your endeavors.

TABLE 1-2
Unit conversion table

Length	1 m = 3.2808 ft = 39.37 in
	1 km = 0.621 mi
	1 mi = 5280 ft = 1.609 km
	1 nm = 6080 ft = 1.853 km
Area	1 m^2 = 10.764 ft^2
	1 cm^2 = 0.155 in^2
Volume	1 gal = 0.13368 ft^3 = 3.785 L
	1 L = 10^{-3} m^3 = 61.02 in^3
Time	1 hr = 3600 sec = 60 min
Mass	1 kg = 1000 g = 2.2046 lbm = 6.8521 × 10^{-2} slug
	1 slug = 1 lbf · sec^2/ft = 32.174 lbm
Density	1 slug/ft^3 = 512.38 kg/m^3
Force	1 N = 1 kg · m/sec^2
	1 lbf = 4.448 N
Energy	1 J = 1 N · m = 1 kg · m^2/sec^2
	1 Btu = 778.16 ft · lbf = 252 cal = 1055 J
	1 cal = 4.186 J
	1 kJ = 0.947813 Btu = 0.23884 kcal

Power	1 W = 1 J/sec = 1 kg · m^2/sec^3
	1 hp = 550 ft · lbf/sec = 2545 Btu/hr = 745.7 W
	1 kW = 3412 Btu/hr = 1.341 hp
Pressure (stress)	1 atm = 14.696 lb/in^2 or psi = 760 torr = 101,325 Pa
	1 atm = 30.0 inHg = 407.2 inH$_2$O
	1 ksi = 1000 psi
	1 mmHg = 0.01934 psi = 1 torr
	1 Pa = 1 N/m^2
	1 inHg = 3376.8 Pa
Energy per unit mass	1 kJ/kg = 0.4299 Btu/lbm
Specific heat	1 kJ/(kg · °C) = 0.23884 Btu/(lbm · °F)
Temperature	1 K = 1.8°R
	K = 273.15 + °C
	°R = 459.69 + °F
Temperature change	1°C = 1.8°F
Specific thrust	1 lbf/(lbm/sec) = 9.8067 N/(kg/sec)
Specific power	1 hp/(lbm/sec) = 1.644 kW/(kg/sec)
Thrust specific fuel consumption (TSFC)	1 lbm/(lbf · hr) = 28.325 mg/(N · sec)
Power specific fuel consumption	1lbm/(hp · hr) = 168.97 mg/(kW · sec)
Strength/weight ratio (σ/ρ)	1 ksi/(slug/ft^3) = 144 ft^2/sec^2 = 13.38 m^2/sec^2

1-3 OPERATIONAL ENVELOPES AND STANDARD ATMOSPHERE

Each engine type will operate only within a certain range of altitudes and Mach numbers (velocities). Similar limitations in velocity and altitude exist for airframes. It is necessary, therefore, to match airframe and propulsion system capabilities. Figure 1-1 shows the approximate velocity and altitude limits, or *corridor of flight,* within which airlift vehicles can operate. The corridor is bounded by a *lift limit,* a *temperature limit,* and an *aerodynamic force limit.* The lift limit is determined by the maximum level-flight altitude at a given velocity. The temperature limit is set by the structural thermal limits of the material used in construction of the aircraft. At any given altitude, the maximum velocity attained is temperature-limited by aerodynamic heating effects. At lower altitudes, velocity is limited by aerodynamic force loads rather than by temperature.

The operating regions of all aircraft lie within the flight corridor. The operating region of a particular aircraft within the corridor is determined by aircraft design, but it is a very small portion of the overall corridor. Superimposed on the flight corridor in Fig. 1-1 are the operational envelopes of various powered aircraft. The operational limits of each propulsion system are determined by limitations of the components of the propulsion system and are shown in Fig. 1-2.

The analyses presented in this text use the properties of the atmosphere to determine both engine and airframe performance. Since these properties vary with location, season, time of day, etc., we will use the U.S. standard

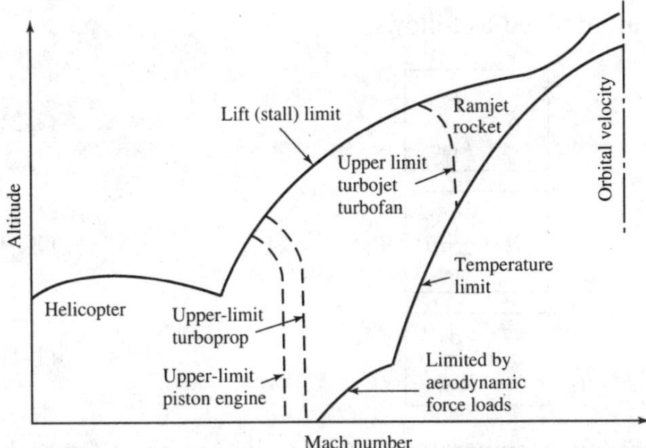

FIGURE 1-1
Flight limits.

atmosphere (Ref. 2) to give a known foundation for our analyses. Appendix A gives the properties of the U.S. standard atmosphere, 1976, in both English and SI units. Values of the pressure P, temperature T, density ρ, and speed of sound a are given in dimensionless ratios of the property at altitude to its value at sea level (SL), (the reference value). The dimensionless ratios of pressure, temperature, and density are given the symbols δ, θ, and σ,

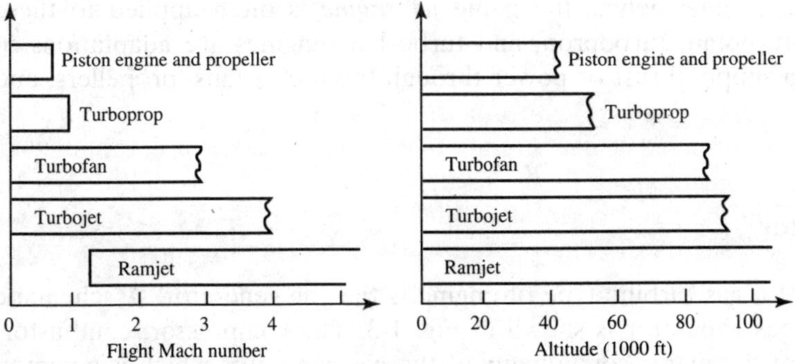

FIGURE 1-2
Engine operational limits.

respectively. These ratios are defined as follows:

$$\boxed{\delta \equiv \frac{P}{P_{\text{ref}}}} \tag{1-2}$$

$$\boxed{\theta \equiv \frac{T}{T_{\text{ref}}}} \tag{1-3}$$

$$\boxed{\sigma \equiv \frac{\rho}{\rho_{\text{ref}}}} \tag{1-4}$$

The reference values of pressure, temperature, and density are given for each unit system at the end of its property table.

For nonstandard conditions such as a hot day, the normal procedure is to use the standard pressure and correct the density, using the perfect gas relationship $\sigma = \delta/\theta$. As an example, we consider a 100°F day at 4-kft altitude. From App. A, we have $\delta = 0.8637$ for the 4-kft altitude. We calculate θ, using the 100°F temperature; $\theta = T/T_{\text{ref}} = (100 + 459.7)/518.7 = 1.079$. Note that absolute temperatures must be used in calculating θ. Then the density ratio is calculated using $\sigma = \delta/\theta = 0.8637/1.079 = 0.8005$.

1-4 AIR-BREATHING ENGINES

The turbojet, turbofan, turboprop, turboshaft, and ramjet engine systems are discussed in this part of Chap. 1. The discussion of these engines is in the context of providing thrust for aircraft. The listed engines are not all the engine types (reciprocating, rockets, combination types, etc.) that are used in providing propulsive thrust to aircraft, nor are they used exclusively on aircraft. The thrust of the turbojet and ramjet results from the action of a fluid jet leaving the engine; hence, the name *jet engine* is often applied to these engines. The turbofan, turboprop, and turboshaft engines are adaptations of the turbojet to supply thrust or power through the use of fans, propellers, and shafts.

Gas Generator

The "heart" of a gas turbine type of engine is the gas generator. A schematic diagram of a gas generator is shown in Fig. 1-3. The compressor, combustor, and turbine are the major components of the gas generator which is common to the turbojet, turbofan, turboprop, and turboshaft engines. The purpose of a gas generator is to supply high-temperature and high-pressure gas.

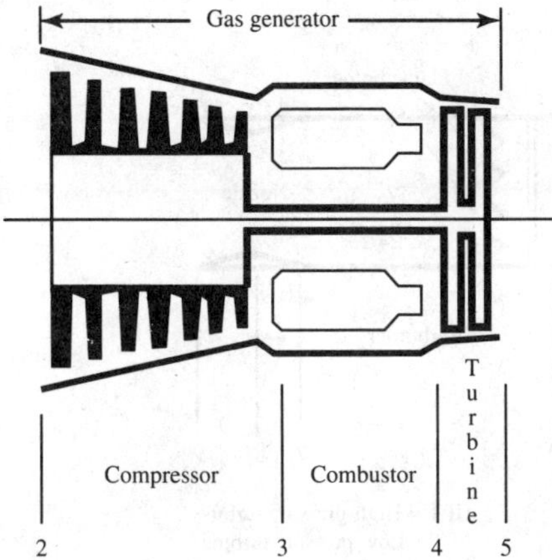

FIGURE 1-3
Schematic diagram of gas generator.

The Turbojet

By adding an inlet and a nozzle to the gas generator, a turbojet engine can be constructed. A schematic diagram of a simple turbojet is shown in Fig. 1-4*a*, and a turbojet with afterburner is shown in Fig. 1-4*b*. In the analysis of a turbojet engine, the major components are treated as sections. Also shown in Figs. 1-4*a* and 1-4*b* are the station numbers for each section.

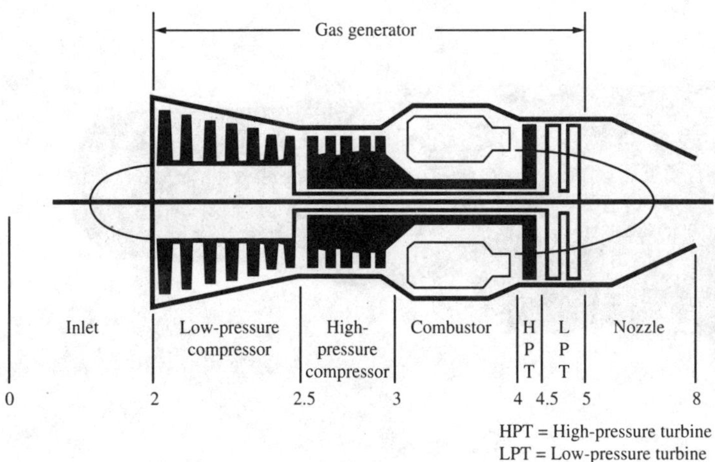

FIGURE 1-4*a*
Schematic diagram of a turbojet (dual axial compressor and turbine).

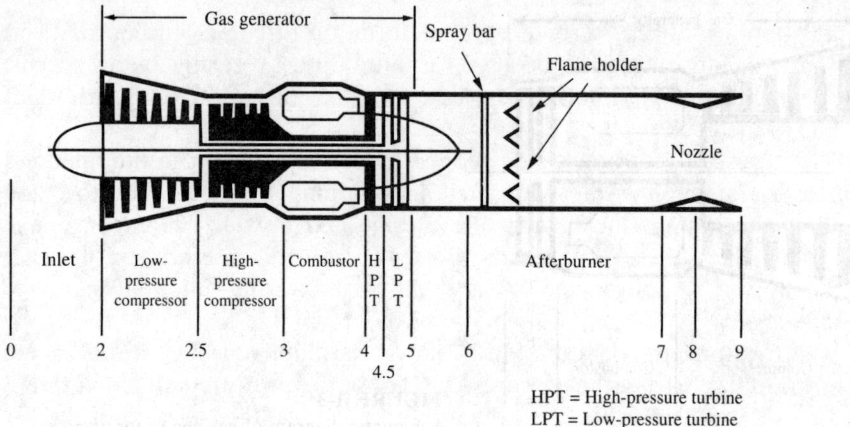

FIGURE 1-4*b*
Schematic diagram of a turbojet with afterburner.

The turbojet was first used as a means of aircraft propulsion by von Ohain (first flight August 27, 1939) and Whittle (first flight May 15, 1941). As development proceeded, the turbojet engine became more efficient and replaced some of the piston engines. A photograph of the J79 turbojet with afterburner used in the F-4 Phantom II and B-58 Hustler is shown in Fig. 1-5.

FIGURE 1-5
General Electric J79 turbojet with afterburner. (*Courtesy of General Electric Aircraft Engines.*)

The adaptations of the turbojet in the form of turbofan, turboprop, and turboshaft engines came with the need for more thrust at relatively low speeds. Some characteristics of different turbojet, turbofan, turboprop, and turboshaft engines are included in App. B.

The thrust of a turbojet is developed by compressing air in the inlet and compressor, mixing the air with fuel and burning in the combustor, and expanding the gas stream through the turbine and nozzle. The expansion of gas through the turbine supplies the power to turn the compressor. The net thrust delivered by the engine is the result of converting internal energy to kinetic energy.

The pressure, temperature, and velocity variations through a J79 engine are shown in Fig. 1-6. In the compressor section, the pressure and temperature increase as a result of work being done on the air. The temperature of the gas is further increased by burning in the combustor. In the turbine section, energy is being removed from the gas stream and converted to shaft power to turn the compressor. The energy is removed by an expansion process which results in a decrease of temperature and pressure. In the nozzle, the gas stream is further expanded to produce a high exit kinetic energy. All the sections of the engine must operate in such a way as to efficiently produce the greatest amount of thrust for a minimum of weight.

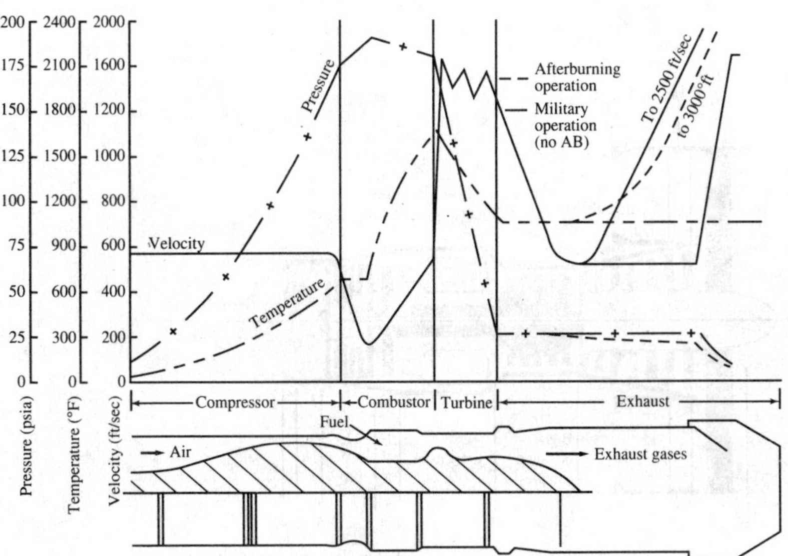

FIGURE 1-6
Property variation through the General Electric J79 afterburning turbojet engine.

The Turbofan

The turbofan engine consists of an inlet, fan, gas generator, and nozzle. A schematic diagram of a turbofan is shown in Fig. 1-7. In the turbofan, a portion of the turbine work is used to supply power to the fan. Generally the turbofan engine is more economical and efficient than the turbojet engine in a limited realm of flight. The *thrust specific fuel consumption* (TSFC, or fuel mass flow rate per unit thrust) is lower for turbofans and indicates a more economical operation. The turbofan also accelerates a larger mass of air to a lower velocity than a turbojet for a higher propulsive efficiency. The frontal area of a turbofan is quite large compared to that of a turbojet, and for this reason more drag and more weight result. The fan diameter is also limited aerodynamically when compressibility effects occur. Several of the current high-bypass-ratio turbofan engines used in subsonic aircraft are shown in Figs. 1-8*a* through 1-8*f*.

Figures 1-9*a* and 1-9*b* show the Pratt & Whitney F100 turbofan and the General Electric F110 turbofan, respectively. These afterburning turbofan engines are used in the F15 Eagle and F16 Falcon supersonic fighter aircraft. In this turbofan, the bypass stream is mixed with the core stream before passing through a common afterburner and exhaust nozzle.

The Turboprop and Turboshaft

A gas generator that drives a propeller is a turboprop engine. The expansion of gas through the turbine supplies the energy required to turn the propeller. A

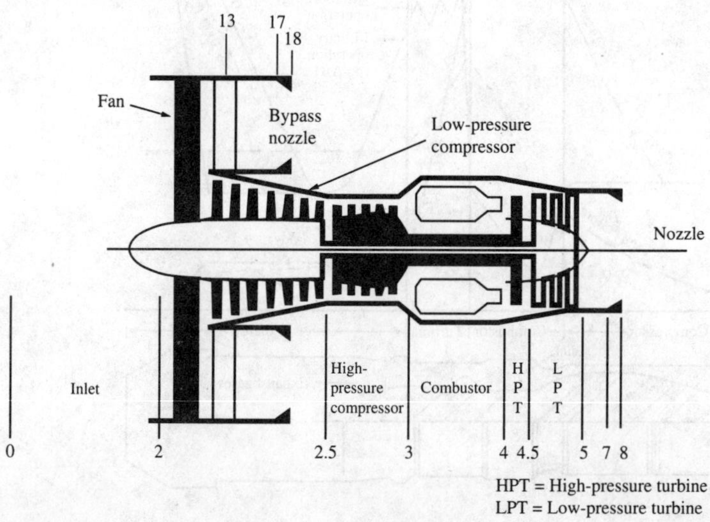

FIGURE 1-7
Schematic diagram of a high-bypass-ratio turbofan.

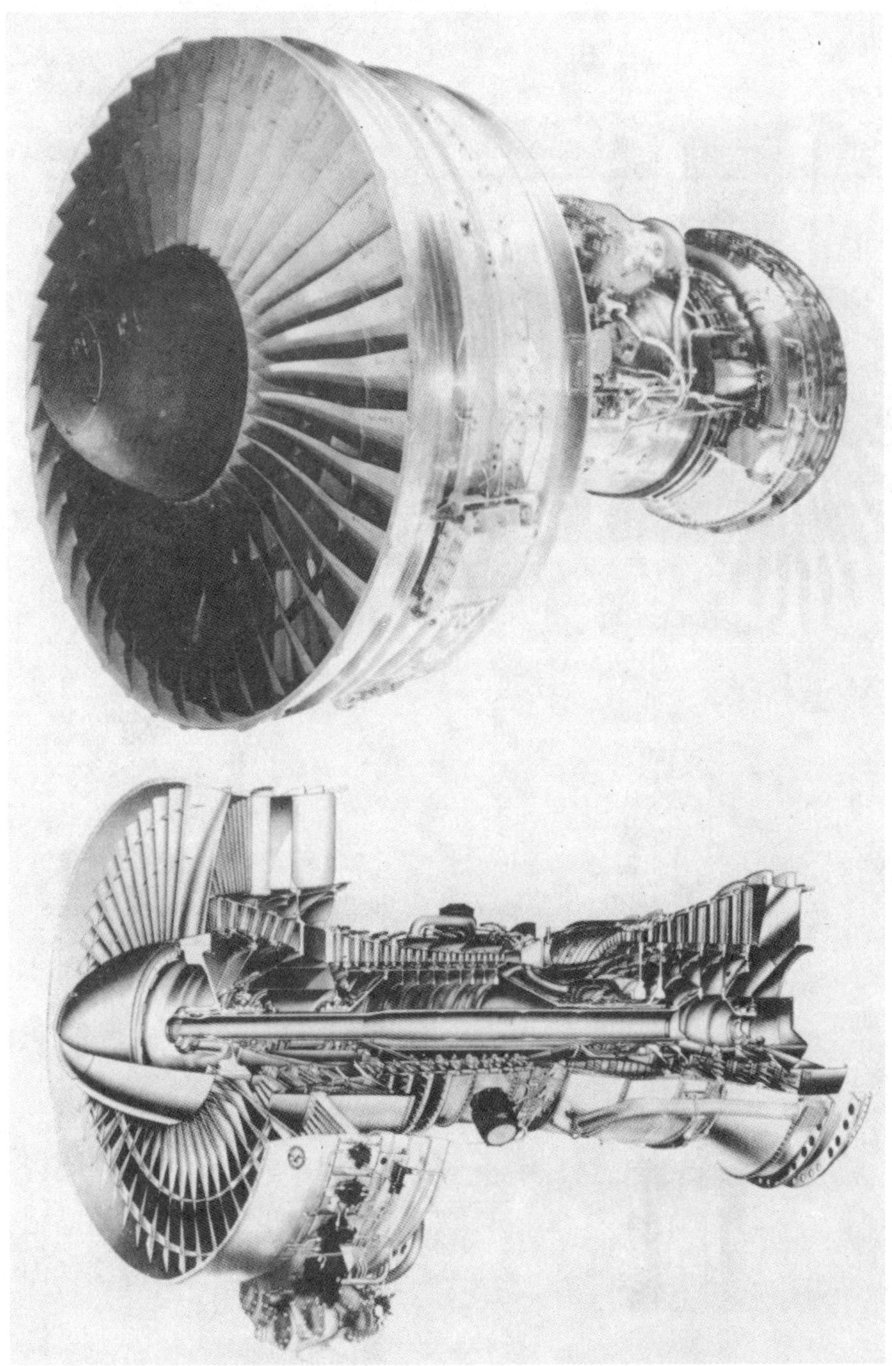

FIGURE 1-8*a*
Pratt & Whitney JT9D turbofan. (*Courtesy of Pratt & Whitney*.)

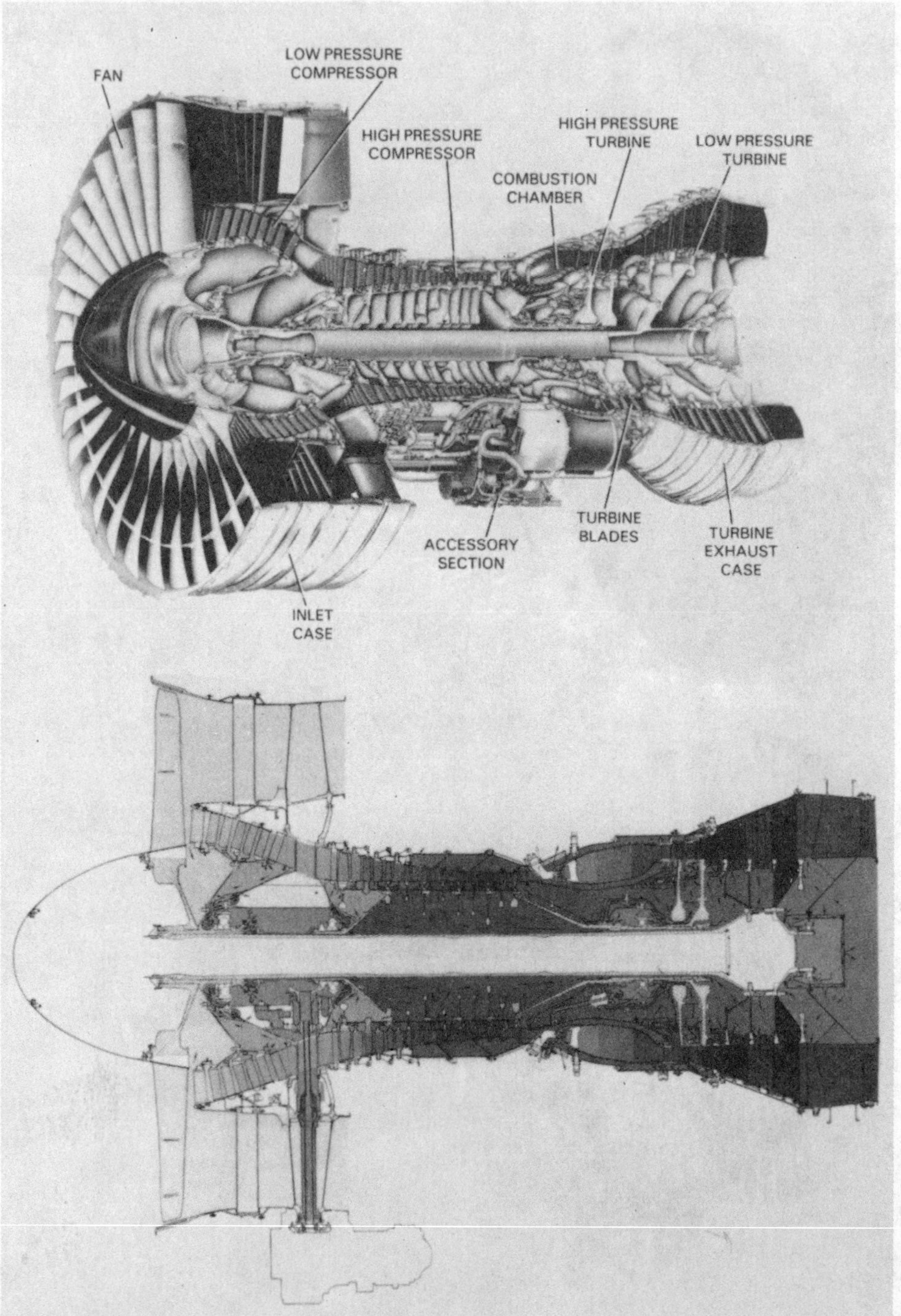

FIGURE 1-8*b*
Pratt & Whitney PW4000 turbofan. (*Courtesy of Pratt & Whitney.*)

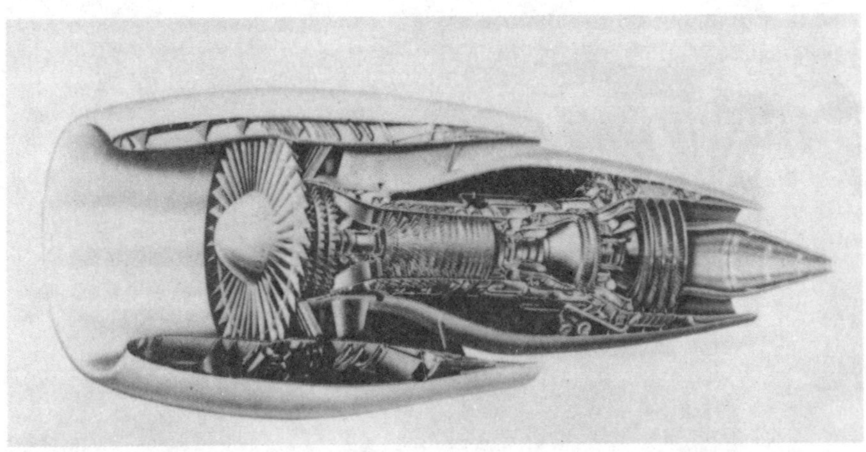

FIGURE 1-8*c*
General Electric CF6 turbofan. (*Courtesy of General Electric Aircraft Engines.*)

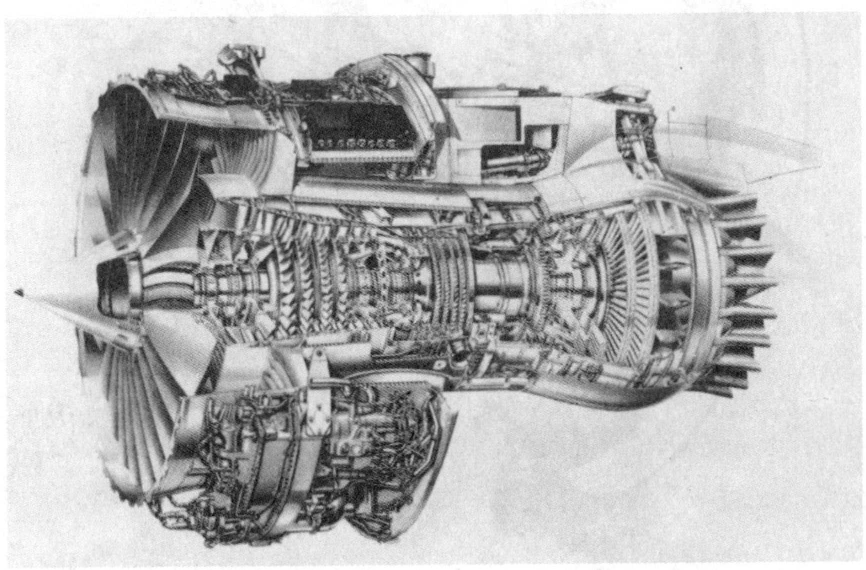

FIGURE 1-8*d*
Rolls-Royce RB-211-524G/H turbofan. (*Courtesy of Rolls-Royce.*)

FIGURE 1-8*e*
General Electric GE90 turbofan. (*Courtesy of General Electric Aircraft Engines.*)

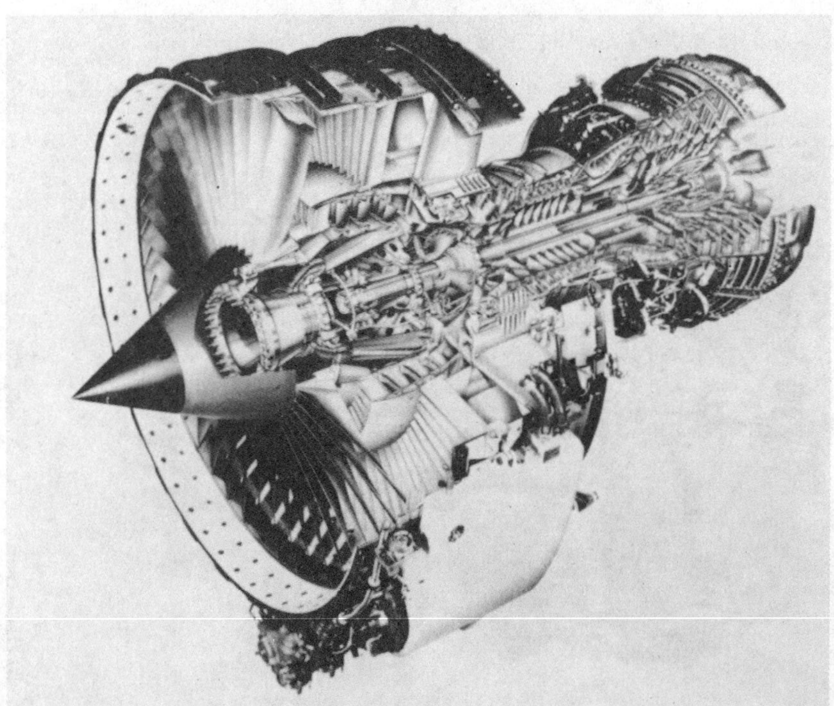

FIGURE 1-8*f*
SNECMA CFM56 turbofan. (*Courtesy of SNECMA.*)

FIGURE 1-9*a*
Pratt & Whitney F100-PW-229 afterburning turbofan. (*Courtesy of Pratt & Whitney.*)

schematic diagram of the turboprop is shown in Fig. 1-10*a*. The turboshaft engine is similar to the turboprop except that power is supplied to a shaft rather than a propeller. The turboshaft engine is used quite extensively for supplying power for helicopters. The turboprop engine may find application in VTOL (vertical takeoff and landing) transporters. The limitations and advantages of the turboprop are those of the propeller. For low-speed flight and short-field takeoff, the propeller has a performance advantage. At speeds approaching the speed of sound, compressibility effects set in and the propeller loses its aerodynamic efficiency. Due to the rotation of the propeller, the propeller tip will approach the speed of sound before the vehicle approaches

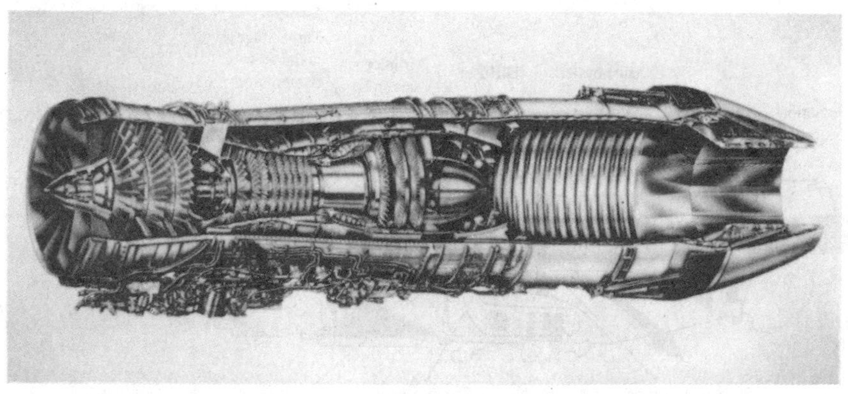

FIGURE 1-9*b*
General Electric F110-GE-129 afterburning turbofan. (*Courtesy of General Electric Aircraft Engines.*)

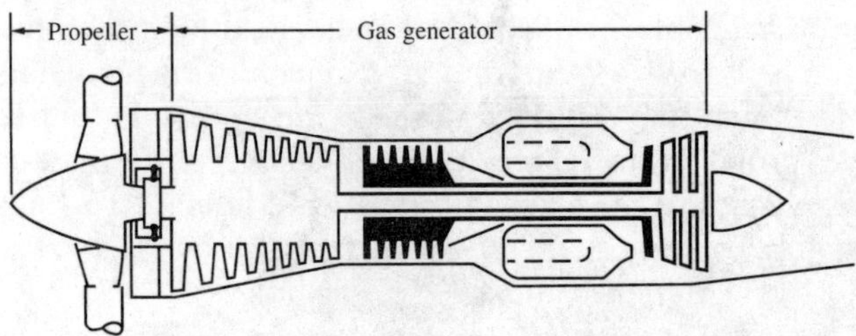

FIGURE 1-10*a*
Schematic diagram of a turboprop.

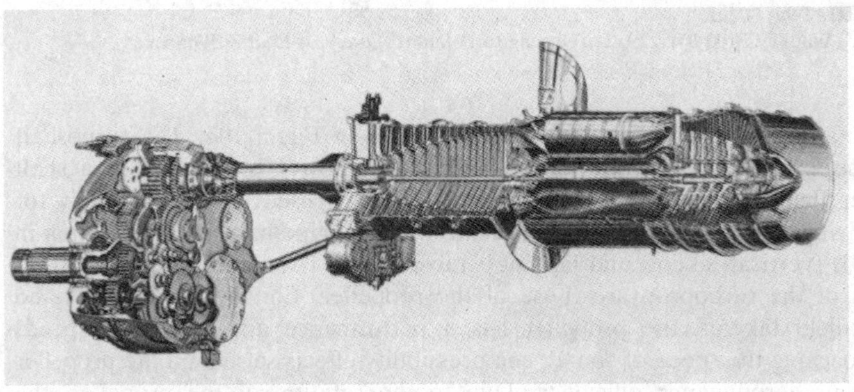

FIGURE 1-10*b*
Allison T56 turboshaft. (*Courtesy of Allison Gas Turbine Division.*)

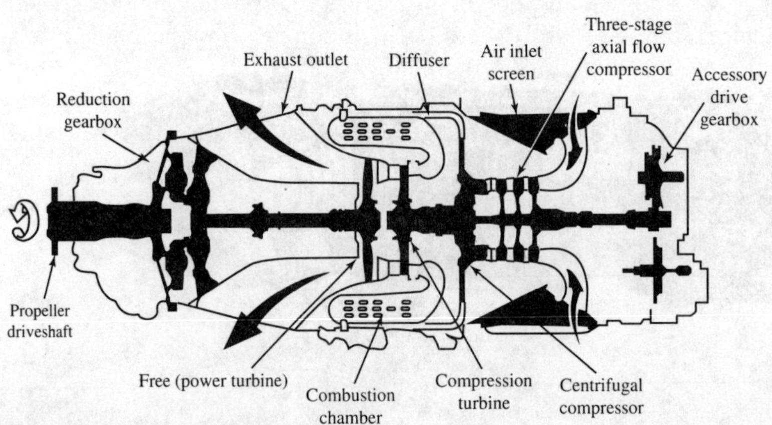

FIGURE 1-10*c*
Canadian Pratt & Whitney PT6 turboshaft. (*Courtesy of Pratt & Whitney of Canada.*)

the speed of sound. This compressibility effect when one approaches the speed of sound limits the design of helicopter rotors and propellers. At high subsonic speeds, the turbofan engine will have a better aerodynamic performance than the turboprop since the turbofan is essentially a *ducted turboprop.* Putting a duct or shroud around a propeller increases its aerodynamic performance. Examples of a turboshaft engine are the Canadian Pratt & Whitney PT6 (Fig. 1-10*c*), used in many small commuter aircraft, and the Allison T56 (Fig. 1-10*b*), used to power the C-130 Hercules and the P-3 Orion.

The Ramjet

The ramjet engine consists of an inlet, a combustion zone, and a nozzle. A schematic diagram of a ramjet is shown in Fig. 1-11. The ramjet does not have the compressor and turbine as the turbojet does. Air enters the inlet where it is compressed and then enters the combustion zone where it is mixed with the fuel and burned. The hot gases are then expelled through the nozzle, developing thrust. The operation of the ramjet depends upon the inlet to decelerate the incoming air to raise the pressure in the combustion zone. The pressure rise makes it possible for the ramjet to operate. The higher the velocity of the incoming air, the greater the pressure rise. It is for this reason that the ramjet operates best at high supersonic velocities. At subsonic velocities, the ramjet is inefficient, and to start the ramjet, air at a relatively higher velocity must enter the inlet.

The combustion process in an ordinary ramjet takes place at low subsonic velocities. At high supersonic flight velocities, a very large pressure rise is developed that is more than sufficient to support operation of the ramjet. Also, if the inlet has to decelerate a supersonic high-velocity airstream to a subsonic velocity, large pressure losses can result. The deceleration process also produces a temperature rise, and at some limiting flight speed, the temperature will approach the limit set by the wall materials and cooling methods. Thus when the temperature increase due to deceleration reaches the limit, it may not be possible to burn fuel in the airstream.

In the past few years, research and development have been done on a ramjet that has the combustion process taking place at supersonic velocities.

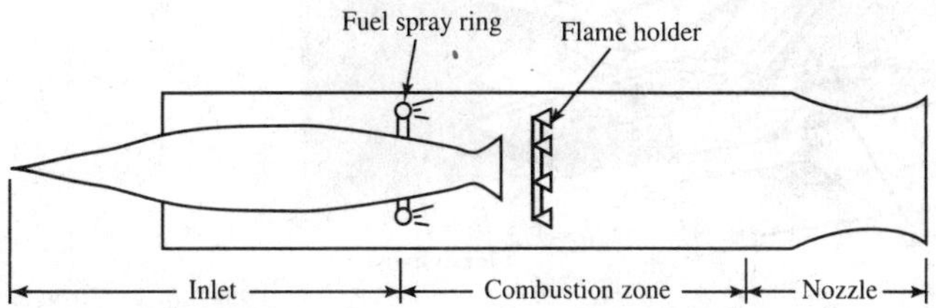

FIGURE 1-11
Schematic diagram of a ramjet.

By using a supersonic combustion process, the temperature rise and pressure loss due to deceleration in the inlet can be reduced. This ramjet with supersonic combustion is known as the *scramjet* (*s*upersonic *c*ombustion *ramjet*). Figure 1-12*a* shows the schematic of a scramjet engine similar to that proposed for the National AeroSpace Plane (NASP) research vehicle, the X-30 shown in Fig. 1-12*b*. Further development of the scramjet for other applications (e.g., the Orient Express) will continue if research and development produces a scramjet engine with sufficient performance gains. Remember that since it takes a relative velocity to start the ramjet or scramjet, another engine system is required to accelerate aircraft like the X-30 to ramjet velocities.

Turbojet/Ramjet Combined-Cycle Engine

Two of the Pratt & Whitney J58 turbojet engines (see Fig. 1-13*a*) are used to power the Lockheed SR71 Blackbird (see Fig. 1-13*b*). This was the fastest aircraft (Mach 3+) when it was retired in 1989. The J58 operates as an afterburning turbojet engine until it reaches high Mach level, at which point the six large tubes (Fig. 1-13*a*) bypass flow to the afterburner. When these tubes are in use, the compressor, burner, and turbine of the turbojet are essentially bypassed and the engine operates as a ramjet with the afterburner acting as the ramjet's burner.

Aircraft Engine Performance Parameters

This section presents several of the air-breathing engine performance parameters that are useful in aircraft propulsion. The first performance parameter is the thrust of the engine which is available for sustained flight (thrust = drag), accelerated flight (thrust > drag), or deceleration (thrust < drag).

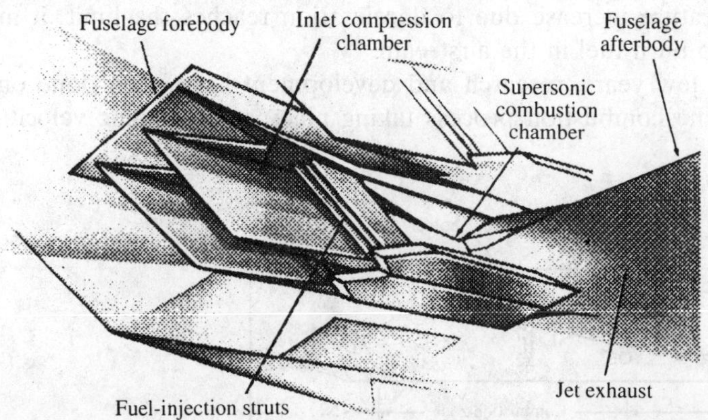

FIGURE 1-12*a*
Schematic diagram of a scramjet.

FIGURE 1-12*b*
Conceptual drawing of the X-30. (*Courtesy of Pratt & Whitney.*)

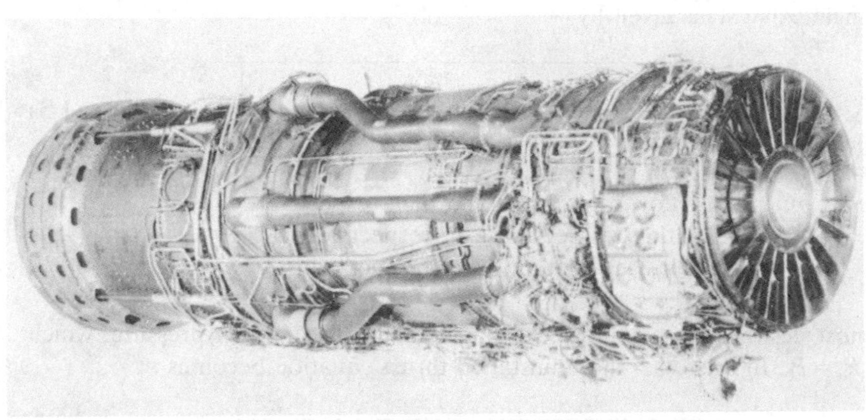

FIGURE 1-13*a*
Pratt & Whitney J58 turbojet. (*Courtesy of Pratt & Whitney.*)

FIGURE 1-13*b*
Lockheed SR71 Blackbird. (*Courtesy of Lockheed.*)

As derived in Chap. 4, the uninstalled thrust F of a jet engine (single inlet and single exhaust) is given by

$$F = \frac{(\dot{m}_0 + \dot{m}_f)V_e + \dot{m}_0 V_0}{g_c} + (P_e - P_0)A_e \tag{1-5}$$

where $\dot{m}_0, \dot{m}_f$ = mass flow rates of air and fuel, respectively
V_0, V_e = velocities at inlet and exit, respectively
P_0, P_e = pressures at inlet and exit, respectively

It is most desirable to expand the exhaust gas to the ambient pressure, which gives $P_e = P_0$. In this case, the uninstalled thrust equation becomes

$$F = \frac{(\dot{m}_0 + \dot{m}_f)V_e - \dot{m}_0 V_0}{g_c} \qquad \text{for } P_e = P_0 \tag{1-6}$$

The installed thrust T is equal to the uninstalled thrust F minus the inlet drag D_{inlet} and minus the nozzle drag D_{noz}, or

$$T = F - D_{\text{inlet}} - D_{\text{noz}} \tag{1-7}$$

Dividing the inlet drag D_{inlet} and nozzle drag D_{noz} by the uninstalled thrust F yields the dimensionless inlet loss coefficient ϕ_{inlet} and nozzle loss coefficient ϕ_{noz}, or

$$\phi_{\text{inlet}} = \frac{D_{\text{inlet}}}{F} \qquad \phi_{\text{noz}} = \frac{D_{\text{noz}}}{F} \tag{1-8}$$

Thus the relationship between the installed thrust T and uninstalled thrust F is simply

$$T = F(1 - \phi_{\text{inlet}} - \phi_{\text{noz}}) \tag{1-9}$$

The second performance parameter is the thrust specific fuel consumption (S and TSFC). This is the rate of fuel use by the propulsion system per unit of thrust produced. The uninstalled fuel consumption S and installed fuel consumption TSFC are written in equation form as

$$S = \frac{\dot{m}_f}{F} \tag{1-10}$$

$$\text{TSFC} = \frac{\dot{m}_f}{T} \tag{1-11}$$

where F = uninstalled thrust
S = uninstalled thrust specific fuel consumption
T = installed engine thrust
TSFC = installed thrust specific fuel consumption
$\dot{m}_f$ = mass flow rate of fuel

The relation between S and TSFC in equation form is given by

$$S = \text{TSFC}\,(1 - \phi_{\text{inlet}} - \phi_{\text{noz}}) \tag{1-12}$$

Values of thrust F and fuel consumption S for various jet engines at sea-level static conditions are listed in App. B. The predicted variations of uninstalled engine thrust F and uninstalled thrust specific fuel consumption S with Mach number and altitude for an advanced fighter engine (from Ref. 3) are plotted in Figs. 1-14*a* through 1-14*d*. Note that the thrust F decreases with altitude and the fuel consumption S also decreases with altitude until 36 kft (the start of the isothermal layer of the atmosphere). Also note that the fuel consumption increases with Mach number and that the thrust varies considerably with the Mach number. The predicted partial-throttle performance of the advanced fighter engine is shown at three flight conditions in Fig. 1-14*e*.

The takeoff thrust of the JT9D high-bypass-ratio turbofan engine is given in Fig. 1-15*a* versus Mach number and ambient air temperature for two versions. Note the rapid falloff of thrust with rising Mach number that is characteristic of this engine cycle and the constant thrust at a Mach number for temperatures of 86°F and below (this is often referred to as a *flat rating*). The partial-throttle performance of both engine versions is given in Fig. 1-15*b* for two combinations of altitude and Mach number.

Although the aircraft gas turbine engine is a very complex machine, the basic tools for modeling its performance are developed in the following chapters. These tools are based on the work of Gordon Oates (Ref. 4). They

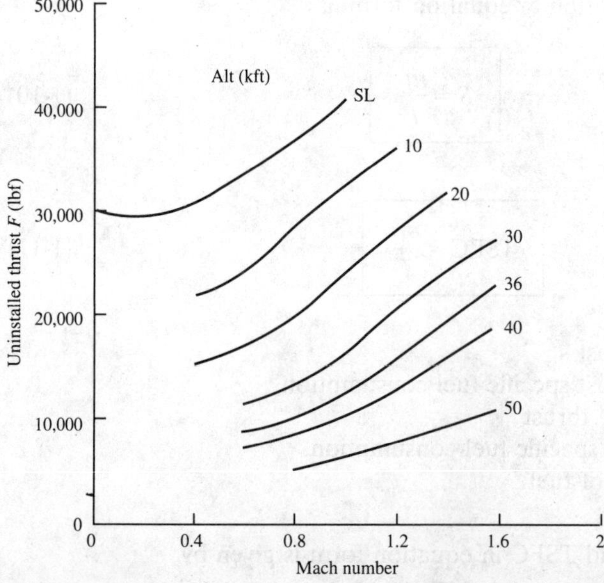

FIGURE 1-14*a*
Uninstalled thrust F of an advanced afterburning fighter engine at maximum power setting, afterburner on. (*Extracted from Ref. 3*.)

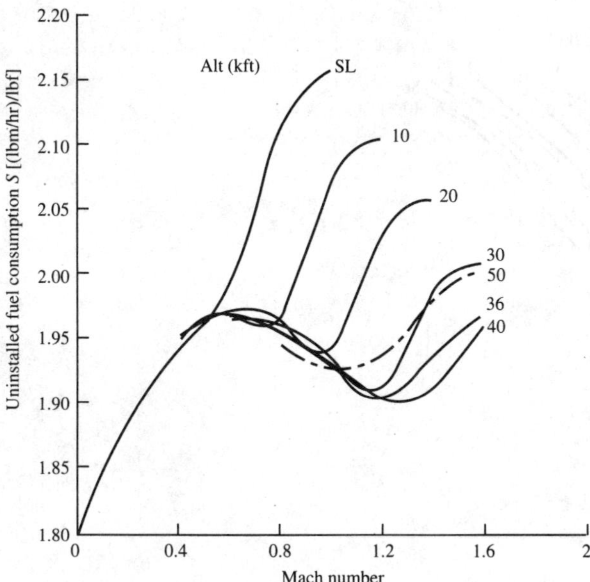

FIGURE 1-14*b*
Uninstalled fuel consumption S of an advanced afterburning fighter engine at maximum power setting, afterburner on. (*Extracted from Ref. 3.*)

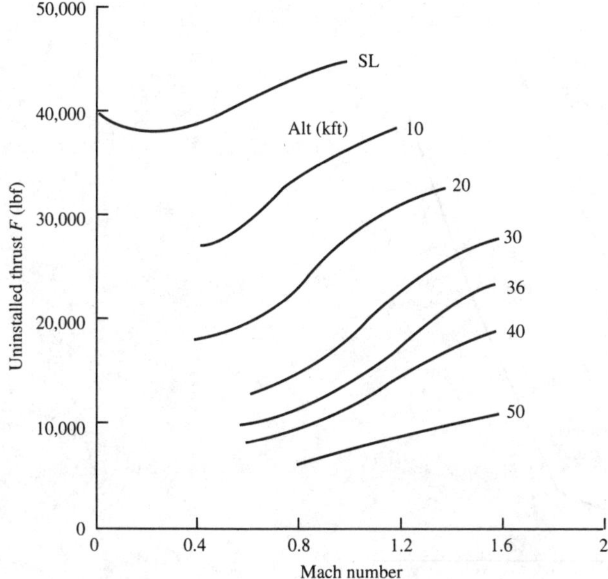

FIGURE 1-14*c*
Uninstalled thrust F of an advanced afterburning fighter engine at military power setting, afterburner off. (*Extracted from Ref. 3.*)

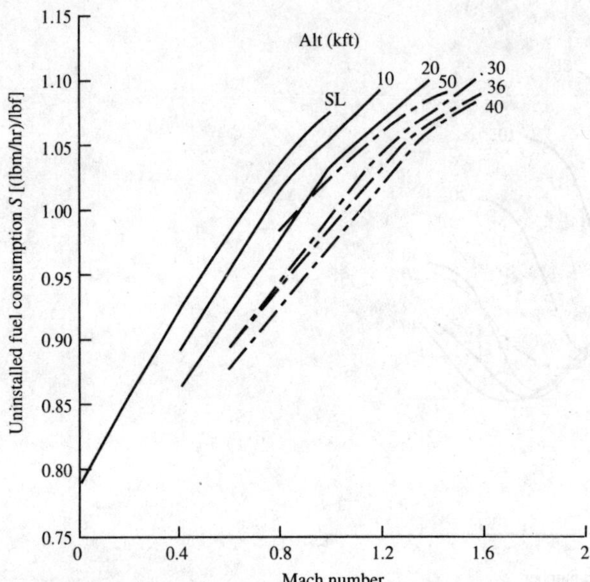

FIGURE 1-14*d*
Uninstalled fuel consumption S of an advanced afterburning fighter engine at military power setting, afterburner off. (*Extracted from Ref. 3.*)

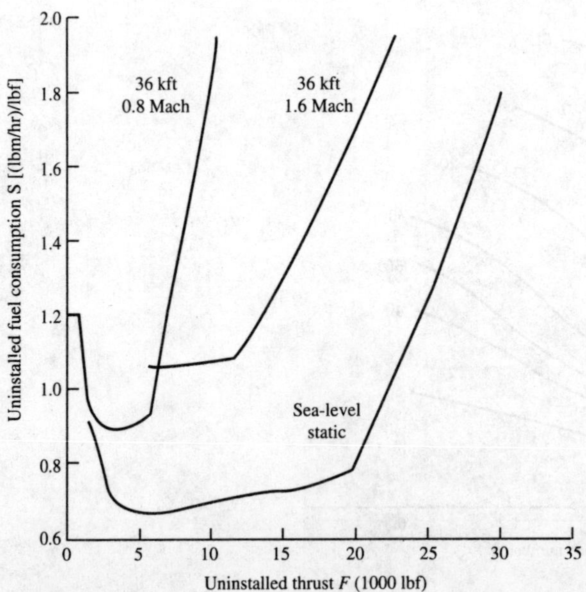

FIGURE 1-14*e*
Partial-throttle performance of an advanced fighter engine. (*Extracted from Ref. 3.*)

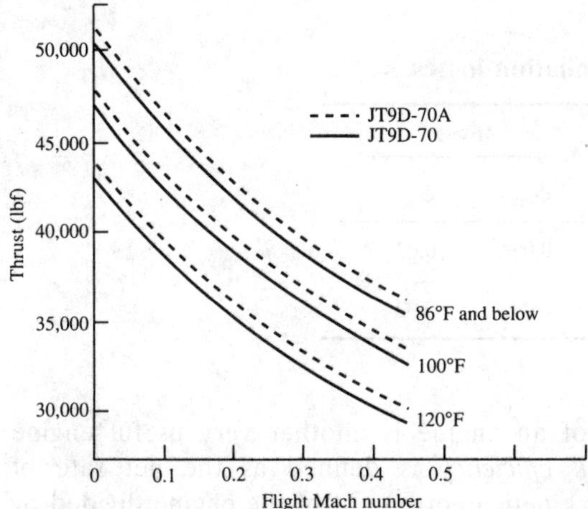

FIGURE 1-15*a*
JT9D-70/-70A turbofan takeoff thrust. (*Courtesy of Pratt & Whitney.*)

permit performance calculations for existing and proposed engines and generate performance curves similar to Figs. 1-14*a* through 1-14*e* and Figs. 1-15*a* and 1-15*b*.

The value of the installation loss coefficient depends on the characteristics of the particular engine/airframe combination, the Mach number, and the engine throttle setting. Typical values are given in Table 1-3 for guidance.

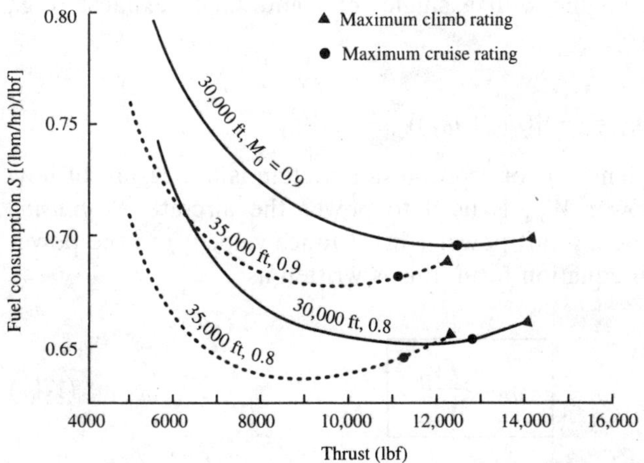

FIGURE 1-15*b*
JT9D-70/-70A turbofan cruise specific fuel consumption. (*Courtesy of Pratt & Whitney.*)

TABLE 1-3
Typical aircraft engine thrust installation losses

Flight condition:	$M<1$		$M>1$	
Aircraft type	ϕ_{inlet}	ϕ_{noz}	ϕ_{inlet}	ϕ_{noz}
Fighter	0.05	0.01	0.05	0.03
Passenger/cargo	0.02	0.01	—	—
Bomber	0.03	0.01	0.04	0.02

The thermal efficiency η_T of an engine is another very useful engine performance parameter. *Thermal efficiency* is defined as the net rate of organized energy (shaft power or kinetic energy) out of the engine divided by the rate of thermal energy available from the fuel in the engine. The fuel's available thermal energy is equal to the mass flow rate of the fuel $\dot{m}_f$ times the fuel heating value h_{PR}. Thermal efficiency can be written in equation form as

$$\boxed{\eta_T = \frac{\dot{W}_{\text{out}}}{\dot{Q}_{\text{in}}}} \tag{1-13}$$

where η_T = thermal efficiency of engine
$\dot{W}_{\text{out}}$ = net power out of engine
$\dot{Q}_{\text{in}}$ = rate of thermal energy released $(\dot{m}_f h_{PR})$

Note: For engines with shaft power output, $\dot{W}_{\text{out}}$ is equal to this shaft power. For engines with no shaft power output (e.g., turbojet engine), $\dot{W}_{\text{out}}$ is equal to the next rate of change of the kinetic energy of the fluid through the engine. The power out of a jet engine with a single inlet and single exhaust (e.g., turbojet engine) is given by

$$\dot{W}_{\text{out}} = \frac{1}{2g_c}[(\dot{m}_0 + \dot{m}_f)V_e^2 - \dot{m}_0 V_0^2]$$

The propulsive efficiency η_P of a propulsion system is a measure of how effectively the engine power $\dot{W}_{\text{out}}$ is used to power the aircraft. *Propulsive efficiency* is the ratio of the aircraft power (thrust times velocity) to the power out of the engine $\dot{W}_{\text{out}}$. In equation form, this is written as

$$\boxed{\eta_P = \frac{TV_0}{\dot{W}_{\text{out}}}} \tag{1-14}$$

where η_P = propulsive efficiency of engine
T = thrust of propulsion system

V_0 = velocity of aircraft
$\dot{W}_{out}$ = net power out of engine

For a jet engine with a single inlet and single exhaust and an exit pressure equal to the ambient pressure, the propulsive efficiency is given by

$$\eta_P = \frac{2(1 - \phi_{inlet} - \phi_{noz})[(\dot{m}_0 + \dot{m}_f)V_e - \dot{m}_0 V_0]V_0}{(\dot{m}_0 + \dot{m}_f)V_e^2 - \dot{m}_0 V_0^2} \tag{1-15}$$

For the case when the mass flow rate of the fuel is much less than that of air and the installation losses are very small, Eq. (1-15) simplifies to the following equation for the propulsive efficiency:

$$\boxed{\eta_P = \frac{2}{V_e/V_0 + 1}} \tag{1-16}$$

Equation (1-16) is plotted versus the velocity ratio V_e/V_0 in Fig. 1-16 and shows that high propulsive efficiency requires the exit velocity to be approximately equal to the inlet velocity. Turbojet engines have high values of the velocity ratio V_e/V_0 with corresponding low propulsive efficiency, whereas turbofan engines have low values of the velocity ratio V_e/V_0 with corresponding high propulsive efficiency.

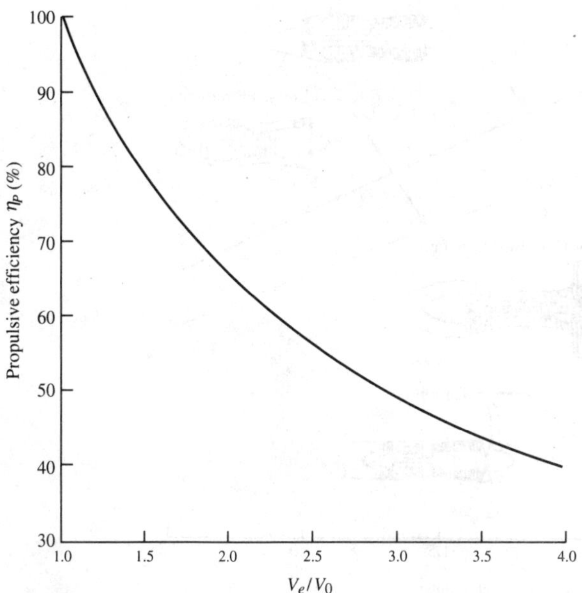

FIGURE 1-16
Propulsive efficiency versus velocity ratio (V_e/V_0).

The thermal and propulsive efficiencies can be combined to give the *overall efficiency* η_O of a propulsion system. Multiplying propulsive efficiency by thermal efficiency, we get the ratio of the aircraft power to the rate of thermal energy released in the engine (the overall efficiency of the propulsion system):

$$\boxed{\eta_O = \eta_P \eta_T} \tag{1-17}$$

$$\boxed{\eta_O = \frac{TV_0}{\dot{Q}_{in}}} \tag{1-18}$$

Several of the above performance parameters are plotted for general types of gas turbine engines in Figs. 1-17*a*, 1-17*b*, and 1-17*c*. These plots can be used to obtain the general trends of these performance parameters with flight velocity for each propulsion system.

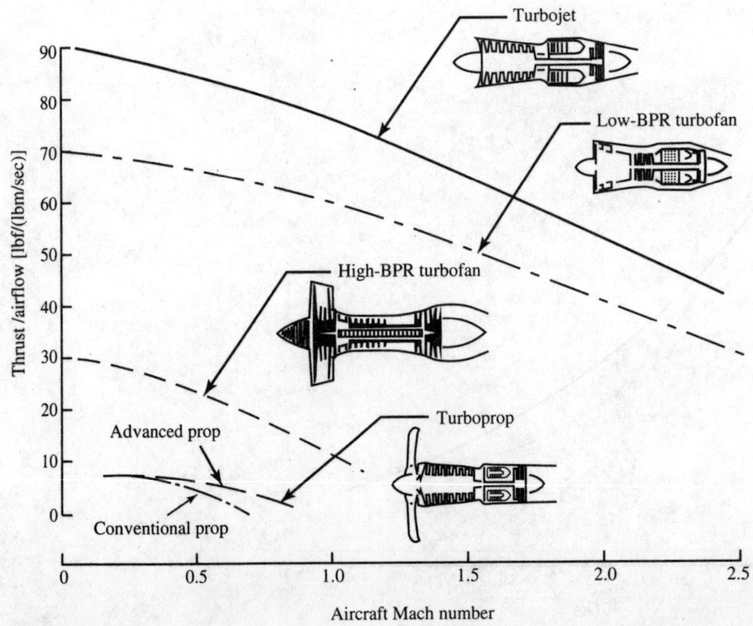

FIGURE 1-17*a*
Specific thrust characteristics of typical aircraft engines. (*Courtesy of Pratt & Whitney*.)

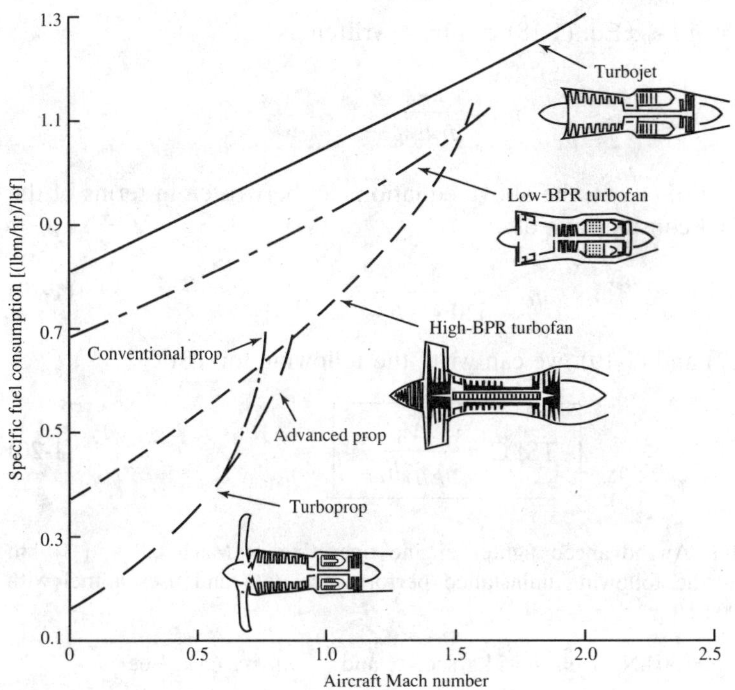

FIGURE 1-17*b*
Thrust specific fuel consumption characteristics of typical aircraft engines. (*Courtesy of Pratt & Whitney.*)

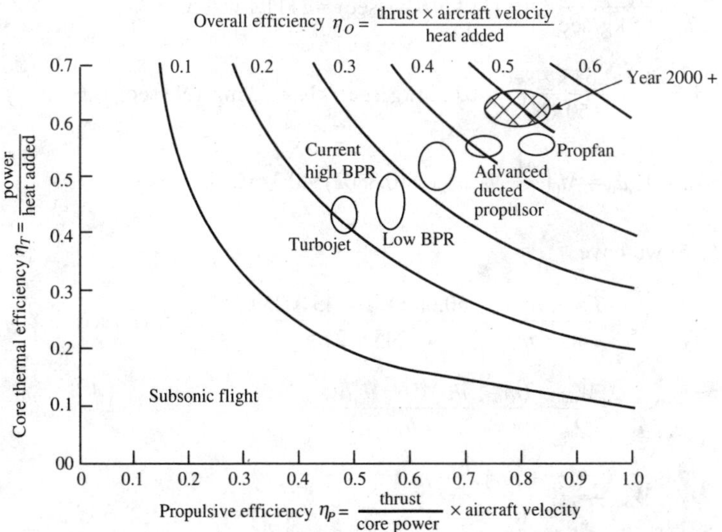

FIGURE 1-17*c*
Efficiency characteristics of typical aircraft engines. (*Courtesy of Pratt & Whitney.*)

Since $\dot{Q}_{\text{in}} = \dot{m}_f h_{PR}$, Eq. (1-18) can be rewritten as

$$\eta_O = \frac{TV_0}{\dot{m}_f h_{PR}}$$

With the help of Eq. (1-11), the above equation can be written in terms of the thrust specific fuel consumption as

$$\eta_O = \frac{V_0}{\text{TSFC} \cdot h_{PR}} \tag{1-19}$$

Using Eqs. (1-17) and (1-19), we can write the following for TSFC:

$$\boxed{\text{TSFC} = \frac{V_0}{\eta_P \eta_T h_{PR}}} \tag{1-20}$$

Example 1-1. An advanced fighter engine operating at Mach 0.8 and 10-km altitude has the following uninstalled performance data and uses a fuel with $h_{PR} = 42{,}800$ kJ/kg:

$$F = 50 \text{ kN} \qquad \dot{m}_0 = 45 \text{ kg/sec} \qquad \text{and} \qquad \dot{m}_f = 2.65 \text{ kg/sec}$$

Determine the specific thrust, thrust specific fuel consumption, exit velocity, thermal efficiency, propulsive efficiency, and overall efficiency (assume exit pressure equal to ambient pressure).

Solution.

$$\frac{F}{\dot{m}_0} = \frac{50 \text{ kN}}{45 \text{ kg/sec}} = 1.1111 \text{ kN/(kg/sec)} = 1111.1 \text{ m/sec}$$

$$S = \frac{\dot{m}_f}{F} = \frac{2.65 \text{ kg/sec}}{50 \text{ kN}} = 0.053 \text{(kg/sec)/kN} = 53 \text{ mg/(N} \cdot \text{sec)}$$

$$V_0 = M_0 a_0 = M_0 \left(\frac{M_0}{a_{\text{ref}}} \right) a_{\text{ref}} = 0.8(0.8802)340.3 = 239.6 \text{ m/sec}$$

From Eq. (1-6) we have

$$V_e = \frac{F g_c + \dot{m}_0 V_0}{\dot{m}_0 + \dot{m}_f} = \frac{50{,}000 \times 1 + 45 \times 239.6}{45 + 2.65} = 1275.6 \text{ m/sec}$$

$$\eta_T = \frac{\dot{W}_{\text{out}}}{\dot{Q}_{\text{in}}} = \frac{(\dot{m}_0 + \dot{m}_f) V_e^2 - \dot{m}_0 V_0^2}{2 g_c \dot{m}_f h_{PR}}$$

$$\dot{W}_{\text{out}} = \frac{(\dot{m}_0 + \dot{m}_f) V_e^2 - \dot{m}_0 V_0^2}{2 g_c}$$

$$= \frac{47.65 \times 1275.6^2 - 45 \times 239.6^2}{2 \times 1} = 37.475 \times 10^6 \text{ W}$$

$$\dot{Q}_{\text{in}} = \dot{m}_f h_{PR} = 2.65 \times 42{,}800 = 113.42 \times 10^6 \text{ W}$$

$$\eta_T = \frac{\dot{W}_{\text{out}}}{\dot{Q}_{\text{in}}} = \frac{37.475 \times 10^6}{113.42 \times 10^6} = 33.04\%$$

$$\eta_P = \frac{FV_0}{\dot{W}_{\text{out}}} = \frac{50{,}000 \times 239.6}{37.475 \times 10^6} = 31.97\%$$

$$\eta_O = \frac{FV_0}{\dot{Q}_{\text{in}}} = \frac{50{,}000 \times 239.6}{113.42 \times 10^6} = 10.56\%$$

Specific Thrust Versus Fuel Consumption

For a jet engine with a single inlet and single exhaust and exit pressure equal to ambient pressure, when the mass flow rate of the fuel is much less than that of air and the installation losses are very small, the specific thrust $F/\dot{m}_0$ can be written as

$$\boxed{\frac{F}{\dot{m}_0} = \frac{V_e - V_0}{g_c}} \tag{1-21}$$

Then the propulsive efficiency of Eq. (1-16) can be rewritten as

$$\eta_P = \frac{2}{Fg_c/(\dot{m}_0 V_0) + 2} \tag{1-22}$$

Substituting Eq. (1-22) into Eq. (1-20) and noting that TSFC $= S$, we obtain the following very enlightening expression:

$$\boxed{S = \frac{Fg_c/\dot{m}_0 + 2V_0}{2\eta_T h_{PR}}} \tag{1-23}$$

Aircraft manufacturers desire engines having low thrust specific fuel consumption S and high specific thrust $F/\dot{m}_0$. Low engine fuel consumption can be directly translated into longer range, increased payload, and/or reduced aircraft size. High specific thrust reduces the cross-sectional area of the engine and has a direct influence on engine weight and installation losses. This desired trend is plotted in Fig. 1-18. Equation (1-23) is also plotted in Fig. 1-18 and shows that fuel consumption and specific thrust are directly proportional. Thus the aircraft manufacturers have to make a tradeoff. The line of Eq. (1-23) shifts in the desired direction when there is an increase in the level of technology (increased thermal efficiency) or an increase in the fuel heating value.

Another very useful measure of merit for the aircraft gas turbine engine is the thrust/weight ratio F/W. For a given engine thrust F, increasing the thrust/weight ratio reduces the weight of the engine. Aircraft manufacturers can use this reduction in engine weight to increase the capabilites of an aricraft (increased payload, increased fuel, or both) or decrease the size (weight) and cost of a new aircraft under development.

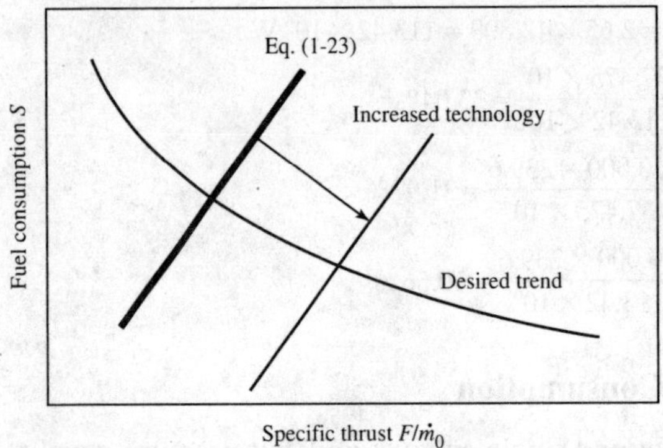

FIGURE 1-18
Relationship between specific thrust and fuel consumption.

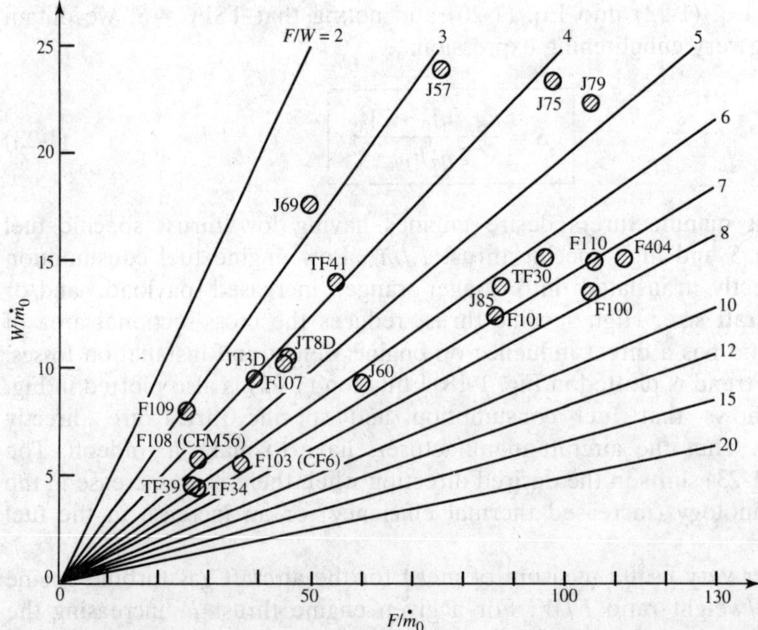

FIGURE 1-19
Engine thrust/weight ratio F/W.

Engine companies expend considerable research and development effort on increasing the thrust/weight ratio of aircraft gas turbine engines. This ratio is equal to the specific thrust $F/\dot{m}_0$ divided by the engine weight per unit of mass flow $W/\dot{m}_0$. For a given engine type, the engine weight per unit mass flow is related to the efficiency of the engine structure, and the specific thrust is related to the engine thermodynamics. The weights per unit mass flow of some existing gas turbine engines are plotted versus specific thrust in Fig. 1-19. Also plotted are lines of constant engine thrust/weight ratio F/W.

Currently, the engine companies, in conjunction with the Department of Defense and NASA, are involved in a large research and development effort to increase the engine thrust/weight ratio F/W and decrease the fuel consumption while maintaining engine durability, maintainability, etc. This program is called the *integrated high-performance turbine engine technology* (IHPTET) *initiative* (see Refs. 5 and 6).

1-5 AIRCRAFT PERFORMANCE

This section on aircraft performance is included so that the reader may get a better understanding of the propulsion requirements of the aircraft (Ref. 7). The coverage is limited to a few significant concepts that directly relate to aircraft engines. It is not intended as a substitute for the many excellent references on this subject (see Refs. 8 through 11).

Performance Equation

Relationships for the performance of an aircraft can be obtained from energy considerations (see Ref. 12). By treating the aircraft (Fig. 1-20) as a moving mass and assuming that the installed propulsive thrust T, aerodynamic drag D, and other resistive forces R act in the same direction as the velocity V, it follows that

$$\underbrace{[T-(D+R)]V}_{\text{rate of mechanical energy input}} = \underbrace{W\frac{dh}{dt}}_{\text{storage rate of potential energy}} + \underbrace{\frac{W}{g}\frac{d}{dt}\left(\frac{V^2}{2}\right)}_{\text{storage rate of kinetic energy}} \tag{1-24}$$

Note that the total resistive force $D+R$ is the sum of the drag of the clean aircraft D and any additional drags R associated with such proturberances as landing gear, external stores, or drag chutes.

By defining the energy height z_e as the sum of the potential and kinetic

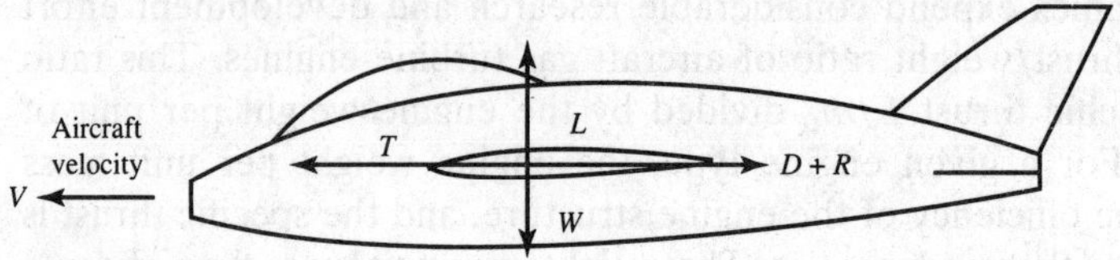

FIGURE 1-20
Forces on aircraft.

energy terms

$$z_e \equiv h + \frac{V^2}{2g} \tag{1-25}$$

Eq. (1-24) can now be written simply as

$$[T - (D + R)]V = W\frac{dz_e}{dt} \tag{1-26}$$

By defining the *weight specific excess power* P_s as

$$P_s \equiv \frac{dz_e}{dt} \tag{1-27}$$

Eq. (1-26) can now be written in its dimensionless form as

$$\frac{T - (D + R)}{W} = \frac{P_s}{V} = \frac{1}{V}\frac{d}{dt}\left(h + \frac{V^2}{2g}\right) \tag{1-28}$$

This is a very powerful equation which gives insight into the dynamics of flight, including both the rate of climb dh/dt and acceleration dV/dt.

Lift and Drag

We use the classical aircraft lift relationship

$$L = nW = C_L q S_w \tag{1-29}$$

where n is the load factor or number of g's perpendicular to V ($n = 1$ for straight and level flight), C_L is the coefficient of lift, S_w is the wing planform area, and q is the dynamic pressure. The dynamic pressure can be expressed in terms of the density ρ and velocity V or the pressure P and Mach number M as

$$q = \frac{1}{2}\rho\frac{V^2}{g_c} = \frac{1}{2}\sigma\rho_{\text{ref}}\frac{V^2}{g_c} \tag{1-30a}$$

or

$$q = \frac{\gamma}{2}PM_0^2 = \frac{\gamma}{2}\delta P_{\text{ref}}M_0^2 \tag{1-30b}$$

where δ and σ are the dimensionless pressure and density ratios defined by Eqs. (1-2) and (1-4), respectively, and γ is the ratio of specific heats ($\gamma = 1.4$ for air). The reference density ρ_{ref} and reference pressure P_{ref} of air are their sea-level values on a standard day and are listed in App. A.

We also use the classical aircraft drag relationship

$$\boxed{D = C_D q S_w} \tag{1-31}$$

Figure 1-21 is a plot of lift coefficient C_L versus drag coefficient C_D, commonly called the *lift-drag polar*, for a typical subsonic passenger aircraft. The drag coefficient curve can be approximated by a second-order equation in C_L written as

$$\boxed{C_D = K_1 C_L^2 + K_2 C_L + C_{D0}} \tag{1-32}$$

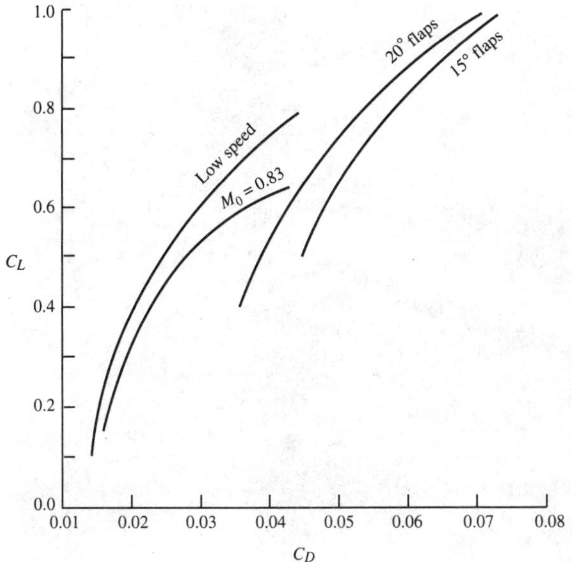

FIGURE 1-21
Typical lift-drag polar.

where the coefficients K_1, K_2, and C_{D0} are typically functions of flight Mach number and wing configuration (flap position, etc.).

The C_{D0} term in Eq. (1-32) is the zero lift drag coefficient which accounts for both frictional and pressure drag in subsonic flight and wave drag in supersonic flight. The K_1 and K_2 terms account for the drag due to lift. Normally K_2 is very small and approximately equal to zero for most fighter aircraft.

Example 1-2. For all the examples given in this section on aircraft performance, two types of aircraft will be considered.

a. An advanced fighter aircraft is approximately modeled after the YF22 Advanced Tactical Fighter shown in Fig. 1-22. For convenience, we will designate our hypothetical fighter aircraft as the HF-1, having the following characteristics:

Maximum gross takeoff weight $W_{TO} = 40{,}000$ lbf (177,920 N)
Empty weight = 24,000 lbf (106,752 N)
Maximum fuel plus payload weight = 16,000 lbf (71,168 N)
Permanent payload = 1600 lbf (7117 N, crew plus return armament)
Expended payload = 2000 lbf (8896 N, missiles plus ammunition)
Maximum fuel capacity = 12,400 lbf (55,155 N)
Wing area $S_w = 720$ ft^2 (66.9 m^2)

FIGURE 1-22
YF22, Advanced Tactical Fighter. (*Photo courtesy of Boeing Defense & Space Group, Military Airplanes Division.*)

TABLE 1-4
Drag coefficients for hypothetical fighter aircraft (HF-1)

M_0	K_1	K_2	C_{D0}
0.0	0.20	0.0	0.0120
0.8	0.20	0.0	0.0120
1.2	0.20	0.0	0.02267
1.4	0.25	0.0	0.0280
2.0	0.40	0.0	0.0270

Engine: low-bypass-ratio, mixed-flow turbofan with afterburner
Maximum lift coefficient $C_{L\,\max} = 1.8$
Drag coefficients given in Table 1-4

b. An advanced 253-passenger commercial aircraft approximately modeled after the Boeing 767 is shown in Fig. 1-23. For convenience, we will designate our hypothetical passenger aircraft as the HP-1, having the following characteristics:

Maximum gross takeoff weight $W_{TO} = 1{,}645{,}760$ N (370,000 lbf)
Empty weight = 822,880 N (185,500 lbf)

FIGURE 1-23
Boeing 767. (*Photo courtesy of Boeing.*)

TABLE 1-5
Drag coefficients for hypothetical passenger aircraft (HP-1)

M_0	K_1	K_2	C_{D0}
0.00	0.056	−0.004	0.0140
0.40	0.056	−0.004	0.0140
0.75	0.056	−0.008	0.0140
0.83	0.056	−0.008	0.0150

Maximum landing weight = 1,356,640 N (305,000 lbf)
Maximum payload = 420,780 N (94,600 lbf, 253 passengers plus 196,000 N of cargo)
Maximum fuel capacity = 716,706 N (161,130 lbf)
Wing area $S_w = 282.5\ \text{m}^2$ ($3040\ \text{ft}^2$)
Engine: high-bypass-ratio turbofan
Maximum lift coefficient $C_{L\,\max} = 2.0$
Drag coefficients given in Table 1-5.

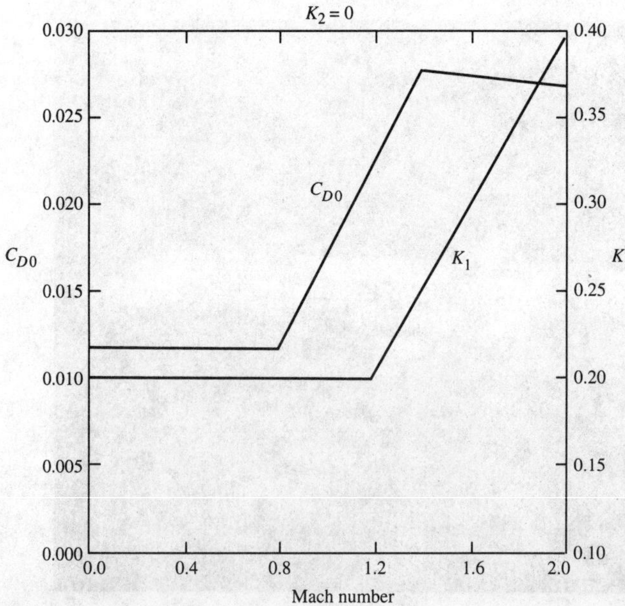

FIGURE 1-24
Values of K_1 and C_{D0} for HF-1 aircraft.

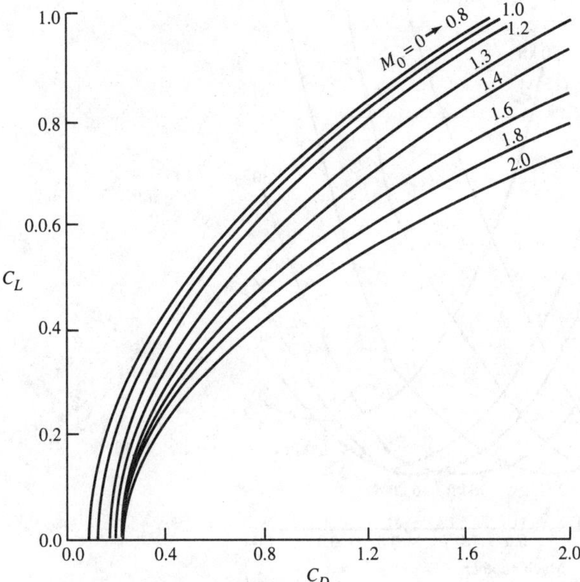

FIGURE 1-25
Lift-drag polar for HF-1 aircraft.

Example 1-3. Determine the drag polar and drag variation for the HF-1 aircraft at 90 percent of maximum gross takeoff weight and the HP-1 aircraft at 95 percent of maximum gross takeoff weight.

a. The variation in C_{D0} and K_1 with Mach number for the HF-1 are plotted in Fig. 1-24 from the data of Table 1-4. Figure 1-25 shows the drag polar at different Mach numbers for the HF-1 aircraft. Using these drag data and the above equations gives the variation in aircraft drag with subsonic Mach number and altitude for level flight ($n = 1$), as shown in Fig. 1-26*a*. Note that the minimum drag is constant for Mach numbers 0 to 0.8 and then increases. This is the same variation as C_{D0}. The variation of drag with load factor n is shown in Fig. 1-26*b* at two altitudes. The drag increases with increasing load factor, and there is a flight Mach number that gives minimum drag for a given altitude and load factor.

b. The variation in C_{D0} and K_2 with Mach number for the HP-1 is plotted in Fig. 1-27 from the data of Table 1-5. Figure 1-28 shows the drag polar at different Mach numbers for the HP-1 aircraft. Using these drag data and the above equations gives the variation in aircraft drag with subsonic Mach number and altitude for level flight ($n = 1$), as shown in Fig. 1-29. Note that the minimum drag is constant for Mach numbers 0 to 0.75 and then increases. This is the same variation as C_{D0}.

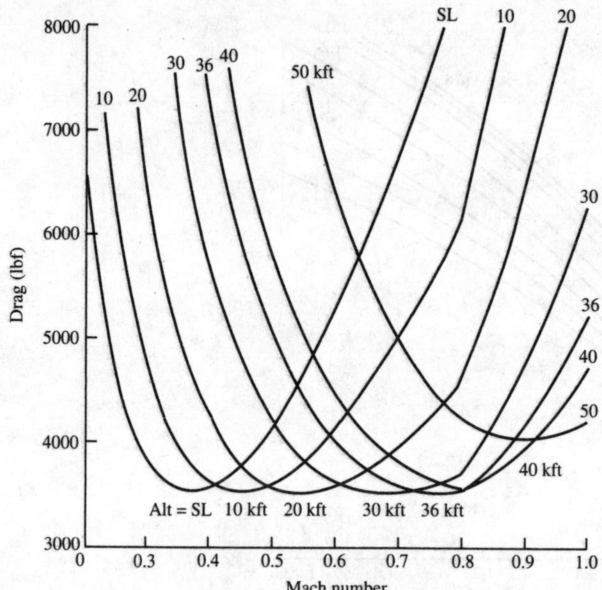

FIGURE 1-26*a*
Drag for level flight ($n = 1$) for HF-1 aircraft.

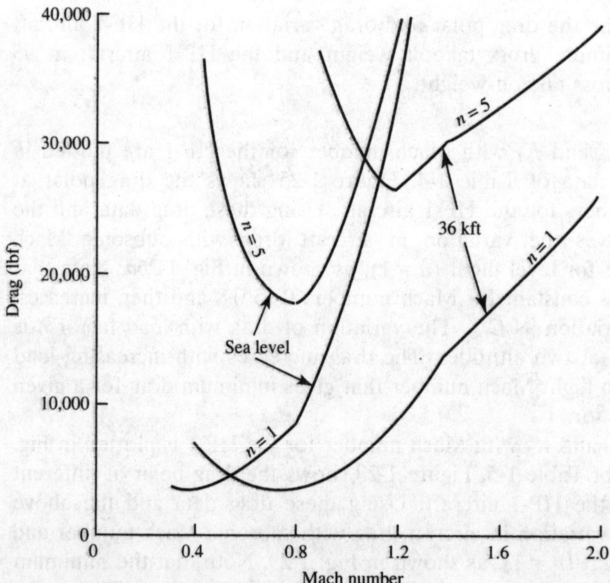

FIGURE 1-26*b*
Drag of HF-1 aircraft at sea level and 36 kft for $n = 1$ and $n = 5$.

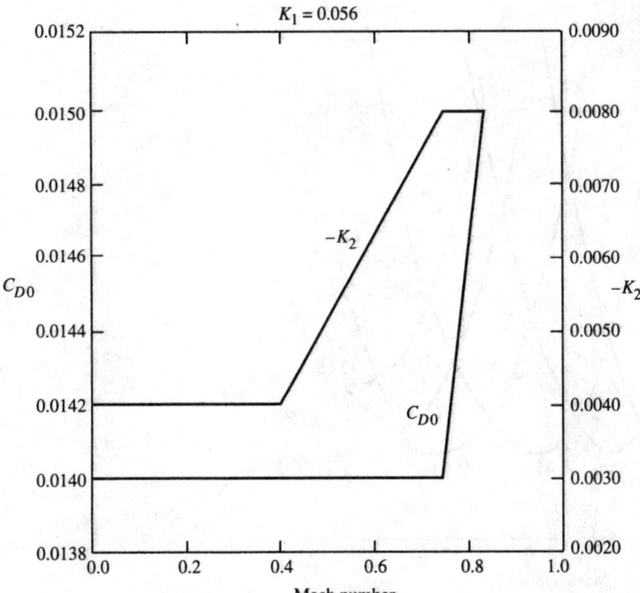

FIGURE 1-27
Values of K_2 and C_{D0} for HP-1 aircraft.

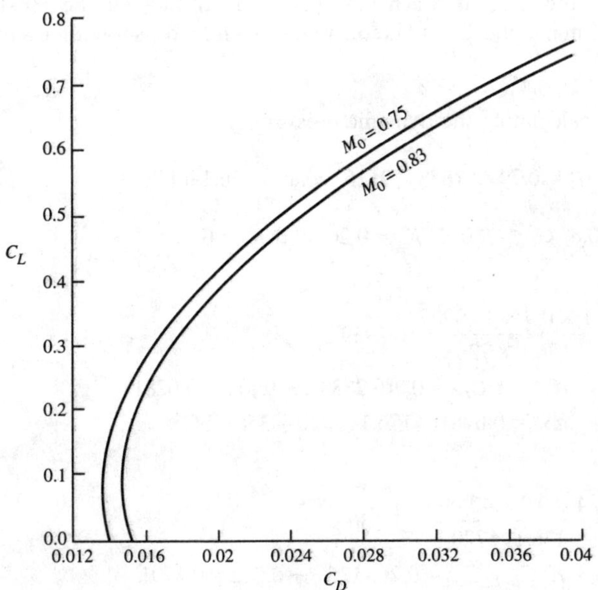

FIGURE 1-28
Lift-drag polar for HP-1 aircraft.

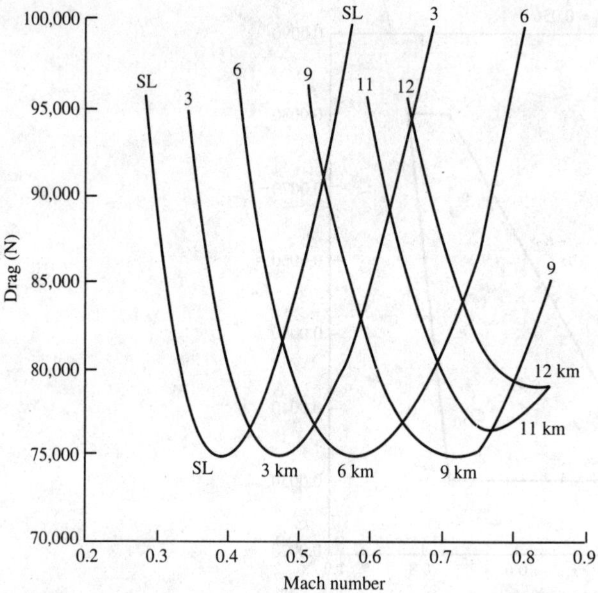

FIGURE 1-29
Drag for level flight ($n = 1$) for HP-1 aircraft.

Example 1-4. Calculate the drag at Mach 0.8 and 40-kft altitude of the HF-1 aircraft at 90 percent of maximum gross takeoff weight with load factors of 1 and 4.

Solution. We begin by calculating the dynamic pressure q.

$$q = \frac{\gamma}{2}\delta P_{\text{ref}} M_0^2 = 0.7 \times 0.1858 \times 2116 \times 0.8^2 = 176.1 \text{ lbf/ft}^2$$

From Fig. 1-24 at $M = 0.8$, $C_{D0} = 0.012$, $K_1 = 0.20$, and $K_2 = 0$.

Case 1: $n = 1$

$$C_L = \frac{nW}{qS_w} = \frac{1 \times 0.9 \times 40{,}000}{176.1 \times 720} = 0.2839$$

$$C_D = K_1 C_L^2 + K_2 C_L + C_{D0} = 0.2(0.2839^2) + 0.012 = 0.0281$$

$$D = C_D q S_w = 0.0281 \times 176.1 \times 720 = 3563 \text{ lbf}$$

Case 2: $n = 4$

$$C_L = \frac{nW}{qS_w} = \frac{4 \times 0.9 \times 40{,}000}{176.1 \times 720} = 1.136$$

$$C_D = K_1 C_L^2 + K_2 C_L + C_{D0} = 0.2(1.136^2) + 0.012 = 0.2701$$

$$D = C_D q S_w = 0.2701 \times 176.1 \times 720 = 34{,}247 \text{ lbf}$$

Note that the drag at $n = 4$ is about 10 times that at $n = 1$.

Stall, Takeoff, and Landing Speeds

Stall is the flight condition when an aircraft's wing loses lift. It is an undesirable condition since vehicle control is lost for a time. During level flight (lift = weight), stall will occur when one tries to obtain a lift coefficient greater than the wing's maximum $C_{L\,\max}$. The *stall speed* is defined as the level flight speed that corresponds to the wing's maximum lift coefficient, or

$$\boxed{V_{\text{stall}} = \sqrt{\frac{2g_c}{\rho C_{L\,\max}} \frac{W}{S_w}}} \tag{1-33}$$

To keep away from stall, aircraft are flown at velocities greater than V_{stall}.

Takeoff and landing are two flight conditions in which the aircraft velocity is close to the stall velocity. For safety, the takeoff speed V_{TO} of an aircraft is typically 20 percent greater than the stall speed, and the landing speed at touchdown V_{TD} is 15 percent greater:

$$\boxed{\begin{aligned} V_{\text{TO}} &= 1.20 V_{\text{stall}} \\ V_{\text{TD}} &= 1.15 V_{\text{stall}} \end{aligned}} \tag{1-34}$$

Example 1-5. Determine the takeoff speed of the HP-1 at sea level with maximum gross takeoff weight and the landing speed with maximum landing weight.

From App. A we have $\rho = 1.255\ \text{kg/m}^3$ for sea level.

From Example 1-2*b* we have $C_{L\,\max} = 2.0$, $W = 1{,}645{,}760\ \text{N}$, $S_w = 282.5\ \text{m}^2$, and

$$V_{\text{stall}} = \sqrt{\frac{2 \times 1}{1.225 \times 2.0} \frac{1{,}645{,}760}{282.5}} = 69.0\ \text{m/sec}$$

Thus $\quad V_{\text{TO}} = 1.20 V_{\text{stall}} = 82.8\ \text{m/sec}\ (\approx 185\ \text{mi/hr})$

For landing, $W = 1{,}356{,}640\ \text{N}$.

$$V_{\text{stall}} = \sqrt{\frac{2 \times 1}{1.225 \times 2.0} \frac{1{,}356{,}640}{282.5}} = 62.6\ \text{m/sec}$$

Thus $\quad V_{\text{TD}} = 1.15 V_{\text{stall}} = 72.0\ \text{m/sec}\ (\approx 161\ \text{mi/hr})$

Fuel Consumption

The rate of change of the aircraft weight dW/dt is due to the fuel consumed by the engines. The mass rate of fuel consumed is equal to the product of the installed thrust T and the installed thrust specific fuel consumption. For constant acceleration of gravity g_0, we can write

$$\frac{dW}{dt} = -\dot{w}_f = -\dot{m}_f \frac{g_0}{g_c} = -T(\text{TSFC})\left(\frac{g_0}{g_c}\right)$$

This equation can be rewritten in dimensionless form as

$$\boxed{\frac{dW}{W} = -\frac{T}{W}(\text{TSFC})\left(\frac{g_0}{g_c}\right) dt} \tag{1-35}$$

ESTIMATE OF TSFC. Equation (1-35) requires estimates of installed engine thrust T and installed TSFC to calculate the change in aircraft weight. For many flight conditions, the installed engine thrust T equals the aircraft drag D. The value of TSFC depends on the engine cycle, altitude, and Mach number. For preliminary analysis, the following equations (from Ref. 7) can be used to estimate TSFC in units of (lbm/hr)/lbf and θ is the dimensionless temperature ratio T/T_{ref}.

a. High-bypass-ratio turbofan

$$\text{TSFC} = (0.4 + 0.45M_0)\sqrt{\theta} \tag{1-36a}$$

b. Low-bypass-ratio, mixed-flow turbofan

Military and lower power settings:

$$\text{TSFC} = (1.0 + 0.35M_0)\sqrt{\theta} \tag{1-36b}$$

Maximum power setting:

$$\text{TSFC} = (1.8 + 0.30M_0)\sqrt{\theta} \tag{1-36c}$$

c. Turbojet

Military and lower power settings:

$$\text{TSFC} = (1.3 + 0.35M_0)\sqrt{\theta} \tag{1-36d}$$

Maximum power setting:

$$\text{TSFC} = (1.7 + 0.26M_0)\sqrt{\theta} \tag{1-36e}$$

d. Turboprop

$$\text{TSFC} = (0.2 + 0.9M_0)\sqrt{\theta} \tag{1-36f}$$

ENDURANCE. For level unaccelerated flight, thrust equals drag ($T = D$) and lift equals weight ($L = W$). Thus Eq. (1-35) is simply

$$\frac{dW}{W} = -\frac{C_D}{C_L}(\text{TSFC})\left(\frac{g_0}{g_c}\right) dt \tag{1-37}$$

We define the endurance factor EF as

$$\text{EF} \equiv \frac{C_L}{C_D(\text{TSFC})}\frac{g_c}{g_0} \tag{1-38}$$

Then Eq. (1-37) becomes

$$\frac{dW}{W} = -\frac{dt}{\text{EF}} \tag{1-39}$$

Note that the minimum fuel consumption for a time t occurs at the flight condition where the endurance factor is maximum.

For the case when the endurance factor EF is constant or nearly constant, Eq. (1-39) can be integrated from the initial to final conditions and the following expression obtained for the aircraft weight fraction:

$$\frac{W_f}{W_i} = \exp\left(-\frac{t}{\text{EF}}\right) \tag{1-40a}$$

or

$$\frac{W_f}{W_i} = \exp\left[-\frac{C_D}{C_L}(\text{TSFC})t\frac{g_0}{g_c}\right] \tag{1-40b}$$

RANGE. For portions of aircraft flight where distance is important, the differential time dt is related to the differential distance ds by

$$ds = V\,dt \tag{1-41}$$

Substituting into Eq. (1-37) gives

$$\frac{dW}{W} = -\frac{C_D}{C_L}\frac{\text{TSFC}}{V}\frac{g_0}{c_g}\,ds \tag{1-42}$$

We define the range factor RF as

$$\text{RF} \equiv \frac{C_L}{C_D}\frac{V}{\text{TSFC}}\frac{g_c}{g_0} \tag{1-43}$$

Then Eq. (1-42) can be simply written as

$$\frac{dW}{W} = -\frac{ds}{\text{RF}} \tag{1-44}$$

Note that the minimum fuel consumption for a distance s occurs at the flight condition where the range factor is maximum.

For the flight conditions where the RF is constant or nearly constant, Eq. (1-42) can be integrated from the initial to final conditions and the following expression obtained for the aircraft weight fraction:

$$\boxed{\frac{W_f}{W_i} = \exp\left(-\frac{s}{\text{RF}}\right)} \tag{1-45a}$$

or

$$\boxed{\frac{W_f}{W_i} = \exp\left(-\frac{C_D}{C_L}\frac{\text{TSFC} \times s}{V}\frac{g_0}{g_c}\right)} \tag{1-45b}$$

This is called the *Breguet range equation.* For the range factor to remain constant, C_L/C_D and V/TSFC need to be constant. Above 36-kft altitude, the ambient temperature is constant and a constant velocity V will correspond to constant Mach and constant TSFC for a fixed throttle setting. If C_L is constant, C_L/C_D will remain constant. Since the aircraft weight W decreases during the flight, the altitude must increase to reduce the density of the ambient air and produce the required lift ($L = W$) while maintaining C_L and velocity constant. This flight profile is called a *cruise climb.*

Example 1-6. Calculate the endurance factor and range factor at Mach 0.8 and 40-kft altitude of hypothetical fighter aircraft HF-1 at 90 percent of maximum gross takeoff weight and a load factor of 1.

Solution.

$$q = \frac{\gamma}{2}\delta P_{\text{ref}}M_0^2 = 0.7 \times 0.1858 \times 2116 \times 0.8^2 = 176.1 \text{ lbf/ft}^2$$

From Fig. 1-24 at $M = 0.8$, $C_{D0} = 0.012$, $K_1 = 0.20$, and $K_2 = 0$.

$$C_L = \frac{nW}{qS_w} = \frac{1 \times 0.9 \times 40{,}000}{176.1 \times 720} = 0.2839$$

$$C_D = K_1C_L^2 + K_2C_L + C_{D0} = 0.2(0.2839^2) + 0.012 = 0.0281$$

Using Eq. (1-36b), we have

$$\text{TSFC} = (1.0 + 0.35M_0)\sqrt{\theta} = (1.0 + 0.35 \times 0.8)\sqrt{0.7519} = 1.110 (\text{lbm/hr})/\text{lbf}$$

Thus $$\text{EF} = \frac{C_L}{C_D(\text{TSFC})}\frac{g_c}{g_0} = \frac{0.2839}{0.0281 \times 1.110}\frac{32.174}{32.174} = 9.102 \text{ hr}$$

$$\text{RF} = \frac{C_L}{D_C}\frac{V}{\text{TSFC}}\frac{g_c}{g_0}$$

$$= \frac{0.2839}{0.0281}\ \frac{0.8 \times 0.8671 \times 1116 \text{ ft/sec}}{1.110(\text{lbm/hr})/\text{lbf}}\ \frac{3600 \text{ sec/hr}}{6080 \text{ ft/nm}}\ \frac{32.174}{32.174}$$

$$= 4170 \text{ nm}$$

Example 1-7. Determine the variation in endurance factor and range factor for the two hypothetical aircraft HF-1 and HP-1.

a. The endurance factor EF is plotted versus Mach number and altitude in Fig. 1-30 for our hypothetical fighter aircraft HF-1 at 90 percent of maximum gross takeoff weight. Note that the best endurance Mach number (minimum fuel consumption) increases with altitude and the best fuel consumption occurs at altitudes of 30 and 36 kft. The range factor is plotted versus Mach number and altitude in Fig. 1-31 for the HF-1 at 90 percent of maximum gross takeoff weight. Note that the best cruise Mach number (minimum fuel consumption) increases with altitude and the best fuel consumption occurs at an altitude of 36 kft and Mach number of 0.8.

b. The endurance factor is plotted versus Mach number and altitude in Fig. 1-32 for our hypothetical passenger aircraft HP-1 at 95 percent of maximum gross takeoff weight. Note that the best endurance Mach number (minimum fuel

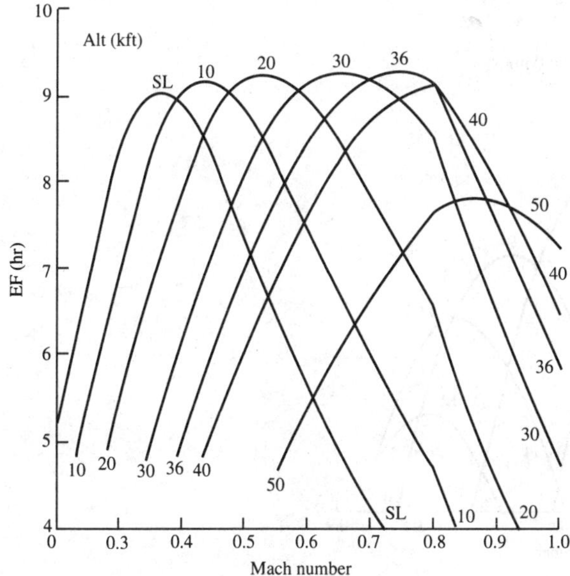

FIGURE 1-30
Endurance factor for HF-1 aircraft.

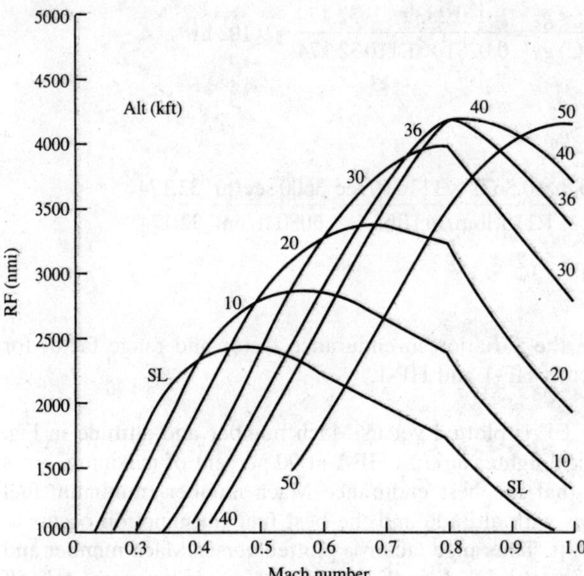

FIGURE 1-31
Range factor for HF-1 aircraft.

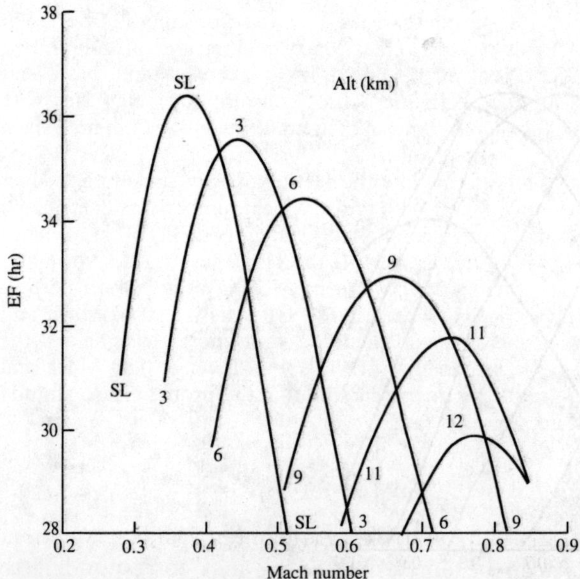

FIGURE 1-32
Endurance factor for HP-1 aircraft.

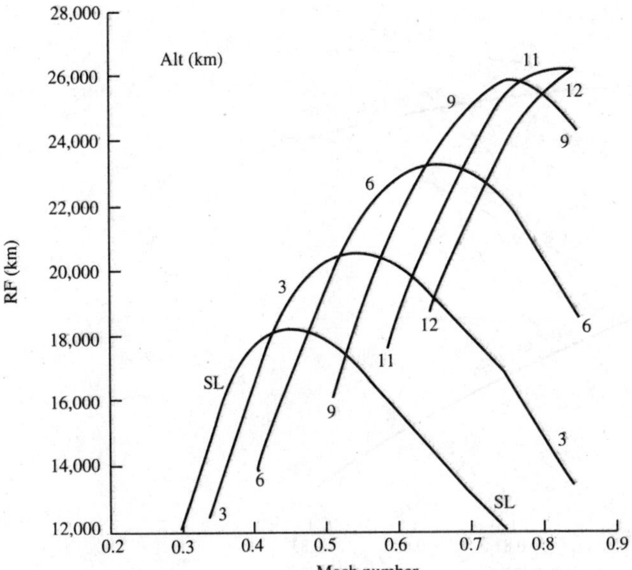

FIGURE 1-33
Range factor for HP-1 aircraft for various altitudes.

consumption) increases with altitude and the best fuel consumption occurs at sea level. The range factor is plotted versus Mach number and altitude in Fig. 1-33 for the HP-1 at 95 percent of maximum gross takeoff weight. Note that the best cruise Mach number (minimum fuel consumption) increases with altitude and the best fuel consumption occurs at an altitude of 11 km and Mach number of about 0.83.

Since the weight of an aircraft like the HP-1 can vary considerably over a flight, the variation in range factor with cruise Mach number was determined for 95 and 70 percent of maximum gross takeoff weight (MGTOW) at altitudes of 11 and 12 km and is plotted in Fig. 1-34. If the HP-1 flew at 0.83 Mach and 12-km altitude, the range factors at 95 percent MGTOW and at 70 percent MGTOW are about the same. However, if the HP-1 flew at 0.83 Mach and 11-km altitude, the range factor would decrease with aircraft weight and the aircraft's range would be less than that of the HP-1 flown at 0.83 Mach and 12-km altitude. One can see from this discussion that the proper cruise altitude can dramatically affect an aircraft's range.

MAXIMUM C_L/C_D. For flight conditions requiring minimum fuel consumption, the optimum flight condition can be approximated by that corresponding to maximum C_L/C_D. From Eq. (1-32), the maximum C_L/C_D (minimum C_D/C_L) can be found by taking the derivative of the following expression, setting it

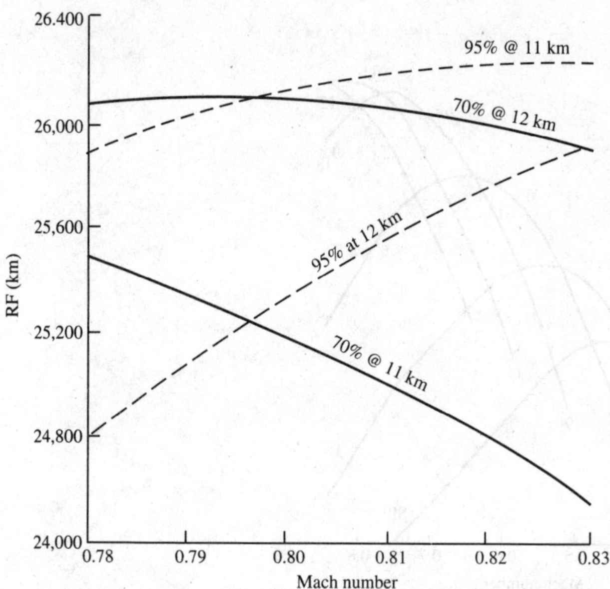

FIGURE 1-34
Range factor for HP-1 aircraft at 70 and 95% MGTOW.

equal to zero, and solving for the C_L that gives minimum C_D/C_L:

$$\frac{C_D}{C_L} = K_1 C_L + K_2 + \frac{C_{D0}}{C_L} \tag{1-46}$$

The lift coefficient that gives maximum C_L/C_D (minimum C_D/C_L) is

$$\boxed{C_L^* = \sqrt{\frac{C_{D0}}{K_1}}} \tag{1-47}$$

and maximum C_L/C_D is given by

$$\boxed{\left(\frac{C_L}{C_D}\right)^* = \frac{1}{2\sqrt{C_{D0}K_1} + K_2}} \tag{1-48}$$

The drag D, range factor, endurance factor, and C_L/C_D versus Mach number at an altitude are plotted in Fig. 1-35 for the HF-1 aircraft and in Fig. 1-36 for the HP-1. Note that the maximum C_L/C_D occurs at Mach 0.8 for the HF-1 and at Mach 0.75 for the HP-1—the same Mach numbers where drags are minimum. The endurance factor is a maximum at a substantially lower Mach number than that corresponding to $(C_L/C_D)^*$ for the HF-1 due to the high TSFC and its increase with Mach number [see Eq. (1-36*b*)]. The endurance factor for the HP-1 is a maximum at the same Mach number that

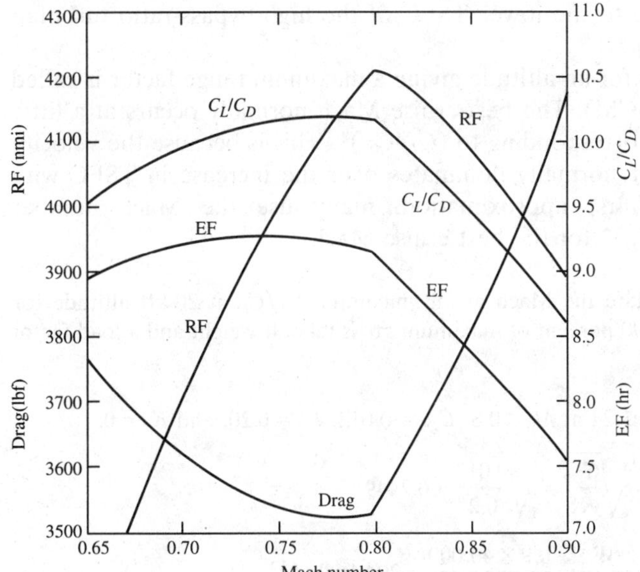

FIGURE 1-35
Comparison of drag C_L/C_D, endurance factor, and range factor for the HF-1 at 36-kft altitude.

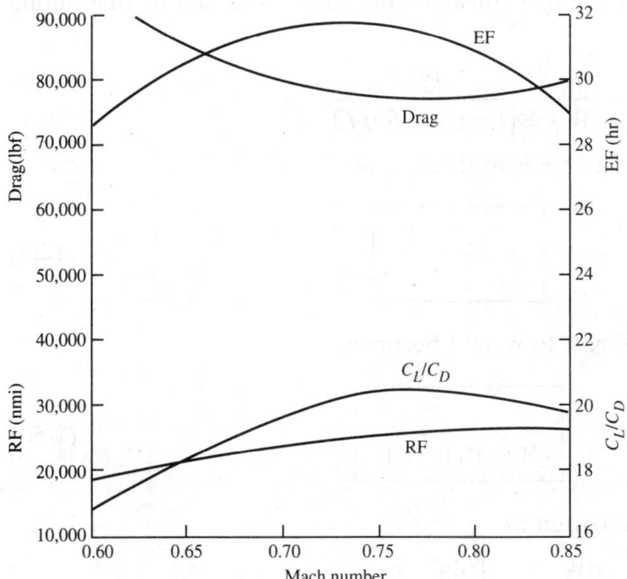

FIGURE 1-36
Comparison of drag C_L/C_D, endurance factor, and range factor for the HP-1 at 11-km altitude.

C_L/C_D is maximum due to the lower TSFC of the high-bypass-ratio turbofan engine [see Eq. (1-36*a*)].

The Mach number for an altitude giving a maximum range factor is called the *best cruise Mach* (BCM). The best cruise Mach normally occurs at a little higher Mach than that corresponding to $(C_L/C_D)^*$. This is because the velocity term in the range factor normally dominates over the increase in TSFC with Mach number. As a first approximation, many use the Mach number corresponding to $(C_L/C_D)^*$ for the best cruise Mach.

Example 1-8. Calculate the Mach giving maximum C_L/C_D at 20-kft altitude for the HF-1 aircraft at 90 percent of maximum gross takeoff weight and a load factor of 1.

Solution. From Fig. 1-24 at $M_0 < 0.8$, $C_{D0} = 0.012$, $K_1 = 0.20$, and $K_2 = 0$.

$$C_L^* = \sqrt{\frac{C_{D0}}{K_1}} = \sqrt{\frac{0.012}{0.2}} = 0.2449$$

$$q = \frac{W}{C_L S_w} = \frac{0.9 \times 40{,}000}{0.2449 \times 720} = 204.16 \text{ lbf/ft}^2$$

$$M_0 = \sqrt{\frac{q}{(\gamma/2)\delta P_{\text{ref}}}} = \sqrt{\frac{204.16}{0.7 \times 0.4599 \times 2116}} = 0.547$$

ACCELERATED FLIGHT. For flight conditions when thrust T is greater than drag D, an expression for the fuel consumption can be obtained by first noting from Eq. (1–28) that

$$\frac{T}{W} = \frac{P_s}{V[1 - (D + R)/T]}$$

We define the ratio of drag $D + R$ to thrust T as

$$u \equiv \frac{D + R}{T} \tag{1-49}$$

The above equation for thrust to weight becomes

$$\frac{T}{W} = \frac{P_s}{V(1 - u)} \tag{1-50}$$

Now Eq. (1-35) can be rewritten as

$$\frac{dW}{W} = -\frac{\text{TSFC}}{V(1 - u)} \frac{g_0}{g_c} P_s \, dt$$

Since $P_s \, dt = dz_e$, the above equation can be expressed in its most useful forms

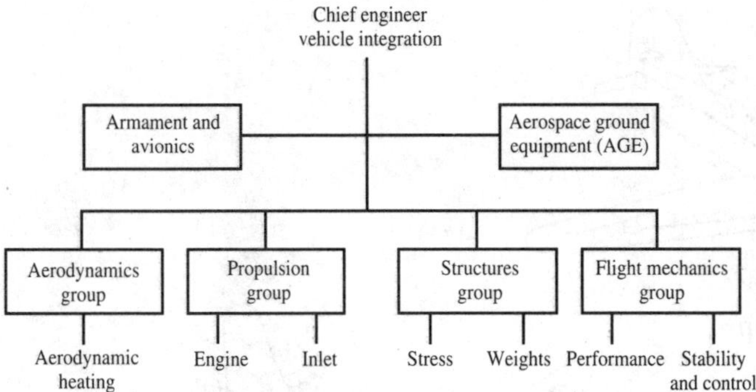

FIGURE 1-37
Organization of a typical vehicle design team.

as

$$\boxed{\frac{dW}{W} = -\frac{\text{TSFC}}{V(1-u)}\frac{g_0}{g_c}\,dz_e = -\frac{\text{TSFC}}{V(1-u)}\frac{g_0}{g_c}\,d\left(h+\frac{V^2}{2g}\right)} \tag{1-51}$$

The term $1-u$ represents the fraction of engine power that goes to increasing the aircraft energy z_e, and u represents that fraction that is lost to aircraft drag $D+R$. Note that this equation applies for cases when u is not unity. When u is unity, either Eq. (1-39) or Eq. (1-44) is used.

To obtain the fuel consumption during an acceleration flight condition, Eq. (1-51) can be easily integrated for known flight paths (values of V and z_e) and known variation of $\text{TSFC}/[V(1-u)]$ with z_e.

Aerospace Vehicle Design—A Team Effort

Aeronautical and mechanical engineers in the aerospace field do many things, but for the most part their efforts all lead to the design of some type of aerospace vehicle. The design team for a new aircraft may be divided into four principal groups: aerodynamics, propulsion, structures, and flight mechanics. The design of a vehicle calls upon the extraordinary talents of engineers in each group. Thus the design is a team effort. A typical design team is shown in Fig. 1-37. The chief engineer serves as the referee and integrates the efforts of everyone into the vehicle design. Figure 1-38 shows the kind of aircraft design which might result if any one group were able to dominate the others.

1-6 ROCKET ENGINES

Non-air-breathing propulsion systems are characterized by the fact that they carry both fuel and the oxidizer within the aerospace vehicle. Such systems

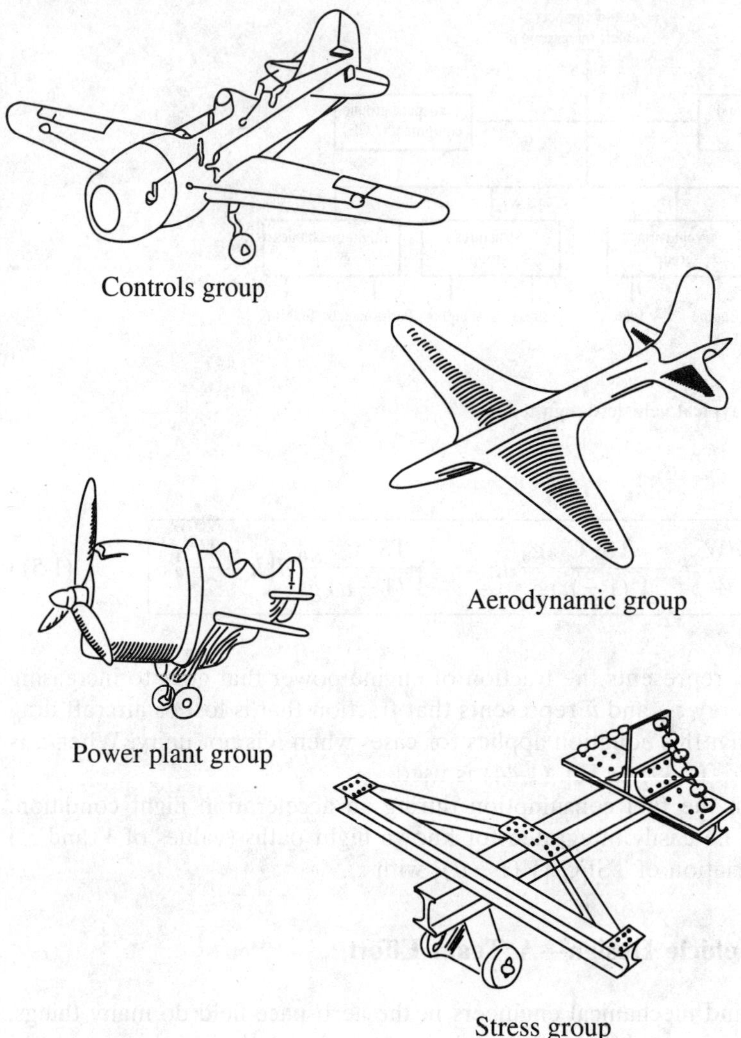

FIGURE 1-38
Aircraft designs.

thus may be used anywhere in space as well as in the atmosphere. Figure 1-39 shows the essential features of a liquid-propellant rocket system. Two propellants (an oxidizer and a fuel) are pumped into the combustion chamber where they ignite. The nozzle accelerates the products of combustion to high velocities and exhausts them to the atmosphere or space.

A solid-propellant rocket motor is the simplest of all propulsion systems. Figure 1-40 shows the essential features of this type of system. In this system, the fuel and oxidizer are mixed together and cast into a solid mass called the *grain.* The grain, usually formed with a hole down the middle called the

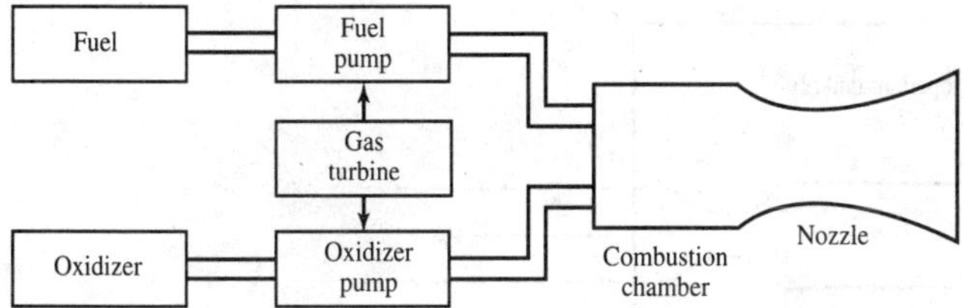

FIGURE 1-39
Liquid-propellant rocket motor.

perforation, is firmly cemented to the inside of the combustion chamber. After ignition, the grain burns radially outward, and the hot combustion gases pass down the perforation and are exhausted through the nozzle.

The absence of a propellant feed system in the solid-propellant rocket is one of its major advantages. Liquid rockets, on the other hand, may be stopped and later restarted, and their thrust may be varied somewhat by changing the speed of the fuel and oxidizer pumps.

Rocket Engine Thrust

A natural starting point in understanding the performance of a rocket is the examination of the static thrust. Application of the momentum equation developed in Chap. 2 will show that the static thrust is a function of the propellant flow rate $\dot{m}_p$, the exhaust velocity V_e and pressure P_e, the exhaust area A_e, and the ambient pressure P_a. Figure 1-41 shows a schematic of a stationary rocket to be considered for analysis. We assume the flow to be one-dimensional, with a steady exit velocity V_e and propellant flow rate $\dot{m}_p$. About this rocket we place a control volume σ whose control surface intersects the exhaust jet perpendicularly through the exit plane of the nozzle. Thrust acts in the direction opposite to the direction of V_e. The reaction to the thrust F necessary to hold the rocket and control volume stationary is shown in Fig. 1-41.

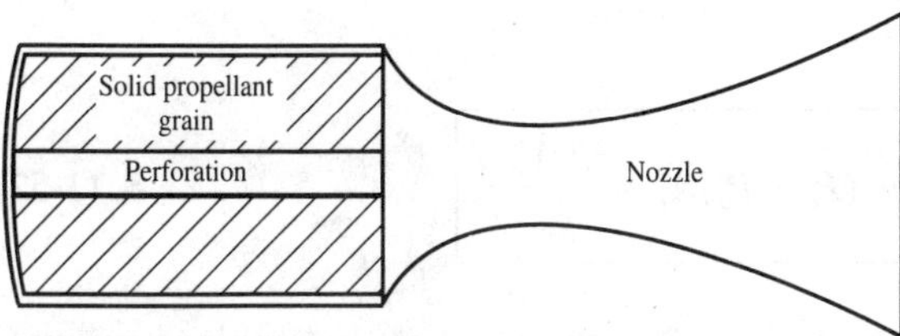

FIGURE 1-40
Solid-propellant rocket motor.

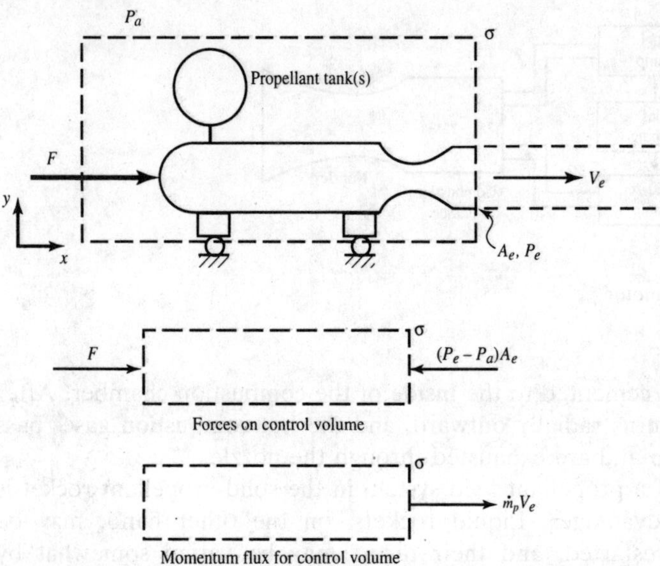

FIGURE 1-41
Schematic diagram of static rocket engine.

The momentum equation applied to this system gives the following:

1. Sum of forces acting on the outside surface of the control volume:

$$\sum F_x = F - (P_e - P_a)A_e$$

2. The net rate of change of momentum for the control volume:

$$\Delta(\text{momentum}) = \dot{M}_{\text{out}} = \frac{\dot{m}_p V_e}{g_c}$$

Since the sum of the forces acting on the outside of the control volume is equal to the net rate of change of the momentum for the control volume, we have

$$\boxed{F - (P_e - P_a)A_e = \frac{\dot{m}_p V_e}{g_c}} \tag{1-52}$$

If the pressure in the exhaust plane P_e is the same as the ambient pressure P_a, the thrust is given by $F = \dot{m}_p V_e / g_c$. The condition $P_e = P_a$ is called *on-design* or *optimum expansion* because it corresponds to maximum thrust for the given chamber conditions. It is convenient to define an *effective exhaust velocity* C such that

$$C \equiv V_e + \frac{(P_e - P_a)A_e g_c}{\dot{m}_p} \tag{1-53}$$

Thus the static thrust of a rocket can be written as

$$F = \frac{\dot{m}_p C}{g_c} \tag{1-54}$$

Specific Impulse

The *specific impulse* I_{sp} for a rocket is defined as the thrust per unit of propellant weight flow

$$I_{sp} \equiv \frac{F}{\dot{w}_p} = \frac{F}{\dot{m}_p}\frac{g_c}{g_0} \tag{1-55}$$

where g_0 is the acceleration due to gravity at sea level. The unit of I_{sp} is the second. From Eqs. (1-54) and (1-55), the specific impulse can also be written as

$$I_{sp} = \frac{C}{g_0} \tag{1-56}$$

Example 1-9. Find the specific impulse of the space shuttle main engine (SSME) which produces 470,000 lbf in a vacuum with a propellant weight flow of 1030 lbf/sec. By using Eq. (1-55), we find that the SSME has a specific impulse I_{sp} of 456 sec (=470,000/1030) in vacuum.

An estimate of the variation in thrust with altitude for the space shuttle main engine is shown in Fig. 1-42. The typical specific impulses for some rocket engines are listed in Table 1-6. Other performance data for rocket engines are contained in App. C.

Rocket Vehicle Acceleration

The mass of a rocket vehicle varies a great deal during flight due to the consumption of the propellant. The velocity that a rocket vehicle attains during powered flight can be determined by considering the vehicle in Fig. 1-43.

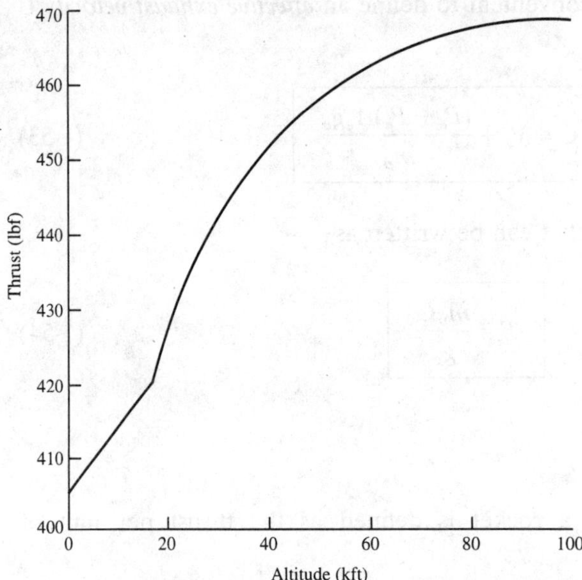

FIGURE 1-42
Rocket thrust variation with altitude.

The figure shows an accelerating rocket vehicle in a gravity field. At some time, the mass of the rocket is m and its velocity is V. In an infinitesimal time dt, the rocket exhausts an incremental mass dm_p with an exhaust velocity V_e relative to the rocket as the rocket velocity changes to $V + dV$. The net change in momentum of the control volume σ is composed of the momentum out of the rocket at the exhaust plus the change of the momentum of the rocket. The momentum out of the rocket in the V direction is $-V_e\, dm_p$, and the change in the momentum of the rocket in the V direction is $m\, dV$. The forces acting on

TABLE 1-6
Ranges of specific impulse I_{sp} for typical rocket engines

Fuel/oxidizer	I_{sp} (sec)
Solid propellant	250
Liquid O_2: kerosene (RP)	310
Liquid O_2: H_2	410
Nuclear fuel: H_2 propellant	840

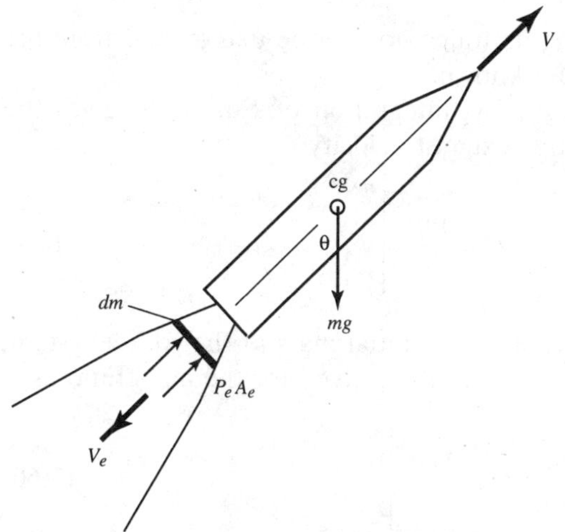

FIGURE 1-43
Rocket vehicle in flight.

the control volume σ are composed of the net pressure force, the drag D, and the gravitational force. The sum of these forces in the V direction is

$$\sum F_V = (P_e - P_a)A_e - D - \frac{mg}{g_c} \cos \theta$$

The resultant impulse on the rocket $(\sum F_V)\,dt$ must equal the momentum change of the system $\Delta(\text{momentum}) = (-V_e\,dm_p + m\,dV)/g_c$. Thus

$$\left[(P_e - P_a)A_e - D - \frac{mg}{g_c} \cos \theta\right] dt = \frac{-V_e\,dm_p + m\,dV}{g_c}$$

From the above relationship, the momentum change of the rocket $(m\,dV)$ is

$$\frac{m\,dV}{g_c} = \left[(P_e - P_a)A_e - D - \frac{mg}{g_c} \cos \theta\right] dt + \frac{V_e\,dm_p}{g_c} \tag{1-57}$$

Since $dm_p = \dot{m}_p\,dt = -(dm/dt)\,dt$, then Eq. (1-57) can be written as

$$\frac{m\,dV}{g_c} = \left[(P_e - P_a)A_e + \frac{\dot{m}_p V_e}{g_c} - D - \frac{mg}{g_c} \cos \theta\right] dt$$

By using Eq. (1-53), the above relationship becomes

$$\frac{m\,dV}{g_c} = \left(\frac{\dot{m}_p}{g_c} C - D - \frac{mg}{g_c} \cos \theta\right) dt$$

or

$$\boxed{dV = -C\frac{dm}{m} - \frac{D g_c}{m}\,dt - g \cos \theta\,dt} \tag{1-58}$$

The velocity of a rocket along its trajectory can be determined from the above equation if C, D, g, and θ are known.

In the absence of drag and gravity, integration of Eq. (1-58) gives the following, assuming constant effective exhaust velocity C:

$$\boxed{\Delta V = C \ln \frac{m_i}{m_f}} \tag{1-59}$$

where ΔV is the change in velocity, m_i is the initial mass of the rocket system, and m_f is the final mass. Equation (1-59) can be solved for the mass ratio as

$$\boxed{\frac{m_i}{m_f} = \exp \frac{\Delta V}{C}} \tag{1-60}$$

Example 1-10. We want to estimate the mass ratio (final to initial) of an H_2-O_2 ($C = 4000$ m/sec) rocket for an earth orbit ($\Delta V = 8000$ m/sec), neglecting drag and gravity. Using Eq. (1-59), we obtain $m_f/m_i = e^{-2} = 0.132$, or a single-stage rocket would be about 13 percent payload and structure and 87 percent propellant.

PROBLEMS

1-1. Calculate the uninstalled thrust for Example 1-1, using Eq. (1-6).

1-2. Develop the following analytical expressions for a turbojet engine:

a. When the fuel flow rate is very small in comparison with the air mass flow rate, the exit pressure is equal to ambient pressure, and the installation loss coefficients are zero, then the installed thrust T is given by

$$T = \frac{\dot{m}_0}{g_c}(V_e - V_0)$$

b. For the above conditions, the thrust specific fuel consumption is given by

$$\text{TSFC} = \frac{Tg_c/\dot{m}_0 + 2V_0}{2\eta_T h_{PR}}$$

c. For $V_0 = 0$ and 500 ft/sec, plot the above equation for TSFC [in (lbm/hr)/lbf] versus specific thrust $T/\dot{m}_0$ [in lbf/(lbm/sec)] for values of specific thrust from 0 to 120. Use $\eta_T = 0.4$ and $h_{PR} = 18{,}400$ Btu/lbm.

d. Explain the trends.

1-3. Repeat 1-2*c*, using SI units. For $V_0 = 0$ to 150 m/sec, plot TSFC [in (mg/sec)/N] versus specific thrust $T/\dot{m}_0$ [in N/(kg/sec)] for values of specific thrust from 0 to 1200. Use $\eta_T = 0.4$ and $h_{PR} = 42{,}800$ kJ/kg.

1-4. A J57 turbojet engine is tested at sea-level, static, standard-day conditions ($P_0 = 14.696$ psia, $T_0 = 518.7$°R, and $V_0 = 0$). At one test point, the thrust is 10,200 lbf while the airflow is 164 lbm/sec and the fuel flow is 8520 lbm/hr. Using these data, estimate the exit velocity V_e for the case of exit pressure equal to ambient pressure ($P_0 = P_e$).

1-5. The thrust for a turbofan engine with separate exhaust streams is equal to the sum of the thrust from the engine core F_C and the thrust from the bypass stream F_B. The bypass ratio of the engine α is the ratio of the mass flow through the bypass stream to the core mass flow, or $\alpha \equiv \dot{m}_B/\dot{m}_C$. When the exit pressures are equal to the ambient pressure, the thrusts of the core and bypass stream are given by

$$F_C = \frac{1}{g_c}[(\dot{m}_C + \dot{m}_f)V_{Ce} - \dot{m}_C V_0]$$

$$F_B = \frac{\dot{m}_B}{g_c}(V_{Be} - V_0)$$

where V_{Ce} and V_{Be} are the exit velocities from the core and bypass, respectively, V_0 is the inlet velocity, and $\dot{m}_f$ is the mass flow rate of fuel burned in the core of the engine.

Show that the specific thrust and thrust specific fuel consumption can be expressed as

$$\frac{F}{\dot{m}_0} = \frac{1}{g_c}\left(\frac{1 + \dot{m}_f/\dot{m}_C}{1+\alpha}V_{Ce} + \frac{\alpha}{1+\alpha}V_{Be} - V_0\right)$$

$$S = \frac{\dot{m}_f}{F} = \frac{\dot{m}_f/\dot{m}_C}{(F/\dot{m}_0)(1+\alpha)}$$

where $\dot{m}_0 = \dot{m}_C + \dot{m}_B$.

1-6. The CF6 turbofan engine has a rated thrust of 40,000 lbf at a fuel flow rate of 13,920 lbm/hr at sea-level static conditions. If the core airflow rate is 225 lbm/sec and the bypass ratio is 6.0, what are the specific thrust [lbf/(lbm/sec)] and thrust specific fuel consumption [(lbm/hr)/lbf]?

1-7. The JT9D high-bypass-ratio turbofan engine at maximum static power ($V_0 = 0$) on a sea-level, standard day ($P_0 = 14.696$ psia, $T_0 = 518.7$°R) has the following data: the air mass flow rate through the core is 247 lbm/sec, the air mass flow rate through the fan bypass duct is 1248 lbm/sec, the exit velocity from the core is 1190 ft/sec, the exit velocity from the bypass duct is 885 ft/sec and the fuel flow rate into the combustor is 15,750 lbm/hr. Estimate the following for the case of exit pressures equal to ambient pressure ($P_0 = P_e$):

a. The thrust of the engine

b. The thermal efficiency of the engine (heating value of jet fuel is about 18,400 Btu/lbm)

c. The propulsive efficiency and thrust specific fuel consumption of the engine

1-8. Repeat Prob. 1-7, using SI units.

1-9. One advanced afterburning fighter engine, whose performance is depicted in Figs. 1-14*a* through 1-14*e*, is installed in the HF-1 fighter aircraft. Using the aircraft drag data of Fig. 1-26*b*, determine and plot the variation of weight specific excess power (P_s in feet per second) versus flight Mach number for level flight ($n = 1$) at 36-kft altitude. Assume the installation losses are constant with values of $\phi_{\text{inlet}} = 0.05$ and $\phi_{\text{noz}} = 0.02$.

1-10. Determine the takeoff speed of the HF-1 aircraft.

1-11. Determine the takeoff speed of the HP-1 aircraft at 90 percent of maximum gross takeoff weight.

1-12. Derive Eqs. (1-47) and (1-48) for maximum C_L/C_D. Start by taking the derivative of Eq. (1-46) with respect to C_L and finding the expression for the lift coefficient that gives maximum C_L/C_D.

1-13. Show that for maximum C_L/C_D, the corresponding drag coefficient C_D is given by

$$C_D = 2C_{D0} + K_2\sqrt{\frac{C_{D0}}{K_1}}$$

1-14. An aircraft with a wing area of 800 ft^2 is in level flight ($n = 1$) at maximum C_L/C_D. Given that the drag coefficients for the aircraft are $C_{D0} = 0.02$, $K_2 = 0$, and $K_1 = 0.2$, find

a. The maximum C_L/C_D and the corresponding values of C_L and C_D

b. The flight altitude [use Eqs. (1-29) and (1-30*b*)] and aircraft drag for an aircraft weight of 45,000 lbf at Mach 0.8

c. The flight altitude and aircraft drag for an aircraft weight of 35,000 lbf at Mach 0.8

d. The range for an installed engine thrust specific fuel consumption rate of 0.8 (lbm/hr)/lbf, if the 10,000-lbf difference in aircraft weight between parts *b* and *c* above is due only to fuel consumption

1-15. An aircraft weighing 110,000 N with a wing area of 42 m^2 is in level flight ($n = 1$) at the maximum value of C_L/C_D. Given that the drag coefficients for the aircraft are $C_{D0} = 0.03$, $K_2 = 0$, and $K_1 = 0.25$, find the following:

a. The maximum C_L/C_D and the corresponding values of C_L and C_D

b. The flight altitude [use Eqs. (1-29) and (1-30*b*)] and aircraft drag at Mach 0.5

c. The flight altitude and aircraft drag at Mach 0.75

1-16. The Breguet range equation [Eq. (1-45*b*)] applies for a cruise climb flight profile with constant range factor RF. Another range equation can be developed for a level cruise flight profile with varying RF. Consider the case where we keep C_L, C_D, and TSFC constant and vary the flight velocity with aircraft weight by the expression

$$V = \sqrt{\frac{2g_c W}{\rho C_L S_w}}$$

Using the subscripts *i* and *f* for the initial and final flight conditions, respectively, show the following:

a. Substitution of this expression for flight velocity into Eq. (1-42) gives

$$\frac{dW}{\sqrt{W}} = -\frac{\sqrt{W_i}}{\text{RF}_i}\,ds$$

b. Integration of the above between the initial *i* and final *f* conditions gives

$$\frac{W_f}{W_i} = \left[1 - \frac{s}{2(\text{RF}_i)}\right]^2$$

c. For a given weight fraction W_f/W_i, the maximum range *s* for this level cruise flight corresponds to starting the flight at the maximum altitude (minimum density) and maximum value of $\sqrt{C_L}/C_D$.

d. For the drag coefficient equation of Eq. (1-32), maximum $\sqrt{C_L}/C_D$ corresponds to $C_L = (1/6K_1)(\sqrt{12K_1C_{D0} + K_2^2} - K_2)$.

1-17. An aircraft begins a cruise at a wing loading W/S_w of 100 lbf/ft^2 and Mach 0.8. The drag coefficients are $K_1 = 0.056$, $K_2 = -0.008$, and $C_{D0} = 0.014$, and the fuel consumption TSFC is constant at 0.8 (lbm/hr)/lbf. For a weight fraction W_f/W_i of 0.9, determine the range and other parameters for two different types of cruise.

a. For a cruise climb (max. C_L/C_D) flight path, determine C_L, C_D, initial and final altitudes, and range.

b. For a level cruise (max. $\sqrt{C_L}/C_D$) flight path, determine C_L, C_D, altitude, initial and final velocities, and range.

1-18. An aircraft weighing 70,000 lbf with a wing area of 1000 ft^2 is in level flight ($n = 1$) at 30-kft altitude. Using the drag coefficients of Fig. 1-24 and the TSFC model of Eq. (1-36*b*), find the following:

a. The maximum C_L/C_D and the corresponding values of C_L, C_D, and Mach number (*Note:* Since the drag coefficients are a function of Mach number and it is an unknown, you must first guess a value for the Mach number to obtain the drag coefficients. Try a Mach number of 0.8 for your first guess.)

b. The C_L, C_D, C_L/C_D, range factor, endurance factor, and drag for flight Mach numbers of 0.74, 0.76, 0.78, 0.80, 0.81, and 0.82

c. The best cruise Mach (maximum RF)

d. The best loiter Mach (maximum EF)

1-19. An aircraft weighing 200,000 N with a wing area of 60 m^2 is in level flight ($n = 1$) at 9-km altitude. Using the drag coefficients of Fig. 1-24 and TSFC model of Eq. (1-36*b*), find the following:

a. The maximum C_L/C_D and the corresponding values of C_L, C_D, and Mach number (*Note:* Since the drag coefficients are a function of the Mach number and it is an unknown, you must first guess a value for the Mach number to obtain the drag coefficients. Try a Mach number of 0.8 for your first guess.)

b. The C_L, C_D, C_L/C_D, range factor, endurance factor, and drag for flight Mach numbers of 0.74, 0.76, 0.78, 0.80, 0.81, and 0.82

c. The best cruise Mach (maximum RF)

d. The best loiter Mach (maximum EF)

1-20. What is the specific impulse in seconds of the JT9D turbofan engine in Prob. 1-7?

1-21. A rocket motor is fired in place on a static test stand. The rocket exhausts 100 lbm/sec at an exit velocity of 2000 ft/sec and pressure of 50 psia. The exit area of the rocket is 0.2 ft^2. For an ambient pressure of 14.7 psia, determine the effective exhaust velocity, the thrust transmitted to the test stand, and the specific impulse.

1-22. A rocket motor under static testing exhausts 50 kg/sec at an exit velocity of 800 m/sec and pressure of 350 kPa. The exit area of the rocket is 0.02 m^2. For an ambient pressure of 100 kPa, determine the effective exhaust velocity, the thrust transmitted to the test stand, and the specific impulse.

1-23. The propellant weight of an orbiting space system amounts to 90 percent of the system gross weight. Given that the system rocket engine has a specific impulse of 300 sec, determine:

a. The maximum attainable velocity if all the propellant is burned and the system's initial velocity is 7930 m/sec *b.* The propellant mass flow rate, given that the rocket engine thrust is 1,670,000 N

1-24. A chemical rocket motor wtih a specific impulse of 400 sec is used in the final stage of a multistage launch vehicle for deep-space exploration. This final stage has a mass ratio (initial to final) of 6, and its single rocket motor is first fired while it orbits the earth at a velocity of 26,000 ft/sec. The final stage must reach a velocity of 36,700 ft/sec to escape the earth's gravitational field. Determine the percentage of fuel that must be used to perform this maneuver (neglect gravity and drag).

1-D1 GAS TURBINE DESIGN PROBLEM 1 (HP-1 AIRCRAFT)

Background

You are to determine the thrust and fuel consumption requirements of the two engines for the hypothetical passenger aircraft, the HP-1. The twin-engine aircraft will cruise at 0.83 Mach and be capable of the following requirements:

1. Takeoff at maximum gross takeoff weight W_{TO} from an airport at 1.6-km pressure altitude on a hot day (38°C) uses a 3650-m (12-kft) runway. The craft is able to maintain a 2.4 percent single-engine climb gradient in the event of engine failure at liftoff.
2. It transports 253 passengers and luggage (90 kg each) over a still-air distance of 11,120 km (6000 nmi). It has 30 min of fuel in reserve at end (loiter).
3. It attains an initial altitude of 11-km at beginning of cruise ($P_s = 1.5$ m/sec).
4. The single-engine craft cruises at 5-km altitude at 0.45 Mach ($P_s = 1.5$ m/sec).

All the data for the HP-1 contained in Example 1-2 apply. Preliminary mission analysis of the HP-1 using the methods of Ref. 12 for the 11,120-km flight with 253 passengers and luggage (22,770-kg payload) gives the following preliminary fuel use:

Description	Distance (km)	Fuel used (kg)
Taxi		200*
Takeoff		840*
Climb and acceleration	330	5,880*
Cruise	10,650	50,240
Descent	140	1,090*
Loiter (30 min at 9-km altitude)		2,350
Land and taxi		600*
	11,120	61,200

* These fuel consumptions can be considered to be constant.

Analysis of takeoff indicates that each engine must produce an installed thrust of 214 kN on a hot day (38°C) at 0.1 Mach and 1.6-km pressure altitude. To provide for reasonable-length landing gear, the maximum diameter of the engine inlet is limited to

2.2 m. Based on standard design practice (see Chap. 10), the maximum mass flow rate per unit area is given by

$$\frac{\dot{m}}{A} = 231.8 \frac{\delta_0}{\sqrt{\theta_0}} \qquad \text{(kg/sec)/m}^2$$

Thus on a hot day (38°C) at 0.1 Mach and 1.6-km pressure altitude, $\theta = (38 + 273.1)/288.2 = 1.079$, $\theta_0 = 1.079 \times 1.002 = 1.081$, $\delta = 0.8256$, $\delta_0 = 0.8256 \times 1.007 = 0.8314$, and the maximum mass flow through the 2.2-m-diameter inlet is 704.6 kg/sec.

Calculations

1. If the HP-1 starts out the cruise at 11-km with a weight of 1,577,940 N, find the allowable TSFC for the distance of 10,650 km for the following cases.
   a. Assume the aircraft performs a cruise climb (flies at a constant C_D/C_L). What is its altitude at the end of the cruise climb?
   b. Assume the aircraft cruises at a constant altitude of 11 km. Determine C_D/C_L at the start and end of cruise. Using the average of these two values, calculate the allowable TSFC.
2. Determine the loiter (endurance) Mach numbers for altitudes of 10, 9, 8, 7, and 6 km when the HP-1 aircraft is at 64 percent of W_{TO}.
3. Determine the aircraft drag at the following points in the HP-1 aircraft's 11,120-km flight based on the fuel consumptions listed above:
   a. Takeoff, $M = 0.23$, sea level
   b. Start of cruise, $M = 0.83$, 11 km
   c. End of cruise climb, $M = 0.83$, altitude = ? ft
   d. End of 11-km cruise, $M = 0.83$, 11 km
   e. Engine out (88 percent of W_{TO}), $M = 0.45$, 5 km

1-D2 GAS TURBINE DESIGN PROBLEM 2 (HF-1 AIRCRAFT)

Background

You are to determine the thrust and fuel consumption requirements of the two engines for the hypothetical fighter aircraft HF-1. This twin-engine fighter will supercruise at 1.6 Mach and will be capable of the following requirements:

1. Takeoff at maximum gross takeoff weight W_{TO} from a 1200-ft (366-m) runway at sea level on a standard day.
2. Supercruise at 1.6 Mach and 40-kft altitude for 250 nmi (463 km) at 92 percent of W_{TO}.
3. Perform 5*g* turns at 1.6 Mach and 30-kft altitude at 88 percent of W_{TO}.
4. Perform 5*g* turns at 0.9 Mach and 30-kft altitude at 88 percent of W_{TO}.
5. Perform the maximum mission listed below.

All the data for the HF-1 contained in Example 1-2 apply. Preliminary mission analysis of the HF-1 using the methods of Ref. 12 for the maximum mission gives the following preliminary fuel use:

Description	Distance (nm)	Fuel used (lbm)
Warmup, taxi, takeoff		700*
Climb and acceleration to 0.9 Mach and 40 kft	35	1,800*
Accelerate from 0.9 to 1.6 Mach	12	700*
Supercruise at 1.6 Mach and 40 kft	203	4,400
Deliver payload of 2000 lbf	0	0*
Perform one 5*g* turn at 1.6 Mach and 30 kft	0	1,000*
Perform two 5*g* turns at 0.9 Mach and 30 kft	0	700*
Climb to best cruise altitude and 0.9 Mach	23	400*
Cruise climb at 0.9 Mach	227	1,600
Loiter (20 min at 30-kft altitude)		1,100
Land		0*
	500	12,400

* These fuel consumptions can be considered to be constant.

Analysis of takeoff indicates that each engine must produce an installed thrust of 23,500 lbf on a standard day at 0.1 Mach and sea-level altitude. To provide for optimum integration into the airframe, the maximum area of the engine inlet is limited to 5 ft². Based on standard design practice (see Chap. 10), the maximum mass flow rate per unit area for subsonic flight conditions is given by

$$\frac{\dot{m}}{A} = 47.5\frac{\delta_0}{\sqrt{\theta_0}} \quad \text{(lbm/sec)/ft}^2$$

Thus at 0.1 Mach and sea-level standard day, $\theta = 1.0$, $\theta_0 = 1.002$, $\delta = 1.0$, $\delta_0 = 1.007$, and the maximum mass flow through the 5-ft² inlet is 238.9 lbm/sec. For supersonic flight conditions, the maximum mass flow rate per unit area is simply the density of the air ρ times its velocity V.

Calculations

1. If the HF-1 starts the supercruise at 40 kft with a weight of 36,800 lbf, find the allowable TSFC for the distance of 203 nmi for the following cases:
   a. Assume the aircraft performs a cruise climb (flies at a constant C_D/C_L). What is its altitude at the end of the cruise climb?
   b. Assume the aircraft cruises at a constant altitude of 40 kft. Determine C_D/C_L at the start and end of cruise. Using the average of these two values, calculate the allowable TSFC.
2. Find the best cruise altitude for the subsonic return cruise at 0.9 Mach and 70.75 percent of W_{TO}.
3. Determine the loiter (endurance) Mach numbers for altitudes of 32, 30, 28, 26, and 24 kft when the HF-1 aircraft is at 67 percent of W_{TO}.
4. Determine the aircraft drag at the following points in the HF-1 aircraft's maximum mission based on the fuel consumptions listed above:
   a. Takeoff, $M = 0.172$, sea level
   b. Start of supercruise, $M = 1.6$, 40 kft
   c. End of supercruise climb, $M = 1.6$, altitude = ? ft
   d. End of 40-kft supercruise, $M = 1.6$, 40 kft
   e. Start of subsonic cruise, $M = 0.9$, altitude = best cruise altitude
   f. Start of loiter, altitude = 30 kft

CHAPTER 2

THERMODYNAMICS REVIEW

2-1 INTRODUCTION

The operation of gas turbine engines and of rocket motors is governed by the laws of mechanics and thermodynamics. The field of mechanics includes the mechanics of both fluids and solids. However, since the process occurring in most propulsion devices involves a flowing fluid, our emphasis will be fluid mechanics or, more specifically, gas dynamics.

With the aid of definitions and experimentally observed phenomena, logical deductions have been made over the years leading to the fundamental laws of mechanics and thermodynamics. Initially the development of these sciences was based on intuition and the accumulation of many different, but not always unrelated, theorems and rules. Frequently the understanding of certain concepts and phenomena was hindered by ambiguous and conflicting definitions. Today, as a result of years of work in mechanics and thermodynamics, we can present an efficient and logical introduction to these sciences based on the schematic outline of Fig. 2-1. In this figure, the terms *fundamental laws, theorems,* and *corollaries* have the following meanings. A *fundamental law* is a statement that can be neither deduced logically from definitions nor established by a finite number of experimental observations. A fundamental law is usually a generalization of experimental results beyond the region covered by the experiments themselves. A *theorem* is a statement whose validity depends upon the validity of a given set of laws. A *corollary* is a more or less self-evident statement following a definition, law, or theorem.

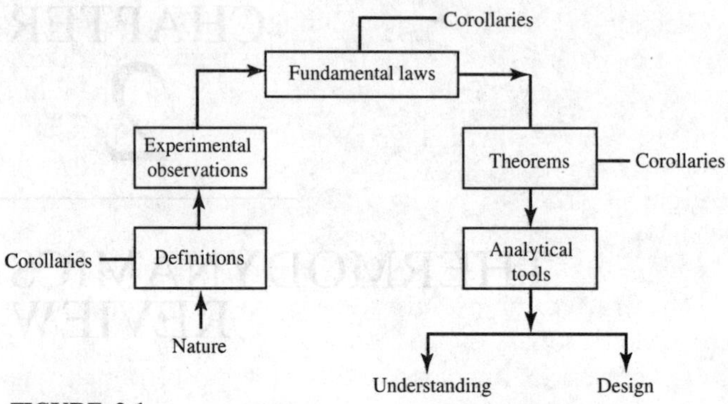

FIGURE 2-1
Interrelationship of definitions, laws, and theorems.

Our approach, then, will be as follows:

1. Definitions will be given which enable us to describe the phenomena of interest.
2. With a necessary and sufficient set of terms so defined, we will indicate how experimental observations of these defined quantities—alone or as they interact with each other—lead to the statement of certain laws of nature.
3. From definitions and laws, corollaries and theorems will be stated and analytical tools shaped. These tools will be used in the study of propulsion systems and the gas flow through components of propulsion devices.

This chapter begins by setting forth the definitions upon which many experimental observations in mechanics and aeronautics are based. The concepts of mass, energy, entropy, and momentum are then introduced, and the basic laws are developed for a system (control mass or closed-system) and control volume (open system). The following chapters use these basic laws in developing analytical tools for the study of one-dimensional gas dynamics, rocket propulsion, and aircraft propulsion.

2-2 DEFINITIONS

Before introducing the concepts of mass, energy, entropy, and momentum, we consider some basic definitions.

System and Control Volume

The system and the control volume play the part in the mechanics of fluids that a free body serves in the mechanics of rigid bodies. In fact, the free body of mechanics is simply a special case of a system.

A *system* is any collection of matter of fixed identity within a prescribed boundary. The boundary of a system is not necessarily rigid; hence, the volume of a system may change. Everything external to the system is called the *surroundings,* and the surface which separates the system from its surroundings is called the *system boundary.* A system, then, is the body or substance which one focuses attention upon in order to observe its behavior alone or as it interacts with the surroundings. Consider Newton's second law of motion in the form $F = ma$. The mass m in this equation is the mass of a system, F is the resultant force (interaction) exerted by the surroundings on the system, and a is the acceleration of the center of mass of the system.

Sometimes it is more convenient to analyze a fluid flow problem by fixing one's attention on a region through which fluid is flowing rather than by studying a fluid system. For this reason we introduce the concept of a control volume.

A *control volume* is any prescribed volume in space bounded by a *control surface* through which matter may flow and across which interactions with the surroundings may occur. Often in our study of fluid flows, we will use the control volume approach rather than the system approach. Each approach is equally valid (Fig. 2-2), and the method selected for a particular problem is simply a matter of convenience.

Classes of Forces

We can identify two classes of forces: boundary or contact forces and distant-acting or body forces. *Boundary forces* act on the boundaries of systems. A boundary force is the force of one system upon another at the point of contact of the two system boundaries. In order for system A to exert a boundary force on system B of magnitude F_{AB}, the boundary of A must be in contact with the boundary of B.

A *body force* is due to distant-acting influences such as gravity, magnetic

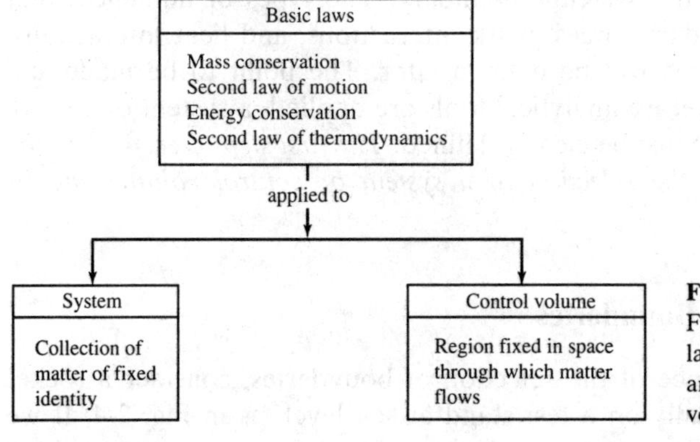

FIGURE 2-2
First step in application of basic laws is the selection of a system and its boundary or a control volume and its boundary.

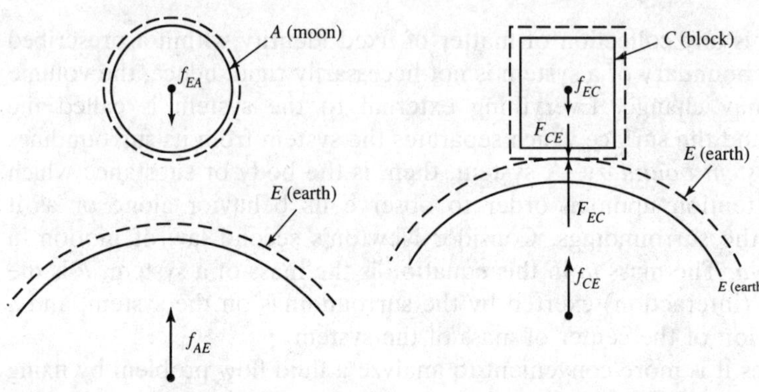

(*a*) Earth and moon exert equal and opposite body forces upon eah other. The body forces act at the center of gravity of each.

(*b*) A block resting on the earth has a body force f_{CE} (its weight) and exerts a body force f_{CE} on the earth. These body forces give rise to the contact forces F_{CE} and F_{EC} at the point of contact of *C* and *E*.

FIGURE 2-3
Body and contact forces.

effects, and electrodynamic forces and is proportional to either the mass or the volume of the body. System *A* need not be in contact with system *B* in order for *A* to exert a body force of magnitude f_{AB} (we use *F* for contact forces and *f* for body forces) on *B*. If *A* and *B* are in contact, however, their mutual body forces can give rise to contact forces as indicated in Fig. 2-3.

Influences and Boundaries

Influences between a system or a control volume region and the environment external to the system (the surroundings) are described in terms of the phenomena occurring at the system's boundary. The types of influences that will concern us are boundary forces, work interactions, and heat interactions. Work and heat interactions will be defined later. The point to be made and emphasized here is that before analytical tools are applied, a system or control volume and its boundary must be clearly defined. *The first step, therefore, in the solution of a problem is the selection of a system or control volume and its boundary.*

Example: Selection of Boundaries

To illustrate the importance of the selection of boundaries, consider a rocket engine mounted horizontally on a test stand at sea level, as in Fig. 2-4. If we wish to examine the various forces acting on the rocket, we must select a

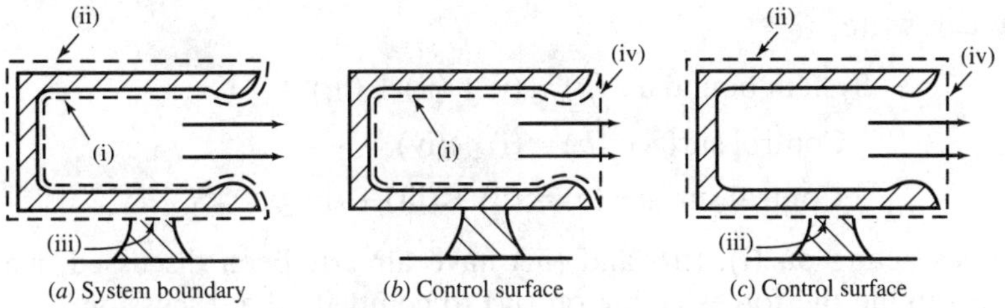

FIGURE 2-4
Three different boundaries for examining forces on a rocket engine.

system or control volume and identify its boundary. Each of three boundaries shown in Fig. 2-4 identifies either a system or a control volume having forces acting thereon.

Let the boundary in (*a*) of the figure define a *system.* The forces of the surroundings on the system are conveniently examined in terms of the portions of the system boundary coincident with (i) the rocket's internal surface, (ii) the rocket's external surface, and (iii) the surface of the strut cut by the boundary. The forces are as follows:

(i) The forces acting on that portion of the system boundary formed by the internal walls of the rocket. These forces are due to the pressure forces of the gases acting perpendicular to the interal surfaces and the frictional forces of the flowing gases acting tangential to the internal surfaces.

(ii) The pressure forces of the surrounding air on that portion of the system boundary formed by the external surface of the rocket. We will assume that the air surrounding the rocket is at rest so that there are no frictional forces between the air and the rocket.

(iii) The force of the strut external to the system acting on the boundary coincident with the strut surface cut by the boundary. This force will have a component perpendicular to the surface counteracting gravity and a component tangential to the boundary due to the imbalance in the horizontal component of the forces acting on the surfaces of (i) and (ii).

The boundaries in (*b*) and (*c*) of Fig. 2-4 each represent a *control surface*—i.e., the surface enclosing a control volume—because mass may flow through a portion of the boundary of each. Surface (i) of system (*a*) is identical with part of the control surface (*b*). We note also that surfaces identified as (ii) and (iii) of (*a*) form a part of the control surface (*c*).

The only part of the boundaries in (*b*) and (*c*) that has not been examined previously is that portion which lies across the exit of the rocket nozzle. Let us designate this portion of the control surface as (iv). With this notation, we can write

$$\text{System boundary } (a) = \text{(i)} + \text{(ii)} + \text{(iii)}$$

$$\text{Control surface } (b) = \text{(i)} + \text{(iv)}$$

$$\text{Control surface } (c) = \text{(ii)} + \text{(iii)} + \text{(iv)}$$

Since the forces acting on (i), (ii), and (iii) have already been discussed, we need only to examine the forces acting on (iv) to complete the discussion.

When a sketch is made of a control surface as in (b) and (c) with a gas flowing across the surface, it represents an instantaneous picture of the flow situation. In this instantaneous picture, we imagine momentarily that the boundary (iv) is occupied by an infinitely thin and massless sheet of material having the instantaneous speed of the fluid at (iv). Now we ask, what are the forces on this sheet and, hence, on the control surface boundary (iv)? The forces on the sheet are the pressure forces of the gas adjacent to it. These forces will be as shown in Fig. 2-5, where *external* and *internal* refer to the outside and the inside of the control volume, respectively. If we are interested in the force of the surroundings on (iv), then we observe that its value is the product of the surface area of (iv) and the pressure at (iv), and that it has a direction, as indicated in the figure. The force of the control volume on the surroundings at (iv) is opposite and equal to this external force.

Other Definitions

Work interaction is an interaction between two systems as a result of a boundary force between the two systems displacing the common boundary through a distance.

Heat interaction is an interaction between two systems as the result of a temperature difference between the two systems.

A *property* is any observable characteristic of a system. Some examples of properties are temperature, volume, pressure, and velocity.

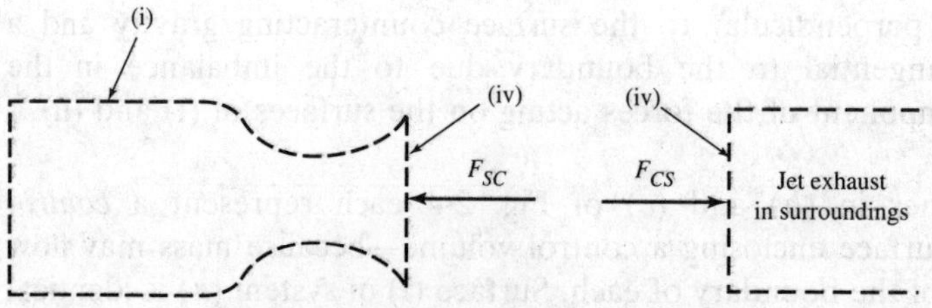

F_{SC} = internal force of control volume C on surroundings S.

F_{CS} = external force of S on C.

FIGURE 2-5
Forces acting on that portion of a control surface through which gas is flowing.

Extensive and intensive properties: Subdivide any homogeneous system A into two parts. Any property of A whose value is the sum of the values of the property for the two parts of A is an extensive property (i.e., mass, volume, kinetic energy). Pressure and temperature are not extensive properties, but are examples of intensive properties.

State is the condition of a system, identified through the properties of the system. Two states of a system are called *identical* if every property of the system is the same in both instances.

Process describes how a system changes from one state to another. A process is fully described only when end states, path, and interactions are specified.

An *adiabatic process* is any process in which there are no heat interactions.

An *isolated system* is a system which can have no interactions with any other system.

Entropy S is a property of matter that measures the degree of randomization or disorder at the microscopic level. The natural state of affairs is for entropy to be produced by all processes. The notion that entropy can be produced, but never destroyed, is the second law of thermodynamics. Entropy changes can be quantified by use of the Gibbs equation

$$dS = \frac{dU + P\,dV}{T} \qquad \text{or} \qquad dS = \frac{dH - V\,dP}{T}$$

2-3 SIMPLE COMPRESSIBLE SYSTEM

The state of a system is described by specifying the value of the properties of the system. Some properties which may be used in describing the state of a system are given in Table 2-1. If the specification of one of the properties in the table fixes the value of a second property, the two properties are called *dependent.* Density and specific volume ($\rho = 1/v$) form an example of two dependent properties. Two properties are *independent* if the specification of

TABLE 2-1
Some thermodynamic properties

Primitive		Derived	
Extensive	**Intensive**	**Extensive**	**Intensive**
Mass m	Density ρ	Energy E	Specific energy e
—	Pressure P	Kinetic energy E_K	Specific kinetic energy $\frac{V^2}{2g_c}$
—	Temperature T	Potential energy E_P	Specific potential energy $\frac{zg}{g_c}$
Volume V	Specific volume v	Internal energy U	Specific internal energy u

one does not fix the value of the other. Temperature and potential energy are two independent properties.

The number of properties required to fix the state of a system is a measure of the system's complexity. We can reduce the complexity of a system by:

a. Restricting the type of material making up the system.
b. Limiting the modes of behavior of the system.

We use both (*a*) and (*b*) in defining a simple system which is easily subject to analysis.

A simple compressible system is:

a. A substance which is homogeneous and invariant in chemical composition, and

b. A system in the absence of motion, force fields (gravity, electric, etc.), capillarity effects, and distortion of solid phases. Let us refer to those modes of behavior listed in (*b*) immediately above as *b*-effects. Gaseous air in the absence of *b*-effects is an example of a simple compressible system. Notice that properties which are related to velocity or position in a gravitational field (momentum, kinetic energy, potential energy) need not be specified in fixing the state of a simple compressible system.

The number of properties required to fix the state of a simple compressible system is very limited. The state of a pure substance in the absence of *b*-effects is *fixed by specifying any two independent intensive properties of the system.*

Once the state of the system is fixed, the values of all other properties of the system are fixed. If, for example, the two independent properties P and ρ of a simple gas system of mass m are specified, then all remaining properties (T, S, U, etc.) are fixed. When we say a derived property such as U is fixed, we mean, of course, that its value relative to some arbitrary datum-state is fixed.

As the restriction on each mode of behavior in the *b*-effects is removed, one more property must be specified to fix the state of the system. Thus the state of a gas of mass m in the presence of motion, but in the absence of other *b*-effects, is fixed by specifying its pressure, temperature, and a third property that fixes its speed or velocity. This third property may be velocity directly or other properties dependent upon velocity such as Mach number, or the properties called *total temperature* and *total pressure* which we will define and use later.

2-4 EQUATIONS OF STATE

The specification of any two independent properties will fix the state of a simple system and, therefore, the values of all other properties of the system. The values of the other properties may be found through equations of state.

By making two coordinates of a three-dimensional axis system correspond to two independent properties of a simple system and letting the third coordinate represent any dependent thermodynamic property, a three-dimensional thermodynamic surface representing the relation between the three properties can be constructed from measured values of the three properties in equilibrium states. If the three properties related in this manner are P, v, and T, the resulting thermodynamic surface is called the *P-v-T surface.* The P-v-T surface for a unit mass of water is shown in Fig. 2-6. Any point on the P-v-T surface of Fig. 2-6 represents an element of the solution of the function

$$f(P, v, T) = 0 \tag{2-1}$$

A function relating one dependent and two independent thermodynamic properties of a simple system of unit mass is called an *equation of state.* When the three properties are P, v, and T as in Eq. (2-1), the equation is called the *thermal equation of state.* In general, we cannot write the functional relationship Eq. (2-1) in the form of an equation in which specified values of the two properties will allow us to determine the value of the third. Although humans may not know what the functional relation Eq. (2-1) is for a given system, one does exist and nature always knows what it is. When the solution set of Eq. (2-1) cannot be determined from relatively simple equations, tables which list the values of P, v, and T (elements of the solution set) satisfying the function may be prepared. This has been done for water (in all its phases), air, and most common gases.

The functional relation between the energy u of a simple system of unit

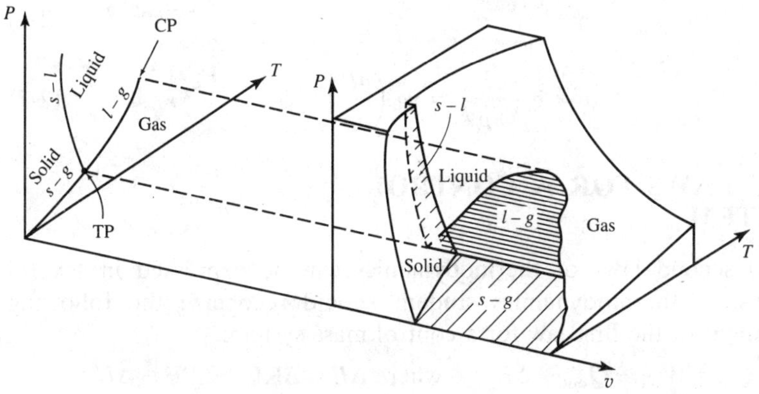

On the ruled surfaces, P and T are dependent properties.
CP = critical point: state beyond which vapor and liquid phases are indistinguishable.
TP = triple point: junction of the solid, liquid, and vapor phase boundaries.

FIGURE 2-6
The P-v-T surface for water.

mass and any two independent properties for the set P, $v(=1/\rho)$, T is called the *energy equation of state.* This equation can be written functionally as

$$u = u(T, v)$$

or
$$u = u(P, v) \tag{2-2}$$

or
$$u = u(P, T)$$

As with the thermal equation of state, we may not be able to write an analytical expression for any of the functional relations of (2-2). The important thing is that energy is a property; hence, the functional relations exist.

If the solution sets of the thermal and energy equations of state of a simple system of unit mass are known, all thermodynamic properties of the system can be found when any two of the three properties P, v, T are specified. From the solution set, we can form a tabulation of v and u against specified values of P and T for all states of the system. From these known values of P, T, v, and u, we can determine any other property of the simple system. For example, the value of the property *enthalpy* h is found for any state of the system by combining the tabulated values of P, v, and u for that state by

$$h \equiv u + Pv \tag{2-3}$$

Four other definitions are listed here for use in the later sections of this chapter: specific heat at constant volume c_v, specific heat at constant pressure c_p, ratio of specific heats γ, and the speed of sound a:

$$c_v \equiv \left(\frac{\partial u}{\partial T}\right)_v \tag{2-4}$$

$$c_p \equiv \left(\frac{\partial h}{\partial T}\right)_P \tag{2-5}$$

$$\gamma \equiv \frac{c_p}{c_v} \tag{2-6}$$

$$a^2 \equiv g_c\left(\frac{\partial P}{\partial \rho}\right)_s = \gamma g_c\left(\frac{\partial P}{\partial \rho}\right)_T \tag{2-7}$$

2-5 BASIC LAWS FOR A CONTROL MASS SYSTEM

The first and second laws of thermodynamics can be expressed in several different ways. A thermodynamics student should recognize the following general statement of the first law for a control mass system:

$$W_{\text{in}} + Q_{\text{in}} = W_{\text{out}} + Q_{\text{out}} + \Delta E \qquad \text{where } \Delta E = \Delta \text{KE} + \Delta \text{PE} + \Delta U$$

The general form of the second law of thermodynamics for a control mass system can be expressed as follows:

$$\Delta S + \left(\frac{Q}{T}\right)_{\text{out}} - \left(\frac{Q}{T}\right)_{\text{in}} \geq 0$$

Both of these expressions allow for work and heat interactions both in and out of a control mass. However, in the study of propulsion, an interesting convention is observed. All heat interactions are assumed to be Q_{in}, while all work interactions are assumed to be W_{out}. Therefore, if you were to analyze a system with a Q_{out}, you would have to consider a Q_{out} as a *negative* Q_{in}. In a similar manner, a W_{in} would be a negative W_{out}. With this convention in mind, the first and second laws for a control mass system can be rewritten as follows:

First law $\quad Q = W + \Delta E \quad$ or $\quad Q - W = \Delta E$

Second law $\quad \Delta S - \dfrac{Q}{T} \geq 0$

The laws of mechanics and thermodynamics, as written in the first instance for a control mass system, are cumbersome to apply to fluid flow problems where one wishes to study a region through which fluid is flowing rather than fix one's attention upon a fixed amount of mass (control mass system). It is extremely useful at the outset, therefore, to convert these laws as written for a control mass system to a form directly applicable to the study of flow through a region fixed in space. This region we may call an *open system* (as is often done in thermodynamics and chemical engineering) or a *control volume*, which is the name customarily used in fluid mechanics and aerodynamics. We follow this latter use. A *control volume* is any prescribed volume in space bounded by a control surface across which matter may flow and heat interactions and work interactions may occur.

We desire, then, to develop control volume relations from the basic laws as written for a system of fixed mass. First, however, we consider the basic laws of interest.

Conservation of mass
$$0 = \frac{dm}{dt} \tag{2-8}$$

Conservation of energy
$$\frac{dQ}{dt} - \frac{dW}{dt} = \frac{dE}{dt} \tag{2-9}$$

Second law of thermodynamics
$$\frac{1}{T}\frac{dQ}{dt} \leq \frac{dS}{dt} \tag{2-10}$$

Momentum equation
$$\sum F_x = \frac{1}{g_c}\frac{dM_x}{dt} \tag{2-11}$$

Equation (2-8) is the mathematical formulation of the fact that matter is neither created nor destroyed. Thus a quantity of matter m cannot vary with time. We assume here that atomic species are conserved, and we dismiss from consideration nuclear reactions. Equation (2-9) relates the change of energy E of a system to the heat interaction Q into a system and the work interaction W out of a system as it proceeds in time dt between two states infinitesimally different from each other. From the second law of thermodynamics and the definition of entropy, we obtain Eq. (2-10), which states that the rate of entropy production dS/dt must be greater than or equal to zero (i.e., the rate of entropy creation in a mass system must be greater than or equal to the rate of inflow associated with the heat interaction). Finally, Newton's second law of motion [Eq. (2-11)] states that the instantaneous rate of change of the momentum M_x in the x direction of a system of fixed mass is equal to the sum of the forces in the x direction acting on the mass at that instant. The subscript x is used to emphasize that momentum and force are vector quantities.

By writing Eqs. (2-8), (2-9), (2-10), and (2-11) in the manner chosen, a similarity or unification of the right-hand side of each equation is evident. Each equation has on the right-hand side the time derivative of a property—mass, energy, entropy, and momentum, respectively. Each of these property time derivatives applies to a mass of fixed identity—a control mass system. In the next section, expressions will be developed that relate each derivative to quantities associated with a control volume. Thus the right-hand sides of Eqs. (2-8) through (2-11) will be put into a form directly applicable to flow through a control volume.

2-6 RELATIONS BETWEEN THE SYSTEM AND CONTROL VOLUME

Suppose that fluid is flowing through the control volume σ in Fig. 2-7 along the streamlines shown. Let the mass contrained within σ at any time be designated as m_σ. At some initial time t_1, suppose that a system is defined to be the mass m of fluid contained in σ (Fig. 2-7). At some later time t_2, this mass system will have moved to the position shown by the boundary S in Fig. 2-8. To relate the system m to the control volume σ, we must evaluate the time derivative of m in terms of control volume quantities. By definition,

$$\frac{dm}{dt} = \lim_{\delta t \to 0} \frac{m_{t_2} - m_{t_1}}{\delta t} \tag{2-12}$$

where $\delta t = t_2 - t_1$

m_{t_1} = mass system at time t_1

m_{t_2} = mass system at time t_2

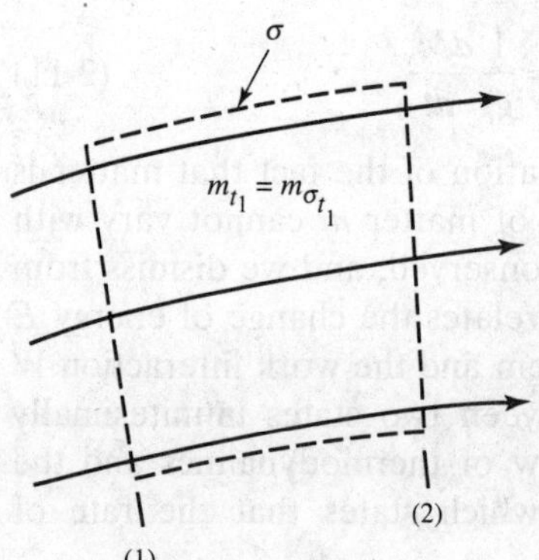

FIGURE 2-7
Mass system within σ at time t_1.

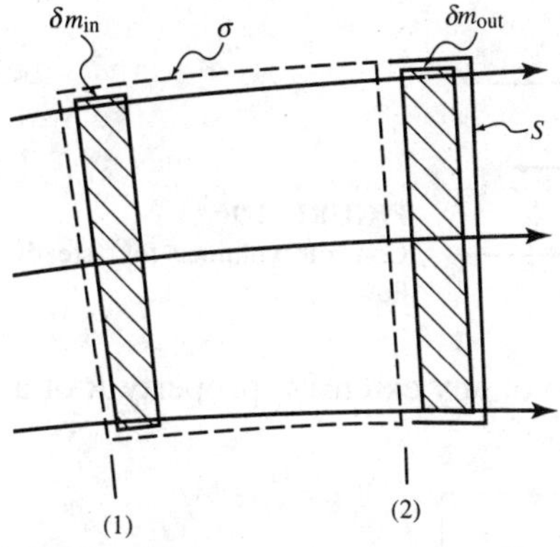

FIGURE 2-8
Mass system not completely in σ at time t_2.

At time t_1, the mass system m completely fills the control volume so that

$$m_{t_1} = m_{\sigma t_1} \tag{2-13}$$

At the later time t_2, the mass system has moved so that a small portion of the mass system, denoted by δm_{out}, has moved out of the control volume at section 2 while the remaining portion of the mass still occupies most of the control volume. During the time interval δt, note that a small element of mass δm_{in} has entered σ through section 1, but this mass is not part of our system of interest. Thus we have

$$m_{t_2} = m_{\sigma t_2} + \delta m_{\text{out}} - \delta m_{\text{in}} \tag{2-14}$$

Substitution of Eqs. (2-13) and (2-14) into Eq. (2-12) and rearranging terms yield

$$\frac{dm}{dt} = \lim_{\delta t \to 0} \left(\frac{m_{\sigma t_2} - m_{\sigma t_1}}{\delta t} + \frac{\delta m_{\text{out}} - \delta m_{\text{in}}}{\delta t} \right) \tag{2-15}$$

The derivative depends, therefore, on two items. The first represents the rate of accumulation of mass within σ which we denote by dm_σ/dt. The second represents the net outflow of mass from σ which we denote by $\dot{m}_{\text{out}} - \dot{m}_{\text{in}}$, where $\dot{m}$ represents the mass flux or flow rate through a control surface. Thus Eq. (2-15) becomes

$$\boxed{\frac{dm}{dt} = \frac{dm_\sigma}{dt} + \dot{m}_{\text{out}} - \dot{m}_{\text{in}}} \tag{2-16}$$

Equation (2-16) is the desired result relating to the system and control volume approaches. In words, the equation reads: The time rate of change of the mass of a system *at the instant it is within a control volume* σ is equal to the accumulation rate of mass within the control volume plus the net mass flux out of the control volume.

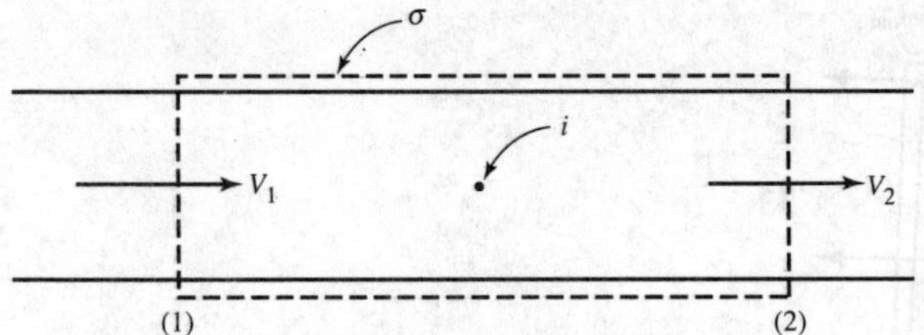

FIGURE 2-9
Control volume for steady flow.

The result expressed in Eq. (2-16) is true of any extensive property R of a system. We may write, therefore,

$$\boxed{\frac{dR}{dt} = \frac{dR_\sigma}{dt} + \dot{R}_{\text{out}} - \dot{R}_{\text{in}}} \tag{2-17}$$

This is the general result we may use to obtain a control volume equation from any system equation involving the rate of change of an extensive property.

DEFINITION OF STEADY FLOW. Consider the flow of fluid through the control volume σ shown in Fig. 2-9. If the properties of the fluid at any point i in the control volume do not vary with time, the flow is called *steady flow*. For such flows we may conclude

$$\frac{dR_\sigma}{dt} = 0 \qquad \text{in steady flow} \tag{2-18}$$

DEFINITION OF ONE-DIMENSIONAL FLOW. If the intensive stream properties at a permeable control surface section normal to the flow directions are uniform, the flow is called *one-dimensional.* Many flows in engineering may be treated as steady one-dimensional flows. The term *one-dimensional* is synonymous in this use with *uniform* and applies only at a control surface section. Thus the overall flow through a control volume may be in more than one dimension and still be uniform (one-dimensional flow) at permeable sections of the control surface normal to the flow direction. The flow in Fig. 2-10 is called

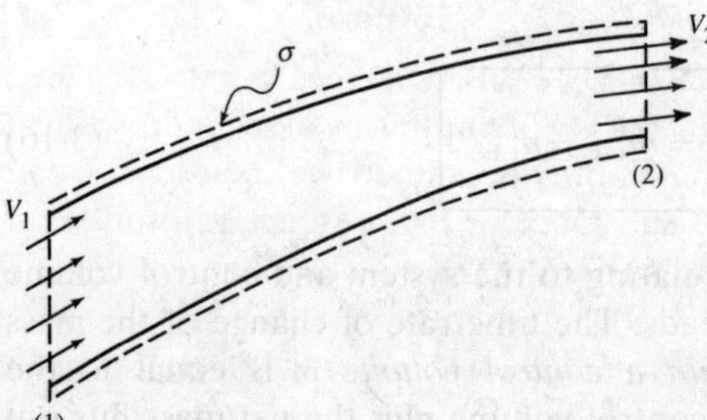

FIGURE 2-10
One-dimensional flow through a convergent duct. The flow is uniform at sections 1 and 2, hence one-dimensional, even though the flow direction may vary elsewhere in the flow.

one-dimensional flow since the intensive properties, such as velocity, density, and temperature, are uniform at sections 1 and 2.

2-7 CONSERVATION OF MASS EQUATION

The law of mass conservation for any system A is simply

$$\frac{dm_A}{dt} = 0 \tag{2-19}$$

Entering this result into Eq. (2-17) yields

$$\frac{dm_\sigma}{dt} + \dot{m}_{\text{out}} - \dot{m}_{\text{in}} = 0 \tag{2-20}$$

which is known as the *conservation of mass equation.* For steady flows through any control volume, Eq. (2-20) simplifies to

$$\boxed{\dot{m}_{\text{out}} = \dot{m}_{\text{in}}} \tag{2-21}$$

If the flow is steady and one-dimensional through a control volume with a single inlet and exit such as shown in Fig. 2-10, $\dot{m} = \rho A V_n$ (where V_n is the velocity component normal to A), and

$$\boxed{\rho_1 A_1 V_{1n} = \rho_2 A_2 V_{2n}} \tag{2-22}$$

2-8 STEADY FLOW ENERGY EQUATION

The energy equation written as a rate question is

$$\dot{Q}_A - \dot{W}_A = \frac{dE_A}{dt} \tag{2-9}$$

where $\dot{Q}_A$ and $\dot{W}_A$ are the rates at which heat and work interactions are occurring at the system boundary. If all the work is due to shaft work, $\dot{W}_A$ represents the shaft power delivered by system A as it receives energy due to a heat interaction at rate $\dot{Q}_A$ and as the energy E of A changes at rate dE_A/dt. It is convenient to have Eq. (2-9) in a form involving terms associated with the boundary of a control volume. With this in mind, we consider steady one-dimensional flow of a fluid (pure substance in the presence of motion and gravity) through a control volume and surface σ (Fig. 2-11). Fluid crosses σ at the in and out stations only. A shaft work interaction $\dot{W}_x$ and heat interaction $\dot{Q}$ occur at the boundary of σ. In addition, flow work interaction occurs at the in and out stations of σ due to the pressure forces at these stations moving

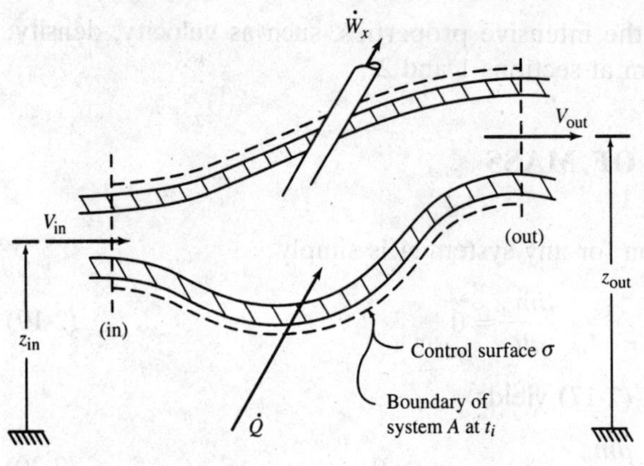

FIGURE 2-11
Steady flow through control volume σ—flow picture at any time t_1.

with the fluid. Since energy is an extensive property, we may write for any instant of time t_i that system A is in σ

$$\frac{dE_A}{dt} = \frac{dE_\sigma}{dt} + \dot{E}_{out} - \dot{E}_{in}$$

Therefore, for steady one-dimensional flow, the right-hand term of Eq. (2-9) becomes

$$\left(\frac{dE_A}{dt}\right)_{t_i} = \left(\frac{dE_\sigma}{dt}\right)_{t_i}^{\nearrow 0} + \dot{E}_{out} - \dot{E}_{in} = (e\dot{m})_{out} - (e\dot{m})_{in}$$

or, with $\dot{m}_{in} = \dot{m}_{out} = \dot{m}$,

$$\left(\frac{dE_A}{dt}\right)_{t_i} = \dot{m}(e_{out} - e_{in}) \tag{i}$$

where $e = u + V^2/(2g_c) + gz/g_c$. For the heat interaction term of Eq. (2-9) we have, for system A at time t_i,

$$(\dot{Q}_A)_{t_i} = \dot{Q} \tag{ii}$$

where $\dot{Q}$ represents the heat interaction rate at the boundary of σ.

For a rigid boundary of the control volume σ, the work interaction term of Eq. (2-9) is due to two effects—the shaft work and flow work rates of A at time t_i. Thus,

$$(\dot{W}_A)_{t_i} = \dot{W}_x + \dot{W}_{flow}$$

where $$\dot{W}_{flow} = (Pv\dot{m})_{out} - (Pv\dot{m})_{in}$$

from $\dot{W}_{\text{flow}}$ = pressure force × velocity = $PA(V) = P(A\,dx/dm)(dm/dt) = Pv\dot{m}$. Now $\dot{m}_{\text{in}} = \dot{m}_{\text{out}} = \dot{m}$, so

$$(\dot{W}_A)_{t_i} = \dot{W}_x + \dot{m}[(Pv)_{\text{out}} - (Pv)_{\text{in}}] \qquad \text{(iii)}$$

When Eqs. (i), (ii), and (iii) are placed in the energy equation for time t_i, we get

$$\dot{Q} - \{\dot{W}_x + \dot{m}[(Pv)_{\text{out}} - (Pv)_{\text{in}}]\} = \dot{m}(e_{\text{out}} - e_{\text{in}}) \qquad \text{(iv)}$$

This is the result sought—an equation in terms of quantities evaluated at the control surface. Some rearrangement of Eq. (iv) will put the equation in a more conventional form. First we assemble all terms involving $\dot{m}$ on the right side of the equation:

$$\boxed{\dot{Q} - \dot{W}_x = \dot{m}(Pv + e)_{\text{out}} - \dot{m}(Pv + e)_{\text{in}}} \qquad \text{(2-23)}$$

Then we divide by $\dot{m}$ and use the expression $e = u + V^2/(2g_c) + gz/g_c$ to get

$$q - w_x = \left(Pv + u + \frac{V^2}{2g_c} + \frac{gz}{g_c}\right)_{\text{out}} - \left(Pv + u + \frac{V^2}{2g_c} + \frac{gz}{g_c}\right)_{\text{in}}$$

where q and w_x are heat and shaft work interactions per unit mass flow through σ. In the last equation, the properties u, P, and v appear again in the arrangement $u + Pv$ which we have called *enthalpy* h. Using h, we obtain the usual form of the *steady flow energy equation*

$$\boxed{q - w_x = \left(h + \frac{v^2}{2g_c} + \frac{gz}{g_c}\right)_{\text{out}} - \left(h + \frac{V^2}{2g_c} + \frac{gz}{g_c}\right)_{\text{in}}} \qquad \text{(2-24)}$$

where all terms have the dimensions of energy per unit mass. If Eq. (2-24) is multiplied by $\dot{m}$, then we get

$$\dot{Q} - \dot{W}_x = \dot{m}\left(h + \frac{V^2}{2g_c} + \frac{gz}{g_c}\right)_{\text{out}} - \dot{m}\left(h + \frac{V^2}{2g_c} + \frac{gz}{g_c}\right)_{\text{in}} \qquad \text{(2-25)}$$

where the dimensions of $\dot{Q}$, $\dot{W}_x$, etc., are those of power or energy per unit time.

Example 2-1. The first step in the application of the steady flow energy equation is a clear definition of a control surface σ. This is so because each term in the equation refers to a quantity at the boundary of a control volume. Thus, to use the equation, one needs only to examine the control surface and identify the applicable terms of the equation.

In the application of Eq. (2-24) to specific flow situations, many of the terms are zero or may be neglected. The following example will illustrate this point.

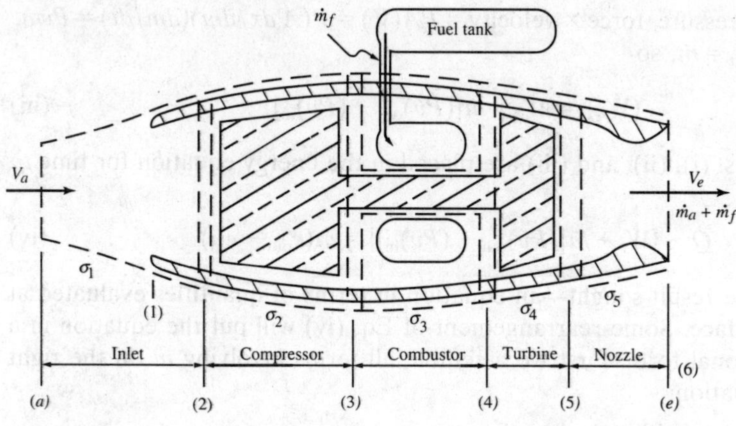

FIGURE 2-12a
Control volume for analyzing each component of a turbojet engine.

Consider a turbojet aircraft engine as shown in Fig. 2-12*a*. We divide the engine into the control volume regions:

σ_1: inlet
σ_2: compressor
σ_3: combustion chamber
σ_4: turbine
σ_5: nozzle

Let us apply the steady flow energy equation to each of these control volumes. In all cases the potential energy change $(gz/g_c)_{\text{out}} - (gz/g_c)_{\text{in}}$ is zero and will be ignored.

It is advisable in using the steady flow energy equation to make two sketches of the applicable control surface σ, showing the heat and shaft work interactions (q, w_x) in one sketch and the fluxes of energy $[h, V^2/(2g_c)]$ in the second sketch. {The term $[h + V^2/(2g_c)]_{\text{out}}$ is a flux per unit mass flow of internal energy u, kinetic energy $V^2/(2g_c)$, and flow work Pv. We will use the expression *flux of energy* to include the flow work flux also.}

a. Inlet and nozzle: σ_1 *and* σ_5. There are no shaft work interactions at control surfaces σ_1 and σ_5. Heat interactions are negligible and may be taken as zero. Therefore, the steady flow energy equation, as depicted in Fig. 2-12*b*, for the inlet or nozzle control surfaces gives the result

$$0 = \left(h + \frac{V^2}{2g_c}\right)_{\text{out}} - \left(h + \frac{V^2}{2g_c}\right)_{\text{in}}$$

Numerical example: Nozzle. Let the gases flowing through the nozzle control volume σ_5 be perfect with $c_p g_c = 6000\ \text{ft}^2/(\text{sec}^2 \cdot {}^\circ\text{R})$. Determine V_6 for $T_5 = 1800^\circ R$, $V_5 = 400$ ft/sec, and $T_6 = 1200^\circ$R.

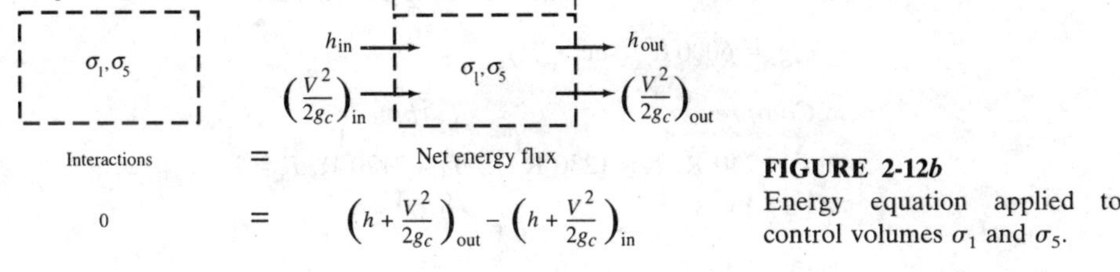

FIGURE 2-12*b*
Energy equation applied to control volumes σ_1 and σ_5.

Solution. From the steady flow energy equation with 5 and 6 the in and out stations respectively, we have

$$h_6 + \frac{V_6^2}{2g_c} = h_5 + \frac{V_5^2}{2g_c}$$

and $$V_6 = \sqrt{2g_c(h_5 - h_6) + V_5^2} = \sqrt{2c_p g_c(T_5 - T_6) + V_5^2}$$

or $$= \sqrt{2(6000)(1800 - 1200) + 400^2}$$

so $$= 2700 \text{ ft/sec}$$

b. Compressor and turbine: *σ_2 and σ_4*. The heat interactions at control surfaces σ_2 and σ_4 are negligibly small. Shaft work interactions are present because each control surface cuts a rotating shaft. The steady flow energy equation for the compressor or for the turbine is depicted in Fig. 2-12*c* and gives

$$-w_x = \left(h + \frac{V^2}{2g_c}\right)_{out} - \left(h + \frac{V^2}{2g_c}\right)_{in}$$

Numerical example: Compressor and turbine. For an equal mass flow† through the compressor and turbine of 185 lb/sec, determine the compressor power and

$w_x < 0$ for σ_2 (compressor)
$w_x > 0$ for σ_4 (turbine)
σ_2, σ_4 — w_x
$q = 0$
(In) (Out)
h_{in} h_{out}
σ_2, σ_4
$\left(\frac{V^2}{2g_c}\right)_{in}$ $\left(\frac{V^2}{2g_c}\right)_{out}$
Interactions = Net energy flux
$-w_x = \left(h + \frac{V^2}{2g_c}\right)_{out} - \left(h + \frac{V^2}{2g_c}\right)_{in}$

FIGURE 2-12*c*
Energy equation applied to control volumes σ_2 and σ_4.

---

† For a typical turbojet engine, 60 to 30 lbm of air enters for each 1 lbm of fuel consumed. It is, therefore, reasonable to assume approximately equal mass flow rates through the compressor and turbine.

the turbine exit temperature T_5 for the following conditions:

$$c_p g_c = 6000 \text{ ft}^2/(\text{sec}^2 \cdot {}^\circ\text{R})$$

Compressor	*Turbine*
$T_2 = 740°\text{R}$, $T_3 = 1230°\text{R}$	$T_4 = 2170°\text{R}$, $T_5 = ?$
$V_2 = V_3$	$V_4 = V_5$

Solution. The compressor power $\dot{W}_c = (\dot{m}w_x)_{\sigma_2}$ is, with $V_2 = V_3$,

$$\dot{W}_c = -\dot{m}(h_3 - h_2) = -\dot{m}c_p(T_3 - T_2)$$

$$= -(185 \text{ lbm/sec}) \frac{6000(\text{ft/sec})^2}{32.174 \text{ ft} \cdot \text{lbf/(lbm} \cdot \text{sec}^2)}(1230 - 740)$$

$$= -16.9 \times 10^6 \text{ ft} \cdot \text{lbf/sec} \times \frac{1 \text{ hp}}{550 \text{ ft} \cdot \text{lbf/sec}}$$

$$= -30{,}700 \text{ hp}$$

The minus sign means the compressor shaft is delivering energy to the air in σ_2.

The turbine drives the compressor so that the turbine power $\dot{W}_t = (\dot{m}w_x)_{\sigma_4}$ is equal in magnitude to the compressor power. Thus $\dot{W}_t = -\dot{W}_c$, where, from the energy equation,

$$\dot{W}_t = \dot{m}(h_4 - h_5) \quad \text{and} \quad \dot{W}_c = -\dot{m}(h_3 - h_2)$$

Thus $$\dot{m}c_p(T_5 - T_4) = -\dot{m}c_p(T_3 - T_2)$$

and $$T_5 = T_4 - (T_3 - T_2)$$

$$= 2170°\text{R} - (1230°\text{R} - 740°\text{R}) = 1680°\text{R} = 1220°\text{F}$$

c. Combustion chamber: σ_3. Let us assume that the fuel and air entering the combustion chamber mix physically in a mixing zone (Fig. 2-12*d*) to form what we will call *reactants* (denoted by subscript R). The reactants then enter a combustion zone where combustion occurs, forming *products* of combustion (subscript P) which leave the combustion chamber. We apply the steady flow energy equation to combustion zone σ_3. Since the temperature in the combustion zone is higher than that of the immediate surroundings, there is a heat interaction between σ_3 and the surroundings which, per unit mass flow of reactants, is negligibly small ($q < 0$ but $q \doteq 0$). Also the velocities of the products leaving and of the reactants entering the combustion zone are approximately equal. There is no shaft work interaction for σ_3. Hence the steady flow energy equation, as depicted in Fig. 2-12*d*, reduces to

$$\boxed{h_{R_3} = h_{P_4}}$$

We must caution the reader about two points concerning this last equation. First, we cannot use the relation $c_p \, \Delta T$ for computing the enthalpy difference between two states of a system when the chemical aggregation of the two states differs. Second, we must measure the enthalpy of each term in the equation

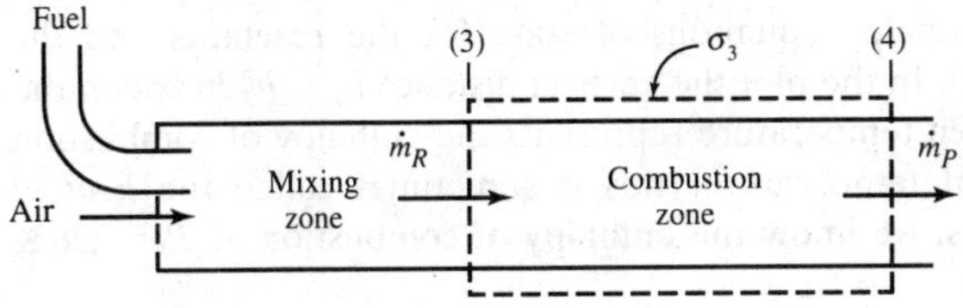

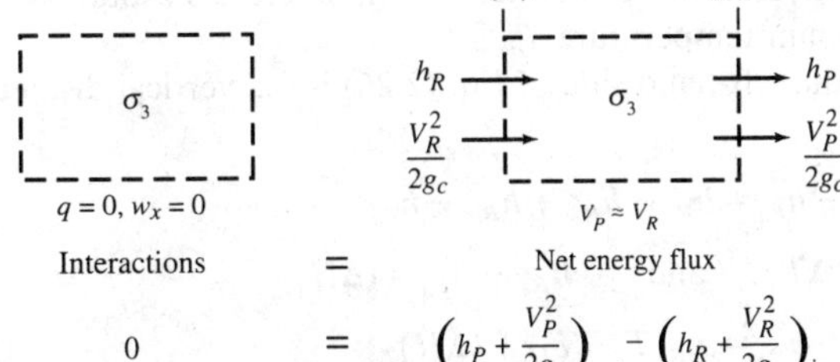

FIGURE 2-12*d*
Energy equation applied to control volume σ_3.

relative to the same datum state. To place emphasis on the first point, we have introduced the additional subscripts R and P to indicate that the chemical aggregations of states 3 and 4 are different.

To emphasize the second point, we select as our common enthalpy datum a state d having the chemical aggregation of the products at a datum temperature T_d. Then, introducing the datum state enthalpy $(h_P)_d$ into the last equation above, we have

$$\boxed{h_{R_3} - h_{P_d} = h_{P_4} - h_{P_d}} \tag{2-26}$$

Equation (2-26) can be used to determine the temperature of the products of combustion leaving an adiabatic combustor for given inlet conditions. If the combustor is not adiabatic, Eq. (2-26), adjusted to include the heat interaction term q on the left-hand side, is applicable. Let us treat the reactants and products as perfect gases and illustrate the use of Eq. (2-26) in determining the temperature of the gases at the exit of a turbojet combustion chamber via an example problem.

Numerical example: Combustion chamber. For the turbojet engine combustion chamber, 45 lbm of air enters with each 1 lbm of JP-4 (kerosene) fuel. Let us assume these reactants enter an adiabatic combustor at 1200°R. The heating value h_{PR} of JP-4 is 18,400 Btu/lbm of fuel at 298 K. [This is also called the *lower heating value* (LHV) of the fuel.] Thus the heat released $(\Delta H)_{298\,\text{K}}$ by the fuel per 1 lbm of the products is 400 Btu/lbm (18,400/46) at 298 K. The following data are known:

$$c_{pP} = 0.267 \text{ Btu/(lbm} \cdot \text{°R)} \qquad \text{and} \qquad c_{pR} = 0.240 \text{ Btu/(lbm} \cdot \text{°R)}$$

Determine the temperature of the products leaving the combustor.

Solution. A plot of the enthalpy equations of state for the reactants and the products is given in Fig. 2-13. In the plot the vertical distance $h_R - h_P$ between the curves of h_R and h_P at a given temperature represents the enthalpy of combustion ΔH of the reactants at that temperature (this is sometimes called the *heat of combustion*). In our analysis, we know the enthalpy of combustion at $T_d = 298$ K (536.4°R).

States 3 and 4, depicted in Fig. 2-13, represent the states of the reactants entering and the products leaving the combustion chamber, respectively. The datum state d is arbitrarily selected to be products at temperature T_d. State d' is the reactants' state at the datum temperature T_d.

In terms of Fig. 2-13, the left-hand side of Eq. (2-26) is the vertical distance between states 3 and d, or

$$h_{R_3} - h_{P_d} = h_{R_3} - h_{R_{d'}} + h_{R_{d'}} - h_{P_d}$$

and since $\quad \Delta h_R = c_{pR}\,\Delta T \qquad$ and $\qquad h_{R_{d'}} - h_{P_d} = (\Delta H)_{T_d}$

then

$$h_{R_3} - h_{P_d} = c_{pR}(T_3 - T_d) + (\Delta H)_{T_d} \tag{i}$$

Similarly, the right-hand side of Eq. (2-26) is

$$h_{P_4} - h_{P_d} = c_{pP}(T_4 - T_d) \tag{ii}$$

Substituting Eqs. (i) and (ii) in Eq. (2-26), we get

$$c_{pR}(T_3 - T_d) + (\Delta H)_{T_d} = c_{pP}(T_4 - T_d) \tag{2-27}$$

We can solve this equation for T_4, which is the temperature of the product gases leaving the combustion chamber. Solving Eq. (2-27) for T_4, we get

$$T_4 = \frac{c_{pR}(T_3 - T_d) + (\Delta H)_{Td}}{c_{pP}} + T_d$$

$$= \frac{0.240(1200 - 536.4) + 400}{0.267} + 536.4$$

$$= 2631°\text{R}\ (2171°\text{F})$$

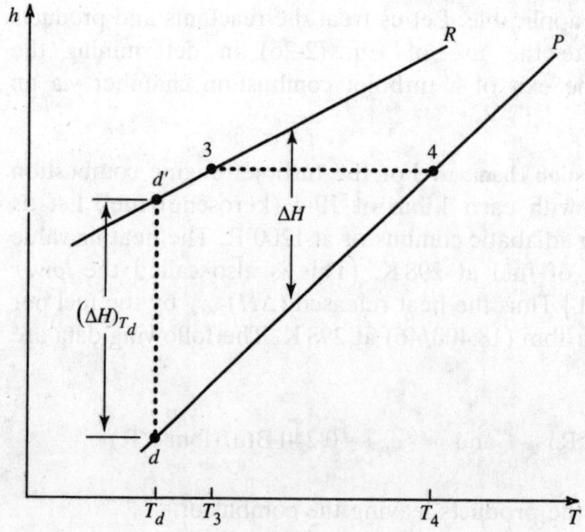

FIGURE 2-13
Enthalpy versus temperature for reactants and products treated as perfect gases.

This is the so-called adiabatic flame temperature of the reactants for a 45:1 weight/mixture ratio of air to fuel.

For the analysis in this book, we choose to sidestep the complex thermochemistry of the combustion process and model it as a simple heating process. The theory and application of thermochemistry to combustion in jet engines are covered in many textbooks, such as the classical text by Penner (see Ref. 13).

2-9 STEADY FLOW ENTROPY EQUATION

From the second law of thermodynamics and the definition of entropy, we have, by Eq. (2-10),

$$\frac{1}{T}\frac{dQ}{dt} \leq \frac{dS}{dt} \tag{2-10}$$

The quantity dQ/dt is a boundary phenomenon for a control volume flow as well as for a system (control mass). Interpreting, therefore, dQ/dt as the heat flux through those parts of the control surface impervious to the flow of matter and using Eq. (2-17) with $R = S$, we obtain

$$\frac{dS_\sigma}{dt} + \dot{S}_{\text{out}} - \dot{S}_{\text{in}} \geq \frac{1}{T}\frac{dQ}{dt} \tag{2-28}$$

where $\dot{S} = \dot{m}s$

This is called the *entropy equation for control volume flow*; dS_σ/dt represents the entropy production rate within the control volume while $\dot{S}_{\text{out}}$ and $\dot{S}_{\text{in}}$ represent the entropy flux into and out of the control volume through the control surface, respectively; dQ/dt is the heat flux through the control surface; and T is the temperature of the fluid adjacent to the control surface.

Steady Flow

For steady flow, Eq. (2-28) becomes

$$\dot{S}_{\text{out}} - \dot{S}_{\text{in}} \geq \frac{1}{T}\frac{dQ}{dt}$$

And, for steady and adiabatic flow through a control volume, this reduces to the statement that the entropy flux out is greater than or equal to the entropy flux in:

$$\dot{S}_{\text{out}} \geq \dot{S}_{\text{in}}$$

For one outlet section (2) and one inlet section (1), this and the continuity condition yield

$$s_2 \geq s_1$$

2-10 MOMENTUM EQUATION

Newton's second law of motion in the form

$$\sum F_A = \frac{1}{g_c}\frac{dM_A}{dt} \tag{2-11}$$

is a system equation relating the net force on system A to the time rate of change of the extensive property momentum M.† We can write an equivalent control volume equation for the second law of motion, using $R = M$ in the general relation

$$\frac{dR_A}{dt} = \frac{dR_\sigma}{dt} + \dot{R}_{\text{out}} - \dot{R}_{\text{in}}$$

to get
$$\sum F_A = \sum F_\sigma = \frac{1}{g_c}\frac{dM_A}{dt} = \frac{1}{g_c}\left(\frac{dM_\sigma}{dt} + \dot{M}_{\text{out}} - \dot{M}_{\text{in}}\right)$$

or
$$\boxed{\sum F_\sigma = \frac{1}{g_c}\left(\frac{dM_\sigma}{dt} + \dot{M}_{\text{out}} - \dot{M}_{\text{in}}\right)} \tag{2-29}$$

In words, Eq. (2-29) says that the net force acting on a fixed control volume σ is equal to the time rate of increase of momentum within σ plus the net flux of momentum from σ. This is the very important momentum equation. It means that the sum of the forces acting on a system A at the instant A occupies control volume σ equals the rate of change of momentum in σ plus the net flux of momentum out of σ. This equation is in fact a *vector* equation, which implies that it must be applied in a specified direction in order to solve for an unknown quantity.

Applying control volume equations to a steady flow problem gives useful results with only a knowledge of conditions at the control surface. Nothing needs to be known about the state of the fluid interior to the control volume. The following examples illustrate the use of the steady one-dimensional flow condition and the momentum equation. We suggest that the procedure of sketching a control surface (and showing the applicable fluxes through the surface and the applicable forces acting on the surface) be followed whenever a control volume equation is used. We illustrate this procedure in the solutions that follow.

Example 2-2. Water ($\rho = 1000\ \text{kg/m}^3$) is flowing at a steady rate through a convergent duct as illustrated in Fig. 2-14(a). For the data given in the figure, find the force of the fluid $F_{\sigma D}$ acting on the convergent duct D between stations 1 and 2.

---

† $M = \int_A V\,dm$ for a fluid system A. This reduces to $M = mV$ for a rigid system of mass m.

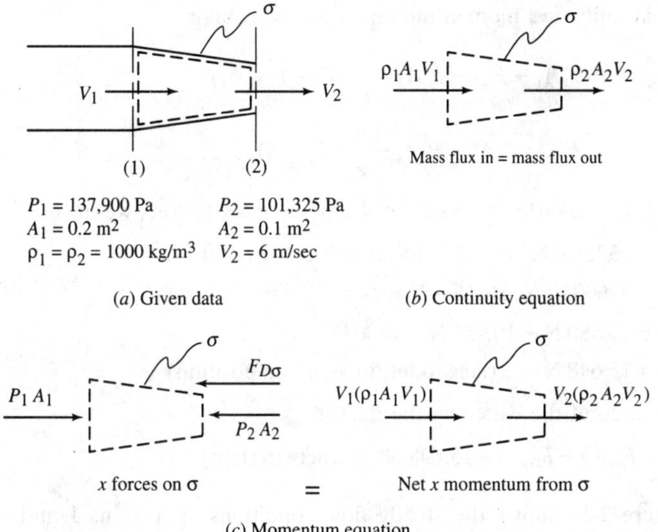

FIGURE 2-14
Flow through a convergent duct.

Solution. We first select the control volume σ such that the force of interest is acting at the control surface. Since we want the force interaction between D and the flowing water, we choose a control surface coincident with the inner wall surface of D bounded by the permeable surfaces 1 and 2, as illustrated in Fig. 2-14(a). By applying the steady one-dimensional continuity equation, Eq. (2-21), as depicted in Fig. 2-14(b), we find V_1 as follows:

$$\rho_1 A_1 V_1 = \rho_2 A_2 V_2$$

$$V_1 = \frac{A_2}{A_1} V_2 \qquad (\rho_1 = \rho_2)$$

$$= 3 \text{ m/sec}$$

With V_1 determined, we can apply the momentum Eq. (2-29) to σ and find the force of the duct walls on σ, denoted by $F_{D\sigma}$ ($F_{\sigma D} = F_{D\sigma}$). By symmetry, $F_{D\sigma}$ is a horizontal force so the horizontal (x) components of forces and momentum fluxes will be considered. The x forces acting on σ are depicted in Fig. 2-14(c) along with the x momentum fluxes through σ.

From Fig. 2-14(c), we have

Momentum equation $\quad P_1 A_1 - F_{D\sigma} - P_2 A_2 = \dfrac{1}{g_c}[(\rho_2 A_2 V_2)V_2 - (\rho_1 A_1 V_1)V_1]$

And by Fig. 2-14(b),

Continuity equation $\quad \rho_1 A_1 V_1 = \rho_2 A_2 V_2 = \dot{m}$

Combining the continuity and momentum equations, we obtain

$$P_1A_1 - F_{D\sigma} - P_2A_2 = \frac{\dot{m}}{g_c}(V_2 - V_1)$$

or

$$F_{D\sigma} = P_1A_1 - P_2A_2 - \frac{\dot{m}}{g_c}(V_2 - V_1)$$

And with $\dot{m} = \rho_1 A_1 V_1 = 1000\ \text{kg/m}^3 \times 0.2\ \text{m}^2 \times 3\ \text{m/sec} = 600\ \text{kg/sec}$, we have

$$F_{D\sigma} = 137{,}900\ \text{N/m}^2 \times 0.2\ \text{m}^2 - 101{,}325\ \text{N/m}^2 \times 0.1\ \text{m}^2$$
$$- 600\ \text{kg/sec} \times (6-3)\ \text{m/sec}$$

or

$$= 27{,}580\ \text{N} - 10{,}132\ \text{N} - 1800\ \text{N}$$

and

$$= 15{,}648\ \text{N} \qquad \text{(acts to left in assumed position)}$$

Finally, the force of the water on the duct is

$$F_{\sigma D} = -F_{D\sigma} = -15{,}648\ \text{N} \qquad \text{(acts to right)}$$

Example 2-3. Figure 2-15 shows the steady flow conditions at sections 1 and 2 about an airfoil mounted in a wind tunnel where the frictional effects at the wall are negligible. Determine the section drag coefficient C_d of this airfoil.

Solution. Since the flow is steady, the continuity equation may be used to find the unknown velocity V_B as follows:

$$(\rho AV)_1 = (\rho AV)_2 \qquad (\text{that is, } \dot{m}_1 = \dot{m}_2)$$

or

$$\rho_1 A_1 V_A = \rho_2(\tfrac{2}{3} V_B + \tfrac{1}{3} V_C)A_2$$

but

$$\rho_1 = \rho_2 \qquad \text{and} \qquad A_1 = A_2$$

$$V_A = \tfrac{2}{3} V_B + \tfrac{1}{3} V_C$$

thus

$$V_B = \tfrac{3}{2} V_A - \tfrac{1}{2} V_C = 31.5\ \text{m/sec}$$

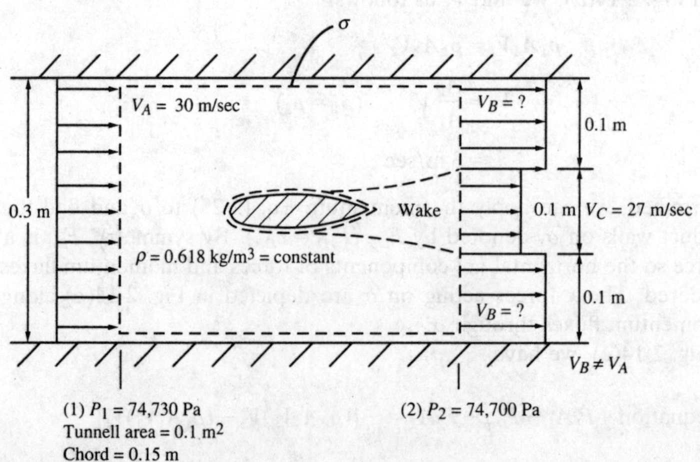

FIGURE 2-15
Wind tunnel drag determination for an Airfoil section.

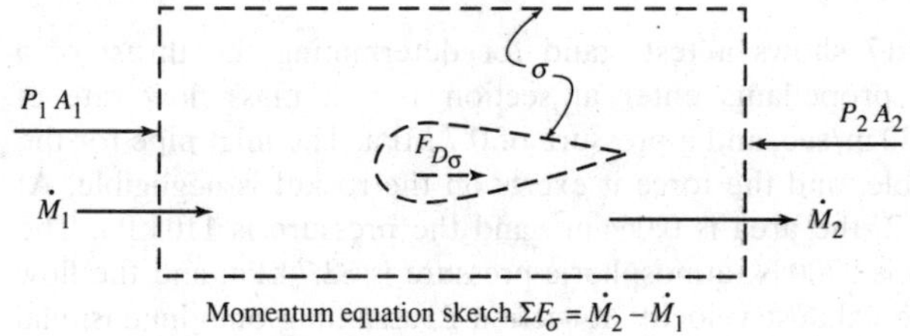

FIGURE 2-16
Sketch of momentum equation for airfoil section.

The momentum equation may now be used to find the drag on the airfoil. This drag force will include both the skin friction and pressure drag. We sketch the control volume σ with the terms of the momentum equation as shown in Fig. 2-16.

Taking forces to right as positive, we have from the sketch above

$$\sum F_\sigma = P_1 A_1 - P_2 A_2 + F_{D\sigma}$$

$$\dot{M}_1 = (\rho_1 A_1 V_A) V_A = \rho_1 A_1 V_A^2$$

$$\dot{M}_2 = \rho_2 \left(\frac{2}{3} A_2\right) V_B^2 + \rho_2 \left(\frac{1}{3} A_2\right) V_C^2$$

$$= \rho_2 A_2 \left(\frac{2}{3} V_B^2 + \frac{1}{3} V_C^2\right)$$

For $\rho = \rho_1 = \rho_2$ and $A = A_1 = A_2$,

$$-F_{D\sigma} = (P_1 - P_2)A + \frac{\rho A}{g_c}\left(V_A^2 - \frac{2}{3} V_B^2 - \frac{1}{3} V_C^2\right)$$

or

$$= (74{,}730 - 74{,}700)0.1 + 0.618$$

$$\times 0.1\left[30^2 - \frac{2}{3}(31.5^2) - \frac{1}{3}(27^2)\right]$$

$$= 3.0\ \text{N} - 0.278\ \text{N}$$

$$= 2.722\ \text{N} \qquad \therefore F_{D\sigma} \text{ acts to left}$$

$$F_{\sigma D} = \text{drag force for section}$$

$$= -F_{D\sigma} \qquad \text{and} \qquad F_{\sigma D} \text{ acts to left}$$

$$F'_D = \frac{F_{\sigma D}}{b} = \frac{2.722\ \text{N}}{0.333\ \text{m}} = 8.174\ \text{N/m}$$

$$C_d = \frac{F'_D}{qc} \qquad \text{and} \qquad q = \frac{\rho V_\infty^2}{2g_c} \qquad \text{where } V_\infty = V_A$$

$$C_d = \frac{F'_D}{[(\rho V_\infty^2)/(2g_c)]c} = \frac{8.174}{(0.618 \times 30^2/2)0.15} = 0.196$$

Example 2-4. Figure 2-17 shows a test stand for determining the thrust of a liquid-fuel rocket. The propellants enter at section 1 at a mass flow rate of 15 kg/sec, a velocity of 30 m/sec, and a pressure of 0.7 MPa. The inlet pipe for the propellants is very flexible, and the force it exerts on the rocket is negligible. At the nozzle exit, section 2, the area is 0.064 m^2, and the pressure is 110 kPa. The force read by the scales is 2700 N, atmospheric pressure is 82.7 kPa, and the flow is steady. Determine the exhaust velocity at section 2, assuming one-dimensional flow exists. Mechanical frictional effects may be neglected.

Solution. First, determine the force on the lever by the rocket to develop a 2700 N scale reading. This may be done by summing moments about the fulcrum point 0 [see Fig. 2-18(*a*)]. Next, draw an external volume around the rocket as shown below, and indicate the horizontal forces and momentum flux [see Fig. 2-18(*b*)].

Gage pressure is used at the exit plane because of the cancellation of atmospheric pressure forces everywhere except at the exit plane where the pressure exceeds atmospheric by an amount equal to $P_2 - P_\infty$, or P_{2g}. Applying the momentum equation to the control volume σ shown in Fig. 2-18(*b*), we obtain

$$\sum F_\sigma = \frac{\dot{M}_{\text{out}_x}}{g_c}$$

Thus
$$F_R - P_{2g}A_2 = \frac{\dot{m}_2 V_2}{g_c}$$

Since the flow is steady, the continuity equation yields $\dot{m}_1 = \dot{m}_2 = 15$ kg/sec. Therefore,

$$\begin{aligned} V_2 &= \frac{F_R - P_{2g}A_2}{\dot{m}_2/g_c} \\ &= \frac{10{,}800\ \text{N} - [(110 - 82.7) \times 10^3\ \text{N/m}^2](0.064\ \text{m}^2)}{15\ \text{kg/sec}} \\ &= 603.5\ \text{m/sec} \end{aligned}$$

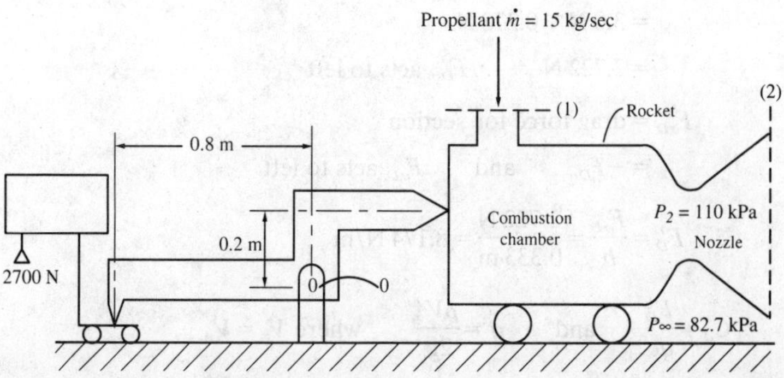

FIGURE 2-17
Liquid-fuel rocket test setup.

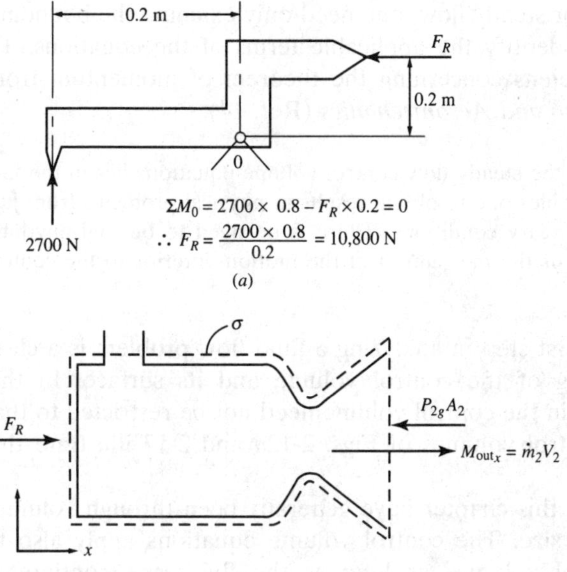

FIGURE 2-18
Moment balance and control volume σ for rocket.

2-11 SUMMARY OF LAWS FOR FLUID FLOW

Table 2-2 gives a convenient summary of the material covered so far in this chapter in the form of a tabulation of the mass, energy, entropy, and momentum equations for a system (control mass) and for control volume flow. For steady flow, all terms of the control volume equations refer to quantities evaluated at the control surface (neglecting body forces). Thus, to use the

TABLE 2-2
Summary of laws

	Closed system of mass	**Control volume flow**
Mass conservation	$\frac{dm}{dt} = 0$	$\frac{dm}{dt} = \frac{dm_\sigma}{dt} + \dot{m}_{\text{out}} - \dot{m}_{\text{in}}$
First law of thermodynamics	$\frac{dQ}{dt} - \frac{dW}{dt} = \frac{dE}{dt}$	$\dot{Q} - \dot{W}_x = \dot{m}(Pv + e)_{\text{out}} - \dot{m}(Pv + e)_{\text{in}} + \frac{dE_\sigma}{dt}$
Second law of thermodynamics	$\frac{dS}{dt} \geq \frac{1}{T}\frac{dQ}{dt}$	$\frac{dS_\sigma}{dt} + \dot{S}_{\text{out}} - \dot{S}_{\text{in}} \geq \frac{1}{T}\frac{dQ}{dt}$
Second law of motion	$\sum F_x = \frac{dM_x}{dt}$	$\sum F_\sigma = \frac{dM_\sigma}{dt} + \dot{M}_{\text{out}} - \dot{M}_{\text{in}}$

control volume equations for steady flow, one need only examine the boundary of the control region and identify the applicable terms of the equations. To paraphrase Prandtl and Tiejens concerning the theorem of momentum from their *Fundamentals of Hydro and Aeromechanics* (Ref. 14):

> The undoubted value of the steady flow control volume equations lies in the fact that their application enables one to obtain results in physical problems from just a knowledge of the boundary conditions. There is no need to be told anything about the state of fluid, or the mechanism of the motion, interior to the control volume.

Needless to say, the first step in analyzing a fluid flow problem is a clear statement or understanding of the control volume and its surface. In this respect, note that the mass in the control volume need not be restricted to that of a flowing fluid. The control volumes of Figs. 2-12*a* and 2-17 illustrate this point.

The flows analyzed in this chapter have generally been through volumes of other than infinitesimal size. The control volume equations apply also to infinitesimally sized control volumes as long as the fluid is a continuum. Examples of the use of an infinitesimal control volume will be given in Chap. 3.

The basic laws discussed in this chapter represent a powerful set of analytical tools which form the starting point in the analysis of any continuum fluid flow problem. Equations (2-8) through (2-11), or Eqs. (2-20), (2-24), (2-28), and (2-29) plus an equation of state relating the thermodynamic properties of the substance under consideration will form the basis of all the analytical work to follow.

Definitions of new quantities may be introduced, but no further fundamental laws will be required. Since the relations presented in this chapter form the starting point of all analytical studies to follow, time spent on the homework problems of this chapter, which are designed to bring out a basic understanding of the fundamental equations, will be well invested.

2-12 PERFECT GAS

General Characteristics

The thermodynamic equations of state for a perfect gas are

$$\boxed{P = \rho RT} \tag{2-30}$$

$$\boxed{u = u(T)} \tag{2-31}$$

where P is the thermodynamic pressure, ρ is the density, R is the gas constant, T is the thermodynamic temperature, and u is the internal energy per unit mass and a function of temperature only. The gas constant R is related to the universal gas constant R_u and the molecular weight of the gas M by

$$R = \frac{R_u}{M}$$

Values of the gas constant and molecular weight for typical gases are presented in Table 2-3 in several unit systems; $R_u = 8.31434\ \mathrm{kJ/(kmol \cdot K)} = 1.98718\ \mathrm{Btu/(mol \cdot {}^\circ R)}$.

From the definition of enthalpy per unit mass h of a substance in Eq. (2-3), this simplifies for a perfect gas to

$$h = u + RT \tag{2-32}$$

Equations (2-31) and (2-32) combined show that the enthalpy per unit mass is also only a function of temperature $h = h(T)$. Differentiating Eq. (2-32) gives

$$dh = du + R\,dT \tag{2-33}$$

The differentials dh and du in Eq. (2-33) are related to the specific heat at constant pressure and specific heat at constant volume [see definitions in Eqs. (2-4) and (2-5)], respectively, as follows:

$$dh = c_p\,dT$$

$$du = c_v\,dT$$

Note that both specific heats can be functions of temperature. These equations can be integrated from state 1 to state 2 to give

$$u_2 - u_1 = \int_{T_1}^{T_2} c_v\,dT \tag{2-34}$$

$$h_2 - h_1 = \int_{T_1}^{T_2} c_p\,dT \tag{2-35}$$

Substitution of the equations for dh and du into Eq. (2-33) gives the relationship between specific heats for a perfect gas

$$\boxed{c_p = c_v + R} \tag{2-36}$$

And γ is the ratio of the specific heat at constant pressure to the specific heat at constant volume, or

$$\boxed{\gamma \equiv \frac{c_p}{c_v}} \tag{2-6}$$

TABLE 2-3
Properties of ideal gases at 298.15 K (536.67°R)

Gas	Molecular weight	c_p [kJ/(kg · K)]	c_p [Btu/(lbm · °R)]	R [kJ/(kg · K)]	R [(ft · lbf)/(lbm · °R)]	γ
Air	28.07	1.004	0.240	0.286	53.34	1.40
Argon	39.94	0.523	0.125	0.208	38.69	1.67
Carbon dioxide	44.01	0.845	0.202	0.189	35.1	1.29
Carbon monoxide	28.01	1.042	0.249	0.297	55.17	1.40
Hydrogen	2.016	14.32	3.42	4.124	766.5	1.40
Nitrogen	28.02	1.038	0.248	0.296	55.15	1.40
Oxygen	32.00	0.917	0.217	0.260	48.29	1.39
Sulfur dioxide	64.07	0.644	0.154	0.130	24.1	1.25
Water vapor	18.016	1.867	0.446	0.461	85.78	1.33

The following relationships result from using Eqs. (2-36) and (2-6):

$$\boxed{\frac{R}{c_v} = \gamma - 1} \tag{2-37}$$

$$\boxed{\frac{R}{c_p} = \frac{\gamma - 1}{\gamma}} \tag{2-38}$$

The Gibbs equation relates the entropy per unit mass s to the other thermodynamic properties of a substance. It can be written as

$$ds = \frac{du + P\,d(1/\rho)}{T} = \frac{dh - (1/\rho)\,dP}{T} \tag{2-39}$$

For a perfect gas, the Gibbs equation can be written simply as

$$\boxed{ds = c_v \frac{dT}{T} + R \frac{d(1/\rho)}{1/\rho}} \tag{2-40}$$

or

$$\boxed{ds = c_p \frac{dT}{T} - R \frac{dP}{P}} \tag{2-41}$$

These equations can be integrated between states 1 and 2 to yield the following expressions for the change in entropy $s_2 - s_1$:

$$s_2 - s_1 = \int_{T_1}^{T_2} c_v \frac{dT}{T} + R \ln \frac{\rho_1}{\rho_2} \tag{2-42}$$

$$s_2 - s_1 = \int_{T_1}^{T_2} c_p \frac{dT}{T} - R \ln \frac{P_2}{P_3} \tag{2-43}$$

If the specific heats are known functions of temperature for a perfect gas, then Eqs. (2-34), (2-35), (2-42), and (2-43) can be integrated from a reference state and tabulated for further use in what are called *gas tables*.

The equation for the speed of sound in a perfect gas is easily obtained by use of Eqs. (2-7) and (2-30) to give

$$\boxed{a = \sqrt{\gamma R g_c T}} \tag{2-44}$$

Calorically Perfect Gas

A *calorically perfect gas* is a perfect gas with constant specific heats (c_p and c_v). In this case, the expressions for changes in internal energy u, enthalpy h, and entropy s simplify to the following:

$$u_2 - u_1 = c_v(T_2 - T_1) \tag{2-45}$$

$$h_2 - h_1 = c_p(T_2 - T_1) \tag{2-46}$$

$$s_2 - s_1 = c_v \ln\frac{T_2}{T_1} - R \ln\frac{\rho_2}{\rho_1} \tag{2-47}$$

$$s_2 - s_1 = c_p \ln\frac{T_2}{T_1} - R \ln\frac{P_2}{P_1} \tag{2-48}$$

Equations (2-47) and (2-48) can be rearranged to give the following equations for the temperature ratio T_2/T_1:

$$\frac{T_2}{T_1} = \left(\frac{\rho_2}{\rho_1}\right)^{R/c_v} \exp\frac{s_2 - s_1}{c_v}$$

$$\frac{T_2}{T_1} = \left(\frac{P_2}{P_1}\right)^{R/c_p} \exp\frac{s_2 - s_1}{c_p}$$

From Eqs. (2-37) and (2-38), these expressions become

$$\frac{T_2}{T_1} = \left(\frac{\rho_2}{\rho_1}\right)^{\gamma-1} \exp\frac{s_2 - s_1}{c_v} \tag{2-49}$$

$$\frac{T_2}{T_1} = \left(\frac{P_2}{P_1}\right)^{(\gamma-1)/\gamma} \exp\frac{s_2 - s_1}{c_p} \tag{2-50}$$

Isentropic Process

For an isentropic process ($s_2 = s_1$), Eqs. (2-49), (2-50), and (2-30) yield the following equations:

$$\boxed{\frac{T_2}{T_1} = \left(\frac{P_2}{P_1}\right)^{(\gamma-1)/\gamma}} \tag{2-51}$$

$$\boxed{\frac{T_2}{T_1} = \left(\frac{\rho_2}{\rho_1}\right)^{\gamma-1}} \tag{2-52}$$

$$\boxed{\frac{P_2}{P_1} = \left(\frac{\rho_2}{\rho_1}\right)^{\gamma}} \tag{2-53}$$

Note that Eqs. (2-51), (2-52), and (2-53) apply only to a calorically perfect gas undergoing an isentropic process.

Example 2-5. Air initially at 20°C and 1 atm is compressed reversibly and adiabatically to a final pressure of 15 atm. Find the final temperature.

Solution. Since the process is isentropic from initial to final state, Eq. (2-51) can be used to solve for the final temperature. The ratio of specific heats for air is 1.4.

$$T_2 = T_1\left(\frac{P_2}{P_1}\right)^{(\gamma-1)/\gamma} = (20 + 273.15)\left(\frac{15}{1}\right)^{0.4/1.4}$$

$$= 293.15 \times 2.1678 = 635.49 \text{ K } (362.34°\text{C})$$

Example 2-6. Air is expanded isentropically through a nozzle from $T_1 = 3000°\text{R}$, $V_1 = 0$, and $P_1 = 10$ atm to $V_2 = 3000$ ft/sec. Find the exit temperature and pressure.

Solution. Application of the first law of thermodynamics to the nozzle gives the following for a calorically perfect gas:

$$c_p T_1 + \frac{V_1^2}{2g_c} = c_p T_2 + \frac{V_2^2}{2g_c}$$

This equation can be rearranged to give T_2:

$$T_2 = T_1 - \frac{V_2^2 - V_1^2}{2g_c c_p} = 3000 - \frac{3000^2}{2 \times 32.174 \times 186.76}$$

$$= 3000 - 748.9 = 2251.1°\text{R}$$

Solving Eq. (2-51) for P_2 gives

$$P_2 = P_1\left(\frac{T_2}{T_1}\right)^{\gamma/(\gamma-1)} = 10\left(\frac{2251.1}{3000}\right)^{3.5} = 3.66 \text{ atm}$$

Mollier Diagram for a Perfect Gas

The Mollier diagram is a thermodynamic state diagram with the coordinates of enthalpy and entropy s. Since the enthalpy of a perfect gas depends upon temperature alone,

$$dh = c_p\, dT$$

temperature can replace enthalpy as the coordinate of a Mollier diagram for a perfect gas. When temperature T and entropy s are the coordinates of a

Mollier diagram, we call it a *T-s diagram.* We can construct lines of constant pressure and density in the *T-s* diagram by using Eqs. (2-42) and (2-43). For a calorically perfect gas, Eqs. (2-47) and (2-48) can be written between any state and the entropy reference state ($s = 0$) as

$$s = c_v \ln \frac{T}{T_{\text{ref}}} - R \ln \frac{\rho}{\rho_{\text{ref}}}$$

$$s = c_p \ln \frac{T}{T_{\text{ref}}} - R \ln \frac{P}{P_{\text{ref}}}$$

where T_{ref}, P_{ref}, and ρ_{ref} are the values of temperature, pressure, and density, respectively, when $s = 0$. Since the most common working fluid in gas turbine engines is air, Fig. 2-19 was constructed for air by using the above equations with these data:

$$c_p = 1.004 \text{ kJ/(kg} \cdot \text{K)} \qquad T_{\text{ref}} = 288.2 \text{ K} \qquad \rho_{\text{ref}} = 1.225 \text{ kg/m}^3$$

$$R = 0.286 \text{ kJ/(kg} \cdot \text{K)} \qquad P_{\text{ref}} = 1 \text{ atm} = 101{,}325 \text{ Pa}$$

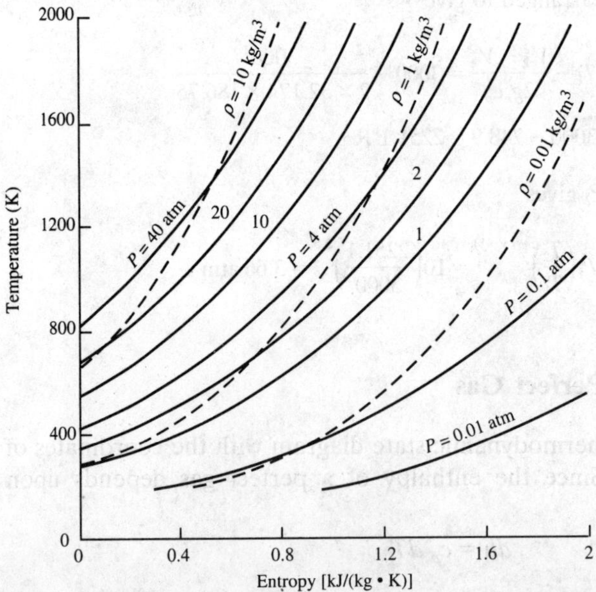

FIGURE 2-19
A *T-s* diagram for air as a calorically perfect gas.

Mixtures of Perfect Gases

We consider a mixture of perfect gases, each obeying the perfect gas equation

$$PV = NR_uT$$

where N is the number of moles and R_u is the universal gas constant. The mixture is idealized as independent perfect gases, each having the temperature T and occupying the volume V. The partial pressure of gas i is

$$P_i = N_iR_u\frac{T}{V}$$

According to the Gibbs-Dalton law, the pressure of the gas mixture of n constituents is the sum of the partial pressures of each constituent:

$$P = \sum_{i=1}^{n} P_i \tag{2-54}$$

The total number of moles N of the gas is

$$N = \sum_{i=1}^{n} N_i \tag{2-55}$$

The ratio of the number of moles of constituent i to the total number of moles in the mixture is called the *mole fraction* χ_i. By using the above equations, the mole fraction of constituent i can be shown to equal the ratio of the partial pressure of constituent i to the pressure of the mixture:

$$\chi_i = \frac{N_i}{N} = \frac{P_i}{P} \tag{2-56}$$

The Gibbs-Dalton law also states that the internal energy, enthalpy, and entropy of a mixture are equal, respectively, to the sum of the internal energies, the enthalpies, and the entropies of the constituents when each alone occupies the volume of the mixture at the mixture temperature. Thus we can write for a mixture of n constituents:

Energy $$U = \sum_{i=1}^{n} U_i = \sum_{i=1}^{n} m_iu_i \tag{2-57}$$

Enthalpy $$H = \sum_{i=1}^{n} H_i = \sum_{i=1}^{n} m_ih_i \tag{2-58}$$

Entropy $$S = \sum_{i=1}^{n} S_i = \sum_{i=1}^{n} m_is_i \tag{2-59}$$

where m_i is the mass of constituent i.

The specific heats of the mixture follow directly the definitions of c_p and c_v and the above equations. For a mixture of n constituents, the specific heats are

$$c_p = \frac{\sum_{i=1}^{n} m_i c_{pi}}{m} \quad \text{and} \quad c_v = \frac{\sum_{i=1}^{n} m_i c_{vi}}{m} \tag{2-60}$$

where m is the total mass of the mixture.

Gas Tables

In the case of a perfect gas with nonconstant specific heats, the variation of the specific heat at constant pressure c_p is normally modeled by several terms of a power series in temperature T. This expression is used in conjunction with the general equations presented above and the new equations that are developed below to generate a gas table for a particular gas (see Ref. 15).

For convenience, we define

$$\boxed{h \equiv \int_{T_{\text{ref}}}^{T} c_p \, dT} \tag{2-61}$$

$$\boxed{\phi \equiv \int_{T_{\text{ref}}}^{T} c_p \frac{dT}{T}} \tag{2-62}$$

$$\boxed{P_r \equiv \exp \frac{\phi - \phi_0}{R}} \tag{2-63}$$

$$\boxed{v_r \equiv \exp\left(-\frac{1}{R} \int_{T_0}^{T} c_v \frac{dT}{T}\right)} \tag{2-64}$$

where P_r and v_r are called the *reduced pressure* and *reduced volume*, respectively. Using the definition of ϕ from Eq. (2-62) in Eq. (2-43) gives

$$s_2 - s_1 = \phi_2 - \phi_1 - R \ln \frac{P_2}{P_1} \tag{2-65}$$

For an isentropic process between states 1 and 2, Eq. (2-65) reduces to

$$\phi_2 - \phi_1 = R \ln \frac{P_2}{P_1}$$

which can be rewritten as

$$\left(\frac{P_2}{P_1}\right)_{s=\text{const}} = \exp\frac{\phi_2 - \phi_1}{R} = \frac{\exp(\phi_2/R)}{\exp(\phi_1/R)}$$

Using Eq. (2-63), we can express this pressure ratio in terms of the reduced pressure P_r as

$$\boxed{\left(\frac{P_2}{P_1}\right)_{s=\text{const}} = \frac{P_{r2}}{P_{r1}}} \tag{2-66}$$

Likewise, it can be shown that

$$\boxed{\left(\frac{v_2}{v_1}\right)_{s=\text{const}} = \frac{v_{r2}}{v_{r1}}} \tag{2-67}$$

For a perfect gas, the properties h, P_r, u, v_r, and ϕ are functions of T, and these can be calculated by starting with a polynomial for c_p. Say we have the seventh-order polynomial

$$c_p = A_0 + A_1T + A_2T^2 + A_3T^3 + A_4T^4 + A_5T^5 + A_6T^6 + A_7T^7 \tag{2-68}$$

The equations for h and ϕ as functions of temperature follow directly from using Eqs. (2-61) and (2-62):

$$h = h_{\text{ref}} + A_0T + \frac{A_1}{2}T^2 + \frac{A_2}{3}T^3 + \frac{A_3}{4}T^4 + \frac{A_4}{5}T^5 + \frac{A_5}{6}T^6 + \frac{A_6}{7}T^7 + \frac{A_7}{8}T^8 \tag{2-69}$$

$$\phi = \phi_{\text{ref}} + A_0 \ln T + A_1T + \frac{A_2}{2}T^2 + \frac{A_3}{3}T^3 + \frac{A_4}{4}T^4 + \frac{A_5}{5}T^5 + \frac{A_6}{6}T^6 + \frac{A_7}{7}T^7 \tag{2-70}$$

After we define reference values, the variations of P_r and v_r follow from Eqs. (2-63), (2-64), and the above.

Appendix D

Typically, air flows through the inlet and compressor of the gas turbine engine whereas products of combustion flow through the engine components downstream of a combustion process. Most gas turbine engines use hydrocarbon fuels of composition $(CH_2)_n$. We can use the above equations to estimate the properties of these gases, given the ratio of the mass of fuel burned to the mass

mass of air. For convenience, we use the fuel/air ratio f, defined as

$$\boxed{f = \frac{\text{mass of fuel}}{\text{mass of air}}} \tag{2-71}$$

The maximum value of f is 0.0676 for the hydrocarbon fuels of composition $(CH_2)_n$.

Given the values of c_p, h, and ϕ for air and the values of combustion products, the values of c_p, h, and ϕ for the mixture follow directly from the mixture equations [Eqs. (2-57) through (2-60)] and are given by

$$R = \frac{1.9857117 \text{ But/(lbm} \cdot {}^\circ\text{R)}}{28.97 - f \times 0.946186} \tag{2-72a}$$

$$c_p = \frac{c_{p\,\text{air}} + f c_{p\,\text{prod}}}{1+f} \tag{2-72b}$$

$$h = \frac{h_{\text{air}} + f h_{\text{prod}}}{1+f} \tag{2-72c}$$

$$\phi = \frac{\phi_{\text{air}} + f \phi_{\text{prod}}}{1+f} \tag{2-72d}$$

Appendix D is a table of the properties h and P_r as functions of the temperature and fuel/air ratio f for air and combustion products [air with hydrocarbon fuels of composition $(CH_2)_n$] at low pressure (perfect gas). These data are based on the above equations and the constants given in Table 2-4, which are valid over the temperature range of 300 to 4000°R. These constants come from the gas turbine engine modeling work of Capt. John S. McKinney

TABLE 2-4
Constants for air and combustion products used in App. D and program AFPROP (Ref. 16)

Air alone		Combustion products of air and $(CH_2)_n$ fuels	
A_0	2.5020051×10^{-1}	A_0	7.3816638×10^{-2}
A_1	$-5.1536879 \times 10^{-5}$	A_1	1.2258630×10^{-3}
A_2	6.5519486×10^{-8}	A_2	$-1.3771901 \times 10^{-6}$
A_3	$-6.7178376 \times 10^{-12}$	A_3	$9.9686793 \times 10^{-10}$
A_4	$-1.5128259 \times 10^{-14}$	A_4	$-4.2051104 \times 10^{-13}$
A_5	$7.6215767 \times 10^{-18}$	A_5	$1.0212913 \times 10^{-16}$
A_6	$-1.4526770 \times 10^{-21}$	A_6	$-1.3335668 \times 10^{-20}$
A_7	$1.0115540 \times 10^{-25}$	A_7	$7.2678710 \times 10^{-25}$
h_{ref}	-1.7558886 But/lbm	h_{ref}	30.58153 But/lbm
ϕ_{ref}	0.0454323 But/(lbm · °R)	ϕ_{ref}	0.6483398 But/(lbm · °R)

(U.S. Air Force) while assigned to the Air Force's Aero Propulsion Laboratory (Ref. 16), and they continue to be widely used in the industry. Appendix D uses a reference value of 2 for P_r at 600°R and $f = 0$.

Computer Program AFPROP

The computer program AFPROP was written by using the above constants for air and products of combustion from air with $(CH_2)_n$. The program can calculate the four primary thermodynamic properties at a state (P, T, h, and s) given the fuel/air ratio f and two independent thermodynamic properties (say, P and h).

To show the use of the gas tables, we will resolve Examples 2-5 and 2-6, using the gas tables of App. D. These problems could also be solved by using the computer program AFPROP.

Example 2-7. Air initially at 100°F and 1 atm is compressed reversibly and adiabatically to a final pressure of 15 atm. Find the final temperature.

Solution. Since the process is isentropic from initial to final state, Eq. (2-66) can be used to solve for the final reduced pressure. From App. D at 20°C (293.15 K) and $f = 0$, $P_r = 1.2768$ and

$$\frac{P_{r2}}{P_{r1}} = \frac{P_2}{P_1} = 15$$

$$P_{r2} = 15 \times 1.2768 = 19.152$$

From App. D for $P_{r2} = 19.152$, the final temperature is 354.42°C (627.57 K). This is 7.9 K lower than the result obtained in Example 2-5 for air as a calorically perfect gas.

Example 2-8. Air is expanded isentropically through a nozzle from $T_1 = 3000°R$, $V_1 = 0$, and $P_1 = 10$ atm to $V_2 = 3000$ ft/sec. Find the exit temperature and pressure.

Solution. Application of the first law of thermodyanics to the nozzle gives the following for a calorically perfect gas:

$$h_1 + \frac{V_1^2}{2g_c} = h_2 + \frac{V_2^2}{2g_c}$$

From App. D at $f = 0$ and $T_1 = 3000°R$, $h_1 = 790.46$ Btu/lbm and $P_{r1} = 938.6$. Solving the above equation for h_2 gives

$$h_2 = h_1 - \frac{V_2^2 - V_1^2}{2g_c} = 790.46 - \frac{3000^2}{2 \times 32.174 \times 778.16}$$

$$= 790.46 - 179.74 = 610.72 \text{ But/lbm}$$

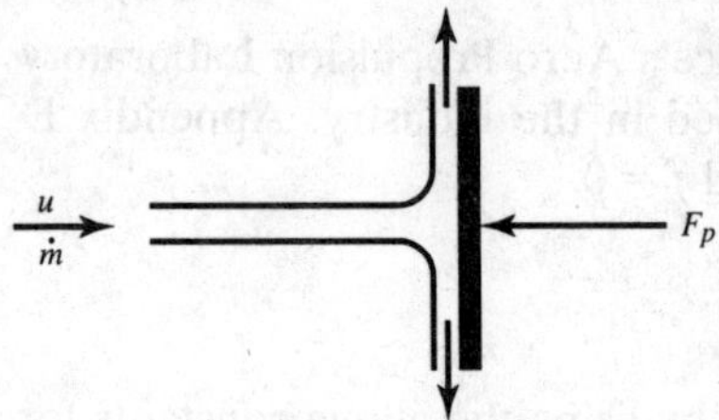

FIGURES P2-1 and P2-2

For $h = 610.72$ Btu/lbm and $f = 0$, App. D gives $T_2 = 2377.7$°R and $P_{r2} = 352.6$. Using Eq. (2-66), we solve for the exit pressure

$$P_2 = P_1 \frac{P_{r2}}{P_{r1}} = 10\left(\frac{352.6}{938.6}\right) = 3.757 \text{ atm}$$

These results for temperature and pressure at station 2 are higher by 126.6°R and 0.097 atm, respectively, than those obtained in Example 2-6 for air as a calorically perfect gas.

PROBLEMS

2-1. A stream of air with velocity of 500 ft/sec and density of 0.07 lbm/ft^3 strikes a stationary plate and is deflected 90°. Select an appropriate control volume and determine the force F_p necessary to hold the plate stationary. Assume that atmospheric pressure surrounds the jet and that the initial jet diameter is 1.0 in.

2-2. An airstream with density of 1.25 kg/m^3 and velocity of 200 m/sec strikes a stationary plate and is deflected 90°. Select an appropriate control volume and determine the force F_p necessary to hold the plate stationary. Assume that atmospheric pressure surrounds the jet and that the initial jet diameter is 1.0 cm.

2-3. Consider the flow shown in Fig. P2-3 of an incompressible fluid. The fluid enters (station 1) a constant-area circular pipe of radius r_0 with uniform velocity V_1 and pressure P_1. The fluid leaves (station 2) with the parabolic velocity profile V_2 given by

$$V_2 = V_{\max}\left[1 - \left(\frac{r}{r_0}\right)^2\right]$$

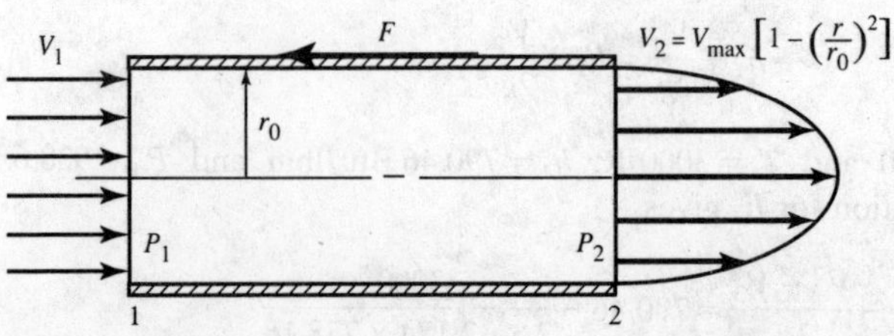

FIGURE P2-3

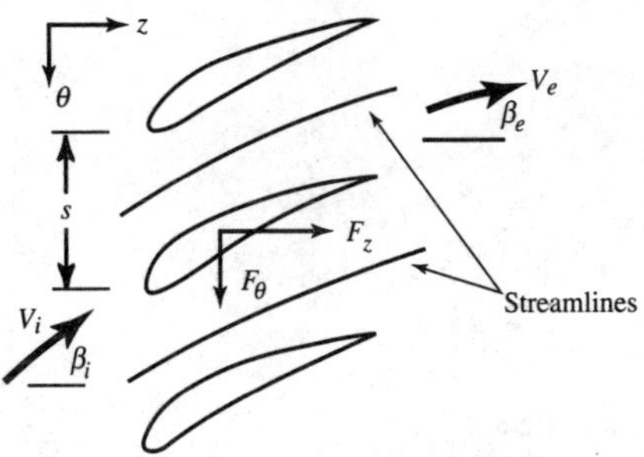

FIGURE P2-4

and uniform pressure P_2. Using the conservation of mass and momentum equations, show that the force F necessary to hold the pipe in place can be expressed as

$$F = \pi r_0^2\left(P_1 - P_2 + \frac{\rho V_1^2}{3g_c}\right)$$

2-4. Consider the flow of an incompressible fluid through a two-dimensional cascade as shown in Fig. P2-4. The airfoils are spaced at a distance s and have unit depth into the page. Application of the conservation of mass requires $V_i \cos \beta_i = V_e \cos \beta_e$.

a. From the tangential momentum equation, show that

$$F_\theta = \frac{\dot{m}}{g_c}(V_I \sin \beta_i - V_e \sin \beta_e)$$

b. From the axial momentum equation, show that

$$F_z = s(P_e - P_i)$$

c. Show that the axial force can be written as

$$F_z = s\left[\frac{\rho}{2g_c}(V_i^2 \sin^2 \beta_i - V_e^2 \sin^2 \beta_e) - (P_{ti} - P_{te})\right]$$

2-5. When a free jet is deflected by a blade surface, a change of momentum occurs and a force is exerted on the blade. If the blade is allowed to move at a velocity, power may be derived from the moving blade. This is the basic principle of the impulse turbine. The jet of Fig. P2-5, which is initially horizontal, is deflected by a fixed blade. Assuming the same pressure surrounds the jet, show that the

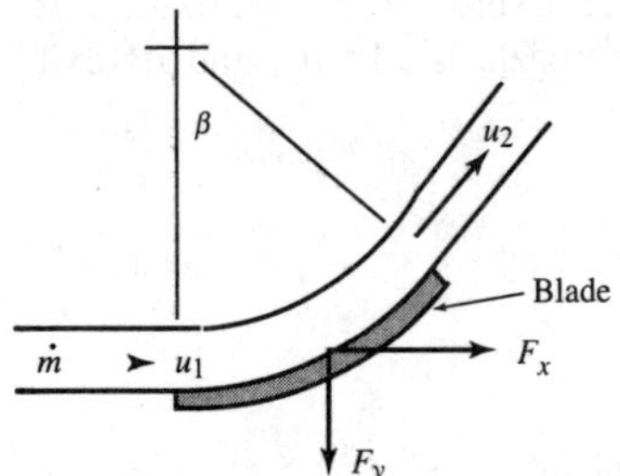

FIGURE P2-5

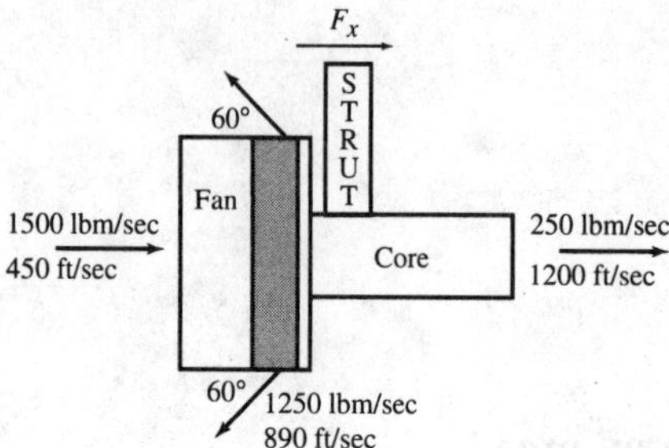

FIGURE P2-6

horizontal (F_x) and vertical forces (F_y) by the fluid on the blade are given by

$$F_x = \frac{\dot{m}(u_1 - u_2 \cos \beta)}{g_c} \qquad \text{and} \qquad F_y = \frac{\dot{m}u_2 \sin \beta}{g_c}$$

Calculate the force F_y for a mass flow rate of 100 lbm/sec, $u_1 = u_2 = 2000$ ft/sec, and $\beta = 60°$.

2-6. One method of reducing an aircarft's landing distance is through the use of thrust reversers. Consider the turbofan engine in Fig. P2-6 with thrust reverser of the bypass airstream. It is given that 1500 lbm/sec of air at 60°F and 14.7 psia enters the engine at a velocity of 450 ft/sec and that 1250 lbm/sec of bypass air leaves the engine at 60° to the horizontal, velocity of 890 ft/sec, and pressure of 14.7 psia. The remaining 250 lbm/sec leaves the engine core at a velocity of 1200 ft/sec and pressure of 14.7 psia. Determine the force on the strut F_x. Assume the outside of the engine sees a pressure of 14.7 psia.

2-7. Air with a density of 0.027 lbm/ft^3 enters a diffuser at a velocity of 2470 ft/sec and a static pressure of 4 psia. The air leaves the diffuser at a velocity of 300 ft/sec and a static pressure of 66 psia. The entrance area of the diffuser is 1.5 ft^2, and its exit area is 1.7 ft^2. Determine the magnitude and direction of the strut force necessary to hold the diffuser stationary when this diffuser is operated in an atmospheric pressure of 4 psia.

2-8. It is given that 50 kg/sec of air enters a diffuser at a velocity of 750 m/sec and a static pressure of 20 kPa. The air leaves the diffuser at a velocity of 90 m/sec and a static pressure of 330 kPa. The entrance area of the diffuser is 0.25 m^2, and its exit area is 0.28 m^2. Determine the magnitude and direction of the strut force necessary to hold the diffuser stationary when this diffuser is operated in an atmospheric pressure of 20 kPa.

2-9. It is given that 100 lbm/sec of air enters a nozzle at a velocity of 600 ft/sec and a static pressure of 70 psia. The air leaves the nozzle at a velocity of 4000 ft/sec and static pressure of 2 psia. The entrance area of the nozzle is 14.5 ft^2, and its exit

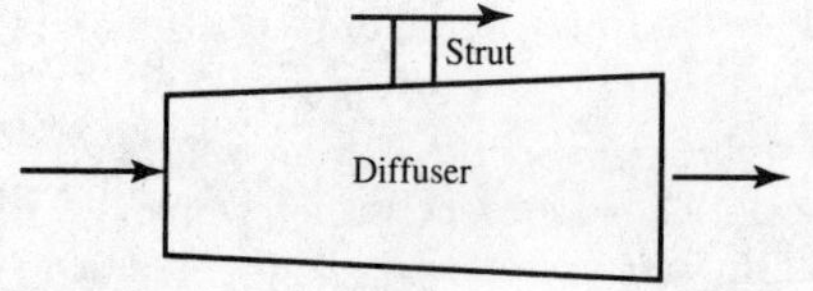

FIGURES P2-7 and 2-8

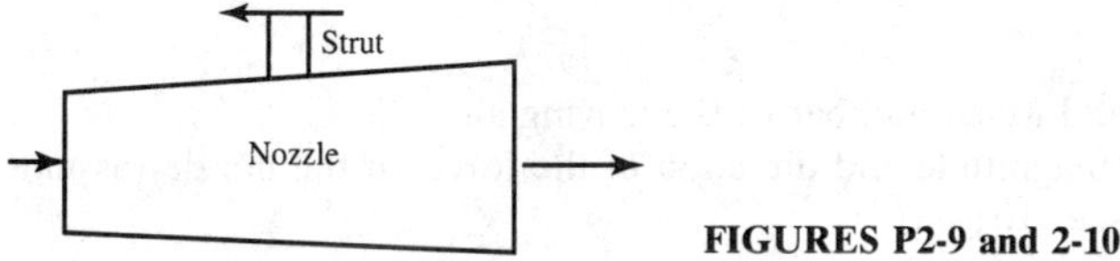

FIGURES P2-9 and 2-10

area is 30 ft^2. Determine the magnitude and direction of the strut force necessary to hold the nozzle stationary when this nozzle is operated in an atmospheric pressure of 4 psia.

2-10. Air with a density of 0.98 kg/m^3 enters a nozzle at a velocity of 180 m/sec and a static pressure of 350 kPa. The air leaves the nozzle at a velocity of 1200 m/sec and a static pressure of 10 kPa. The entrance area of the nozzle is 1.0 m^2, and its exit area is 2.07 m^2. Determine the magnitude and direction of the strut force necessary to hold the nozzle stationary when this nozzle is operated in an atmospheric pressure of 10 kPa.

2-11. For a calorically perfect gas, show that $P + \rho V^2/g_c$ can be written as $P(1 + \gamma M^2)$. Note that the Mach number M is defined as the velocity V divided by the speed of sound a.

2-12. Air at 1400 K, 8 atm, and 0.3 Mach expands isentropically through a nozzle to 1 atm. Assuming a calorically perfect gas, find the exit temperature and the inlet and exit areas for a mass flow rate of 100 kg/sec.

2-13. It is given that 250 lbm/sec of air at 2000°F, 10 atm, and 0.2 Mach expands isentropically through a nozzle to 1 atm. Assuming a calorically perfect gas, find the exit temperature and the inlet and exit areas.

2-14. Air at 518.7°R is isentropically compressed from 1 to 10 atm. Assuming a calorically perfect gas, determine the exit temperature and the compressor's input power for a mass flow rate of 150 lbm/sec.

2-15. It is given that 50 kg/sec of air at 288.2 K is isentropically compressed from 1 to 12 atm. Assuming a calorically perfect gas, determine the exit temperature and the compressor's input power.

2-16. Air at −55°F, 4 psia, and $M = 2.5$ enters an isentropic diffuser with an inlet area of 1.5 ft^2 and leaves at $M = 0.2$. Assuming a calorically perfect gas, determine:

a. The mass flow rate of the entering air

b. The pressure and temperature of the leaving air

c. The exit area and magnitude and direction of the force on the diffuser (assume outside of diffuser sees 4 psia)

2-17. Air at 225 K, 28 kPa, and $M = 2.0$ enters an isentropic diffuser with an inlet area of 0.2 m^2 and leaves at $M = 0.2$. Assuming a calorically perfect gas, determine:

a. The mass flow rate of the entering air

b. The pressure and temperature of the leaving air

c. The exit area and magnitude and direction of the force on the diffuser (assume outside of diffuser sees 28 kPa)

2-18. Air at 1800°F, 40 psia, and $M = 0.4$ enters an isentropic nozzle with an inlet area of 1.45 ft^2 and leaves at 10 psia. Assuming a calorically perfect gas, determine:

a. The velocity and mass flow rate of the entering air

b. The temperature and Mach number of the leaving air
c. The exit area and magnitude and direction of the force on the nozzle (assume outside of nozzle sees 10 psia)

2-19. Air at 1500 K, 300 kPa, and $M = 0.3$ enters an isentropic nozzle with an inlet area of 0.5 m^2 and leaves at 75 kPa. Assuming a calorically perfect gas, determine:
a. The velocity and mass flow rate of the entering air
b. The temperature and Mach number of the leaving air
c. The exit area and magnitude and direction of the force on the nozzle (assume outside of nozzle sees 75 kPa)

2-20. It is given that 100 lb/sec of air enters a steady flow compressor at 1 atm and 68°F. It leaves at 20 atm and 800°F. If the process is adiabatic, find the input power, specific volume at exit, and change in entropy. Is the process reversible? (Assume a calorically perfect gas.)

2-21. It is given that 50 kg/sec of air enters a steady flow compressor at 1 atm and 20°C. It leaves at 20 atm and 427°C. If the process is adiabatic, find the input power, specific volume at exit, and change in entropy. Is the process reversible? (Assume a calorically perfect gas.)

2-22. It is given that 200 lb/sec of air enters a steady flow turbine at 20 atm and 3400°R. It leaves at 10 atm. For a turbine efficiency of 85 percent, determine the exit temperature, output power, and change in entropy. (Assume a calorically perfect gas.)

2-23. It is given that 80 kg/sec of air enters a steady flow turbine at 30 atm and 2000 K. It leaves at 15 atm. For a turbine efficiency of 85 percent, determine the exit temperature, output power, and change in entropy. (Assume a calorically perfect gas.)

2-24. Air at 140°F, 300 psia, and 300 ft/sec enters a long insulated pipe of uniform diameter. At the exit, the pressure has dropped to 102.9 psia. Assuming a calorically perfect gas, determine:
a. The temperature and velocity at the exit [*Hint:* Since both the mass flow rate and the area are constant for this problem, ρV is constant. Also, from the first law of thermodynamics, $c_p T + V^2/(2g_c)$ is constant. Using the first law of thermodynamics, substitute for the exit velocity and solve for the exit temperature.]
b. The change in entropy

2-25. Air at 300 K, 20 atm, and 70 m/sec enters a long insulated pipe of uniform diameter. At the exit, the pressure has dropped to 6.46 atm. Assuming a calorically perfect gas, determine:
a. The temperature and velocity at the exit [*Hint:* Since both the mass flow rate and the area are constant for this problem, ρV is constant. Also, from the first law of thermodynamics, $c_p T + V^2/(2g_c)$ is constant. Using the first law of thermodynamics, substititue for the exit velocity and solve for the exit temperature.]
b. The change in entropy

2-26. Rework Prob. 2-13 for variable specific heats, using App. D or the program AFPROP. Compare your results to Prob. 2-13.

2-27. Rework Prob. 2-15 for variable specific heats, using App. D or the program AFPROP. Compare your results to Prob. 2-15.

2-28. Rework Prob. 2-16 for variable specific heats, using App. D or the program AFPROP. Compare your results to Prob. 2-16.

2-29. Rework Prob. 2-19 for variable specific heats, using App. D or the program AFPROP. Compare your results to Prob. 2-19.

2-30. Rework Prob. 2-20 for variable specific heats, using App. D or the program AFPROP. Compare your results to Prob. 2-20.

2-31. Rework Prob. 2-23 for variable specific heats, using App. D or the program AFPROP. Compare your results to Prob. 2-23.

CHAPTER

3

COMPRESSIBLE FLOW

3-1 INTRODUCTION

For a simple compressible system, we learned that the state of a unit mass of gas is fixed by two independent intensive properties such as pressure and temperature. To fully describe the condition and thus fix the state of this same gas when it is in motion requires the specification of a further property which will fix the speed of the gas. Thus three independent intensive properties are required to fully specify the state of a gas in motion.

At any given point in a compressible fluid flow field, the thermodynamic state of the gas is fixed by specifying, at that point, the velocity of the gas and any two independent properties such as pressure and temperature. However, we find that to specify the velocity directly is not always the most useful or the most convenient way to describe one-dimensional flow. There are other properties of the gas in motion which are dependent upon the speed of the gas and which may be used in place of the speed to describe the state of the flowing gas. Some of these properties are the Mach number, total pressure, and total temperature. In this chapter we define these properties and describe briefly some of the characteristics of compressible flow.

3-2 COMPRESSIBLE FLOW PROPERTIES

Total Enthalpy and Total Temperature

The steady flow energy equation in the absence of gravity effects is

$$q - w_x = \left(h + \frac{V^2}{2g_c}\right)_{\text{out}} - \left(h + \frac{V^2}{2g_c}\right)_{\text{in}}$$

For a calorically perfect gas this becomes

$$q - w_x = c_p\left(T + \frac{V^2}{2g_c c_p}\right)_{\text{out}} - c_p\left(T + \frac{V^2}{2g_c c_p}\right)_{\text{in}}$$

The quantities $h + V^2/(2g_c)$ and $T + V^2/(2g_c c_p)$ in these equations are called the *stagnation* or *total enthalpy* h_t and the *stagnation* or *total temperature* T_t, respectively. Thus

Total enthalpy
$$\boxed{h_t \equiv h + \frac{V^2}{2g_c}} \tag{3-1}$$

Total temperature
$$\boxed{T_t \equiv T + \frac{V^2}{2g_c c_p}} \tag{3-2}$$

The temperature T is sometimes called the *static temperature* to distinguish it from the total temperature T_t. When $V = 0$, the static and total temperatures are identical. From the definitions above, it follows that, for a calorically perfect gas,

$$\Delta h_t = c_p \, \Delta T_t$$

Using these new definitions, we see that the steady flow energy equation in the absence of gravity effects becomes

$$q - w_x = h_{t\text{out}} - h_{t\text{in}} \tag{3-3}$$

or, for a calorically perfect gas,

$$q - w_x = c_p(T_{t\text{out}} - T_{t\text{in}}) \tag{3-4}$$

If $q - w_x = 0$, we see from (3-3) and (3-4) that $h_{t\text{out}} = h_{t\text{in}}$ and that, for a calorically perfect gas, $T_{t\text{out}} = T_{t\text{in}}$.

Consider an airplane in flight at a velocity V_a. To an observer riding with the airplane, the airflow about the wing of the plane appears as in Fig. 3-1. We mark out a control volume σ as shown in the figure between a station far upstream from the wing and a station just adjacent to the wing's leading edge stagnation point, where the velocity of the airstream is reduced to a negligibly small magnitude. Applying the steady flow energy equation to the flow through σ of Fig. 3-1, we have

$$q - w_x = \left(h + \cancel{\frac{V^2}{2g_c}}^{\,0}\right)_1 - \left(h + \frac{V^2}{2g_c}\right)_2$$

or

$$0 = c_p T_1 - c_p\left(T + \frac{V^2}{2g_c c_p}\right)_2$$

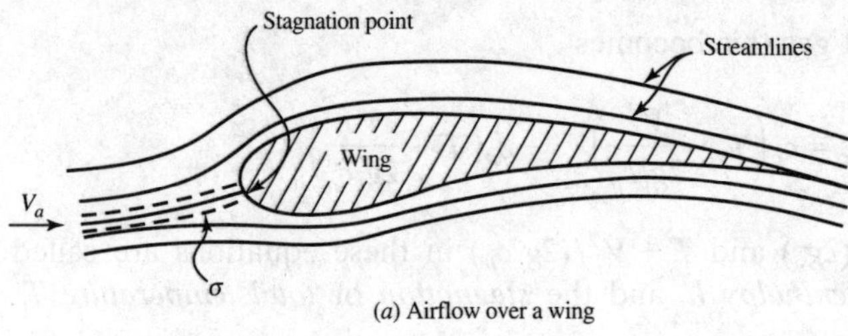

(a) Airflow over a wing

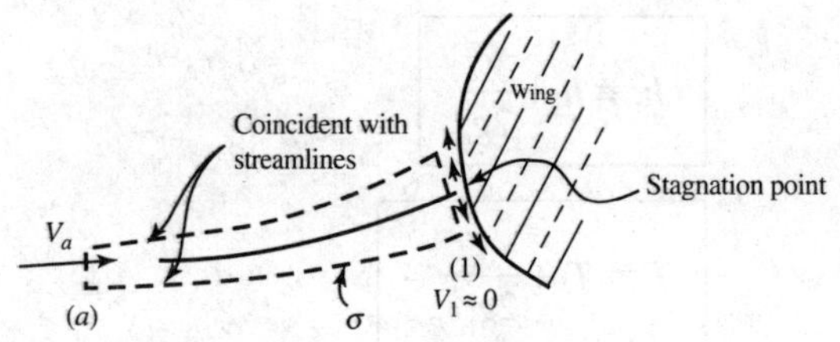

(b) Enlarged view of flow in the neighborhood of the stagnation point

FIGURE 3-1
Control volume *s* with free stream inlet and stagnation exit conditions (reference system at rest relative to wing).

From this equation, we find that the temperature of the air at the stagnation point of the wing is

$$T_1 = T_a + \frac{V_a^2}{2g_c c_p} = T_{ta}$$

Thus we see that the temperature, which the leading edge of the wing "feels," is the total temperature T_{ta}.

At high flight speeds, the free stream total temperature T_{ta} is significantly different from the free stream ambient temperature T_a. This is illustrated in Fig. 3-2 where $T_{ta} - T_a$ is plotted against V_a by using the relation

$$(T_t - T)_a = \frac{V_a^2}{2g_c c_p} = \frac{V_a^2}{12{,}000} \approx \left(\frac{V_a}{110}\right)^2 \ {}^\circ\mathrm{R}$$

with V_a expressed in feet per second.

Since the speed of sound at 25,000 ft is 1000 ft/sec, a Mach number scale for 25,000 ft is easily obtained by dividing the scale for V_a in Fig. 3-2 by 1000. (Mach number M equals V_a divided by the local speed of sound.) Therefore, Mach number scales are also given on the graphs.

Referring to Fig. 3-2, we find that at a fiight speed of 8000 ft/sec corresponding to a Mach number of 0.8 at 25,000-ft altitude, the stagnation

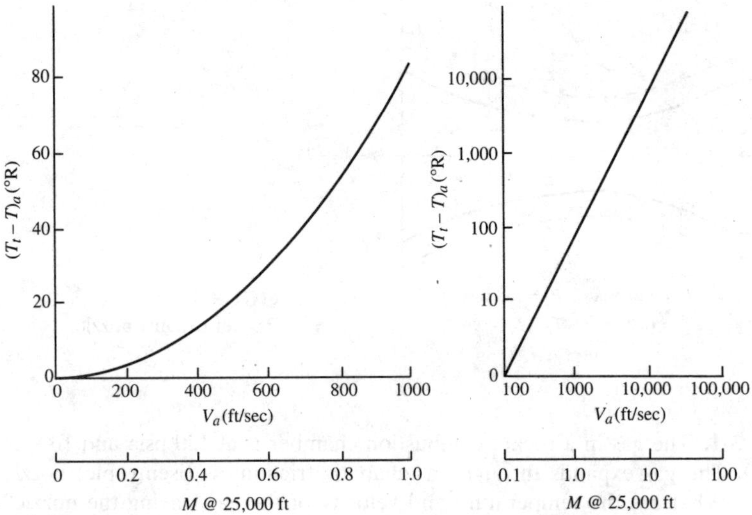

FIGURE 3-2
Total temperature minus ambient temperature versus flight speed and versus flight Mach number at 25,000 ft. [$g_c c_p$ is assumed constant at 6000 ft^2/(sec$^2 \cdot$ °R). Therefore these are approximate curves.]

points on an airplane experience a temperature which is about 50°R higher than ambient temperature. At 3300 ft/sec ($M = 3.3$ at 25,000 ft), the total temperature is 900°R higher than ambient! It should be evident from these numbers that vehicles such as the X-15 airplane and reentry bodies experience high temperatures at their high flight speeds.

These high temperatures are produced as the kinetic energy of the air impinging on the surfaces of a vehicle is reduced and the enthalpy (hence, temperature) of the air is increased a like amount. This follows directly from the steady flow energy equation which gives, with $q = w_x = 0$,

$$\left(h + \frac{V^2}{2g_c}\right)_{\text{in}} = \left(h + \frac{V^2}{2g_c}\right)_{\text{out}}$$

or

$$\Delta h = c_p\,\Delta T = -\Delta\left(\frac{V^2}{2g_c}\right)$$

and

$$\Delta T = -\frac{\Delta V^2}{2g_c c_p}$$

Thus a decrease in the kinetic energy of air produces a rise in the air temperature and a consequent heat interaction between the air and the surfaces of an air vehicle. This heat interaction effect is referred to as *aerodynamic heating.*

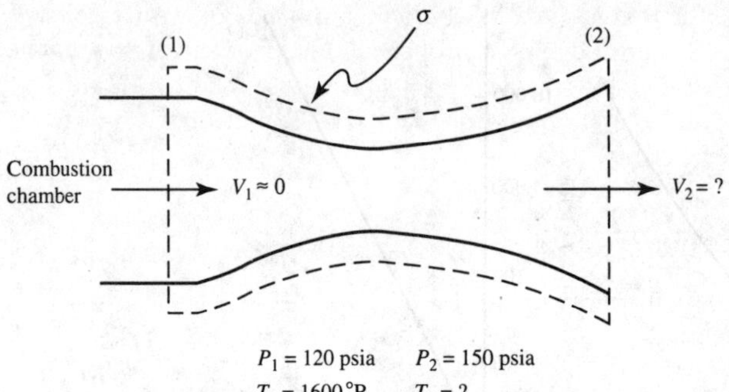

FIGURE 3-3
Rocket exhaust nozzle.

Example 3-1. The gas in a rocket combustion chamber is at 120 psia and 1600°R (Fig. 3-3). The gas expands through an adiabatic frictionless (isentropic) nozzle to 15 psia. What are the temperature and velocity of the gas leaving the nozzle? Treat the gas as the calorically perfect gas air with $\gamma = 1.4$ and $g_c c_p = 6000 \text{ ft}^2/(\text{sec}^2 \cdot °\text{R})$.

Solution. Locate the state of the combustion chamber gas entering control volume σ on a T-s diagram like Fig. 2-19 in the manner depicted in Fig. 3-4. Then, from the diagram, find s_1. Since the process is isentropic, $s_2 = s_1$. The entropy at 2, along with the known value of P_2, fixes the static state of 2. With 2 located in the T-s diagram, we can read T_2 from the temperature scale as 885°R, and we can verify this graphical solution for T_2 by using the isentropic relation (2-51) with $\gamma = 1.4$. Thus $T_2 = (1600°\text{R})(15/120)^{0.286} = 885°\text{R}$ (checks).

If, in addition to P_2 and T_2, the total temperature T_{t2} of the flowing gas at 2

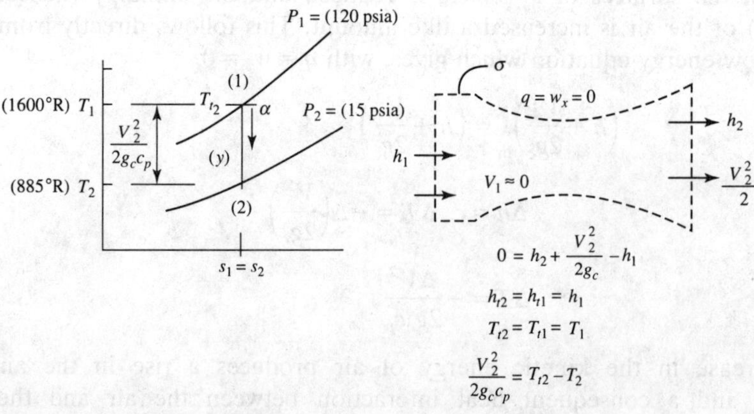

FIGURE 3-4
Process plot for example rocket nozzle.

is known, then the state of the gas at 2 is completely fixed. For with P_2 and T_2 specified, the values of all thermodynamic properties independent of speed (the *static* properties) are fixed, and the speed of the gas is determined by T_2 and T_{t2}.

From the steady flow energy equation (Fig. 3-4), we find that $T_{t2} = T_{t1} = T_1$ and, hence, V_2 from the relation

$$\frac{V_2^2}{2g_c c_p} = T_{t2} - T_2$$

We see from this equation that the vertical distance $T_{t2} - T_2$ in the T-s diagram is indicative of the speed of the gas at 2, which is $V_2^2 = 2(6000)(1600 - 885)\text{ft}^2/\text{sec}^2$. Thus $V_2 = 2930$ ft/sec.

The series of states through which the gas progresses in the nozzle as it flows from the combustion chamber (nozzle inlet) to the nozzle exit is represented by path line α in the T-s diagram. The speed of the gas at any intermediate state y in the nozzle is represented by the vertical distance on the path line from 1 to the state in question. This follows from the relations

$$T_{ty} = T_1 \qquad \text{and} \qquad \frac{V_y^2}{2g_c c_p} = T_{ty} - T_y = T_1 - T_y$$

Stagnation or Total Pressure

In the adiabatic, no-shaft-work slowing of a flowing perfect gas to zero speed, the gas attains the same final stagnation temperature whether it is brought to rest through frictional effects (irreversible) or without them (reversible). This follows from the energy control volume equation applied to σ of Fig. 3-5 for a calorically perfect gas. Thus, from

$$q - w_x = c_p(T_y - T_1) + \frac{V_y^2 - V_1^2}{2g_c}$$

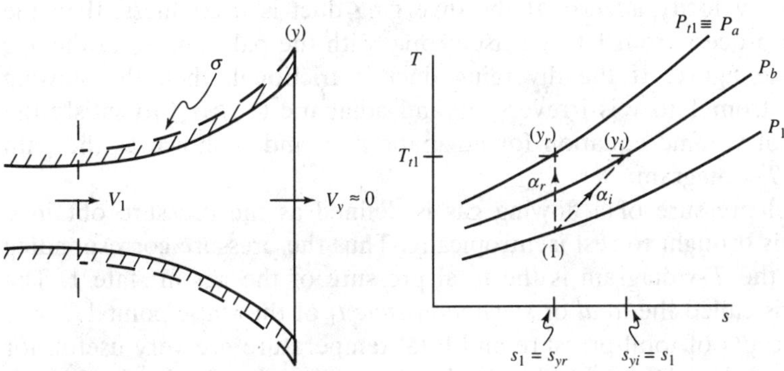

FIGURE 3-5
Definition of total pressure.

with $q = w_x = 0$ and $V_y = 0$, T_y becomes

$$T_y = T_0 = T_1 + \frac{V_1^2}{2g_c c_p} \tag{3-5}$$

Since the energy control volume equation is valid for frictional or frictionless flow, $T_y = T_0$ is constant and independent of the degree of friction between 1 and y as long as $q = w_x = V_y = 0$.

Although the gas attains the same final temperature T_0 in reversible or irreversible processes, its final pressure will vary with the degree of irreversibility associated with the slowing down process. The entropy state and control volume equations for the flow through σ are

$$c_p \ln \frac{T_y}{T_1} - R \ln \frac{P_y}{P_1} = s_y - s_1 \geq 0 \tag{3-6}$$

Since $T_y = T_0 =$ constant from Eq. (3-5), the final value of P_y depends upon the entropy increase $s_y - s_1$, which in turn is a measure of the degree of irreversibility between 1 and y.

When the slowing down process between 1 and y is reversible, with $s_y - s_1 = 0$, the final pressure is defined as the total pressure P_t; the final state is called the *total state* t_1 of the static state 1. Using this definition of total pressure, we have, from Eq. (2-51),

$$\boxed{P_t \equiv P\left(\frac{T_t}{T}\right)^{\gamma/(\gamma-1)}} \tag{3-7}$$

These ideas are illustrated in the T-s diagram of Fig. 3-5. Let us imagine the flowing gas at station 1 to be brought to rest adiabatically with no shaft work by means of a duct diverging to an extremely large area at station y, where the flow velocity is zero. If the diverging duct is frictionless, then the slowing down process from 1 to y is isentropic with the path line α_r in the T-s diagram of the figure. If the diverging duct is frictional, then the slowing down process from 1 to y is irreversible and adiabatic ($s_{yi} > s_1$) to satisfy the entropy control volume equation for adiabatic flow and is shown as the path line α_i in the T-s diagram.

The total pressure of a flowing gas is defined as the pressure obtained when the gas is brought to rest isentropically. Thus the pressure corresponding to state y_r of the T-s diagram is the total pressure of the gas in state 1. The state point y_r is called the *total* or *stagnation state* t_1 of the static point 1.

The concepts of total pressure and total temperature are very useful, for these two properties along with the third property (pressure) of a flowing gas are readily measured, and they fix the state of the flowing gas. We measure these three properties in flight with pitot-static and total temperature probes

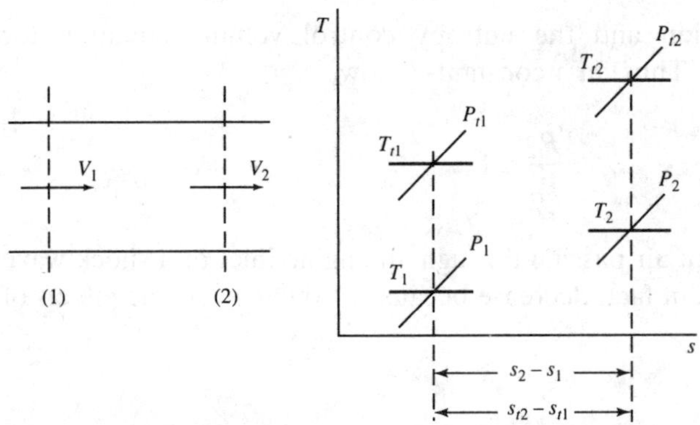

FIGURE 3-6
Entropy change in terms of the stagnation properties T_t and P_t.

on modern high-speed airplanes, and these properties are used to determine speed and Mach number and to provide other data for many aircraft subsystems.

Consider a gas flowing in a duct in which P and T may change due to heat interaction and friction effects. The flow total state points t_1 and t_2 and the static state points 1 and 2, each of which corresponds to flow stations 1 and 2, are located in the T-s diagram of Fig. 3-6. By definition, the entropy of the total state at any given point in a gas flow has the same value as the entropy of the static state properties at that point. Therefore, $s_{t1} = s_1$ and $s_{t2} = s_2$.

From the entropy equation of state of a perfect gas, the entropy change between 1 and 2 is

$$s_2 - s_1 = c_p \ln \frac{T_2}{T_1} - R \ln \frac{P_2}{P_1}$$

The entropy change between total state points t_1 and t_2 is

$$\boxed{s_{t2} - s_{t1} = c_p \ln \frac{T_{t2}}{T_{t1}} - R \ln \frac{P_{t2}}{P_{t1}}} \tag{3-8}$$

Since $s_{t1} = s_1$ and $s_{t2} = s_2$, we have

$$s_{t2} - s_{t1} = s_2 - s_1$$

Therefore, the change of entropy between two states of a flowing gas can be determined by using total properties in place of static properties.

Equation (3-8) indicates that in an adiabatic and no-shaft-work constant-T_t flow (such as exists in an airplane engine inlet or flow through a shock wave), we have

$$s_2 - s_1 = -R \ln \frac{P_{t2}}{P_{t1}}$$

By virtue of this equation and the entropy control volume equation for adiabatic flow, $s_2 - s_1 \geq 0$. Thus, in a constant-T_t flow,

$$\frac{P_{t2}}{P_{t1}} \leq 1$$

Hence the total pressure of air passing through an engine inlet or a shock wave cannot increase and must, in fact, decrease because of the irreversible effects of friction.

T/T_t and P/P_t as Functions of Mach Number

The speed of sound a in a perfect gas is given by

$$a = \sqrt{\gamma g_c R T}$$

Using this relation for the speed of sound, we can write the Mach number in the following form:

$$M^2 = \frac{V^2}{\gamma g_c R T}$$

With the help of this expression for the Mach number, we can obtain many useful relations that give gas flow property ratios in terms of the flow Mach number alone. Two such relations for T/T_t and P/P_t are

$$\boxed{\frac{T}{T_t} = \left(1 + \frac{\gamma - 1}{2} M^2\right)^{-1}} \tag{3-9}$$

$$\boxed{\frac{P}{P_t} = \left(1 + \frac{\gamma - 1}{2} M^2\right)^{-\gamma/(\gamma-1)}} \tag{3-10}$$

Equations (3-9) and (3-10) appear graphically in Fig. 3-7 and are tabulated in App. E for γ values of 1.4 and 1.3. These equations show that for each free stream Mach number (hence, for each flight Mach number of an airplane), the ratios P/P_t and T/T_t have unique values.

Both Fig. 3-7 and the corresponding equations provide Mach numbers and ambient temperatures for known values of P, P_t, and T_t. For example, we are given the following in-flight measurements:

$$P = 35.4 \text{ kPa} \qquad T_t = 300 \text{ K} \qquad \text{and} \qquad P_t = 60.0 \text{ kPa}$$

From these data, $P/P_t = 0.59$. If we enter Fig. 3-7 with this value of P/P_t, we

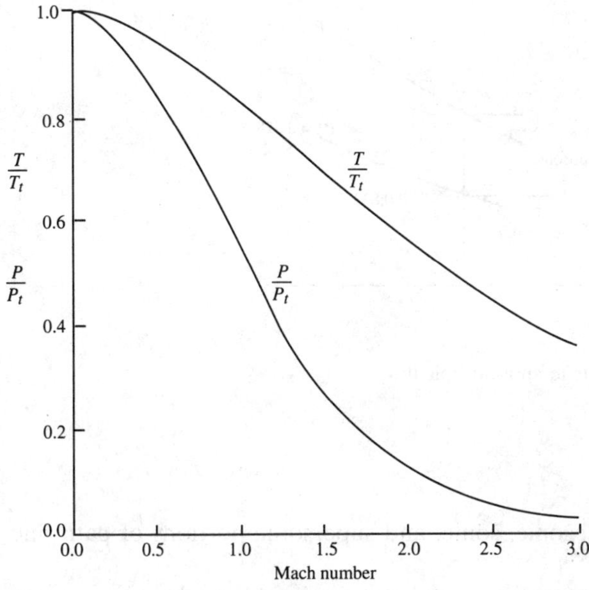

FIGURE 3-7
T/T_t and P/P_t versus Mach number ($\gamma = 1.4$).

find $M = 0.9$ and $T/T_t = 0.86$. Then we obtain the ambient temperature by using $T = (T/T_t)T_t = 0.86(300) = 258°\text{R}$.

Figure 3-7 shows that in a sonic ($M = 1.0$) stream of gas with $\gamma = 1.4$,

$$\frac{P}{P_t} = 0.528 \qquad \text{and} \qquad \frac{T}{T_t} = 0.833$$

and for supersonic flow,

$$\frac{P}{P_t} < 0.528 \qquad \text{and} \qquad \frac{T}{T_t} < 0.833$$

Consider the one-dimensional steady flow of a gas in a duct with T_t and P_t constant at all stations along the duct. This means a total temperature probe will measure the same value of T_t at each duct station, and an isentropic total pressure probe will measure the same value of P_t at each station. The path line of α of the flow is a vertical line in the T-s diagram. The state points on the path line can be categorized as follows:

Subsonic	$T > 0.883T_t$	$P > 0.528P_t$
Sonic	$T = 0.833T_t$	$P = 0.528P_t$
Supersonic	$T < 0.833T_t$	$P < 0.528P_t$

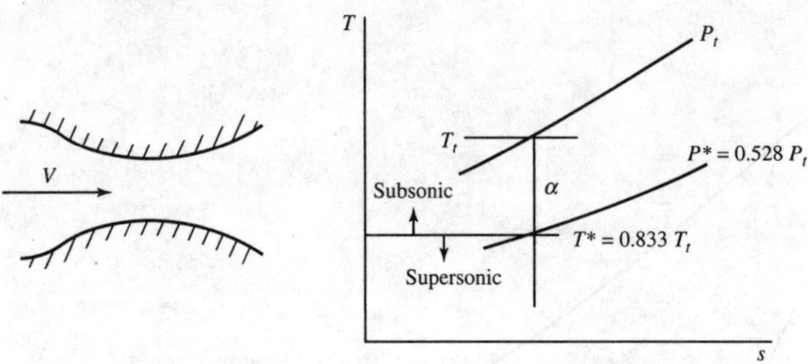

FIGURE 3-8
Subsonic and supersonic state points in an isentropic flow.

Figure 3-8 delineates the subsonic, sonic, and supersonic portions of path line α.

The thermodynamic properties at the state point where $M = 1$ on α are denoted by P^*, T^*, V^*, etc. (read as P star, etc.). In addition, the cross-sectional flow area at the $M = 1$ point is indicated by A^*. The magnitude of A^* is determined by the relation

$$\boxed{A^* = \frac{\dot{m}}{\rho^* V^*}} \tag{3-11}$$

Mass Flow Parameter (MFP)

The stream properties at any general station of a calorically perfect gas are related by Eqs. (2-30), (2-44), (3-2), (3-7), (3-9), (3-10), and the one-dimensional mass flow equation

$$\dot{m} = \rho A V$$

For convenience, we define the following grouping of terms which are a function only of M, R, and γ:

$$\boxed{\text{MFP} \equiv \frac{\dot{m}\sqrt{T_t}}{P_t A}} \tag{3-12}$$

noting that

$$\frac{\dot{m}}{A} = \rho V = \frac{PV}{RT} = \frac{V}{\sqrt{\gamma g_c RT}}\,\frac{P\sqrt{\gamma g_c}}{\sqrt{RT}} = M\sqrt{\frac{\gamma g_c}{R}}\,\frac{P}{\sqrt{T}}$$

we then see that multiplying through by $\sqrt{T_t}/P_t$ gives

$$\frac{\dot{m}\sqrt{T_t}}{P_t A} = M \sqrt{\frac{\gamma g_c}{R} \frac{P/P_t}{\sqrt{T/T_t}}}$$

Replacing the static/total property ratios with Eqs. (3-9) and (3-10) gives

$$\frac{\dot{m}\sqrt{T_t}}{P_t A} = M \sqrt{\frac{\gamma g_c}{R}} \left(1 + \frac{\gamma - 1}{2} M^2\right)^{-\gamma/(\gamma-1)+1/2}$$

or finally

$$\boxed{\text{MFP}(M) = \frac{\dot{m}\sqrt{T_t}}{P_t A} = \frac{M\sqrt{\gamma g_c/R}}{\{1 + [(\gamma - 1)/2]M^2\}^{(\gamma+1)/[2(\gamma-1)]}}} \tag{3-13}$$

Thus from a combination of other thermodynamic properties, we have defined the new property—the *mass flow parameter* (MFP)—that is a unique function of the Mach number in a calorically perfect gas. Values of the mass flow parameter are plotted in Fig. 3-9 for $\gamma = 1.4$ and $\gamma = 1.3$, and App. E tabulates MFP versus Mach number for γ values of 1.4, 1.33, and 1.3. From Fig. 3-9 and App. E, one sees that the maximum value of the mass flow parameter occurs when the Mach number is unity. Thus, for a given total temperature and pressure T_t and P_t, the maximum mass flow rate per area corresponds to a flow Mach number of 1.

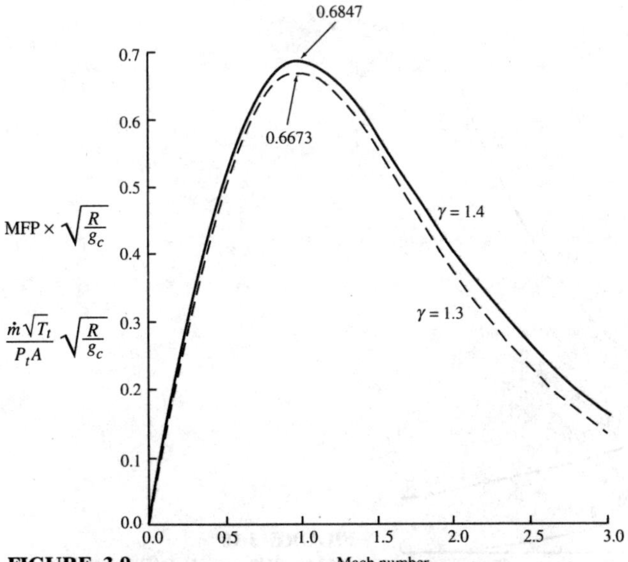

FIGURE 3-9
Mass flow parameter versus Mach number ($\gamma = 1.4$ and $\gamma = 1.3$).

Isentropic Area Ratio A/A^*

The ratio of the one-dimensional flow area A at any flow station to the one-dimensional area for that same flow rate at sonic velocity A^* is a unique function of the Mach number M at the flow station and the ratio of specific heats γ. Consider the isentropic flow of a calorically perfect gas in an isentropic duct from ρ, M, P, T, and A to the sonic state where the properties are ρ^*, $M^*=1$, P^*, T^*, and A^*. Since both states have the same mass flow, we write

$$\dot{m} = \rho A V = \rho^* A^* V^*$$

Rewriting gives

$$\frac{A}{A^*} = \frac{\rho^* V^*}{\rho V} = \frac{P^*}{T^*}\frac{T}{P}\frac{1}{M}\frac{a^*}{a} = \frac{1}{M}\frac{P^*/P}{T^*/T}\sqrt{T^*/T} = \frac{1}{M}\frac{P^*/P}{\sqrt{T^*/T}} \tag{i}$$

However,

$$\frac{T}{T^*} = \frac{T/T_t}{T^*/T_t} = \left[\frac{2}{\gamma+1}\left(1+\frac{\gamma-1}{2}M^2\right)\right]^{-1} \tag{ii}$$

and
$$\frac{P}{P^*} = \frac{P/P_t}{P^*/P_t} = \left[\frac{2}{\gamma+1}\left(1+\frac{\gamma-1}{2}M^2\right)\right]^{-\gamma/(\gamma-1)} \tag{iii}$$

Substitution of Eqs. (ii) and (iii) gives

$$\boxed{\frac{A}{A^*} = \frac{1}{M}\left[\frac{2}{\gamma+1}\left(1+\frac{\gamma-1}{2}M^2\right)\right]^{(\gamma+1)/[2(\gamma-1)]}} \tag{3-14}$$

and A/A^*, P/P_t, and T/T_t are plotted versus Mach number in Fig. 3-10 for $\gamma = 1.4$ and tabulated in App. E for γ values of 1.4, 1.33, and 1.3.

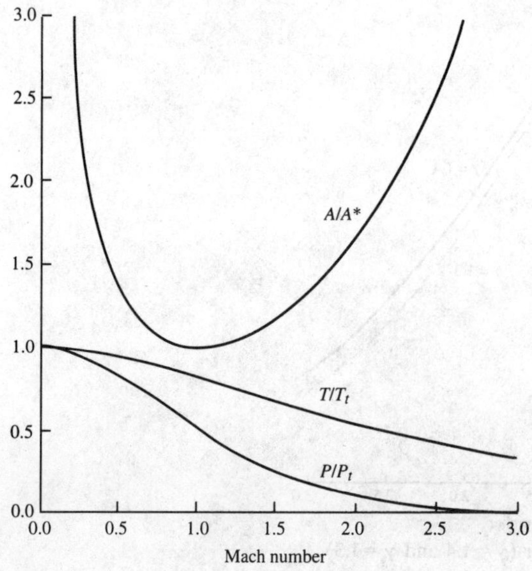

FIGURE 3-10
A/A^*, T/T_t, and P/P_t versus Mach number ($\gamma = 1.4$).

Example 3-2. Air at a total temperature of 300 K and total pressure of 1 atm flows through a 2-m^2 duct at a Mach number of 0.5.

a. What must the area of the duct be for the flow to isentropically accelerate to Mach 1?

b. What is the mass flow rate of air through the duct?

Solution. From App. E for $M = 0.5$ and $\gamma = 1.4$, $A/A^* = 1.33984$ and $\text{MFP}\sqrt{R/g_c} = 0.511053$.

a. The area of the duct at $M = 1$ is then

$$A^* = \frac{A}{A/A^*} = \frac{2\ \text{m}^2}{1.33984} = 1.4927\ \text{m}^2$$

b. The mass flow rate can be calculated by using the MFP as follows:

$$\dot{m} = \frac{P_t A}{\sqrt{T_t}} \frac{\text{MFP}\sqrt{R/g_c}}{\sqrt{R/g_c}} = \frac{101{,}325 \times 2\ \text{N}}{\sqrt{300\ \text{K}}} \frac{0.511053}{16.9115} \text{kg} \cdot \sqrt{\text{K}}/(\text{N} \cdot \text{sec}) = 353.57\ \text{kg/sec}$$

Velocity-Area Variation

The variation of density in a compressible flow field introduces a variable which is not present in an incompressible flow. This added variable produces some marked differences between compressible and incompressible flow characteristics. An often-quoted example is the variation of stream area with stream velocity. Consider a steady one-dimension incompressible flow with uniform stream properties at each cross section of the flow. For this flow, the equation of continuity reduces to

$$AV = \text{const}$$

It is clear from this that as the cross-sectional area of the flow increases, the velocity decreases and vice versa (Fig. 3-11). This can be observed in a flowing stream of water—where the stream runs deep, the current is slow and, in the

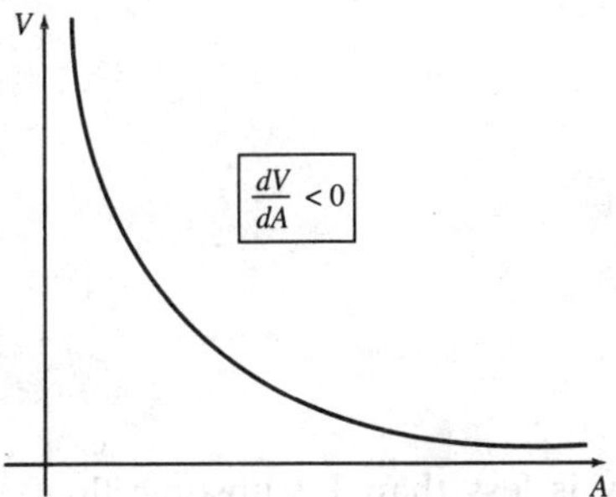

FIGURE 3-11
Velocity area variation for incompressible flow.

shallow depths of the stream, the current runs faster. A mathematical statement of this simple physical fact is obtained by differentiating the above relation and solving for the rate of change of velocity with area

$$\frac{dV}{dA} = -\frac{V}{A}$$

Thus the change of velocity with area is always negative, and for decreasing areas, we obtain increasing velocities, which is in accordance with experience. These facts are shown graphically in Fig. 3-11.

For compressible flow, the equation of continuity for one-dimensional steady flow with uniform properties at each section of the flow is

$$\rho AV = \text{const}$$

As a result of the added variable ρ in this equation, it is not immediately clear how the velocity of the flow will vary with the flow area. To obtain further insights into this question, we can form the derivative of velocity of continuity, and solving for the desired result gives

$$\frac{dV}{dA} = -\frac{V}{A}\left(1 + \frac{A}{\rho}\frac{d\rho}{dA}\right)$$

which is the incompressible velocity-area derivative expression with an added term that takes into account the variable density factor. From this, we see that the change of the velocity with area may be negative or positive in compressible flows, depending upon the sign and magnitude of the density variation with area. To get an explicit answer for the sign of the velocity-area derivative, we must know the density-area derivative. The development of this derivative is given later in Section 3.5. For the purpose of this discussion, let us simply state the results. It is found that for frictionless adiabatic flow of a perfect gas, dP/dA depends upon the local Mach number M of the flow (ratio of the stream and sound velocities) in the following manner:

$$\frac{d\rho}{dA} = \frac{\rho}{A}\frac{M^2}{1 - M^2}$$

Using this in the expression for dV/dA, we get

$$\frac{dV}{dA} = -\frac{V}{A}\frac{1}{1 - M^2}$$

Thus when the Mach number of the flow is less than 1 (subsonic flow),

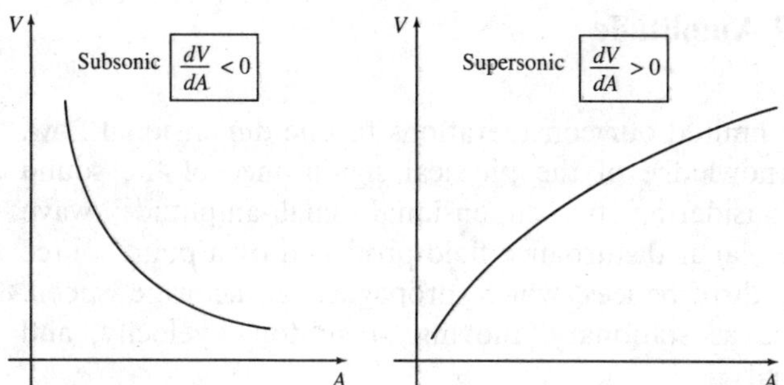

FIGURE 3-12
Velocity-area variation for compressible flow.

dV/dA is negative and the variation of velocity with flow area is similar to that experienced with incompressible flow. However, when the Mach number is greater than 1 (supersonic flow), dV/dA is positive since the variation of density with area is such that to increase the velocity requires an increase in area to pass the same mass at the lower densities associated with the higher velocities (Fig. 3-12).

Another way of saying the same thing is to consider flow sections 1 and 2 having two different velocities, areas, and densities. For these two sections, we have

$$\rho_1 A_1 V_1 = \rho_2 A_2 V_2$$

In terms of this equation, we have just found that in supersonic flow, if $V_2 > V_1$, then the density at 2 is sufficiently less than the density at 1, $\rho_2 \ll \rho_1$, that in order to maintain the equality required by mass conservation, the area at 2 must be larger than that at 1, or $A_2 > A_1$. This explains the reason for the converging-diverging shape of rocket nozzles. The gases leaving the combustion chamber are accelerated in the converging portion of the nozzle until the gases attain a sonic speed at the throat. Beyond the nozzle throat, the flow is supersonic, and the nozzle area must be increased to attain higher velocities at the much lower densities encountered in this phase of the expansion process.

From the above discussion, it is clear that the speed of sound and the variation of fluid density are important parameters in compressible flows. Now, the change in density of a flowing gas is usually the result of pressure variations in the gas, and it should be expected, therefore, that the rate of change of density with pressure is also important in compressible flow studies. We will find that the density variation with pressure and the speed of sound are intimately connected. The reciprocal of $dP/d\rho$, in fact, is equal to the square of the speed of sound. It is because of the importance of the speed of sound in compressible fluid flows that we next consider the propagation of sound waves in a medium.

Two-Dimensional Small-Amplitude Wave Propagation

Up to this point, we have limited our considerations to one-dimensional flow. We may obtain further knowledge of the physical significance of the sound velocity, however, by considering two-dimensional small-amplitude wave propagation. Consider the planar disturbance field produced by a point source as it sends out periodic disturbances which propagate at acoustic speed. Consider the point source as stationary, moving at subsonic velocity, and moving at supersonic velocity.

The pulses emanating periodically from the source will propagate spherically outward at the speed of sound. After any given time interval, the pulse loci form the planar patterns shown in Fig. 3-13. The number of each

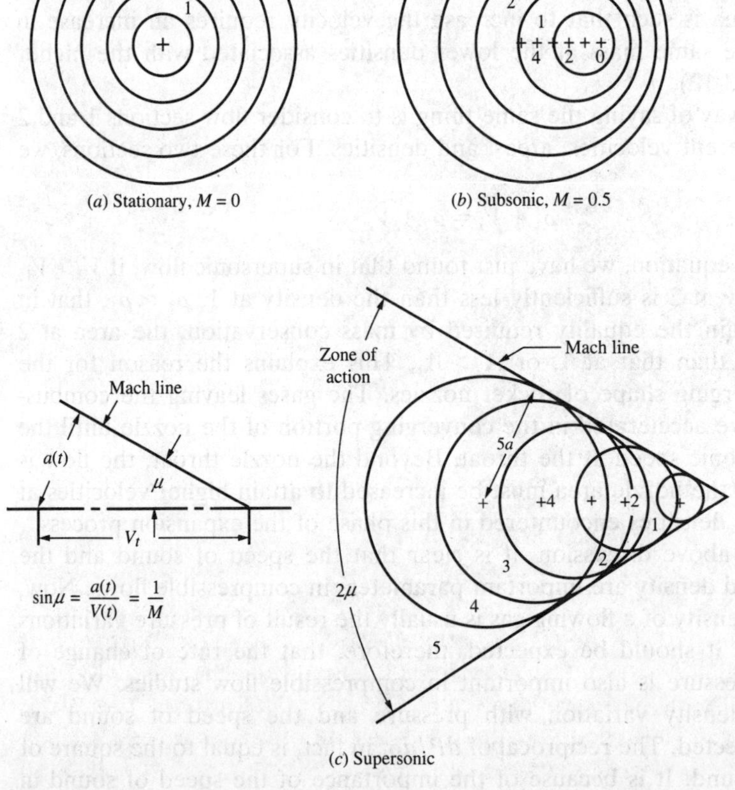

FIGURE 3-13
Point source moving in a gas.

pulse indicates its age. Pulse 4 is 4 sec old, having begun 4 sec prior to the time of the picture when the point source was at the center of the circle formed by the pulse.

These patterns are easily observed in the form of gravity waves on the surface of a body of water which are distributed periodically by drops of water from the tip of a paddle freshly withdrawn from the water. By moving the paddle at the proper speed relative to the water, any of the patterns shown can be reproduced by the surface wavelets formed as water droplets from the paddle strike the water's surface.

For Fig. 3-13(a), the point source is stationary, and concentric circles are formed by the pulse loci. When, as in Fig. 3-13(b), the source moves at a speed less than that of the pulse propagation speed, the pulse loci, which form circles about their point of origin, are no longer concentric since the source emanated each pulse from a different location. When the point source speed exceeds the pulse propagation speed, in Fig. 3-13(c), circular pulse lines are formed, and these pulse circles are tangent to a line at angle μ with the direction of the source speed such that

$$\sin \mu = \frac{a(t)}{V(t)} = \frac{1}{M}$$

This tangent line is called a *Mach line,* and the angle μ is called the *Mach angle.*

The wave pulse patterns of Fig. 3-13 indicate that for other than supersonic speeds, the disturbance field produced by the point source extends to infinite distances about the source as time progresses (in the absence of viscous effects). At supersonic speeds, however, note that the fluid field is completely undisturbed forward of the Mach cone; the fluid is disturbed only within the cone.

The pattern of Fig. 3-13(c) illustrates the three rules of supersonic flow given by von Karman in 1947 in the tenth Wright brothers lecture (Ref. 17). These rules are based on the assumption of small disturbances and are applicable at a given instant of time. They are qualitatively applicable, however, to large disturbances. The rules are:

1. *The rule of forbidden signals.* The effect of pressure changes produced by a point source moving at a speed faster than sound cannot reach points ahead of the point source.
2. *The zone of action and the zone of silence.* All effects produced by a point source moving at a supersonic speed are contained within the zone of action bounded by the Mach cone and extending downstream from the body. The region outside of the cone of action at any instant of time is called the *zone of silence.*
3. *The rule of concentrated action.* The effects produced by the motion of a point source at supersonic speeds are concentrated along the Mach lines.

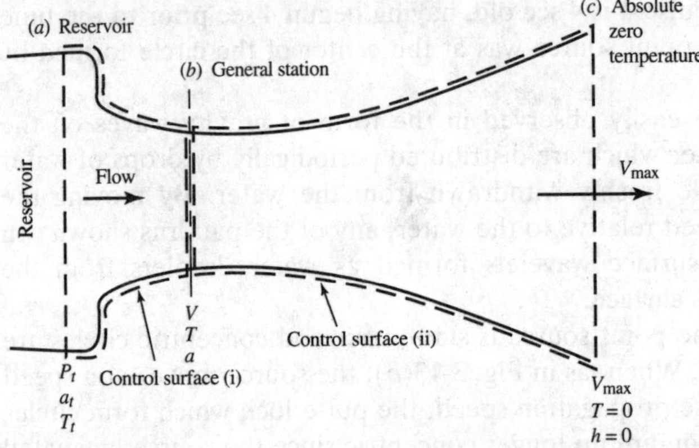

FIGURE 3-14
Gas flow to zero absolute temperature.

Extrapolating this rule to large disturbances, we can observe its qualitative application in the concentration of effects along a shock wave accompanying a body at supersonic speeds.

Summary: Realms of Compressible Flow

Let us consider the steady flow of a perfect gas in the absence of heat flow and shaft work. Between any "in" and "out" sections of a control surface in such a flow, the steady flow energy equation is

$$\left(h + \frac{V^2}{2g_c}\right)_{\text{in}} = \left(h + \frac{V^2}{2g_c}\right)_{\text{out}}$$

To fix ideas more explicitly, we can imagine the flow to originate in a large reservoir supplied by a gas pump. The velocity of the gas in the large reservoir is negligible so that stagnation conditions exist in the tank. From this reservoir, the gas expands through a channel of varying area to lower pressures and temperatures. Figure 3-14 depicts the reservoir and channel. Three channel sections of interest and shown in the flow are as follows:

- The reservoir station [Fig. 3-14(a)], designated as station t since stagnation conditions exist.
- Any general station [Fig. 3-14(b)]. The stream properties are written with no subscript.
- Absolute zero temperature station [Fig. 3-14(c)]. At this section in the flow, it is imagined that the gas has expanded to an absolute zero temperature, attaining the maximum velocity possible.

For control surfaces i and ii, the steady flow energy equation becomes

$$h_t = h + \frac{V^2}{2g_c} \tag{i}$$

$$h + \frac{V^2}{2g_c} = \frac{V_{max}^2}{2g_c} \tag{ii}$$

or, by combining Eqs. (i) and (ii),

$$h_t = h + \frac{V^2}{2g_c} = \frac{V_{max}^2}{2g_c} = \text{const}$$

where the constant, or the total enthalpy, of any given flow is dependent upon the given reservoir conditions. For unchanging conditions, then, the total enthalpy is constant throughout the flow. The last equation above is simply a mathematical statement of the following facts. In the reservoir, there is no kinetic energy contribution to the total enthalpy, and the static and total enthalpies are identical. At any general station in the flow, there are kinetic energy and static enthalpy contributions to the total enthalpy. At the zero absolute temperature station, the stream velocity has attained its maximum value, and the total enthalpy is made up of kinetic energy only with the static enthalpy zero.

The flow process of Fig. 3-14 is shown on the enthalpy-entropy diagrams of Fig. 3-15. The kinetic energy of the flow, being equal to an enthalpy change, can also be shown on the diagrams as indicated. Each part of the figure is identical except for the *label* of the enthalpy axis. Since we are considering flow of a calorically perfect gas, the enthalpy, measured relative to a zero datum at zero absolute temperature, can be expressed as

$$h - h_{datum} = c_p(T - T_{datum})$$

$$h = c_pT \qquad \text{since } h_{datum} = 0 \text{ and } T_{datum} = 0$$

This result is used in Fig. 3-15(b), where the enthalpy axis is labeled c_pT.

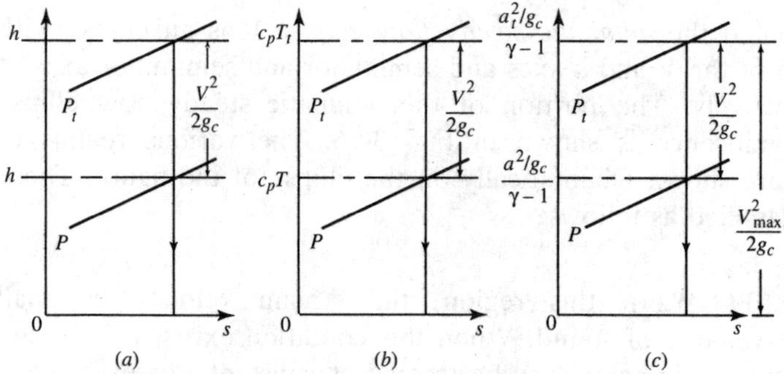

FIGURE 3-15
The h-s diagram for flow of Fig. 3-14.

By making use of the fact that the speed of sound is dependent only upon temperature for a perfect gas, the enthalpy can be written in terms of the speed of sound a. We have

$$a^2 = \gamma g_c RT \qquad \text{or} \qquad T = \frac{a^2}{\gamma g_c R}$$

whence

$$h = c_p \frac{a^2}{\gamma g_c R}$$

or, with

$$\frac{c_p}{R} = \frac{\gamma}{\gamma - 1}$$

$$h = \frac{a^2/g_c}{\gamma - 1} = c_p T$$

Thus we can label the enthalpy axis $[(a^2/g_c)/(\gamma - 1)]$ as in Fig. 3-15(*c*). Of course, a_t is the velocity of sound at the stagnation (reservoir) conditions of the stream.

By compressing the enthalpy in terms of the speed of sound, the realms of compressible flow can be conveniently summarized on the so-called adiabatic steady flow ellipse. From the steady flow energy equation for adiabatic, no-shaft-work flow, we have $h_t = h + V^2/(2g_c) = V^2_{max}/(2g_c)$ or, for a perfect gas,

$$\frac{a_t^2}{\gamma - 1} = \frac{a^2}{\gamma - 1} + \frac{V^2}{2} = \frac{V^2_{max}}{2}$$

Dividing the enthalpy term $a^2/(\gamma - 1)$ of this equation by the stagnation enthalpy $a_t^2/(\gamma - 1)$ and the kinetic energy term by $V^2_{max}/2$ [this is permissible since $a_t^2/(\gamma - 1) = V^2_{max}/2$], we get

$$\frac{a^2}{a_t^2} + \frac{V^2}{V^2_{max}} = 1 \tag{3-15}$$

This equation is called the *adiabatic steady flow ellipse.* It is an ellipse with center at the origin of the V and a axes and semimajor and semiminor axes of V_{max} and a_t, respectively. The portion of the adiabatic steady flow ellipse having physical significance is shown in Fig. 3-16. The various realms of compressible flow are shown schematically on the ellipse of the figure. These flow regimes are classified as follows.

INCOMPRESSIBLE FLOW. In this region, the stream velocity is small compared with the velocity of sound. When this condition exists, the density of even highly compressible gases may be treated as constant. An example is airflow over wings of low-speed (120-kn) airplanes. A further example is found in the flow of natural gas in transcontinental pipelines. To avoid

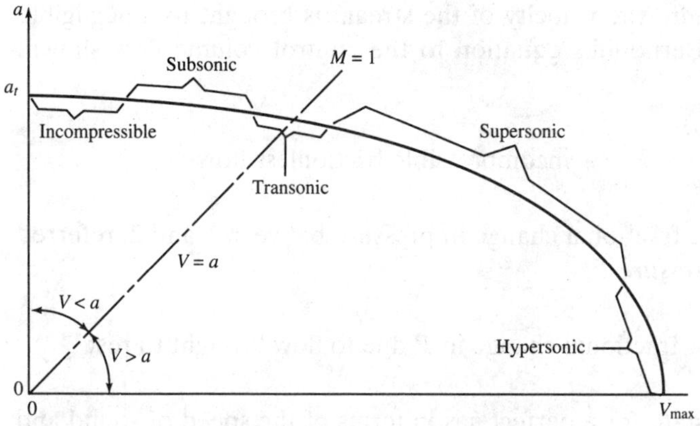

FIGURE 3-16
Realms of compressible flow. (*After Shapiro, Ref. 84.*)

excessive pressure losses in these exceptionally long pipelines, the gas velocities employed are extremely small compared to the velocity of sound.

SUBSONIC COMPRESSIBLE FLOW. We may think of this realm of flow as being bounded roughly by Mach numbers 0.2 and 0.8. In the lower range of subsonic compressible flow, good engineering results may be obtained by neglecting compressibility in pressure variation computations. This is possible since, *at the lower subsonic velocities, the pressure variations are sufficiently small to permit the assumption of no change in density.* The incompressible Bernoulli equation may be used to demonstrate this point in frictionless flow. Consider a ballistic missile in unaccelerated flight moving at a velocity V_1 through air at rest. To an observer at rest relative to the missile (we take this point of view to reduce the analysis to one of steady flow), the flow situation appears as in Fig. 3-17. Mark out a control volume in the flow, as shown between a point far upstream from the missile and a point just adjacent to the

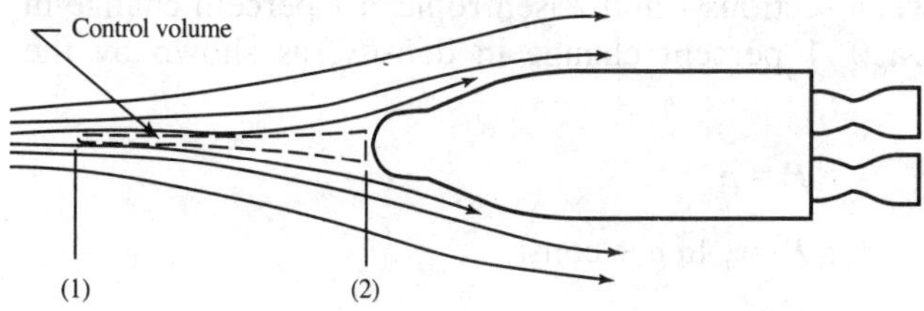

FIGURE 3-17
Flow approaching missile.

nose of the missile, where the velocity of the stream is brought to a negligible magnitude. Applying Bernoulli's equation to the control volume flow shown, we have

$$P_1 + \frac{\rho_1 V_1^2}{2g_c} = P_2 \qquad \text{incompressible frictionless flow}$$

Now, consider the fractional change in pressure between 1 and 2, referred to as the *free stream pressure P*;

$$\frac{P_2 - P_1}{P_1} = \frac{\rho_1 V_1^2}{2g_c P_1} \qquad \text{fractional change in } P \text{ due to flow brought to rest}$$

From the equation of state for a perfect gas in terms of the speed of sound and the definition of Mach number, we have

$$P = \rho RT = \frac{\rho(\gamma g_c RT)}{\gamma g_c} = \frac{\rho a^2}{\gamma g_c}$$

Then

$$\frac{\rho_1}{P_1} = \frac{\gamma g_c}{a_1^2}$$

so

$$\frac{\rho_1 V_1^2}{2g_c P_1} = \frac{\gamma g_c}{a_1^2}\frac{V_1^2}{2g_c} = \frac{\gamma M_1^2}{2}$$

and

$$\frac{P_2 - P_1}{P_1} = \frac{\Delta P}{P_1} = \frac{\gamma M_1^2}{2} \tag{3-16}$$

This gives the fractional change in pressure between stations 1 and 2 in terms of the free stream Mach number. With this relation, we can verify the italicized statement above that *at the lower subsonic velocities, the pressure variations are sufficiently small.* We find the percentage change in pressure at Mach numbers 0.2 and 0.4 to be 2.8 and 11.2 percent, respectively, for $\gamma = 1.4$.

It appears, therefore, that at a flight speed of about 0.4 Mach, the order of magnitude of the pressure change is becoming rather significant. However, our main concern here is how this pressure change affects the density which was assumed constant (since Bernoulli's equation for incompressible flow was used). With the flow between sections 1 and 2 isentropic, a 1 percent change in pressure corresponds to a 0.71 percent change in density, as shown by the following:

$$P = \rho^\gamma$$

whence

$$\ln P = \gamma \ln \rho + \text{const}$$

and, differentiating in terms of finite differences, we have

$$\frac{\Delta P}{P} = \gamma \frac{\Delta \rho}{\rho}$$

or $$\frac{\Delta\rho}{\rho}=\frac{1}{\gamma}\frac{\Delta P}{P}=0.71\frac{\Delta P}{P} \qquad (\gamma=1.4)$$

and $$\frac{\Delta\rho}{\rho_1}=\frac{M_1^2}{2} \quad \text{fractional change in density due to flow brought to rest} \tag{3-17}$$

This permits a check on the last part of the italicized words above which state *to permit the assumption of no change in density.* The percentage change in density between sections 1 and 2 of the flow of Fig. 3-17 at Mach 0.2 and 0.4 is 2 and 8 percent, respectively. Hence at Mach numbers less than about 0.4, it is permissible, within an engineering accuracy range of 8 percent, to neglect the compressibility of air in pressure computations.

In the upper Mach number range of the subsonic compressible flow regime, compressibility effects become more and more important. Density variations must, therefore, be taken into account in computational work in this range.

TRANSONIC FLOW. The word *transonic* was coined by von Karman and Dryden to identify the flow regime about a Mach number of 1 (from, say, 0.8 to 1.3) where the flow over a body is partly subsonic and partly supersonic. The analytical solution of transonic flow is extremely difficult due to the striking difference in the nature of the differential equations that describe subsonic flow and supersonic flow.

> Dryden and I invented the word *transonic*. . . We could not agree whether it should be written with one "s" or two. Dryden was logical and wanted two "s"'s, I thought it wasn't necessary . . . so wrote it with one "s." I introduced the term in this form in a report to the Air Force. I am not sure whether the general who read it knew what it meant, but his answer contained the word, so it seemed to be officially accepted. (Ref. 18).

SUPERSONIC FLOW. It is clear from Fig. 3-16 that changes in the stream velocity and the speed of sound are of comparable magnitude in this realm of flow. Correspondingly, the Mach number of the flow may change materially through changes in either the speed of sound or the stream velocity. Calculation of supersonic flows is much simpler than the corresponding problem for subsonic flow due to the availabilty of linearized approximations that give adequate accuracy in supersonic flow.

HYPERSONIC FLOW. In this regime of flow, the Mach number is very high, and the stream velocity is very small relative to the speed of sound variation. This realm of flow is encountered in the flight of missiles at very high speeds. Hypersonic flow about missiles or nose cones at very high altitudes, where the air density is relatively low, must be analyzed by the use of the kinetic theory of gases rather than continuum mechanics.

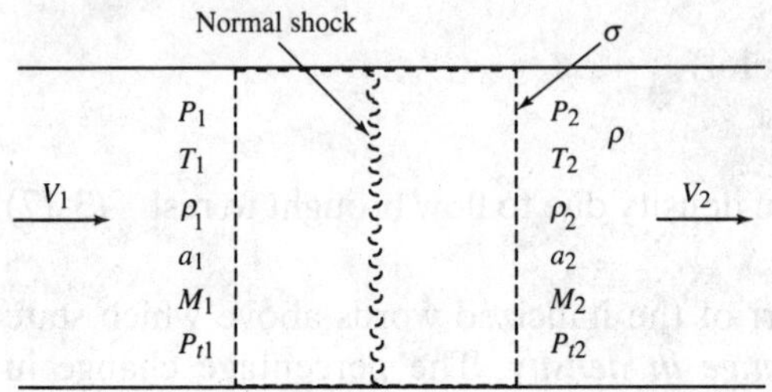

FIGURE 3-18
Normal shock wave in σ with steady flow through σ.

3-3 NORMAL SHOCK WAVE

Let us investigate this problem: For given inlet conditions to the control volume enclosing the normal shock wave of Fig. 3-18, we are interested in determining the exit conditions, and this requires simultaneous solution of seven equations, one for each exit stream property of the figure. These equations are obtained by application of the mass, momentum, energy, and entropy control volume equations; the state equations for a perfect gas; the speed of sound equation for a perfect gas; and the definition of Mach number:

1. Mass control volume equation
2. Momentum control volume equation normal to wave
3. Energy control volume equation
4. Thermal state equation
5. Entropy control volume equation
6. Speed of sound in perfect gas
7. Definition of Mach number

The seven equations derived from these are as follows:

Mass $$\rho_1 V_1 = \rho_2 V_2 \tag{3-18}$$

Momentum $$\frac{P_1 + \rho_1 V_1^2}{g_c} = \frac{P_2 + \rho_2 V_2^2}{g_c} \tag{3-19}$$

Energy $$\frac{c_p T_1 + V_1^2}{2g_c} = \frac{c_p T_2 + V_2^2}{2g_c} \tag{3-20}$$

State $$\frac{P_1}{\rho_1 T_1} = \frac{P_2}{\rho_2 T_2} \tag{3-21}$$

Entropy $$P_{t1}\left(\frac{P_1}{\rho_1^\gamma}\right)^{1/(\gamma-1)} = P_{t2}\left(\frac{P_2}{\rho_2^\gamma}\right)^{1/(\gamma-1)} \quad \text{[from Eq. (2-40)]} \tag{3-22}$$

$$P_{t1} \geq P_{t2}$$

Sound $$\frac{a_1^2}{T_1} = \frac{a_2^2}{T_2} \tag{3-23}$$

Mach $$\frac{M_1^2 T_1}{V_1^2} = \frac{M_2^2 T_2}{V_2^2} \tag{3-24}$$

Some algebra is required to solve Eqs. (3-18) through (3-24) and obtain the five functions listed below. These five functions and the equations $a_2^2 = \gamma R g_c T_2$ and $V_2 = a_2 M_2$ determine the seven exit properties listed in Fig. 3-18 and tabulated in App. F for $\gamma = 1.4$.

$$\frac{P_2}{P_1} = f_1(M_1) = \frac{2\gamma}{\gamma+1} M_1^2 - \frac{\gamma-1}{\gamma+1} \tag{3-25}$$

$$\frac{\rho_2}{\rho_1} = f_2(M_1) = \frac{M_1^2}{\dfrac{\gamma-1}{\gamma+1} M_1^2 + \dfrac{2}{\gamma+1}} \tag{3-26}$$

$$\frac{T_2}{T_1} = f_3(M_1) = \frac{\left(\dfrac{2\gamma}{\gamma-1} M_1^2 - 1\right)\left(1 + \dfrac{\gamma-1}{2} M_1^2\right)}{\dfrac{(\gamma+1)^2}{2(\gamma-1)} M_1^2} \tag{3-27}$$

$$\frac{P_{t2}}{P_{t1}} = f_4(M_1) = \left(\frac{\dfrac{\gamma+1}{2} M_1^2}{1 + \dfrac{\gamma-1}{2} M_1^2}\right)^{\gamma/(\gamma-1)} \left(\frac{2\gamma}{\gamma+1} M_1^2 - \frac{\gamma-1}{\gamma+1}\right)^{-1/(\gamma-1)} \tag{3-28}$$

$$M_2 = f_5(M_1) = \left(\frac{M_1^2 + \dfrac{2}{\gamma-1}}{\dfrac{2\gamma}{\gamma-1} M_1^2 - 1}\right)^{1/2} \tag{3-29}$$

Figure 3-19 presents a plot of the five functions listed above versus M ($\gamma = 1.4$). The static property ratios of the figure may be interpreted as the ratios occurring across a normal shock from the point of view of an observer at rest relative to the wave or at rest relative to the gas into which the wave is propagating. From the latter's point of view, a shock wave advancing through sea-level air at Mach 2.1 produces a pressure rise of 5:1. The air immediately behind such a shock wave would have a pressure of approximately 75 psia.

The curves of M_2 and P_{t2}/P_{t1} of the figure show that the higher the inlet Mach number to a normal shock, the lower the exit Mach number and the

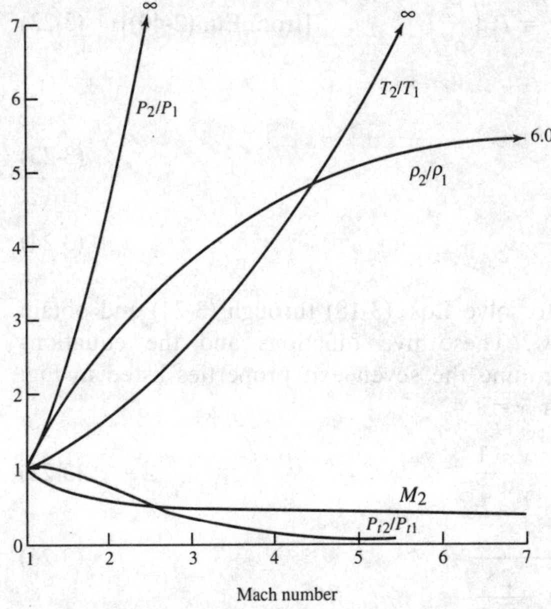

FIGURE 3-19
Property variations across a normal shock ($\gamma = 1.4$).

total pressure ratio across the shock wave. Contrary to the static property ratio curves which, by definition, are independent of an observer's reference velocity, these two curves depend upon the observer's reference velocity and cannot be used directly by an observer not riding on the wave.

Normal Shock Wave Propagation Speed

Equation (3-25) gives the relationship for the normal shock wave pressure ratio as

$$f_1(M_1) = \frac{P_2}{P_1} = \frac{2\gamma}{\gamma - 1} M_1^2 - \frac{\gamma - 1}{\gamma + 1} \tag{3-25}$$

From the point of view of a normal shock wave advancing into gas at rest, M_1 (in this equation) is the ratio of the wave propagation speed V_w and the speed of sound in the gas in advance of the wave. Consequently, by solving Eq. (3-25) for V_1, we obtain the speed of propagation of a normal shock wave into a gas at rest. The result can be put in the form

$$V_w^2 = a_1^2\left[1 + \frac{\gamma + 1}{2\gamma}\left(\frac{P_2 - P_1}{P_1}\right)\right] \tag{3-30}$$

This verifies that the propagating speed of a normal shock wave depends upon the wave strength and equals the speed of a sound pulse as ΔP approaches zero.

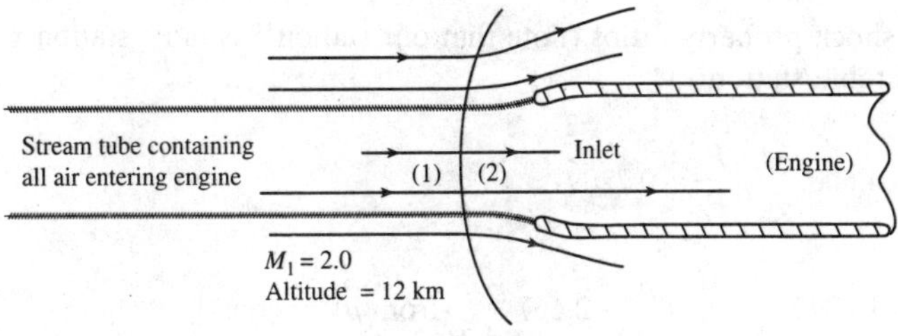

FIGURE 3-20
Normal shock in front of engine inlet.

Example 3.3. A steady stream of air passes through a normal shock which stands ahead of the engine inlet of a supersonic airplane flying at Mach 2 at 12 km (see Fig. 3-20). Find the properties of the air at the inlet and exit of the normal shock wave.

Solution. Standard atmosphere tables (App. A) give for 12 km

$$\delta = 0.1915 \qquad \theta = 0.7519 \qquad \text{and} \qquad \frac{a}{a_{\text{ref}}} = 0.8671$$

Thus

$$P_1 = \delta P_{\text{ref}} = 0.1915 \times 101{,}300 = 19{,}400 \text{ Pa}$$

$$T_1 = \theta T_{\text{ref}} = 0.7519 \times 288.2 = 216.7 \text{ K}$$

$$a_1 = \frac{a}{a_{\text{ref}}} a_{\text{ref}} = 0.8671 \times 340.3 = 295.1 \text{ m/sec}$$

Plots (Fig. 3-10), tabulations (App. E), or equations [Eqs. (3-9) and (3-10)] of P/P_t and T/T_t versus Mach number give, for $M_1 = 2.0$ and $\gamma = 1.4$,

$$\left(\frac{P}{P_t}\right)_1 = 0.1278 \qquad \left(\frac{T}{T_t}\right)_1 = 0.5556$$

From these data, we obtain

$$P_{t1} = \frac{P_1}{(P/P_t)_1} = \frac{19{,}400}{0.1278} = 151{,}800 \text{ Pa}$$

$$T_{t1} = \frac{T_1}{(T/T_t)_1} = \frac{216.7}{0.5556} = 390.0 \text{ K}$$

$$V_1 = M_1 a_1 = 2(295.1) = 590.2 \text{ m/sec}$$

We have now determined, at the shock inlet,

$$M_1 = 2.0 \qquad V_1 = 590.2 \text{ m/sec} \qquad T_1 = 216.7 \text{ K}$$

$$T_{t1} = 390.0 \text{ K} \qquad P_1 = 19{,}400 \text{ Pa} \qquad P_{t1} = 151{,}800 \text{ Pa}$$

From tabulations in App. F (for higher accuracy) of Fig. 3-19, at $M_1 = 2.0$

we find the normal shock property ratios (note that our station 1 is table station x and our station 2 is table station y)

$$\frac{P_2}{P_1} = 4.500 \qquad \frac{P_{t2}}{P_{t1}} = 0.7209$$

$$\frac{T_2}{T_1} = 1.6875 \qquad \frac{V_1}{V_2} = \frac{\rho_2}{\rho_1} = 2.667 \qquad \text{(from } \rho V = \text{const)}$$

and the exit Mach number

$$M_2 = 0.5774$$

These numbers may be checked, grossly, by Fig. 3-19. The normal shock exit stream properties are

$$P_2 = P_1 \frac{P_2}{P_1} = 19{,}400 \times 4.500 = 87{,}300 \text{ Pa}$$

$$P_{t2} = P_{t1} \frac{P_{t2}}{P_{t1}} = 151{,}800 \times 0.7209 = 109{,}430 \text{ Pa}$$

$$T_2 = T_1 \frac{T_2}{T_1} = 216.7 \times 1.6875 = 365.7 \text{ K}$$

$$V_2 = \frac{V_1}{V_1/V_2} = \frac{590.2}{2.667} = 221.3 \text{ m/sec}$$

The results are summarized in Fig. 3-21. Notice that there is a 28 percent decrease in total pressure through the normal shock. Supersonic inlets are designed to keep this total pressure loss to a minimum.

Example 3-4. This example will illustrate a procedure for determining stream

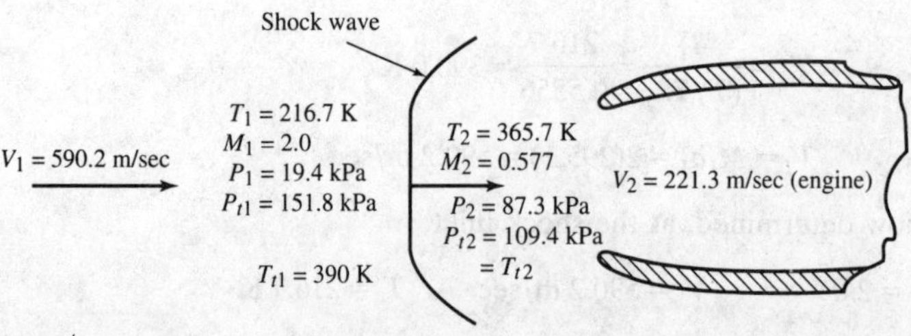

FIGURE 3-21
Flow properties' variation across normal shock.

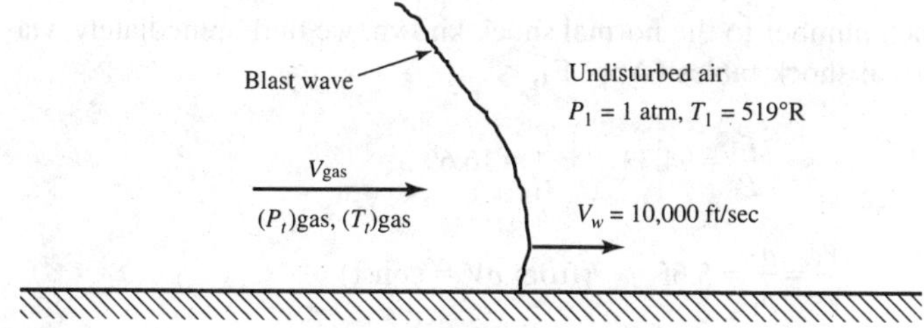

FIGURE 3-22
Blast wave propagating into air at rest.

properties in the wake of a normal shock wave advancing into gas at rest. The property ratios in Eqs. (3-25) through (3-28) were derived from the point of view of an observer riding on the shock wave. Since total pressure and total temperature depend upon stream velocity, the ratios developed for these two properties apply only to a velocity reference system that rides on the wave. Static properties of a flowing gas do not depend upon the stream's velocity. As a result, the static property ratios developed for a stationary shock front are also applicable across a shock wave propagating into a gas at rest.

Suppose a blast wave, perhaps created by a bomb explosion, is traveling through air at standard sea-level conditions with a speed of 10,000 ft/sec (see Fig. 3-22). Let us treat the spherical portion of the wave adjacent to the ground as a normal shock wave in order to estimate the state of the air in the blast wave's wake.

Estimate the value of the following stream properties in the wake of the blast wave:

a. Pressure P_2
b. Temperature T_2
c. Velocity V_{gas}
d. Mach number M_{gas}
e. Total temperature $P_{t\,gas}$
f. Total pressure $T_{t\,gas}$

Solution. We first reduce the problem to one of steady-state flow (see Fig. 3-23). For the flow in the steady-state reference frame, we have

$$P_1 = 1 \text{ atm} \qquad T_1 = 518.7°\text{R} \qquad a_1 = 1116 \text{ ft/sec} \qquad V_1 = 10{,}000 \text{ ft/sec}$$

Thus

$$M_1 = \frac{V_1}{a_1} = \frac{10{,}000}{1116} \approx 9.0$$

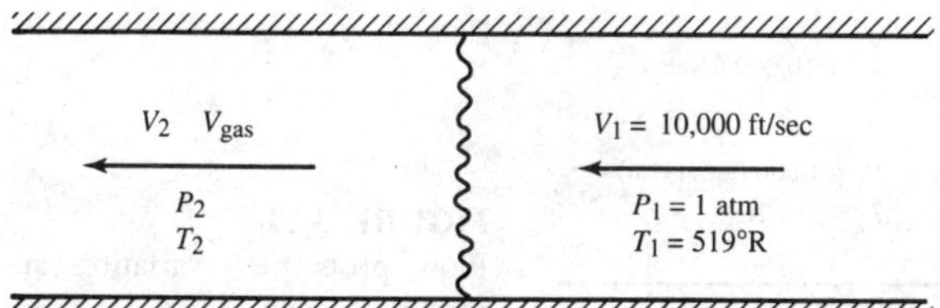

FIGURE 3-23
Blast wave reduced to steady-state flow.

With the inlet Mach number to the normal shock known, we find immediately, via tabulations in normal shock tables (App. F),

$$\frac{P_2}{P_1} = 94.33 \qquad \frac{T_2}{T_1} = 16.69$$

$$\frac{V_1}{V_2} = \frac{\rho_2}{\rho_1} = 5.65 \qquad \text{(from } \rho V = \text{const)}$$

These data give the static pressure and temperature in either frame of reference whence

a. $$P_2 = P_1 \frac{P_2}{P_1} = 94.33 \text{ atm}$$

b. $$T_2 = T_1 \frac{T_2}{T_1} = 518.7(16.69) = 8658°\text{R}$$

The velocity V_2 in the steady-state reference frame is

$$V_2 = \frac{V_1}{V_1/V_2} = \frac{10{,}000}{5.65} = 1770 \text{ ft/sec}$$

To determine the velocity of the gas V_{gas} in the wake of the blast, we algebraically add 10,000 ft/sec to V_2 and obtain

c. $V_{\text{gas}} = 10{,}000 - 1770 = 8230 \text{ ft/sec} = V_{\text{gas}}$ in direction of wave movement

Figure 3-24 illustrates the solution of the problem thus far. The values of M_{gas}, $T_{t\text{gas}}$, and $P_{t\text{gas}}$ remain to be found.

The Mach number of the gas in the blast wave's wake is

d. $$M_{\text{gas}} = \frac{V_{\text{gas}}}{a_2} = \frac{V_{\text{gas}}}{a_1\sqrt{T_2/T_1}} = \frac{8230}{1116\sqrt{16.69}} = \frac{8230}{4559} = 1.8$$

Determine the total temperature and total pressure now, based on your knowledge of the fact that the static/total ratios of these two properties are functions of the flow Mach number. From

$$\frac{T}{T_t} = \left(1 + \frac{\gamma - 1}{2} M^2\right)^{-1}$$

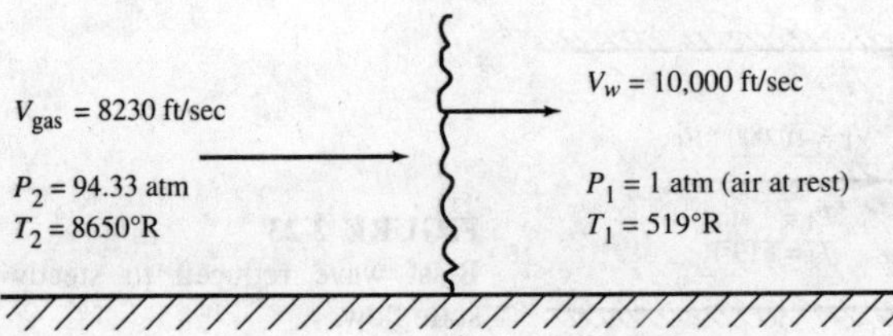

FIGURE 3-24
Flow properties' variation across blast wave.

we find for $M_{gas} = 1.8$

$$\frac{T}{T_t} = 0.6068 \qquad \text{(by calculation or tables)}$$

whence

e.
$$T_{t\,gas} = \frac{T_2}{T/T_t} = \frac{8658}{0.6068} = 14{,}270°\text{R}$$

From
$$\frac{P}{P_t} = \left(\frac{T}{T_t}\right)^{\gamma/(\gamma-1)} = \left(1 + \frac{\gamma-1}{2}M^2\right)^{-\gamma/(\gamma-1)}$$

we find for $M_{gas} = 1.8$

$$\frac{P}{P_t} = 0.1740 \qquad \text{(by calculation of tables)}$$

whence

f.
$$P_{t\,gas} = \frac{P_2}{P/P_t} = \frac{94.33}{0.1740} = 542 \text{ atm}$$

The total temperature and total pressure are felt by a stationary structure in the path of the blast wave. Obviously, a stationary structure exposed to a blast wave of this strength would not be stationary long. Some estimates indicate that a nuclear shock wave travels at speeds on the order of 200,000 ft/sec (20 times the wave speed of the example) and produces a total pressure in its wake on the order of 40,000 atm!

3-4 OBLIQUE SHOCK WAVE

When a wedge-shaped object is placed in a two-dimensional supersonic flow, a plane-attached shock wave may emanate from the nose of the body, or a detached shock wave may arise. The latter is curved and stands in front of the object (Fig. 3-25). The flow Mach number and the wedge angle θ together determine which of these two types of shocks will occur.

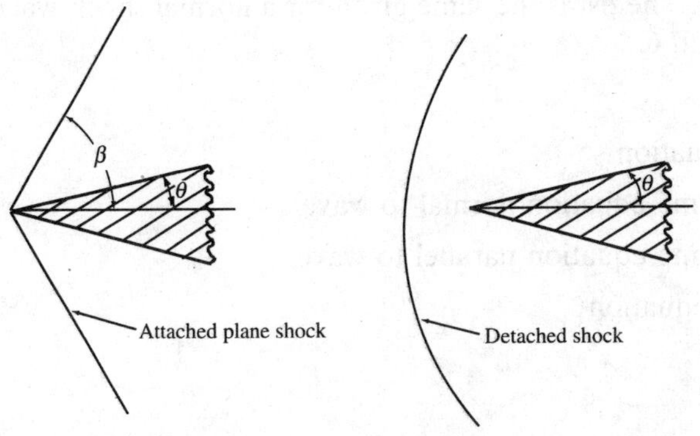

FIGURE 3-25
Attached and detached shocks in supersonic flow.

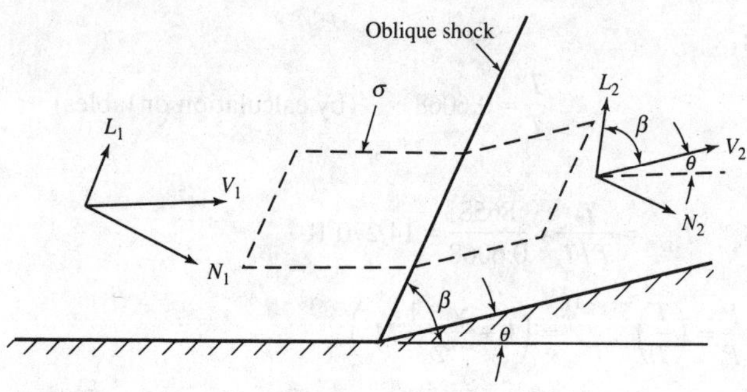

FIGURE 3-26
Control volume for oblique shock analysis.

Consider the analysis of oblique shock waves with the following purposes in mind:

1. To determine the exit conditions from an attached oblique shock wave, given the inlet conditions and either the stream deflection angle θ or the shock angle β
2. To determine the limitations on upstream Mach M_1 and θ for an attached shock to occur
3. To show that the normal shock wave is a special case of the oblique shock with $\theta = 0$

In Fig. 3-26, a flow is deflected through an angle θ as it passes through a shock wave which makes an angle β with the upstream flow velocity. A proper control volume, indicated by the dashed lines, will have its upper and lower sides coincident with the flow streamlines and its ends parallel to the shock front. For convenience, assume the area through which the fluid enters and leaves to be unity, and apply the physical laws and definitions below to the flow through the control volume. The list is the same given for a normal shock wave except for added items 3 and 6.

1. Mass control volume equation
2. Momentum control volume equation normal to wave
3. Momentum control volume equation parallel to wave
4. Energy control volume equation
5. Thermal state equation
6. Geometry of figure

7. Entropy control volume equation
8. Speed of sound
9. Definition of Mach number

These equations follow from application of the above nine conditions:

Mass $$\rho_1 N_1 = \rho_2 N_2 \tag{3-31a}$$

N_{momentum} $$P_1 + \rho_1 N_1^2 = P_2 + \rho_2 N_2^2 \tag{3-31b}$$

L_{momentum} $$\rho_1 N_1 L_1 = \rho_2 N_2 L_2 \tag{3-31c}$$

Energy $$c_p T_1 + \frac{N_1^2 + L_1^2}{2g_c} = c_p T_2 + \frac{N_2^2 + L_2^2}{2g_c} \tag{3-31d}$$

State $$\frac{P_1}{\rho_1 T_1} = \frac{P_2}{\rho_2 T_2} \tag{3-31e}$$

Geometry $$\tan(\beta - \theta) = \frac{N_2}{L_2} \tag{3-31f}$$

Entropy $$P_{t1}\left(\frac{P_1}{\rho_1^\gamma}\right)^{1/(\gamma-1)} = P_{t2}\left(\frac{P_2}{\rho_2^\gamma}\right)^{1/(\gamma-1)} \tag{3-31g}$$

$$P_{t1} \geq P_{t2}$$

Sound $$\frac{a_1^2}{T_1} = \frac{a_2^2}{T_2} \tag{3-31h}$$

Mach $$\frac{M_1\sqrt{T_1}\sin\beta}{N_1} = \frac{M_2\sqrt{T_2}\sin(\beta-\theta)}{N_2} \tag{3-31i}$$

Solution of this set of equations gives the following relationships:

$$\frac{P_2}{P_1} = f_1(M_1 \sin\beta) \tag{3-32a}$$

$$\frac{\rho_2}{\rho_1} = f_2(M_1 \sin\beta) \tag{3-32b}$$

$$\frac{T_2}{T_1} = f_3(M_1 \sin\beta) \tag{3-32c}$$

$$\frac{P_{t2}}{P_{t1}} = f_4(M_1 \sin \beta) \tag{3-32d}$$

$$M_2 \sin (\beta - \theta) = f_5(M_1 \sin \beta) \tag{3-32e}$$

$$\tan (\beta - \theta) = \frac{2/(\gamma + 1) + [(\gamma - 1)/(\gamma + 1)]M_1^2 \sin^2 \beta}{M_1^2 \sin \beta \cos \beta} \tag{3-32f}$$

Here the functions f_1, f_2, etc., are identical with those for a normal shock wave when $\beta = 90°$ and $\theta = 0°$.

It is convenient to present the last equation, Eq. (3-32*f*), graphically by plotting β versus θ for values of M_1, as shown in Fig. 3-27. Equation (3-32*f*) is given in tabular form in App. G. When a solution does not exist for that combination of Mach number M_1 and wedge angle θ, the maximum value of the wedge angle θ_{max} and the corresponding shock angle β are given.

The functions f_1, f_2, f_4, and f_5 are given graphically in Figs. 3-28 through 3-31.

Observe from the graph of Fig. 3-27 that there exist three possible solutions for a given wedge angle θ:

1. Two values of β for a given M_1. For example, $\theta = 20°$, $M_1 = 4.0$ gives $\beta = 32°$ or $\beta = 84°$. Either value of β may occur depending upon the boundary conditions of the flow. Usually, the wave with the smaller shock angle occurs. However, a proper adjustment of the downstream pressure will produce the wave with the larger shock angle.
2. One value of β for a given M_1. For example, $\theta = 23°$, $M_1 = 2.0$, $\beta = 65°$.
3. No value of β for a given M_1. For example, $\theta = 20°$, $M_1 = 1.5$. When this condition exists, a detached shock wave results.

Figures 3-28 through 3-31 give the oblique shock stream property ratios and exit Mach numbers for various values of the stream deflection (half wedge) angle θ for $\gamma = 1.4$. The family of curves on each graph is bounded by a normal shock curve and a Mach line curve.

Thus these graphs include the curves for the normal shock relations [excluding T_2/T_1 which may be found from $T_2/T_1 = (P_2/P_1)/(\rho_2/\rho_1)$] of Fig. 3-19. The normal shock conditions correspond to the limiting strong oblique shock solutions of Figs. 3-28 through 3-31 as the stream deflection angle goes to zero. The Mach line, or Mach wave, conditions are the limiting weak oblique shock solutions of Figs. 3-28 through 3-31 as the stream deflection angle goes to zero. Notice that the stream properties do not change through a Mach line; this is in keeping with the concept of a Mach line being formed from sound pulses which produce infinitesimally small changes in stream properties.

There are numerous references that present the shock relations for the oblique and normal shocks in either graphical or tabular form (see Refs. 15, 19, 20, and 21).

In the analysis of the oblique shock, we have developed a series of

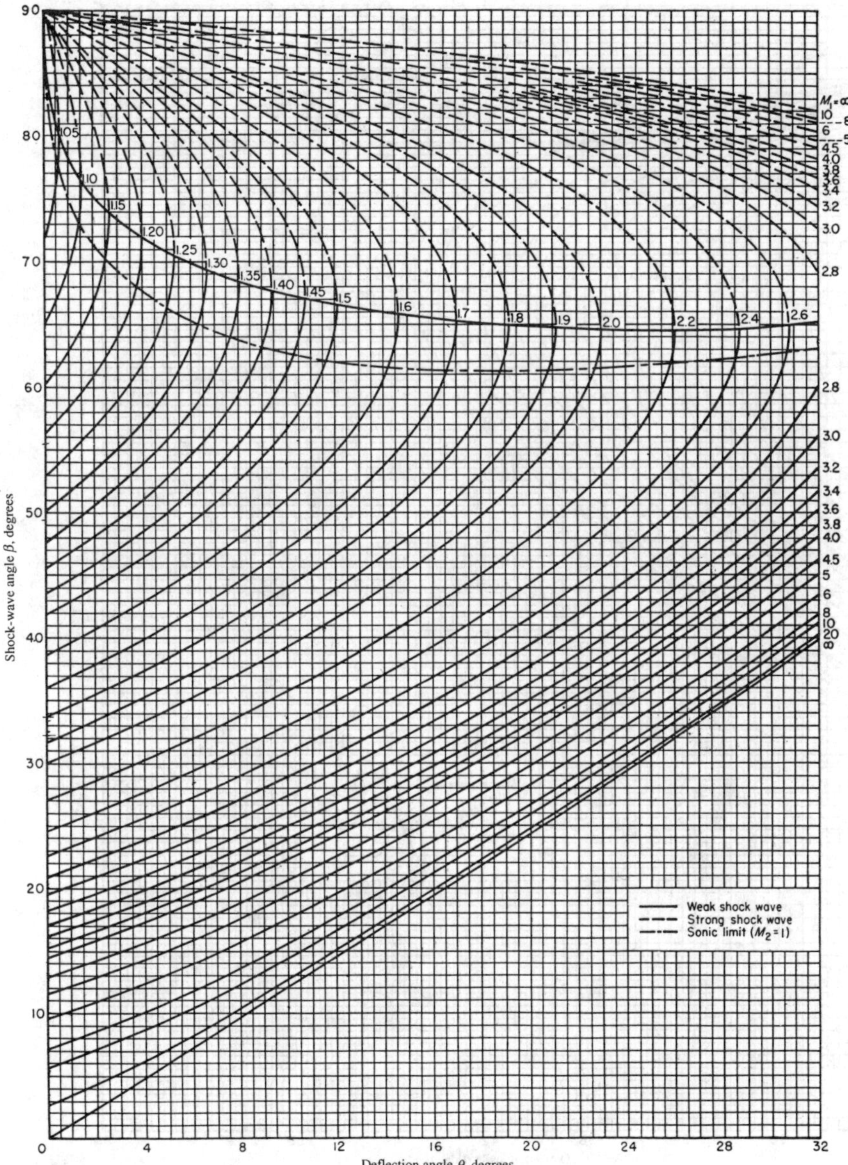

FIGURE 3-27
Relation between M_1, β, and θ for oblique shock ($\gamma = 1.4$).

equations from which it is possible to find the oblique shock exit conditions, given the inlet conditions and β or θ. We have seen that each of the equations in this series reduces to its normal shock counterpart as β approaches 90° and θ approaches 0°. Moreover, the expression relating β, θ, and M_1 (Fig. 3-27) enables us to determine the limiting values of M and θ for an attached shock when a wedge is placed in a supersonic flow.

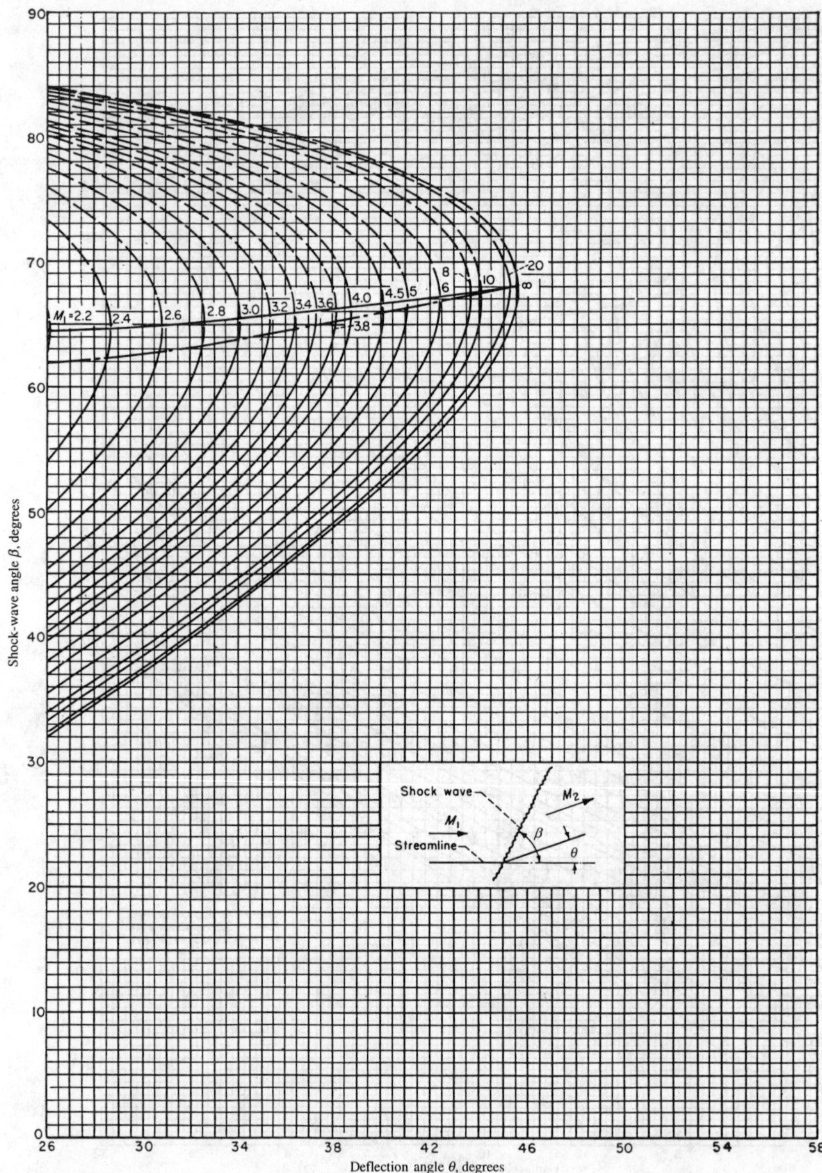

FIGURE 3-27
(*Continued.*)

Example 3-5. A steady supersonic stream of air at an altitude of 12 km and Mach number of 2.0 approaches a wedge with an included angle of 40° (Fig. 3-32). Find the stream properties downstream of the weak oblique shock wave attached to the wedge and the angle that the shock makes with the original direction of flow.

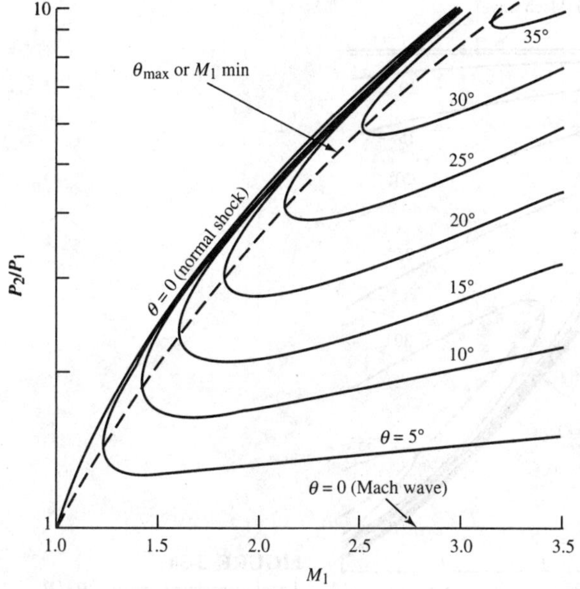

FIGURE 3-28
Pressure ratio P_2/P_1 for oblique shock ($\gamma = 1.4$).

Solution. From App. A at 12 km we have $P_1 = \delta P_{ref} = 19{,}400$ Pa and $T_1 = \theta T_{ref} = 216.7$ K. Figure 3-27 indicates that an attached shock will occur for $\theta = 20°$ and $M_1 = 2.0$. Thus we may proceed with the solution. Of the two shock angles possible for the given conditions, the smaller angle generally occurs. Accordingly, we read $\beta = 53°$ from Fig. 3-27. The following data are obtained from Figs. 3-28

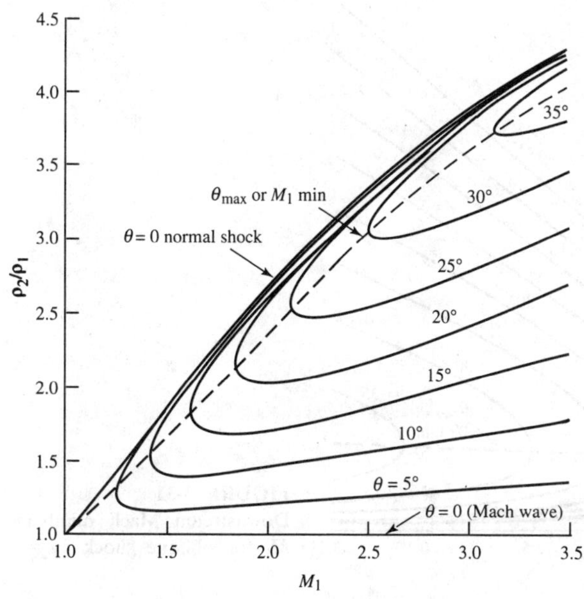

FIGURE 3-29
Density ratio ρ_2/ρ_1 for oblique shock ($\gamma = 1.4$).

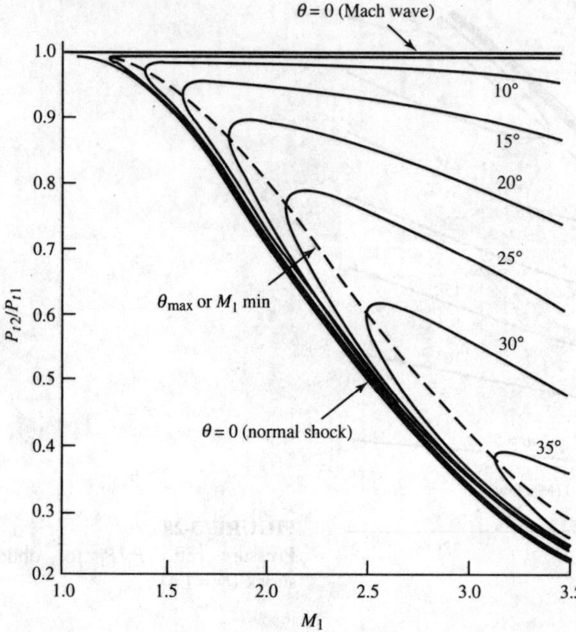

FIGURE 3-30
Total pressure ratio P_{t2}/P_{t1} for oblique shock ($\gamma = 1.4$).

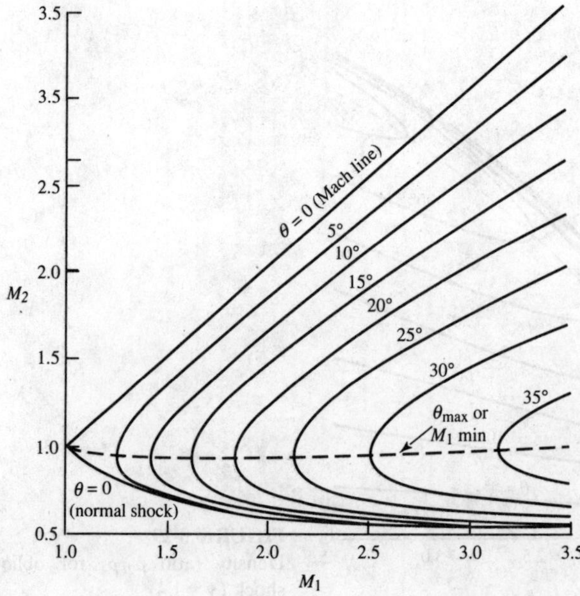

FIGURE 3-31
Downstream Mach number M_2 for oblique shock ($\gamma = 1.4$).

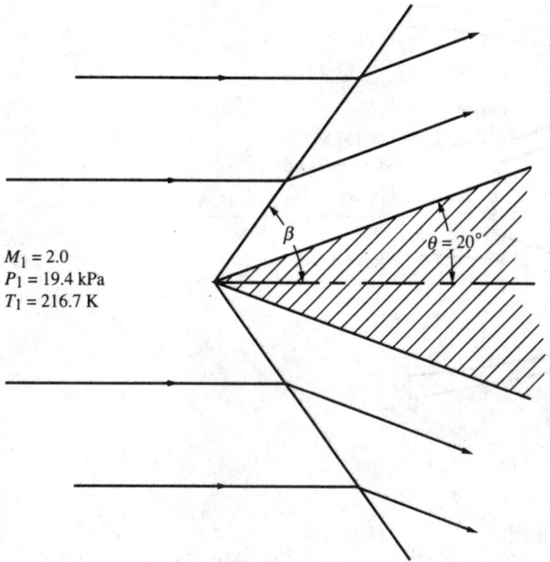

FIGURE 3-32
A 20° half-angle wedge in supersonic flow.

through 3-31:

$$\frac{P_2}{P_1} = 2.8 \qquad \frac{\rho_2}{\rho_1} = 2.03 \qquad \frac{P_{t2}}{P_{t1}} = 0.89 \qquad M_2 = 1.22$$

The approaching total temperature and total pressure were found to be

$$P_{t1} = \frac{P_1}{(P/P_t)_1} = \frac{19{,}400}{0.1278} = 151{,}800 \text{ Pa}$$

$$T_{t1} = \frac{T_1}{(T/T_t)_1} = \frac{216.7}{0.5556} = 390.0 \text{ K}$$

From these data, we may determine the downstream properties.

$$P_2 = P_1 \frac{P_2}{P_1} = 19{,}400(2.8) = 54{,}320 \text{ Pa}$$

$$P_{t2} = P_{t1} \frac{P_{t2}}{P_{t1}} = 151{,}800(0.89) = 135{,}100 \text{ Pa}$$

$$T_2 = T_1 \frac{P_2 \rho_1}{P_1 \rho_2} = 216.7\left(\frac{2.8}{2.03}\right) = 298.9 \text{ K}$$

To find T_2 alternately, use $(T/T_t)_2$ for $M_2 = 1.22$ in the relation

$$T_2 = T_{t2}\left(\frac{T}{T_t}\right)_2 = T_{t1}\left(\frac{T}{T_t}\right)_2 = 390(0.7706) = 300.5 \text{ K}$$

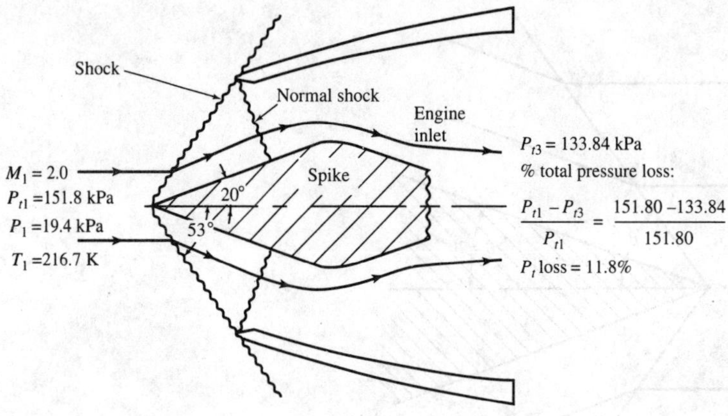

FIGURE 3-33
Example 3-6 external compression inlet.

This is a more accurate value of T_2 since T/T_t was read from tables and not from a graph.

Example 3-6. The inlet of the engine of Example 3-3 (normal shocks) incorporates a spike having a cone angle of 40°. As a result, the inlet air at 12 km and Mach 2.0 passes through an oblique shock attached to the spike and a normal shock at the inlet's cowl lip (Fig. 3-33). Determine the total pressure and Mach number at the exit of the normal shock. Compare the losses through this inlet with those of Example 3-3.

Solution. Although the shock of the spike is a conical shock wave, we may make a sufficiently accurate approximate analysis by using two-dimensional oblique shock theory. We found the stream properties in zone 2 of Fig. 3-32 (Example 3–5) to be

$$M_2 = 1.22 \qquad P_{t2} = 135{,}100 \text{ Pa}$$

From App. F, the total pressure ratio across a normal shock with an inlet Mach number of 1.22 is $P_{t3}/P_{t2} = 0.9907$, and the Mach number in zone 3 is 0.83. The total pressure in zone 3 is, therefore,

$$P_{t3} = P_{t2}\frac{P_{t3}}{P_{t2}} = 135{,}100(0.9907) = 133{,}840 \text{ Pa}$$

Assuming no total pressure losses except through shock waves, the spike inlet of this example has a 12 percent total pressure loss. The inlet of Example 3-3 has a 28 percent total pressure loss. If we define efficiency as the total pressure at the inlet shock pattern exit divided by the initial total pressure of the free stream, the spike inlet is then more efficient. The result of this comparison (inlet of Example 3-3 versus Example 3-6) is not an isolated case. It is generally true that, for a given supersonic flow, the total pressure loss through a series of shocks consisting of oblique shocks terminating in a normal shock is less than the total pressure loss through a single normal shock.

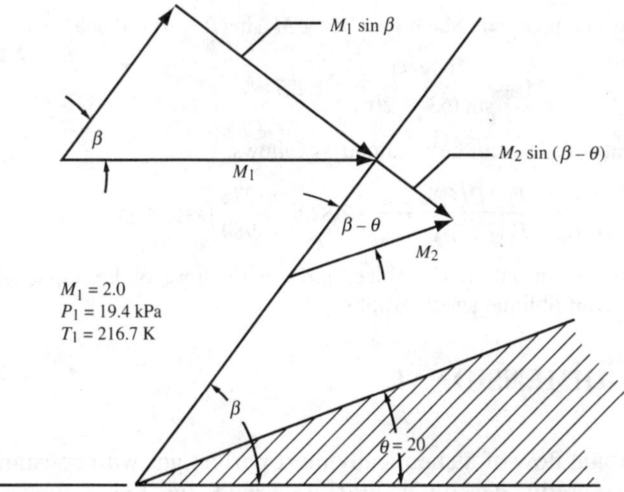

FIGURE 3-34
Flow across an oblique shock.

Example 3-7. Normal shock analysis shows that the exit Mach number and the stream property ratios across a normal shock are expressible in terms of the inlet Mach number. Figure 3-19 graphically represents the functional relationships between normal shock properties and the inlet Mach number. Oblique shock analysis indicates that the normal shock functional relationships, and thus Fig. 3-19, are also applicable to the oblique shock wave if, in using the normal shock relations for an oblique shock, the inlet and exit Mach numbers (M_1 and M_2 of Fig. 3-18) are replaced with the normal components of the corresponding Mach numbers for the oblique shock. This example will illustrate how, by using this procedure, one may use tabulations of normal shock relations in oblique shock analysis.

For the oblique shock flow shown in Fig. 3-34, determine the following quantities from normal shock tabulations of them:

$$\frac{P_2}{P_1} \qquad \frac{\rho_2}{\rho_1} \qquad \frac{T_2}{T_1} \qquad \frac{P_{t2}}{P_{t1}} \qquad M_2$$

Compare the results with those of Example 3-5.

Solution. Use Fig. 3-27 to determine the shock angle β. Taking the value of β corresponding to the shock which normally occurs, we get $\beta = 53°$. [*Note*: A more accurate value of β can be obtained by using Eq. (3-32*f*) or App. G.] Then the normal component of inlet Mach number $= M_1 \sin\beta = 2 \sin 53° = 1.6$.

From normal shock tables at a Mach number of 1.6,

$$\frac{P_2}{P_1} = 2.820 \qquad \frac{\rho_2}{\rho_1} = 2.032 \qquad \frac{T_2}{T_1} = 1.388$$

and the normal component of exit Mach number = $M_2 \sin(\beta - \theta) = 0.6684$, so

$$M_2 = \frac{0.6684}{\sin(53° - 20°)} = 1.227$$

The total pressure ratio P_{t2}/P_{t1} can be obtained as follows:

$$\frac{P_{t2}}{P_{t1}} = \frac{P_2}{P_1}\frac{(P/P_t)_{M_1}}{(P/p_t)_{M_2}} = \frac{P_2}{P_1}\frac{(P/P_t)_{M=2.0}}{(P/P_t)_{M=1.227}} = 2.820\left(\frac{0.1278}{0.3980}\right) = 0.9055$$

These results, based on normal shock tables, agree with those of Example 3-5 which were derived from oblique shock graphs.

3-5 STEADY ONE-DIMENSIONAL GAS DYNAMICS

The steady one-dimensional flow of a chemically inert perfect gas with constant specific heats is conveniently described and governed by the following definitions and physical laws.

Definitions

Perfect gas $\qquad P = \rho RT \qquad$ (i)

Mach number $\qquad M^2 = \dfrac{V^2}{\gamma R g_c T} \qquad$ (ii)

Total temperature $\qquad T_t = T\left(1 + \dfrac{\gamma - 1}{2} M^2\right) \qquad$ (iii)

Total pressure $\qquad P_t = P\left(1 + \dfrac{\gamma - 1}{2} M^2\right)^{\gamma/(\gamma-1)} \qquad$ (iv)

Physical Laws

For one-dimensional flow through a control volume having a single inlet and exit sections 1 and 2, respectively, we have

One-dimensional mass flow $\qquad \rho_1 A_1 V_1 = \rho_2 A_2 V_2 \qquad$ (v)

Momentum $\qquad F_{\text{frict}} = -\Delta\left(PA + \dfrac{\rho A V^2}{g_c}\right) \qquad$ (vi)

Energy equation (no shaft work) $\qquad q = c_p(T_{t2} - T_{t1}) \qquad$ (vii)

Entropy equation (adiabatic flow) $\qquad s_2 \geq s_1 \qquad$ (viii)

where F_{frict} is the frictional force of a solid control surface boundary on the flowing gas and A is the flow cross-sectional area normal to the velocity V.

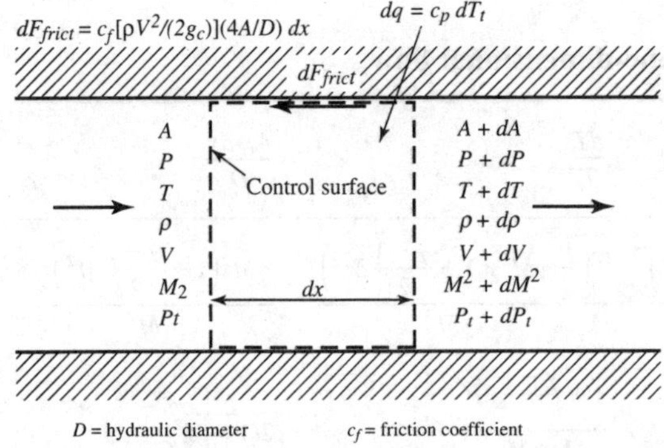

FIGURE 3-35
Independent and dependent variables for one-dimensional flow.

Now consider the differential element of duct with length dx, as shown in Fig. 3-35. The independent variables are the area change, total temperature change, and frictional force. The dependent variables are P, T, ρ, V, M^2, and P_t. The application of Eqs. (i) through (vi) to flow in Fig. 3-35, having the presence of the simultaneous effects of area change, heat interaction, and friction, results in the following set of equations for the infinitesimal element dx:

Perfect gas†
$$-\frac{dP}{P} + \frac{d\rho}{\rho} + \frac{dT}{T} = 0 \qquad (3\text{-}33a)$$

Total temperature†
$$\frac{dT}{T} + \frac{[(\gamma-1)/2]M^2}{1+[(\gamma-1)/2]M^2}\frac{dM^2}{M^2} = \frac{dT_t}{T_t} \qquad (3\text{-}33b)$$

One-dimensional mass flow†
$$\frac{d\rho}{\rho} + \frac{dA}{A} + \frac{dV}{V} = 0 \qquad (3\text{-}33c)$$

Total pressure†
$$\frac{dP}{P} + \frac{(\gamma/2)M^2}{1+[(\gamma-1)/2]M^2}\frac{dM^2}{M^2} = \frac{dP_t}{P_t} \qquad (3\text{-}33d)$$

Momentum
$$\frac{dP}{P} + \gamma M^2\frac{dV}{V} + 2\gamma M^2 c_f\frac{dx}{D} = 0 \qquad (3\text{-}33e)$$

Mach number†
$$2\frac{dV}{V} - \frac{dT}{T} = \frac{dM^2}{M^2} \qquad (3\text{-}33f)$$

In these equations, heat interaction effects are measured in terms of the total temperature change according to Eq. (vii). The entropy condition of Eq. (viii) is also applicable if $dT_t = 0$. If dT_t is not zero, then the entropy requirement is $ds = dq/T$. The six dependent variables M^2, V, P, ρ, T, and P_t in the above set of six linear algebraic equations may be expressed in terms of

† These equations are obtained by taking the derivative of the natural log of Eqs. (i) through (v).

TABLE 3-1
Influence coefficients for steady one-dimensional flow

Dependent \ Independent	$\dfrac{dA}{A}$	$\dfrac{dT_t}{T_t}$	$\dfrac{4c_f\,dx}{D}$
$\dfrac{dM^2}{M^2}$	$-\dfrac{2\left(1+\dfrac{\gamma-1}{2}M^2\right)}{1-M^2}$	$\dfrac{(1+\gamma M^2)\left(1+\dfrac{\gamma-1}{2}M^2\right)}{1-M^2}$	$\dfrac{\gamma M^2\left(1+\dfrac{\gamma-1}{2}M^2\right)}{1-M^2}$
$\dfrac{dV}{V}$	$-\dfrac{1}{1-M^2}$	$\dfrac{1+\dfrac{\gamma-1}{2}M^2}{1-M^2}$	$\dfrac{\gamma M^2}{2(1-M^2)}$
$\dfrac{dP}{P}$	$\dfrac{\gamma M^2}{1-M^2}$	$\dfrac{-\gamma M^2\left(1+\dfrac{\gamma-1}{2}M^2\right)}{1-M^2}$	$\dfrac{-\gamma M^2[1+(\gamma-1)M^2]}{2(1-M^2)}$
$\dfrac{d\rho}{\rho}$	$\dfrac{M^2}{1-M^2}$	$\dfrac{-\left(1+\dfrac{\gamma-1}{2}M^2\right)}{1-M^2}$	$\dfrac{-\gamma M^2}{2(1-M^2)}$
$\dfrac{dT}{T}$	$\dfrac{(\gamma-1)M^2}{1-M^2}$	$\dfrac{(1-\gamma M^2)\left(1+\dfrac{\gamma-1}{2}M^2\right)}{1-M^2}$	$\dfrac{-\gamma(\gamma-1)M^4}{2(1-M^2)}$
$\dfrac{dP_t}{P_t}$	0	$\dfrac{-\gamma M^2}{2}$	$\dfrac{-\gamma M^2}{2}$

This table is read:

$$\frac{dV}{V}=\left(-\frac{1}{1-M^2}\right)\frac{dA}{A}+\frac{1+\dfrac{\gamma-1}{2}M^2}{1-M^2}\frac{dT_t}{T_t}+\frac{\gamma M^2}{2(1-M^2)}\frac{4c_f\,dx}{D}$$

the three independent variables A, T_t, and $4c_f\,dx/D$. The solution is given in Table 3-1.

General conclusions can be made relative to the variation of the stream properties of the flow with each of the independent variables by the relations of Table 3-1. As an example, the relationship given for dV/V at the bottom of the table indicates that, in a constant-area adiabatic flow, friction will increase the stream velocity in subsonic flow and will decrease the velocity in supersonic flow. Similar reasoning may be applied to determine the manner in which any dependent property varies with a single independent variable.

Example 3-8. Consider the one-dimensional flow of a perfect gas in a channel of circular cross section. The flow is adiabatic, and we wish to design the duct so that its area varies with x such that the velocity remains constant.

a. Show that in such a flow, the temperature must be a constant, hence the Mach number must be a constant.

b. Show that the total pressure varies inversely with the cross-sectional area.

c. Show that $2\,dA/C = \gamma M^2 c_f\,dx$, where C is the circumference.

d. For a constant c_f and a circular channel of diameter D, show that the diameter must vary in accordance with the following equation to keep the velocity constant:

$$D = D_i + \gamma M^2 c_f x$$

Solution. This problem requires that we apply the relationships of Table 3-1 and other fundamental relationships.

a. Since the flow is adiabatic, the total temperature is constant. From the definition of the total temperature, we have $T_t = T + V^2/(2c_p g_c)$. Since T_t and V are constant in the duct, the above equation requires that the static temperature remain constant. With the static temperature of the gas constant, the speed of sound will be constant ($a = \sqrt{\gamma R g_c T}$). With constant velocity and speed of sound, the Mach number will be constant.

b. Application of the continuity equation to the constant-velocity flow gives $A_i/A = \rho/\rho_i$. For a perfect gas with constant static temperature, we have $\rho/\rho_i = P/P_i$, and from Eq. (iv) for constant-Mach flow, we get $P_t/P_{ti} = P/P_i$. Thus $P_t/P_{ti} = A_i/A$.

c. To obtain this relationship, we need to get a relationship between two independent properties to keep the dependent property of velocity constant. Table 3-1 gives the basic relationships between dependent and independent properties for one-dimensional flow. We are interested in the case where velocity is constant, and thus we write the equation listed as an example at the bottom of Table 3-1 for the case where both dV and dT_t are zero:

$$0 = \left(-\frac{1}{1 - M^2}\right)\frac{dA}{A} + 0 + \frac{\gamma M^2}{2(1 - M^2)}\frac{4c_f\,dx}{D}$$

The area of the duct is equal to the circumference C times one quarter of the diameter D. Thus $A = CD/4$, and the above relationship reduces to

$$\boxed{2\frac{dA}{C} = \gamma M^2 c_f\,dx}$$

d. For a circular cross section, $A = \pi D^2/4$ and $C = \pi D$. Thus $2\,dA/C = dD$. Substitution of this relationship into the above equation and integration give the desired result (at $x = 0$, $D = D_i$):

$$\boxed{D = D_i + \gamma M^2 c_f x}$$

3-6 SIMPLE FLOWS

There is a class of gas flows in which a single independent variable controls the change in the flow properties. The flow of a perfect gas through an ideal nozzle, with area treated as the independent variable, is an example from this class of flows. The purpose of this section is to study several types of flow that are in this class.

Consider a nonreacting gas to be flowing steadily through a duct which satisfies the following conditions:

1. Constant area
2. Frictionless
3. Constant total temperature
4. No gas injection into the flow

Excluding shocks and electrical effects, the stream properties of such a flow would remain constant throughout the flow field, and we would have what is called a *trivial flow*. By removing any one or a combination of the flow restrictions listed above, the stream properties would change with the effect present (variable area, friction, heating, or gas injection).

Thus if the area is changed at will in a flexible duct with no friction, heating, or gas injection [Fig. 3-36(*a*)], the stream properties will vary as the area is changed. In this case, the area is the single independent variable upon which the stream properties depend. (We assume here that a reservoir and a discharge region maintained at constant but different pressures are available to produce the flow considered.) Flows in which only a single independent effect produces variations in the stream properties are called *simple flows*. The flow shown in Fig. 3-36(*a*) is a simple type of flow, called *simple area flow*.

In the work to follow, we will study how the stream properties of a flowing gas vary in simple types of flow and in flows with combined effects. The simple flows to be analyzed are shown in Fig. 3-36. Each of these flows has a direct practical application even though a truly simple flow is seldom

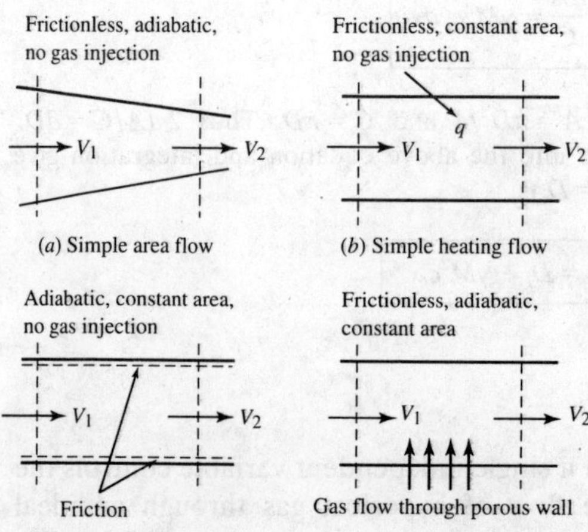

FIGURE 3-36
Simple types of flow.

encountered in practice. Often, however, in a flow with combined area, friction, or gas injection effects, one of these greatly outweighs the effect of all others so that the variation in stream properties is determined mainly by a single independent variable. Examples of real flows which may be treated as simple flows are given below for each type of simple flow of Fig. 3-36.

In Fig. 3-36(*a*), gas flow through a real nozzle represents a flow with the combined effects of area, friction, and heat transfer present. In large nozzles, the effect of the area change on the stream properties greatly exceeds the frictional and heating effects; however, excellent agreement between theory and experiment is obtained by treating the flow as simple area flow.

In Fig. 3-36(*b*), the total temperature change occurring in a gas turbine combustor, or in a rocket combustion chamber between the injector plate and the nozzle inlet, can be analyzed as a simple heating flow. By ignoring friction and the change in molecular weight and specific heat of the gases, the adiabatic combustion process can be replaced by an equivalent simple heating process producing the same total temperature rise. This is an effective model for studying the variation of stream properties with total temperature in these combustion chambers.

In Fig. 3-36(*c*), some rocket propulsion installations employ a relatively long constant-area blast tube between the combustion chamber and nozzle. The gas flow in this blast tube is, for all practical purposes, adiabatic and is an example of simple frictional flow.

In Fig. 3-36(*d*), in transonic wind tunnel test sections, gas is withdrawn from the main flow through porous tunnel walls in order to eliminate shock reflections from the walls. This represents a simple gas injection flow with negative injection (gas withdrawl).

3-7 SIMPLE AREA FLOW—NOZZLE FLOW

Figure 3-37 shows simple area flow through a nozzle from a subsonic flow (state 1) through the sonic conditions (state x) to supersonic flow (state 2).

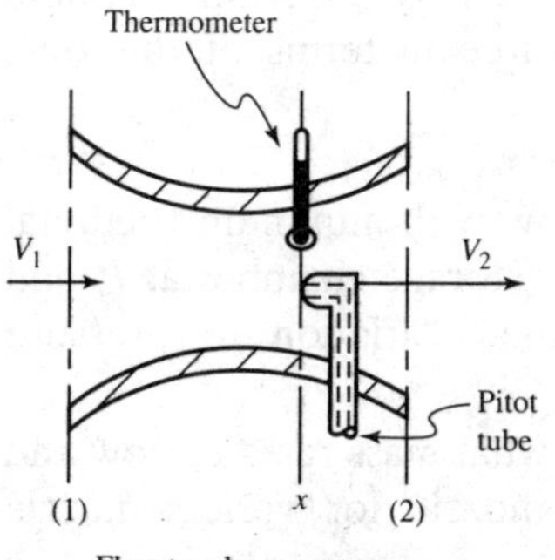

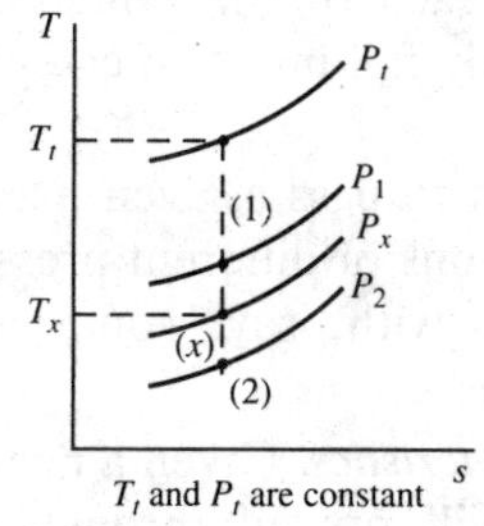

FIGURE 3-37
Simple area flow.

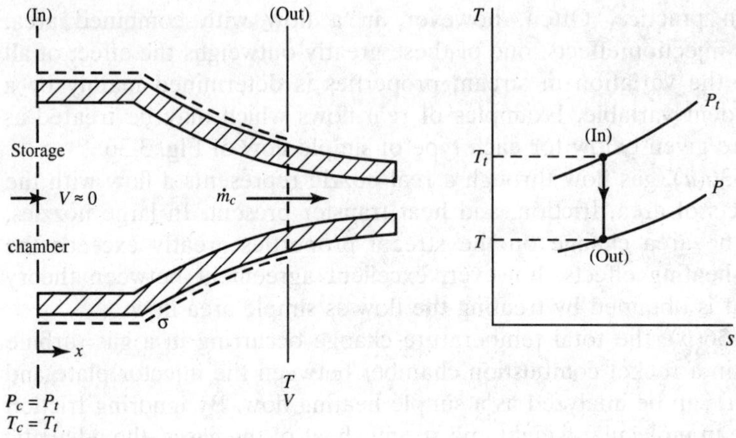

FIGURE 3-38
Control volume for simple area flow.

The flow is isentropic, and both the total temperature and total pressure are constant. For analysis, we consider accelerating a gas through a nozzle in a simple area flow with mass flow rate $\dot{m}_c$. Let the flow originate in a large storage chamber (Fig. 3-38) at chamber pressure $P_c = P_t$ and chamber temperature $T_c = T_t$. The stream properties at any station in the flow are related by the following equations:

$$P_c = P_t = P\left(\frac{T_t}{T}\right)^{\gamma/(\gamma-1)} \tag{i}$$

$$T_c = T_t = T + \frac{V^2}{2g_c c_p} \tag{ii}$$

$$\dot{m}_c = \rho AV = \frac{P}{RT}AV \tag{iii}$$

For given chamber gas conditions P_c, T_c, R, γ, and known $\dot{m}_c$, there are four variables P, T, V, A in these three equations. We may select one variable as independent and find each of the remaining three in terms of this one. Practical problems generally fall into two categories.

1. *Nozzle design.* We wish to pass a given mass flow with minimum frictional losses between two regions of different pressure (storage chamber at P_c and exhaust region at P_a) with, say, some assumed variation in pressure between the two regions.
2. *Nozzle operating characteristics.* Given a nozzle, what mass rates of flow and pressure distribution will prevail through the nozzle for various nozzle pressure ratios ($P_n = P_c/P_a$)?

In case 1, our independent, or known, variable is pressure P, which is a function of position x. In case 2, the variation of the flow area A with x as the known variable. We will consider each case in turn.

Nozzle Design

We shall illustrate the design of a nozzle by example.

Example 3-9. Assume we wish to expand gases at 28 lbm/sec from a high-altitude second-stage rocket combustion chamber to an ambient pressure of 0.618 psia (~70,000 ft altitude). Pertinent data simulating the Agena rocket engine are as follows:

$P_c = 206$ psia	$c_p g_c = 6000\ \text{ft}^2/(\text{sec}^2 \cdot {}^\circ\text{R})$
$T_c = 5000^\circ\text{R}$	Nozzle length = 30 in
$\dot{m} = 28$ lbm/sec	Pressure variation—Fig. 3-39
$Rg_c = 1715\ \text{ft}^2/(\text{sec}^2 \cdot {}^\circ\text{R})$	Exit pressure = 0.618 psia

To solve the problem, we must determine the flow area, gas temperature, velocity, and Mach number A, T, V, and M at each nozzle station. Assume all sections of the nozzle are circular, and assume simple area flow. Figure 3-39 provides the length of, and pressure in, the nozzle to be designed.

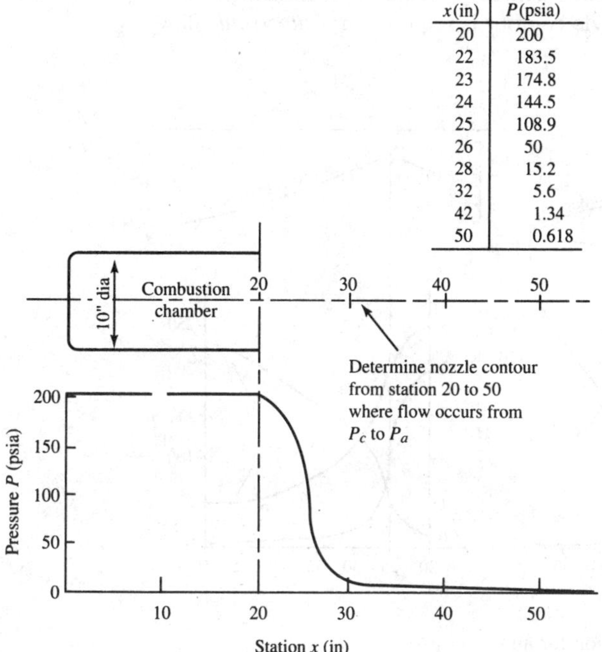

x(in)	P(psia)
20	200
22	183.5
23	174.8
24	144.5
25	108.9
26	50
28	15.2
32	5.6
42	1.34
50	0.618

FIGURE 3-39
Pressure distribution.

Solution. For the given conditions, the constants of Eqs. (i) through (iii) are known. Thus

$$P_t = P_c = 206 \text{ psia} \qquad Rg_c = 1715 \text{ ft}^2/(\text{sec}^2 \cdot {}^\circ\text{R})$$

$$T_t = T_c = 5000^\circ\text{R} \qquad c_p g_c = 6000 \text{ ft}^2/(\text{sec}^2 \cdot {}^\circ\text{R})$$

$$\dot{m} = 28 \text{ lbm/sec} \qquad \gamma = 1.4$$

Rewrite Eqs. (i) through (iii) as

$$T = T_t\left(\frac{P}{P_t}\right)^{(\gamma-1)/\gamma} \tag{iv}$$

$$V = \sqrt{2c_p g_c(T_t - T)} \tag{v}$$

$$A = \frac{\dot{m}RT}{PV} \tag{vi}$$

With P known (Fig. 3-39), use Eq. (iv) to find T at any given station. Equation (v) will then give V. With T and V determined, and $\dot{m}$, R, and P known, Eq. (vi) gives the nozzle area A at the selected station. In this manner, the nozzle area and gas properties can be found at all stations. The Mach number follows from

$$M = \frac{V}{\sqrt{\gamma R g_c T}} \tag{vii}$$

The results of the computation outlined are plotted in Fig. 3-40. The curves and nozzle contour in this figure illustrate that in order to *decrease P* and *increase V* in a simple area flow:

- A *converging* nozzle contour is required in *subsonic* flow.
- A *diverging* nozzle contour is required in a *supersonic* flow.

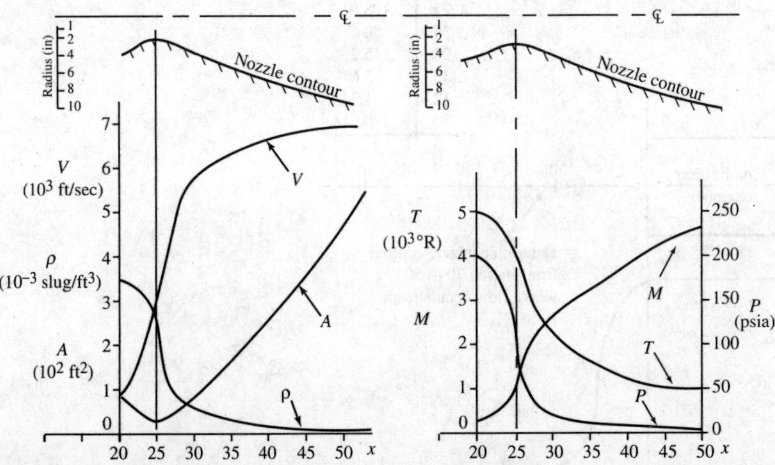

FIGURE 3-40
Nozzle flow properties versus station for air.

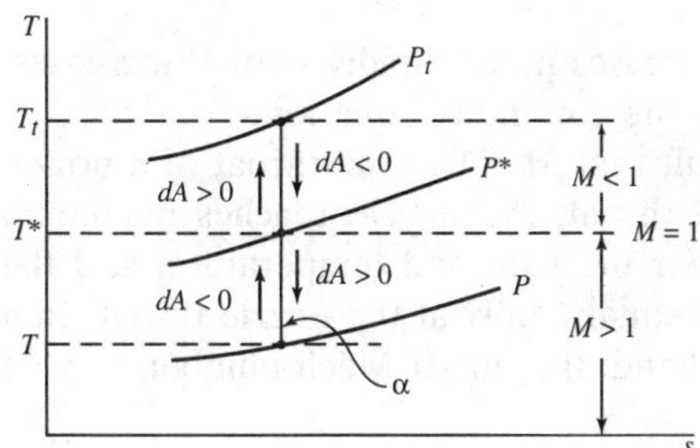

FIGURE 3-41
Isentrope line α.

Thus we find that the typical shape of a nozzle which is accelerating a gas from rest to supersonic speeds is convergent-divergent (C-D). At the design operating point of a *supersonic* C-D nozzle, the flow is subsonic up to the throat, sonic at the throat, and supersonic after the throat. The exit plane pressure P_e equals the exhaust region pressure P_a. We shall denote the nozzle pressure ratio for the design point as $P_{\bar{n}}$, where

$$\boxed{P_{\bar{n}} = (P_n)_{\text{des}} = \left(\frac{P_c}{P_a}\right)_{\text{des}}}$$

The path line of an isentropic flow is called an *isentrope.* The area variation required to progress along an isentrope in a given direction is shown in the T-s diagram of Fig. 3-41. To progress *downward* along the isentrope requires a converging area ($dA < 0$) in subsonic flow and diverging area ($dA > 0$) in a supersonic stream. To progress *upward* along the isentrope requires a converging area ($dA < 0$) in supersonic flow and diverging area ($dA > 0$) in subsonic flow. This is why the engine intakes on the XB-70 and various other supersonic aircraft converge from the inlet entrance to a throat and then diverge to the compressor face. This design reduces the speed of the air entering the compressor. Since P, T, ρ, and $V^2/(2c_pg_c)$ can be displayed in the T-s diagram, the isentrope line properly interpreted summarizes most of the characteristics of isentropic flow.

The stream area/velocity variations discussed above can be explained on the basis of the continuity equation by examining how the gas density varies with velocity in an isentropic flow. Area, velocity, and density are related as follows by the one-dimensional steady flow continuity equation:

$$A = \frac{\dot{m}}{\rho V} \qquad (\dot{m} = \text{const})$$

By reference to a T-s diagram, with lines of constant density thereon, we know that in an isentropic flow, ρ decreases as V increases. In subsonic flow, V increases faster than ρ decreases so that, according to the above equation, A

must decrease. In supersonic flow, ρ decreases more rapidly than V increases, and therefore A must increase to satisfy the continuity equation.

Lastly, we have the important result that $M = 1$ in the throat of a nozzle accelerating a gas. When $M = 1$ at the throat, the nozzle reaches maximum possible mass flow for the given chamber pressure and temperature, and the nozzle is said to be *choked.* And M will equal 1 only at the nozzle throat. In a decelerating diffuser flow, on the other hand, the throat Mach number may be less than, equal to, or greater than 1.

Nozzle Operating Characteristics for Isentropic Flow

Having designed a nozzle for a specific operating condition, we now examine its off-design operating characteristics. We wish to answer the following question: Given a nozzle, what are the possible isentropic pressure distributions and mass flow rates through the nozzle?

A simple way to investigate this question is to deal with a single equation which contains all the restrictions placed on the flow by the perfect gas state equations and the control volume equations. The governing equations may be combined into a single equation. We have

Mass $$\dot{m} = \frac{PAV}{RT} \tag{viii}$$

Energy $$T_t = T + \frac{V^2}{2c_p g_c} \tag{ix}$$

Entropy $$P = P_t\left(\frac{T}{T_t}\right)^{\gamma/(\gamma-1)} \tag{x}$$

Equation (viii) can be written as

$$\frac{\dot{m}}{A} = \frac{PV}{RT} \tag{xi}$$

wherein $$P = P_t\left(\frac{P}{P_t}\right) \qquad T = T_t\left(\frac{T}{T_t}\right)$$

and $$V = \sqrt{2c_p g_c(T_t - T)} = \left\{2c_p g_c T_t\left[1 - \left(\frac{P}{P_t}\right)^{(\gamma-1)/\gamma}\right]\right\}^{1/2}$$

Substituting these expressions for P, T, and V in Eq. (xi) and simplifying, we obtain a single equation representing the simultaneous solution of Eqs. (viii), (ix), and (x):

$$\boxed{\frac{\dot{m}}{A} = \frac{P_t}{\sqrt{T_t}}\sqrt{\frac{2g_c}{R}\frac{\gamma}{\gamma-1}\left[\left(\frac{P}{P_t}\right)^{2/\gamma} - \left(\frac{P}{P_t}\right)^{(\gamma+1)/\gamma}\right]}} \tag{3-34}$$

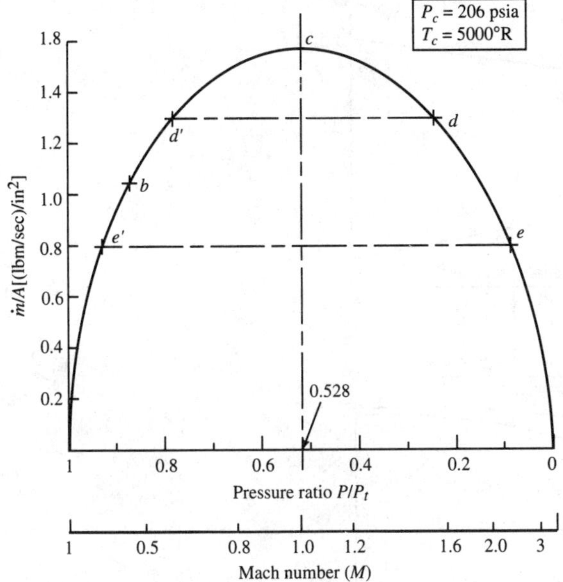

FIGURE 3-42
$\dot{m}/A$ versus P/P_t and Mach number for air.

If Eq. (3-34) is satisfied at every station of the flow through a nozzle, it follows that the conditions imposed on the flow by the thermal state equation and the mass, energy, and entropy control volume equations are satisfied. With P_c and T_c known in any given nozzle flow, we may effect a graphical solution of Eq. (3-34) by plotting $\dot{m}/A$ versus P/P_t. In a physical flow, P/P_t may vary from 1.0 in a storage chamber ($P = P_c = P_t$) to 0 in a vacuum ($P = 0$). A graph of $\dot{m}/A$ versus P/P_t is given in Fig. 3-42 for $P_c = 206$ psia and $T_c = 5000$°R. Since there is a unique value of M for each P/P_t, we show a Mach number scale along with the P/P_t axis. Notice that M increases as P/P_t decreases from left to right in the figure.

We note that for a given value of $\dot{m}/A$, there are two possible values of P/P_t in Fig. 3-42. In a particular problem, we can determine which value of P/P_t is applicable by examining the physical aspects of the flow.

Assume the nozzle depicted in Fig. 3-43 is discharging air isentropically from a storage chamber with $P_c = 206$ psia and $T_c = 5000$°R. Let us plot the nozzle pressure distributions for various nozzle mass flows. We shall determine the pressure distribution for maximum mass flow first.

With the chamber pressure and temperature known, the $\dot{m}/A$ versus P/P_t plot of Fig. 3-42 is made. Then, since for maximum mass flow $M = 1$ at the nozzle throat, $\dot{m}_{\text{max}}$ is determined by the relation

$$\dot{m}_{\text{max}} = \left(\frac{\dot{m}}{A}\right)_{M=1} A_{\text{throat}}$$
$$= [1.55(\text{lbm/sec})/\text{in}^2](14.4\ \text{in}^2) = 22.3\ \text{lbm/sec}$$

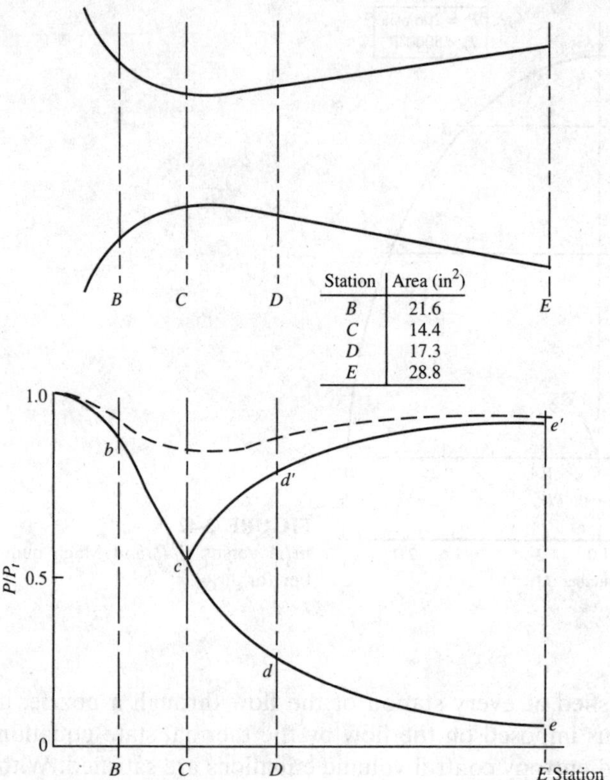

Station	Area (in^2)
B	21.6
C	14.4
D	17.3
E	28.8

FIGURE 3-43
Nozzle pressure distributions.

With $\dot{m}$ and the areas at nozzle stations B, C, D, and E of Fig. 3-43 known, we determine $\dot{m}/A$ at these stations. With these values of $\dot{m}/A$, we locate state points b, c, d, and e, as shown in Fig. 3-42, and read values of P/P_t corresponding to stations B, C, D, and E.

Beginning at the storage chamber, $P/P_t = 1$. Then as A decreases and $\dot{m}/A$ increases, P/P_t decreases from 1.0 to b and c at the throat, as indicated in Figs. 3-42 and 3-43. After passing through the nozzle throat, A increases and $\dot{m}/A$ decreases. Now there may physically exist either value of the ratio P/P_t, corresponding to a given $\dot{m}/A$ with a continuous variation in pressure through the nozzle being maintained. Thus at section D, the pressure may be that corresponding to d or d' in Figs. 3-42 and 3-43. Whichever value exists depends upon the nozzle pressure ratio $P_n = P_c/P_a$. The isentropic nozzle pressure distributions for maximum mass flow are the solid lines labeled I and II in the graph of Fig. 3-43. The dashed line represents a nozzle pressure distribution for a mass flow less than maximum and, hence, subsonic flow through the nozzle.

The nozzle pressure distribution corresponding to flow in I of Fig. 3-43 can be produced by nozzle pressure ratios other than the design value $P_{\bar{n}}$. However, the nozzle exit plane pressure P_e and the exhaust region pressure P_a are equal only for the design nozzle pressure ratio $P_{\bar{n}}$. At the off-design pressure ratios producing flow I, P_e remains the same, as given by

$$P_e = \frac{P_c}{P_{\bar{n}}}$$

but is either greater than or less than the exhaust region pressure P_a.

When $P_e > P_a$, the nozzle is said to be *underexpanded.* Under these conditions, the gas in the nozzle has not expanded down to the exhaust region pressure. Similarly, when $P_e < P_a$, the nozzle is said to be *overexpanded* because the gas in the nozzle has expanded to a value below the exhaust region pressure.

We see from Fig. 3-42 that there are no solutions of the equation

$$\frac{\dot{m}}{A} = f\left(\frac{P}{P_t}\right)$$

which gives $P_e = P_a$ for exhaust region P_a between $P_{e'}$ and P_e. Physically, it is possible to have a discharge region pressure in this range. What happens when such an exhaust region pressure exists? To answer this question, let us discuss the operating characteristics of a nozzle which might be used as a high-speed wind tunnel.

Nozzle Flow and Shock Waves

Figure 3-44 shows a wind tunnel nozzle which we shall use for purposes of discussion. The tunnel operates between an air storage chamber maintained at P_c and T_c and an evacuated receiver. The pressure of the receiver P_a increases as air flows from the storage chamber through the tunnel into the receiver. In this way, the nozzle pressure ratio $P_n = P_c/P_a$ decreases from a very high value (due to a low P_a initially) to a value of 1 when the receiver pressure becomes equal to the storage chamber pressure and flow ceases. A rocket engine nozzle descending through the atmosphere would experience a similar decrease in pressure ratio as P_a increases and P_c remains constant.

During the operation of the tunnel, the air flowing into the evacuated receiver raises the pressure in the nozzle exhaust region P_a and decreases the nozzle pressure ratio P_n. As a result, seven distinct nozzle pressure ratio operating conditions are present. They are depicted in Figs. 3-44 and 3-46 and tabulated in Fig. 3-45. The coordinates of the operating diagram in Fig. 3-46 are the nozzle pressure ratio and nozzle area ratio ε, where ε is the ratio of the nozzle exit area A_e to the nozzle throat area A_t. If we assume the tunnel of Fig. 3-44 has an area ratio of $\varepsilon = 2$, then the operating points of the tunnel all lie

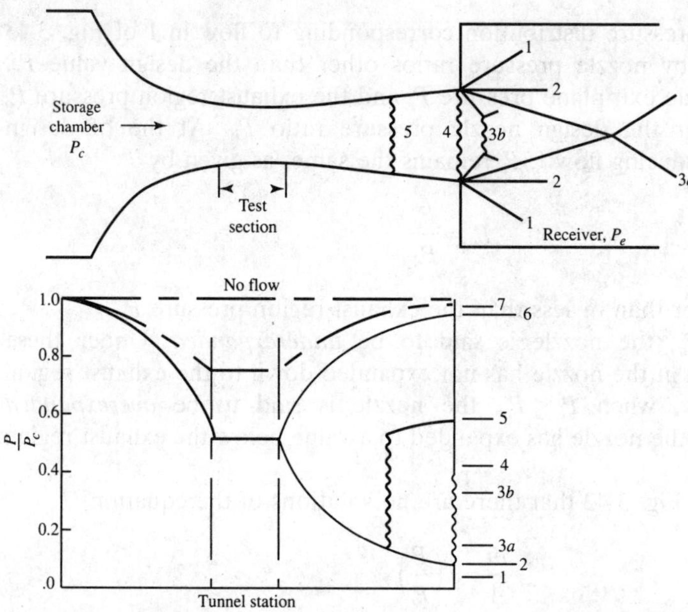

FIGURE 3-44
Nozzle flow with shock waves.

	Operand point	Exit section pressure P_e		Nozzle pressure ratio $P_n = P_C/P_a$	Mass flow rate
1	Underexpanded	$P_e > P_a$		$P_n > P_{\bar{n}}$	Maximum
2	Design	$P_e = P_a$	$P_e = \dfrac{P_c}{P_{\bar{n}}}$	$P_n = P_{\bar{n}}$	Maximum
3	Overexpanded (a) Reg. reflection (b) Mach reflection	$P_e < P_a$		$P_n < P_{\bar{n}}$	Maximum
4	Normal shock at exit	$(P_e)_x < (P_e)_y = P_a$		$P_n < P_{\bar{n}}$	Maximum
5	Normal shock in divergent section	$P_e = P_a$		$P_n > P_{\bar{n}}$	Maximum
6	Sonic at throat subsonic elsewhere	$P_e = P_a$		$P_n < P_{\bar{n}}$	Maximum
7	Subsonic everywhere	$P_e = P_a$		$P_n < P_{\bar{n}}$	Less than Maximum

FIGURE 3-45
Nozzle operating points.

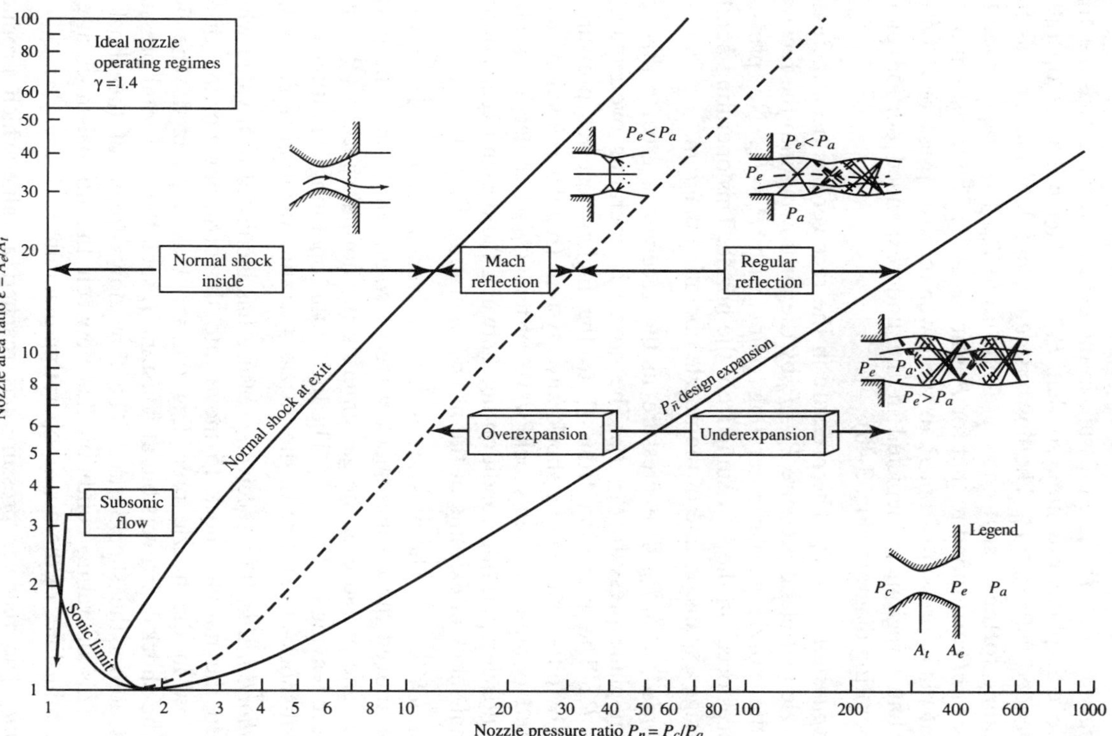

FIGURE 3-46
Nozzle operating diagram.

along the horizontal line $\varepsilon = 2$ in the nozzle operating diagram of Fig. 3-46. The following conditions are possible:

1. *Underexpanded,* $P_n > P_{\bar{n}}$. The pressure in the evacuated receiver is less than the nozzle exit plane pressure, so that $P_e > P_a$. The nozzle is operating underexpanded with $P_n > P_{\bar{n}}$. The flow *inside* the nozzle is the same as that corresponding to the design point pressure ratio $P_{\bar{n}}$. The flow *outside* the nozzle *does not* correspond to that for $P_{\bar{n}}$ since $P_e \neq P_a$. The transition of the nozzle exit plane pressure from P_e to the lower receiver pressure P_a occurs in the exhaust region, as depicted in the underexpanded portion of the nozzle operating diagram (Fig. 3-46).
2. *Design expansion,* $P_n = P_{\bar{n}}$. The pressure in the receiver has been increased to the nozzle exit plane pressure $P_e = P_a$ by the air flowing into the receiver. This is the nozzle design operating point with $P_n = P_{\bar{n}}$. No pressure disturbances occur in the jet issuing from the nozzle. This operating point is on the design expansion line of the nozzle operating diagram.
3. *Overexpanded,* $P_n < P_{\bar{n}}$. The pressure in the receiver is greater than the nozzle exit plane pressure $P_e < P_a$. The nozzle is operating overexpanded with $P_n < P_{\bar{n}}$. The transition from P_e to the higher receiver pressure is produced by either an oblique shock wave system (regular reflection 3*a*) or a combined oblique-normal shock wave system (Mach reflection pattern 3*b*). This nozzle operating condition lies between the design expansion line and normal-shock-at-exit line of the nozzle operating diagram.
4. *Normal shock at exit.* The pressure in the receiver has increased to a value which has moved the normal shock wave of condition 3*b* into the nozzle exit plane. The pressure of the gas entering the normal shock is $(P_e)_x$, and the pressure leaving is $(P_e)_y = P_a$. The loci of this operating condition are on the normal-shock-at-exit line of the nozzle operating diagram (Fig. 3-46).
5. *Normal shock inside.* The receiver pressure has increased to a value which has caused the normal shock to move into the diverging portion of the nozzle. Flow in the nozzle preceding the shock is unaffected. The flow through the shock is irreversible at constant T_t such that the total pressure decreases across the shock wave. The flow downstream of the shock is subsonic. This operating condition lies between the normal-shock-at-exit and sonic limit lines of the nozzle operating diagram.
6. *Sonic limit.* The receiver pressure has reached a value which produces isentropic shock-free flow throughout the nozzle with sonic throat conditions and subsonic flow elsewhere. The nozzle pressure ratios corresponding to this operating condition lie on the sonic limit line of the nozzle operating diagram. This nozzle flow corresponds to flow II of Fig. 3-43.
7. *Subsonic flow.* The receiver pressure has risen to a value producing subsonic flow throughout with a reduced mass flow. This operating condition is

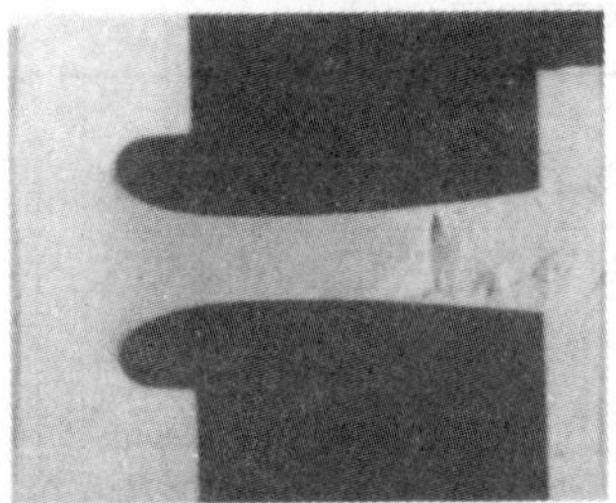

(*a*) $P_n = 1.5$, normal shock, inside

(*b*) $P_n = 2.5$, Mach reflection, overexpansion

(*c*) $P_n = 4.5$, regular reflection, overexpansion

(*d*) $P_n = 8.0$, underexpansion

FIGURE 3-47
Spark Schlieren photographs of nozzle exhaust flow patterns for an area ratio of 1.5. (*Department of Aero-Mechanical Engineering, AFIT, WPAFB, Ohio.*)

bounded by the sonic limit and the $P_n = 1$ (no-flow) lines of the nozzle operating diagram.

Figure 3-47 is a picture of several nozzle exhaust flow patterns for a conical nozzle with an area ratio of $\varepsilon = 1.5$. For $P_n = 1.5$, the normal shock is located well within the nozzle. As P_n is increased to 2.5, the flow is overexpanded in the Mach reflection regime, as evidenced by the clearly defined normal shock internal to the flow. Further increase in P_n causes this normal shock in the Mach reflection pattern to move farther out and diminish in size. It disappears when the regular reflection pattern is obtained. For $P_n = 4.5$, the nozzle is overexpanded in the regular reflection regime. The photograph with $P_n = 8.0$ corresponds to an underexpanded operating point with the exhaust gas expanding down to the ambient pressure in the jet plume.

Nozzle Characteristics of Some Operational Engines

The operating point of a nozzle is determined by the nozzle pressure ratio P_n and area ratio ε. These ratios are presented in Table 3-2 along with other data

TABLE 3-2
Some nozzle characteristics of rocket and turbojet engines

Engine		Chamber pressure P_c (psia)	Area ratio ε	$P_{\bar{n}}$	$(P_n)_{\text{operate}}$
Saturn	F-1 without extension	965	10	140	Varies with
	F-1 with extension	965	16	275	altitude P_a
	J-2	763	27.5	610	
Atlas	Booster	703	8	100	Varies with
	Sustainer	543	25	528	altitude P_a
Subsonic air-breathing turbojet (40,000 ft)		8–14	1.0	1.9	3–5
Supersonic air-breathing turbojet (40,000 ft)		8–56	1–2	1.9–8	3–20

for some operational nozzles. The data in Table 3-2 permit us to locate the operating points of the Saturn and Atlas engines at a given ε in the nozzle operating diagram (Fig. 3-36). In the Saturn F-1 engine, $\varepsilon = 16$ and $P_c =$ 965 psia. Thus at 46,000 ft with $P_a = 2$ psia, we have $P_n = 965/2 = 482$ and a nozzle operating point of (482, 16). This operating point (assuming $\gamma = 1.4$) indicates that the F-1 nozzle is operating above the nozzle design point (underexpanded) at 46,000 ft. At sea level for the F-1, P_n is about 65, and the operating point of the engine nozzle (assuming $\gamma = 1.4$) is in the overexpanded regular reflection region.

The turbojet engines of high-performance, air-breathing, subsonic aircraft generally use convergent nozzles ($\varepsilon = 1.0$) and operate with nozzle pressure ratios greater than the design value of 1.9 (assuming $\gamma = 1.4$). These nozzles therefore operate in the underexpanded operating regime. Turbojet engines of supersonic aircraft, however, have converging-diverging ejectors.

3-8 SIMPLE HEATING FLOW—RAYLEIGH LINE

Consider the flow of a perfect gas with simple heating effects. This flow alternatively may be called *simple T_t flow* since the total temperature is the independent property controlled through the heating effect, as noted by the steady flow energy equation with no shaft work

$$q = c_p \, \Delta T_t$$

By simple heating flow, we mean the following to apply: steady, frictionless flow of a nonreacting perfect gas with no area change or shaft work. The temperature-entropy locus of fluid states that may possibly be attained by a gas in a simple heating flow is called the *simple heating flow line* or, more commonly, the *Rayleigh line.* Let us determine the simple heating flow line and discuss some of its characteristics.

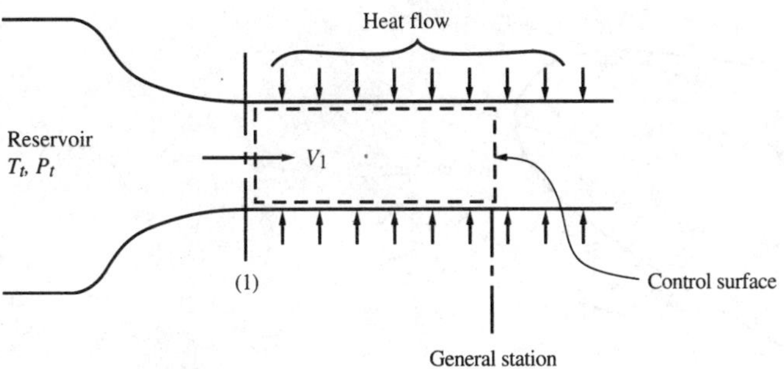

FIGURE 3-48
Simple heating flow.

In Fig. 3-48, a perfect gas is shown to flow steadily from a large reservoir through a convergent nozzle and then into a constant-area frictionless duct with heating effects. We designate the duct inlet as station 1. A relation between the stream properties at 1 and the pressure and temperature downstream of 1 can be obtained by combining the momentum and continuity equations for the flow through the control surface of Fig. 3-48. We have

Momentum $$P_1 + \frac{\rho_1 V_1^2}{g_c} = P + \frac{\rho V^2}{g_c}$$

Continuity $$\rho_1 V_1 = \rho V = \frac{\dot{m}}{A} = \text{const}$$

Replacing V in the momentum equation with $(\dot{m}/A)(1/\rho)$ from the continuity equation gives, after we use $\rho = P/(RT)$,

$$P_1 + \frac{\rho_1 V_1^2}{g_c} = P + \frac{R}{g_c}\left(\frac{\dot{m}}{A}\right)^2 \frac{T}{P} \tag{3-35}$$

This is the equation of a family of lines relating P and T for parameter values of P_1, V_1, and ρ_1 (hence $\dot{m}/A$). For given inlet conditions, therefore, this equation represents a relation between pressure and temperature (P and T) that must be satisfied at stations downstream of station 1 in the flow of Fig. 3-48. By assuming values of pressure in the flow, the corresponding values of temperature which must exist in order to satisfy the momentum and continuity equations can be found from Eq. (3-35). These values of P and T can then be substituted into the following equation to determine the corresponding values of entropy:

$$s = c_p \ln \frac{T}{T_1} - R \ln \frac{P}{P_1} + s_1 \tag{3-36}$$

In this manner, the perfect gas state points satisfying the continuity and momentum equations in simple heating flow can be determined. The

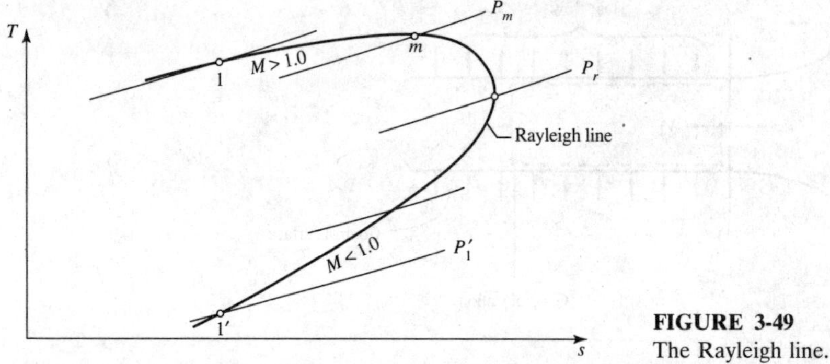

FIGURE 3-49
The Rayleigh line.

temperature-entropy locus of such points is called the *Rayleigh line.* A Rayleigh line obtained by this procedure is sketched in Fig. 3-49. If the assumed values of P_1, T_1, and V_1 correspond to a subsonic condition, station 1 is located on the upper branch of the Rayleigh line. Supersonic values of state 1 properties for the same $\dot{m}/A$ would place this state point on the lower branch of the Rayleigh line at 1′. Thus the Rayleigh line's upper branch corresponds to subsonic state points while the lower branch is in the locus of supersonic flow states.

Treating the simultaneous solution of Eqs. (3-35) and (3-36) as a purely mathematical exercise, for the present, we observe the following: By assuming values of P successively less than P_1, it is found that T and s initially increase until, at P_m, T attains a maximum and, at P_r, s reaches a maximum. For values of P less than P_m, the temperature decreases. And for P less than P_r, the entropy is seen to decrease. Finally, we note that by assuming values of P greater than P_1, we get monotonically decreasing values of T and s. Physically, how can the gas flowing through the duct of Fig. 3-48 be made to attain the pressures assumed in the mathematical solution of Eqs. (3-35) and (3-36)? That is, beginning at state 1 on the Rayleigh line of Fig. 3-49 and at station 1 in Fig. 3-48, how can the gas be made to proceed through the Rayleigh line state points?

The definition of entropy

$$ds = \left(\frac{dq}{T}\right)_{\text{rev}}$$

indicates that one can proceed to higher or lower entropy states on the Rayleigh line by a heat flow to or from the gas, respectively. Heat flow *from* the gas downstream of station 1, therefore, will cause the gas to proceed to the left of the Rayleigh line to states of lower entropy, higher pressure, and lower temperature. Heat flow *to* the gas downstream of station 1, on the other hand, is represented by a progression of the gas along the Rayleigh line to the right to states of higher entropy, lower pressure, and higher temperature up to point m. After state m is reached, further heat flow to the gas produces a decrease in temperature but will continue to decrease the pressure and, up to the point r, increase the entropy. It is impossible to reach values of entropy higher than state r on the Rayleigh line passing through state 1. It is not possible, therefore, to have heat flow in excess of that which takes the gas to r and still remain on the same Rayleigh line.

Let us show that point r is a sonic state point on the Rayleigh line. This can be done as follows: For simple heating flow we have, between any two states infinitesimally close to each other,

$$dq = T\,ds = dh - \frac{dP}{\rho}$$

and

$$dq = dh_t = dh + \frac{V\,dV}{g_c}$$

whence

$$\frac{dP}{\rho} = -\frac{V\,dV}{g_c} \tag{i}$$

Also, by the continuity equation,

$$\frac{d\rho}{\rho} = -\frac{dV}{V} \tag{ii}$$

Eliminating dV from Eqs. (i) and (ii), we find that at any point on the Rayleigh line, the pressure-density gradient equals the square of the stream velocity:

$$\frac{dP}{d\rho} = \frac{V^2}{g_c} \tag{iii}$$

Now we observe that $dP/d\rho$, evaluated at r on Rayleigh line, corresponds to an isentropic $dP/d\rho$ since $ds = 0$ at r. But an isentropic $dP/d\rho$ equals the velocity of sound squared, so $V^2 = a^2$ at r, and the Mach number at this point on the Rayleigh line is 1. We accordingly refer to the stream properties at this sonic point on the Rayleigh line (Fig. 3-50) as P_r^*, T_r^*, etc. The subscript r is used to emphasize that these starred properties are Rayleigh line sonic properties and are not the isentropic P^*, T^* introduced previously. The quantities of P_r^*, T_r^*, etc., are constant in a given simple heating flow, whereas P^*, T^*, etc., will vary from point to point in the same flow because T_t and P_t vary along a Rayleigh line. Note that if Eq. (iii) is evaluated at the maximum temperature point on the Rayleigh line, $M = 1/\sqrt{\gamma}$ at this point.

After state point r has been reached by a heat flow to the gas stream of Fig. 3-50 between 1 and r, the gas can theoretically proceed to lower pressure and entropy by a heat flow from the gas downstream of station r as shown schematically in the figure. (It seems quite probable, however, that one could obtain, experimentally, the transition from subsonic to supersonic flow by this method.) This corresponds to accelerating the gas from subsonic to supersonic flow by reversing the direction of heat flow downstream of point r. This situation is the simple heating counterpart to reversing the area effect from

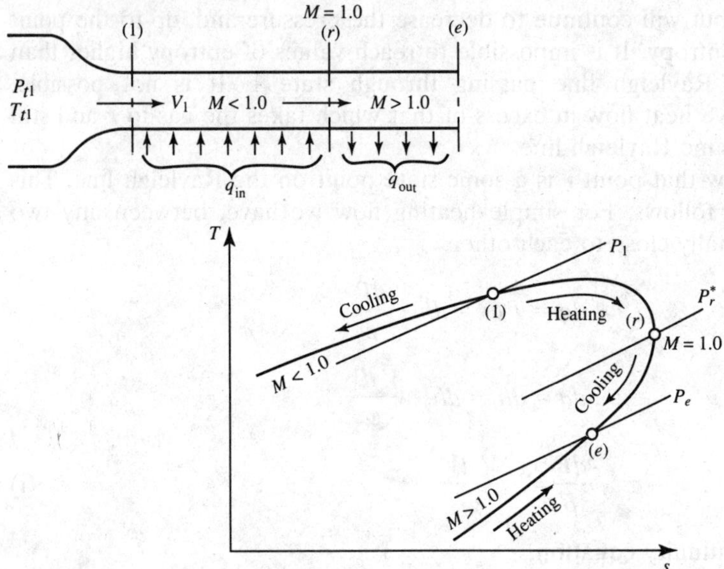

FIGURE 3-50
Transition through sonic point in simple heating flow.

converging to diverging in a simple area flow in order to accelerate the gas from subsonic to supersonic conditions.

Consider a subsonic simple heating flow in which sufficient heat flow is present to produce sonic exit conditions at the duct exit. The process is represented in Fig. 3-51 where 1 represents the duct inlet station and 2

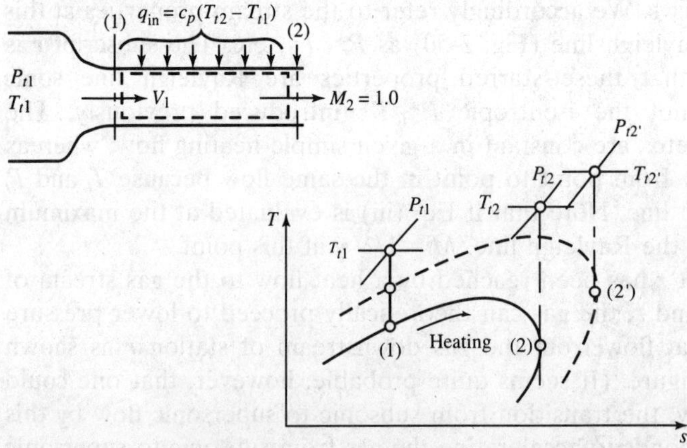

FIGURE 3-51
Choked simple heating flow.

represents the exit. What happens if the heat flow is increased to a value in excess of that required to produce sonic flow at the exit? This added heat flow produces a readjustment in the gas flow which results in a reduced mass flow rate and operation on a different Rayleigh line with a Mach number of 1 still maintained at the exit. The new flow process lies on a Rayleigh line such as the dashed one in the figure with the flow proceeding from 1′ to 2′ and with $T_{t2'} > T_{t2}$. This choking phenomenon is analogous to choking in a simple convergent nozzle flow with sonic exit conditions. If the nozzle exit area is reduced, the mass flow is reduced and sonic conditions continue to be maintained at the exit.

Analytical Relations for Simple Heating Flow

The stream properties in a simple heating flow must satisfy the following equations:

$$T_t = T\left(1 + \frac{\gamma - 1}{2} M^2\right) \tag{3-37}$$

$$P_t = P\left(1 + \frac{\gamma - 1}{2} M^2\right)^{\gamma/(\gamma-1)} \tag{3-38}$$

$$\frac{\dot{m}}{A} = \rho V = \text{const} \tag{3-39}$$

$$R = \frac{P}{\rho T} = \text{const} \tag{3-40}$$

$$\frac{1}{\gamma R g_c} = \frac{M^2 T}{V^2} = \text{const} \tag{3-41}$$

This set of equations is identical to the applicable equations for simple area flow except that in this set, A is constant and P_t and T_t are variables. We have five equations in the six variables T_t, P_t, T, P, M^2, and V. We select T_t as the independent variable, and T_t is controlled by heat flow to the gas. The dependent properties P_t, T, P, M^2, and V can be found in terms of the independent property T_t by writing Eqs. (3-37) through (3-41) in logarithmic differential form and solving for the dependent quantities in terms of the independent variable T_t. Equations (3-37) through (3-41), written in differential form, become, respectively,

Energy
$$\frac{dT}{T} + \frac{[(\gamma - 1)/2]M^2}{1 + [(\gamma - 1)/2]M^2}\frac{dM^2}{M^2} = \frac{dT_t}{T_t} \tag{3-42}$$

Total pressure
$$\frac{dP}{P} + \frac{(\gamma/2)M^2}{1 + [(\gamma - 1)/2]M^2}\frac{dM^2}{M^2} = \frac{dP_t}{P_t} \tag{3-43}$$

Continuity
$$\frac{d\rho}{\rho} + \frac{dV}{V} = 0 \tag{3-44}$$

TABLE 3-3
Simple heating flow

	$\dfrac{dT_t}{T_t}$
$\dfrac{dM^2}{M^2}$	$\dfrac{(1+\gamma M^2)\left(1+\dfrac{\gamma-1}{2}M^2\right)}{1-M^2}$
$\dfrac{dV}{V}$	$\dfrac{1+\dfrac{\gamma-1}{2}M^2}{1-M^2}$
$\dfrac{dP}{P}$	$\dfrac{-\gamma M^2\left(1+\dfrac{\gamma-1}{2}M^2\right)}{1-M^2}$
$\dfrac{d\rho}{\rho}$	$\dfrac{-\left(1+\dfrac{\gamma-1}{2}M^2\right)}{1-M^2}$
$\dfrac{dT}{T}$	$\dfrac{(1-\gamma M^2)\left(1+\dfrac{\gamma-1}{2}M^2\right)}{1-M^2}$
$\dfrac{dP_t}{P_t}$	$\dfrac{-\gamma M^2}{2}$

TABLE 3-4
Simple frictional flow

	$\dfrac{4c_f\,dx}{D}$
$\dfrac{dM^2}{M^2}$	$\dfrac{\gamma M^2\{1+[(\gamma-1)/2]M^2\}}{1-M^2}$
$\dfrac{dV}{V}$	$\dfrac{\gamma M^2}{2(1-M^2)}$
$\dfrac{dP}{P}$	$\dfrac{-\gamma M^2[1+(\gamma-1)M^2]}{2(1-M^2)}$
$\dfrac{d\rho}{\rho}$	$\dfrac{-\gamma M^2}{2(1-M^2)}$
$\dfrac{dT}{T}$	$\dfrac{-\gamma(\gamma-1)M^4}{2(1-M^2)}$
$\dfrac{dP_t}{P_t}$	$\dfrac{-\gamma M^2}{2}$

State
$$\frac{dP}{P}-\frac{d\rho}{\rho}-\frac{dT}{T}=0 \tag{3-45}$$

Mach number
$$\frac{dM^2}{M^2}+\frac{dT}{T}-2\frac{dV}{V}=0 \tag{3-46}$$

The algebraic solution of these equations, to give each dependent variable in terms of T_t, is summarized in Table 3-3.

General conclusions can be drawn from Table 3-3 concerning the variation of the gas properties in a simple heating flow. We see from the relation

$$\frac{dP_t}{P_t}=-\frac{\gamma M^2}{2}\frac{dT_t}{T_t} \tag{3-47}$$

that increasing the total temperature (heat flow to the gas) causes a decrease in total pressure. This indicates, e.g., that in a turbojet engine combustion chamber, a total pressure loss occurs due to the rise of total temperature. This loss is over and above the loss in total pressure due to frictional effects.

Each coefficient of dT_t/T_t in Table 3-3, except the coefficient of Eq. (3-47), has the term $1-M^2$. As a result, the variation of M, P, T, ρ, and V with total temperature is of opposite sign in subsonic and supersonic flow. This is the mathematical proof of the variations already discussed graphically by using the Rayleigh line.

T_t/T_t^*, P_t/P_t^*, etc., for Simple Heating Flow

It was found in simple area flow that A/A^* was a function of the Mach number. A comparable relation in simple heating flow is that T_t/T_t^* is a function of the Mach number. In this ratio, T_t^* represents the total temperature at the sonic point on the Rayleigh line of a given flow. The ratio T_t/T_t^* and similar functions of the Mach number for simple heating flow can be found by integration of the relations in Table 3-3. The first equation in the table can be solved for dT_t/T_t to give

$$\frac{dT_t}{T_t} = \frac{1 - M^2}{(1 + \gamma M^2)\{1 + [(\gamma - 1)/2]M^2\}} \frac{dM^2}{M^2} \tag{3-48}$$

This can be integrated between $M = M$, $T_t = T_t$ and the sonic point where $M = 1$, $T_t = T_t^*$ to obtain T_t/T_t^* as a function of the Mach number. The final result is

$$\boxed{\frac{T_t}{T_t^*} = \frac{2(\gamma + 1)M^2\{1 + [(\gamma - 1)/2]M^2\}}{(1 + \gamma M^2)^2}} \tag{3-49}$$

This equation shows that the total temperature at any given point in a simple heating flow divided by the total temperature required to produce sonic conditions is a function of the Mach number at the given point. In terms of the flow of Fig. 3-52, this means that the total temperature at station 1 divided by

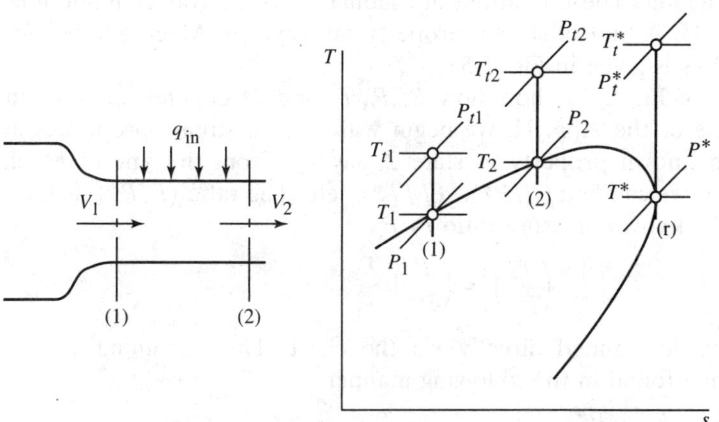

FIGURE 3-52
Interpretation of T/T^* in simple heating flow.

T_t^* at point r on the Rayleigh line explicitly determines the Mach number at state 1. Similarly, $(T_t/T_t^*)_2$ is related to M_2. It should be made clear that it is not necessary that T_t^* physically occur anywhere in the flow. And T_t^* is the total temperature that would be obtained if sufficient heat flow were present to take the flow along the Rayleigh line from state 1 to a Mach number of 1 at state r.

Through Eq. (3-49), one can evaluate the effect of total temperature changes on the flow Mach number. Suppose, e.g., that $M_1 = 0.34$ and that q_{in} is such that $T_{t2}/T_{t1} = 2.0$. Substituting $M_1 = 0.34$ into Eq. (3-49), we find $(T_t/T_t^*)_1 = 0.42$. Then

$$\left(\frac{T_t}{T_t^*}\right)_2 = \left(\frac{T_t}{T_t^*}\right)_1 \frac{T_{t2}}{T_{t1}}$$

gives $(T_t/T_t^*)_2 = 0.84$. A tabulation of Eq. (3-49) (see App. H), giving T_t/T_t^* versus M, shows that for this value of $(T_t/T_t^*)_2$, $M_2 = 0.62$.

Not only is the ratio of T_{t1} to T_t^* a function of Mach number at 1, but also the ratio of any *stream property at state* 1 *to the corresponding property at the sonic state point r of the Rayleigh line is a function of Mach number at state* 1. That is, P/P^*, T/T^*, P_t/P_t^*, etc., are all functions of Mach number in simple heating flow. These functional relationships can be determined by replacing dT_t/T_t in the equations of Table 3-3 by Eq. (3-48), to obtain relations which can be integrated between any general state point on the Rayleigh line and the sonic state point r. To illustrate, we have from the third line of Table 3-3 and Eq. (3-48)

$$\frac{dP_t}{P_t} = -\frac{\gamma M^2}{2}\frac{dT_t}{T_t} = \frac{-\gamma M^2(1 - M^2)}{2(1 + \gamma M^2)\{1 + [(\gamma - 1)/2]M^2\}}\frac{dM^2}{M^2}$$

Integrating between the limits $M = M$, $P_t = P_t$ and $M = 1$, $P_t = P_t^*$, we obtain P_t/P_t^* in terms of M.

The integrated relations for simple heating flow are given in Table 3-5 at the end of this chapter. These relations are tabulated as the Rayleigh line flow function in App. H. A plot of stream property ratios versus Mach number for simple heating flow is given in Fig. 3-53.

The curves of Fig. 3-53 show how P, P_t, T, and M depend upon T_t. In using these charts or the App. H, we begin with known stream properties at state 1 and with known property at state 2, say P_2. From the known Mach number at state 1, we can find $(P/P^*)_1$, $(T_t/T_t^*)_1$, etc. The ratio $(P/P^*)_2$ is then found through the known pressure ratio P_2/P_1:

$$\left(\frac{P}{P^*}\right)_2 = \left(\frac{P}{P^*}\right)_1 \frac{P_2}{P_1}$$

From this, M_2 is determined directly via the chart. The remaining state 2 properties are then found in the following manner:

$$P_{t2} = \left(\frac{P_t}{P_t^*}\right)_2 \left(\frac{P_t^*}{P_t}\right)_1 P_{t1} \qquad T_2 = \left(\frac{T}{T^*}\right)_2 \left(\frac{T^*}{T}\right)_1 T_1 \qquad \text{etc.}$$

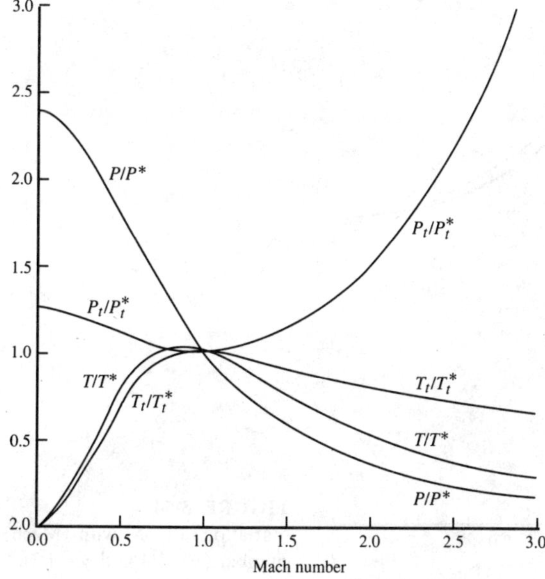

FIGURE 3-53
Variation of stream properties with Mach number in simple heating flow ($\gamma = 1.4$).

In many problems, we know the entering Mach number, total temperature, and heat interaction, and we want to find the leaving Mach number. For a gas with $\gamma = 1.4$, we can use the tables in App. H. However, for other values of γ, we must solve the analytic expression of Eq. (3-49) for the Mach number.

Writing Eq. (3-49) for a heat interaction between states 1 and 2, we obtain

$$\boxed{\frac{T_{t2}}{T_{t1}} = \frac{\phi(M_2^2)}{\phi(M_1^2)}} \tag{3-50}$$

where

$$\boxed{\phi(M^2) = \frac{M^2\{1 + [(\gamma - 1)/2]M^2\}}{(1 + \gamma M^2)^2}} \tag{3-51}$$

Note that

$$\boxed{\frac{T_{t2}}{T_{t1}} = 1 + \frac{q_{\text{in}}}{c_p T_{t1}}} \tag{3-52}$$

The effect of a heat interaction is easily interpreted by plotting the

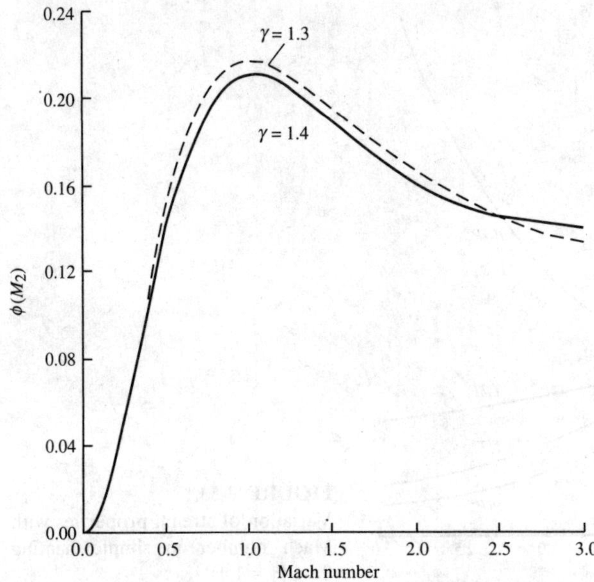

FIGURE 3-54
Variation of ϕ with Mach number ($\gamma = 1.4$ and $\gamma = 1.3$).

function of $f(M^2)$. Thus noting that $\phi(0) = 0$, $\phi(1) = 1/[2(\gamma+1)]$, and $\phi(\infty) = (\gamma-1)/(2\gamma)$, we have a plot of $\phi(M^2)$ as sketched in Fig. 3-54.

Note that for a positive heat interaction, $\phi(M_2^2)$ must be larger than $\phi(M_1^2)$. Thus we see that the Mach number *moves toward unity*. However, if $\phi(M_2^2)$ is greater than $1/[2(\gamma+1)]$, there is no solution. When M reaches 1, the flow is said to be *thermally choked*. Further heat additions would then lead to changes in the *upstream* conditions.

Consider a turbojet. The flow is usually choked at the turbine nozzle throat. The Mach number at the exit of the combustion chamber M_{exit} is fixed by the area ratio of the combustor exit to the turbine nozzle throat. If a further heat interaction occurs, M_{exit} cannot increase. Instead, the combustion chamber pressure will increase. Hopefully, the compressor can supply this pressure (with the increased work input from the turbine).

Solution for the Downstream Variables

We may solve for M_2 by writing

$$\boxed{\begin{aligned}\Phi = \phi(M_2^2) &= \frac{M_2^2\{1 + [(\gamma-1)/2]M_2^2\}}{(1+\gamma M_2^2)^2} \\ &= \frac{M_1^2\{1 + [(\gamma-1)/2]M_1^2\}}{(1+\gamma M_1^2)^2}\left(1 + \frac{q_{\text{in}}}{c_p T_{t1}}\right)\end{aligned}} \tag{3-53}$$

In this expression, M_1 and $q_{\text{in}}(c_p T_{t1})$ are known. This is a quadratic equation for M_2^2:

$$M_2^2\left(1+\frac{\gamma-1}{2}M_2^2\right)=\Phi(1+\gamma M_2^2)^2$$

or

$$M_2^4\left(\frac{\gamma-1}{2}-\gamma^2\Phi\right)+M_2^2(1-2\gamma\Phi)-\Phi=0$$

Thus

$$M_2^2=\frac{2\gamma\Phi-1\pm\sqrt{1-2(\gamma+1)\Phi}}{\gamma-1-2\gamma^2\Phi}$$

Note that if $\Phi=(\gamma-1)/(2\gamma^2)$, the denominator goes to zero. This corresponds to $M=\infty$ in the supersonic case. But, for the subsonic case, the numerator also goes to zero. To *remove* this singularity, multiply the numerator and denominator by $2\gamma\Phi-1\mp\sqrt{1-2(\gamma+1)\Phi}$. Then

$$M_2^2=\frac{(2\gamma\Phi-1)^2-[1-2(\gamma+1)\Phi]}{(\gamma-1-2\gamma^2\Phi)[2\gamma\Phi-1\mp\sqrt{1-2(\gamma+1)\Phi}]}$$

$$=\frac{2\Phi[2\gamma^2\Phi-(\gamma-1)]}{(\gamma-1-2\gamma^2\Phi)[2\gamma\Phi-1\mp\sqrt{1-2(\gamma+1)\Phi}]}$$

or

$$=\frac{-2\Phi}{2\gamma\Phi-1\mp\sqrt{1-2(\gamma+1)\Phi}}$$

This may be written as

$$\boxed{M_2^2=1-\frac{\Delta(1+\Delta)}{1-2\gamma\Phi+\Delta}} \tag{3-54}$$

where

$$\boxed{\Delta=\pm\sqrt{1-2(\gamma+1)\Phi}} \tag{3-55}$$

Here, plus is for subsonic flow and minus is for supersonic flow.

For the static pressure, we use the momentum equation

$$d\left(P+\frac{\rho V^2}{g_c}\right)=0$$

or

$$d[P(1+\gamma M^2)]=0$$

So

$$\boxed{\frac{P_2}{P_1}=\frac{1+\gamma M_1^2}{1+\gamma M_2^2}} \tag{3-56}$$

For the total pressure, we have

$$\frac{P_{t2}}{P_{t1}}=\frac{P_2}{P_1}\left\{\frac{1+[(\gamma-1)/2]M_2^2}{1+[(\gamma-1)/2]M_1^2}\right\}^{\gamma/(\gamma-1)}$$

Thus

$$\boxed{\frac{P_{t2}}{P_{t1}}=\frac{1+\gamma M_1^2}{1+\gamma M_2^2}\left\{\frac{1+[(\gamma-1)/2]M_2^2}{1+[(\gamma-1)/2]M_1^2}\right\}^{\gamma/(\gamma-1)}} \tag{3-57}$$

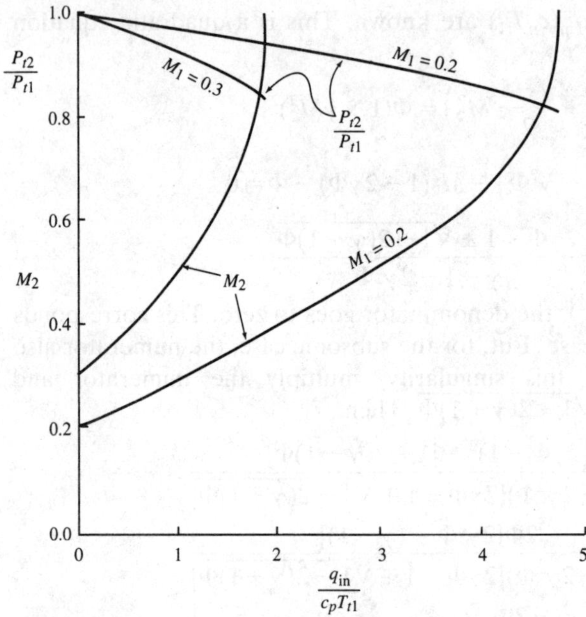

FIGURE 3-55
Total pressure ratio and exit Mach number versus heating rate ($\gamma = 1.4$).

We can plot these results for the total pressure ratio. For example, for a gas with $M_1 = 0.2$ and 0.3, we get the curves shown in Fig. 3-55.

Example 3-10. One-dimensional flow of a perfect gas occurs in a frictionless, constant-area duct while energy is added to the gas by a heat interaction, as depicted in the sketch of Fig. 3-56. The perfect gas has $\gamma = 1.33$ and $c_p = 0.276$ Btu/(lbm · °R). The gas enters the duct with a total temperature of 1000°R, a total pressure of 135 psia, and a Mach number of 0.4.

a. Find the leaving Mach number and the T_{t2}/T_{t1}, P_2/P_1, and P_{t2}/P_{t1} property ratios for heat interactions of 30, 60, 90, 120, 150, 180, 210, 240, and 270 Btu/lbm.

b. Find the leaving total temperature and heat interaction that will choke the flow at the exit ($M_2 = 1$).

c. Determine what must happen to upstream conditions when the heat interaction is 300 Btu/lbm.

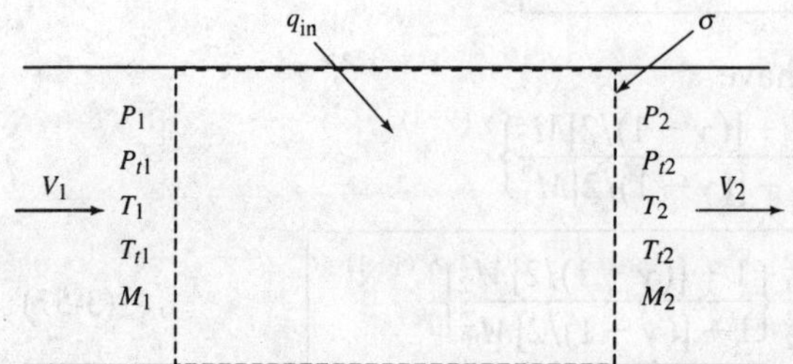

FIGURE 3-56
Sketch of control volume for Example 3-10.

Solution. The applicable equations for the solution of this problem are these:

$$\frac{T_{t2}}{T_{t1}} = 1 + \frac{q_{\text{in}}}{c_p T_{t1}} \tag{3-52}$$

$$\Phi = \phi(M_2^2) = \frac{M_2^2\{1 + [(\gamma - 1)/2]M_2^2\}}{(1 + \gamma M_2^2)^2} = \frac{M_1^2\{1 + [(\gamma - 1)/2]M_1^2\}}{(1 + \gamma M_1^2)^2}\left(1 + \frac{q_{\text{in}}}{c_p T_{t1}}\right) \tag{3-53}$$

$$M_2^2 = 1 - \frac{\Delta(1 + \Delta)}{1 + 2\gamma\Phi + \Delta} \tag{3-54}$$

$$\Delta = \sqrt{1 - 2(\gamma + 1)\Phi} \tag{3-55}$$

$$\frac{P_2}{P_1} = \frac{1 + \gamma M_1^2}{1 + \gamma M_2^2} \tag{3-56}$$

$$\frac{P_{t2}}{P_{t1}} = \frac{1 + \gamma M_1^2}{1 + \gamma M_2^2}\left\{\frac{1 + [(\gamma - 1)/2]M_2^2}{1 + [(\gamma - 1)/2]M_1^2}\right\}^{\gamma/(\gamma-1)} \tag{3-57}$$

a. For the heat-interactions and entering total temperature, we obtain the following values listed in tabular form:

q_{in} **(Btu/lbm)**	T_{t2}/T_{t1}	Φ	Δ	M_2	P_2/P_2	P_{t2}/P_{t1}
30	1.1087	0.123786	0.650506	0.452873	0.970851	0.988187
60	1.2174	0.135922	0.605479	0.467478	0.939679	0.975828
90	1.3261	0.148057	0.556823	0.504594	0.905995	0.962827
120	1.4348	0.160193	0.503487	0.545323	0.869072	0.949052
150	1.5435	0.171329	0.443786	0.591412	0.827741	0.934314
180	1.6522	0.184465	0.374691	0.646015	0.779908	0.918320
210	1.7609	0.196601	0.289551	0.716185	0.720967	0.900544
240	1.8696	0.208737	0.165187	0.827310	0.634871	0.879752
270	1.9783	0.220870	$\sqrt{-0.029}$	—	—	—

The calculations for a heat interaction of 270 Btu/lbm are not completed because the results for Δ indicate that the flow will be choked at the exit and the upstream properties must change.

b. For choked flow at the exit, we use Eq. (3-49) to determine $T_{t2}(=T_{t1}^*)$.

$$\frac{T_t}{T_t^*} = \frac{2(\gamma + 1)M^2\left(1 + \frac{\gamma - 1}{2}M^2\right)}{(1 + \gamma M^2)^2}$$

$$\frac{T_{t1}}{T_{t1}^*} = \frac{2(2.33)(0.16)(1.0264)}{1.2128} = 0.520288 \tag{3-49}$$

$$T_{t1}^* = 1922°\text{R}$$

$$q_{\text{in}_{\max}} = c_p(T_{t1}^* - T_{t1}) = 0.276(922) = 254.47 \text{ Btu/lbm}$$

c. A heat interaction of 300 Btu/lbm will choke the flow at the exit and entrance Mach number, and the static pressure will change. The new entering Mach number can be determined by using Eqs. (3-52) and (3-49) as follows:

$$\frac{T_{t1}^*}{T_{t1}} = \frac{T_{t2}}{T_{t1}} = 1 + \frac{q_{\text{in}}}{c_p T_{t1}} = 2.086957$$

Thus $T_{t2} = T_{t1}^* = 2087°\text{R}$.

Noting that Eq. (3-49) is equal to $2(\gamma + 1)$ times the function $\phi(M^2)$, as given by Eq. (3-51), we can write

$$\phi(M_1^2) = \frac{1}{2(\gamma+1)}\frac{T_{t1}}{T_{t1}^*} = \frac{1}{2(2.33)}\frac{1}{2.086957} = 0.102825$$

Equation (3-51) can be solved for the Mach number, as was done for Eq. (3-53). The solution is the same as that given by Eqs. (3-54) and (3-55) with Φ replaced by $\phi(M_1^2)$. Thus

$$\Phi = \phi(M_1^2) = 0.102825$$

$$\Delta = \sqrt{1 - 2(\gamma+1)\Phi} = 0.7216878$$

$$M_1^2 = 1 - \frac{\Delta(1+\Delta)}{1 - 2\gamma\Phi + \Delta} = 0.142007$$

or

$$M_1 = 0.3768$$

Thus the entering Mach number has reduced from 0.4 to 0.3768 when the heat interaction increased from 254.47 to 300 Btu/lbm. For the same entering total temperature and total pressure, we can determine the entering flow properties for these two cases [assuming $R = 53.34$ ft · lbf/(lbm · °R)]:

Quantity	$q_{in} \leq q_{in_{max}}$	q_{in} **= 300 Btu/lbm**
T_{t1} (°R)	1000	1000
P_{t1} (psia)	135	135
M_1	0.4000	0.3768
T_1 (°R)	974.28	977.11
P_1 (psia)	123.23	124.49
a_1 (ft/sec)	1490.7	1492.9
V_1 (ft/sec)	596.28	562.52
$\frac{\dot{m}}{A} = \rho_1 V_1$ [lbm/(ft^2 · sec)]	203.60	193.48

Thus the heat interaction of 300 Btu/lbm reduced the mass flow rate per unit area by 5 percent and increased the entering static pressure by 1 percent versus the values for unchoked flow.

A basic model for the combustion process can be a simple heating flow. In a turbojet engine, the combustor increases the thermal energy of the gas by burning fuel as it is pumped in. If the mass flow rate of air goes down and we continue to pump fuel in at the same rate, the heat interaction per unit mass of gas will go up even higher, and our upstream Mach number M_1 will continue to decrease until we can get no flow through the compressor. At this point, the compressor stalls, and no airflow is available for the burner—so we also get flameout.

Example 3-11. One-dimensional flow of air, a perfect gas, occurs in a frictionless, constant-area duct while energy is added to the heat by a heat interaction. The air enters the duct with a total temperature of 450 K, a total pressure of 8 atm, and a Mach number of 0.3.

a. Find the heat interaction that will choke the flow at the exit ($M = 1$) and the exit total temperature and total pressure.

b. For an exit Mach number of 0.6, determine the heat interaction and the exit total temperature and total pressure.

Solution. For solution of this problem, we will use the tables in App. H and check our answers by using Fig. 3-55.

a. For the entering condition of $M = 0.3$, we have from App. H

$$\frac{T_{t1}}{T_{t1}^*} = 0.346860 \qquad \text{and} \qquad \frac{P_{t1}}{P_{t1}^*} = 1.19854$$

Since the exit condition corresponds to $M = 1$,

$$T_{t2} = T_{t1}^* \qquad \text{and} \qquad P_{t2} = P_{t1}^*$$

Thus

$$T_{t2} = \frac{T_{t1}}{T_{t1}/T_{t1}^*} = \frac{450}{0.346860} = 1297.4 \text{ K}$$

$$P_{t2} = \frac{P_{t1}}{P_{t1}/P_{t1}^*} = \frac{8}{1.19854} = 6.675 \text{ atm}$$

$$q_{\text{in}} = c_p(t_{t2} - T_{t1}) = 1.004(1297.4 - 450) = 850.79 \text{ kJ/kg}$$

and

$$\frac{q_{\text{in}}}{c_p T_{t1}} = 1.883 \qquad \text{which checks with Fig. 3-55}$$

b. For the exit Mach number of 0.6, we have from App. H

$$\frac{T_{t2}}{T_{t2}^*} = 0.818923 \qquad \text{and} \qquad \frac{P_{t2}}{P_{t2}^*} = 1.07525$$

Since $T_{t1}^* = T_{t2}^*$ and $P_{t1}^* = P_{t2}^*$, then

$$T_{t2} = T_{t1}\frac{T_{t2}/T_{t2}^*}{t_{t1}/T_{t1}^*} = 450\left(\frac{0.818923}{0.346860}\right) = 1062.4°\text{R}$$

$$P_{t2} = P_{t1}\frac{P_{t2}/P_{t2}^*}{P_{t1}/P_{t1}^*} = 8\left(\frac{1.07525}{1.19854}\right) = 7.177 \text{ atm}$$

$$q_{\text{in}} = c_p(t_{t2} - T_{t1}) = 1.004(1062.4 - 450) = 614.85 \text{ kJ/kg}$$

and

$$\frac{q_{\text{in}}}{c_p T_{t1}} = 1.361 \qquad \text{which checks with Fig. 3.55}$$

3-9 SIMPLE FRICTIONAL FLOW—FANNO LINE

The steady flow of a nonreacting perfect gas in a constant-area, adiabatic duct with friction is called *simple frictional flow*. For such a flow, a relation between the stream properties at a given station and the pressure and temperature at any general station in the flow can be obtained from the steady flow energy equation and the continuity equation. For the flow of Fig. 3-57,

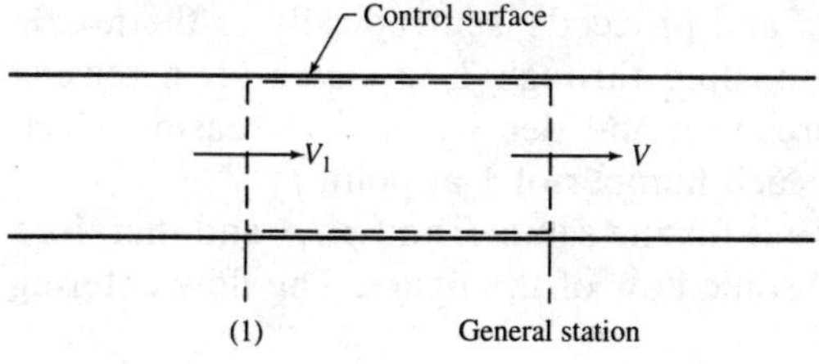

FIGURE 3-57
Simple frictional flow.

these equations take the forms

Energy $$T_1 + \frac{V_1^2}{2c_p g_c} = T_t = T + \frac{V^2}{2c_p g_c} = \text{const}$$

Continuity $$\rho_1 V_1 = \rho V = \frac{\dot{m}}{A} = \text{const}$$

Solving the continuity equation for the velocity V and using $P = \rho RT$ gives

$$V = \frac{\dot{m}}{A}\frac{1}{\rho} = \frac{\dot{m}}{A}\frac{RT}{P}$$

Replacing V in the energy equation by $(\dot{m}/A)/(RT/P)$, we get

$$T_1 + \frac{V_1^2}{2c_p g_c} = T_t = T + \frac{1}{2c_p g_c}\left(\frac{\dot{m}}{A}\right)^2\left(\frac{RT}{P}\right)^2 \tag{3-58}$$

For given inlet conditions at station 1, this equation represents a relation in terms of pressure and temperature that must be satisfied at any point in the flow. By assuming values of T to exist at points in the flow, it is possible, with Eq. (3-58), to determine the corresponding values of P, thus fixing the state of the gas (P, T, T_t) at these points in the flow. Further, by arbitrarily assuming a value of entropy s_1, the entropy at any other point of known T and P is determined by

$$s = c_p \ln\frac{T}{T_1} - R\ln\frac{P}{P_1} + s_1 \tag{3-59}$$

Since the flow is irreversible and adiabatic, the values of P and T that may occur physically downstream of station 1 are further restricted by the fact that the gas must proceed through values of T and P corresponding to states of higher entropy.

The temperature-entropy locus of the fluid states, satisfying Eqs. (3-58) and (3-59), is called the *simple frictional flow line*, or the *Fanno line*. Equation (3-58) relates P and T for fixed values of T_t and $\dot{m}/A$. The family of Fanno lines obtained for parametric values of T_t with fixed $\dot{m}/A$ is shown in Fig. 3-58(a), while Fig. 3-58(b) shows the family of Fanno lines corresponding to parametric values of $\dot{m}/A$ with T_t held constant.

As an illustration of flows along a Fanno line, consider a perfect gas to be flowing from a large reservoir through a nozzle and then through a simple frictional duct. Two cases, one subsonic and one supersonic, are illustrated in Fig. 3-59. In the subsonic case, flow begins in the reservoir at state point (P_t, T_t) on the temperature-entropy diagram and proceeds isentropically to the nozzle exit at (P_1, T_1); then along the Fanno line through 1 to states of increasing entropy; decreasing temperature, pressure, and density; and increasing Mach number; tending toward a limiting Mach number of 1 at point f.

The supersonic flow of Fig. 3-59 is for the same T_t and $\dot{m}/A$ and therefore is on the same Fanno line as the subsonic flow of the figure. The flow entering

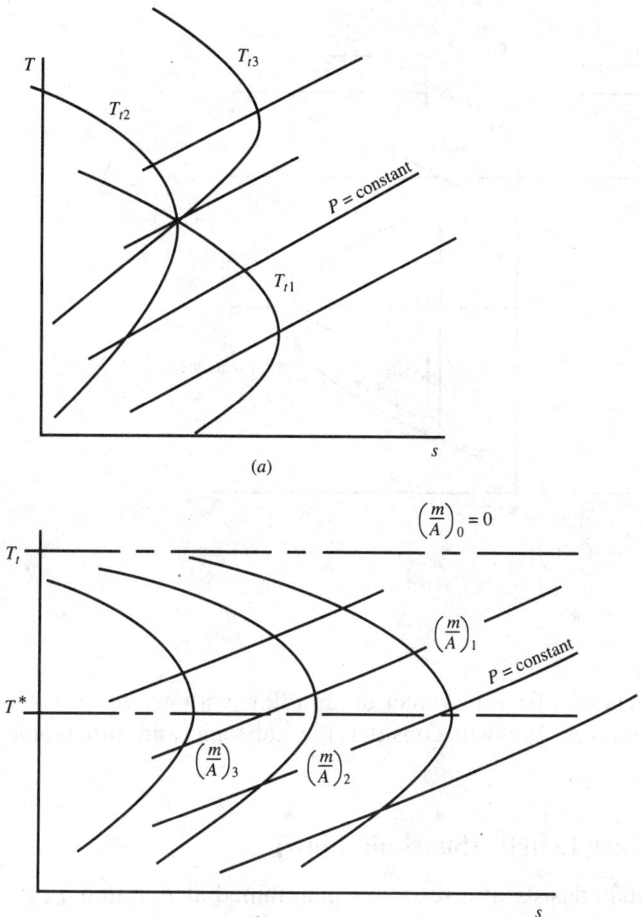

FIGURE 3-58
Fanno lines.

the frictional duct at station 1 progresses along the supersonic branch of the Fanno line to higher entropy, temperature, pressure, and density, and to a limiting Mach number of 1 at *f*. From this example, we see that the effect of friction on P, T, ρ, V, and M in supersonic flow is the opposite of its effect on these properties in subsonic flow. In all cases of simple frictional flow, P_t decreases and s increases.

For given inlet conditions to a simple frictional duct, there exists a Fanno line representing the *possible* states that the flow may proceed through in the duct. Whether a portion of or all these possible states are attained by the gas as it flows through the duct depends upon the amount of frictional duct length and pressures imposed upon the boundaries (inlet and exit) of the flow system.

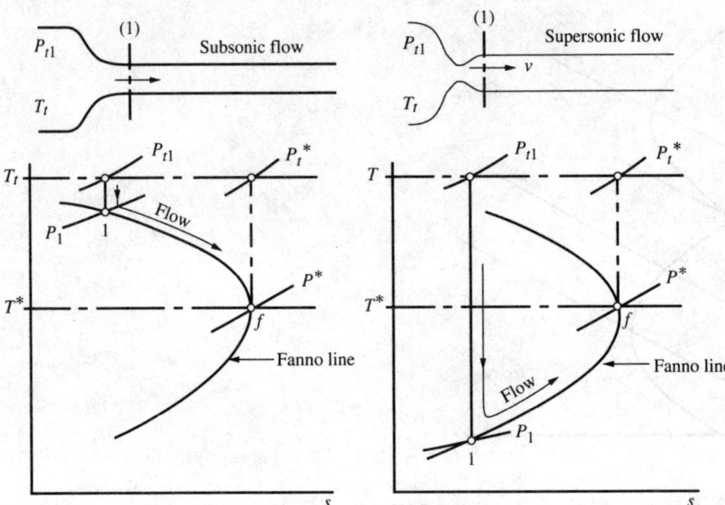

FIGURE 3-59
Simple frictional flow.

Let us examine the effects of a frictional duct upon a flow with given reservoir and exhaust region pressures. We will consider the subsonic and supersonic cases separately.

Effect of Frictional Duct Length (Subsonic Flow)

The flow unit of Fig. 3-60 consists of a reservoir maintained at $P_{t\,\text{res}}$ and T_t, an exhaust region of constant ambient pressure P_a, a convergent nozzle, and a constant-area pipe whose length can be adjusted to terminate at station 1, 2, 3, or 4. As a starting point, let the unit be such that at its exit $M = 1$ and the exhaust region is just attained.

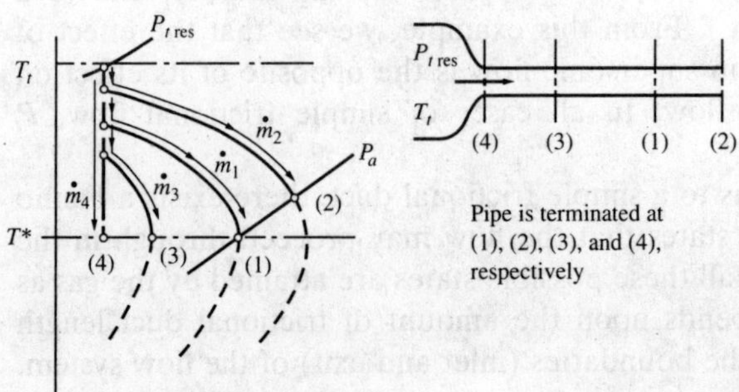

FIGURE 3-60
Effect of duct length in subsonic flow.

For this case (Fig. 3-60), the flow through the unit from (P_t, T_t) follows isentropically down to the inlet of the simple frictional duct and then along a Fanno line corresponding to $\dot{m}_1$ to $M = 1$ at the duct exit section 1. If now the duct length is increased to 2, everything else remaining the same, we find the flow process to follow along a Fanno line corresponding to a lower mass rate of flow $\dot{m}_2$. Throughout this latter flow, $M < 1$. If the duct length is increased further beyond station 2, the mass flow in the unit continues to decrease and, in the limit, $\dot{m}$ tends to zero as the duct length tends to infinity. Now, on the other hand, if the duct length is decreased to station 3, we find the flow process to proceed isentropically down to the duct inlet and then along a Fanno line of mass flow rate $\dot{m}_3 > \dot{m}_1$. As the duct length goes to zero, the Mach number at the nozzle exit increases to 1, corresponding to a maximum mass rate of flow $\dot{m}_4$ through the nozzle (as the duct length goes to zero, the unit becomes a simple convergent nozzle). Beginning at condition 4, we observe that adding duct lengths to the nozzle produces a decrease in mass flow, i.e., the flow is "choked" by friction.

Effect of Frictional Duct Length (Supersonic Flow)

Let the unit of Fig. 3-61 be operating such that the flow leaving the pipe is at $M = 1$ and at the exhaust region pressure with a mass rate of flow $\dot{m}_1$. This

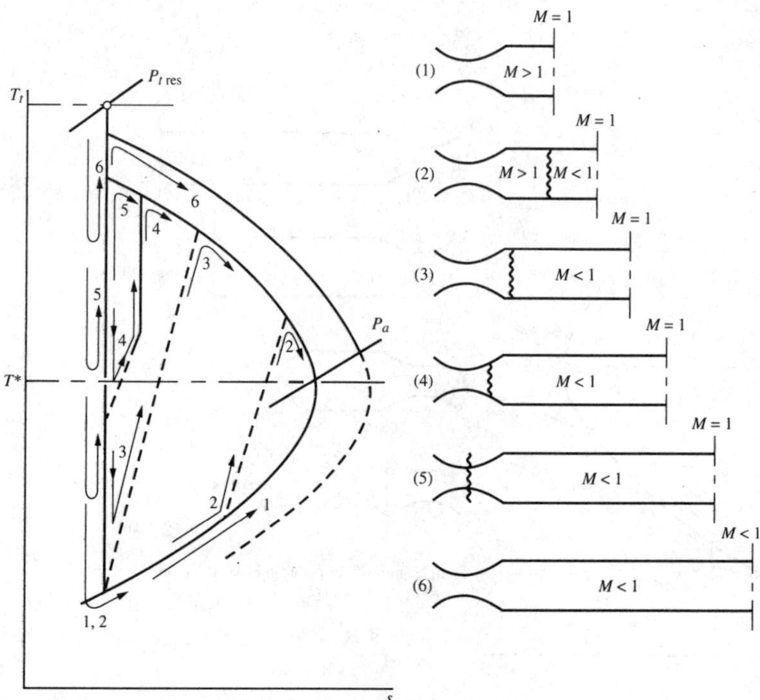

FIGURE 3-61
Flow along Fanno line with normal shocks.

condition is indicated on the T-s diagram where the flow process originates at P_t, T_t, proceeds isentropically to the supersonic branch of the Fanno line corresponding to $\dot{m}_1$, and then follows along this Fanno line to $M = 1$ and P_a. Now, as the duct length is increased to condition 2, we find that the new boundary condition of increased duct length can be satisfied by assuming a normal shock to occur at a point in the duct such that the combination of duct length preceding and duct length following the flow discontinuity produces a Mach number of 1 at the duct exit. The flow process corresponding to this condition is shown by the arrows numbered 2. As the duct length is increased further, the normal shock progresses upstream to the duct inlet, then into the nozzle until it reaches the nozzle throat at 5. Further increase in length, beyond that corresponding to 5, reduces the mass rate of flow through the unit, and the flow progresses through the duct for these cases along Fanno lines of lower mass flows as indicated by 6.

Suppose, now, a flow corresponding to condition 1 exists, and let the duct length be reduced. In this case, we find that the stream properties in the remaining portion are unaffected and that as the duct length is reduced to zero, the flow reduces to that through a convergent-divergent nozzle, exhausting to the discharge region through a system of oblique shock waves set up in the exhaust region. These conditions are illustrated schematically in Fig. 3-62. For condition 1, the flow proceeds isentropically to the duct inlet, then along a

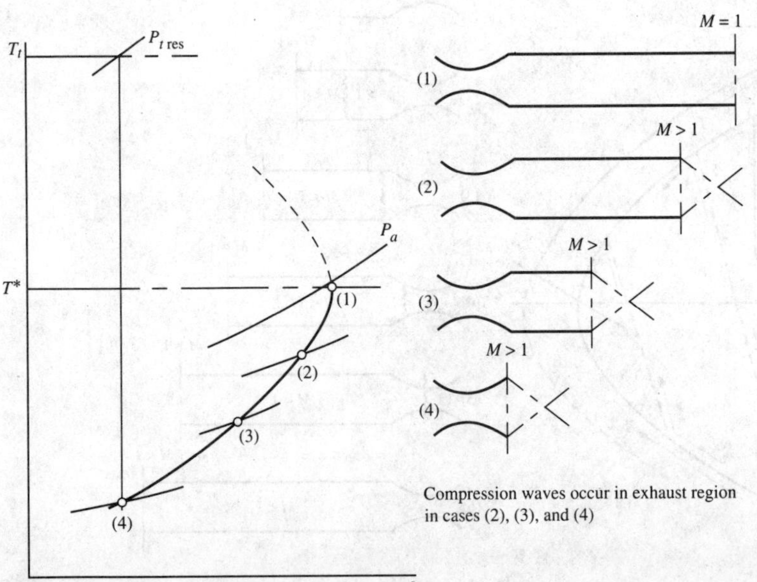

FIGURE 3-62
Flow along supersonic branch of Fanno line.

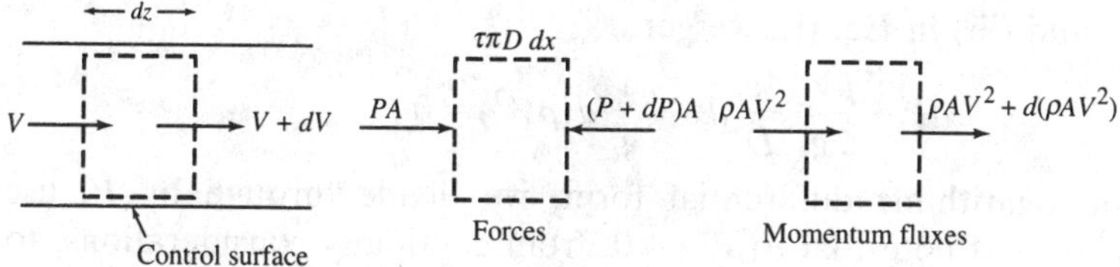

FIGURE 3-63
Momentum equation for simple frictional flow.

Fanno line to $M = 1$ at 1. For 2, 3, and 4, the exit conditions from the unit are as indicated on the T-s diagram. Notice that P_2, P_3 and P_4 are each less than P_a. The rise in pressure to P_a in these cases is attained through a series of oblique shock waves set up from the exit of the duct.

Analytical Relations for Simple Frictional Flow

To develop equations expressing the relations between the dependent stream properties and the independent frictional duct length in a simple frictional flow, we must apply the momentum equation to introduce the duct friction factor c_f and duct length x into the analysis. These terms arise in the momentum equation by evaluating the force of the duct on fluid for the flow. The momentum equation is applied to the flow through the control surface in the simple frictional flow of Fig. 3-63 to obtain

$$-A\,dP - \tau\pi D\,dx = \frac{1}{g_c}\,d(\rho A V^2) \tag{i}$$

In this equation, D is the duct diameter, and τ is the shear stress at the wall acting over the wetted area $\pi D\,dx$. The pipe friction factor c_f is defined as

$$\boxed{c_f \equiv \frac{\tau}{\rho V^2/(2g_c)}}$$

so that

$$\tau = \frac{c_f \rho V^2}{2g_c} \tag{ii}$$

The pipe circumference can be expressed in terms of the pipe area as follows:

$$\pi D = 4\frac{\pi D^2}{4D} = \frac{4A}{D} \tag{iii}$$

Using Eqs. (ii) and (iii) in Eq. (i), we get

$$dP + \frac{\rho V^2}{2g_c}\frac{4c_f}{D}dx + \frac{1}{g_c}d(\rho V^2) = 0$$

To put this in logarithmic differential form, we divide through by P, use $\rho V^2/(Pg_c) = \gamma M^2$, and note that $d(\rho V) = 0$, from continuity considerations, to obtain finally

$$\frac{dP}{p} + \frac{\gamma M^2}{2}\frac{4c_f}{D}dx + \gamma M^2 \frac{dV}{V} = 0$$

We now have the following set of linear algebraic equations with variables in logarithmic differential form which must be satisfied in simple frictional flow:

State $$\frac{dP}{P} - \frac{d\rho}{\rho} - \frac{dT}{T} = 0 \tag{3-60}$$

Energy $$\frac{dT}{T} + \frac{[(\gamma-1)/2]M^2}{1+[(\gamma-1)/2]M^2}\frac{dM^2}{M^2} = 0 \tag{3-61}$$

Continuity $$\frac{d\rho}{\rho} + \frac{dV}{V} = 0 \tag{3-62}$$

Total pressure $$\frac{dP}{P} + \frac{(\gamma/2)M^2}{1+[(\gamma-1)/2]M^2}\frac{dM^2}{M^2} = \frac{dP_t}{P_t} \tag{3-63}$$

Momentum $$\frac{dP}{P} + \frac{\gamma M^2}{2}\frac{4c_f}{D}dx + \gamma M^2 \frac{dV}{V} = 0 \tag{3-64}$$

Mach number $$\frac{dM^2}{M^2} + \frac{dT}{T} - 2\frac{dV}{V} = 0 \tag{3-65}$$

The quantity $4c_f\,dx/D$ is selected as the independent variable because the frictional duct length is the physical phenomenon producing changes in state. This leaves P, ρ, T, M^2, V, and P_t as our six dependent variables in a set of six equations. The usual methods for solving simultaneous linear algebraic equations are used to obtain the relations of Table 3-4 (see page 180). A procedure to obtain the first entry is outlined as follows: By using the momentum equation, Eq. (3-64), P can be eliminated from the equation of state, Eq. (3-60), to give a relation in V, x, P, and T. Next ρ is eliminated from this result by the continuity equation, Eq. (3-62), to obtain a relation in V, x, and T. Then Eq. (3-65) is used to eliminate V in favor of M^2, giving an equation in M^2, x, and T. Finally, the energy equation is used to replace T with M^2 to give the first equation in Table 3-4 on page 180.

The results of Table 3-4 indicate that except for P_t, the sign of a property gradient in simple frictional flow depends upon the flow Mach number. For example,

$$\frac{dV}{dx} = \frac{\gamma M^2}{2(M^2-1)}\frac{4c_f}{D}V$$

Consequently, friction accelerates the gas in subsonic flow and reduces the velocity in a supersonic simple frictional flow. The relations of Table 3-4 constitute the analytical verification of facts determined graphically from the

Fanno line. It is interesting to note that friction causes the velocity to increase in subsonic flow and produces a pressure rise in supersonic simple frictional flow.

Fanno Line Stream Properties as Functions of Mach Number

For computational work in simple frictional flow, it is convenient to have the stream properties as functions of the flow Mach number. For this purpose, the Mach number is treated as the independent variable. The first entry in Table 3-4 can be written

$$\frac{4c_f\,dx}{D}=\frac{1-M^2}{\gamma M^2\{1+[(\gamma-1)/2]M^2\}}\frac{dM^2}{M^2} \tag{3-66}$$

With this relation, it is possible to determine the frictional duct required beyond any given station in the flow to produce a Mach number of 1 by integrating from any pipe station L and Mach number M to the pipe station L^* where the Mach number is 1 (Fig. 3-64). During the integration, we assume a constant value of c_f so that the left-hand side of Eq. (3-66) becomes

$$\int_L^{L^*}\frac{4c_f\,dx}{D}=\frac{4c_f}{D}(L^*-L)=\frac{4c_fL_{\max}}{D}$$

The integration of $L_{\max}$ is given with the help of Fig. 3-64. It is the maximum pipe length that can be added beyond a given station without affecting the stream properties at the station, regardless of the exhaust region pressure. When this maximum length exists, sonic flow conditions will occur at the pipe exit.

Integration of the right-hand side of Eq. (3-66) gives finally

$$\boxed{\frac{4c_fL_{\max}}{D}=\frac{1-m^2}{\gamma M^2}+\frac{\gamma+1}{2\gamma}\ln\frac{(\gamma+1)M^2}{2\{1+[(\gamma-1)/2]M^2\}}} \tag{3-67}$$

A plot of Eq. (3-67) is given in Fig. 3-65. The graph shows that the effect of friction on the stream properties is much greater in supersonic flow than in

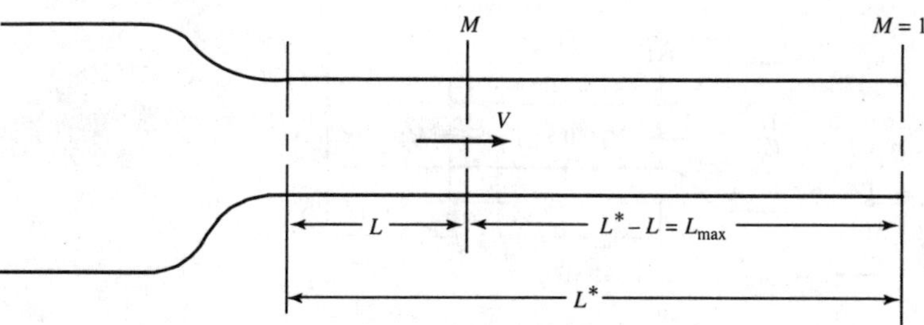

FIGURE 3-64
Simple frictional flow with sonic exit conditions.

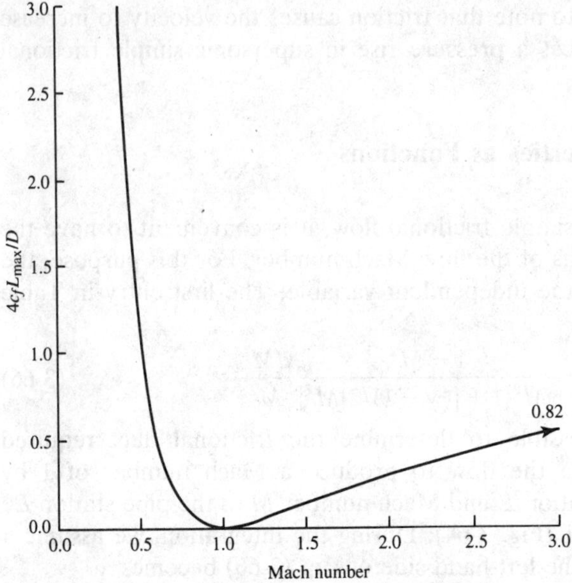

FIGURE 3-65
$4c_fL_{max}/D$ as a function of Mach number ($\gamma = 1.4$).

subsonic flow. To illustrate, for a pipe of diameter D with a friction factor of 0.01, the figure indicates that the frictional duct length L_{max} required to take a flow from $M = \infty$ to $M = 1.0$ is such that $4c_fL_{max}/D = 0.82$, and L_{max} is

$$L_{max} = 0.82\frac{D}{4c_f} = 0.82\frac{D}{4(0.01)} = 20 \text{ diameters}$$

In subsonic flow, the frictional effect is such that $4c_fL_{max}/D = 0.82$ at $M = 0.65$ and $L_{max} = 20$ diameters will only change the Mach number from 0.65 to 1.0. In supersonic flow, the same length would produce a Mach number change from infinity to 1.0.

Example 3-12. Air is flowing through a pipe 2 m long with a 2-cm diameter and mean friction factor of $c_f = 0.0025$. The Mach number of the flow at the pipe inlet is 0.5. What is the exit Mach number from the pipe?

Solution. Figure 3-66 illustrates the flow under consideration. At station 1,

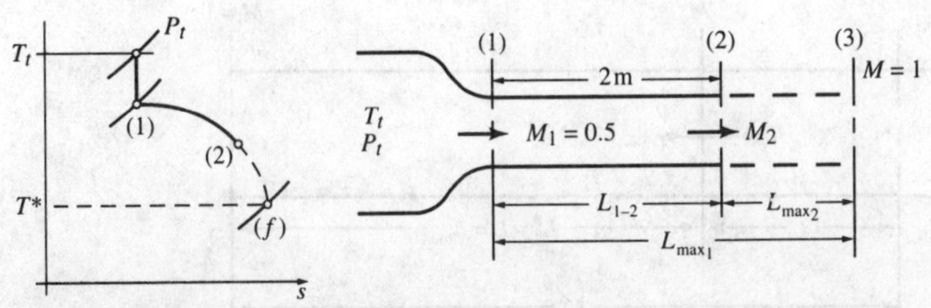

FIGURE 3-66
Illustration of use of L_{max} concept.

$M = 0.5$ and, from Fig. 3-65, we have $(4c_f L_{max}/D)_1 = 1.07$. Now, from the geometry of Fig. 3-66, we see that

$$L_{max_2} = L_{max_1} - L_{1\text{-}2}$$

Multiplying this equation by $4c_f/D$ gives

$$\left(\frac{4cfL_{max}}{D}\right)_2 = \left(\frac{4c_f L_{max}}{D}\right)_1 - \frac{4c_f L_{1\text{-}2}}{D}$$

Then $$\left(\frac{4c_f L_{max}}{D}\right)_2 = 1.07 - \frac{4(0.0025)2}{0.02} = 1.07 - 1.00 = 0.07$$

From Fig. 3-65, the Mach number corresponding to this value of $4c_f L_{max}/D$ is 0.8, and, therefore, $M_2 = 0.8$.

The interpretation of the relation $4c_f L_{max}/D = f(M)$ in conjunction with the Fanno line (Fig. 3-67) is that for a given simple frictional flow, the pipe length required to cause the flow to proceed from a given state 1 on the Fanno line to state f, corresponding to a Mach number of 1, is a function of the Mach number at state 1.

Similarly, converting the equations of Table 3-4 to relations with Mach number as the independent variable through the use of Eq. (3-66), we can show that $(P_t/P_{tf})_1$, $(P/P_f^*)_1$, etc., are functions of the Mach number at state 1. We use a subscript f on the starred quantities of the Fanno line for the present to distinguish these starred quantities from the isentropic starred property at any station. As is evident from Fig. 3-67, P_f^* is constant for a given Fanno line while the isentropic P^* will vary from state point to state point on a Fanno line. The subscript f will not generally be used for a Fanno line starred property. One must be careful, therefore, to avoid confusing isentropic, Rayleigh line, and Fanno line starred quantities.

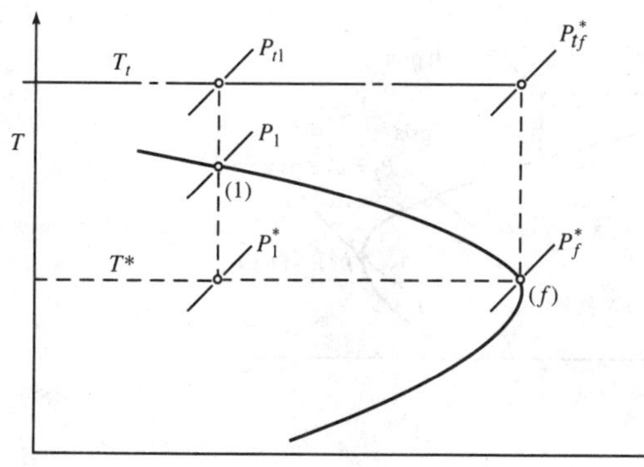

FIGURE 3-67
Fanno line interpretation of $4c_f L_{max}/D$, P/P_f^* and P_t/P_{tf}^*.

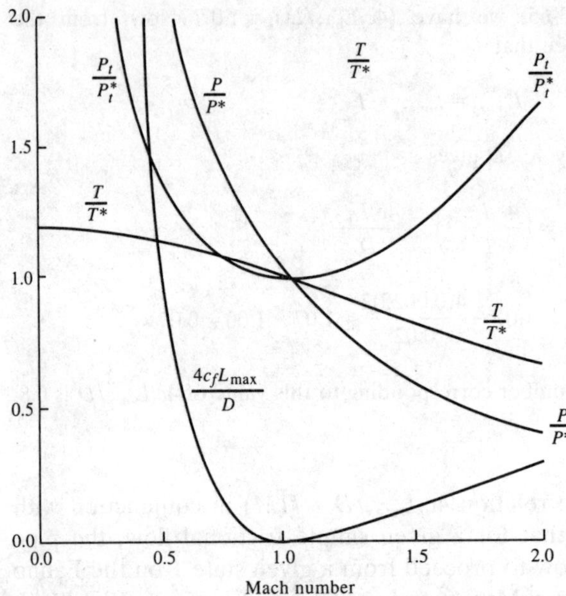

FIGURE 3-68
Fanno line relations ($\gamma = 1.4$).

After replacing, in Table 3-4, the dependent variable $4c_f\,dx/D$ with dM^2/M^2 as the dependent variable via Eq. (3-66), we obtain relations that may be integrated to give P/P^*, P_t/P_t^*, T/T^*, etc., as functions of the Mach number. The integrated results are given in Table 3-5 at the end of this chapter. These relations are tabulated as the Fanno line flow function in App. I. Figure 3-68 shows a plot of the more important integrated simple frictional flow relations.

Example 3-13. We can illustrate the use of Fig. 3-68, or the tabulated counterpart in App. I, with an example. Figure 3-69 shows the data taken from an

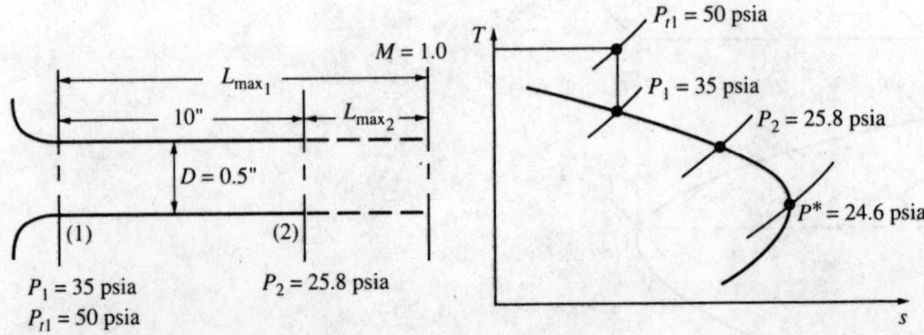

FIGURE 3-69
Experimental data for determining the friction factor.

experimental setup to determine the friction factor between stations 1 and 2 in an airflow experiment.

Solution. From the data given in the figure, we have $P/P_{t1} = 0.7$ and hence $M_1 = 0.73$. This value of the Mach number gives $(P/P^*)_1 = 1.426$ from Fig. 3-68. With this and P_2 and P_1, we can find $(P/P^*)_2$ via

$$\left(\frac{P}{P^*}\right)_2 = \left(\frac{P}{P^*}\right)_1 \frac{P_2}{P_1} = 1.426\left(\frac{25.8}{35}\right) = 1.05$$

The Mach number corresponding to this value of $(P/P^*)_2$ is found to be (Fig. 3-68) $M_2 = 0.955$. From the same figure, we find

$$\left(\frac{4c_f L_{max}}{D}\right)_1 = 0.156 \qquad \text{and} \qquad \left(\frac{4c_f L_{max}}{D}\right)_2 = 0.0026$$

Using the relation

$$\left(\frac{4c_f L_{max}}{D}\right)_1 = \frac{4c_f L_{1\text{-}2}}{D} + \left(\frac{4c_f L_{max}}{D}\right)_2$$

we find

$$\frac{4c_f L_{1\text{-}2}}{D} = 0.156 - 0.0026 = 0.153$$

Finally, the friction factor is

$$c_f = \frac{4c_f L_{1\text{-}2}}{D}\frac{D}{4L_{1\text{-}2}} = 0.153\frac{0.5}{4 \times 10} = 0.0019$$

Notice in simple frictional flow that the basic relation relating station 1 properties to station 2 properties in terms of the frictional duct producing the change is

$$\left(\frac{4c_f L_{max}}{D}\right)_2 = \left(\frac{4c_f L_{max}}{D}\right)_1 - \frac{4c_f L_{1\text{-}2}}{D}$$

In simple frictional flow and simple heating flow, the analogous relations in terms of the primary independent variables are

$$\left(\frac{A}{A^*}\right)_2 = \left(\frac{A}{A^*}\right)_1 \frac{A_2}{A_1} \qquad \text{and} \qquad \left(\frac{T_t}{T_t^*}\right)_2 = \left(\frac{T_t}{T_t^*}\right)_1 \frac{T_{t2}}{T_{t1}}$$

The problem represented in Fig. 3-69 can be worked by using App. I in the following manner:

$$\left(\frac{P}{P_t}\right)_1 = 0.7$$

We obtain M_1 from App. E and get $M_1 = 0.73$. At $M_1 = 0.73$, App. I gives the following:

$$\left(\frac{4c_f L^*}{D}\right)_1 = 0.156054 \qquad \left(\frac{I}{I^*}\right)_1 = 1.03783 \qquad \left(\frac{T}{T^*}\right)_1 = 1.08442$$

$$\left(\frac{P_t}{P_t^*}\right)_1 = 1.07419 \qquad \left(\frac{P}{P^*}\right)_1 = 1.42652$$

Thus $$\left(\frac{P}{P^*}\right)_2 = \left(\frac{P}{P^*}\right)_1 \frac{P_2}{P_1} = 1.42652\left(\frac{25.8}{35}\right) = 1.051549$$

Entering App. I with this value of $(P/P^*)_2$, we get

$$M_2 = 0.9576 \qquad \left(\frac{4c_f L^*}{D}\right)_2 = 0.002345 \qquad \left(\frac{I}{I^*}\right)_2 = 1.00067$$

$$\left(\frac{T}{T^*}\right)_2 = 1.014 \qquad \left(\frac{P_t}{P_t^*}\right)_2 = 1.001546$$

Thus $$\frac{4c_f L_{1\text{-}2}}{D} = 0.156054 - 0.002345 = 0.15371$$

and $$c_f = \frac{0.15371 \times 0.5}{4 \times 10} = 0.00192$$ which is very close to the value obtained from Fig. 3.68

Also we can obtain the total pressure at station 2 by

$$P_{t2} = P_{t1}\left(\frac{P_t}{P_t^*}\right)_2 \left(\frac{P_t^*}{P_t}\right)_1 = 50\left(\frac{1.001546}{1.07419}\right) = 46.62 \text{ psia}$$

The force necessary to hold the 10-ft segment of duct in place can be obtained by using the values of the impulse function I contained in App. I and defined by

$$\boxed{I \equiv PA + \frac{\dot{m}V}{g_c} = \left(P + \frac{\rho V^2}{g_c}\right)A = PA(1 + \gamma M^2)} \qquad (3\text{-}68)$$

From the momentum equation applied to the length of constant-area duct, we obtain the following equation for the force F:

$$F = \left[\left(P + \frac{\rho V^2}{g_c}\right)_2 - \left(P + \frac{\rho V^2}{g_c}\right)_1\right]A$$

Thus $$\boxed{F = I_2 - I_1} \qquad (3\text{-}69)$$

For simple frictional flow, the impulse function I is tabulated in App. I as the ratio I/I^*. Since the flow area is constant, this ratio can be written as follows for simple frictional flow:

$$\frac{I}{I^*} = \frac{P}{P^*} \frac{1 + \gamma M^2}{1 + \gamma} \tag{3-70}$$

Equation (3-69) can be rewritten in terms of the tabulated ratio I/I^* as

$$F = \left[\left(\frac{I}{I^*} \right)_2 - \left(\frac{I}{I^*} \right)_1 \right] I^* \tag{3-71}$$

where $$I^* = P^* A(1 + \gamma)$$

Thus $$F = (1.00067 - 1.03783) I^* = -0.03716 I^*$$

Using the pressure and area at station 1 to obtain I^*, we have

$$I^* = P^* A(1 + \gamma) = \frac{35}{1.42652}(0.19635)(2.4)$$

$$= (24.587)(0.19635)(2.4) = 11.586 \text{ lbf}$$

Thus $$F = -0.43 \text{ lbf}$$

3-10 SUMMARY OF SIMPLE FLOWS

A simple flow is defined as one in which all but one of the independent variables in Table 3-1 are zero. Three types of simple flows are summarized in Table 3-5 by presenting for each simple flow (1) the independent effects present; (2) a schematic of the flow situation; (3) the locus on a temperature-entropy diagram of the possible states attained for each flow; and (4) useful functions obtained by integration of the relations of Table 3-1 or the basic Eqs. (3-33*a*) through (3-33*f*).

In the temperature-entropy diagrams of Table 3-5, the path lines of states corresponding to simple area flow, simple heating flow, and simple frictional flow, respectively, are shown. These path lines are called the *isentrope, Rayleigh*, and *Fanno lines,* respectively.

To proceed downward along the *isentrope line* from point a of the diagram, the flow area is decreased until the sonic point at b is reached. The area must be increased after point b in order to continue down to point c. By proper adjustments in the flow area and boundary pressures, the flow may be made to proceed through point b in either direction along the isentrope line.

TABLE 3-5
Simple flows

		Simple area	Simple heating	Simple friction
Effects	Area	Present	0	0
	Heating	0	Present	0
	Friction	0	0	Present
Schematic of flow situation		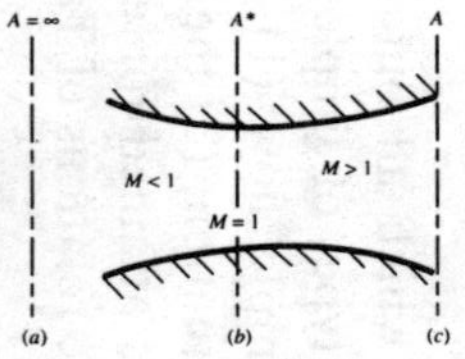	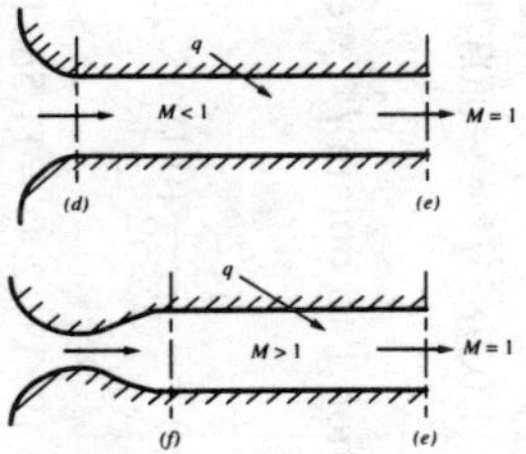	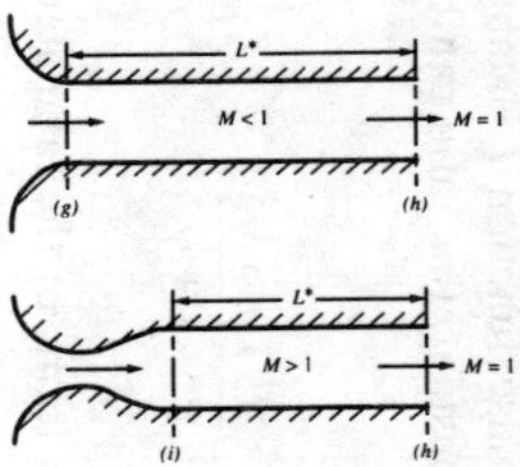
Temperature-entropy path line		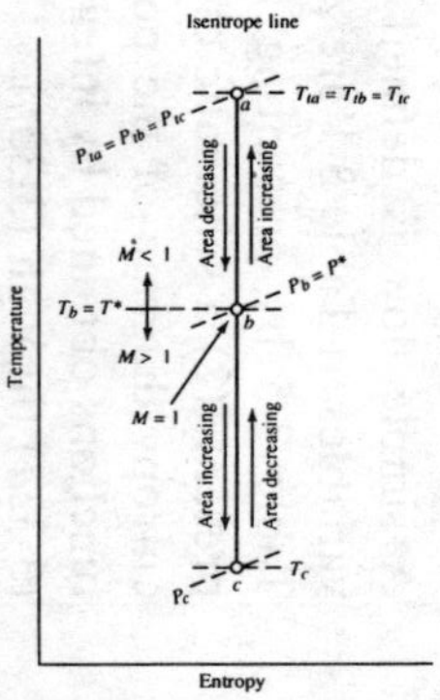	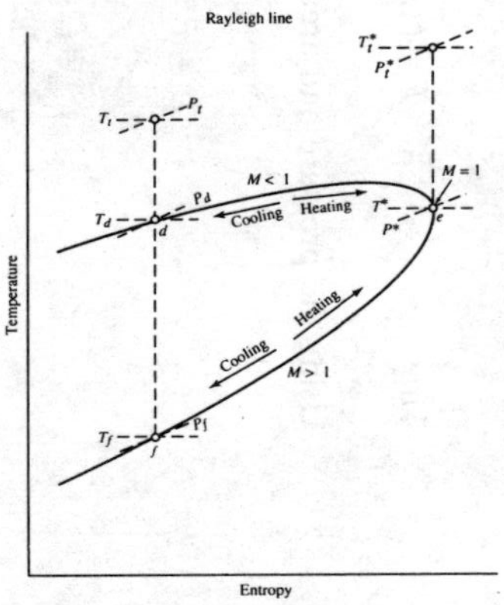	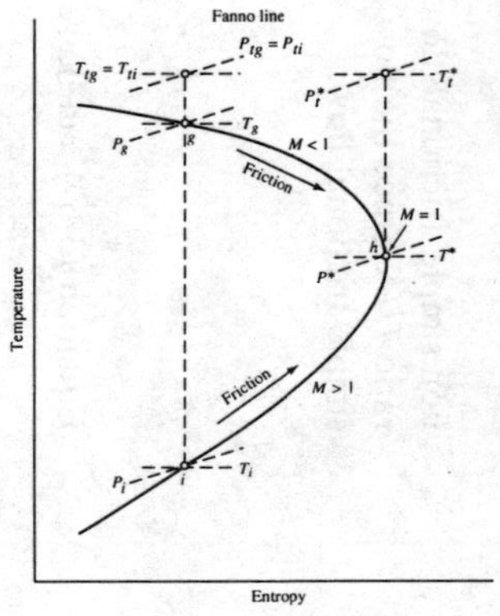

Useful functions			
Graphical	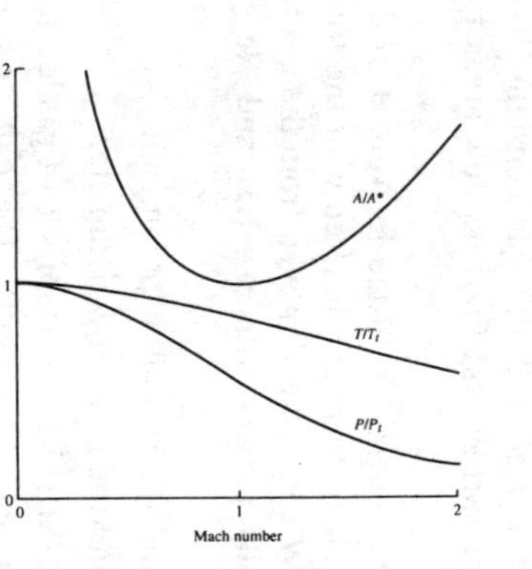	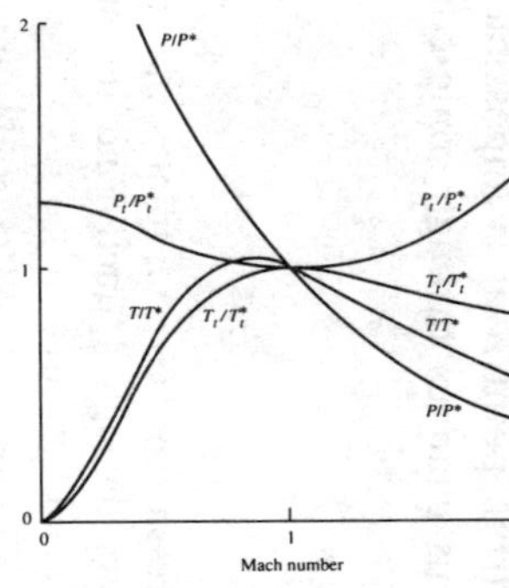	
Analytic	$\frac{A}{A^*}=\frac{1}{M}\left[\frac{2}{\gamma+1}\left(1+\frac{\gamma-1}{2}M^2\right)\right]^{(\gamma+1)/[2(\gamma-1)]}$ $\frac{T}{T_t}=\left(1+\frac{\gamma-1}{2}M^2\right)^{-1}$ $\frac{P}{P_t}=\left(1+\frac{\gamma-1}{2}M^2\right)^{-\gamma/(\gamma-1)}$	$\frac{T_t}{T_t^*}=\frac{2(\gamma+1)M^2}{(1+\gamma M^2)^2}\left(1+\frac{\gamma-1}{2}M^2\right)$ $\frac{P}{P^*}=\frac{\gamma+1}{1+\gamma M^2}$ $\frac{T}{T^*}=\frac{(\gamma+1)^2M^2}{(1+\gamma M^2)^2}$ $\frac{P_t}{P_t^*}=\frac{\gamma+1}{1+\gamma M^2}\left[\frac{2}{\gamma+1}\left(1+\frac{\gamma-1}{2}M^2\right)\right]^{\gamma/(\gamma-1)}$	$\frac{P}{P^*}=\frac{1}{\sqrt{\frac{2}{\gamma+1}\left(1+\frac{\gamma-1}{2}M^2\right)}}$ $\frac{T}{T^*}=\left[\frac{2}{\gamma+1}\left(1+\frac{\gamma-1}{2}M^2\right)\right]^{-1}$ $\frac{P_t}{P_t^*}=\frac{1}{M}\left[\frac{2}{\gamma+1}\left(1+\frac{\gamma-1}{2}M^2\right)\right]^{(\gamma+1)/[2(\gamma-1)]}$ $\frac{4c_fL^*}{D}=\frac{1-M^2}{\gamma M^2}+\frac{\gamma+1}{2\gamma}\ln\frac{M^2}{\frac{2}{\gamma+1}\left(1+\frac{\gamma-1}{2}M^2\right)}$

Point a represents the isentropic stagnation condition for all points on the isentrope $a - c$.

The *Rayleigh line* shows the series of possible states in a steady, frictionless, constant-area flow. Motion along the Rayleigh line is caused by changes in the stagnation temperature produced by heating effects which, in turn, produce entropy changes in the manner indicated on the line. Heating in an initially subsonic (point d) flow causes the flow Mach number to approach 1 (point e). Neither heating nor cooling can continuously alter the flow from subsonic to supersonic speeds, or from supersonic to subsonic speeds.

The *Fanno line* represents the possible series of states in a steady, constant-area, constant-stagnation-temperature flow. Frictional effects alone produce motion along the Fanno line. Consequently, the flow progression along the line must always be one of increasing entropy toward the sonic point h. The flow is subsonic on the Fanno line above h and supersonic below. Since the entropy decreases along the Fanno line from point h, it is impossible, in simple friction flow, to proceed by continuous changes through sonic conditions at point h.

PROBLEMS

3-1. It is given that 100 lbm/sec of air at total pressure of 100 psia, total temperature of 40°F, and static pressure of 20 psia flows through a duct. Find the static temperature, Mach number, velocity (ft/sec), and flow area (ft^2).

3-2. Products of combustion ($\gamma = 1.3$) at a static pressure of 2.0 MPa, static temperature of 2000 K, and Mach number of 0.05 are accelerated in an isentropic nozzle to a Mach number of 1.3. Find the downstream static pressure and static temperature. If the mass flow rate is 100 kg/sec and the gas constant R is 286 J/(kg · K), use the mass flow parameter (MFP) and find the flow areas for $M = 0.5$ and $M = 1.3$.

3-3. Data for the JT9D high-bypass-ratio turbofan engine are listed in App. B. If the gas flow through the turbines (from station 4 to 5) is 251 lbm/sec with the total properties listed, what amount of power (kW and hp) is removed from the gas by the turbines? Assume the gas is calorically perfect with $\gamma = 1.31$ and $Rg_c = 1716\ ft^2/(sec^2 \cdot °R)$.

3-4. Rework Prob. 2-12, using total properties and the mass flow parameter.

3-5. Rework Prob. 2-13, using total properties and the mass flow parameter.

3-6. At launch, the space shuttle main engine (SSME) has 1030 lbm/sec of gas leaving the combustion chamber at $P_t = 3000$ psia and $T_t = 7350°R$. The exit area of the SSME nozzle is 77 times the throat area. If the flow through the nozzle is considered to be reversible and adiabatic (isentropic) with $Rg_c = 3800\ ft^2/(sec^2 \cdot °R)$ and $\gamma = 1.25$, find the area of the nozzle throat (in^2) and the exit Mach number. *Hint*: Use the mass flow parameter to get the throat area and Eq. (3-14) to get the exit Mach number.

3-7. The experimental evaluation of a gas turbine engine's performance requires the accurate measurement of the inlet air mass flow rate into the engine. A bell-mouth engine inlet (shown schematically below) can be used for this purpose

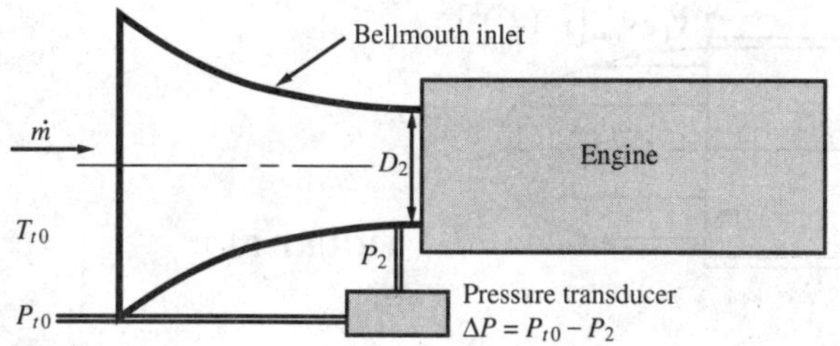

FIGURE P3-7

in the static test of an engine. The free stream velocity V_0 is assumed to be zero, and the flow through the bell mouth is assumed to be adiabatic and reversible. See Fig. P3-7.

Measurements are made of the free stream pressure P_{t0} and the static pressure at station 2 (P_2), and the exit diameter of the inlet D_2.

a. For the bell-mouth inlet, show that the Mach number at station 2 is given by

$$M_2 = \sqrt{\frac{2}{\gamma - 1}\left[\left(\frac{P_{t0}}{P_{t0} - \Delta P}\right)^{(\gamma-1)/\gamma} - 1\right]}$$

and the inlet mass flow rate is given by

$$\dot{m} = \frac{P_{t0}}{\sqrt{T_{t0}}} \frac{\pi D_2^2}{4} \sqrt{\frac{2g_c}{R}\frac{\gamma}{\gamma - 1}\left[\left(\frac{P_{t0} - \Delta P}{P_{t0}}\right)^{2/\gamma} - \left(\frac{P_{t0} - \Delta P}{P_{t0}}\right)^{(\gamma+1)/\gamma}\right]}$$

b. For the following measured data, determine the inlet air mass flow rate, Mach number M_2, static temperature T_2, and velocity V_2:

$$T_{t0} = 7°\text{C} \qquad P_{t0} = 77.80 \text{ kPa}$$

$$\Delta P = 3.66 \text{ kPa} \qquad D_2 = 0.332 \text{ m}$$

3-8. An ideal ramjet (see Fig. P3-8) is operated at 50,000-ft altitude with a flight Mach number of 3. The diffuser and nozzle are assumed to be isentropic, and the combustion is to be modeled as an ideal heat interaction at constant Mach number with constant total pressure. The cross-sectional area and Mach number for certain engine stations are given in the table below. The total temperature leaving the combustor T_{t4} is 4000°R. Assume ambient pressure surrounding the engine flow passage.

a. Determine the mass flow rate of air through the engine (lbm/sec).

b. Complete the table with flow areas, static pressures, static temperatures, and velocities.

c. Find the thrust (magnitude and direction) of the diffuser, combustor, and nozzle.

d. Find the thrust (magnitude and direction) of the ramjet.

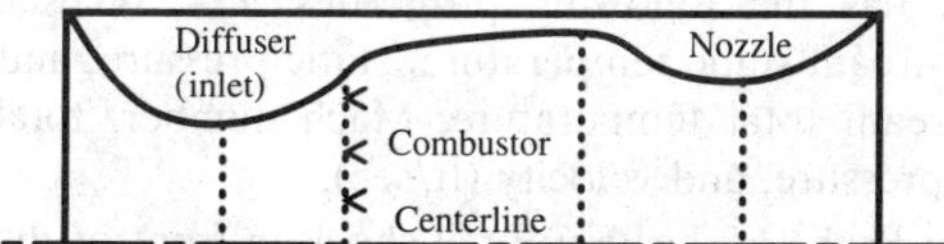

FIGURE P3-8

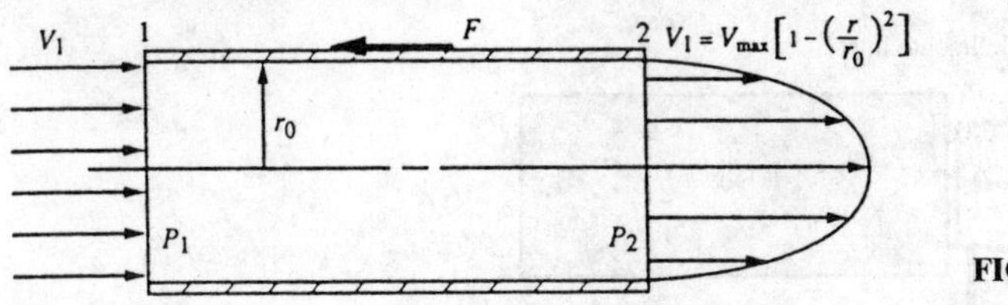

FIGURE P3-9

Station:	1	2	3	4	5	6
Area (ft^2)	4.235					
Mach	3	1	0.15	0.15	1	3
P (psia)						
T (°R)						
V (ft/sec)						

3-9. Consider the adiabatic flow shown in Fig. P3-9 of a calorically perfect gas. The gas enters a constant-area circular pipe with uniform velocity V_1, pressure P_1, and temperature T_1. The fluid leaves with the parabolic velocity profile V_2 given by

$$V_2 = V_{max}\left[1 - \left(\frac{r}{r_0}\right)^2\right]$$

and with uniform pressure P_2 and uniform temperature T_2. Using the conservation of mass, momentum, and energy equations, derive an expression for:

a. The force F necessary to hold the pipe in place
b. The exit total temperature profile
c. The mass average total temperature at the exit
d. The exit total pressure profile
e. The mass average total pressure at the exit

Note: The mass average of any fluid property Z is defined by

$$\bar{Z} = \frac{1}{\dot{m}} \int Z\, d\dot{m} = \frac{1}{\dot{m}} \int_A \rho V Z\, dA$$

3-10. If the flow enters the diffuser of Prob. 2-7 at −55°F, is the process isentropic?

3-11. If the flow enters the nozzle of Prob. 2-10 at 1250 K, is the process isentropic?

3-12. Solve Prob. 2-16, using total properties and the mass flow parameter.

3-13. Solve Prob. 2-17, using total properties and the mass flow parameter.

3-14. Solve Prob. 2-18, using total properties and the mass flow parameter.

3-15. Solve Prob. 2-19, using total properties and the mass flow parameter.

3-16. Air at 20 kPa, 260 K, and Mach 3 passes through a normal shock. Determine:

a. Total temperature and pressure upstream of the shock
b. Total temperature and pressure downstream of the shock
c. Static temperature and pressure downstream of the shock

3-17. Air upstream of a normal shock has the following properties: $P_t = 100$ psia, $T_t = 100$°F, and $M = 2$. Find the upstream static temperature, static pressure, and velocity (ft/sec). Find the downstream total temperature, Mach number, total pressure, static temperature, static pressure, and velocity (ft/sec).

3-18. If the diffuser of the ideal ramjet in Prob. 3-8 has a normal shock in front of the inlet, determine:

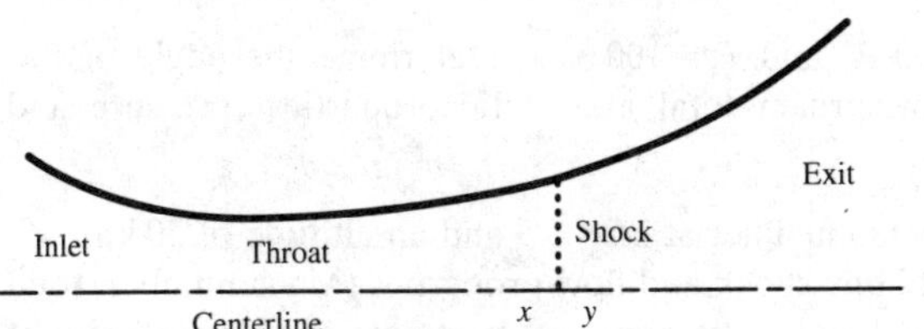

FIGURE P3-19

a. The total and static pressures and the static temperature downstream of the shock
b. The mass flow rate through the engine (lbm/sec) (assume choked flow at diffuser throat)
c. The thrust of the engine

3-19. Air at a total pressure of 1.4 MPa, total temperature of 350 K, and Mach number of 0.5 is accelerated isentropically in a nozzle (see sketch in Fig. P3-19) to a Mach number of 3 (station x), passes through a normal shock (x to y), and then flows isentropically to the exit. Given a nozzle throat area of 0.05 m^2 and the exit area of 0.5 m^2:
a. Find the area at the shock
b. Find the static pressure and static temperature upstream of the shock (station x)
c. Find the Mach number and the total and static pressures and temperatures downstream of the shock (station y)
d. Find the Mach number, static pressure, and static temperature at the exit

3-20. Air flows through an isentropic nozzle with inlet conditions of $T_t = 2000°\text{R}$ and $P_t = 100$ psia. The throat area is 2 ft^2, and the exit area is 10.32 ft^2. If the flow is choked at the throat, find:
a. Mass flow rate through the nozzle
b. Mach number, static temperature, and static pressure at exit without a shock
c. Mach number, static temperature, and static pressure at exit with a shock in the divergent section where the flow area is 4.06 ft^2 (see Fig. P3-19)

3-21. Air at a total pressure of 400 psia, total temperature of 500°C, and subsonic Mach number is accelerated isentropically in a nozzle (see sketch in Fig. P3-19) to a supersonic Mach number (station x), passes through a normal shock (x to y), and then flows isentropically to the exit. Given a nozzle inlet area of 3 ft^2, throat area of 1 ft^2, and exit area of 6 ft^2:
a. Find the Mach number at the inlet
b. Find the Mach number upstream of the shock (station x)
c. Find the static pressure and static temperature upstream of the shock (station x)
d. Find the Mach number and the total and static pressures and temperatures downstream of the shock (station y)
e. Find the Mach number, static pressure, and static temperature at the exit

3-22. A 20° wedge (see Fig. P3-22) is to be used in a wind tunnel using air with test

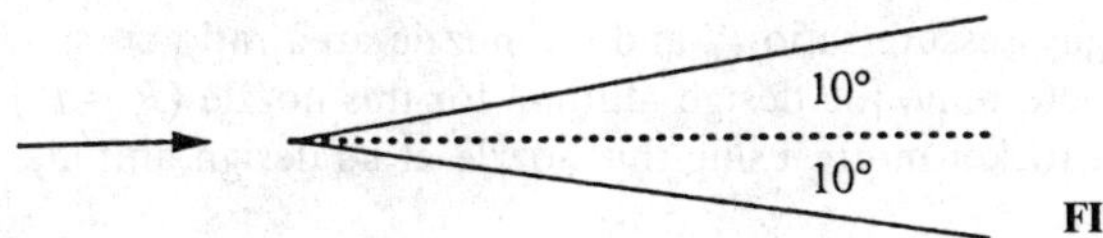

FIGURE P3-22

conditions of $M = 3$, $T_t = 500°\text{R}$, and $P_t = 100$ psia. Determine the angle of the oblique shocks and the downstream total and static properties (pressure and temperature).

3-23. A 15° ramp is used on a supersonic inlet at $M = 3.5$ and an altitude of 20 km.

a. Determine the angle of oblique shock and flow properties (Mach number, total and static temperature, total and static pressure) upstream and downstream of the shock

b. At what Mach number does the shock detach from the ramp?

3-24. Show that Eq. (3-22*f*) can be solved for θ in terms of M_1 and β to give

$$\tan\theta = \frac{2\cot\beta(M_1^2\sin^2\beta - 1)}{2 + M_1^2(\gamma + 1 - 2\sin^2\beta)}$$

3-25. A calorically perfect gas undergoes an ideal heat interaction in a duct. The area of the duct is varied to hold the static pressure constant. Using the influence coefficients of Table 3-1, show the following:

a. The area variation required to hold the static pressure constant is given by

$$\frac{dA}{A} = \left(1 + \frac{\gamma - 1}{2}M^2\right)\frac{dT_t}{T_t}$$

b. The relationship between the Mach number and total temperature, for the above area variation, is given by

$$\frac{dM^2}{M^2} = -\left(1 + \frac{\gamma - 1}{2}M^2\right)\frac{dT_t}{T_t}$$

c. The relationship for the area of the duct in terms of the Mach number is given by

$$A_2 = A_1\left(\frac{M_1}{M_2}\right)^2 \quad \text{where subscripts refer to states 1 and 2}$$

3-26. You are required to design a nozzle to pass a given mass flow rate of air with minimum frictional losses between a storage pressure chamber P_c and an exhaust region P_e with a given variation in pressure between the two regions. The design conditions are

$$\dot{m} = 1000 \text{ lbm/sec} \qquad P_c = 3000 \text{ psia} \qquad T_c = 3700°\text{R}$$

a. Using the design conditions, complete the table below

b. Make a plot of the nozzle contour (see Fig. 3-40)

c. Calculate the nozzle design pressure ratio $P_{\bar{n}}$ and the nozzle area ratio ε

d. Using the altitude table, determine the design altitude for this nozzle ($P_e = P_a$)

e. Determine the thrust of a rocket motor using this nozzle at its design altitude

Station x (in)	P (psia)	P/P_t	M	T/T_t	A/A^*	T (°R)	a (ft/sec)	V (ft/sec)	A (in²)	D (in)
0	2918									
2	2841									
4	2687									
6	2529									
8	2124									
10 (throat)	1585									
12	727									
16	218									
24	19.8									
41	3.21									
60	1.17									

3-27. A perfect gas enters a constant-area heater at a Mach number of 0.3, total pressure of 600 kPa, and total temperature of 500 K. A heat interaction of 500 kJ/kg into the gas occurs. Determine the Mach number, total pressure, and total temperature after the heat interaction for the following gases:

a. $\gamma = 1.4$ and $c_p = 1.004$ kJ/(kg · K)

b. $\gamma = 1.325$ and $c_p = 1.171$ kJ/(kg · K)

3-28. A perfect gas enters a constant-area heater at a Mach number of 0.5, total pressure of 200 psia, and total temperature of 1000°R. A heat interaction of 100 Btu/lbm into the gas occurs. Determine the Mach number, total pressure, and total temperature after the heat interaction for the following gases:

a. $\gamma = 1.4$ and $c_p = 0.24$ Btu/(lbm · °R)

b. $\gamma = 1.325$ and $c_p = 0.28$ Btu/(lbm · °R)

3-29. A convergent-only nozzle is to be used on an afterburning gas turbine engine as shown in Fig. P3-29. Model the afterburner (station 6 to station 7) as a constant-area duct ($A_6 = A_7$) with simple heat interaction q_{in} into the air. The flow through the nozzle (station 7 to station 8) is isentropic. The exit area of the nozzle A_8 is varied with the afterburner setting T_{t7} to keep sonic ($M = 1$) flow at station 8 and the inlet conditions (mass flow rate, P_t, and T_t) constant at station 6.

a. Using the mass flow parameter, show that the area ratio A_8/A_6 is given by

$$\frac{A_8}{A_6} = \frac{P_{t6}}{P_{t7}} \sqrt{\frac{T_{t7}}{T_{t6}}} \frac{\text{MFP}(M_6)}{\text{MFP}(M=1)} = \frac{P_{t6}}{P_{t7}} \sqrt{\frac{T_{t7}}{T_{t6}}} \left(\frac{A}{A^*}\right)_{M_6}$$

b. For $M_6 = 0.4$, determine the area ratio A_8/A_6 for the following values of T_{t7}/T_{t6}: 1.0, 1.1, 1.2, 1.3, 1.4, 1.5, 1.6, and $T_{t7} = T_t^*$

3-30. Air at a static pressure of 200 kPa, static temperature of 300 K, and velocity of 150 m/sec enters a constant-area adiabatic circular duct with an inside diameter of

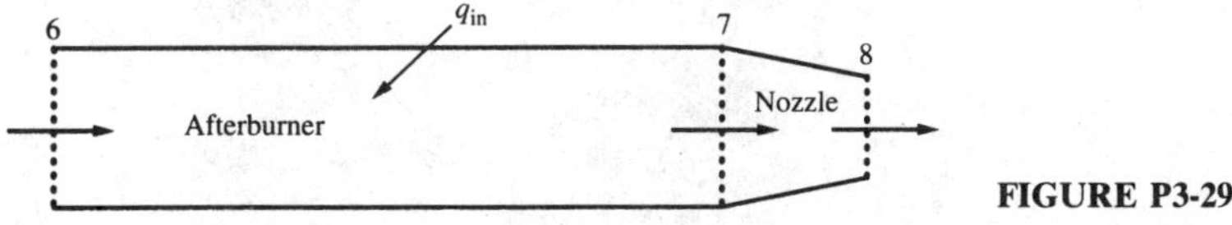

FIGURE P3-29

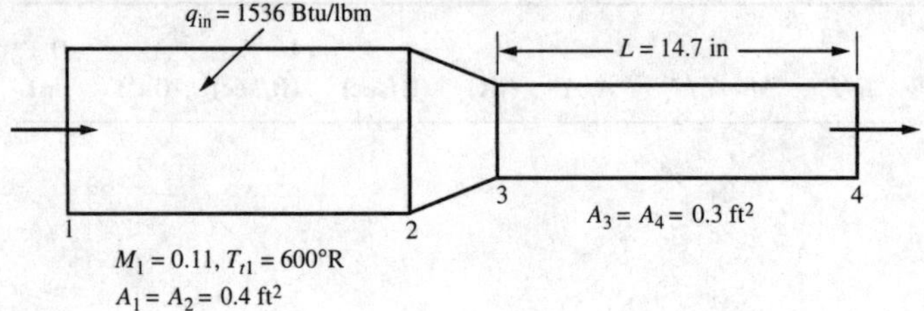

FIGURE P3-36

0.1 m. The duct has a constant coefficient of friction c_f equal to 0.005. Determine the following:

a. The maximum length L_{max} for this duct with constant inlet conditions

b. Static pressure, total pressure, and static temperature at the exit whose length is L_{max}

c. Static pressure, total pressure, and static temperature at the exit whose length is $L_{max}/2$

3-31. Air at a static pressure of 80 psia, static temperature of 500°R, and velocity of 500 ft/sec enters a constant-area adiabatic circular duct with an inside diameter of 3 in. The duct has a constant coefficient of friction c_f equal to 0.004. Determine the following:

a. The maximum length L_{max} for this duct and constant inlet conditions

b. Static pressure, total pressure, and static temperature at the exit whose length is L_{max}

c. Static pressure, total pressure, and static temperature at the exit whose length is $L_{max}/2$

3.32. Air flows through a constant-area duct of 20 in^2. The air enters at $M = 0.65$, $P_t = 100$ psia, and $T_t = 500$°R. Assuming $c_f = 0.012$, determine:

a. Duct length needed to choke the flow at the exit and the exit total pressure

b. Duct length needed for an exit total pressure of 95 psia and the exit Mach number

3-33. Air flows through a constant-area duct of 0.1 m^2. The air enters at $M = 0.5$, $P_t = 200$ kPa, and $T_t = 300$ K. Assuming $c_f = 0.010$, determine:

a. Duct length needed to choke the flow at the exit and the exit total pressure

b. Duct length needed for an exit total pressure of 160 kPa and the exit Mach number

3-34. Solve Prob. 2-24, using the Fanno line flow functions.

3-35. Solve Prob. 2-25, using the Fanno line flow functions.

3-36. Determine the static temperature at station 4 of the duct shown in Fig. P3-36 for the flow of air using the techniques of simple heating, area, and friction flows. Assume a calorically perfect gas.

CHAPTER 4

AIRCRAFT GAS TURBINE ENGINE

4-1 INTRODUCTION

The introductory fundamentals of aircraft propulsion systems are covered in this chapter. Emphasis is placed upon propulsion systems which operate on the so-called Brayton cycle. Such systems include turbojets, turboprops, turbofans, ramjets, and combinations thereof. Before taking up the thermodynamic processes involved in these systems, we consider the forces acting on a propulsive duct and the effect of installation on the net propulsive force.

4-2 THRUST EQUATION

We define a *propulsion system* as a unit submerged in a fluid medium about and through which the fluid flows. The propulsion system contains an energy-transfer mechanism which increases the kinetic energy of the fluid passing through the system. This mechanism is called the *engine.* In Fig. 4-1, the engine is shown schematically in a nacelle housing which forms the second portion of the propulsion system. Thus the propulsion system contains:

1. An engine (the nozzle is considered to be part of the engine in our terminology)
2. Housing about the engine (nacelle or duct)

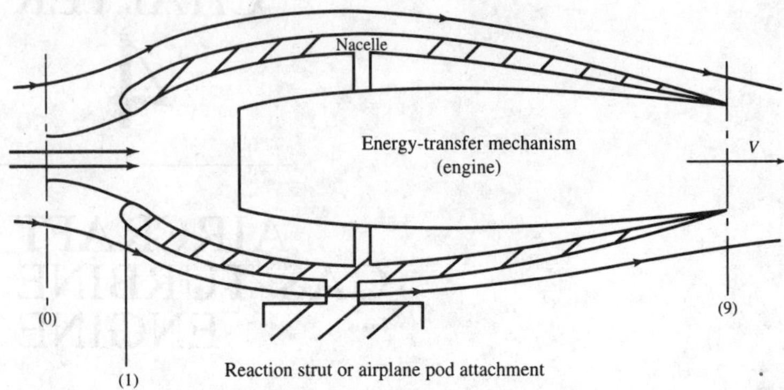

FIGURE 4-1
Propulsion system.

Several different aircraft systems may use the same engine submerged in different-shaped nacelles. Thus one propulsion system may use engine X in a pod installation hanging from a wing while, in another system, engine X may be surrounded by a nacelle which is, in fact, the airplane's fuselage—examples are the B-52 versus F-100 propulsion systems which use the J57 turbojet engine. The thrust of a propulsion system will depend upon

- Its engine
- Its nacelle

As a result, it is conventional to speak of *uninstalled engine thrust* and *installed engine thrust.* The uninstalled engine thrust should depend on the engine alone and hence must be independent of the nacelle. The installed engine thrust is the thrust produced by both the engine and the nacelle. *Installed engine thrust* T is defined as the shear force in the reaction strut of Fig. 4-1.

Uninstalled engine thrust F is defined as the force F_{int} acting on the internal surface of the propulsion system from 1 to 9 plus the force F'_{int} acting on the internal surface of the stream tube 0 to 1 which contains the air flowing into the engine. It will be shown that F is independent of the nacelle.

To evaluate the uninstalled engine thrust, defined as $F_{int} + F'_{int}$, we apply the momentum equation to the control surface of Fig. 4-2. In so doing, we use the convention that all pressures used will be gauge pressures. We adopt this convention because it is used by the external aerodynamicist in computing the drag and lift forces on the airplane. To be consistent, then, the internal aerodynamicist must do the same. Figure 4-3 shows the momentum equation for assumed steady flow applied to flow through the control surface of Fig. 4-2.

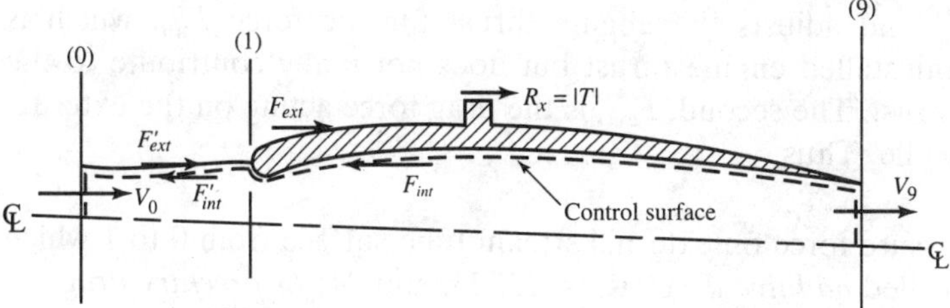

FIGURE 4-2
Forces on propulsion system.

Referring to Fig. 4-3 and equating forces to the change in momentum flux, we get

$$F'_{\text{int}} + F_{\text{int}} + (P_0 - P_0)A_0 - (P_9 - P_0)A_9 = \frac{\dot{m}_9 V_9 - \dot{m}_0 V_0}{g_c}$$

$$F \quad + \quad 0 \quad - (P_9 - P_0)A_9 = \frac{\dot{m}_9 V_9 - \dot{m}_0 V_0}{g_c}$$

$$\text{Uninstalled engine thrust } F = \frac{\dot{m}_9 V_9 - \dot{m}_0 V_0}{g_c} + (P_9 - P_0)A_9 \tag{4-1}$$

This equation for the uninstalled engine thrust is seen to contain terms completely independent of the nacelle of the propulsion system. The terms $\dot{m}$, V_9, A_9, and P_9 are fixed by the engine while the terms V_0 and P_0 are fixed by the flight condition.

To obtain the installed engine thrust, we must "subtract" from the uninstalled engine thrust the drag forces F'_{ext} and F_{ext}. The first, F'_{ext}, is equal in

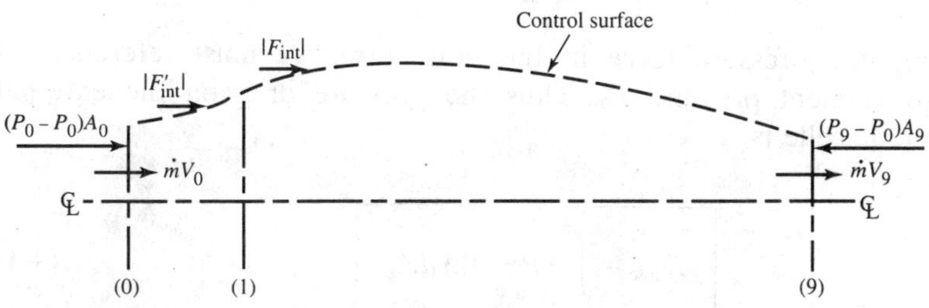

FIGURE 4-3
Control surface forces and momentum fluxes for evaluating F (pressure referred to P_0).

magnitude to F'_{int} and adjusts the engine thrust for the force F'_{int}, which is credited to the uninstalled engine thrust but does not really contribute to the installed engine thrust. The second, F_{ext}, is the drag force acting on the external surface of the nacelle. Thus

F'_{ext} = pressure force on external stream tube surface from 0 to 1 which is called *additive drag* (Refs. 22, 23, and 24) or *preentry drag* (Ref. 25)

and F_{ext} = pressure force on nacelle's external surface

In the accounting system of viscous and pressure forces acting on the airframe and engine, the viscous forces on the nacelle are included in the airframe drag, and the pressure forces on the nacelle are included in the installed engine thrust.

The installed engine thrust T is then

$$\text{Shear force in strut of Fig. 4-1} = T = F_{\text{int}} - F_{\text{ext}}$$

$$= F_{\text{int}} + F'_{\text{int}} - (F_{\text{ext}} + F'_{\text{ext}})$$

where $F_{\text{ext}} + F'_{\text{ext}}$ is called the *drag D* and where, as above, $F_{\text{int}} + F'_{\text{int}}$ is called the *uninstalled engine thrust F*. Using this notation, we have

$$\boxed{\text{Installed engine thrust } T = T - D} \tag{4-2}$$

The two forces F_{ext} and F'_{ext} that make up the drag D are called the *nacelle drag* D_{nac} and the *additive drag* D_{add}, respectively. Thus the drag force can be written as

$$\boxed{D = D_{\text{nac}} + D_{\text{add}}} \tag{4-3}$$

In computing the pressure force in the drag term, we must reference all pressures to ambient pressure P_0. Thus the pressure drag on the external surface of the nacelle is

$$\boxed{D_{\text{nac}} = \int_1^9 (P - P_0)\, dA_y} \tag{4-4}$$

where P is the absolute pressure on the nacelle surface dA which has a vertical

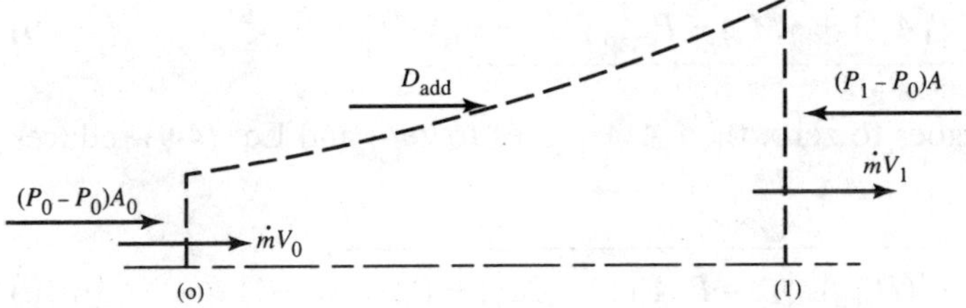

FIGURE 4-4
Momentum equation applied to stream tube of engine air from 0 to 1.

component of dA_y. The additive drag is the pressure drag on the stream tube bounding the internal flow between stations 0 and 1, or

$$\boxed{D_{add} = \int_0^1 (P - P_0)\, dA_y} \tag{4-5}$$

Application of the momentum equation to the stream tube shown in Fig. 4-4 between stations 0 and 1 gives

Forces on stream tube = change in momentum flux

$$\int_0^1 (P - P_0)\, dA_y - \int_1 (P - P_0)\, dA_y = \int_1 \frac{\rho V^2}{g_c}\, dA_y - \int_0 \frac{\rho V^2}{g_c}\, dA_y$$

Thus $$D_{add} = \int_1 \left(P + \frac{\rho V^2}{g_c}\right) dA_y - \int_0 \frac{\rho V^2}{g_c}\, dA_y - P_0 A_1$$

or $$D_{add} = \int_1 \left(P + \frac{\rho V^2}{g_c}\right) dA_y - \int_0 \left(P + \frac{\rho V^2}{g_c}\right) dA_y - P_0(A_1 - A_0) \tag{4-6}$$

The term $P + \rho V^2/g_c$ within the integrals is called the *total momentum flux,* and for a perfect gas

$$\boxed{P + \frac{\rho V^2}{g_c} = P(1 + \gamma M^2)} \tag{4-7}$$

Thus Eq. (4-6) can be expressed as

$$D_{add} = \int_1 P(1 + \gamma M^2)\, dA_y - \int_0 P(1 + \gamma M^2)\, dA_y - P_0(A_1 - A_0)$$

For one-dimensional flow, the above equation becomes

$$\boxed{D_{add} = P_1 A_1(1 + \gamma M_1^2) - P_0 A_0(1 + \gamma M_0^2) - P_0(A_1 - A_0)} \tag{4-8}$$

or

$$D_{\text{add}} = P_1A_1(1+\gamma M_1^2) - P_0A_0\gamma M_0^2 - P_0A_1 \tag{4-9}$$

In the limit, as M_0 goes to zero, then $A_0M_0^2$ goes to zero and Eq. (4-9) reduces to

$$(D_{\text{add}})_{M_0=0} = P_1A_1(1+\gamma M_1^2) - P_0A_1 \tag{4-10}$$

Example 4-1. Two nacelles with inlet areas of (1) $A_1 = 0.20\ \text{m}^2$ and (2) $A_1 = 0.26\ \text{m}^2$ are being considered for use with a gas turbine engine X which produces an uninstalled thrust F of 20,000 N at sea level and $M_0 = 0.5$. Compare the installed engine thrust obtained with nacelle 1 and engine X to the installed engine thrust for nacelle 2 and engine X at $M_0 = 0.5$ and sea level. Engine X has a mass flow of 41.75 kg/sec. Nacelles 1 and 2 each have the same nacelle drag of 900 N.

Solution. The installed engine thrust is given by

$$T = F - D = F - D_{\text{nac}} - D_{\text{add}}$$

Since both the unistalled engine thrust F and nacelle drag D_{nac} are known, only the additive drag D_{add} need be determined for both nacelles. Either Eq. (4-8) or Eq. (4-9) can be used to calculate D_{add}, and both require the evaluation of P_1, M_1, and A_0. Since the mass flow rate into engine X is the same for both nacelles, A_0 will be determined first. The *mass flow parameter* (MFP) can be used to find A_0 once the total temperature and pressure are known at station 0:

$$T_{t0} = T_0\left(1 + \frac{\gamma-1}{2}M_0^2\right) = 288.2(1 + 0.2 \times 0.5^2) = 302.6\ \text{K}$$

$$P_{t0} = P_0\left(1 + \frac{\gamma-1}{2}M_0^2\right)^{\gamma/(\gamma-1)} = 101{,}300(1 + 0.2 \times 0.5^2)^{3.5} = 120{,}160\ \text{Pa}$$

$$\text{MFP}(0.5)\sqrt{\frac{R}{g_c}} = \frac{\dot{m}\sqrt{T_{t0}}}{P_{t0}A_0}\sqrt{\frac{R}{g_c}} = 0.511053 \qquad \text{(from App. E)}$$

Thus

$$A_0 = \frac{\dot{m}\sqrt{T_{t0}}\sqrt{R/g_c}}{P_{t0}[\text{MFP}(0.5)\sqrt{R/g_c}]} = \frac{41.75\sqrt{302.6}(16.9115)}{120{,}160(0.511053)}$$

$$= 0.200\ \text{m}^2$$

With subsonic flow between stations 0 and 1, the flow between these two stations is assumed to be isentropic. Thus the total pressure and total temperature at station 1 are 120,160 Pa and 302.6 K. Since the mass flow rate, area, and total properties are known at station 1 for both nacelles, the Mach number M_1 and static pressure P_1 needed to calculate the additive drag can be determined as follows:

1. Calculate $\text{MFP}\sqrt{R/g_c}$ at station 1, and find M_1 from App. E.

2. Calculate P_1, using Eq. (3-10) or P/P_t from App. E.

Nacelle 1. Since the inlet area A_1 for nacelle 1 is the same as flow area A_0 and the flow process is isentropic, then $M_1 = 0.5$ and $P_1 = 101{,}300$ Pa. From Eq. (4-8), the additive drag is zero, and the installed thrust is

$$T = F - D_{\text{nac}} - D_{\text{add}} = 20{,}000 - 900 - 0 = 19{,}100 \text{ N}$$

Nacelle 2. Calculating $\text{MFP}\sqrt{R/g_c}$ at station 1, we find

$$\text{MFP}(M_1)\sqrt{\frac{R}{g_c}} = \frac{\dot{m}\sqrt{T_{t1}}\sqrt{R/g_c}}{P_{t1}A_1} = \frac{41.75\sqrt{302.6}(16.9115)}{120{,}160(0.26)}$$
$$= 0.393133$$

From App. E, $M_1 = 0.3586$ and

$$P_1 = \frac{P_{t1}}{\{1 + [(\gamma - 1)/2]M_1^2\}^{(\gamma-1)/\gamma}} = \frac{120{,}160 \text{ Pa}}{1.09295} = 109{,}940 \text{ Pa}$$

Then, using Eq. (4-8), we have

$$D_{\text{add}} = P_1A_1(1 + \gamma M_1^2) - P_0A_0(1 + \gamma M_0^2) - P_0(A_1 - A_0)$$
$$= 109{,}940 \times 0.26(1 + 1.4 \times 0.3586^2) - 101{,}300$$
$$\times 0.2(1 + 1.4 \times 0.5^2) - 101{,}300(0.26 - 0.20)$$
$$= 33{,}730 - 27{,}351 - 6078 = 301 \text{ N}$$

$$T = F - D_{\text{nac}} - D_{\text{add}} = 20{,}000 - 900 - 301 = 18{,}799 \text{ N}$$

Conclusion. A comparision of the installed engine thrust T of nacelle 1 to that of nacelle 2 shows that nacelle 1 gives a higher installed engine thrust and is better than nacelle 2 at the conditions calculated.

Example 4-2. An inlet of about 48 ft^2 (a little larger than the inlet on one of the C-5A's engines) is designed to have an inlet Mach number of 0.8 at sea level. Determine the variation of the additive drag with flight Mach number from $M_0 = 0$ to 0.9. Assume that M_1 remains constant at 0.8.

Solution. We will be using Eqs. (4-8) and (4-10) to solve this problem. The following values are known:

$$P_0 = 14.696 \text{ psia} \qquad M_1 = 0.8 \qquad A_1 = 48 \text{ ft} \qquad \gamma = 1.4$$

Thus we must find values of A_0 and P_1 for each flight Mach number M_0. We assume isentropic flow between stations 0 and 1 and therefore P_t and A^* are constant. Using the relations for isentropic flow, we can write

$$P_1 = P_0 \frac{P_{t0}}{P_0} \frac{P_1}{P_{t1}} = P_0 \frac{(P/P_t)_1}{(P/P_t)_0}$$

$$A_0 = A_1 \frac{A_1^*}{A_1} \frac{A_0}{A_0^*} = A_1 \frac{(A/A^*)_0}{(A/A^*)_1}$$

We obtain values of P/P_t and A/A^* from the isentropic table (App. E). At a flight Mach number of 0.9, we have

$$P_1 = P_0 \frac{(P/P_t)_1}{(P/P_t)_0} = 14.696\left(\frac{0.65602}{0.59126}\right) = 16.306 \text{ psia}$$

$$A_0 = A_1 \frac{(A/A^*)_0}{(A/A^*)_1} = 48\left(\frac{1.0089}{1.0382}\right) = 46.65 \text{ ft}^2$$

Thus

$$\begin{aligned} D_{\text{add}} &= P_1 A_1(1 + \gamma M_1^2) - P_0 A_0(1 + \gamma M_0^2) - P_0(A_1 - A_0) \\ &= 16.306(144)(48)(1.896) - 14.696(144)(46.65)(2.134) \\ &\quad - 14.696(144)(1.35) \\ &= 213{,}693 - 210{,}672 - 2857 \\ &= 164 \text{ lbf} \end{aligned}$$

At a flight Mach number of 0, we have

$$(D_{\text{add}})_{M_0=0} = P_1 A_1(1 + \gamma M_1^2) - P_0 A_1$$

$$P_1 = (14.696)(0.65602) = 9.641 \text{ psia}$$

Thus

$$\begin{aligned} D_{\text{add}} &= 9.641(144)(48)(1.896) - 14.696(144)(48) \\ &= 126{,}347 - 101{,}579 \\ &= 24{,}768 \text{ lbf} \end{aligned}$$

Table 4-1 presents the results of this inlet's additive drag in the range of flight Mach numbers requested. As indicated in this table, the additive drag is largest at low flight Mach numbers for this fixed-area inlet.

As will be shown in the next section, most of the additive drag D_{add} can be offset by the forebody portion of the nacelle drag (D_w, a negative drag or thrust), provided that the flow does not separate (in perfect flow, we will show that $D_{\text{add}} + D_w = 0$). With the large variation in M_0 and the fixed value of M_1, the path of the streamlines entering the inlet must go through large changes in geometry, as shown in Fig. 4-5. Boundary-layer separation on the forebody of the nacelle can occur when the inlet must turn the flow through large angles

TABLE 4-1
Summary of additive calculations for Example 4-2

M_0	$\left(\frac{P}{P_t}\right)_0$	P_1 (psia)	$\left(\frac{A}{A^*}\right)_0$	A_0 (ft^2)	$1+\gamma M_0^2$	D_{add} (lbf)
0.0	1.00000	9.641	—	—	1.000	24,768
0.1	0.99303	9.711	5.8218	269.16	1.014	17,711
0.2	0.97250	9.916	2.9635	137.01	1.056	12,135
0.3	0.93947	10.265	2.0351	94.09	1.126	7,857
0.4	0.89561	10.768	1.5901	73.52	1.224	4,687
0.5	0.84302	11.439	1.3398	61.94	1.350	2,453
0.6	0.78400	12.300	1.1882	54.94	1.504	1,017
0.7	0.72093	13.376	1.0944	50.60	1.686	258
0.8	0.65602	14.696	1.0382	48.00	1.896	0
0.9	0.59126	16.306	1.0089	46.65	2.134	164

with a resulting decrease in the magnitude of the drag on the forebody portion of the nacelle and increase in the net drag $D_{add} + D_w$ on the front portion of the inlet. To reduce the additive drag at low flight Mach numbers, some subsonic inlets have blow-in doors (see Fig. 4-5) that increase the inlet area at the low flight Mach numbers (full-throttle operation) and thus reduce the additive drag.

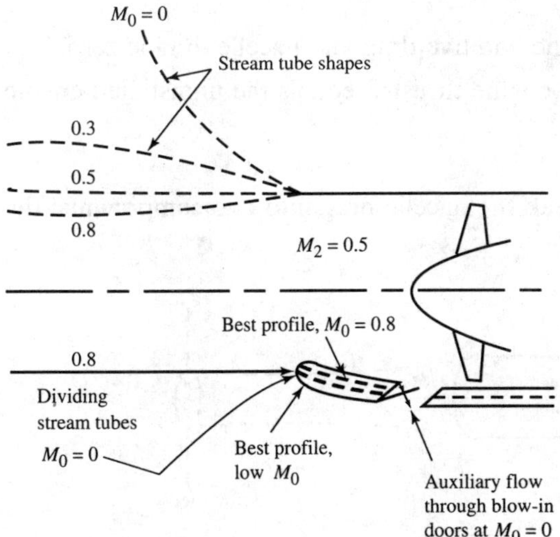

FIGURE 4-5
Subsonic inlet at different flight Mach numbers (*top*) with auxiliary blow-in door (*bottom*). (Source: Kerrebrock, Aircraft Engines and Gas Turbines, MIT Press, 1977)

Relationship between Nacelle Drag and Additive Drag

The nacelle drag and the additive drag are interdependent. We can learn something about this interdependence by considering a *perfect nacelle,* i.e., a nacelle with no external viscous drag or form drag.

We now consider a control volume for all the fluid flowing external to the engine, i.e., all the fluid outside the stream tube shown in Fig. 4-6. Because the flow is perfect (no shocks, no boundary layers, etc.), the fluid conditions are identical at the entrance 0 and exit 9 of our control volume.

Since the momentum of the fluid flowing through the control volume does not change, the sum of the pressure forces acting on the inside of the stream tube must equal zero. For perfect flow, we have

$$\int_0^1 (P - P_0)\, dA_y + \int_1^9 (P - P_0)\, dA_y + \int_9^\infty (P - P_0)\, dA_y = 0$$

or

$$D_{\text{add}} + D_{\text{nac}} = -\int_9^\infty (P - P_0)\, dA_y \tag{4-11}$$

For the case of a perfect fluid, we can combine Eqs. (4-11), (4-6), (4-3), and (4-2) to obtain

$$T = F + \int_9^\infty (P - P_0)\, dA_y \tag{4-12}$$

For a perfectly expanded nozzle ($P_9 = P_0$) and a jet that is parallel to the free stream ($dA_y = 0$), the following conclusions can be made:

1. From Eq. (4-11), the sum of the additive drag and nacelle drag is zero.
2. From Eq. (4-12), the installed engine thrust T equals the uninstalled engine thrust F.

It is industry practice to break the nacelle drag into two components: the

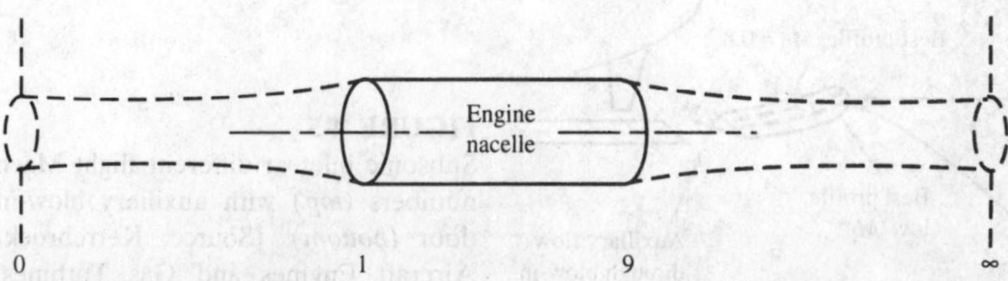

FIGURE 4-6
Stream tube of flow through engine nacelle.

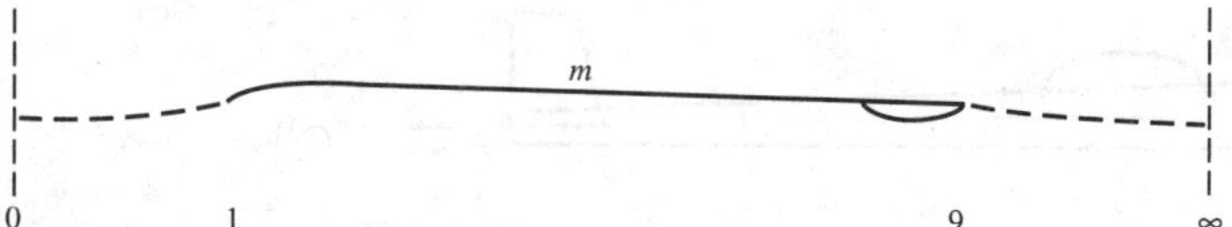

FIGURE 4-7
Ideal long nacelle.

drag associated with the forebody (front half of nacelle) D_w and the drag associated with the afterbody (rear half of nacelle) D_b. This is usually a reasonable approach because often lip separation dominates near the inlet and boat-tail drag near the exit. Assuming the division of nacelle drag to be meaningful, we can interpret the two drag terms by considering the nacelle to be very long and parallel in the middle, as shown in Fig. 4-7.

In this case, perfect flow would give us P_0, etc., at the middle. Application of the momentum equation to a control volume from 0 to m containing all the fluid outside the engine's stream tube will give

$$\int_0^1 (P - P_0)\, dA_y + \int_1^m (P - P_0)\, dA_y = 0$$

That is, in perfect flow,

$$D_{\text{add}} + D_w = 0 \tag{4-13}$$

Similarly, application of the momentum equation to a control from m to ∞ containing all the fluid outside the engine's stream tube will give

$$D_b + \int_9^\infty (P - P_0)\, dA_y = 0 \tag{4-14}$$

4-3 NOTE ON PROPULSIVE EFFICIENCY

The kinetic energy of the fluid flowing through an aircraft propulsion system is increased by an energy-transfer mechanism consisting of a series of processes constituting an engine cycle. From the point of view of an observer riding on the propulsion unit (see Fig. 4-8*a*), the engine cycle output is the increase of

FIGURE 4-8*a*
Velocity change by observer on aircraft.

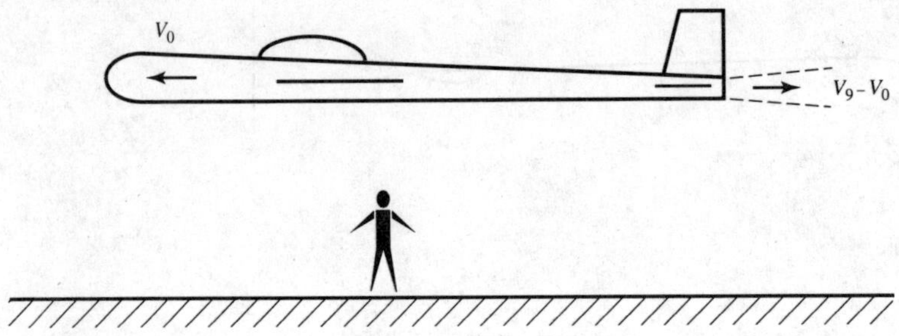

FIGURE 4-8*b*
Velocity change by observer on ground.

kinetic energy received by the air passing through the engine, which is $(V_9^2 - V_0^2)/(2g_c)$. From this observer's point of view, the total power output of the engine is the kinetic energy increase imparted to the air per unit time. On the other hand, from the point of view of an observer on the ground (see Fig. 4-8*b*), one sees the aircraft propulsion system's thrust moving at a velocity V_0 and observes the still air to receive an increase in kinetic energy, after passing through the engine, by an amount $(V_9 - V_0)^2/(2g_c)$. From this point of view, therefore, the total effect of the engine (and its output) is the sum of the propulsive power FV_0 and the kinetic energy per unit time imparted to the air passing through the engine. The sole purpose of the engine is to produce a propulsive power, and this is called the *useful power output* of the propulsion system. The ratio of the useful power output to the total power output of the propulsion system is called the *propulsive efficiency* [see Eq. (1-14)].

4-4 GAS TURBINE ENGINE COMPONENTS

The inlet, compressor, combustor, turbine, and nozzle are the main components of the gas turbine engine. The purpose and operation of these components and two thrust augmentation techniques are discussed in this section.

Inlets

An inlet reduces the entering air velocity to a level suitable for the compressor. The air velocity is reduced by a compression process which increases the air pressure. The operation and design of the inlet are described in terms of the efficiency of the compression process, the external drag of the inlet, and the mass flow into the inlet. The design and operation of the inlet depend on whether the air entering the duct is subsonic or supersonic. As the aircraft approaches the speed of sound, the air tends to be compressed more, and at

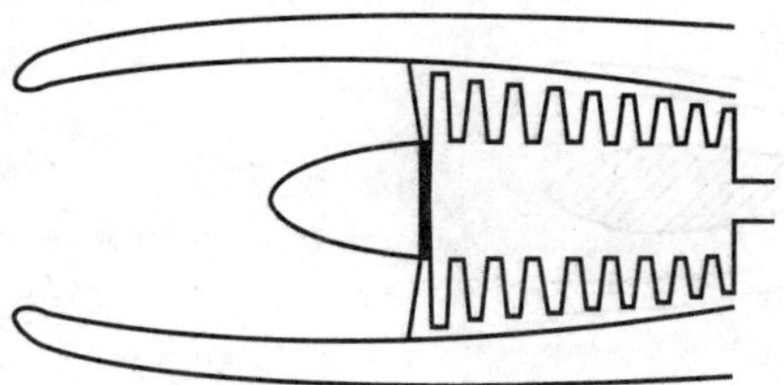

FIGURE 4-9
Subsonic inlet.

Mach 1, shock waves occur. Shock waves are compression waves, and at higher Mach numbers, these compression waves are stronger. Compression by shock waves is inefficient. In subsonic flow, there are no shock waves, and the air compression takes place quite efficiently. In supersonic flow, there are shock waves present. Shock waves and the compressibility of air then influence the design of inlets.

SUBSONIC INLET. The subsonic inlet can be a divergent duct, as shown in Fig. 4-9. This duct is satisfactory until the Mach number becomes greater than 1, at which time a shock wave occurs at the mouth and the compression process becomes inefficient. The subsonic divergent duct operates best at one velocity (design point), and at other velocities, the compression process is less efficient and the external drag is greater. The airflow patterns for the subsonic inlet are shown in Fig. 4-10.

SUPERSONIC INLET. Since shock waves will occur in supersonic flow, the geometry of supersonic inlets is designed to obtain the most efficient compression with a minimum of weight. If the velocity is reduced from a supersonic speed to a subsonic speed with one normal shock wave, the compression process is relatively inefficient. If several oblique shock waves are employed to reduce the velocity, the compression process is more efficient. Two typical supersonic inlets are the *ramp* (two-dimensional wedge) and the

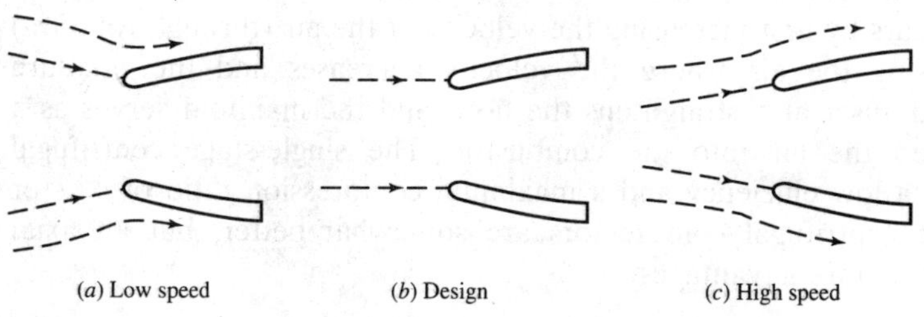

FIGURE 4-10
Subsonic inlet flow patterns.

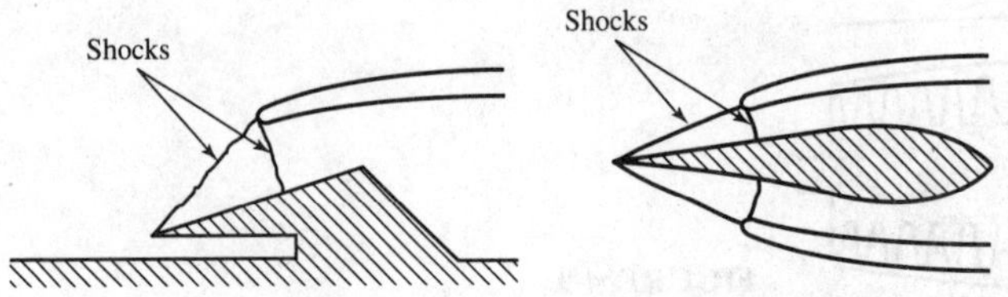

FIGURE 4-11
Supersonic inlets.

centerbody (three-dimensional spike), which are shown in Fig. 4-11. The shock wave positions in Fig. 4-11 are for the design condition of the inlet. At off-design Mach numbers, the positions of the shock waves change, thus affecting the external drag and the efficiency of compression. A more efficient ramp or centerbody inlet can be designed by using more than two shock waves to compress the entering air. Also, if the geometry is designed to be variable, the inlet operates more efficiently over a range of Mach numbers.

Compressors

The function of the compressor is to increase the pressure of the incoming air so that the combustion process and the power extraction process after combustion can be carried out more efficiently. By increasing the pressure of the air, the volume of the air is reduced, which means that the combustion of the fuel/air mixture will occur in a smaller volume.

CENTRIFUGAL COMPRESSOR. The compressor was the main stumbling block during the early years of turbojet engine development. Great Britain's Sir Frank Whittle solved the problem by using a centrifugal compressor. This type of compressor is still being used in many of the smaller gas turbine engines. A typical single-stage centrifugal compressor is shown in Fig. 4-12. The compressor consists of three main parts: an impeller, a diffuser, and a compressor manifold. Air enters the compressor near the hub of the impeller and is then compressed by the rotational motion of the impeller. The compression occurs by first increasing the velocity of the air (through rotation) and then diffusing the air where the velocity decreases and the pressure increases. The diffuser also straightens the flow, and the manifold serves as a collector to feed the air into the combustor. The single-stage centrifugal compressor has a low efficiency and a maximum compression ratio of 4 : 1 or 5 : 1. Multistage centrifugal compressors are somewhat better, but an axial compressor offers more advantages.

AXIAL COMPRESSORS. An axial compressor is shown in Fig. 4-13. The air in an axial compressor flows in an axial direction through a series of rotating

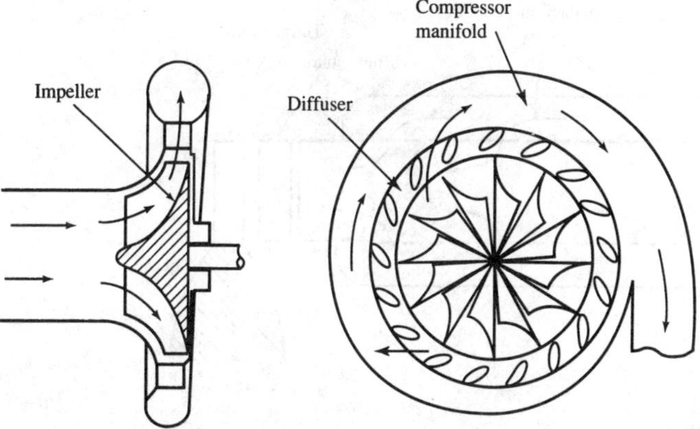

FIGURE 4-12
Single-stage centrifugal compressor.

rotor blades and stationary *stator* vanes which are concentric with the axis of rotation. Each set of rotor blades and stator vanes is known as a *stage.* The flow path in an axial compressor decreases in the cross-sectional area in the direction of flow. The decrease of area is in proportion to the increased density of the air as the compression progresses from stage to stage. Figure 4-13 contains a schematic of an axial compressor. Each stage of an axial compressor produces a small compression pressure ratio (1.1 : 1 to 1.2 : 1) at a high efficiency. Therefore, for high pressure ratios (12 : 1), multiple stages are used. Axial compressors are also more compact and have a smaller frontal area than a centrifugal compressor, which are added advantages. For the best axial compressor efficiency, the compressor operates at a constant axial velocity, as shown in Fig. 1-6. At high compression ratios, multistaging a single axial compressor does not produce as efficient an operation as a dual axial compressor would (see Fig. 1-4*a*). For a single rotational speed, there is a limit in the balance operation between the first and last stages of the compressor. To obtain more flexibility and a more uniform loading of each compressor stage,

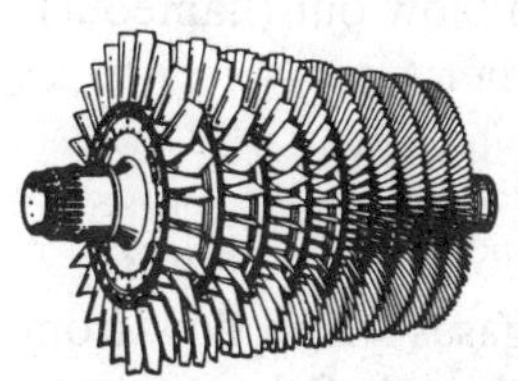

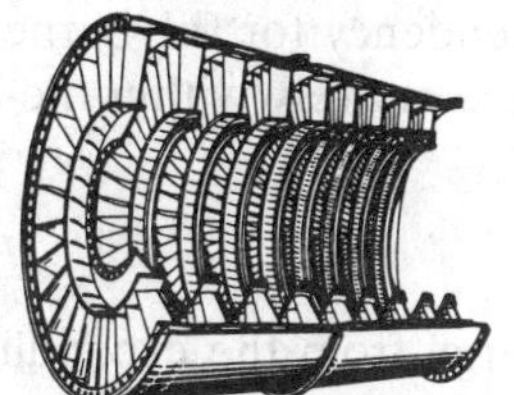

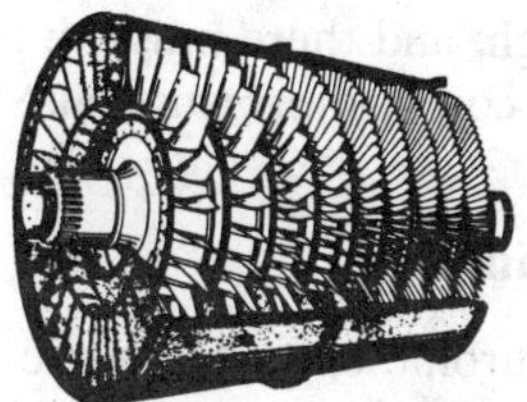

FIGURE 4-13
Multistage axial compressor.

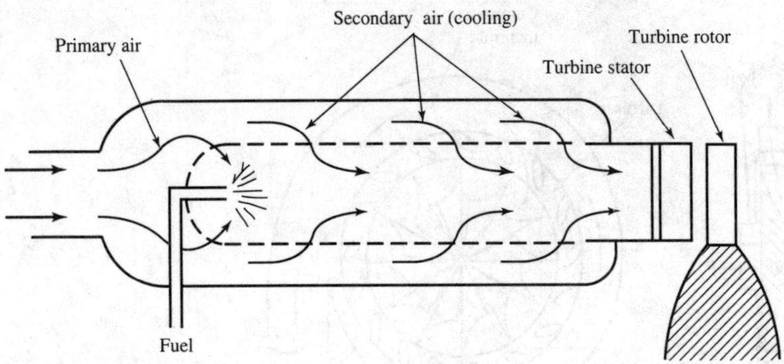

FIGURE 4-14
Straight-through flow combustor.

a dual compressor with two different rotational speeds is generally used in high-compression-ratio axial compressors.

Combustor or Main Burner

The combustor is designed to burn a mixture of fuel and air and to deliver the resulting gases to the turbine at a uniform temperature. The gas temperature must not exceed the allowable structural temperature of the turbine. A schematic of a combustor is shown in Fig. 4-14. Less than one-half of the total volume of air entering the burner mixes with the fuel and burns. The rest of the air—secondary air—is simply heated or may be thought of as cooling the products of combustion and cooling the burner surfaces. The ratio of total air to fuel varies among the different types of engines from 30 to 60 parts of air to 1 part of fuel by weight. The average ratio in new engine designs is about 40 : 1, but only 15 parts are used for burning (since the combustion process demands that the number of parts of air to fuel must be within certain limits at a given pressure for combustion to occur). Combustion chambers may be of the can, the annular, or the can-annular type, as shown in Fig. 4-15.

For an acceptable burner design, the pressure loss as the gases pass through the burner must be held to a minimum, the combustion efficiency must be high, and there must be no tendency for the burner to blow out (flameout). Also, combustion must take place entirely within the burner.

Turbines

The turbine extracts kinetic energy from the expanding gases which flow from the combustion chamber. The kinetic energy is converted to shaft horsepower to drive the compressor and the accessories. Nearly three-fourths of all the energy available from the products of combustion is required to drive the

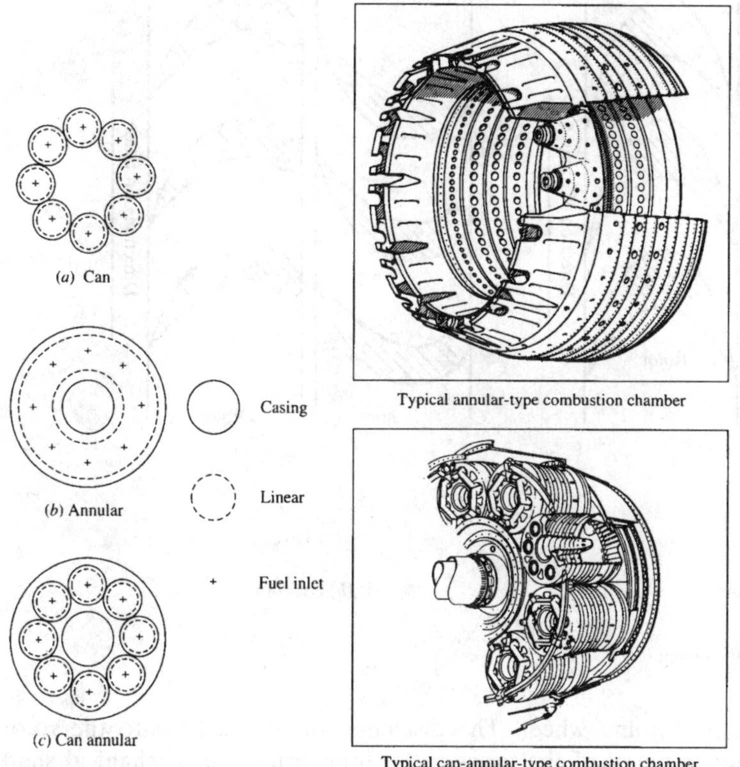

FIGURE 4-15
Cross sections of combustion chambers.

compressor. The axial-flow turbine consists of a turbine wheel *rotor* and a set of stationary vanes *stator,* as shown in Fig. 4-16. The set of stationary vanes of the turbine is a plane of vanes (concentric with the axis of the turbine) that are set at an angle to form a series of small nozzles which discharge the gases onto

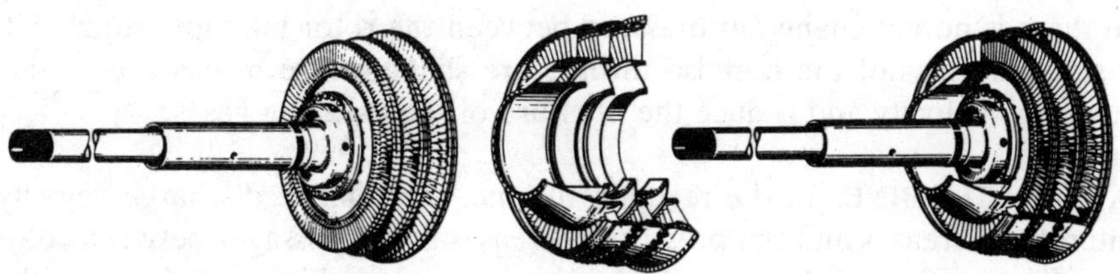

FIGURE 4-16
Axial-flow turbine components.

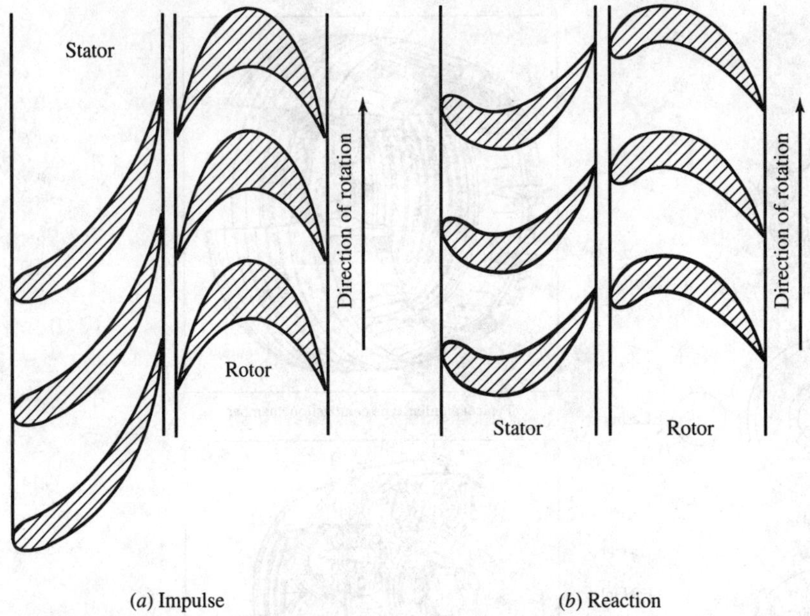

FIGURE 04-17
Impulse and reaction stages.

the blades of the turbine wheel. The discharge of the gases onto the rotor allows the kinetic energy of the gases to be transformed to mechanical shaft energy.

Like the axial compressor, the axial turbine is usually multistaged. There are generally fewer turbine stages than compressor stages since in the turbine the pressure is decreasing (expansion process) whereas, in the compressor the pressure is increasing (compression process). In each of the processes (expansion or compression), the blades of the axial turbine or axial compressor act as airfoils, and the airflow over the airfoil is more favorable in the expansion process.

IMPULSE TURBINE. The impulse turbine and the reaction turbine are the two basic types of axial turbines, as shown in Fig. 4-17. In the impulse type, the relative discharge velocity of the rotor is the same as the relative inlet velocity since there is no net change in pressure between the rotor inlet and rotor exit. The stator nozzles of the impulse turbine are shaped to form passages which increase the velocity and reduce the pressure of the escaping gases.

REACTION TURBINE. In the reaction turbine, the relative discharge velocity of the rotor increases and the pressure decreases in the passages between rotor blades. The stator nozzle passages of the reaction turbine merely alter the direction of the flow.

Most turbines in jet engines are a combination of impulse and reaction turbines. In the design of turbines, the following items must be considered: (1) shaft rotational speed, (2) gas flow rate, (3) inlet and outlet temperatures, (4) inlet and outlet pressures, (5) exhaust velocity, and (6) required power output. If the jet engine is equipped with a dual compressor, the turbine must also be dual or split.

Exhaust Nozzle

The purpose of the exhaust nozzle is to increase the velocity of the exhaust gas before discharge from the nozzle and to collect and straighten gas flow from the turbine. In operating, the gas turbine engine converts the internal energy of the fuel to kinetic energy in the exhaust gas stream. The net thrust (or force) of the engine is the result of this operation, and it can be calculated by applying Newton's second law of motion (see Chap. 2). For large values of specific thrust, the kinetic energy of the exhaust gas must be high, which implies a high exhaust velocity. The nozzle supplies a high exit velocity by expanding the exhaust gas in an expansion process which requires a decrease in pressure. The pressure ratio across the nozzle controls the expansion process, and the maximum thrust for a given engine is obtained when the exit pressure equals the ambient pressure. Nozzles and their operation are discussed further in Chaps. 3 and 10. The two basic types of nozzles used in jet engines are the convergent and convergent-divergent nozzles.

CONVERGENT NOZZLE. The convergent nozzle is a simple convergent duct, as shown in Fig. 4-18. When the nozzle pressure ratio (turbine exit pressure to nozzle exit pressure) is low (less than about 2), the convergent nozzle is used. The convergent nozzle has generally been used in low thrust engines for subsonic aircraft.

CONVERGENT-DIVERGENT NOZZLE. The convergent-divergent nozzle can be a convergent duct followed by a divergent duct. Where the cross-sectional

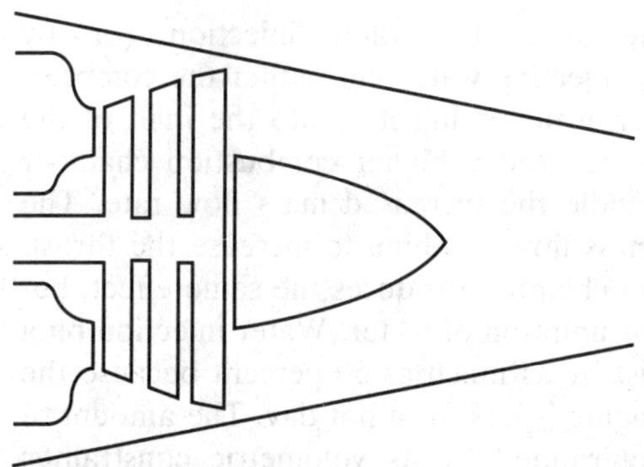

FIGURE 4-18
Convergent exhaust nozzle.

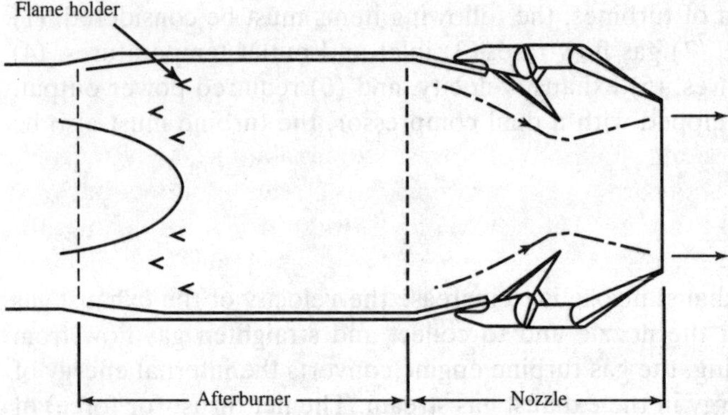

FIGURE 4-19
Convergent-divergent ejector exhaust nozzle.

area of the duct is a minimum, the nozzle is said to have a *throat* at that position. Most convergent-divergent nozzles used in supersonic aircraft are not simple ducts, but incorporate variable geometry and other aerodynamic features, as shown in Fig. 4-19. Only the throat area and exit area of the nozzle in Fig. 4-19 are set mechanically, the nozzle walls being determined aerodynamically by the gas flow. The convergent-divergent nozzle is used if the nozzle pressure ratio is high. High-specific-thrust engines in supersonic aircraft generally have some form of convergent-divergent nozzle. If the engine incorporates an afterburner, the nozzle throat and exit area must be varied to match the different flow conditions and to produce the maximum available thrust.

Thrust Augmentation

Thrust augmentation can be accomplished by either water injection or afterburning.

WATER INJECTION. Thrust augmentation by water injection (or by water/alcohol mixture) is achieved by injecting water into either the compressor or the combustion chamber. When water is injected into the inlet of the compressor, the mass flow rate increases and a higher combustion chamber pressure results if the turbine can handle the increased mass flow rate. The higher pressure and the increase in mass flow combine to increase the thrust. Injection of water into the combustion chamber produces the same effect, but to a lesser degree and with greater consumption of water. Water injection on a hot day can increase the takeoff thrust by as much as 50 percent because the original mass of air entering the jet engine is less for a hot day. The amount of air entering any turbomachine is determined by its volumetric constraints;

therefore, it follows that the mass flow on a hot day will be less since the air is less dense on a hot day.

AFTERBURNING. Another method of thrust augmentation is by burning additional fuel in the afterburner. The afterburner is a section of duct between the turbine and exhaust nozzle. The schematic diagram in Fig. 4-19 shows the afterburner section. The afterburner consists of the duct section, fuel injectors, and flame holders. It is possible to have afterburning because, in the main burner section, the combustion products are air-rich. The effect of the afterburning operation is to raise the temperature of the exhaust gases which, when exhausted through the nozzle, will reach a higher exit velocity. The pressure/temperature velocity profile for afterburning is also shown in Fig. 1-6. The J79 for afterburner operation has a thrust of 17,900 lbf and a *thrust specific fuel consumption* (TSFC) of 1.965 [(lbm/hr)/lbf]/hr, and for military operation (no afterburning) it has a thrust of 11,870 lbf and a TSFC of 0.84 [(lbm/hr)/lbf]/hr. We then see that afterburning produces large thrust gains at the expense of fuel economy.

4-5 BRAYTON CYCLE

The Brayton power cycle is a model used in thermodynamics for an ideal gas turbine power cycle. It is composed of the four following processes, which are also shown in Fig. 4-20(*a*):

1. Isentropic compression (2 to 3)
2. Constant-pressure heat addition (3 to 4)

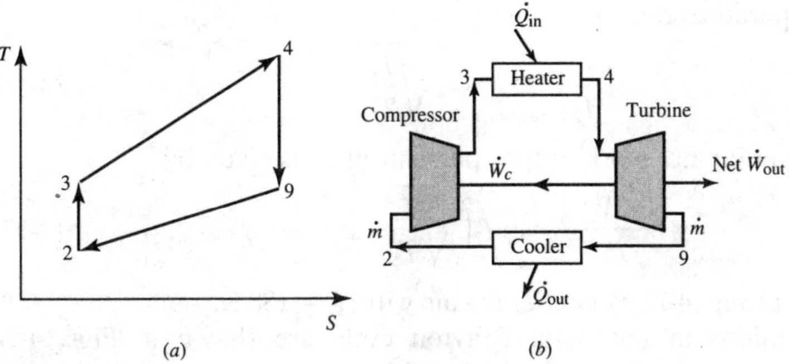

FIGURE 4-20
Brayton cycle.

3. Isentropic expansion (4 to 9)
4. Constant-pressure heat rejection (9 to 2)

The basic components of the Brayton cycle are shown to the right in Fig. 4-20(*b*). In the ideal cycle, the processes through both the compressor and the turbine are considered to be reversible and adiabatic (isentropic). The processes through the heater and cooler are considered to be constant-pressure in the ideal cycle.

For a calorically perfect gas, thermodynamic analysis of the ideal Brayton cycle gives the following equations for the rate of energy transfer of each component:

$$\dot{W}_c = \dot{m}c_p(T_3 - T_2) \qquad \dot{Q}_{\text{in}} = \dot{m}c_p(T_4 - T_3)$$
$$\dot{W}_t = \dot{m}c_p(T_4 - T_9) \qquad \dot{Q}_{\text{out}} = \dot{m}c_p(T_9 - T_2)$$
$$\text{Net } \dot{W}_{\text{out}} = \dot{W}_t - \dot{W}_c = \dot{m}c_p[T_4 - T_9 - (T_3 - T_2)]$$

Now, the thermal efficiency of the cycle is $\eta_T = \text{net } \dot{W}_{\text{out}}/\dot{Q}_{\text{in}}$. Noting that $(P_3/P_2)^{(\gamma-1)/\gamma} = T_3/T_2 = T_4/T_9$, we see that the thermal efficiency for the ideal Brayton cycle can be shown to be given by

$$\boxed{\eta_T = 1 - \left(\frac{1}{\text{PR}}\right)^{(\gamma-1)/\gamma}} \tag{4-15}$$

where PR is the *pressure ratio* P_3/P_2. The thermal efficiency is plotted in Fig. 4-21 as a function of the compressor pressure ratio for two ratios of specific heats.

For an ideal Brayton cycle with fixed compressor inlet temperature T_2 and heater exit temperature T_4, simple calculus yields an expression for the pressure ratio P_3/P_2 and associated temperature ratio T_3/T_2 giving the maximum net work output per unit mass. This optimum compressor pressure, or temperature ratio, corresponds to the maximum area within the cycle on a T-s diagram, as shown in Fig. 4-22. One can show that the optimum compressor temperature ratio is given by

$$\left(\frac{T_3}{T_2}\right)_{\text{max work}} = \sqrt{\frac{T_4}{T_2}} \tag{4-16}$$

and the corresponding net work output per unit mass is given by

$$\frac{\text{Net } \dot{W}_{\text{out}}}{\dot{m}} = c_p T_2 \left(\sqrt{\frac{T_4}{T_2}} - 1\right)^2 \tag{4-17}$$

which is plotted in Fig. 4-23 versus T_4 for air with $T_2 = 288$ K.

Three variations in the basic Brayton cycle are shown in Figs. 4-24 through 4-26. Figure 4-24 shows the cycle with a *high-pressure* (HP) turbine driving the compressor and a free-power turbine providing the output power. This cycle has the same thermal efficiency as the ideal Brayton cycle of Fig.

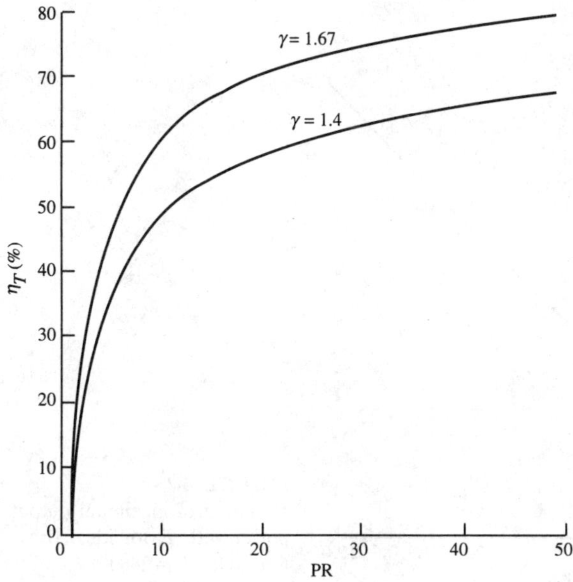

FIGURE 4-21
Thermal efficiency of ideal Brayton cycle.

4-20. Figure 4-25 shows the Brayton cycle with reheat. Addition of reheat to the cycle increases the specfic power of the free turbine and reduces the thermal efficiency.

Figure 4-26 shows the ideal Brayton cycle with regeneration. When regeneration is added to the basic Brayton cycle, the energy input to the heater is reduced, which increases the cycle's thermal efficiency. For an ideal regenerator, we have

$$T_{3.5} = T_9 \qquad \text{and} \qquad T_{9.5} = T_3$$

Note that regeneration is possible only when T_9 is greater than T_3, which requires low cycle pressure ratios. The thermal efficiency of an ideal Brayton cycle with regeneration is shown in Fig. 4-27 for several values of T_4/T_2 along

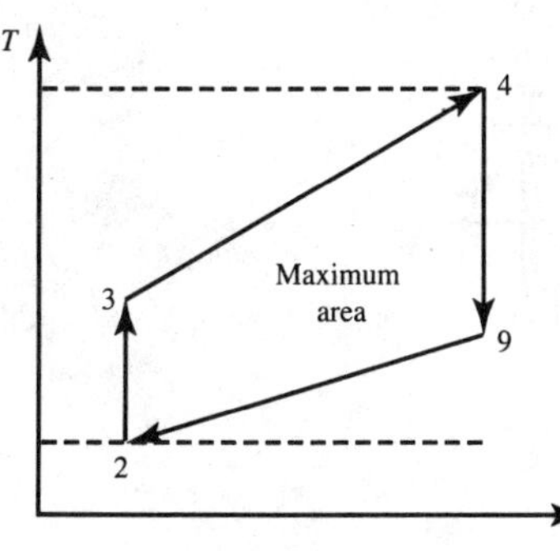

FIGURE 4-22
Maximum-power-output Brayton cycle.

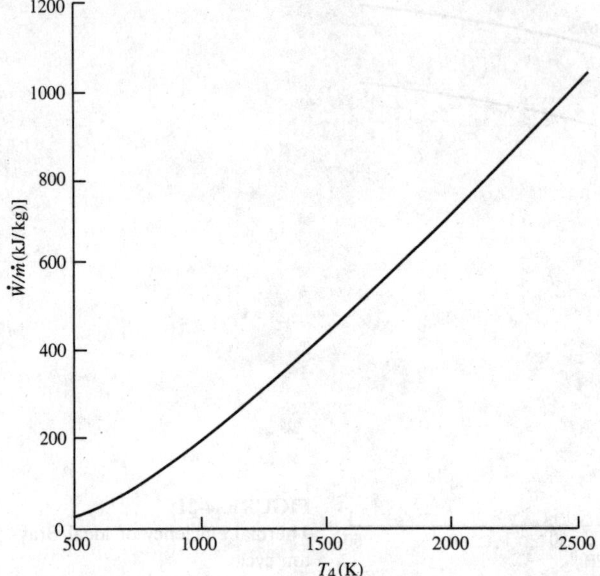

FIGURE 4-23
Variation of maximum output power with T_4 for ideal Brayton cycle ($T_2 = 288$ K).

with the thermal efficiency of the cycle without regeneration. The thermal efficiency of the ideal Brayton cycle with regeneration is given by

$$\eta_T = 1 - \frac{(\text{PR})^{(\gamma-1)/\gamma}}{T_4/T_2} \tag{4-18}$$

4-6 AIRCRAFT ENGINE DESIGN

This introductory chapter to aircraft propulsion systems has presented the basic engine components and ideal engines. The following chapters present the cycle analysis (thermodynamic design-point study) of ideal and real engines,

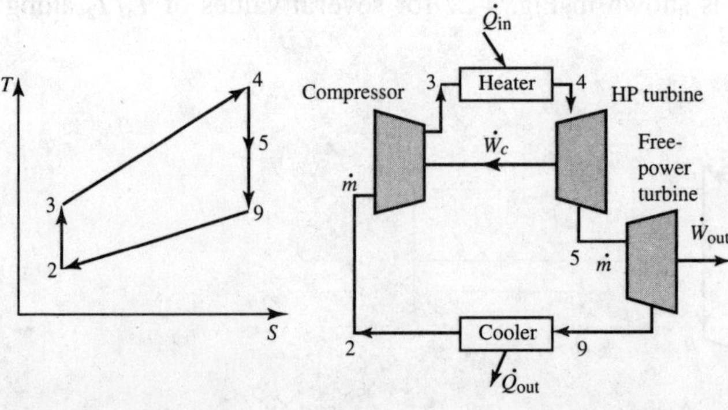

FIGURE 4-24
Brayton cycle with free-power turbine.

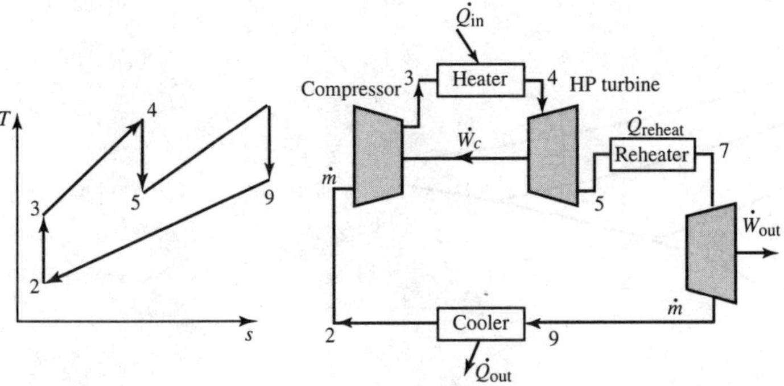

FIGURE 4-25
Brayton cycle with reheat.

off-design performance, and an introduction to the aerodynamics of engine components. The design procedure for a typical gas turbine engine, shown in Fig. 4-28, requires that thermodynamic design-point studies (cycle analysis) and off-design performance be in the initial steps of design. The iterative nature of design is indicated in Fig. 4-28 by the feedback loops. Although only a few loops are shown, many more exist.

PROBLEMS

4-1. The inlet for a high-bypass-ratio turbofan engine has an area A_1 of 6.0 m^2 and is designed to have an inlet Mach number M_1 of 0.6. Determine the additive drag at the flight conditions of sea-level static test and Mach number of 0.8 at 12-km altitude.

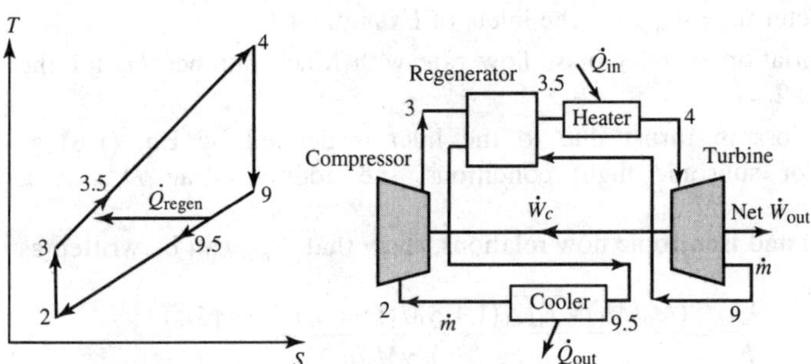

FIGURE 4-26
Ideal Brayton cycle with regeneration.

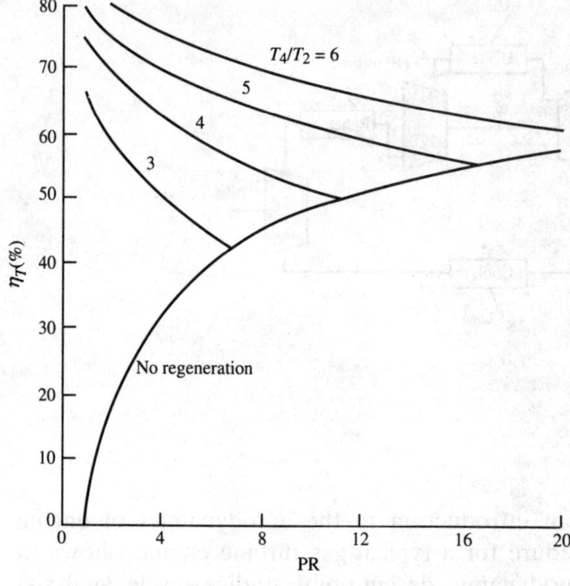

FIGURE 4-27
Thermal efficiency of ideal Brayton cycle with regeneration.

4-2. An inlet with an area A_1 of 10 ft^2 is designed to have an inlet Mach number M_1 of 0.6. Determine the additive drag at the flight conditions of sea-level static test and Mach number of 0.8 at 40-kft altitude.

4-3. Determine the additive drag for an inlet having an area A_1 of 7000 in^2 and a Mach number M_1 of 0.8 while flying at a Mach number M_0 of 0.4 at an altitude of 2000 ft.

4-4. Determine the additive drag for an inlet having an area A_1 of 5.0 m^2 and a Mach number M_1 of 0.7 while flying at a Mach number M_0 of 0.3 at an altitude of 1 km.

4-5. A turbojet engine under static test ($M_0 = 0$) has air with a mass flow of 100 kg/sec flowing through an inlet area A_1 of 0.56 m^2 with a total pressure of 1 atm and total temperature of 288.8 K. Determine the additive drag of the inlet.

4-6. In Chap. 1, the loss in thrust due to the inlet is defined by Eq. (1-8) as $\phi_{\text{inlet}} = D_{\text{inlet}}/F$. Determine ϕ_{inlet} for the inlets of Example 4-1.

4-7. Determine the variation of inlet mass flow rate with Mach number M_0 for the inlet of Example 4-2.

4-8. In Chap. 1, the loss in thrust due to the inlet is defined by Eq. (1-8) as $\phi_{\text{inlet}} = D_{\text{inlet}}/F$. For subsonic flight conditions, the additive drag D_{add} is a conservative estimate of D_{inlet}.

a. Using Eq. (4-9) and isentropic flow relations, show that ϕ_{inlet} can be written as

$$\phi_{\text{inlet}} = \frac{D_{\text{add}}}{F} = \frac{(M_0/M_1)\sqrt{T_1/T_0}(1 + \gamma M_1^2) - (A_1/A_0 + \gamma M_0^2)}{(Fg_c/\dot{m}_0)(\gamma M_0/a_0)}$$

b. Calculate and plot the variation of ϕ_{inlet} with flight Mach number M_0 from 0.2 to 0.9 for inlet Mach numbers M_1 of 0.6 and 0.8 with $(Fg_c/\dot{m}_0)(\gamma/a_0) = 4.5$.

4-9. A bell-mouth inlet (see Fig. P3-7) is installed for static testing of jet engines.

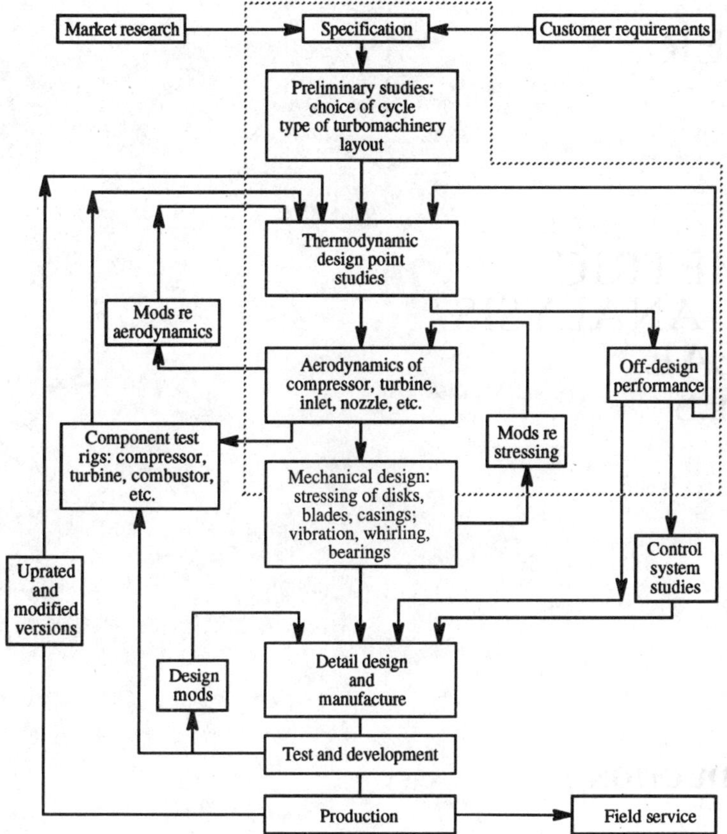

FIGURE 4-28
Typical aircraft gas turbine design procedure.

Determine the force on the bell-mouth inlet with the data of Prob. 3-7*b* for an inlet area that is 8 times the area at station 2 (assume that the inlet wall is a stream tube and that the outside of the bell-mouth inlet sees a static pressure equal to P_{t0}).

4-10. The maximum power out of an ideal Brayton cycle operating between temperatures T_2 and T_4 is given by Eq. (4-17). By taking the derivative of the net work out of an ideal Brayton cycle with respect to the pressure ratio (PR) and setting it equal to zero, show that Eq. (4-16) gives the resulting compressor temperature ratio and Eq. (4-17) gives the net work out.

4-11. Show that Eq. (4-18) gives the thermal efficiency for the ideal Brayton cycle with regeneration.

4-12. For the ideal Brayton cycle with regeneration, regeneration is desirable when $T_9 \geq T_3$. Show that the maximum compressor pressure ratio $\text{PR}_{\max}$ for regeneration ($T_9 = T_3$) is given by

$$\text{PR}_{\max} = \left(\frac{T_4}{T_2}\right)^{\gamma/[2(\gamma-1)]}$$

CHAPTER 5

PARAMETRIC CYCLE ANALYSIS OF IDEAL ENGINES

5-1 INTRODUCTION

Cycle analysis studies the thermodynamic changes of the working fluid (air and products of combustion in most cases) as it flows through the engine. It is divided into two types of analysis: *parametric cycle analysis* (also called *design-point* or *on-design*) and *engine performance analysis* (also called *off-design*). Parametric cycle analysis determines the performance of engines at different flight conditions and values of design choice (e.g., compressor pressure ratio) and design limit (e.g., combustor exit temperature) parameters. Engine performance analysis determines the performance of a specific engine at all flight conditions and throttle settings.

In both forms of analysis, the components of an engine are characterized by the change in properties they produce. For example, the compressor is described by a total pressure ratio and efficiency. A certain engine's behavior is determined by its geometry, and a compressor will develop a certain total pressure ratio for a given geometry, speed, and airflow. Since the geometry is not included in parametric cycle analysis, the plots of specific thrust $F/\dot{m}_0$ and thrust specific fuel consumption S versus, say, Mach number or compressor pressure ratio are not portraying the behavior of a specific engine. Each point on such plots represents a different engine. The geometry for each plotted engine will be different, and thus we say that parametric cycle analysis represents a "rubber engine." Parametric cycle analysis is also called *design-point analysis* or *on-design analysis* since each plotted engine is operating at its so-called design point (Refs. 4, 12, and 26).

The main objective of parametric cycle analysis is to relate the engine performance parameters (primarily thrust F and thrust specific fuel consumption S) to design choices (compressor pressure ratio, fan pressure ratio, bypass ratio, etc.), to design limitations (burner exit temperature, compressor exit pressure, etc.), and to flight environment (Mach number, ambient temperature, etc.). From parametric cycle analysis, we can easily determine which engine type (e.g., turbofan) and component design characteristics (range of design choices) best satisfy a particular need.

The value of parametric cycle analysis depends directly on the realism with which the engine components are characterized. For example, if a compressor is specified by the total pressure ratio and the isentropic efficiency, and if the analysis purports to select the best total pressure ratio for a particular mission, then the choice may depend on the variation of efficiency with pressure ratio. For the conclusions to be useful, a realistic variation of efficiency with total pressure ratio must be included in the analysis.

The parametric cycle analysis of engines will be developed in stages. First the general steps applicable to the parametric cycle analysis of engines will be introduced. Next these steps will be followed to analyze engines where all engine components are taken to be ideal. Trends of these ideal engines will be analyzed, given that only basic conclusions can be deduced. The parametric cycle analysis of ideal engines allows us to look at the characteristics of the several types of aircraft engines in the simplest possible ways so that they can be compared. Following this, realistic assumptions as to component losses will be introduced in Chap. 6 and the parametric cycle analysis repeated for the different aircraft engines in Chap. 7. Performance trends of these engines with losses (real engines) will also be analyzed.

In the last chapter on engine cycle analysis, models will be developed for the performance characteristics of the engine components. The aerothermodynamic relationships between the engine components will be analyzed for several types of aircraft engines. Then the performance of specific engines at all flight conditions and throttle settings will be predicted.

5-2 NOTATION

The *total* or *stagnation temperature* is defined as that temperature reached when a steadily flowing fluid is brought to rest (stagnated) adiabatically. If T_t denotes the total temperature, T the static (thermodynamic) temperature, and V the flow velocity, then application of the first law of thermodynamics to a calorically perfect gas gives $T_t = T + V^2/(2g_c c_p)$. However, the Mach number $M = V/a = V/\sqrt{\gamma g_c RT}$ can be introduced into the above equation to give

$$T_t = T\left(1 + \frac{\gamma - 1}{2} M^2\right) \tag{5-1}$$

The *total* or *stagnation pressure* P_t is defined as the pressure reached when a steady flowing stream is brought to rest adiabatically and reversibly (i.e., isentropically). Since $P_t/P = (T_t/T)^{(\gamma-1)/\gamma}$, then

$$P_t = P\left(1 + \frac{\gamma - 1}{2} M^2\right)^{\gamma/(\gamma-1)} \tag{5-2}$$

Ratios of total temperatures and pressures will be used extensively in this text, and a special notation is adopted for them. We denote a *ratio of total pressures* across a component by π, with a subscript indicating the component: d for diffuser (inlet), c for compressor, b for burner, t for turbine, n for nozzle, and f for fan:

$$\boxed{\pi_a = \frac{\text{total pressure leaving component } a}{\text{total pressure entering component } a}} \tag{5-3}$$

Similarly, the *ratio of total temperatures* is denoted by τ, and

$$\boxed{\tau_a = \frac{\text{total temperature leaving component } a}{\text{total temperature entering component } a}} \tag{5-4}$$

Exceptions

1. We define the total/static temperature and pressure ratios of the free stream (τ_r and π_r) by

$$\boxed{\tau_r = \frac{T_{t0}}{T_0} = 1 + \frac{\gamma - 1}{2} M_0^2} \tag{5-5}$$

$$\boxed{\pi_r = \frac{P_{t0}}{P_0} = \left(1 + \frac{\gamma - 1}{2} M_0^2\right)^{\gamma/(\gamma-1)}} \tag{5-6}$$

Thus the total temperature and pressure of the free stream can be written as

$$T_{t0} = T_0 \tau_r \qquad P_{t0} = P_0 \pi_r$$

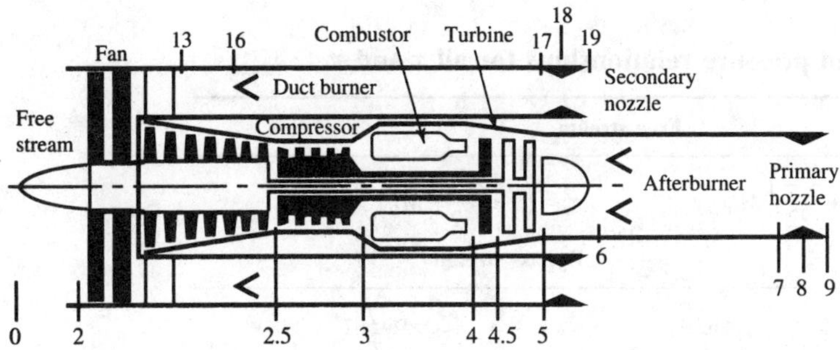

FIGURE 5-1
Station numbering for gas turbine engines.

2. Also, τ_λ is defined as the ratio of the burner exit enthalpy $c_p T_t$ to the ambient enthalpy $c_p T_0$:

$$\boxed{\tau_\lambda = \frac{h_{t\,\text{burner exit}}}{h_0} = \frac{(c_p T_t)_{\text{burner exit}}}{(c_p T)_0}} \tag{5-7}$$

Figure 5-1 shows the cross section and station numbering of a turbofan engine with both afterburning and duct burning. This station numbering is in accordance with Aerospace Recommended Practice (ARP) 755A (Ref. 27). Note that the station numbers 13 through 19 are used for the bypass stream and decimal numbers such as station number 4.5 are used to indicate an intermediate station.

Table 5-1 contains most of the short-form notation temperature ratios (τ's) and pressure ratios (π's) that we will use in our analysis. (Note that the τ_λ's are expressed for calorically perfect gases.) These ratios are shown in terms of the standard station numbering (Ref. 26).

5-3 DESIGN INPUTS

The total temperature ratios, total pressure ratios, etc., can be classified into one of four categories:

1. Flight conditions P_0, T_0, M_0, c_p, τ_r, π_r

2. Design limits $(c_p T_t)_{\text{burner exit}}$

TABLE 5-1
Temperature and pressure relationships for all τ and π

Free stream			
	$\tau_r = 1 + \frac{\gamma - 1}{2} M_0^2$	$\pi_r = \left(1 + \frac{\gamma - 1}{2} M_0^2\right)^{\gamma/(\gamma-1)}$	
Core stream		**Bypass stream**	
$\tau_\lambda = \frac{c_{pt} T_{t4}}{c_{pc} T_0}$	$\tau_{\lambda \mathrm{AB}} = \frac{c_{p\mathrm{AB}} T_{t7}}{c_{pc} T_0}$	$\tau_{\lambda \mathrm{DB}} = \frac{c_{p\mathrm{DB}} T_{t17}}{c_{pc} T_0}$	
$\tau_d = \frac{T_{t2}}{T_{t0}}$	$\pi_d = \frac{P_{t2}}{P_{t0}}$	$\tau_f = \frac{T_{t13}}{T_{t2}}$	$\pi_f = \frac{P_{t13}}{P_{t2}}$
$\tau_c = \frac{T_{t3}}{T_{t2}}$	$\pi_c = \frac{P_{t3}}{P_{t2}}$	$\tau_{\mathrm{DB}} = \frac{T_{t17}}{T_{t13}}$	$\pi_{\mathrm{DB}} = \frac{P_{t17}}{P_{t13}}$
$\tau_b = \frac{T_{t4}}{T_{t3}}$	$\pi_b = \frac{P_{t4}}{P_{t3}}$	$\tau_{fn} = \frac{T_{t19}}{T_{t17}}$	$\pi_{fn} = \frac{P_{t19}}{P_{t17}}$
$\tau_t = \frac{T_{t5}}{T_{t4}}$	$\pi_t = \frac{P_{t5}}{P_{t4}}$		
$\tau_{\mathrm{AB}} = \frac{T_{t7}}{T_{t5}}$	$\pi_{\mathrm{AB}} = \frac{P_{t7}}{P_{t5}}$		
$\tau_n = \frac{T_{t9}}{T_{t7}}$	$\pi_n = \frac{P_{t9}}{P_{t7}}$		

3. Component performance π_d, π_b, π_n, etc.
4. Design choices π_c, π_f, etc.

5-4 STEPS OF ENGINE PARAMETRIC CYCLE ANALYSIS

The steps of engine parametric cycle analysis listed below are based on a jet engine with a single inlet and single exhaust. Thus these steps will use only the station numbers for the core engine flow (from 0 to 9) shown in Fig. 5-1. We will use these steps in this chapter and Chap. 7. When more than one exhaust stream is present (e.g., high-bypass-ratio turbofan engine), the steps will be modified.

Parametric cycle analysis desires to determine how the engine performance (specific thrust and fuel consumption) varies with changes in the flight conditions (e.g., Mach number), design limits (e.g., main burner exit temperature), component performance (e.g., turbine efficiency), and design choices (e.g., compressor pressure ratio).

1. Starting with an equation for uninstalled engine thrust, we rewrite this equation in terms of the total pressure and total temperature ratios: the ambient pressure P_0, temperature T_0, and speed of sound a_0, and the flight

Mach number M_0 as follows:

$$F = \frac{1}{g_c}(\dot{m}_9 V_e - \dot{m}_0 V_0) + A_9(P_9 - P_0)$$

$$\frac{F}{\dot{m}_0} = \frac{a_0}{g_c}\left(\frac{\dot{m}_9}{\dot{m}_0}\frac{V_9}{a_0} - M_0\right) + \frac{A_9 P_9}{\dot{m}_0}\left(1 - \frac{P_0}{P_9}\right)$$

2. Next express the velocity ratio(s) V_9/a_0 in terms of Mach numbers, temperatures, and gas properties of states 0 and 9:

$$\left(\frac{V_9}{a_0}\right)^2 = \frac{a_9^2 M_9^2}{a_0^2} = \frac{\gamma_9 R_9 g_c T_9}{\gamma_0 R_0 g_c T_0} M_9^2$$

3. Find the exit Mach number M_9. Since

$$P_{t9} = P_9\left(1 + \frac{\gamma - 1}{2} M_9^2\right)^{\gamma/(\gamma-1)}$$

then

$$M_9^2 = \frac{2}{\gamma - 1}\left[\left(\frac{P_{t9}}{P_9}\right)^{(\gamma-1)/\gamma} - 1\right]$$

where

$$\frac{P_{t9}}{P_9} = \frac{P_0}{P_9}\frac{P_{t0}}{P_0}\frac{P_{t2}}{P_{t0}}\frac{P_{t3}}{P_{t2}}\frac{P_{t4}}{P_{t3}}\frac{P_{t5}}{P_{t4}}\frac{P_{t7}}{P_{t5}}\frac{P_{t9}}{P_{t7}}$$

$$= \frac{P_0}{P_9}\pi_r \pi_d \pi_c \pi_b \pi_t \pi_{AB} \pi_n$$

4. Find the temperature ratio T_9/T_0:

$$\frac{T_9}{T_0} = \frac{T_{t9}/T_0}{T_{t9}/T_9} = \frac{T_{t9}/T_0}{(P_{t9}/P_9)^{(\gamma-1)/\gamma}}$$

where

$$\frac{T_{t9}}{T_0} = \frac{T_{t0}}{T_0}\frac{T_{t2}}{T_{t0}}\frac{T_{t3}}{T_{t2}}\frac{T_{t4}}{T_{t3}}\frac{T_{t5}}{T_{t4}}\frac{T_{t7}}{T_{t5}}\frac{T_{t9}}{T_{t7}} = \tau_r \tau_d \tau_c \tau_b \tau_t \tau_{AB} \tau_n$$

5. Apply the first law of thermodynamics to the burner (combustor), and find an expression for the fuel/air ratio f in terms of τ's, etc:

$$\dot{m}_0 c_p T_{t3} + \dot{m}_f h_{PR} = \dot{m}_0 c_p T_{t4}$$

6. When applicable, find an expression for the total temperature ratio across the turbine τ_t by relating the turbine power output to the compressor, fan, and/or propeller power requirements. This allows us to find τ_t in terms of other variables.
7. Evaluate the specific thrust, using the above results.
8. Evaluate the thrust specific fuel consumption S, using the results for specific thrust and fuel/air ratio:

$$S = \frac{f}{F/\dot{m}_0} \tag{5-8}$$

9. Develop expressions for the thermal and propulsive efficiencies.

5-5 ASSUMPTIONS OF IDEAL CYCLE ANALYSIS

For analysis of ideal cycles, we assume the following:

1. There are isentropic (reversible and adiabatic) compression and expansion processes in the inlet (diffuser), compressor, fan, turbine, and nozzle. Thus we have the following relationships:

$$\tau_d = \tau_n = 1 \qquad \pi_d = \pi_n = 1 \qquad \tau_c = \pi_c^{(\gamma-1)/\gamma} \qquad \tau_t = \pi_t^{(\gamma-1)/\gamma}$$

2. Constant-pressure combustion ($\pi_b = 1$) is idealized as a heat interaction into the combustor. The fuel flow rate is much less than the airflow rate through the combustor such that

$$\frac{\dot{m}_f}{\dot{m}_c} \ll 1 \qquad \text{and} \qquad \dot{m}_c + \dot{m}_f \cong \dot{m}_c$$

3. The working fluid is air which behaves as a perfect gas with constant specific heats.
4. The engine exhaust nozzles expand the gas to the ambient pressure ($P_e = P_0$).

5-6 IDEAL RAMJET

A schematic diagram of a ramjet engine is shown in Fig. 5-2, and the ideal

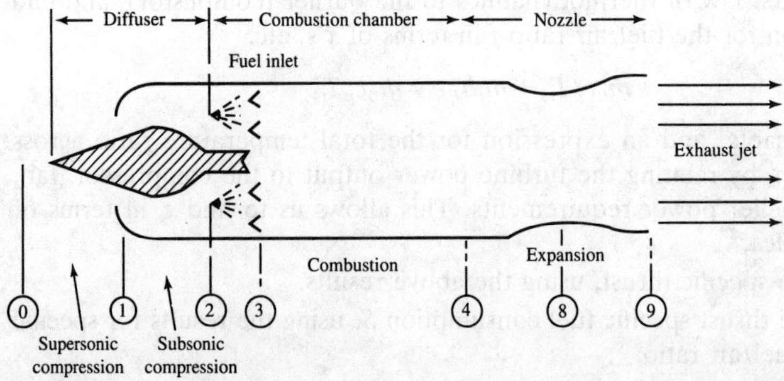

FIGURE 5-2
Typical ramjet engine.

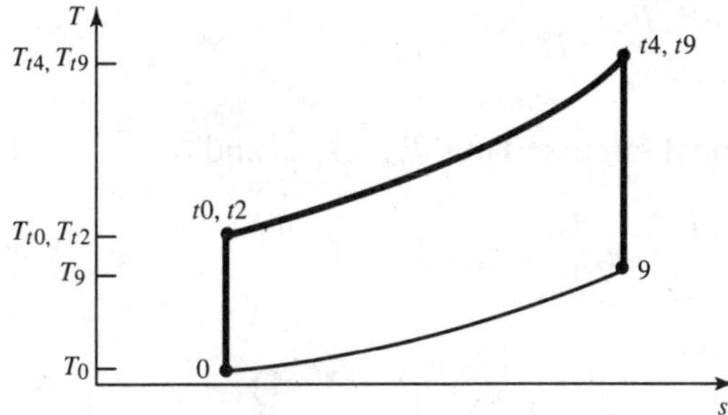

FIGURE 5-3
The T-s diagram of an ideal ramjet engine.

cycle is plotted on a temperature-entropy (T-s) diagram in Fig. 5-3. A ramjet engine is conceptually the simplest aircraft engine and consists of an inlet or diffuser, a combustor or burner, and a nozzle. The inlet or diffuser slows the air velocity relative to the engine from the flight velocity V_0 to a smaller value V_2. This decrease in velocity increases both the static pressure P_2 and static temperature T_2. In the combustor or burner, fuel is added and its chemical energy is converted to thermal energy in the combustion process. This addition of thermal energy increases the static temperature T_4, and the combustion process occurs at a nearly constant pressure for $M_4 \ll 1$. The nozzle expands the gas to or near the ambient pressure, and the temperature decreases from T_4 to T_9 with a corresponding increase in the kinetic energy per unit mass $(V_9^2 - V_4^2)/(2g_c)$.

Cycle Analysis

Application of the steps of cycle analysis to the ideal ramjet of Fig. 5-2 is presented below in the order listed in Sec. 5-4:

Step 1.
$$F = \frac{1}{g_c}(\dot{m}_9 V_9 - \dot{m}_0 V_0) + A_9(P_9 - P_0)$$

However, $P_9 = P_0$ and $\dot{m}_9 \cong \dot{m}_0$ for the ideal engine. Thus

$$F = \frac{\dot{m}_0}{g_c}(V_9 - V_0) = \frac{\dot{m}_0 a_0}{g_c}\left(\frac{V_9}{a_0} - M_0\right) \tag{5-9}$$

Step 2.
$$\left(\frac{V_9}{a_0}\right)^2 = \frac{a_9^2 M_9^2}{a_0^2} = \frac{\gamma_9 R_9 g_c T_9 M_9^2}{\gamma_0 R_0 g_c T_0}$$

However, $\gamma_9 = \gamma_0 = \gamma$ and $R_9 = R_0 = R$ for an ideal engine. Thus

$$\left(\frac{V_9}{a_0}\right)^2 = \frac{T_9}{T_0} M_9^2 \tag{5-10}$$

Step 3.
$$P_{t9} = P_0 \frac{P_{t0}}{P_0}\frac{P_{t2}}{P_{t0}}\frac{P_{t4}}{P_{t2}}\frac{P_{t9}}{P_{t4}} = P_0 \pi_r \pi_d \pi_b \pi_n$$

However, $\pi_d = \pi_b = \pi_n = 1$ for an ideal engine. Thus $P_{t9} = P_0 \pi_r$ and

$$\frac{P_{t9}}{P_9} = \frac{P_{t9}}{P_0}\frac{P_0}{P_9} = \pi_r \frac{P_0}{P_9} = \pi_r$$

$$M_9^2 = \frac{2}{\gamma - 1}\left[\left(\frac{P_{t9}}{P_9}\right)^{(\gamma-1)/\gamma} - 1\right] = \frac{2}{\gamma - 1}(\pi_r^{(\gamma-1)/\gamma} - 1)$$

However,
$$\pi_r^{(\gamma-1)/\gamma} = \tau_r$$

Thus
$$M_9^2 = \frac{2}{\gamma - 1}(\tau_r - 1) = M_0^2 \quad \text{or} \quad \boxed{M_9 = M_0} \tag{5-11}$$

Step 4.
$$T_{t9} = T_0 \frac{T_{t0}}{T_0}\frac{T_{t2}}{T_{t0}}\frac{T_{t4}}{T_{t2}}\frac{T_{t9}}{T_{t4}} = T_0 \tau_r \tau_d \tau_b \tau_n = T_0 \tau_r \tau_b$$

$$\frac{T_{t9}}{T_9} = \left(\frac{P_{t9}}{P_9}\right)^{(\gamma-1)/\gamma}$$

$$\frac{T_9}{T_0} = \frac{T_{t9}/T_0}{T_{t9}/T_9} = \frac{\tau_r \tau_b}{(P_{t9}/P_9)^{(\gamma-1)/\gamma}} = \frac{\tau_r \tau_b}{\tau_r}$$

$$\boxed{\frac{T_9}{T_0} = \tau_b} \tag{5-12}$$

Step 5. Application of the steady flow energy equation (first law of thermodynamics) to the control volume about the burner or combustor shown in Fig. 5-4 gives

$$\dot{m}_0 h_{t2} + \dot{m}_f h_{PR} = (\dot{m}_0 + \dot{m}_f) h_{t4}$$

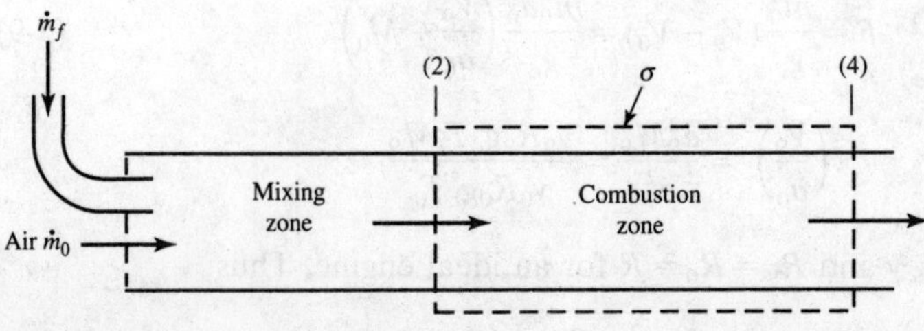

FIGURE 5-4
Combustor model.

where h_{PR} is the thermal energy released by the fuel during combustion. For an ideal engine,

$$\dot{m}_0 + \dot{m}_f \cong \dot{m}_0 \qquad \text{and} \qquad c_{p2} = c_{p4} = c_p$$

Thus the above equation becomes

$$\dot{m}_0 c_p T_{t2} + \dot{m}_f h_{PR} = \dot{m}_0 c_p T_{t4}$$

or

$$\dot{m}_f h_{PR} = \dot{m}_0 c_p (T_{t4} - T_{t2}) = \dot{m}_0 c_p T_{t2}\left(\frac{T_{t4}}{T_{t2}} - 1\right)$$

The *fuel/air ratio* f is defined as

$$f \equiv \frac{\dot{m}_f}{\dot{m}_0} = \frac{c_p T_{t2}}{h_{PR}}\left(\frac{T_{t4}}{T_{t2}} - 1\right) \tag{5-13a}$$

For the ideal ramjet, $T_{t0} = T_{t2} = T_0 \tau_r$ and $T_{t4}/T_{t2} = \tau_b$. Thus Eq. (5-13*a*) becomes

$$f = \frac{c_p T_0 \tau_r}{h_{PR}}(\tau_b - 1) \tag{5-13b}$$

However,

$$\tau_\lambda = \frac{c_{p4} T_{t4}}{c_{p0} T_0} = \frac{T_{t4}}{T_0} = \frac{T_{t2}}{T_0}\frac{T_{t4}}{T_{t2}} = \tau_r \tau_b$$

for the ramjet, and Eq. (5-13*b*) can be written as

$$\boxed{f = \frac{c_p T_0}{h_{PR}}(\tau_\lambda - \tau_r)} \tag{5-13c}$$

Step 6. This is not applicable for the ramjet engine.
Step 7. Since $M_9 = M_0$ and $T_9/T_0 = \tau_b$, then

$$\left(\frac{V_9}{a_0}\right)^2 = \frac{T_9}{T_0} M_9^2 = \tau_b M_0^2 \tag{5-14}$$

and the expression for thrust can be rewritten as

$$F = \frac{\dot{m}_0 a_0 M_0}{g_c}(\sqrt{\tau_b} - 1) = \frac{\dot{m}_0 a_0 M_0}{g_c}\left(\sqrt{\frac{\tau_\lambda}{\tau_r}} - 1\right) \tag{5-15a}$$

or

$$\boxed{\frac{F}{\dot{m}_0} = \frac{a_0 M_0}{g_c}(\sqrt{\tau_b} - 1) = \frac{a_0 M_0}{g_c}\left(\sqrt{\frac{\tau_\lambda}{\tau_r}} - 1\right)} \tag{5-15b}$$

Step 8.

$$S = \frac{f}{F/\dot{m}_0}$$

$$\boxed{S = \frac{c_p T_0 g_c (\tau_\lambda - \tau_r)}{a_0 M_0 h_{PR}(\sqrt{\tau_\lambda/\tau_r} - 1)}} \tag{5-16a}$$

or

$$S = \frac{c_p T_0 g_c \tau_r(\tau_b - 1)}{a_0 M_0 h_{PR}(\sqrt{\tau_b} - 1)} \tag{5-16b}$$

Step 9. Development of the following efficiency expressions is left to the reader:

Thermal efficiency
$$\eta_T = 1 - \frac{1}{\tau_r} \tag{5-17a}$$

Propulsive efficiency
$$\eta_P = \frac{2}{\sqrt{\tau_\lambda/\tau_r} + 1} \tag{5-17b}$$

Overall efficiency
$$\eta_O = \eta_T \eta_P = \frac{2(\tau_r - 1)}{\sqrt{\tau_\lambda \tau_r} + \tau_r} \tag{5-17c}$$

Summary of Equations—Ideal Ramjet

INPUTS: M_0, T_0(K, °R), γ, $c_p\left(\frac{\text{kJ}}{\text{kg}\cdot\text{K}}, \frac{\text{Btu}}{\text{lbm}\cdot{}^\circ\text{R}}\right)$, $h_{PR}\left(\frac{\text{kJ}}{\text{kg}}, \frac{\text{Btu}}{\text{lbm}}\right)$, T_{t4}(K, °R)

OUTPUTS: $\frac{F}{\dot{m}_0}\left(\frac{\text{N}}{\text{kg/sec}}, \frac{\text{lbf}}{\text{lbm/sec}}\right)$, f, $S\left(\frac{\text{mg/sec}}{\text{N}}, \frac{\text{lbm/hr}}{\text{lbf}}\right)$, η_T, η_P, η_O

EQUATIONS:

$$R = \frac{\gamma - 1}{\gamma} c_p \tag{5-18a}$$

$$a_0 = \sqrt{\gamma R g_c T_0} \tag{5-18b}$$

$$\tau_r = 1 + \frac{\gamma - 1}{2} M_0^2 \tag{5-18c}$$

$$\tau_\lambda = \frac{T_{t4}}{T_0} \tag{5-18d}$$

$$\frac{V_9}{a_0} = M_0 \sqrt{\frac{\tau_\lambda}{\tau_r}} \tag{5-18e}$$

$$\frac{F}{\dot{m}_0} = \frac{a_0}{g_c}\left(\frac{V_9}{a_0} - M_0\right) \tag{5-18f}$$

$$f = \frac{c_p T_0}{h_{PR}}(\tau_\lambda - \tau_r) \tag{5-18g}$$

$$S = \frac{f}{F/\dot{m}_0} \tag{5-18h}$$

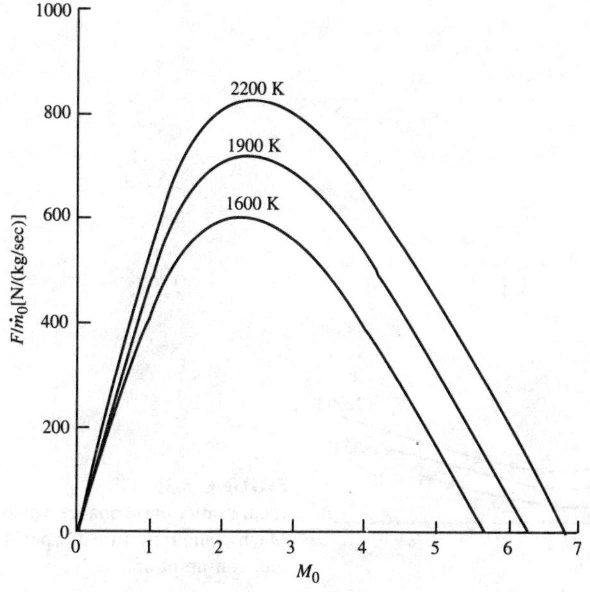

FIGURE 5-5*a*
Ideal ramjet performance versus Mach number: specific thrust.

$$\eta_T = 1 - \frac{1}{\tau_r} \tag{5-18i}$$

$$\eta_P = \frac{2}{\sqrt{\tau_\lambda/\tau_r} + 1} \tag{5-18j}$$

$$\eta_O = \eta_T \eta_P = \frac{2(\tau_r - 1)}{\sqrt{\tau_\lambda \tau_r} + \tau_r} \tag{5-18k}$$

Example 5-1. The performance of ideal ramjets is plotted in Figs. 5-5*a* through 5-5*d* versus flight Mach number M_0 for different values of the total temperature leaving the combustor. Calculations were performed for the following input data:

$$T_0 = 216.7\text{ K} \qquad \gamma = 1.4 \qquad c_p = 1.004\text{ kJ/(kg}\cdot\text{K)} \qquad h_{PR} = 42{,}800\text{ kJ/kg}$$

$$T_{t4} = 1600,\ 1900,\ \text{and } 2200\text{ K}$$

Optimum Mach Number

The plot of specific thrust versus Mach number shows that the maximum value of specific thrust is exhibited at a certain Mach number for each value of T_{t4}. An analytical expression for this optimum Mach number can be found by

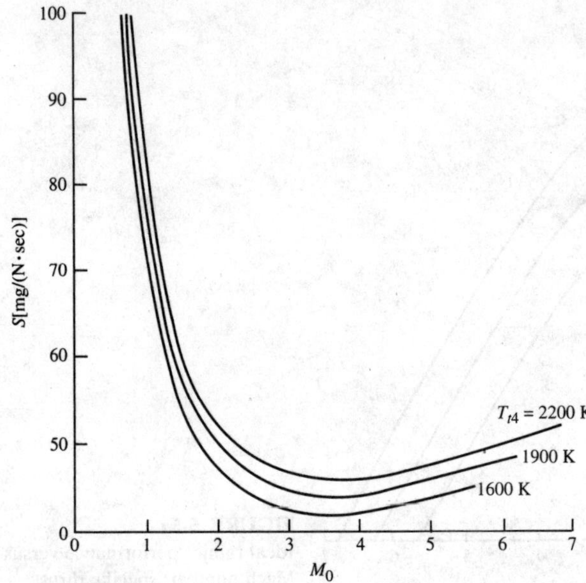

FIGURE 5-5*b*
Ideal ramjet performance versus Mach number: thrust specific fuel consumption.

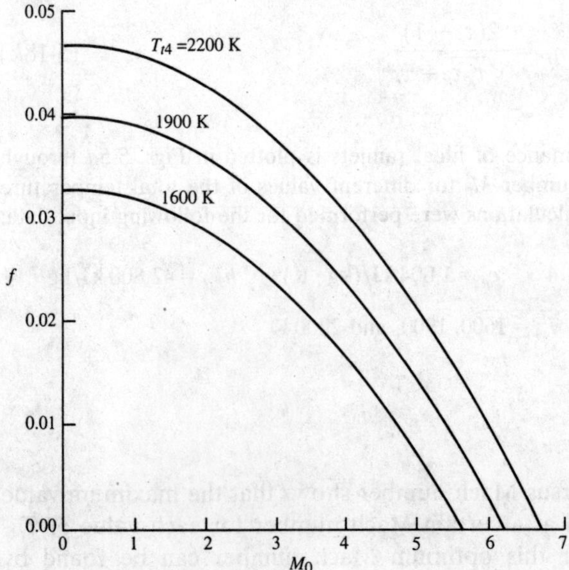

FIGURE 5-5*c*
Ideal ramjet performance versus Mach number: fuel/air ratio.

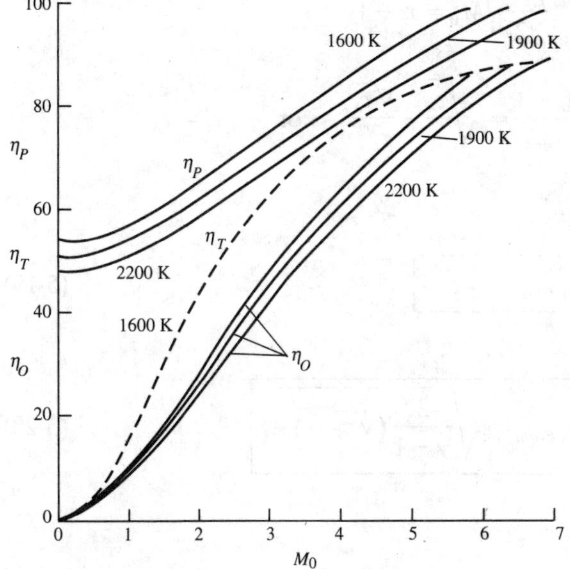

FIGURE 5-5*d*
Ideal ramjet performance versus Mach number: efficiencies.

taking the partial derivative of the equation for specific thrust with respect to flight Mach number, setting this equal to zero, and solving as follows.

Combining Eqs. (5-18*e*) and (5-18*f*) and differentiating gives

$$\frac{\partial}{\partial M_0}\left(\frac{F}{\dot{m}_0}\right) = \frac{a_0}{g_c}\frac{\partial}{\partial M_0}\left[M_0\left(\sqrt{\frac{\tau_\lambda}{\tau_r}} - 1\right)\right] = 0$$

$$\sqrt{\frac{\tau_\lambda}{\tau_r}} - 1 + M_0\sqrt{\tau_\lambda}\,\frac{\partial}{\partial M_0}\left(\frac{1}{\sqrt{\tau_r}}\right) = 0$$

Now
$$\frac{\partial}{\partial M_0}\left(\frac{1}{\sqrt{\tau_r}}\right) = -\frac{1}{2}\frac{1}{\tau_r^{3/2}}\frac{\partial \tau_r}{\partial M_0} = -\frac{1}{2\tau_r^{3/2}}\frac{\partial}{\partial M_0}\left(1 + \frac{\gamma-1}{2}M_0^2\right)$$

$$= -\frac{(\gamma-1)M_0}{2\tau_r^{3/2}}$$

Thus
$$\sqrt{\frac{\tau_\lambda}{\tau_r}} - 1 = M_0\sqrt{\tau_\lambda}\,\frac{(\gamma-1)M_0}{2\tau_r^{3/2}}$$

or
$$\sqrt{\frac{\tau_\lambda}{\tau_r}} - 1 = \sqrt{\frac{\tau_\lambda}{\tau_r}}\,\frac{(\gamma-1)M_0^2}{2\tau_r}$$

But $$\frac{\gamma-1}{2}M_0^2=\tau_r-1$$

then $$\sqrt{\frac{\tau_\lambda}{\tau_r}}-1=\sqrt{\frac{\tau_\lambda}{\tau_r}\frac{\tau_r-1}{\tau_r}}=\sqrt{\frac{\tau_\lambda}{\tau_r}-\frac{\sqrt{\tau_\lambda}}{\tau_r^{3/2}}}\quad\text{or}\quad\tau_r^3=\tau_\lambda$$

Thus $F/\dot{m}_0$ is maximum when

$$\boxed{\tau_{r\,\max F/\dot{m}_0}=\sqrt[3]{\tau_\lambda}}\tag{5-19}$$

or $$\boxed{M_{0\,\max F/\dot{m}_0}=\sqrt{\frac{2}{\gamma-1}(\sqrt[3]{\tau_\lambda}-1)}}\tag{5-20}$$

Mass Ingested by an Ideal Ramjet

Since the specific thrust of a ramjet has a maximum at the fight Mach number given by Eq. (5-20) and decreases at higher Mach numbers, one might question how the thrust of a given ramjet will vary with the Mach number. Does the thrust of a ramjet vary as its specific thrust? Since the thrust of a given ramjet will depend on its physical size (flow areas), the variation in thrust per unit area with Mach number will give the trend we seek. For a ramjet, the diffuser exit Mach number (station 2) is essentially constant over the flight Mach number operating range ($M_2 = 0.5$). Using this fact, we can find the engine mass flow rate in terms of A_2, M_0, M_2, and the ambient pressure and temperature. With this flow rate, we can then find the thrust per unit area at station 2 from

$$\frac{F}{A_2}=\frac{F}{\dot{m}_0}\frac{\dot{m}_0}{A_2}$$

As we shall see, the mass flow rate is a strong function of flight Mach number and altitude. For our case,

$$\frac{\dot{m}_0}{A_2}=\frac{\dot{m}_2}{A_2}=\frac{\dot{m}_2}{A_2^*}\frac{A_2^*}{A_2}=\frac{\dot{m}_2}{A_2^*}\left(\frac{A^*}{A}\right)_{M_2}\tag{i}$$

However, $$\text{MFP}(M_i)=\frac{\dot{m}_i\sqrt{T_{ti}}}{A_iP_{ti}}$$

and $$\text{MFP}^* = \text{MFF}(@M=1) = \frac{\dot{m}\sqrt{T_t}}{A^* P_t}$$

Then $$\frac{\dot{m}_2}{A_2^*} = \text{MFP}^* \frac{P_{t2}}{\sqrt{T_{t2}}} \qquad T_{t2} = T_{t0} \quad \text{and} \quad P_{t2} = \pi_d P_{t0} \tag{ii}$$

where $$\frac{P_{t2}}{\sqrt{T_{t2}}} = \frac{\pi_d P_{t0}}{\sqrt{T_{t0}}} = \frac{\pi_d P_0}{\sqrt{T_0}} \frac{P_{t0}/P_0}{\sqrt{T_{t0}/T_0}} = \frac{\pi_d P_0}{\sqrt{T_0}} \frac{(T_{t0}/T_0)^{\gamma/(\gamma-1)}}{\sqrt{T_{t0}/T_0}}$$

or $$\frac{P_{t2}}{\sqrt{T_{t2}}} = \frac{\pi_d P_0}{\sqrt{T_0}} \left(\frac{T_{t0}}{T_0}\right)^{\gamma/(\gamma-1)-1/2} = \frac{\pi_d P_0}{\sqrt{T_0}} (\tau_r)^{(\gamma+1)/[2(\gamma-1)]} \tag{iii}$$

For air, $\gamma = 1.4$ and $(\gamma+1)/[2(\gamma-1)] = 3$. Thus, combining Eqs. (i), (ii), and (iii), we get

$$\boxed{\frac{\dot{m}_0}{A_2} = \text{MFP}^* \left(\frac{A^*}{A}\right)_{M_2} \frac{\pi_d P_0 \tau_r^3}{\sqrt{T_0}}} \tag{5-21}$$

The variations of mass flow per unit area [Eq. (5-21)], specific thrust, and thrust per unit area at station 2 with flight Mach number are plotted in Fig. 5-6 for M_2 of 0.5, altitude of 12 km, T_{t4} of 1900 K, and π_d of 1.0. Although the specific thrust variation with Mach number reaches a maximum at Mach 2.30 and then falls off, the thrust of an ideal ramjet continues to increase with flight Mach number until about Mach 5.25 due to the very rapid increase in mass flow per unit area.

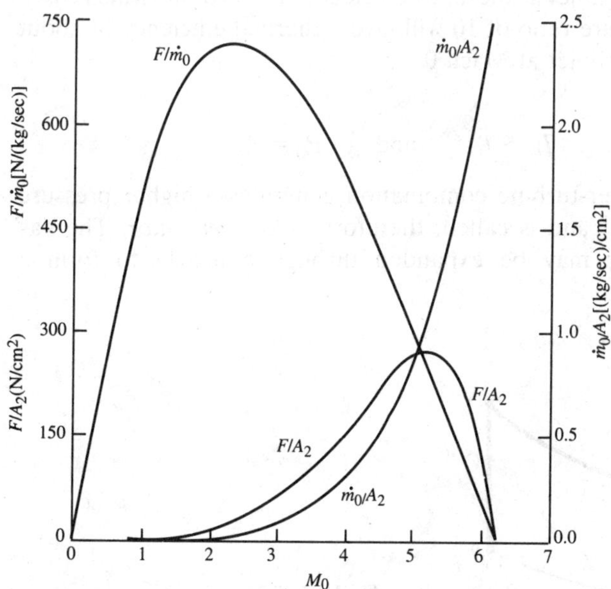

FIGURE 5-6
Ideal ramjet thrust per unit area versus Mach number.

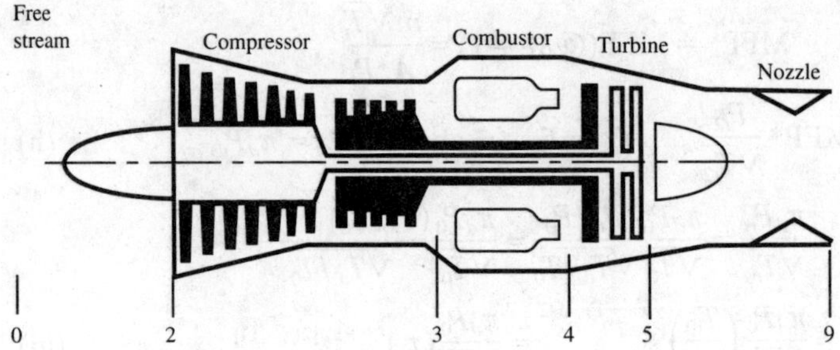

FIGURE 5-7*a*
Station numbring of ideal turbojet engine.

5-7 IDEAL TURBOJET

The thrust of a ramjet tends to zero as the Mach number goes to zero. This poor performance can be overcome by the addition of a compressor-turbine unit to the basic Brayton cycle, as shown in Fig. 5-7*a*. The thermal efficiency of this ideal cycle is now

$$\eta_T = 1 - \frac{T_0}{T_{t3}} = 1 - \frac{1}{\tau_r \tau_c} \tag{5-22}$$

Whereas an ideal ramjet's thermal efficiency is zero at Mach 0, a compressor having a pressure ratio of 10 will give a thermal efficiency of about 50 percent for the ideal turbojet at Mach 0.

For the ideal turbojet

$$\dot{W}_t = \dot{W}_c \qquad T_{t4} > T_{t3} \qquad \text{and} \qquad P_{t4} = P_{t3}$$

Thus the compressor-burner-turbine combination generates a higher pressure and temperature at its exit and is called, therefore, a *gas generator*. The gas leaving the gas generator may be expanded through a nozzle to form a

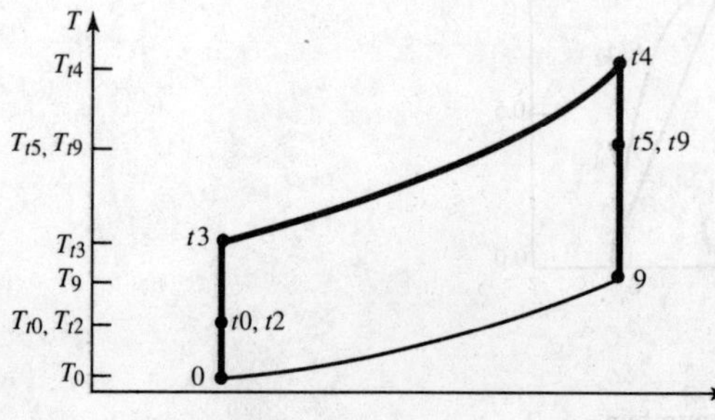

FIGURE 5-7*b*
The *T-s* diagram of an ideal turbojet engine.

turbojet, as depicted in Figs. 5-7*a* and 5-7*b*. Or the gases may be expanded through a turbine to drive a fan (turbofan), a propeller (turboprop), a generator (gas turbine), an automobile (gas turbine), or a helicopter rotor (gas turbine).

We will analyze the ideal turbojet cycle as we did the ideal ramjet cycle and will determine the trends in the variation of thrust, thrust specific fuel consumption, and fuel/air ratio with compressor pressure ratio and flight Mach number.

Cycle Analysis

Application of these steps of cycle analysis to the ideal turbojet engine is presented below in the order listed in Sec. 5-4.

Step 1.

$$\frac{F}{\dot{m}_0}=\frac{1}{g_c}(V_9-V_0)=\frac{a_0}{g_c}\left(\frac{V_9}{a_0}-M_0\right)$$

Step 2.

$$\left(\frac{V_9}{a_0}\right)^2=\frac{a_9^2M_9^2}{a_0^2}=\frac{\gamma_9R_9g_cT_9M_9^2}{\gamma_0R_0g_cT_0}=\frac{T_9}{T_0}M_9^2$$

Step 3.

$$P_{t9}=P_9\left(1+\frac{\gamma-1}{2}M_9^2\right)^{\gamma/(\gamma-1)}$$

and

$$P_{t9}=P_0\frac{P_{t0}}{P_0}\frac{P_{t2}}{P_{t0}}\frac{P_{t3}}{P_{t2}}\frac{P_{t4}}{P_{t3}}\frac{P_{t5}}{P_{t4}}\frac{P_{t9}}{P_{t5}}=P_0\pi_r\pi_d\pi_c\pi_b\pi_t\pi_n$$

However, $\pi_d=\pi_b=\pi_n=1$, thus $P_{t9}=P_0\pi_r\pi_c\pi_t$ and so

$$M_9^2=\frac{2}{\gamma-1}\left[\left(\frac{P_{t9}}{P_9}\right)^{(\gamma-1)/\gamma}-1\right]$$

where

$$\frac{P_{t9}}{P_9}=\frac{P_{t9}}{P_0}\frac{P_0}{P_9}=\pi_r\pi_c\pi_t\frac{P_0}{P_9}=\pi_r\pi_c\pi_t$$

Then

$$M_9^2=\frac{2}{\gamma-1}[(\pi_r\pi_c\pi_t)^{(\gamma-1)/\gamma}-1]$$

However, $\pi_r^{(\gamma-1)/\gamma}=\tau_r$ and for an ideal turbojet $\pi_c^{(\gamma-1)/\gamma}=\tau_c$ and $\pi_t^{(\gamma-1)/\gamma}=\tau_t$. Thus

$$\boxed{M_9^2=\frac{2}{\gamma-1}(\tau_r\tau_c\tau_t-1)} \tag{5-23}$$

Step 4.

$$T_{t9}=T_0\frac{T_{t0}}{T_0}\frac{T_{t2}}{T_{t0}}\frac{T_{t3}}{T_{t2}}\frac{T_{t4}}{T_{t3}}\frac{T_{t5}}{T_{t4}}\frac{T_{t9}}{T_{t5}}=T_0\tau_r\tau_d\tau_c\tau_b\tau_t\tau_n=T_0\tau_r\tau_c\tau_b\tau_t.$$

Then

$$\frac{T_9}{T_0}=\frac{T_{t9}/T_0}{T_{t9}/T_9}=\frac{\tau_r\tau_c\tau_b\tau_t}{(P_{t9}/P_9)^{(\gamma-1)/\gamma}}=\frac{\tau_t\tau_c\tau_b\tau_t}{-(\pi_r\pi_c\pi_t)^{(\gamma-1)/\gamma}}=\frac{\tau_r\tau_c\tau_b\tau_t}{\tau_r\tau_c\tau_t}$$

Thus $$\boxed{\frac{T_9}{T_0} = \tau_b} \tag{5-24}$$

Step 5. Application of the steady flow energy equation to the burner gives

$$\dot{m}_0 h_{t3} + \dot{m}_f h_{PR} = (\dot{m}_0 + \dot{m}_f) h_{t4}$$

For an ideal cycle, $\dot{m}_0 + \dot{m}_f \cong \dot{m}_0$ and $c_{p3} = c_{p4} = c_p$. Thus

$$\dot{m}_0 c_p T_{t3} + \dot{m}_f h_{PR} = \dot{m}_0 c_p T_{t4}$$

$$\dot{m}_f h_{PR} = \dot{m}_0 c_p (T_{t4} - T_{t3}) = \dot{m}_0 c_p T_0 \left(\frac{T_{t4}}{T_0} - \frac{T_{t3}}{T_0} \right)$$

or $$f = \frac{\dot{m}_f}{\dot{m}_0} = \frac{c_p T_0}{h_{PR}} \left(\frac{T_{t4}}{T_0} - \frac{T_{t3}}{T_0} \right)$$

However, $$\tau_\lambda = \frac{T_{t4}}{T_0} \quad \text{and} \quad \tau_r \tau_c = \frac{T_{t3}}{T_0}$$

then $$\boxed{f = \frac{\dot{m}_f}{\dot{m}_0} = \frac{c_p T_0}{h_{PR}} (\tau_\lambda - \tau_r \tau_c)} \tag{5-25}$$

or $$f = \frac{\dot{m}_f}{\dot{m}_0} = \frac{c_p T_0 \tau_r \tau_c}{h_{PR}} (\tau_b - 1) \tag{5-26}$$

Step 6. The power out of the turbine is

$$\dot{W}_t = (\dot{m}_0 + \dot{m}_f)(h_{t4} - h_{t5}) \cong \dot{m}_0 c_p (T_{t4} - T_{t5})$$
$$= \dot{m}_0 c_p T_{t4} \left(1 - \frac{T_{t5}}{T_{t4}} \right) = \dot{m}_0 c_p T_{t4} (1 - \tau_t)$$

The power required to drive the compressor is

$$\dot{W}_c = \dot{m}_0 (h_{t3} - h_{t2}) = \dot{m}_0 c_p (T_{t3} - T_{t2})$$
$$= \dot{m}_0 c_p T_{t2} \left(\frac{T_{t3}}{T_{t2}} - 1 \right) = \dot{m}_0 c_p T_{t2} (\tau_c - 1)$$

Since $\dot{W}_c = \dot{W}_t$ for the ideal turbojet, then

$$\dot{m}_0 c_p T_{t2} (\tau_c - 1) = \dot{m}_0 c_p T_{t4} (1 - \tau_t)$$

or $$\tau_t = 1 - \frac{T_{t2}}{T_{t4}} (\tau_c - 1)$$

thus $$\boxed{\tau_t = 1 - \frac{\tau_r}{\tau_\lambda} (\tau_c - 1)} \tag{5-27}$$

Step 7. $$\boxed{\left(\frac{V_9}{a_0} \right)^2 = \frac{T_9}{T_0} M_9^2 = \frac{2}{\gamma - 1} \frac{\tau_\lambda}{\tau_r \tau_c} (\tau_r \tau_c \tau_t - 1)} \tag{5-28}$$

but $$\frac{F}{\dot{m}_0} = \frac{a_0}{g_c} \left(\frac{V_9}{a_0} - M_0 \right)$$

thus

$$\frac{F}{\dot{m}_0}=\frac{a_0}{g_c}\left[\sqrt{\frac{2}{\gamma-1}\frac{\tau_\lambda}{\tau_t\tau_c}(\tau_r\tau_c\tau_t-1)}-M_0\right] \tag{5-29}$$

Step 8.

$$S=\frac{f}{F/\dot{m}_0} \tag{5-8}$$

The thrust specific fuel consumption S can be calculated by first calculating the fuel/air ratio f and the thrust per unit of airflow $F/\dot{m}_0$, using Eqs. (5-25) and (5-29), respectively, and then substituting these values into the above equation. An analytical expression for S can be obtained by substituting Eqs. (5-25) and (5-29) into Eq. (5-8) to get the following:

$$S=\frac{c_pT_0g_c(\tau_\lambda-\tau_r\tau_c)}{a_0h_{PR}\left[\sqrt{\frac{2}{\gamma-1}\frac{\tau_\lambda}{\tau_r\tau_c}(\tau_r\tau_c\tau_t-1)}-M_0\right]} \tag{5-30}$$

Step 9. Again the development of these expressions is left to the reader:

Thermal efficiency $$\eta_T=1-\frac{1}{\tau_r\tau_c} \tag{5-31a}$$

Propulsive efficiency $$\eta_P=\frac{2M_0}{V_9/a_0+M_0} \tag{5-31b}$$

Overall efficiency $$\eta_O=\eta_P\eta_T \tag{5-31c}$$

Summary of Equations—Ideal Turbojet

INPUTS: M_0, T_0(K, °R), γ, $c_p\left(\frac{\text{kJ}}{\text{kg}\cdot\text{K}}, \frac{\text{Btu}}{\text{lbm}\cdot{}^\circ\text{R}}\right)$, $h_{PR}\left(\frac{\text{kJ}}{\text{kg}}, \frac{\text{Btu}}{\text{lbm}}\right)$, T_{t4}(K, °R), π_c

OUTPUTS: $\frac{F}{\dot{m}_0}\left(\frac{\text{N}}{\text{kg/sec}}, \frac{\text{lbf}}{\text{lbm/sec}}\right)$, f, $S\left(\frac{\text{mg/sec}}{\text{N}}, \frac{\text{lbm/hr}}{\text{lbf}}\right)$ η_T, η_P, η_O

EQUATIONS:

$$R=\frac{\gamma-1}{\gamma}c_p \tag{5-32a}$$

$$a_0=\sqrt{\gamma Rg_cT_0} \tag{5-32b}$$

$$\tau_r=1+\frac{\gamma-1}{2}M_0^2 \tag{5-32c}$$

$$\tau_\lambda=\frac{T_{t4}}{T_C} \tag{5-32d}$$

$$\tau_c=(\pi_c)^{(\gamma-1)/\gamma} \tag{5-32e}$$

$$\tau_t=1-\frac{\tau_r}{\tau_\lambda}(\tau_c-1) \tag{5-32f}$$

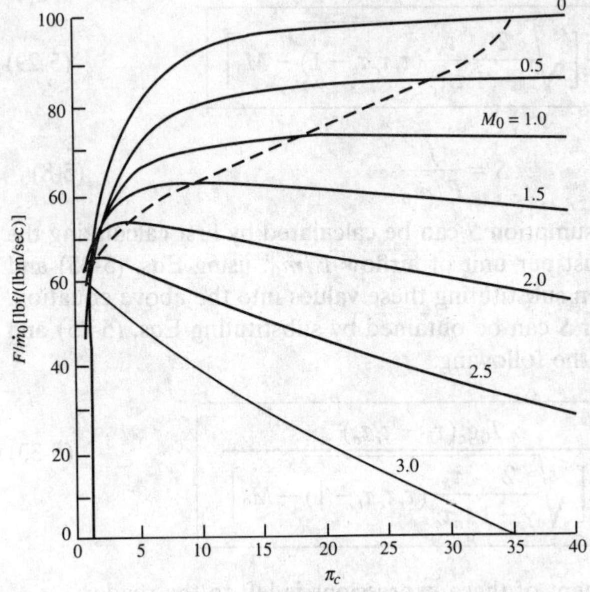

FIGURE 5-8a
Ideal turbojet performance versus compressor pressure ratio: specific thrust.

$$\frac{V_9}{a_0} = \sqrt{\frac{2}{\gamma - 1} \frac{\tau_\lambda}{\tau_r \tau_c} (\tau_r \tau_c \tau_t - 1)} \tag{5-32g}$$

$$\frac{F}{\dot{m}_0} = \frac{a_0}{g_c}\left(\frac{V_9}{a_0} - M_0\right) \tag{5-32h}$$

$$f = \frac{c_p T_0}{h_{PR}} (\tau_\lambda - \tau_r \tau_c) \tag{5-32i}$$

$$S = \frac{f}{F/\dot{m}_0} \tag{5-32j}$$

$$\eta_T = 1 - \frac{1}{\tau_r \tau_c} \tag{5-32k}$$

$$\eta_P = \frac{2M_0}{V_9/a_0 + M_0} \tag{5-32l}$$

$$\eta_O = \eta_P \eta_T \tag{5-32m}$$

Example 5-2. In Figs. 5-8*a* through 5-8*d*, the performance of ideal turbojets is plotted versus compressor pressure ratio π_c for different values of flight Mach number M_0. Figures 5-9*a* through 5-9*d* plot the performance versus flight Mach number M_0 for different values of the compressor pressure ratio π_c. Calculations were performed for the following input data:

$$T_0 = 390°\text{R} \qquad \gamma = 1.4 \qquad c_p = 0.24\ \text{Btu/(lbm} \cdot °\text{R)}$$

$$h_{PR} = 18{,}400\ \text{Btu/lbm} \qquad T_{t4} = 3000°R$$

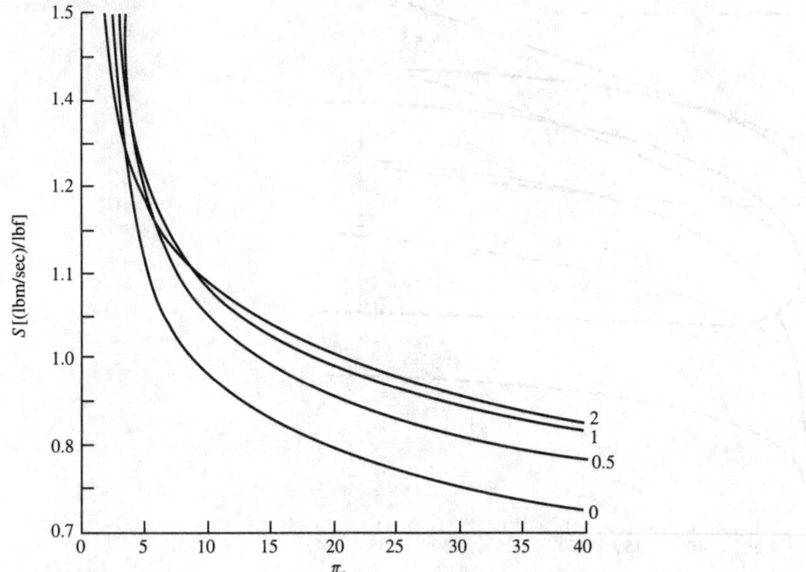

FIGURE 5-8*b*
Ideal turbojet performance versus compressor pressure ratio: thrust specific fuel consumption.

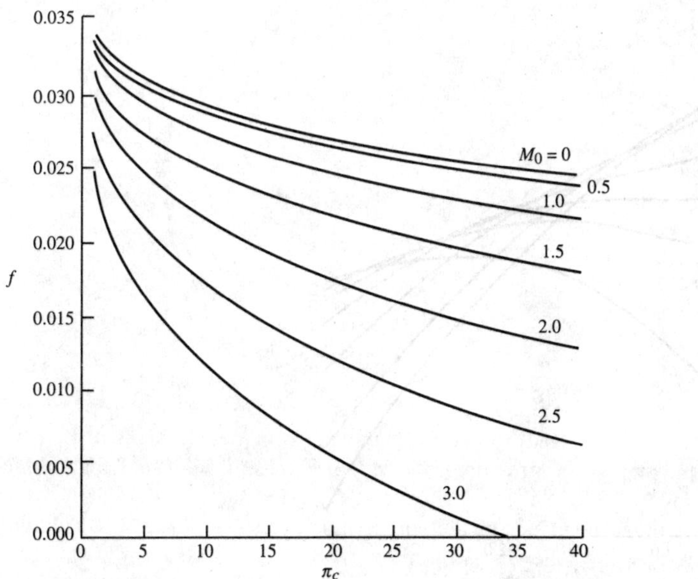

FIGURE 5-8*c*
Ideal turbojet performance versus compressor pressure ratio: fuel/air ratio.

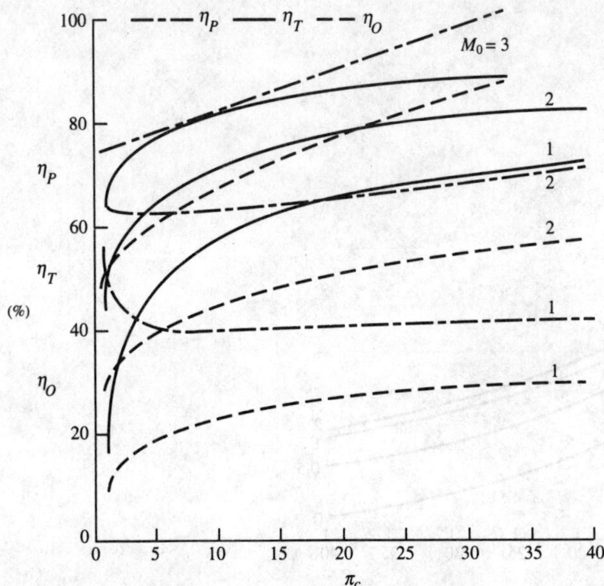

FIGURE 5-8*d*
Ideal turbojet performance versus compressor pressure ratio: efficiencies.

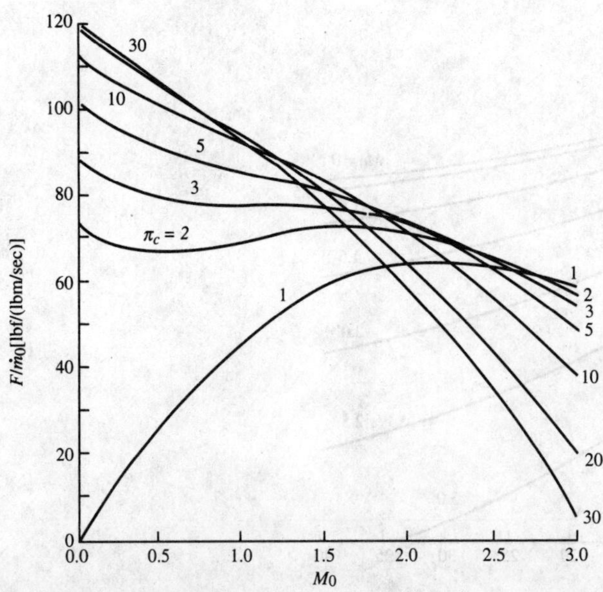

FIGURE 5-9*a*
Ideal turbojet performance versus flight Mach number: specific thrust.

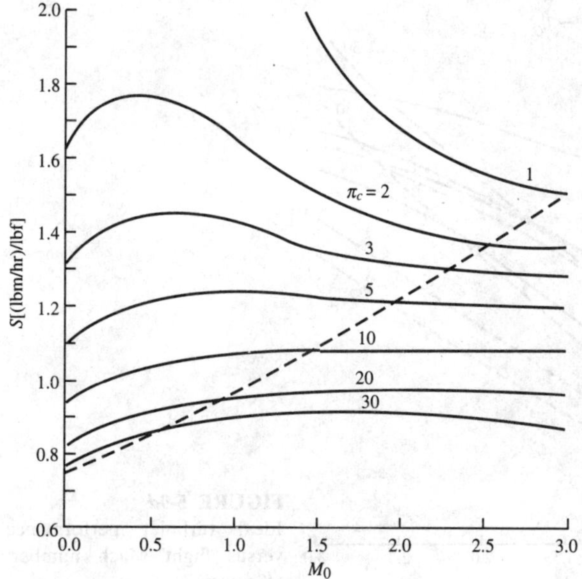

FIGURE 5-9*b*
Ideal turbojet performance versus flight Mach number: thrust specific fuel consumption.

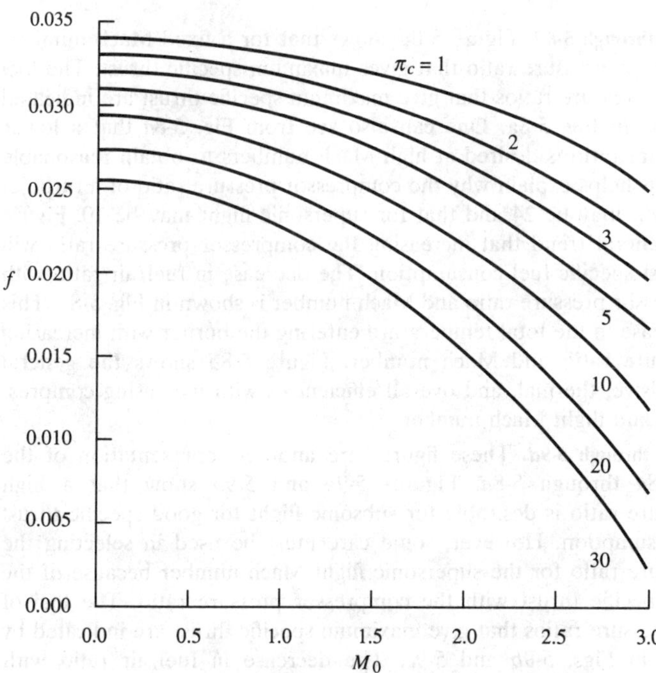

FIGURE 5-9*c*
Ideal turbojet performance versus flight Mach number: fuel/air ratio.

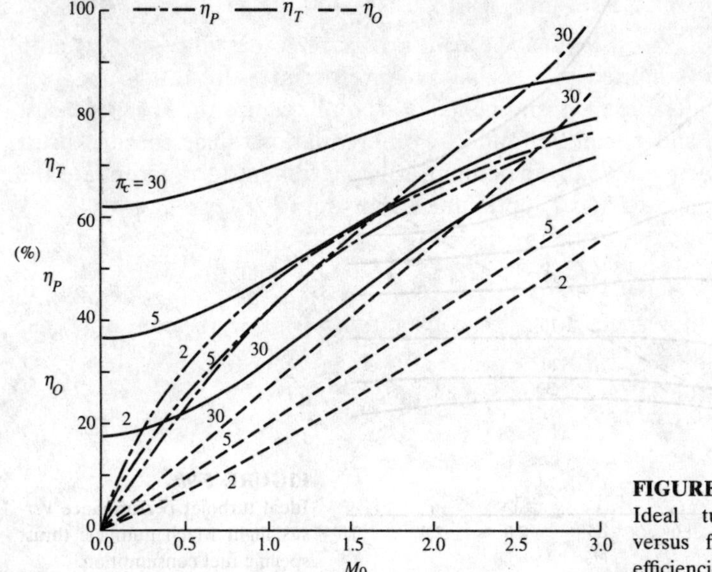

FIGURE 5-9*d*
Ideal turbojet performance versus flight Mach number: efficiencies.

Figures 5-8*a* through 5-8*d*. Figure 5-8*a* shows that for a fixed Mach number, there is a compressor pressure ratio that gives maximum specific thrust. The loci of the compressor pressure ratios that give maximum specific thrust are indicated by the dashed line in Fig. 5-8a. One can also see from Fig. 5-8*a* that a lower compressor pressure ratio is desired at high Mach numbers to obtain reasonable specific thrust. This helps explain why the compressor pressure ratio of a turbojet for a subsonic flight may be 24 and that for supersonic flight may be 10. Figure 5-8*b* shows the general trend that increasing the compressor pressure ratio will decrease the thrust specific fuel consumption. The decrease in fuel/air ratio with increasing compressor pressure ratio and Mach number is shown in Fig. 5-8*c*. This is due to the increase in the total temperature entering the burner with increasing compressor pressure ratio and Mach number. Figure 5-8*d* shows the general increase in propulsive, thermal, and overall efficiencies with increasing compressor pressure ratio and flight Mach number.

Figures 5-9*a* through 5-9*d*. These figures are another representation of the data of Figs. 5-8*a* through 5-8*d*. Figures 5-9*a* and 5-9*b* show that a high compressor pressure ratio is desirable for subsonic flight for good specific thrust and low fuel consumption. However, some care must be used in selecting the compressor pressure ratio for the supersonic flight Mach number because of the rapid fall-off in specific thrust with the compressor pressure ratio. The loci of the compressor pressure ratios that give maximum specific thrust are indicated by the dashed lines in Figs. 5-9*b* and 5-9*c*. The decrease in fuel/air ratio with increasing Mach number and compressor pressure ratio is shown in Fig. 5-9*c*. Figure 5-9*d* shows the dominant influence of flight Mach number on propulsive efficiency. The performance of the ideal ramjet is shown in Fig. 5-9*a* through 5-9*c* by curves for the compressor pressure ratio equal to 1.

Optimum Compressor Pressure Ratio

The plot of specific thrust versus the compressor pressure ratio shows that a maximum value is exhibited at a certain compressor pressure ratio at a given M_0, a_0, and τ_λ. The value of τ_c and hence of π_c to maximize the specific thrust at a given M_0, a_0, and τ_λ can be found by differentiation. Since specific thrust will be maximum when V_9/a_0 is maximum, it is convenient to differentiate the expression for $(V_9/a_0)^2$ to find τ_c optimum. From Eq. (5-28), we have

$$\frac{\partial}{\partial \tau_c}\left[\left(\frac{V_9}{a_0}\right)^2\right] = \frac{2}{\gamma-1}\frac{\partial}{\partial \tau_c}\left[\frac{\tau_\lambda}{\tau_r \tau_c}(\tau_r \tau_c \tau_t - 1)\right] = 0$$

Differentiating with respect to τ_c at constant M_0 (thus τ_r is constant) and constant τ_λ, we obtain

$$-\frac{\tau_\lambda}{\tau_r \tau_c^2}(\tau_r \tau_c \tau_t - 1) + \frac{\tau_{t\lambda}}{\tau_r \tau_c}\left(\tau_r \tau_t + \tau_r \tau_c \frac{\partial T_t}{\partial \tau_c}\right) = 0$$

or
$$-\frac{\tau_\lambda \tau_t}{\tau_c} + \frac{\tau_\lambda}{\tau_r \tau_c^2} + \frac{\tau_\lambda \tau_t}{\tau_c} + \tau_\lambda \frac{\partial \tau_t}{\partial \tau_c} = 0$$

Then
$$\frac{1}{\tau_r \tau_c^2} + \frac{\partial \tau_t}{\partial \tau_c} = 0 \qquad \text{where} \qquad \frac{\partial \tau_t}{\partial \tau_c} = -\frac{\tau_t}{\tau_\lambda}$$

Thus
$$\frac{1}{\tau_r \tau_c^2} = \frac{\tau_t}{\tau_\lambda}$$

which results in

$$\boxed{(\tau_c)_{\max F/\dot{m}_0} = \frac{\sqrt{\tau_\lambda}}{\tau_r}} \tag{5-33a}$$

or
$$(\pi_c)_{\max F/\dot{m}_0} = (\tau_c)_{\max F/\dot{m}_0}^{\gamma/(\gamma-1)} \tag{5-33b}$$

An expression for the maximum V_9/a_0 can be found by substituting Eq. (5-33*a*) into Eqs. (5-28) and (5-27) to obtain

$$\frac{V_9}{a_0} = \sqrt{\frac{2}{\gamma-1}\sqrt{\tau_\lambda}(\sqrt{\tau_\lambda}\tau_t - 1)}$$

and
$$\tau_t = 1 - \left(\frac{1}{\sqrt{\tau_\lambda}} - \frac{\tau_r}{\tau_\lambda}\right)$$

Thus
$$\frac{V_9}{a_0} = \sqrt{\frac{2}{\gamma-1}[(\sqrt{\tau_\lambda}-1)^2 + \tau_r - 1]} \tag{5-33c}$$

The specific thrust can then be written as

$$\frac{F}{\dot{m}_0} = \frac{a_0}{g_c}\left\{\sqrt{\frac{2}{\gamma-1}[(\sqrt{\tau_\lambda}-1)^2 + \tau_r - 1]} - M_0\right\} \tag{5-33d}$$

The fuel/air ratio f for the optimum turbojet can be written as

$$f = \frac{c_p T_0}{h_{PR}}(\tau_\lambda - \sqrt{\tau_\lambda}) \tag{5-33e}$$

and the thrust specific fuel consumption S as

$$S = \frac{c_p T_0 g_c(\tau_\lambda - \sqrt{\tau_\lambda})}{a_0 h_{PR}\{\sqrt{[2/(\gamma-1)][(\sqrt{\tau_\lambda}-1)^2+\tau_r-1]}-M_0\}} \tag{5-33f}$$

For the optimum ideal turbojet, it can be easily shown that $T_{t3} = T_9$. As the Mach number is changed in the optimum ideal turbojet at a fixed τ_λ and fixed altitude, the cycle and its enclosed area remain the same in the T-s diagram. The area enclosed by the cycle in the T-s diagram equals the net work output (kinetic energy change, for our case) of the cycle per unit mass flow. Even though this output is constant as M_0 increases, the thrust per unit mass flow decreases as M_0 increases. This can be shown as follows.

The kinetic energy change per unit mass is constant, and we can write

$$V_9^2 - V_0^2 = C$$

and, therefore,

$$(V_9 - V_0)(V_9 + V_0) = C$$

or

$$\frac{F}{\dot{m}_0} = \frac{V_9 - V_0}{g_c} = \frac{C/g_c}{V_9 + V_0} \tag{5-34}$$

Referring to the T-s diagram of Fig. 5-7b, we see that as V_0 increases, T_{t2} increases and thus so does T_{t5}. But if T_{t5} increases, V_9 increases also. Consequently $V_9 + V_0$ becomes larger as M_0 increases. Therefore, from Eq. (5-34), $V_9 - V_0$ must decrease as M_0 increases. It follows that the thrust per unit mass flow decreases with increasing M_0 even though the cycle work output per unit mass flow remains constant.

5-8 IDEAL TURBOJET WITH AFTERBURNER

The thrust of a turbojet can be increased by the addition of a second combustion chamber, called an *afterburner,* aft of the turbine, as shown in Fig. 5-10. The total temperature leaving the afterburner has a higher limiting value than the total temperature leaving the main combustor because the gases

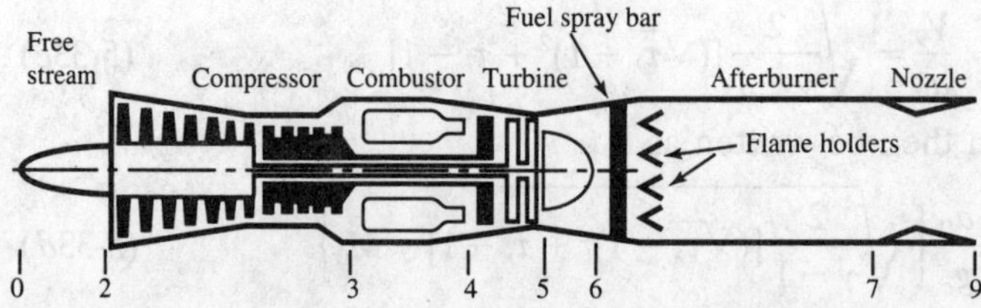

FIGURE 5-10
Station numbering of an ideal afterburning turbojet engine.

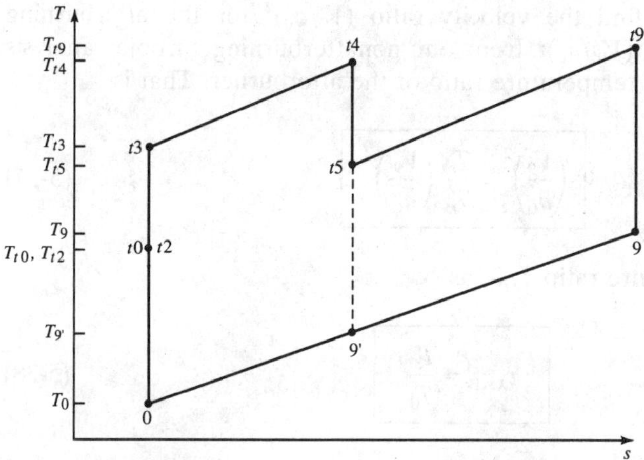

FIGURE 5-11
The T-s diagram for an ideal afterburning turbojet engine.

leaving the afterburner do not have a turbine to pass through. The station numbering is indicated in Figs. 5-10 and 5-11 with 9′ representing the nozzle exit for the case of no afterburning.

Cycle Analysis

Rather than go through the complete steps of cycle analysis, we will use the results of the ideal turbojet and modify the equations to include afterburning. The gas velocity at the nozzle exit is given by

$$\frac{V_9^2}{2g_c c_p} = T_{t9} - T_9 = T_{t9}\left[1 - \left(\frac{P_9}{P_{t9}}\right)^{(\gamma-1)/\gamma}\right] \tag{5-35}$$

and for the nonafterburning (subscript dry) and afterburning (subscript AB for afterburning) cases, we have

$$\frac{P_9}{P_{t9}} = \left(\frac{P_{9'}}{P_{t5}}\right)_{\text{dry}} = \left(\frac{P_9}{P_{t9}}\right)_{\text{AB}}$$

Thus we have

$$\boxed{\left(\frac{V_9}{V_{9'}}\right)^2 = \frac{T_{t9}}{T_{t5}}} \tag{5-36}$$

Consequently, we can find the velocity ratio $(V_9/a_0)^2$ for the afterburning turbojet by multiplying $(V_{9'}/a_0)^2$ from our nonafterburning turbojet analysis [Eq. (5-28)] by the total temperature ratio of the afterburner. That is,

$$\left(\frac{V_9}{a_0}\right)^2 = \frac{T_{t9}}{T_{t5}}\left(\frac{V_{9'}}{a_0}\right)^2 \tag{5-37}$$

We define the temperature ratio $\tau_{\lambda \mathrm{AB}}$ as

$$\tau_{\lambda \mathrm{AB}} = \frac{T_{t7}}{T_0} \tag{5-38}$$

Thus we can write the total temperature ratio of the afterburner as

$$\frac{T_{t9}}{T_{t5}} = \frac{(T_{t9}/T_{t7})(T_{t7}/T_0)}{(T_{t5}/T_{t4})(T_{t4}/T_0)} = \frac{\tau_{\lambda \mathrm{AB}}}{\tau_\lambda \tau_t} \tag{5-39}$$

Using Eqs. (5-27), (5-28), (5-37), and (5-39), we get the following expressions for V_9/a_0:

$$\left(\frac{V_9}{a_0}\right)^2 = \frac{2}{\gamma - 1}\frac{\tau_{\lambda \mathrm{AB}}}{\tau_\lambda \tau_t}\frac{\tau_\lambda}{\tau_r \tau_c}(\tau_r \tau_c \tau_t - 1) = \frac{2}{\gamma - 1}\tau_{\lambda \mathrm{AB}}\left(1 - \frac{1}{\tau_r \tau_c \tau_t}\right)$$

$$\left(\frac{V_9}{a_0}\right)^2 = \frac{2}{\gamma - 1}\tau_{\lambda \mathrm{AB}}\left[1 - \frac{\tau_\lambda/(\tau_r \tau_c)}{\tau_\lambda - \tau_r(\tau_c - 1)}\right] \tag{5-40}$$

We find the total fuel flow rate to the burner and afterburner by an energy balance across the engine from station 0 to station 9, as sketched in Fig. 5-12.

The chemical energy of the fuel introduced between stations 0 and 9 is

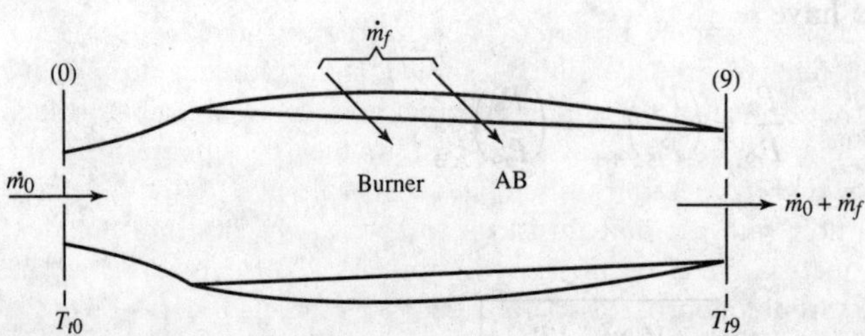

FIGURE 5-12
Total fuel flow rate control volume.

converted to thermal and kinetic energy of the gases, as measured by the total temperature rise $T_{t9} - T_{t0}$. Thus we can write for this ideal engine

$$\dot{m}_{f\,\text{tot}} h_{PR} = \dot{m}_0 c_p (T_{t9} - T_{t0}) = \dot{m}_0 c_p T_0 \left(\frac{T_{t9}}{T_0} - \frac{T_{t0}}{T_0} \right)$$

Thus

$$\boxed{f_{\text{tot}} = \frac{\dot{m}_f}{\dot{m}_0} = \frac{c_p T_0}{h_{PR}} (\tau_{\lambda\text{AB}} - \tau_r)} \tag{5-41}$$

The thermal efficiency is given by

$$\boxed{\eta_T = \frac{(\gamma - 1) c_p T_0 [(V_9/a_0)^2 - M_0^2]}{2 f_{\text{tot}} h_{PR}}} \tag{5-42}$$

Summary of Equations—Ideal Turbojet with Afterburner

INPUTS: M_0, T_0(K, °R), γ, $c_p \left(\frac{\text{kJ}}{\text{kg} \cdot \text{K}}, \frac{\text{Btu}}{\text{lbm} \cdot {}^\circ\text{R}} \right)$, $h_{PR} \left(\frac{\text{kJ}}{\text{kg}}, \frac{\text{Btu}}{\text{lbm}} \right)$, T_{t4}(K, °R), T_{t7}(K, °R), π_c

OUTPUTS: $\frac{F}{\dot{m}_0} \left(\frac{\text{N}}{\text{kg/sec}}, \frac{\text{lbf}}{\text{lbm/sec}} \right)$, f_{tot}, $S \left(\frac{\text{mg/sec}}{\text{N}}, \frac{\text{lbm/hr}}{\text{lbf}} \right)$, η_T, η_P, η_O

EQUATIONS: Equations (5-32*a*) through (5-32*f*), (5-40), (5-32*h*), (5-41), (5-32*j*) with f replaced by f_{tot}, (5-42), (5-32*l*), and (5-32*m*)

Example 5-3. We consider the performance of an ideal turbojet engine with afterburner. For comparison with the nonafterburning (simple) turbojet of Example 5-2, we select the following input data:

$T_0 = 390°\text{R}$ $\quad \gamma = 1.4$ $\quad c_p = 0.24\ \text{Btu/(lbm} \cdot {}^\circ\text{R)}$ $\quad h_{PR} = 18{,}400\ \text{Btu/lbm}$

$T_{t4} = 3000°\text{R}$ $\quad T_{t7} = 4000°\text{R}$

Figure 5-13 compares the performance of two turbojet engines with a compressor pressure ratio of 10, an afterburning turbojet and a simple turbojet. The graph of specific thrust versus M_0 indicates the thrust increase available by adding an afterburner to a simple turbojet. The afterburner increases the static thrust about 22 percent for the conditions shown and continues to provide significant thrust as the thrust of the simple turbojet goes to zero at about Mach 3.8. The graph of Fig. 5-13 also shows the cost in fuel consumption of the increased thrust provided by the afterburner. The cost is about a 20 to 30 percent increase in the fuel flow rate per unit thrust up to about $M_0 = 2.0$. In a nonideal turbojet, the same increase in S occurs up to about $M_0 = 2.0$. However, as the thrust of the simple turbojet approaches zero in the real case, its S rises above the afterburning engine's S so that the afterburning engine at the higher M_0 has a lower S and higher specific thrust than the simple turbojet.

Figures 5-14*a* through 5-14*d* show the variation of engine performance with

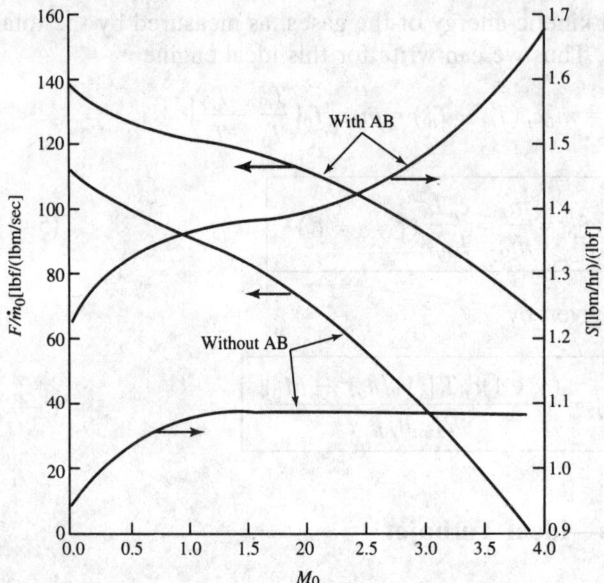

FIGURE 5-13
Engine performance versus M_0 for an ideal afterburning turbojet.

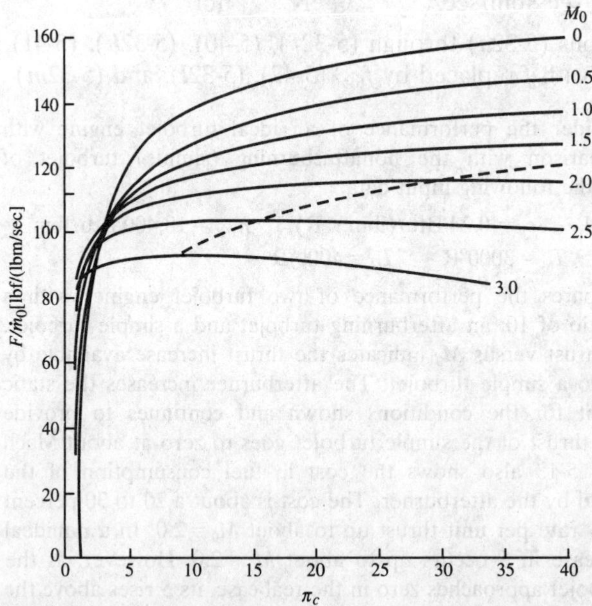

FIGURE 5-14*a*
Ideal afterburning turbojet engine performance versus compressor pressure ratio: specific thrust.

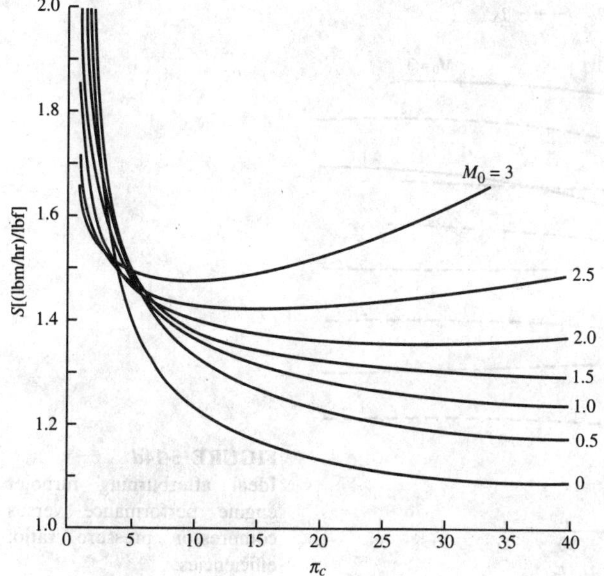

FIGURE 5-14*b*
Ideal afterburning turbojet engine performance versus compressor pressure ratio: thrust specific fuel consumption.

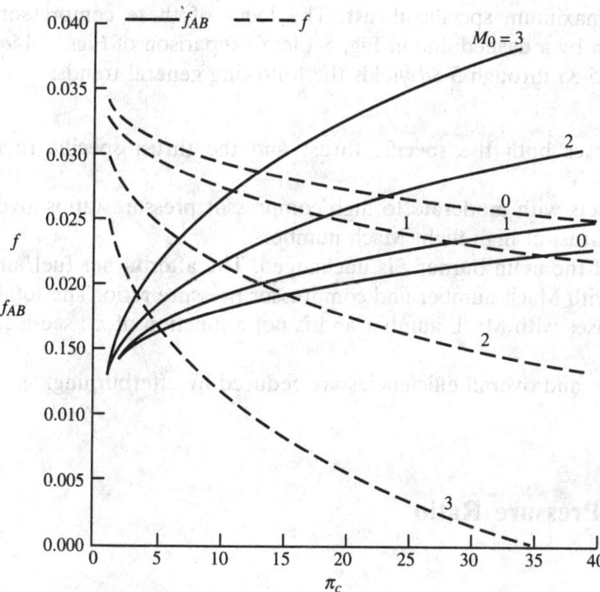

FIGURE 5-14*c*
Ideal afterburning turbojet engine performance versus compressor pressure ratio: fuel/air ratios.

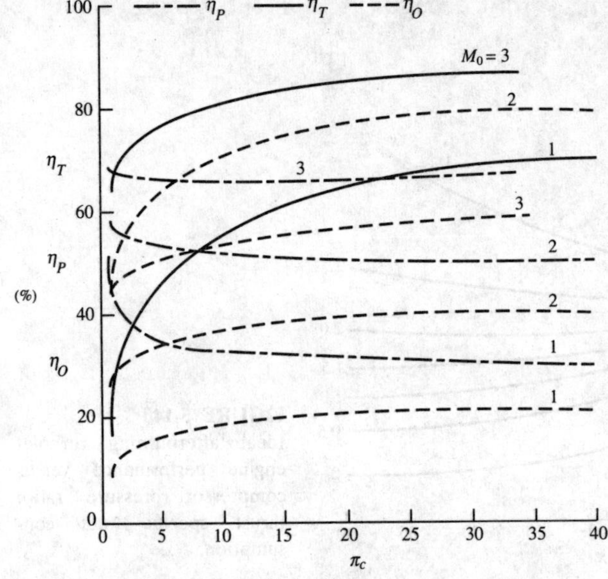

FIGURE 5-14*d*
Ideal afterburning turbojet engine performance versus compressor pressure ratio: efficiencies.

both Mach number and compressor pressure ratio for the afterburning turbojet. These should be compared to their counterparts in Figs. 5-8*a* through 5-8*d*. For a fixed flight Mach number, the ideal afterburning turbojet has a compressor pressure ratio giving maximum specific thrust. The locus of these compressor pressure ratios is shown by a dashed line in Fig. 5-14*a*. Comparison of Figs. 5-14*a* through 5-14*d* to Figs. 5-8*a* through 5-8*d* yields the following general trends:

1. Afterburning increases both the specific thrust and the thrust specific fuel consumption.
2. Afterburning turbojets with moderate to high compressor pressure ratios give very good specific thrust at high flight Mach numbers.
3. The fuel/air ratio of the main burner f is unchanged. The afterburner fuel/air ratio f_{AB} increases with Mach number and compressor pressure ratio. The total fuel/air ratio decreases with Mach number and is not a function of π_c; see Eq. (5-41).
4. Thermal, propulsive, and overall efficiencies are reduced by afterburning.

Optimum Compressor Pressure Ratio with Afterburner

The value of the compressor pressure ratio to maximize the specific thrust at a given M_0, τ_r, τ_λ, and altitude can be found by differentiating V_9/a_0 with respect to τ_c since the specific thrust depends upon τ_c only through the ratio V_9/a_0 in the equation

$$\frac{F}{\dot{m}_0} = \frac{a_0}{g_c}\left(\frac{V_9}{a_0} - M_0\right)$$

We have for $(V_9/a_0)^2$, from Eq. (5-40),

$$\left(\frac{V_9}{a_0}\right)^2 = \frac{2}{\gamma - 1}\tau_{\lambda AB}\left[1 - \frac{\tau_\lambda/(\tau_r\tau_c)}{\tau_\lambda - \tau_r(\tau_c - 1)}\right]$$

Differentiating with respect to τ_c at constant M_0, τ_r, and τ_λ and setting it equal to zero, we get

$$\frac{\partial}{\partial\tau_c}\left[\left(\frac{V_9}{a_0}\right)^2\right] = \frac{2}{\gamma - 1}\tau_{\lambda AB}\frac{\partial}{\partial\tau_c}\left[1 - \frac{\tau_\lambda/(\tau_r\tau_c)}{\tau_\lambda - \tau_r(\tau_c - 1)}\right] = 0$$

Thus
$$\frac{\tau_\lambda}{\tau_r\tau_c^2}\frac{1}{\tau_\lambda - \tau_r(\tau_c - 1)} + \frac{\tau_\lambda/(\tau_r\tau_c)}{[\tau_\lambda - \tau_r(\tau_c - 1)]^2}(-\tau_r) = 0$$

or
$$\frac{1}{\tau_c} - \frac{\tau_r}{\tau_\lambda - \tau_r(\tau_c - 1)} = 0$$

which becomes
$$\tau_r\tau_c = \tau_\lambda - \tau_r(\tau_c - 1)$$

resulting in
$$\tau_{c\,\max F/\dot{m}AB} = \frac{1}{2}\left(\frac{\tau_\lambda}{\tau_r} + 1\right) \tag{5-43}$$

Placing Eq. (5-43) into Eq. (5-40), we get

$$\left(\frac{V_9}{a_0}\right)^2 = \frac{2}{\gamma - 1}\tau_{\lambda AB}\left[1 - \frac{4\tau_\lambda}{(\tau_\lambda + \tau_r)^2}\right] \tag{5-44}$$

so that
$$\frac{F}{\dot{m}_0} = \frac{a_0}{g_c}\left\{\sqrt{\frac{2}{\gamma - 1}\tau_{\lambda AB}\left[1 - \frac{4\tau_\lambda}{(\tau_\lambda + \tau_r)^2}\right]} - M_0\right\} \tag{5-45}$$

The locus of specific thrust versus π_c and M_0 for optimum afterburning turbojets is plotted as a dashed line in Fig. 5-14a. Note that the pressure ratio giving the maximum specific thrust decreases with the flight Mach number.

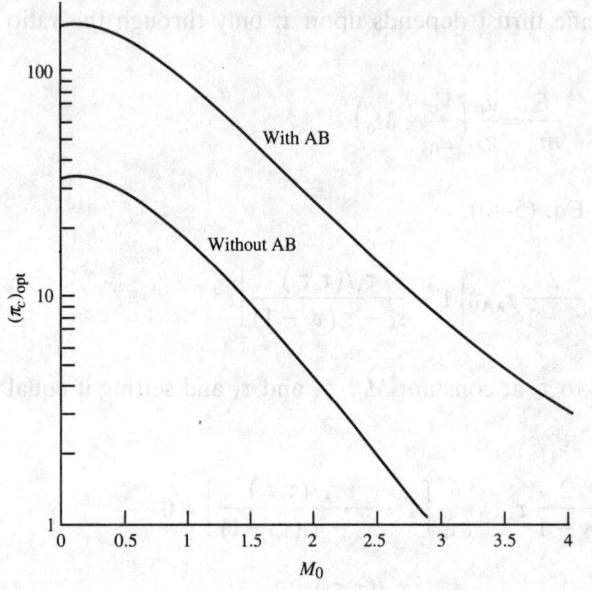

FIGURE 5-15
Optimum ideal turbojet compressor pressure ratio ($\tau_\lambda = 7.5$).

Optimum Simple Turbojet and Optimum Afterburning Turbojet—Comparison

Figures 5-8*a* and 5-14*a* plot the thrust per unit mass flow versus the compressor pressure ratio for different values of the flight Mach number for the ideal turbojet without afterburner and the ideal turbojet with afterburner, respectively. These figures show that the thrust per unit mass flow is higher for the engine with afterburner and that the optimum compressor pressure ratio is also higher for the engine with afterburner. The thrust per unit mass flow, thrust specific fuel consumption, and compressor pressure ratio for an optimum simple and an optimum afterburning turbojet are shown versus the Mach number for representative conditions in Figs. 5-15 and 5-16. The optimum afterburning π_c and specific thrust are higher at all Mach numbers. Considering a given engine with, say, a compressor pressure ratio of 30, we see from Fig. 5-15 that it can operate optimally at Mach 2 with afterburning and near optimum conditions subsonically without afterburning where less thrust is required and available and where the fuel consumption is much lower. Figure 5-16 shows that at $M_0 = 2.7$, the specific fuel consumption of an afterburning engine with $\pi_c = 12$ is the same as that of a simple turbojet with $\pi_c = 1.5$. From Fig. 5-16, we see that at $M_0 = 2.7$, the thrust per unit mass flow of the afterburning engine is 50 percent higher. Based on these data, which engine would you select for a supersonic transport (SST) to cruise at $M_0 = 2.7$?

The higher-pressure-ratio afterburning engine is the logical choice for cruise at $M_0 = 2.7$ since it provides a smaller engine with the same fuel

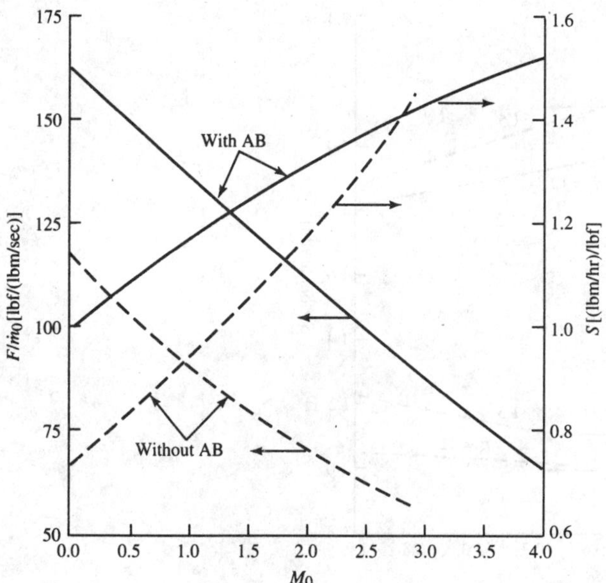

FIGURE 5-16
Optimum ideal turbojet performance ($T_0 = 390°R$, $\tau_\lambda = 7.5$, $\tau_{\lambda AB} = 10$).

consumption as the nonafterburning, low-pressure-ratio engine. The final choice of an engine depends upon the engine's subsonic performance also.

The plots of Fig. 5-17 provide a comparison of the nonafterburning $\pi_c = 12$ and $\pi_c = 1.5$ engines at subsonic flight speeds. It is evident that the higher-pressure-ratio engine operating in the nonafterburning mode has the better subsonic performance. The higher-pressure-ratio engine is, therefore, the best choice overall.

Although our conclusions that an afterburning high-pressure-ratio ($\pi_c = 12$) turbojet engine is a proper engine for an SST are based on a simple ideal cycle analysis, they agree with practice. The Concorde uses four Olympus 593 afterburning turbojet engines (see Figs. 5-18*a*, 5-18*b*, and 5-18*c*) for supersonic cruise. In addition, the GE4 that was being developed by General Electric for the Boeing SST was an afterburning turbojet engine with a pressure ratio of about 12! This SST engine is shown in Fig. 5-19.

5-9 IDEAL TURBOFAN

The propulsive efficiency of a simple turbojet engine can be improved by extracting a portion of the energy from the engine's gas generator to drive a ducted propeller, called a *fan*. The fan increases the propellant mass flow rate with an accompanying decrease in the required propellant exit velocity for a given thrust. Since the rate of production of "wasted" kinetic energy in the

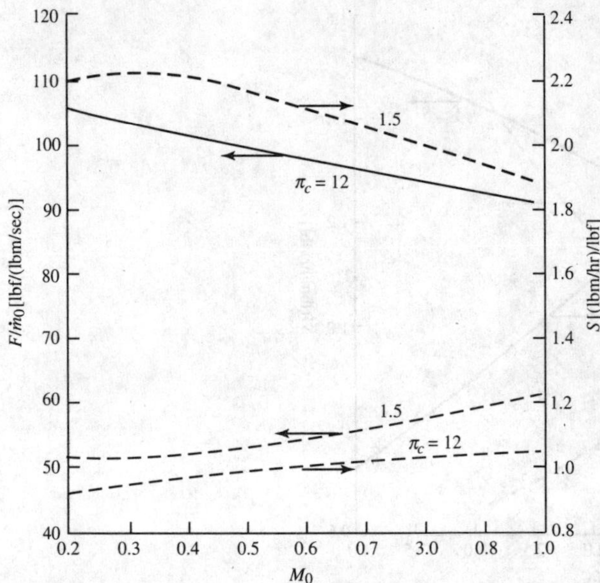

FIGURE 5-17
Ideal turbojet without afterburning ($T_0 = 390°\text{R}$, $\tau_\lambda = 7.5$).

exit propellant gases varies as the first power with mass flow rate and as the square of the exit velocity, the net effect of increasing the mass flow rate and decreasing the exit velocity is to reduce the wasted kinetic energy production and to improve the propulsive efficiency.

Our station numbering for the turbofan cycle analysis is given in Fig. 5-20, and the T-s diagrams for ideal flow through the fan and the core engine are given in Figs. 5-21 and 5-22, respectively. The temperature drop through the turbine ($T_{t4} - T_{t5}$) is now greater than the temperature rise through the compressor ($T_{t3} - T_{t2}$) since the turbine drives the fan in addition to the compressor.

The fan exit is station 13, and the fan total pressure ratio and the fan total temperature ratio are π_f and τ_f, respectively. The fan flow nozzle exit is station 19, and the fan nozzle total pressure ratio and the fan nozzle total temperature ratio are π_{fn} and τ_{fn}, respectively. These four ratios are listed below.

$$\pi_f = \frac{P_{t13}}{P_{t2}} \qquad \tau_f = \frac{T_{t13}}{T_{t2}} \qquad \pi_{fn} = \frac{P_{t19}}{P_{t13}} \qquad \text{and} \qquad \tau_{fn} = \frac{T_{t19}}{T_{t13}}$$

The gas flow through the core engine is $\dot{m}_C$, and the gas flow through the fan

FIGURE 5-18*a*
Olympus 593 turbojet engine used in the Concorde. (*Courtesy of Rolls-Royce.*)

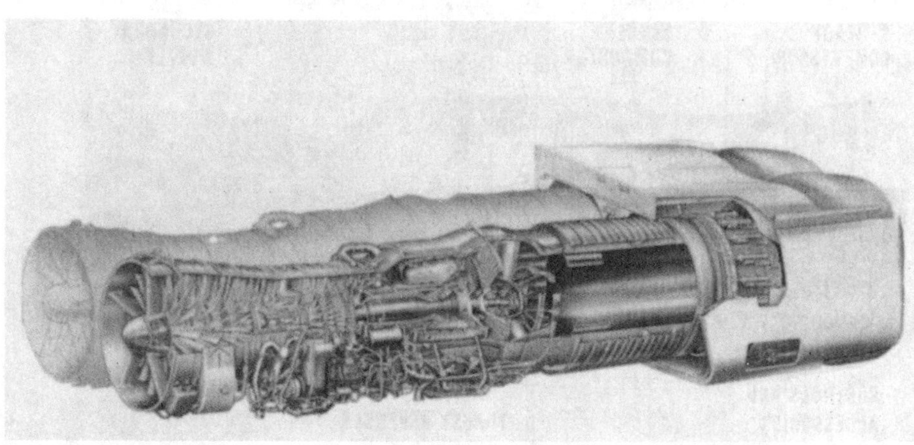

FIGURE 5-18*b*
Two Olympus engines with thrust-reversing nozzles. (*Courtesy of Rolls-Royce.*)

FIGURE 5-18c
Concorde supersonic transport. (*Courtesy of Rolls-Royce.*)

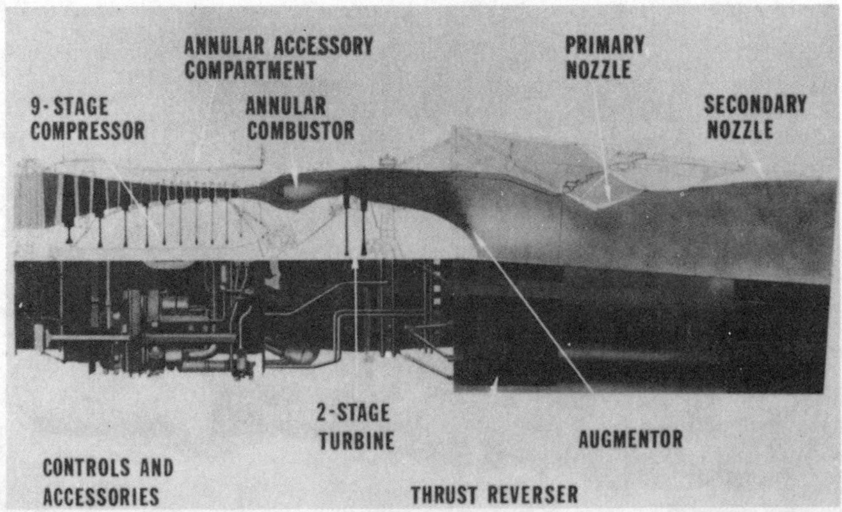

FIGURE 5-19
General Electric GE4 turbojet engine (developed for Boeing SST). (*Courtesy of General Electric.*)

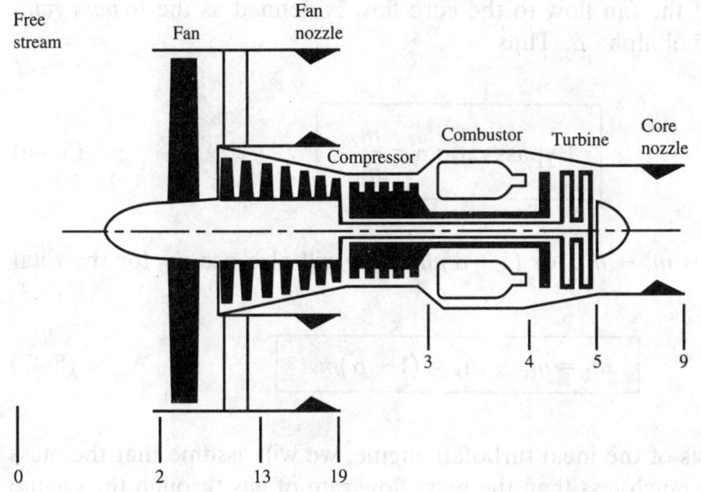

FIGURE 5-20
Station numbering of a turbofan engine.

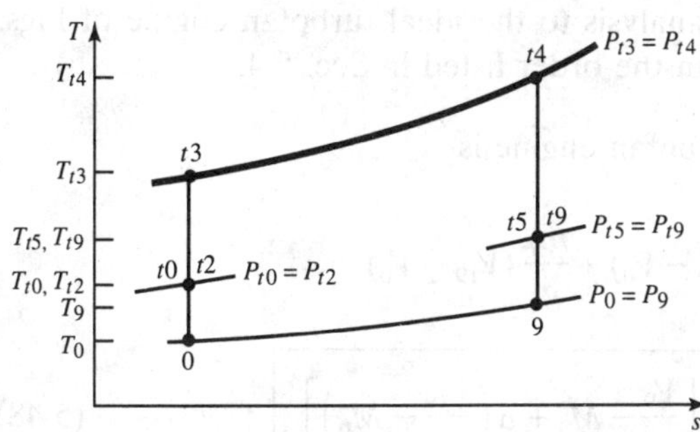

FIGURE 5-21
The *T-s* diagram for core stream of ideal turbofan engine.

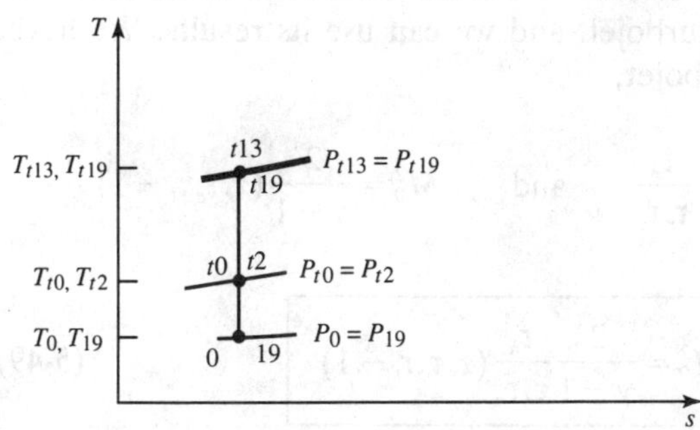

FIGURE 5-22
The *T-s* diagram for fan stream of ideal turbofan engine.

is $\dot{m}_F$. The ratio of the fan flow to the core flow is defined as the *bypass ratio* and given the symbol alpha α. Thus

$$\text{Bypass ratio } \alpha = \frac{\dot{m}_F}{\dot{m}_C} \tag{5–46}$$

the total gas flow is $\dot{m}_C + \dot{m}_F$, or $(1+\alpha)\dot{m}_C$. We will also use $\dot{m}_0$ for the total gas flow. Thus

$$\dot{m}_0 = \dot{m}_C + \dot{m}_F = (1+\alpha)\dot{m}_C \tag{5-47}$$

In the analysis of the ideal turbofan engine, we will assume that the mass flow rate of fuel is much less than the mass flow rate of gas through the engine core. We will also assume that both the engine core nozzle and the fan nozzle are designed so that $P_0 = P_9 = P_{19}$.

Cycle Analysis

Application of the steps of cycle analysis to the ideal turbofan engine of Figs. 5-20 and 5-21 is presented below in the order listed in Sec. 5-4.

Step 1. The thrust of the ideal turbofan engine is

$$F = \frac{\dot{m}_C}{g_c}(V_9 - V_0) + \frac{\dot{m}_F}{g_c}(V_{19} - V_0)$$

Thus

$$\frac{F}{\dot{m}_0} = \frac{a_0}{g_c}\frac{1}{1+\alpha}\left[\frac{V_9}{a_0} - M_0 + \alpha\left(\frac{V_{19}}{a_0} - M_0\right)\right] \tag{5-48}$$

Steps 2 through 4. First, the core stream of the turbofan encounters the same engine components as the ideal turbojet, and we can use its results. We have, from the analysis of the ideal turbojet,

$$\left(\frac{V_9}{a_0}\right)^2 = \frac{T_9}{T_0}M_9^2 \qquad \frac{T_9}{T_0} = \tau_b = \frac{\tau_\lambda}{\tau_r\tau_c} \qquad \text{and} \qquad M_9^2 = \frac{2}{\gamma-1}(\tau_r\tau_c\tau_t - 1)$$

Thus

$$\left(\frac{V_9}{a_0}\right)^2 = \frac{T_9}{T_0}M_9^2 = \frac{2}{\gamma-1}\frac{\tau_\lambda}{\tau_r\tau_c}(\tau_r\tau_c\tau_t - 1) \tag{5-49}$$

Second, compared to the core stream, the fan stream of the turbofan contains a fan rather than a compressor and does not have either a combustor or a turbine. Thus the above equations for the core stream of the ideal turbofan can be adapted for the fan stream as follows:

$$\left(\frac{V_{19}}{a_0}\right)^2 = \frac{T_{19}}{T_0} M_{19}^2 \qquad \boxed{T_{19} = T_0} \qquad \text{and} \qquad M_{19}^2 = \frac{2}{\gamma - 1}(\tau_r \tau_f - 1)$$

$$\boxed{\left(\frac{V_{19}}{a_0}\right)^2 = M_{19}^2 = \frac{2}{\gamma - 1}(\tau_r \tau_f - 1)} \tag{5-50}$$

Step 5. Application of the steady flow energy equation to the burner gives

$$\dot{m}_C c_p T_{t3} + \dot{m}_f h_{PR} = (\dot{m}_C + \dot{m}_f) c_p T_{t4}$$

We define the fuel/air ratio f in terms of the mass flow rate of air through the burner $\dot{m}_C$, and we obtain

$$\boxed{f = \frac{\dot{m}_f}{\dot{m}_C} = \frac{c_p T_0}{h_{PR}}(\tau_\lambda - \tau_r \tau_c)} \tag{5-51}$$

Step 6. The power out of the turbine is

$$\dot{W}_t = (\dot{m}_C + \dot{m}_f) c_p (T_{t4} - T_{t5}) \cong \dot{m}_C c_p T_{t4}(1 - \tau_t)$$

The power required to drive the compressor is

$$\dot{W}_c = \dot{m}_C c_p (T_{t3} - T_{t2}) = \dot{m}_C c_p T_{t2}(\tau_c - 1)$$

The power required to drive the fan is

$$\dot{W}_f = \dot{m}_F c_p (T_{t13} - T_{t2}) = \dot{m}_F c_p T_{t2}(\tau_f - 1)$$

Since $\dot{W}_t = \dot{W}_c + \dot{W}_f$ for the ideal turbofan, then

$$T_{t4}(1 - \tau_t) = T_{t2}(\tau_c - 1) + \alpha T_{t2}(\tau_f - 1)$$

$$\tau_t = 1 - \frac{T_{t2}}{T_{t4}}[\tau_c - 1 + \alpha(\tau_f - 1)]$$

$$\boxed{\tau_t = 1 - \frac{\tau_r}{\tau_\lambda}[\tau_c - 1 + \alpha(\tau_f - 1)]} \tag{5-52}$$

Step 7. Combining Eqs. (5-49) and (5-52), we get

$$\left(\frac{V_9}{a_0}\right)^2 = \frac{2}{\gamma - 1}\frac{\tau_\lambda}{\tau_r\tau_c}\left(\tau_r\tau_c\left\{1 - \frac{\tau_r}{\tau_\lambda}[\tau_c - 1 + \alpha(\tau_f - 1)]\right\} - 1\right)$$

which can be simplified to

$$\left(\frac{V_9}{a_0}\right)^2 = \frac{2}{\gamma - 1}\left\{\tau_\lambda - \tau_r[\tau_c - 1 + \alpha(\tau_f - 1)] - \frac{\tau_\lambda}{\tau_r\tau_c}\right\} \tag{5-53}$$

Thus the specific thrust of the ideal turbojet is given by Eqs. (5-48), (5-50), and (5-53).

Step 8

$$S = \frac{\dot{m}_f}{F} = \frac{f}{F/\dot{m}_C} = \frac{f}{(\dot{m}_0/\dot{m}_C)(F/\dot{m}_0)}$$

$$S = \frac{f}{(1+\alpha)(F/\dot{m}_0)} \tag{5-54}$$

Step 9. The thermal efficiency of an ideal turbofan engine is the same as that of an ideal turbojet engine. That is,

$$\eta_T = 1 - \frac{1}{\tau_r\tau_c} \tag{5-22}$$

This may seem surprising since the net power out of a turbojet is $\dot{m}_0(V_9^2 - V_0^2)/(2g_c)$, while for a turbofan it is $\dot{m}_C(V_9^2 - V_0^2)/(2g_c) + \dot{m}_F(V_{19}^2 - V_0^2)/(2g_c)$. The reason that the thermal efficiency is the same is that power extracted from the core stream of the turbofan engine is added to the bypass stream without loss in the ideal case. Thus the net power out remains the same.

One can easily show that the propulsive efficiency of the ideal turbofan engine is given by

$$\eta_P = 2\frac{V_9/V_0 - 1 + \alpha(V_{19}/V_0 - 1)}{V_9^2/V_0^2 - 1 + \alpha(V_{19}^2/V_0^2 - 1)} \tag{5-55}$$

A useful performance parameter for the turbofan engine is the ratio of the specific thrust per unit mass flow of the core stream to that of the fan stream. We give this *thrust ratio* the symbol FR and define

$$\text{FR} \equiv \frac{F_C/\dot{m}_C}{F_F/\dot{m}_F} \tag{5-56}$$

For the ideal turbofan engine, the thrust ratio FR can be expressed as

$$\text{FR} = \frac{V_9/a_0 - M_0}{V_{19}/a_0 - M_0} \tag{5-57}$$

We will discover in the analysis of optimum turbofan engines that we will want a certain thrust ratio for minimum thrust specific fuel consumption.

Summary of Equations—Ideal Turbofan

INPUTS: M_0, T_0(K, °R), γ, $c_p\left(\frac{\text{kJ}}{\text{kg}\cdot\text{K}}, \frac{\text{Btu}}{\text{lbm}\cdot°\text{R}}\right)$, $h_{PR}\left(\frac{\text{kJ}}{\text{kg}}, \frac{\text{Btu}}{\text{lbm}}\right)$, T_{t4}(K, °R), π_c, π_f, α

OUTPUTS: $\frac{F}{\dot{m}_0}\left(\frac{\text{N}}{\text{kg/sec}}, \frac{\text{lbf}}{\text{lbm/sec}}\right)$, f, $S\left(\frac{\text{mg/sec}}{\text{N}}, \frac{\text{lbm/hr}}{\text{lbf}}\right)$, η_T, η_P, η_O, FR

EQUATIONS:

$$R = \frac{\gamma - 1}{\gamma} c_p \tag{5-58a}$$

$$a_0 = \sqrt{\gamma R g_c T_0} \tag{5-58b}$$

$$\tau_r = 1 + \frac{\gamma - 1}{2} M_0^2 \tag{5-58c}$$

$$\tau_\lambda = \frac{T_{t4}}{T_0} \tag{5-58d}$$

$$\tau_c = (\pi_c)^{(\gamma-1)/\gamma} \tag{5-58e}$$

$$\tau_f = (\pi_f)^{(\gamma-1)/\gamma} \tag{5-58f}$$

$$\frac{V_9}{a_0} = \sqrt{\frac{2}{\gamma - 1}\left\{\tau_\lambda - \tau_r[\tau_c - 1 + \alpha(\tau_f - 1)] - \frac{\tau_\lambda}{\tau_r \tau_c}\right\}} \tag{5-58g}$$

$$\frac{V_{19}}{a_0} = \sqrt{\frac{2}{\gamma - 1}(\tau_r \tau_f - 1)} \tag{5-58h}$$

$$\frac{F}{\dot{m}_0} = \frac{a_0}{g_c}\frac{1}{1+\alpha}\left[\frac{V_9}{a_0} - M_0 + \alpha\left(\frac{V_{19}}{a_0} - M_0\right)\right] \tag{5-58i}$$

$$f = \frac{c_p T_0}{h_{PR}}(\tau_\lambda - \tau_r \tau_c) \tag{5-58j}$$

$$S = \frac{f}{(1+\alpha)(F/\dot{m}_0)} \tag{5-58k}$$

$$\eta_T = 1 - \frac{1}{\tau_r \tau_c} \tag{5-58l}$$

$$\eta_P = 2M_0 \frac{V_9/a_0 - M_0 + \alpha(V_{19}/a_0 - M_0)}{V_9^2/a_0^2 - M_0^2 + \alpha(V_{19}^2/a_0^2 - M_0^2)} \tag{5-58m}$$

$$\eta_O = \eta_T \eta_P \tag{5-58n}$$

$$\text{FR} = \frac{V_9/a_0 - M_0}{V_{19}/a_0 - M_0} \tag{5-58o}$$

Example 5-4. The turbofan engine has three design variables:

- Compressor pressure ratio π_c
- Fan pressure ratio π_f
- Bypass ratio α

Since this engine has two more design variables than the turbojet, this section contains many more plots of engine performance than were required for the turbojet. First, we will look at the variation of each of the three design variables for an engine that will operate at a flight Mach number of 0.9. Then we will look at the variation of design performance with flight Mach number. In all the calculations for this section, the following values are held constant:

$$T_0 = 216.7\,\text{K} \quad \gamma = 1.4 \quad c_p = 1.004\,\text{kJ/(kg}\cdot\text{K)} \quad h_{PR} = 42{,}800\,\text{kJ/kg} \quad T_{t4} = 1670\,\text{K}$$

Figures 5-23*a* through 5-23*e*. Specific thrust and thrust specific fuel consumption are plotted versus the compressor pressure ratio for different values of the bypass ratio in Figs. 5-23*a* and 5-23*b*. The fan pressure ratio is held constant in these plots. Figure 5-23*a* shows that specific thrust remains essentially constant with respect to the compressor pressure ratio for values of π_c from 15 to 25, and that specific thrust decreases with increasing bypass ratio. Figure 5-23*b* shows that thrust specific fuel consumption decreases with increasing compressor pressure ratio π_c and increasing bypass ratio α.

Figure 5-23*c* shows that the fuel/air ratio decreases with compressor pressure ratio, the thermal efficiency increases with compressor pressure ratio, and both are independent of the engine bypass ratio. From Fig. 5-23*d*, we can see that the propulsive efficiency increases with engine bypass ratio and varies very little with compressor pressure ratio. The overall efficiency, shown also in Fig. 5-23*d*, increases with both compressor pressure ratio and bypass ratio.

The thrust ratio is plotted versus compressor pressure ratio and bypass ratio in Fig. 5-23*e*. As can be seen, the thrust ratio decreases with increasing bypass ratio and varies very little with compressor pressure ratio.

Figures 5-24*a* through 5-24*e*. Specific thrust and thrust specific fuel consumption are plotted versus the compressor pressure ratio π_c for different values of the fan pressure ratio π_f. The bypass ratio α is held constant in these plots. Figure 5-24*a* shows that the specific thrust remains essentially constant with respect to the compressor pressure ratio for values of π_c from 15 to 25, and that the specific thrust has a maximum with respect to the fan pressure ratio π_f. Figure 5-24*b* shows that thrust specific fuel consumption decreases with increasing compressor pressure ratio π_c and that S has a minimum with respect to fan pressure ratio π_f. We will look at this optimum fan pressure ratio in more detail in another section of this chapter.

Propulsive and overall efficiencies are plotted versus compressor pressure ratio and fan pressure ratio in Figs. 5-24*c* and 5-24*d*. Figure 5-24*c* shows that propulsive efficiency increases with fan pressure ratio until a value of $\pi_f = 3.5$ and then decreases. There is a fan pressure ratio giving maximum propulsive efficiency. Propulsive efficiency is essentially constant for values of the compressor pressure ratio above 15. Also from Fig. 5-24*d*, we can see that overall efficiency increases with compressor pressure ratio and increases with fan pressure ratio until a value of $\pi_f = 3.5$ and then decreases. There is a fan pressure ratio giving maximum overall efficiency.

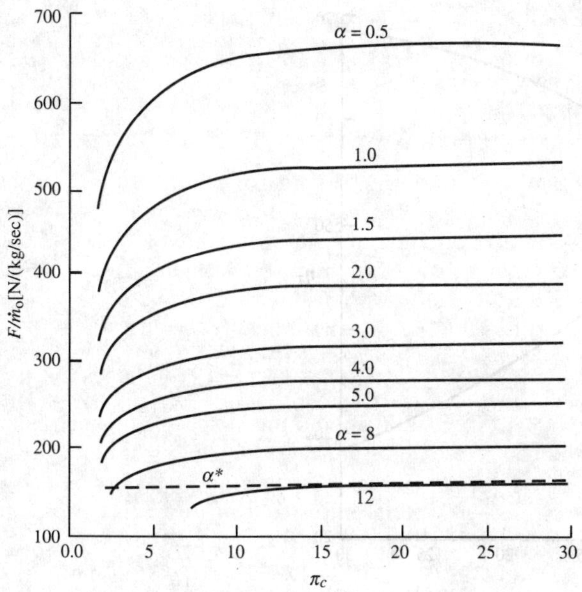

FIGURE 5-23*a*
Ideal turbofan performance versus π_c, for $\pi_f = 2$ and $M_0 = 0.9$: specific thrust.

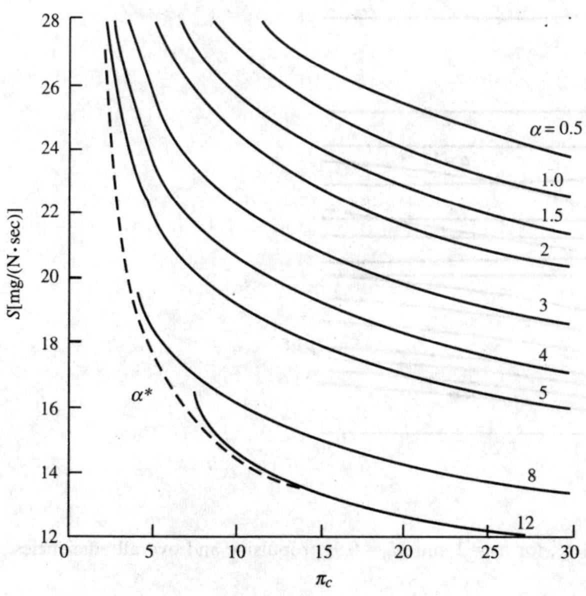

FIGURE 5-23*b*
Ideal turbofan performance versus π_c, for $\pi_f = 2$ and $M_0 = 0.9$: thrust specific fuel consumption.

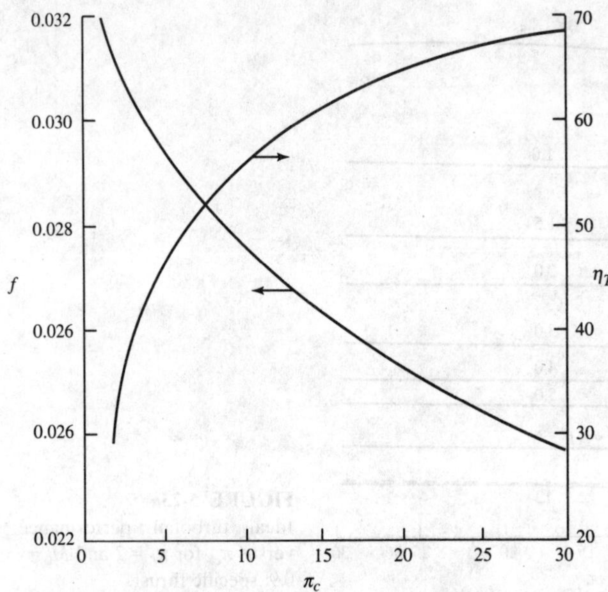

FIGURE 5-23c
Ideal turbofan performance versus π_c, for $\pi_f = 2$ and $M_0 = 0.9$: fuel/air ratio and thermal efficiency.

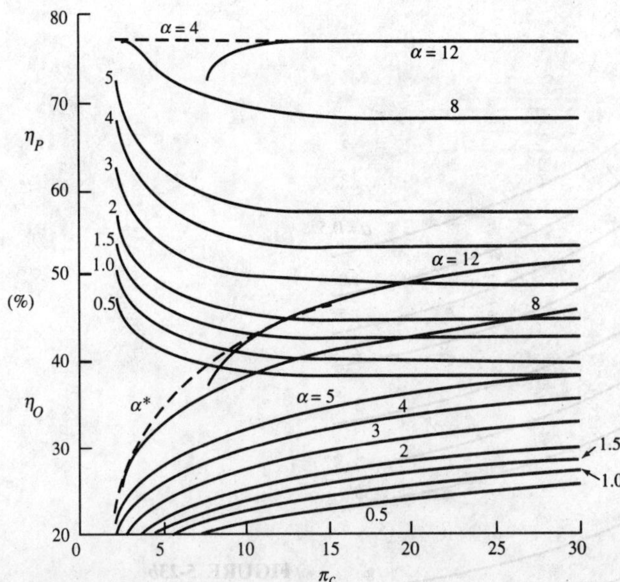

FIGURE 5-23d
Ideal turbofan performance versus π_c, for $\pi_f = 2$ and $M_0 = 0.9$: propulsive and overall efficiencies.

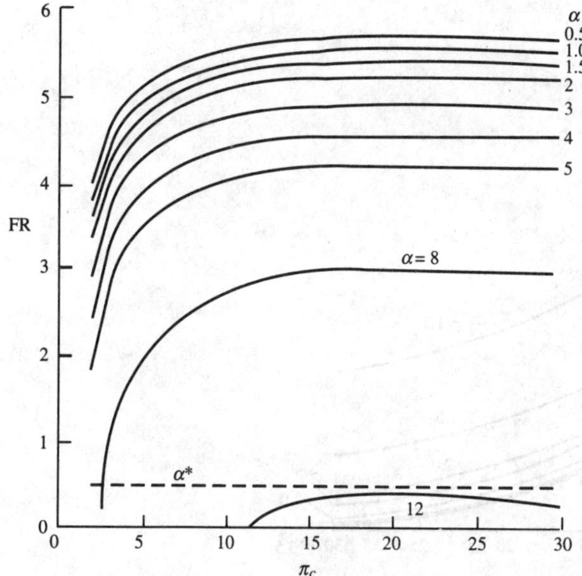

FIGURE 5-23*e*
Ideal turbofan performance versus π_c, for $\pi_f = 2$ and $M_0 = 0.9$: thrust ratio.

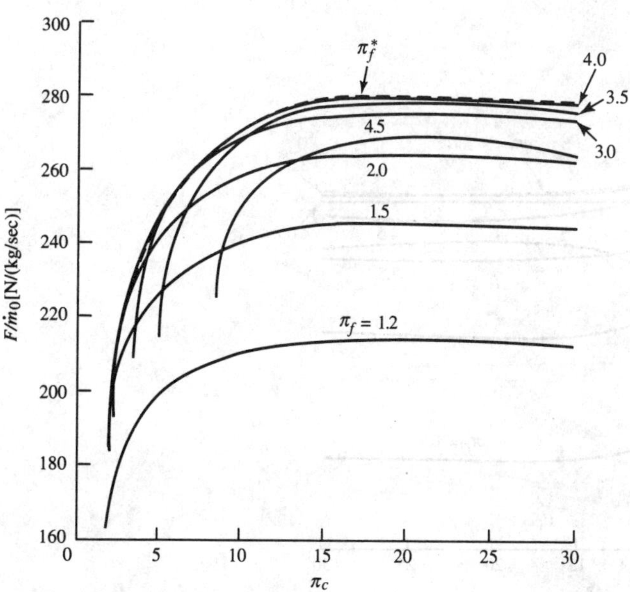

FIGURE 5-24*a*
Ideal turbofan performance versus π_c, for $\alpha = 5$ for $M_0 = 0.9$: specific thrust.

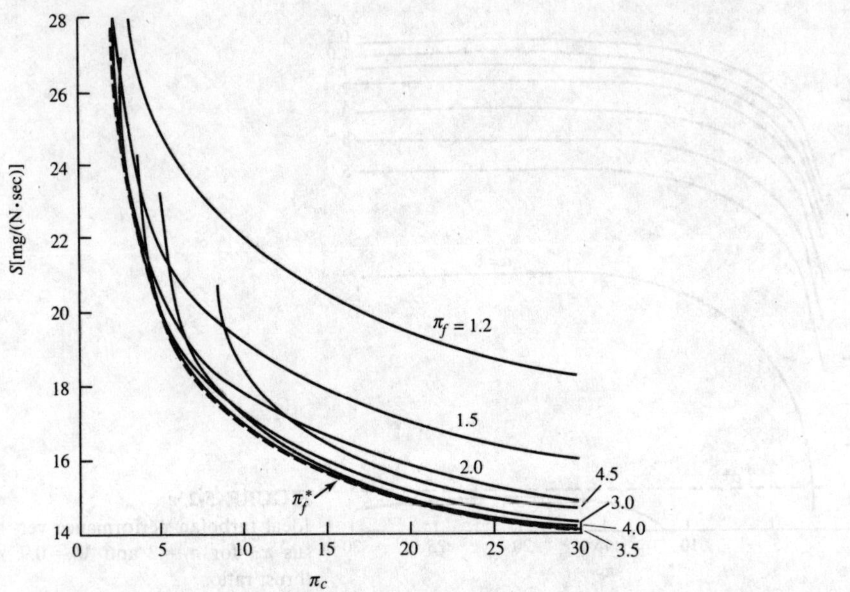

FIGURE 5-24*b*
Ideal turbofan performance versus π_c, for $\alpha = 5$ and $M_0 = 0.9$: thrust specific fuel consumption.

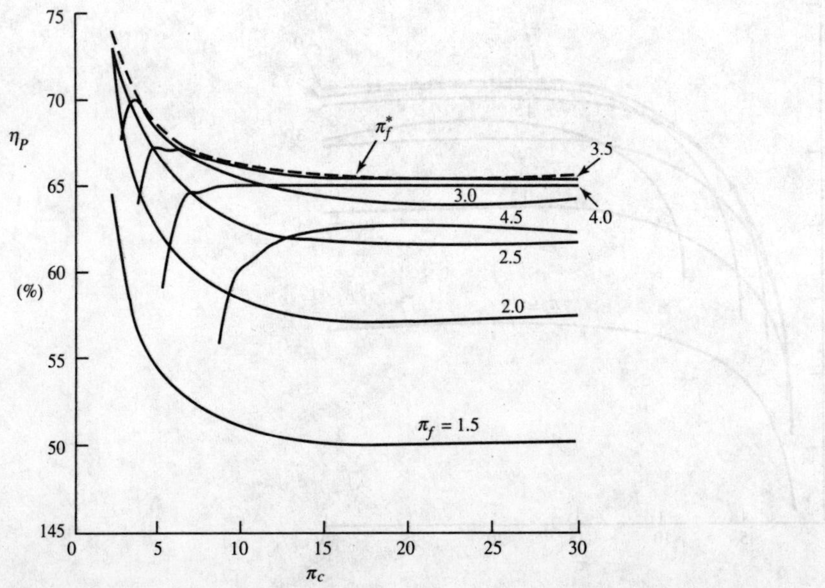

FIGURE 5-24*c*
Ideal turbofan performance versus π_c, for $\alpha = 5$ and $M_0 = 0.9$: propulsive efficiency.

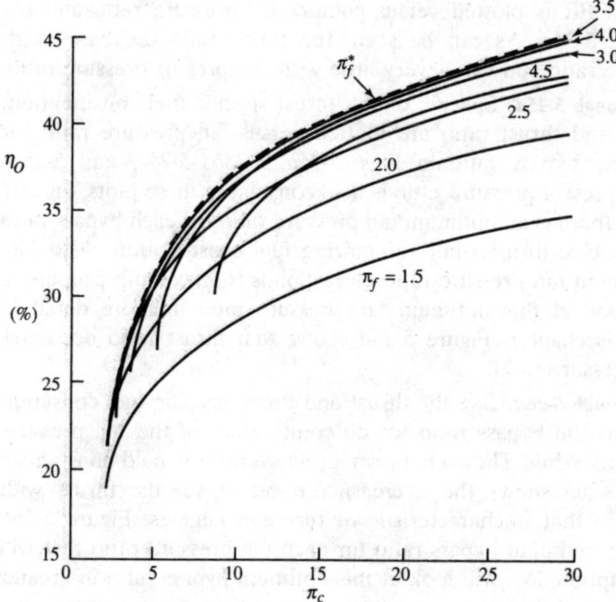

FIGURE 5-24*d*
Ideal turbofan performance versus π_c, for $\alpha = 5$ and $M_0 = 0.9$: overall efficiency.

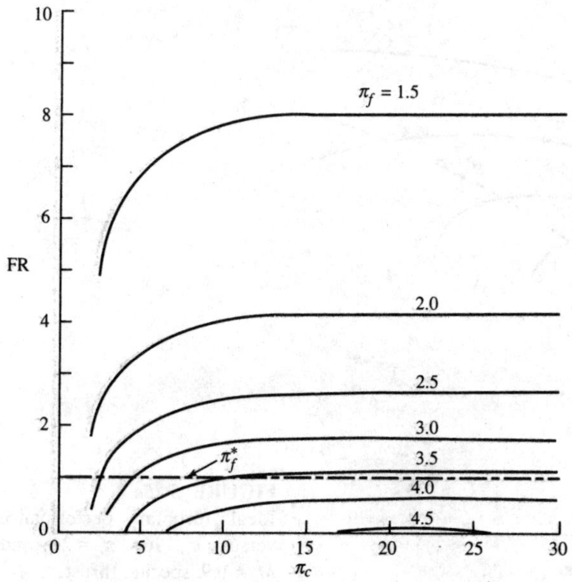

FIGURE 5-24*e*
Ideal turbofan performance versus π_c, for $\alpha = 5$ and $M_0 = 0.9$: thrust ratio.

The thrust ratio FR is plotted versus compressor pressure ratio and fan pressure ratio in Fig. 5-24*e*. As can be seen, the thrust ratio decreases with increasing fan pressure ratio and varies very little with compressor pressure ratio.

Figures 5-25*a* through 5-25*d*. Specific thrust, thrust specific fuel consumption, propulsive efficiency, and thrust ratio are plotted versus fan pressure ratio for different values of the bypass ratio in Figs. 5-25*a*, 5-25*b*, 5-25*c*, and 5-25*d*, respectively. The compressor pressure ratio is held constant in these plots. Figures 5-25*a* and 5-25*b* show there is an optimum fan pressure ratio for each bypass ratio that will maximize specific thrust while minimizing fuel consumption. Also Fig. 5-25*c* shows the optimum fan pressure ratio corresponds to maximum propulsive efficiency. We will look at this optimum fan pressure ratio in more detail in another section of this chapter. Figure 5-25*d* shows that thrust ratio decreases with increasing fan pressure ratio.

Figures 5-26*a* through 5-26*d*. Specific thrust and thrust specific fuel consumption are plotted versus the bypass ratio for different values of the fan pressure ratio in Figs. 5-26*a* and 5-26*b*. The compressor pressure ratio is held constant in these plots. Figure 5-26*a* shows the decreasing trend in specific thrust with increasing bypass ratio that is characteristic of turbofan engines. Figure 5-26*b* shows that there is an optimum bypass ratio for each fan pressure ratio that will minimize fuel consumption. We will look at this optimum bypass ratio in greater detail in another section of this chapter.

Propulsive efficiency and thrust ratio are plotted versus the bypass ratio in Figs. 5-26*c* and 5-26*d*, respectively. Figure 5-26*c* shows there is an optimum bypass ratio for each fan pressure ratio that will maximize propulsive efficiency. Figure 5-26*d* shows that thrust ratio decreases with both increasing bypass ratio and increasing fan pressure ratio.

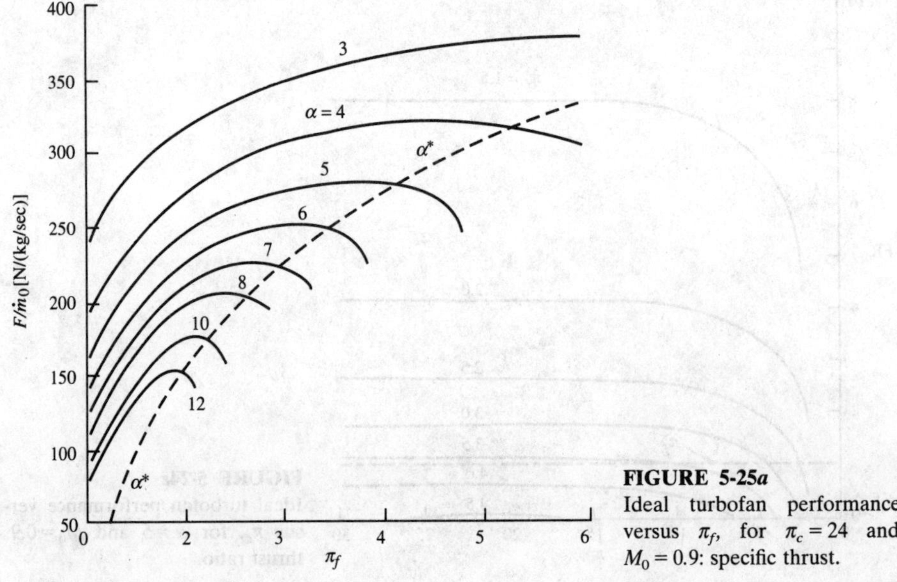

FIGURE 5-25*a*
Ideal turbofan performance versus π_f, for $\pi_c = 24$ and $M_0 = 0.9$: specific thrust.

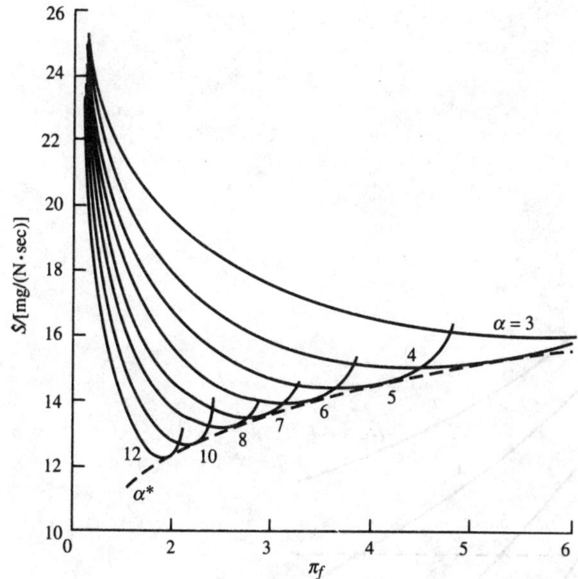

FIGURE 5-25b
Ideal turbofan performance versus π_f, for $\pi_c = 24$ and $M_0 = 0.9$: thrust specific fuel consumption.

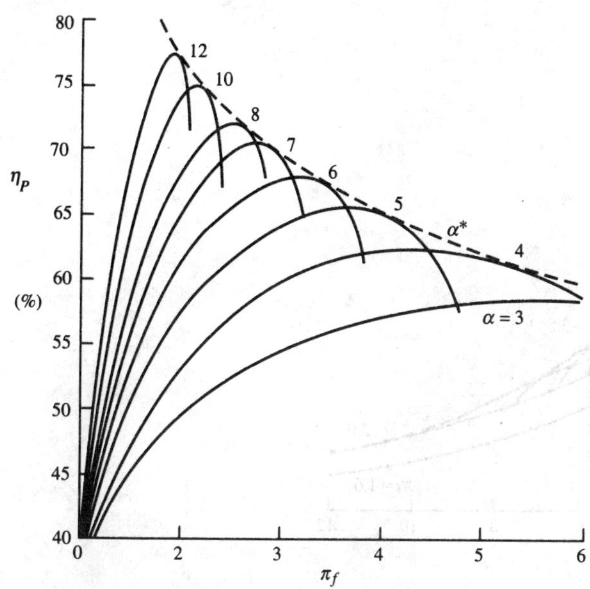

FIGURE 5-25c
Ideal turbofan performance versus π_f, for $\pi_c = 24$ and $M_0 = 0.9$: propulsive efficiency.

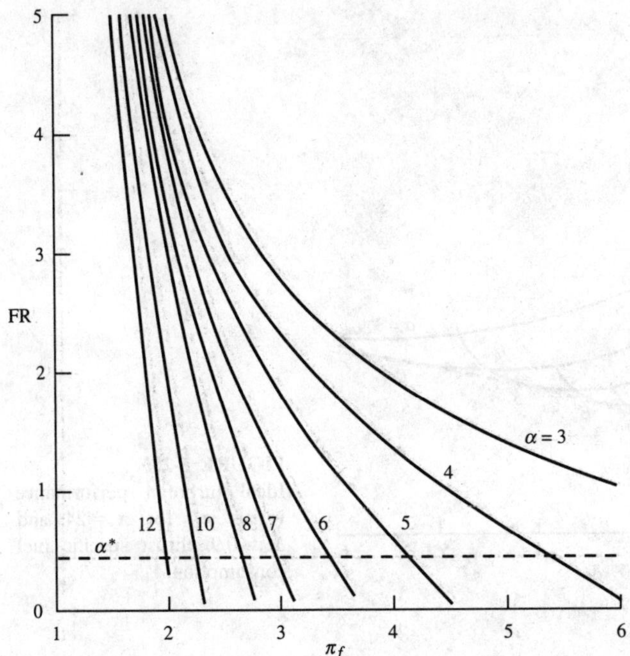

FIGURE 5-25*d*
Ideal turbofan performance versus π_f, for $\pi_c = 24$ and $M_0 = 0.9$: thrust ratio.

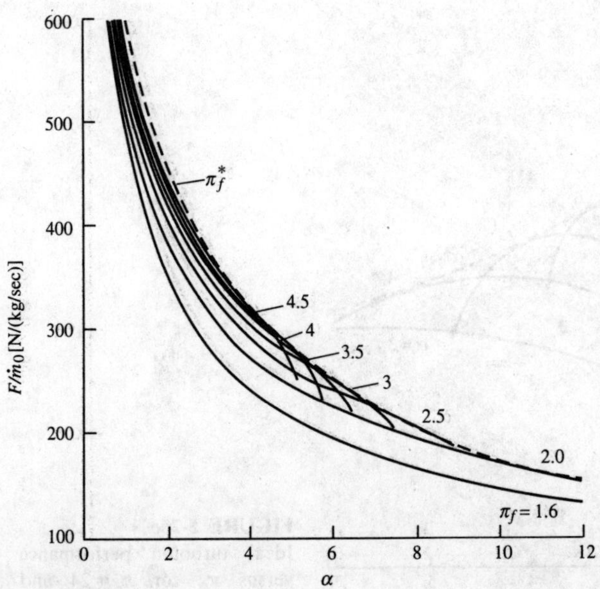

FIGURE 5-26*a*
Ideal turbofan performance versus α, for $\pi_c = 24$ and $M_0 = 0.9$: specific thrust.

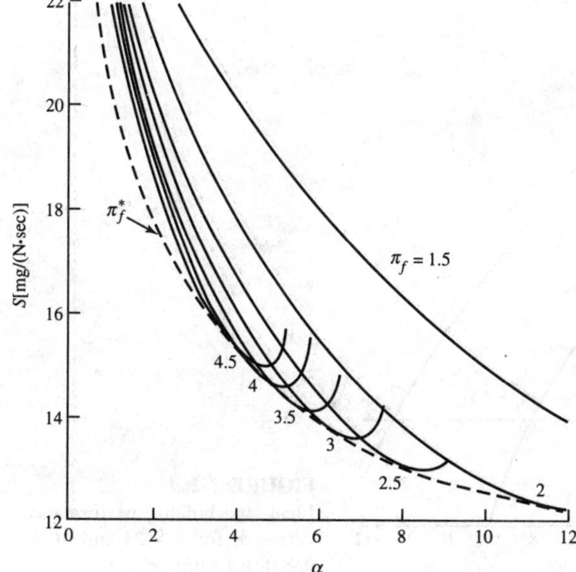

FIGURE 5-26b
Ideal turbofan performance versus α, for $\pi_c = 24$ and $M_0 = 0.9$: thrust specific fuel consumption.

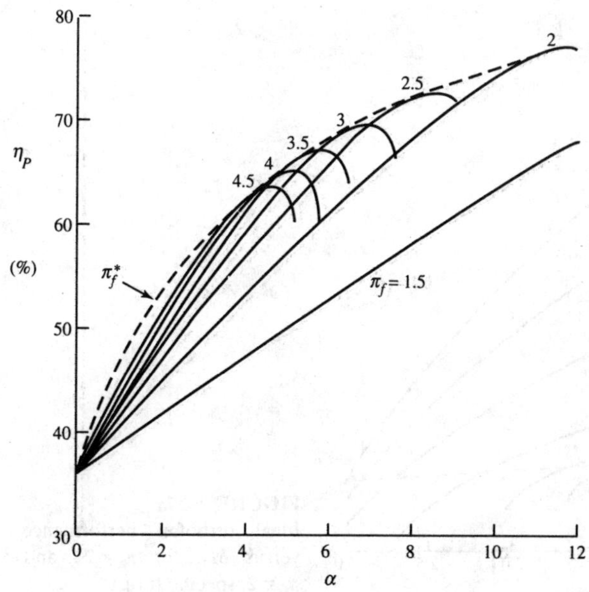

FIGURE 5-26c
Ideal turbofan performance versus α, for $\pi_c = 24$ and $M_0 = 0.9$: propulsive efficiency.

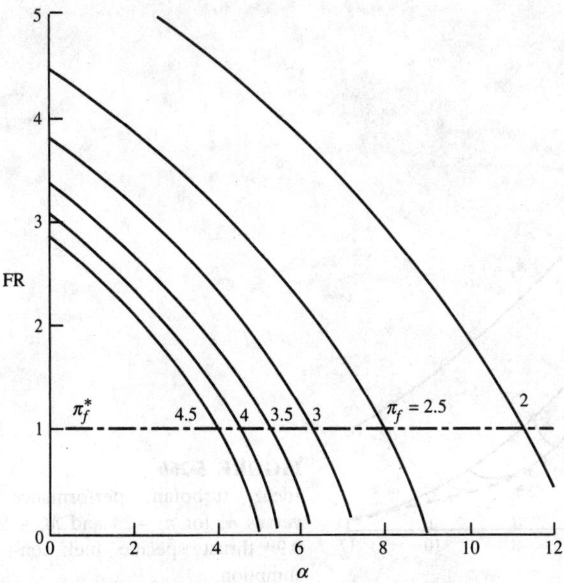

FIGURE 5-26*d*
Ideal turbofan performance versus α, for $\pi_c = 24$ and $M_0 = 0.9$: thrust ratio.

Figures 5-27*a* through 5-28*e*. Specific thrust and the specific fuel consumption are plotted versus the flight Mach number for different values of the bypass ratio in Figs. 5-27*a*, 5-27*b*, 5-28*a*, and 5-28*b*. The compressor pressure ratio has a value of 24 for all four plots, and the fan pressure ratio is held constant at a value of 2

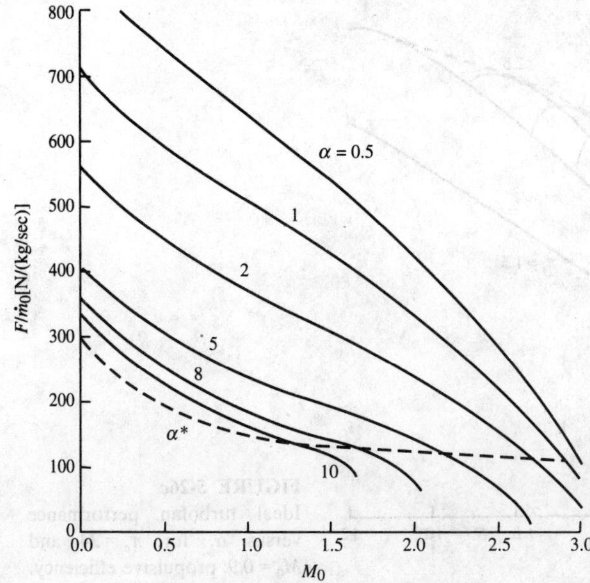

FIGURE 5-27*a*
Ideal turbofan performance versus M_0, for $\pi_c = 24$ and $\pi_f = 2$: specific thrust.

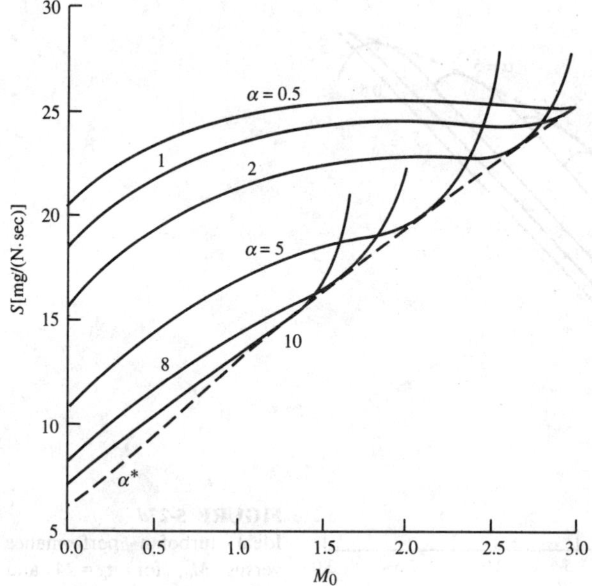

FIGURE 5-27*b*
Ideal turbofan performance versus M_0, for $\pi_c = 24$ and $\pi_f = 2$: thrust specific fuel consumption.

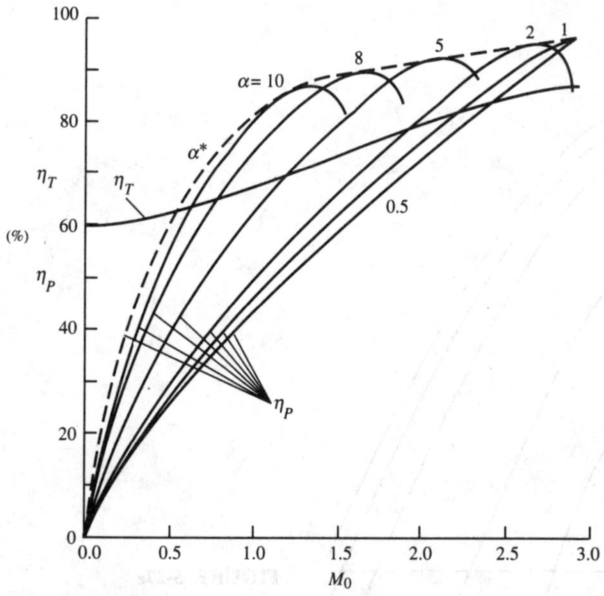

FIGURE 5-27*c*
Ideal turbofan performance versus M_0, for $\pi_c = 24$ and $\pi_f = 2$: thermal and propulsive efficiencies.

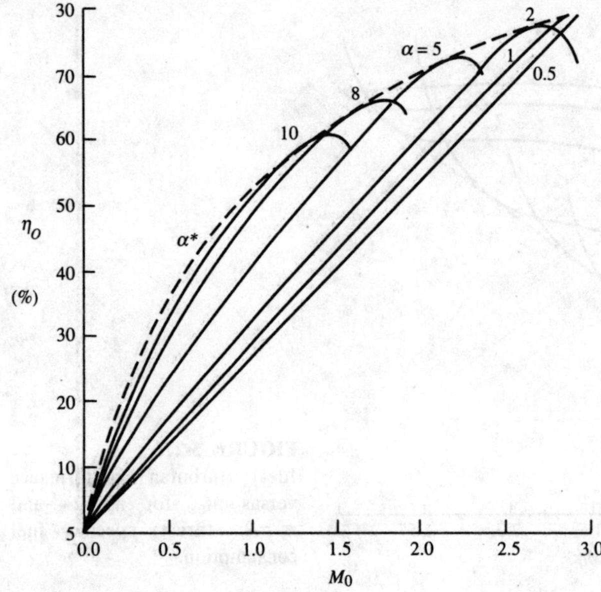

FIGURE 5-27*d*
Ideal turbofan performance versus M_0, for $\pi_c = 24$ and $\pi_f = 2$: overall efficiency.

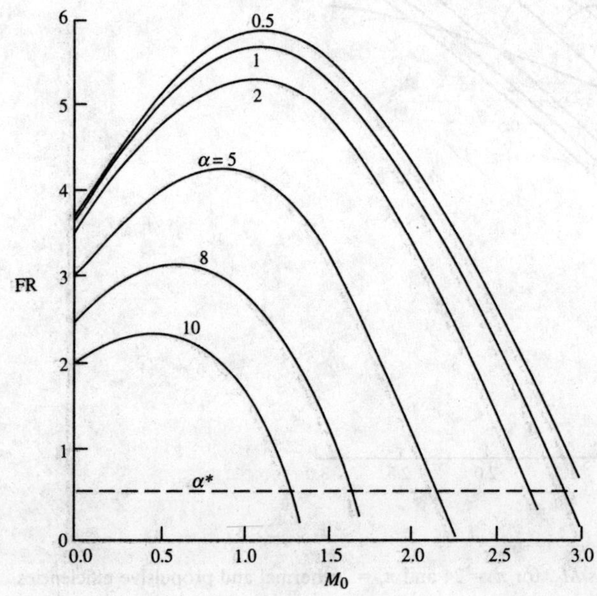

FIGURE 5-27*e*
Ideal turbofan performance versus M_0, for $\pi_c = 24$ and $\pi_f = 2$: thrust ratio.

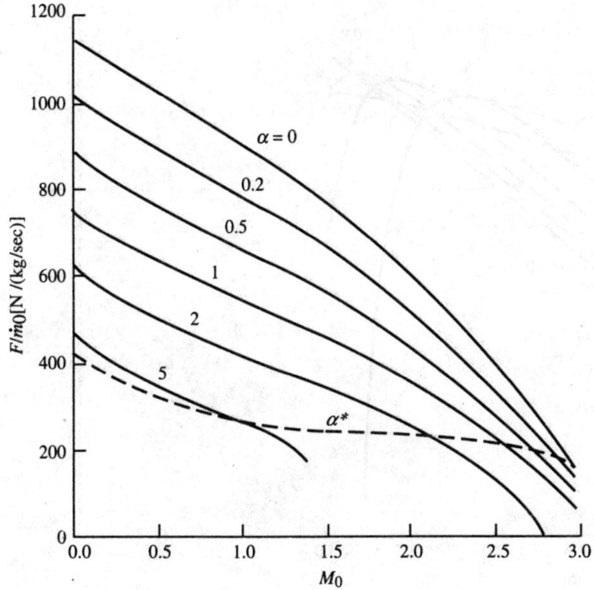

FIGURE 5-28a
Ideal turbofan performance versus M_0, for $\pi_c = 24$ and $\pi_f = 3$: specific thrust.

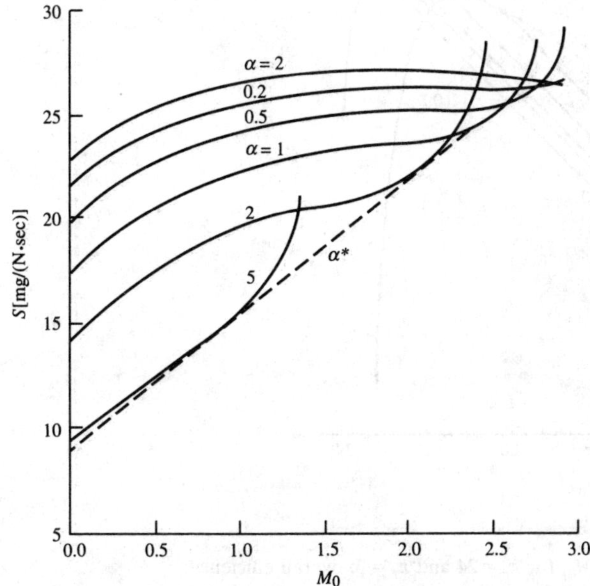

FIGURE 5-28b
Ideal turbofan performance versus M_0, for $\pi_c = 24$ and $\pi_f = 3$: thrust specific fuel consumption.

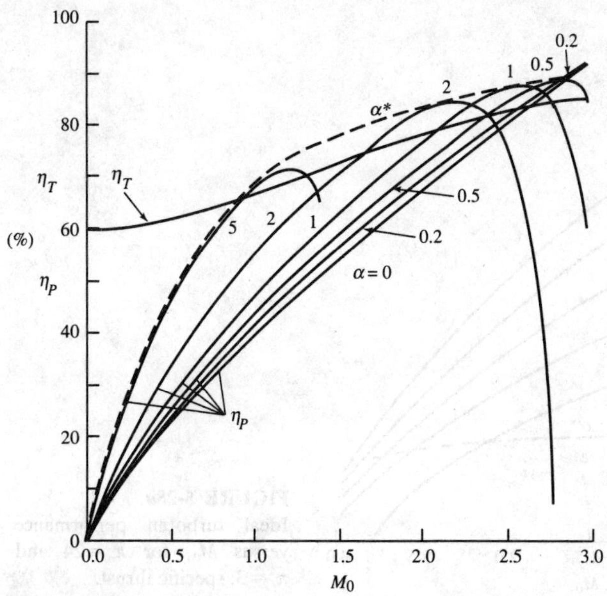

FIGURE 5-28c
Ideal turbofan performance versus M_0, for $\pi_c = 24$ and $\pi_f = 3$: thermal and propulsive efficiencies.

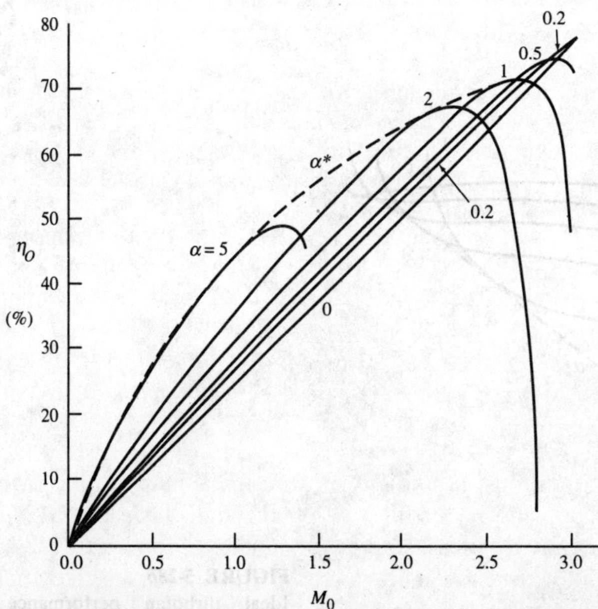

FIGURE 5-28d
Ideal turbofan performance versus M_0, for $\pi_c = 24$ and $\pi_f = 3$: overall efficiency.

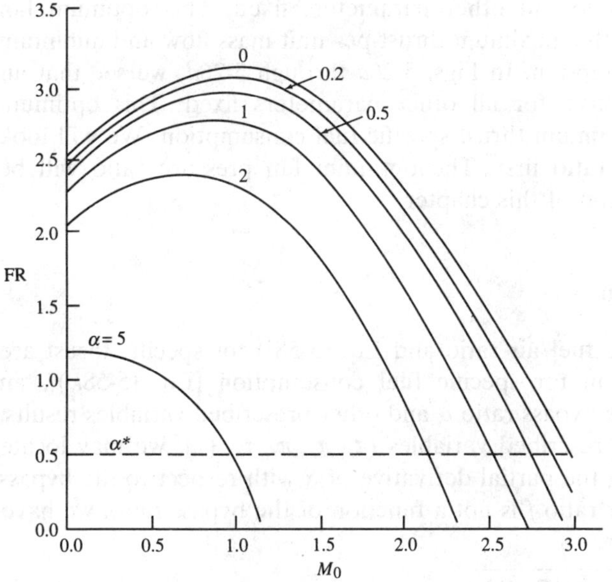

FIGURE 5-28*e*
Ideal turbofan performance versus M_0, for $\pi_c = 24$ and $\pi_f = 3$: thrust ratio.

for Figs. 5-27*a* and 5-27*b* and at a value of 3 for Figs. 5-28*a* and 5-28*b*. Figures 5-27*a* and 5-28*a* show that specific thrust decreases with increasing flight Mach number and with increasing bypass ratio. These four figures also show that the high-bypass-ratio engines are limited to lower flight Mach numbers and that a low-bypass-ratio engine is required for the higher flight Mach numbers.

Propulsive, thermal, and overall efficiencies are plotted versus the flight Mach number for different values of the bypass ratio in Figs. 5-27*c*, 5-27*d*, 5-28*c*, and 5-28*d*. We can see that propulsive efficiency increases with flight Mach number and that there is an optimum bypass ratio for each flight Mach number that gives maximum propulsive and overall efficiencies.

The thrust ratio is plotted versus flight Mach number for different values of the bypass ratio in Figs. 5-27*e* and 5-28*e*. These plots show that thrust ratio decreases with increasing bypass ratio and generally decreases with increasing flight Mach number.

5-10 IDEAL TURBOFAN WITH OPTIMUM BYPASS RATIO

For a given set of flight conditions T_0 and M_0 and design limit τ_λ, there are three design variables: π_c, π_f, and α. In Figs. 5-23*a* through 5-23*e* and 5-24*a* through 5-24*e*, we can see that by increasing the compressor ratio π_c we can increase the thrust per unit mass flow and decrease the thrust specific fuel consumption. Increases in the compressor pressure ratio above a value of 20 do not increase the thrust per unit mass flow but do decrease the thrust specific fuel consumption. In Figs. 5-25*a* through 5-25*d*, we can see that an optimum fan pressure ratio exists for all other parameters fixed. This optimum fan pressure ratio gives both the maximum thrust per unit mass flow and minimum thrust specific fuel consumption. In Figs. 5-26*a* through 5-26*d*, we see that an optimum bypass ratio exists for all other parameters fixed. This optimum bypass ratio gives the minimum thrust specific fuel consumption. We will look at this optimum bypass ratio first. The optimum fan pressure ratio will be analyzed in the next section of this chapter.

Optimum Bypass Ratio α^*

When Eq. (5-58*j*) for the fuel/air ratio and Eq. (5-58*i*) for specific thrust are inserted into the equation for specific fuel consumption [Eq. (5-58*k*)], an expression in terms of the bypass ratio α and other prescribed variables results. For a given set of such prescribed variables (τ_r, π_c, π_f, τ_λ, V_0), we may locate the minimum S by taking the partial derivative of S with respect to the bypass ratio α. Since the fuel/air ratio f is not a function of the bypass ratio, we have

$$S = \frac{f}{(1+\alpha)(F/\dot{m}_0)}$$

$$\frac{\partial S}{\partial \alpha} = \frac{\partial}{\partial \alpha}\left[\frac{f}{(1+\alpha)(F/\dot{m}_0)}\right] = 0$$

$$\frac{\partial S}{\partial \alpha} = \frac{-f}{[(1+\alpha)(F/\dot{m}_0)]^2}\frac{\partial}{\partial \alpha}\left[(1+\alpha)\left(\frac{F}{\dot{m}_0}\right)\right] = 0$$

Thus $\partial S/\partial \alpha = 0$ is satisfied by

$$\frac{\partial}{\partial \alpha}\left[\frac{g_c}{V_0}(1+\alpha)\left(\frac{F}{\dot{m}_0}\right)\right] = 0$$

where $$\frac{g_c}{V_0}(1+\alpha)\left(\frac{F}{\dot{m}_0}\right) = \frac{V_9}{V_0} - 1 + \alpha\left(\frac{V_{19}}{V_0} - 1\right)$$

Then the optimum bypass ratio is given by

$$\frac{\partial}{\partial \alpha}\left[\frac{V_9}{V_0} - 1 + \alpha\left(\frac{V_{19}}{V_0} - 1\right)\right] = \frac{\partial}{\partial \alpha}\left(\frac{V_9}{V_0}\right) + \frac{V_{19}}{V_0} - 1 = 0 \qquad \text{(i)}$$

However, $$\frac{1}{2V_9/V_0}\frac{\partial}{\partial \alpha}\left[\left(\frac{V_9}{V_0}\right)^2\right] = \frac{\partial}{\partial \alpha}\left(\frac{V_9}{V_0}\right)$$

Thus Eq. (i) becomes

$$\frac{1}{2V_9/V_0}\frac{\partial}{\partial \alpha}\left[\left(\frac{V_9}{V_0}\right)^2\right] + \frac{V_{19}}{V_0} - 1 = 0 \qquad \text{(ii)}$$

Since $$\left(\frac{V_9}{V_0}\right)^2 = \frac{1}{M_0^2}\left(\frac{V_9}{a_0}\right)^2 = \frac{1}{[(\gamma-1)/2](\tau_r - 1)}\left(\frac{V_9}{a_0}\right)^2$$
$$= \frac{\tau_\lambda - \tau_r[\tau_c - 1 + \alpha(\tau_f - 1)] - \tau_\lambda/(\tau_r\tau_c)}{\tau_r - 1}$$

then $$\frac{\partial}{\partial\alpha}\left[\left(\frac{V_9}{V_0}\right)^2\right] = \frac{\partial}{\partial\alpha}\left\{\frac{\tau_\lambda - \tau_r[\tau_c - 1 + \alpha(\tau_f - 1)] - \tau_\lambda/(\tau_r\tau_c)}{\tau_r - 1}\right\}$$

giving $$\frac{\partial}{\partial\alpha}\left[\left(\frac{V_9}{V_0}\right)^2\right] = -\frac{\tau_r(\tau_f - 1)}{\tau_r - 1} \tag{iii}$$

Since $$\left(\frac{V_{19}}{V_0}\right)^2 = \frac{1}{M_0^2}\left(\frac{V_{19}}{a_0}\right)^2 = \frac{1}{[(\gamma-1)/2](\tau_r - 1)}\left(\frac{V_{19}}{a_0}\right)^2 = \frac{\tau_r\tau_f - 1}{\tau_r - 1} \tag{iv}$$

then Eqs. (iii) and (iv), substituted into Eq. (ii), give

$$\frac{1}{2V_9/V_0}\left[-\frac{\tau_r(\tau_f - 1)}{\tau_r - 1}\right] + \sqrt{\frac{\tau_r\tau_f - 1}{\tau_r - 1}} - 1 = 0$$

Substitution of the equation for V_9/V_0 gives

$$\frac{1}{2}\frac{-\tau_r(\tau_f - 1)}{\sqrt{\{\tau_\lambda - \tau_r[\tau_c - 1 + \alpha^*(\tau_f - 1)] - \tau_\lambda/(\tau_r\tau_c)\}/(\tau_r - 1)}} + \sqrt{\frac{\tau_r\tau_f - 1}{\tau_r - 1}} - 1 = 0$$

or $$\frac{1}{2}\frac{\tau_r(\tau_f - 1)}{\sqrt{\{\tau_\lambda - \tau_r[\tau_c - 1 + \alpha^*(\tau_f - 1)] - \tau_\lambda/(\tau_r\tau_c)\}/(\tau_r - 1)}} = \sqrt{\frac{\tau_r\tau_f - 1}{\tau_r - 1}} - 1$$

Squaring both sides, we have

$$\frac{1}{4}\frac{[\tau_r(\tau_f - 1)]^2}{\{\tau_\lambda - \tau_r[\tau_c - 1 + \alpha^*(\tau_f - 1)] - \tau_\lambda/(\tau_r\tau_c)\}/(\tau_r - 1)} = \left(\sqrt{\frac{\tau_r\tau_f - 1}{\tau_r - 1}} - 1\right)^2$$

or $$\frac{1}{4}\frac{[\tau_r(\tau_f - 1)]^2}{[\sqrt{(\tau_r\tau_f - 1)/(\tau_r - 1)} - 1]^2} = \frac{\tau_\lambda - \tau_r[\tau_c - 1 + \alpha^*(\tau_f - 1)] - \tau_\lambda/(\tau_r\tau_c)}{\tau_r - 1} \tag{v}$$

An expression for the bypass ratio giving the minimum fuel consumption is obtained by solving Eq. (v) for α^*. Thus

$$\alpha^* = \frac{\tau_r - 1}{\tau_r(\tau_f - 1)}\left[\frac{\tau_\lambda - \tau_r(\tau_c - 1) - \tau_\lambda/(\tau_r\tau_c)}{\tau_r - 1} - \frac{1}{4}\left(\sqrt{\frac{\tau_r\tau_f - 1}{\tau_r - 1}} + 1\right)^2\right]$$

or $$\boxed{\alpha^* = \frac{1}{\tau_r(\tau_f - 1)}\left[\tau_\lambda - \tau_r(\tau_c - 1) - \frac{\tau_\lambda}{\tau_r\tau_c} - \frac{1}{4}(\sqrt{\tau_r\tau_f - 1} + \sqrt{\tau_r - 1})^2\right]} \tag{5-59}$$

Now note that we may write

$$\frac{\tau_r(\tau_f - 1)}{\tau_r - 1} = \frac{\tau_r\tau_f - \tau_r + 1 - 1}{\tau_r - 1} = \frac{\tau_r\tau_f - 1}{\tau_r - 1} - 1$$

So then Eq. (v) becomes

$$\frac{1}{4}\left[\frac{\left(\sqrt{\dfrac{\tau_r\tau_f-1}{\tau_r-1}}\right)^2-1}{\sqrt{\dfrac{\tau_r\tau_f-1}{\tau_r-1}}-1}\right]^2=\frac{\tau_\lambda-\tau_r[\tau_c-1+\alpha^*(\tau_f-1]-\dfrac{\tau_\lambda}{\tau_r\tau_c}}{\tau_r-1}$$

Taking the square root of both sides of this equation gives

$$\frac{1}{2}\left(\sqrt{\frac{\tau_r\tau_f-1}{\tau_r-1}}+1\right)=\sqrt{\frac{\tau_\lambda-\tau_r[\tau_c-1+\alpha^*(\tau_f-1)]-\tau_\lambda/(\tau_r\tau_c)}{\tau_r-1}}$$

or

$$\frac{1}{2}\left(\sqrt{\frac{\tau_r\tau_f-1}{\tau_r-1}}-1\right)=\sqrt{\frac{\tau_\lambda-\tau_r[\tau_c-1+\alpha^*(\tau_f-1)]-\tau_\lambda/(\tau_r\tau_c)}{\tau_r-1}}-1 \qquad \text{(vi)}$$

Noting from Eqs. (5-50) and (5-53) that the term within the square root on the left side of the equals sign is the velocity ratio V_{19}/V_0, and that the term within the square root on the right side is the velocity ratio V_9/V_0, we see that Eq. (vi) becomes

$$\frac{1}{2}\left(\frac{V_{19}}{V_0}-1\right)=\frac{V_9}{V_0}-1 \quad \text{or} \quad V_9-V_0=\frac{1}{2}(V_{19}-V_0)$$

Thus

$$\text{FR}=\frac{V_9-V_0}{V_{19}-V_0}=\frac{1}{2} \qquad \text{(5-60)}$$

We thus note from Eq. (5-60) that when the bypass ratio is chosen to give the minimum specific fuel consumption, the thrust per unit mass flow of the engine core is one-half that of the fan. Thus the thrust ratio of an optimum-bypass-ratio ideal turbofan is 0.5. Using this fact, we may write the equation for the specific thrust simply as

$$\left(\frac{F}{\dot{m}_0}\right)_{\alpha^*}=\frac{a_0}{g_c}\frac{1+2\alpha^*}{2(1+\alpha^*)}\left[\sqrt{\frac{2}{\gamma-1}(\tau_r\tau_f-1)}-M_0\right] \qquad \text{(5-61)}$$

where α^* is obtained from Eq. (5-59).

One can easily show that the propulsive efficiency at the optimum bypass ratio is given by

$$(\eta_P)_{\min S}=\frac{4(1+2\alpha^*)V_0}{(3+4\alpha^*)V_0+(1+4\alpha^*)V_{19}} \qquad \text{(5-62)}$$

Summary of Equations—Optimum-Bypass-Ratio Ideal Turbofan

INPUTS: M_0, $T_0(\text{K}, °\text{R})$, γ, $c_p\left(\frac{\text{kJ}}{\text{kg}\cdot\text{K}}, \frac{\text{Btu}}{\text{lbm}\cdot°\text{R}}\right)$, $h_{PR}\left(\frac{\text{kJ}}{\text{kg}}, \frac{\text{Btu}}{\text{lbm}}\right)$, $T_{t4}(\text{K}, °\text{R})$, π_c, π_f

OUTPUTS: $\frac{F}{\dot{m}_0}\left(\frac{\text{N}}{\text{kg/sec}}, \frac{\text{lbf}}{\text{lbm/sec}}\right)$, f, $S\left(\frac{\text{mg/sec}}{\text{N}}, \frac{\text{lbm/hr}}{\text{lbf}}\right)$, η_T, η_P, η_O, α^*

EQUATIONS: Equations (5-58*a*) through (5-58*h*) plus

$$\alpha^* = \frac{1}{\tau_r(\tau_f - 1)}\left[\tau_\lambda - \tau_r(\tau_c - 1) - \frac{\tau_\lambda}{\tau_r\tau_c} - \frac{1}{4}\left(\sqrt{\tau_r\tau_f - 1} + \sqrt{\tau_r - 1}\right)^2\right] \tag{5-63a}$$

$$\frac{F}{\dot{m}_0} = \frac{a_0}{g_c}\frac{1 + 2\alpha^*}{2(1 + \alpha^*)}\left[\sqrt{\frac{2}{\gamma - 1}(\tau_r\tau_f - 1)} - M_0\right] \tag{5-63b}$$

$$\eta_P = \frac{4(1 + 2\alpha^*)M_0}{(3 + 4\alpha^*)M_0 + (1 + 4\alpha^*)(V_{19}/a_0)} \tag{5-63c}$$

and Eqs. (5-58*j*), (5-58*k*), (5-58*l*), (5-58*n*)

Example 5-5. The engine we looked at in Sec. 5-9 is used again in this section for an example. The following values are held constant for all plots:

$$T_0 = 216.7\ \text{K} \qquad \gamma = 1.4 \qquad c_p = 1.004\ \text{kJ/(kg}\cdot\text{K)}$$
$$h_{PR} = 42{,}800\ \text{kJ/kg} \qquad T_{t4} = 1670\ \text{K}$$

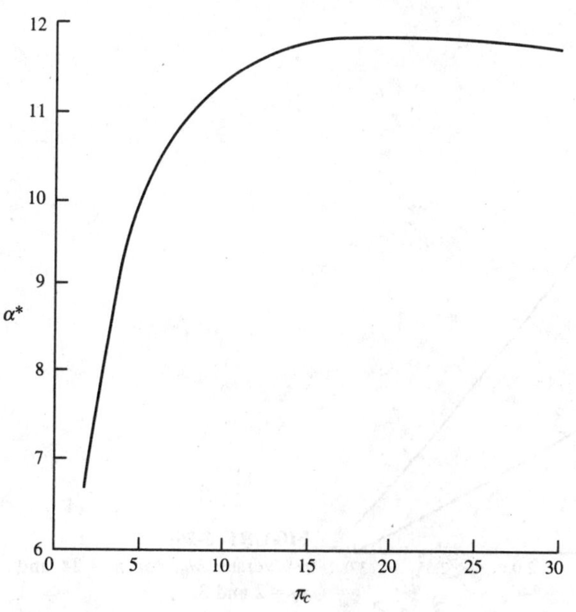

FIGURE 5-29*a*
α^* versus π_c, for $\pi_f = 2$ and $M_0 = 0.9$.

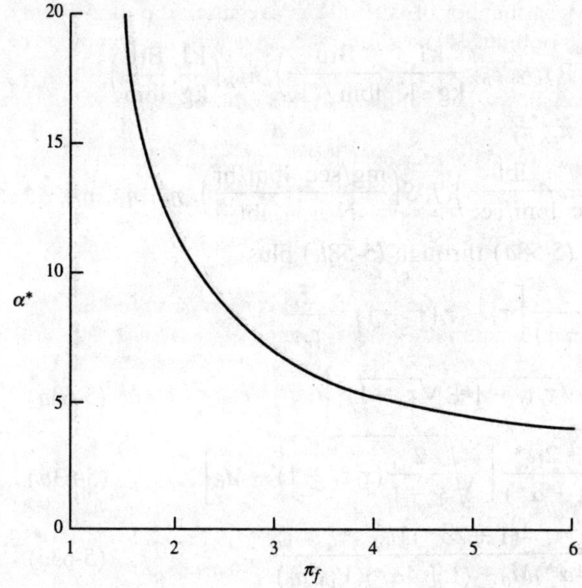

FIGURE 5-29*b*
α^* versus π_f, for $\pi_c = 24$ and $M_0 = 0.9$.

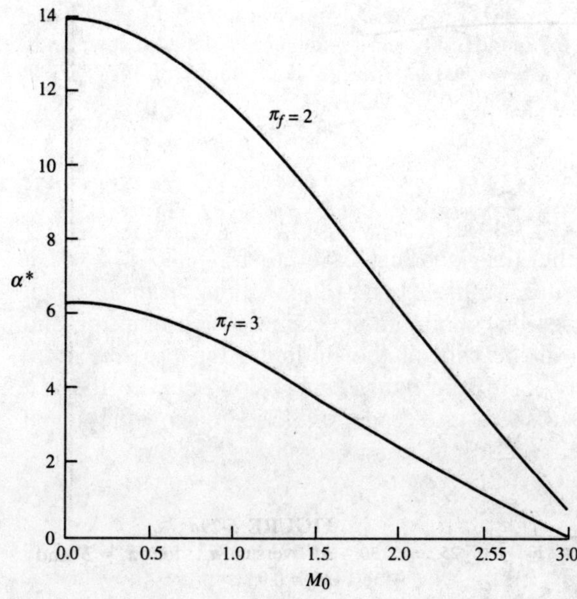

FIGURE 5-29*c*
α^* versus M_0, for $\pi_c = 24$ and $\pi_f = 2$ and 3.

The optimum bypass ratio is plotted in Fig. 5-29*a* versus the compressor pressure ratio for a flight Mach number of 0.9 and fan pressure ratio of 2. From this plot, we can see that the optimum bypass ratio increases with the compressor pressure ratio. The optimum bypass ratio is plotted in Fig. 5-29*b* versus the fan pressure ratio, and this figure shows that optimum bypass ratio decreases with fan pressure ratio.

The optimum bypass ratio versus the flight Mach number is plotted in Fig. 5-29*c* for fan pressure ratios of 2 and 3. From these plots, we can see that the optimum bypass ratio decreases with the flight Mach number. Note that the optimum engine is a turbojet at a Mach number of about 3.0 for a fan pressure ratio of 3.

The plots of specific thrust and thrust specific fuel consumption for an ideal turbofan engine with optimum bypass ratio versus compressor pressure ratio are superimposed on Figs. 5-23*a* through 5-23*e* by a dashed line marked α^*. The optimum-bypass-ratio ideal turbofan has the minimum thrust specific fuel consumption.

The plots of specific thrust and thrust specific fuel consumption for the optimum-bypass-ratio ideal turbofan versus fan pressure ratio are superimposed on Figs. 5-25*a* through 5-25*d* by a dashed line marked α^*. As shown in these figures, the plot for α^* is the locus of the minimum value of S for each π_f.

The plots of specific thrust and thrust specific fuel consumption for the optimum-bypass-ratio ideal turbofan versus flight Mach number are superimposed on Figs. 5-27*a* through 5-27*e* for a fan pressure ratio of 2 and on Figs. 5-28*a* through 5-28*e* for a fan pressure ratio of 3. As shown in these figures, the plots for α^* are the locus of the minimum value of S for fixed values of π_c and π_f.

The thermal efficiency of an optimum-bypass-ratio ideal turbofan is the same as that of an ideal turbojet. The bypass ratio of an ideal turbofan affects only the propulsive efficiency. The propulsive efficiency of an optimum-bypass-ratio ideal turbofan is superimposed on those of Figs. 5-23*d*, 5-25*c*, 5-27*c*, and 5-28*c*. As can be seen, the optimum bypass ratio gives the maximum propulsive efficiency. Likewise, as shown in Figs. 5-23*d*, 5-25*c*, 5-27*d*, and 5-28*d*, the optimum bypass ratio gives the maximum overall efficiency. The thrust ratio of an optimum-bypass-ratio ideal turbofan is superimposed on those of Figs. 5-23*e*, 5-25*d*, 5-27*e*, and 5-28*e* and is equal to 0.5.

5-11 IDEAL TURBOFAN WITH OPTIMUM FAN PRESSURE RATIO

Figures 5-25*a* and 5-25*b* show that for given flight conditions T_0 and M_0, design limit τ_λ, compressor pressure ratio π_c, and bypass ratio α, there is an optimum fan pressure ratio π_f which gives the minimum specific fuel consumption and maximum specific thrust. As will be shown, the optimum fan pressure ratio corresponds to the exit velocity V_{19} of the fan stream, being equal to the exit velocity of the core stream V_9. It is left, as a reader exercise, to show that equal exit velocities ($V_9 = V_{19}$) correspond to maximum propulsive efficiency.

Optimum Fan Pressure Ratio π_f^*

For a given set of prescribed variables (τ_r, π_c, τ_λ, V_0, α), we may locate the optimum fan pressure ratio by taking the partial derivative of the specific thrust with respect to the fan total temperature ratio. The derivation of an expression for the optimum fan total temperature ratio and, by Eq. (5-58*f*), the optimum fan pressure ratio follows. From Eq. (5-54), we have

$$\frac{\partial S}{\partial \tau_f} = \frac{-f}{[(1+\alpha)(F/\dot{m}_0)]^2} \frac{\partial}{\partial \tau_f}\left[(1+\alpha)\left(\frac{F}{\dot{m}_0}\right)\right] = 0$$

Thus $\dfrac{\partial S}{\partial \tau_f} = 0$ is satisfied by $\dfrac{\partial}{\partial \tau_f}\left[\dfrac{g_c}{V_0}(1+\alpha)\left(\dfrac{F}{\dot{m}_0}\right)\right] = 0$

where $\dfrac{g_c}{V_0}(1+\alpha)\left(\dfrac{F}{\dot{m}_0}\right) = \dfrac{V_9}{V_0} - 1 + \alpha\left(\dfrac{V_{19}}{V_0} - 1\right)$

Hence the optimum fan pressure ratio is given by solution of

$$\frac{\partial}{\partial \tau_f}\left[\frac{V_9}{V_0} - 1 + \alpha\left(\frac{V_{19}}{V_0} - 1\right)\right] = \frac{\partial}{\partial \tau_f}\left(\frac{V_9}{V_0}\right) + \alpha\frac{\partial}{\partial \tau_f}\left(\frac{V_{19}}{V_0}\right) = 0 \qquad \text{(i)}$$

Since $\dfrac{\partial}{\partial \tau_f}\left(\dfrac{V_9}{V_0}\right) = \dfrac{1}{2V_9/V_0}\dfrac{\partial}{\partial \tau_f}\left[\left(\dfrac{V_9}{V_0}\right)^2\right]$

and $\dfrac{\partial}{\partial \tau_f}\left(\dfrac{V_{19}}{V_0}\right) = \dfrac{1}{2V_{19}/V_0}\dfrac{\partial}{\partial \tau_f}\left[\left(\dfrac{V_{19}}{V_0}\right)^2\right]$

Eq. (i) becomes

$$\frac{1}{2V_9/V_0}\frac{\partial}{\partial \tau_f}\left[\left(\frac{V_9}{V_0}\right)^2\right] + \alpha\frac{1}{2V_{19}/V_0}\frac{\partial}{\partial \tau_f}\left[\left(\frac{V_{19}}{V_0}\right)^2\right] = 0 \qquad \text{(ii)}$$

To determine the first term of Eq. (ii), we start with

$$\left(\frac{V_9}{V_0}\right)^2 = \frac{1}{M_0^2}\left(\frac{V_9}{a_0}\right)^2 = \frac{1}{[(\gamma-1)/2](\tau_r - 1)}\left(\frac{V_9}{a_0}\right)^2$$

$$= \frac{\tau_\lambda - \tau_r[\tau_c - 1 + \alpha(\tau_f - 1)] - \tau_\lambda/(\tau_r\tau_c)}{\tau_r - 1} \qquad \text{(iii)}$$

Thus $\dfrac{\partial}{\partial \tau_f}\left[\left(\dfrac{V_9}{V_0}\right)^2\right] = \dfrac{-\alpha\tau_r}{\tau_r - 1}$ (iv)

To determine the second term of Eq. (ii), we start with

$$\left(\frac{V_{19}}{V_0}\right)^2 = \frac{1}{M_0^2}\left(\frac{V_{19}}{a_0}\right)^2 = \frac{1}{[(\gamma-1)/2](\tau_r - 1)}\left(\frac{V_{19}}{a_0}\right)^2 = \frac{\tau_r\tau_f - 1}{\tau_r - 1} \qquad \text{(v)}$$

Thus $\dfrac{\partial}{\partial \tau_f}\left[\left(\dfrac{V_{19}}{V_0}\right)^2\right] = \dfrac{\tau_r}{\tau_r - 1}$ (vi)

Substitution of Eqs. (iv) and (vi) into Eq. (ii) gives

$$\frac{1}{2V_9/V_0}\left(\frac{-\alpha\tau_r}{\tau_r-1}\right)+\alpha\frac{1}{2V_{19}/V_0}\frac{\tau_r}{\tau_r-1}=0 \tag{vii}$$

Thus we can conclude from Eq. (vii) that the optimum fan pressure ratio corresponds to that value of τ_f yielding

$$\boxed{V_9=V_{19}} \tag{5-64}$$

Also

$$\boxed{\text{FR}=1} \tag{5-65}$$

To solve for the optimum fan temperature ratio, we equate Eqs. (iii) and (v):

$$\left(\frac{V_9}{V_0}\right)^2=\frac{\tau_\lambda-\tau_r[\tau_c-1+\alpha(\tau_f-1)]-\tau_\lambda/(\tau_r\tau_c)}{\tau_r-1}$$

$$=\left(\frac{V_{19}}{V_0}\right)^2=\frac{\tau_r\tau_f-1}{\tau_r-1}$$

giving

$$\boxed{\tau_f^*=\frac{\tau_\lambda\tau_r(\tau_c-1)-\tau_\lambda/(\tau_r\tau_c)+\alpha\tau_r+1}{\tau_r(1+\alpha)}} \tag{5-66}$$

An equation for the specific thrust of an optimum-fan-pressure-ratio turbofan can be obtained by starting with the simplified expression

$$\left(\frac{F}{\dot{m}_0}\right)_{\tau_f^*}=\frac{a_0}{g_c}\left(\frac{V_{19}}{a_0}-M_0\right)$$

which becomes

$$\boxed{\left(\frac{F}{\dot{m}_0}\right)_{\tau_f^*}=\frac{a_0}{g_c}\left[\sqrt{\frac{2}{\gamma-1}(\tau_r\tau_f^*-1)}-M_0\right]} \tag{5-67}$$

The propulsive efficiency for the optimum-fan-pressure-ratio turbofan engine is simply

$$\boxed{(\eta_P)_{\tau_f^*}=\frac{2}{V_{19}/V_0+1}} \tag{5-68}$$

Summary of Equations—Optimum-Fan-Pressure-Ratio Ideal Turbofan

INPUTS: $M_0, T_0(\text{K}, °\text{R}), \gamma, c_p\left(\frac{\text{kJ}}{\text{kg}\cdot\text{K}}, \frac{\text{Btu}}{\text{lbm}\cdot°\text{R}}\right), h_{PR}\left(\frac{\text{kJ}}{\text{kg}}, \frac{\text{Btu}}{\text{lbm}}\right),$

$T_{t4}(\text{K}, °\text{R}), \pi_c, \alpha$

OUTPUTS: $\frac{F}{\dot{m}_0}\left(\frac{\text{N}}{\text{kg/sec}}, \frac{\text{lbf}}{\text{lbm/sec}}\right), f, S\left(\frac{\text{mg/sec}}{\text{N}}, \frac{\text{lbm/hr}}{\text{lbf}}\right), \eta_T, \eta_P, \eta_O, \pi_f^*$

EQUATIONS: Equations (5-58*a*) through (5-58*e*), (5-58*j*), (5-58*l*), plus

$$\tau_f^* = \frac{\tau_\lambda - \tau_r(\tau_c - 1) - \tau_\lambda/(\tau_r\tau_c) + \alpha\tau_r + 1}{\tau_r(1+\alpha)} \tag{5-69a}$$

$$\pi_f^* = (\tau_f^*)^{\gamma/(\gamma-1)} \tag{5-69b}$$

$$\frac{V_{19}}{a_0} = \sqrt{\frac{2}{\gamma - 1}(\tau_r\tau_f^* - 1)} \tag{5-69c}$$

$$\frac{F}{\dot{m}_0} = \frac{a_0}{g_c}\left(\frac{V_{19}}{a_0} - M_0\right) \tag{5-69d}$$

$$\eta_P = \frac{2M_0}{V_{19}/a_0 + M_0} \tag{5-69e}$$

and Eqs. (5-58*k*) and (5-58*n*)

Effect of Bypass Ratio on Specific Thrust and Fuel Consumption

Data for several turbofan engines are listed in Table 5-2. The bypass ratio ranges from 0.76 for the engine in the smaller A-7D fighter attack airplane to 5 for engines in the commercial transports, to 8 for the C-5A/B heavy logistics military transport engine. The specific thrust and specific fuel consumption for the fighter are about twice their values for the three transport-type airplanes. Let us look at the interrelationship between the bypass ratio, specific thrust,

TABLE 5-2

Engine	Bypass ratio α	$F/\dot{m}_0$ {[N/(kg/sec)] [lbf/(lbm/sec)]}	S {[(mg/sec)/N] [(lbm/hr)/lbf]}	π_f	π_c	Aircraft
TF-39	8.0	251.8 (25.68)	8.87 (0.313)	1.45	22.0	C5A/B
JT9D	5.1	253.4 (25.84)	9.80 (0.346)	1.54	22.3	Boeing 747
CF6	4.32	255.6 (26.06)	9.86 (0.348)	1.71	30.2	DC-10
TF-41	0.76	498.0 (50.78)	17.8 (0.629)	2.45	21.0	A-7D

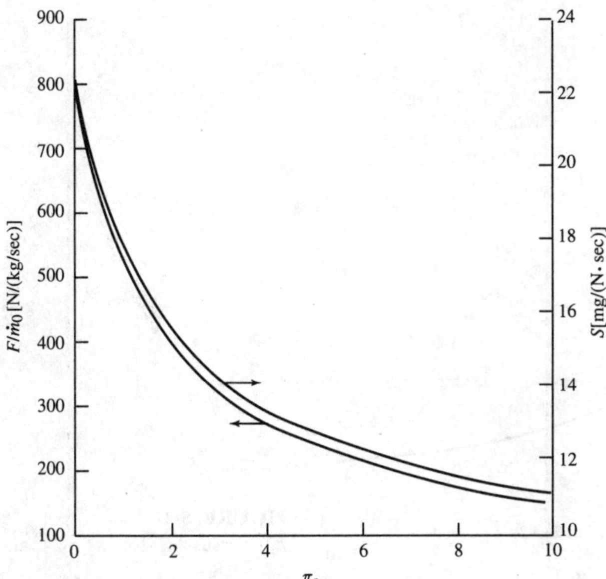

FIGURE 5-30
Performance at π_f^* versus α, for $\pi_c = 24$ and $M_0 = 0.8$.

and specific fuel consumption to help explain the trends in the values of these quantities, as exhibited by the table.

We can examine how these quantities interact for the ideal turbofan with optimum fan pressure ratio by plotting specific thrust and thrust specific fuel consumption versus bypass ratio. Such plots are given in Fig. 5-30 for $M_0 = 0.8$, $T_0 = 216.7$ K, $\tau_\lambda = 6.5$, $\pi_c = 24$, $h_{PR} = 42{,}800$ kJ/kg, $\gamma = 1.4$, and $c_p = 1.004$ kJ/(kg · K). The optimum fan pressure ratio which gives $V_9 = V_{19}$ is plotted versus the bypass ratio α in Fig. 5-31.

We can see, in Fig. 5-30, a sharp reduction in specific fuel consumption as α increases from zero. An equally marked, but unfavorable, decrease in thrust per unit mass flow occurs. A large fraction of the beneficial decrease in S is obtained by selecting an α of about 5, as was done for the engines in the DC-10 and 747 transports. At a bypass ratio of 8, corresponding to the C-5A engines, a further decrease in specific fuel consumption is realized. Since engine weight is a small fraction of the takeoff gross weight for these airplanes, it is of secondary importance compared to fuel weight and hence specific fuel consumption. Thus we find a relatively large bypass ratio for the engines in the transporters tabulated compared to the 0.76 value of the A-7D engine.

Example 5-6. The engine that we looked at in Sec. 5-9 is used again in this section for an example. The following values are held constant for all plots:

$T_0 = 216.7$ K $\quad \gamma = 1.4 \quad c_p = 1.004$ kJ/(kg K) $\quad h_{PR} = 42{,}800$ kJ/kg $\quad T_{t4} = 1670$ K

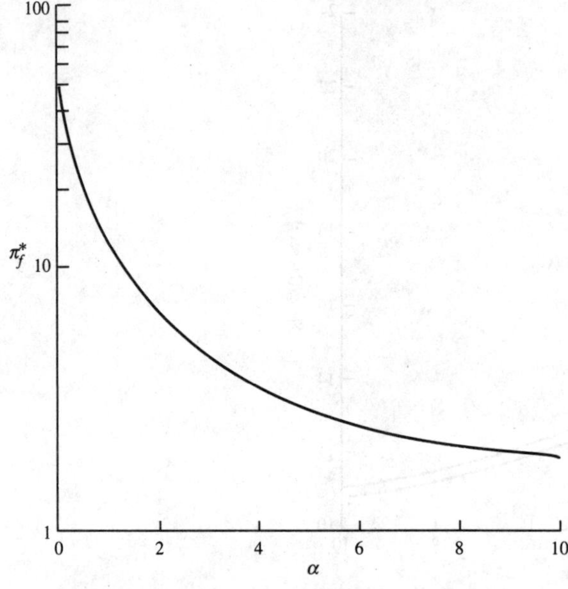

FIGURE 5-31
π_f^* versus α, for $\pi_c = 24$ and $M_0 = 0.8$.

The optimum fan pressure ratio is plotted versus the compressor pressure ratio in Fig. 5-32 and versus the bypass ratio in Fig. 5-33. From Fig. 5-32, we can see that the optimum fan pressure ratio increases with the compressor pressure ratio. Figure 5-33 shows that the optimum fan pressure ratio decreases with the bypass ratio.

Plots of specific thrust, thrust specific fuel consumption, propulsive efficiency, overall efficiency, and thrust ratio for the optimum-fan-pressure-ratio ideal turbofan engines are superimposed on Figs. 5-24 and 5-26 as dashed lines marked π_f^*. The plots for optimum fan pressure ratio are the loci of the optimums for specific thrust, thrust specific fuel consumption, propulsive efficiency, and overall efficiency. The thrust ratio of the optimum-fan-pressure-ratio ideal turbofan engines is equal to 1.

Comparison of Optimum Ideal Turbofans

A comparison of the two optimum ideal turbofan engines can be made by looking at contour plots of specific thrust $F/\dot{m}_0$ and thrust specific fuel consumption S versus fan pressure ratio π_f and bypass ratio α. For our example problem (Examples 5-4, 5-5, and 5-6), contours of constant specific thrust values and contours of constant thrust specific fuel consumption are plotted in Figs. 5-34*a* and 5-34*b*, respectively. Also plotted are the curves for π_f^* and α^* for each optimum engine. Figures 5-34*a* and 5-34*b* show that π_f^* is the fan pressure ratio giving maximum specific thrust and minimum thrust specific fuel consumption for a given bypass ratio. Figure 5-34*b* shows that α^* is the bypass ratio giving minimum thrust specific fuel consumption for a given fan pressure

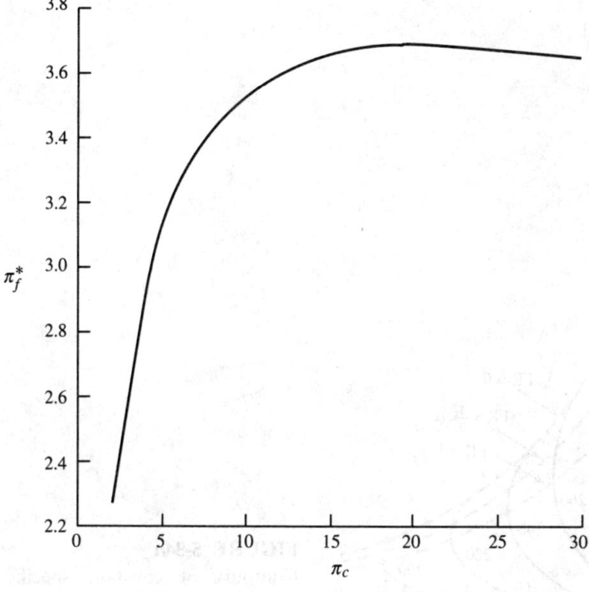

FIGURE 5-32
π_f^* versus π_c, for $M_0 = 0.9$ and $\alpha = 5$.

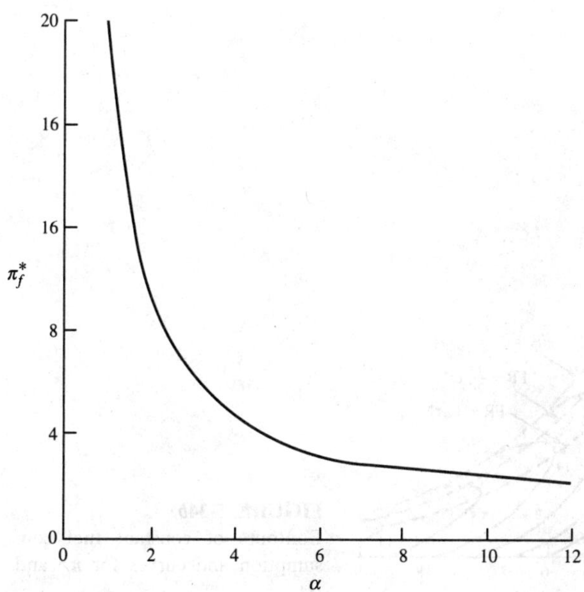

FIGURE 5-33
π_f^* versus α, for $M_0 = 0.9$ and $\pi_c = 24$.

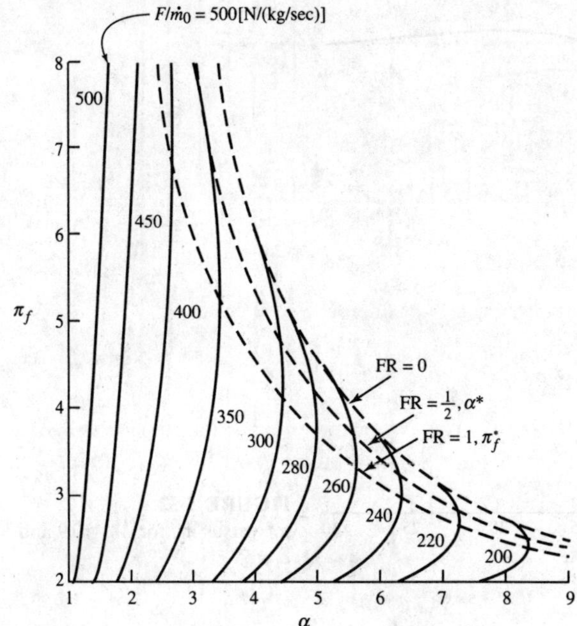

FIGURE 5-34*a*
Contours of constant specific thrust and curves for π_f^* and α^*.

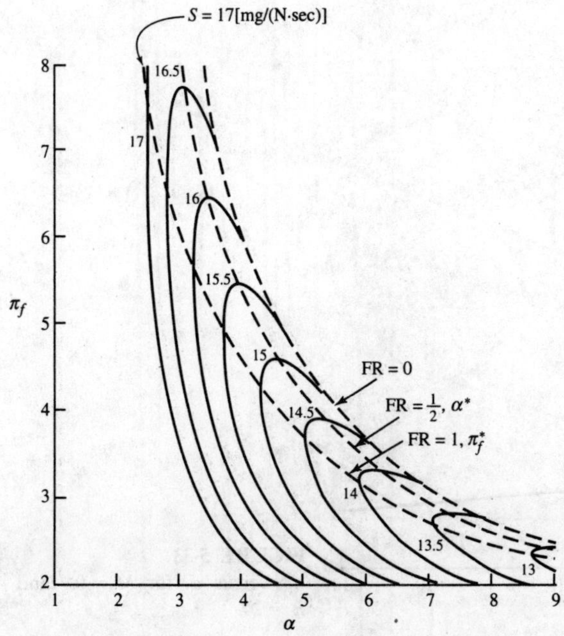

FIGURE 5-34*b*
Contours of constant fuel consumption and curves for π_f^* and α^*.

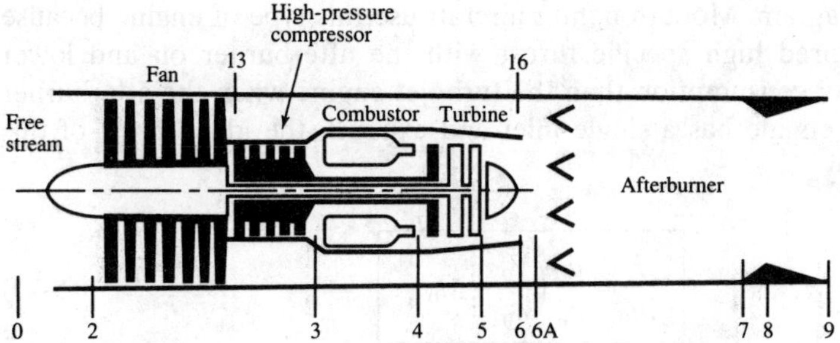

FIGURE 5-35
Station numbering for mixed-flow turbofan engine with afterburner.

ratio. Also shown in Fig. 5-34*b* are that the α^* curve is the locus of horizontal tangents to contours of constant S and the π_f^* curve is the locus of vertical tangents to contours of constant S.

5-12 IDEAL MIXED-FLOW TURBOFAN WITH AFTERBURNING

We consider the turbofan engine in which the core flow and bypass flow are mixed together before passing through an afterburner and nozzle. Figure 5-35 shows a view of such a turbofan engine, and Fig. 5-36 shows the ideal engine

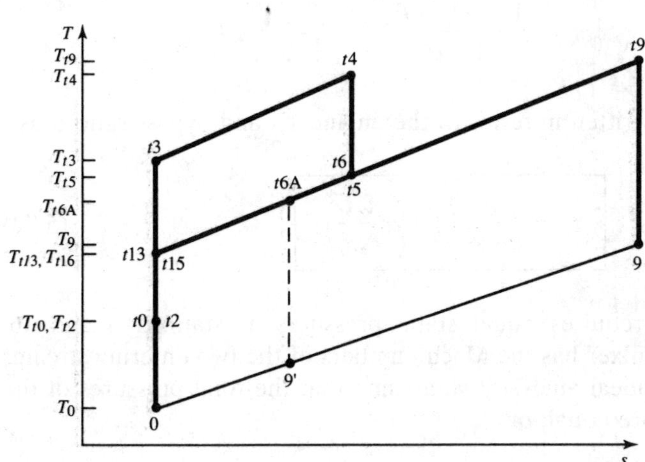

FIGURE 5-36
The *T-s* diagram for mixed-flow turbofan engine.

cycle on a T-s diagram. Modern fighter aircraft use this type of engine because it gives the required high specific thrust with the afterburner on and lower thrust specific fuel consumption than the turbojet engine when the afterburner is off. Since this engine has a single inlet and exhaust, the ideal thrust of this engine is given by

$$\boxed{\frac{F}{\dot{m}_0} = \frac{a_0}{g_c}\left(\frac{V_9}{a_0} - M_0\right)} \tag{5-70}$$

The analysis of this engine requires the definition of the total temperature and total pressure ratios across the mixer. We define

$$\boxed{\tau_M = \frac{T_{t6\text{A}}}{T_{t6}} \quad \text{and} \quad \pi_M = \frac{P_{t6\text{A}}}{P_{t6}}} \tag{5-71}$$

The flow in the bypass duct from station 13 to 16 is considered to be reversible and adiabatic. The bypass stream enters the mixer at station 16 with the same total properties as the fan discharge. An energy balance of the mixer gives

$$\dot{m}_6 c_p T_{t6} + \dot{m}_{16} c_p T_{t16} = \dot{m}_{6\text{A}} c_p T_{t6\text{A}}$$

or

$$T_{t6} + \alpha T_{t13} = (1 + \alpha) T_{t6\text{A}}$$

Since $T_{t6} = T_{t5}$, then

$$\tau_M = \frac{1 + \alpha T_{t13}/T_{t5}}{1 + \alpha}$$

This equation can be written in terms of the engine τ's and bypass ratio α as

$$\boxed{\tau_M = \frac{1}{1 + \alpha}\left(1 + \alpha \frac{\tau_r \tau_f}{\tau_\lambda \tau_t}\right)} \tag{5-72}$$

Fluid dynamics requires equal static pressures at stations 6 and 16. Normal design of the mixer has the Mach numbers of the two entering streams nearly equal. For this ideal analysis, we assume that the total pressures of the two entering streams are equal, or

$$\boxed{P_{t6} = P_{t16}} \tag{5-73}$$

The total pressure ratio of the mixer in this ideal turbofan engine is assumed to be unity, or

$$\boxed{\pi_M = \frac{P_{t6A}}{P_{t6}} = 1} \tag{5-74}$$

Equal total pressures at stations 6 and 16 require that the total pressure ratio of stations 3 to 13 equal that of stations 3 to 6. The total pressure ratio across the burner is unity, which allows us to write

$$\frac{P_{t3}}{P_{t13}} = \frac{P_{t3}/P_{t2}}{T_{t13}/P_{t2}} = \frac{\pi_c}{\pi_f} = \frac{P_{t3}}{P_{t6}} = \frac{P_{t4}}{P_{t5}} = \frac{1}{\pi_t}$$

We note, from Fig. 5-36, that stations 13, 16, 6, 6A, and 9 all have the same total pressure. When the afterburner is *on*, the isentropic process between states $t9$ and 9 represents the flow through the exhaust nozzle. When the afterburner is *off*, the flow enters the exhaust nozzle at state $t6A$ and exists at 9′.

Since the compression and expansion processes are isentropic, the above expression becomes

$$\boxed{\frac{1}{\tau_t} = \frac{\tau_c}{\tau_f}} \tag{5-75}$$

Cycle Analysis

The power balance between the turbine, fan, and compressor is developed in a previous section and gives the following relationship between the total temperature ratios across these components:

$$\boxed{\tau_t = 1 - \frac{\tau_r}{\tau_\lambda}[\tau_c - 1 + \alpha(\tau_f - 1)]} \tag{5-52}$$

For given values of τ_r, τ_λ, and τ_c, there is one value of τ_f for each value of α that satisfies both Eq. (5-75) and Eq. (5-52). From these two equations, we can obtain an expression for the bypass ratio α in terms of the other variables and an expression for the fan total temperature ratio τ_f. From Eqs. (5-75) and (5-52), we have

$$\frac{\tau_f}{\tau_c} = 1 - \frac{\tau_r}{\tau_\lambda}[\tau_c - 1 + \alpha(\tau_f - 1)]$$

or

$$\tau_f = \tau_c - \frac{\tau_r \tau_c}{\tau_\lambda}[\tau_c - 1 + \alpha(\tau_f - 1)] \tag{i}$$

Case 1. Fan pressure ratio π_f is specified. Equation (i), solved for the bypass ratio α, yields

$$\boxed{\alpha = \frac{\tau_\lambda(\tau_c - \tau_f)}{\tau_r\tau_c(\tau_f - 1)} - \frac{\tau_c - 1}{\tau_f - 1}} \tag{5-76}$$

Case 2. Bypass ratio α is specified. Equation (i), solved for τ_f, yields

$$\boxed{\tau_f = \frac{\tau_\lambda/\tau_r - (\tau_c - 1) + \alpha}{\tau_\lambda/(\tau_r\tau_c) + \alpha}} \tag{5-77}$$

The velocity ratio V_9/a_0 is given by

$$\left(\frac{V_9}{a_0}\right)^2 = \frac{T_9}{T_0} M_9^2$$

where

$$\boxed{M_9^2 = \frac{2}{\gamma - 1}(\tau_r\tau_f - 1)} \tag{5-78}$$

The temperature ratio T_9/T_0 depends on the operation of the afterburner. When the afterburner is *on*, then

$$\boxed{\frac{T_9}{T_0} = \frac{T_{t9}/T_0}{(P_{t9}/P_9)^{(\gamma-1)/\gamma}} = \frac{\tau_{\lambda AB}}{\tau_r\tau_f} \quad \text{afterburner } on} \tag{5-79}$$

When the afterburner is *off*, we have

$$\boxed{\frac{T_9}{T_0} = \frac{T_{t9}/T_0}{(P_{t9}/P_9)^{(\gamma-1)/\gamma}} = \frac{\tau_\lambda\tau_t\tau_M}{\tau_r\tau_f} \quad \text{afterburner } off} \tag{5-80}$$

The fuel/air ratio of the burner is given by Eq. (5-51). The fuel/air ratio of the afterburner is obtained by an energy balance between stations 6A and 7. We write

$$\dot{m}_{fAB}h_{PR} + \dot{m}_0 c_p T_{t6A} = \dot{m}_0 c_p T_{t7}$$

$$\boxed{f_{AB} = \frac{\dot{m}_{fAB}}{\dot{m}_0} = \frac{c_p T_0}{h_{PR}}(\tau_{\lambda AB} - \tau_\lambda\tau_t\tau_M)} \tag{5-81}$$

The *overall fuel/air ratio* f_O is defined as the total fuel flow rate divided by the total airflow rate, or

$$f_O \equiv \frac{\dot{m}_f + \dot{m}_{f\mathrm{AB}}}{\dot{m}_0} \tag{5-82}$$

For this engine, the overall fuel/air ratio can be written in terms of the fuel/air ratios of the burner and afterburner as

$$f_O = \frac{f}{1+\alpha} + f_{\mathrm{AB}} \tag{5-83}$$

The thrust specific fuel consumption S is then given by

$$S = \frac{f_O}{F/\dot{m}_0} \tag{5-84}$$

Equation (5-31*b*) gives the propulsive efficiency η_P for this cycle, and the thermal efficiency η_T is given by

$$\eta_T = \frac{\gamma - 1}{2}\frac{c_p T_0}{f_O h_{PR}}\left[\left(\frac{V_9}{a_0}\right)^2 - M_0^2\right] \tag{5-85}$$

Summary of Equations—Ideal Mixed-Flow Turbofan Engine

INPUTS: M_0, T_0(K, °R), γ, $c_p\left(\frac{\mathrm{kJ}}{\mathrm{kg\cdot K}}, \frac{\mathrm{Btu}}{\mathrm{lbm\cdot °R}}\right)$, $h_{PR}\left(\frac{\mathrm{kJ}}{\mathrm{kg}}, \frac{\mathrm{Btu}}{\mathrm{lbm}}\right)$,

T_{t4}(K, °R), T_{t7}(K, °R), π_c, and π_f or α

OUTPUTS: $\frac{F}{\dot{m}_0}\left(\frac{\mathrm{N}}{\mathrm{kg/sec}}, \frac{\mathrm{lbf}}{\mathrm{lbm/sec}}\right)$, f, f_{AB}, f_O, $S\left(\frac{\mathrm{mg/sec}}{\mathrm{N}}, \frac{\mathrm{lbm/hr}}{\mathrm{lbf}}\right)$,

η_T, η_P, η_O, and α or π_f

EQUATIONS:

$$R = \frac{\gamma - 1}{\gamma} c_p \tag{5-86a}$$

$$a_0 = \sqrt{\gamma R g_c T_0} \tag{5-86b}$$

$$\tau_r = 1 + \frac{\gamma - 1}{2} M_0^2 \tag{5-86c}$$

$$\tau_\lambda = \frac{T_{t4}}{T_0} \tag{5-86d}$$

$$\tau_c = (\pi_c)^{(\gamma-1)/\gamma} \tag{5-86e}$$

Case 1. π_f is specified:

$$\tau_f = (\pi_f)^{(\gamma-1)/\gamma} \tag{5-86f}$$

$$\alpha = \frac{\tau_\lambda(\tau_c - \tau_f)}{\tau_r \tau_c(\tau_f - 1)} - \frac{\tau_c - 1}{\tau_f - 1} \tag{5-86g}$$

If $\alpha < 0$, then $\alpha = 0$.

Case 2. α is specified:

$$\tau_f = \frac{\tau_\lambda/\tau_r - (\tau_c - 1) + \alpha}{\tau_\lambda/(\tau_r \tau_c) + \alpha} \tag{5-86h}$$

$$\pi_f = (\tau_f)^{\gamma/(\gamma-1)} \tag{5-86i}$$

We continue:

$$\tau_t = 1 - \frac{\tau_r}{\tau_\lambda}[\tau_c - 1 + \alpha(\tau_f - 1)] \tag{5-86j}$$

$$f = \frac{c_p T_0}{h_{PR}}(\tau_\lambda - \tau_r \tau_c) \tag{5-86k}$$

$$\tau_M = \frac{1}{1+\alpha}\left(1 + \alpha \frac{\tau_r \tau_f}{\tau_\lambda \tau_t}\right) \tag{5-86l}$$

If the afterburner is on, then

$$\tau_{\lambda \mathrm{AB}} = \frac{T_{t7}}{T_0} \tag{5-86m}$$

$$f_{\mathrm{AB}} = \frac{c_p T_0}{h_{PR}}(\tau_{\lambda \mathrm{AB}} - \tau_\lambda \tau_t \tau_M) \tag{5-86n}$$

$$\frac{T_9}{T_0} = \frac{\tau_{\lambda \mathrm{AB}}}{\tau_r \tau_f} \tag{5-86o}$$

If the afterburner is off, then

$$f_{\mathrm{AB}} = 0 \tag{5-86p}$$

$$\frac{T_9}{T_0} = \frac{\tau_\lambda \tau_t \tau_M}{\tau_r \tau_f} \tag{5-86q}$$

We continue:

$$M_9 = \sqrt{\frac{2}{\gamma - 1}(\tau_r \tau_f - 1)} \tag{5-86r}$$

$$\frac{V_9}{a_0} = \sqrt{\frac{T_9}{T_0}} M_9 \tag{5-86s}$$

$$f_O = \frac{f}{1+\alpha} + f_{\mathrm{AB}} \tag{5-86t}$$

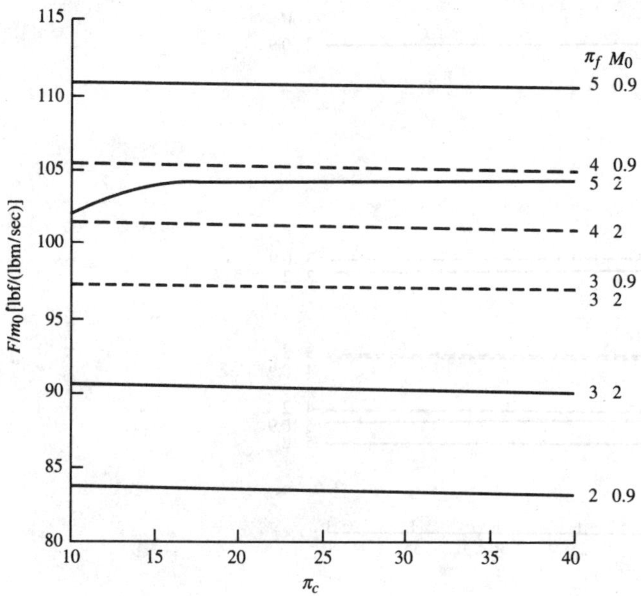

FIGURE 5-37*a*
Specific thrust of a mixed-flow turbofan engine (afterburner on).

$$\frac{F}{\dot{m}_0} = \frac{a_0}{g_c}\left(\frac{V_9}{a_0} - M_0\right) \tag{5-86u}$$

$$S = \frac{f_O}{F/\dot{m}_0} \tag{5-86v}$$

$$\eta_T = \frac{\gamma - 1}{2}\frac{c_p T_0}{f_O h_{PR}}\left[\left(\frac{V_9}{a_0}\right)^2 - M_0^2\right] \tag{5-86w}$$

$$\eta_P = \frac{2M_0}{V_9/a_0 + M_0} \tag{5-86x}$$

$$\eta_O = \eta_P \eta_T \tag{5-86y}$$

Example 5-7. The afterburning and nonafterburning performances of ideal mixed-flow turbofan engines are plotted in Figs. 5-37*a* through 5-38*b* versus compressor pressure ratio π_c for different values of the fan pressure ratio π_f at two flight Mach numbers M_0. Figures 5-39*a* and 5-39*b* plot the required bypass ratio α versus compressor pressure ratio π_c for the different values of fan pressure ratio π_f at flight Mach numbers of 0.9 and 2, respectively. Calculations were performed for the following input data:

$T_0 = 390°\text{R}$ $\quad\gamma = 1.4\quad$ $c_p = 0.24\ \text{Btu/(lbm}\cdot°\text{R)}$ $\quad h_{PR} = 18{,}400\ \text{Btu/lbm}$

$T_{t4} = 3000°\text{R}$ $\quad T_{t7} = 3600°\text{R}\quad$ $\pi_c = 10 \rightarrow 40$ $\quad\pi_f = 2 \rightarrow 5\quad$ $M_0 = 0.9, 2$

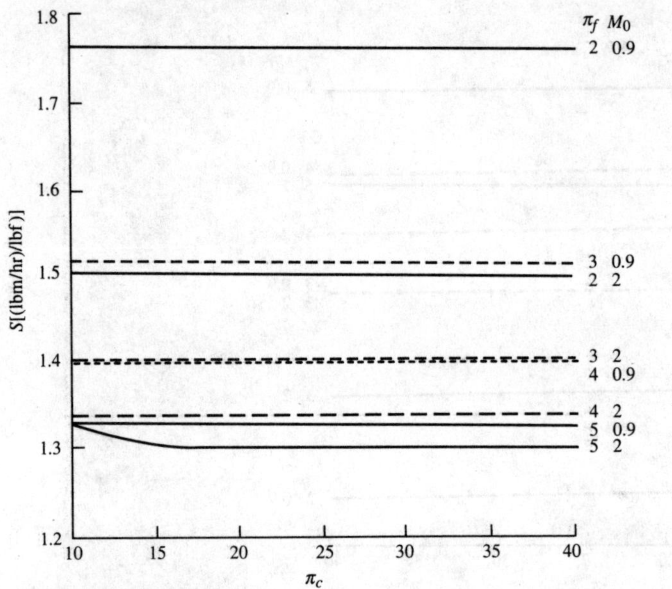

FIGURE 5-37*b*
Thrust specific fuel consumption of a mixed-flow turbofan engine (afterburner on).

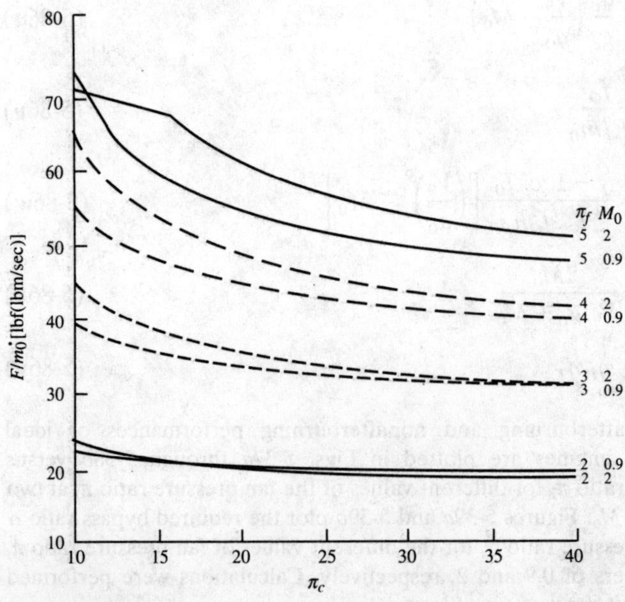

FIGURE 5-38*a*
Specific thrust of a mixed-flow turbofan engine (afterburner off).

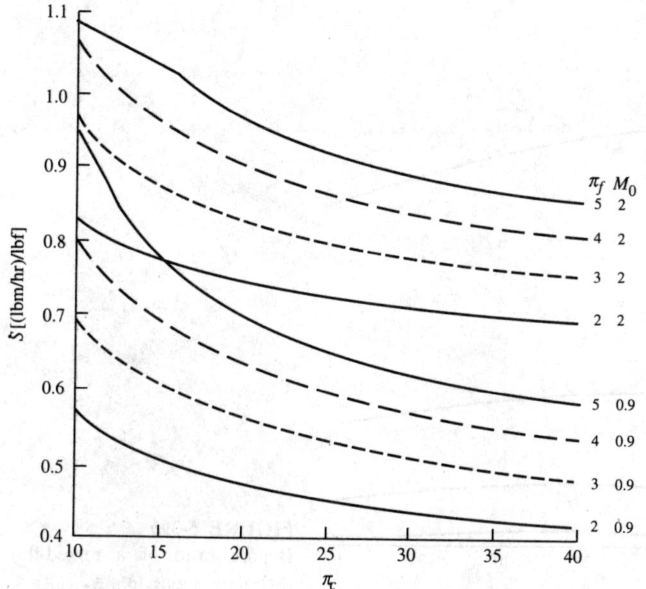

FIGURE 5-38*b*
Thrust specific fuel consumption of a mixed-flow turbofan engine (afterburner off).

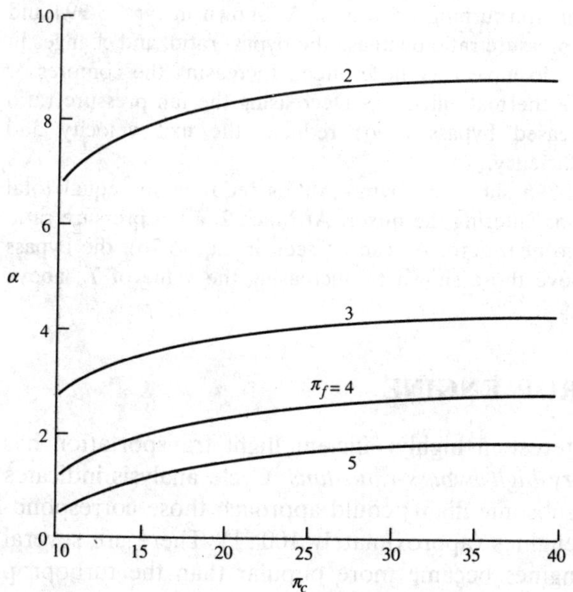

FIGURE 5-39*a*
Bypass ratio of a mixed-flow turbofan engine, $M_0 = 0.9$.

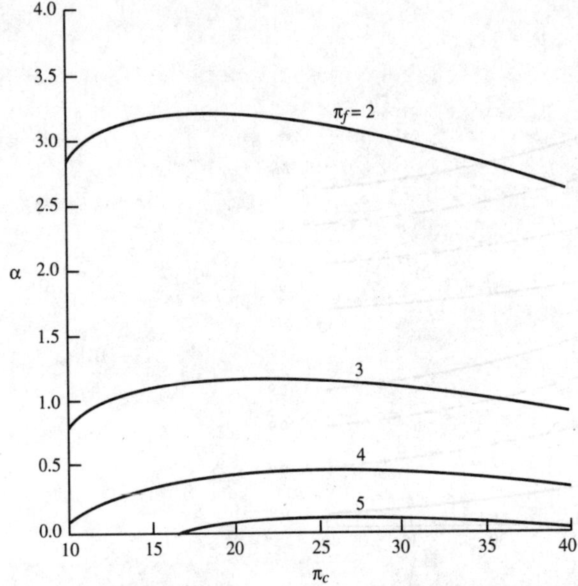

FIGURE 5-39*b*
Bypass ratio of a mixed-flow turbofan engine, $M_0 = 2$.

Figures 5-37*a* and 5-37*b* show that the performance of the afterburning engine is a function of only the fan pressure ratio and flight Mach number. The fuel/air ratio is proportional to the total temperature rise across the engine $(T_{t9} - T_{t0})$, essentially a constant. The specific thrust increases with the nozzle pressure ratio $(P_{t9}/P_9 = \pi_r \pi_f)$. As a result, increasing the fan pressure ratio increases the specific thrust and decreases the fuel consumption.

Figures 5-38*a* and 5-38*b* show the performance trends of the mixed-flow turbofan engine during nonafterburning operation. As shown in Figs. 5-39*a* and 5-39*b,* increases in the fan pressure ratio decrease the bypass ratio, and changes in the compressor pressure ratio have very little effect. Increasing the compressor pressure ratio increases the thermal efficiency. Decreasing the fan pressure ratio (with corresponding increased bypass ratio) reduces the exit velocity and increases the propulsive efficiency.

Figures 5-39*a* and 5-39*b* show the bypass ratios required for equal total pressures of the two streams entering the mixer. At Mach 2, a fan pressure ratio of 5 requires a bypass ratio near zero. As can be seen in Eq. (5-76), the bypass ratio can be increased above those shown by increasing the value of T_{t4} above 3000°R.

5-13 IDEAL TURBOPROP ENGINE

In recent years, renewed interest in highly efficient flight transportation has spurred investigation into *very-high-bypass-ratio fans.* Cycle analysis indicates that such bypass ratios (for subsonic flight) could approach those corresponding to the "old" turboprop engines (approximately 100 : 1). There are several reasons why the turbofan engines became more popular than the turboprop engines, and it is wise to review such reasons so that we can comprehend why similar concepts are again gaining in popularity.

A major reason for the success of the turbofan was its high (subsonic) Mach number capability. In a turboprop, the propeller tip Mach numbers became very large above approximately $M = 0.7$, and the resultant loss in propeller efficiency limits the turboprop use to Mach numbers less than 0.7. With a turbofan, the onset of high-Mach-number effects is reduced by the diffusion within the duct. In addition, the individual blade loading can be much reduced by utilizing many blades. A second important benefit of conventional turbofans is that they require no gearbox to reduce the tip speeds of their relatively short blades. (Note, of course, that usually a turbofan engine has multiple spools.) Turboprop gearboxes have, to date, been heavy and subject to reliability problems. Finally, the high tip speed of the turboprops led to high noise levels, both in the airport vicinity and within the aircraft at flight speeds.

Recent studies of the very-high-bypass-ratio engines have, however, suggested some compromise designs that show high promise. Thus if a bypass ratio of, say, 25 is selected, the corresponding cowl could have identified with it both weight penalties and drag penalties that do not compensate for the benefits of the inlet diffusion and of the reduction in tip losses. By considering this "in between" bypass ratio, the required shaft speed reduction will be reduced with the result that a lighter and simpler gearbox may be utilized. The effects of tip losses and noise production may be somewhat curtailed by utilizing many (about eight) of the smaller blades and by sweeping the blades to reduce the relative Mach numbers. An additional benefit is available in that the blades may be made variable-pitch which will allow high propeller efficiencies to be maintained over a wide operating range. Recall [Eq. (1-16)] that the propulsive efficiency of a single-exhaust engine is $\eta_P = 2V_0/(V_j + V_0)$, where V_0 = flight speed and V_j = jet speed.

This expression is appropriate for a propeller also, and it serves to emphasize that we want a large propeller [to reduce V_j for a given thrust $F = \dot{m}_0(V_j - V_0)/g_c$] if the propulsive efficiency is to be high. The *propulsive efficiency* represents the ideal limit of the propeller efficiency and is defined as

$$\eta_{\text{prop}} = \frac{\text{power to vehicle}}{\text{power to propeller}} = \frac{F_{\text{prop}} V_0}{\dot{W}_{\text{prop}}} \tag{5-87}$$

Thus

$$\eta_{\text{prop}} = \frac{F_{\text{prop}} V_0}{\dot{W}_{\text{prop}}} = \frac{\dot{m}_{\text{prop}}(V_j - V_0)}{\frac{1}{2}\dot{m}_{\text{prop}}(V_j^2 - V_0^2)} \frac{\frac{1}{2}\dot{m}_{\text{prop}}(V_j^2 - V_0^2)}{\dot{W}_{\text{prop}}} \equiv \eta_P \eta_L \tag{5-88}$$

where $\dot{W}_{\text{prop}}$ = propeller power in, η_P is the propulsive efficiency and

$$\eta_L = \frac{\frac{1}{2}\dot{m}_{\text{prop}}(V_j^2 - V_0^2)}{\dot{W}_{\text{prop}}} \tag{5-89}$$

represents the power output of the propeller to the stream divided by the power input to the propeller.

Thus we expect the propeller efficiency to increase with propeller size simply because the ideal propeller efficiency (i.e., the propulsive efficiency) increases. This, of course, relates the propeller efficiency and bypass ratio. The propeller size will, in practice, be limited by the onset of tip Mach number losses, etc., which would be reflected in a reduced η_L.

Cycle Analysis

It is appropriate in analyzing the turboprop class of engine to consider the work supplied to the vehicle, rather than the thrust. To facilitate this, we introduce the dimensionless *work output coefficient C*, defined as

$$C = \frac{\text{power interaction/mass flow of air through engine core}}{h_0} \tag{5-90}$$

For the thrust of the core stream, we define its work output coefficient as

$$C_C = \frac{F_C V_0}{\dot{m}_0 c_p T_0} \tag{5-91}$$

Thus the work output coefficient for the total turboprop engine is

$$C_{\text{tot}} = C_{\text{prop}} + C_C \tag{5-92}$$

and the corresponding thrust is

$$F = F_{\text{prop}} + F_C = \frac{C_{\text{tot}}\dot{m}_0 c_p T_0}{V_0} \tag{5-93}$$

It is usual, with turboprop engines, to have the core stream exit nozzles unchoked, so the pressure imbalance term will not contribute in the expression for the thrust. We consider the numbering stations indicated in Figs.

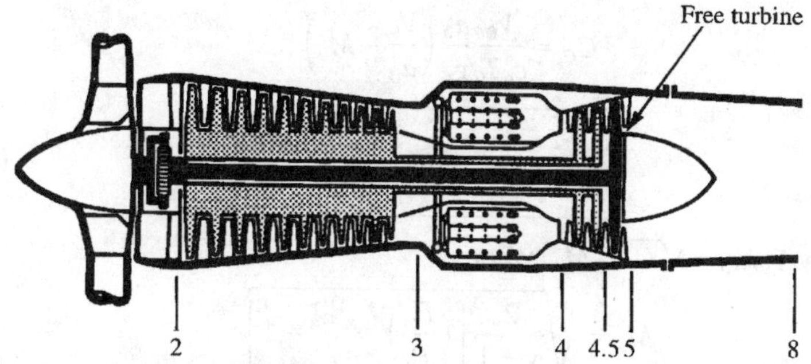

FIGURE 5-40a
Station numbering of turboprop engine. (*Courtesy of Pratt & Whitney.*)

5-40*a* and 5-40*b*, and we proceed with the analysis in much the same way as with the previously considered engine types.

For a turboprop engine, we have two design variables—the compressor pressure ratio and the low-pressure (free or power) turbine temperature ratio. We want to develop the cycle equations in terms of the pressure and temperature ratios across both the high-pressure turbine (drives the compressor) and the low-pressure turbine. With station number 4.5 between the high- and low-pressure turbines, we define

$$\boxed{\pi_{tH} = \frac{P_{t4.5}}{P_{t4}} \qquad \tau_{tH} = \frac{T_{t4.5}}{T_{t4}} \qquad \pi_{tL} = \frac{T_{t5}}{T_{t4.5}} \qquad \tau_{tL} = \frac{T_{t5}}{T_{t4.5}}} \tag{5-94}$$

Step 1. We have for the engine core

$$\frac{F_C}{\dot{m}_0} = \frac{a_0}{g_c}\left(\frac{V_9}{a_0} - M_0\right)$$

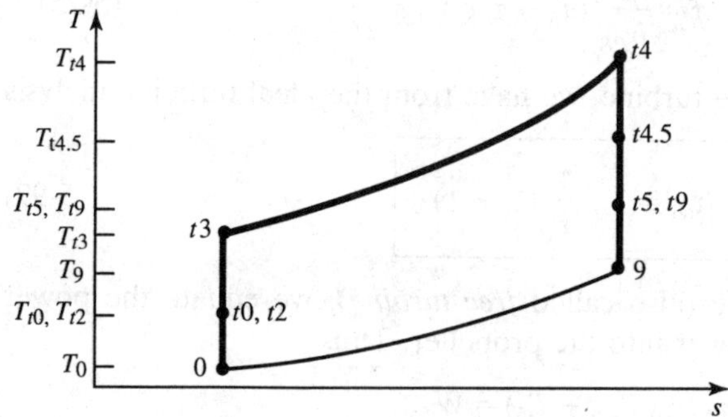

FIGURE 5-40b
The *T-s* diagram of ideal turboprop engine.

Then
$$C_C = \frac{V_0}{c_p T_0} \frac{a_0}{g_c} \left(\frac{V_9}{a_0} - M_0 \right)$$

Thus
$$\boxed{C_C = (\gamma - 1) M_0 \left(\frac{V_9}{a_0} - M_0 \right)} \tag{5-95}$$

Step 2. Now $V_9/a_0 = \sqrt{T_9/T_0} M_9$, where

$$M_9 = \sqrt{\frac{2}{\gamma - 1} \left[\left(\frac{P_{t9}}{P_9} \right)^{(\gamma-1)/\gamma} - 1 \right]} \tag{5-96}$$

Step 3.
$$\frac{P_{t9}}{P_9} = \frac{P_0}{P_9} \pi_r \pi_d \pi_c \pi_b \pi_{tH} \pi_{tL} \pi_n = \pi_r \pi_c \pi_{tH} \pi_{tL}$$

$$\boxed{M_9 = \sqrt{\frac{2}{\gamma - 1} (\tau_r \tau_c \tau_{tH} \tau_{tL} - 1)}} \tag{5-97}$$

Step 4.
$$\frac{T_9}{T_0} = \frac{T_{t9}/T_0}{T_{t9}/T_9} = \frac{T_{t9}/T_0}{(P_{t9}/P_9)^{(\gamma-1)/\gamma}}$$

where
$$\frac{T_{t9}}{T_0} = \tau_\lambda \tau_{tH} \tau_{tL} \tau_n = \tau_\lambda \tau_{tH} \tau_{tL}$$

and
$$\left(\frac{P_{t9}}{P_9} \right)^{(\gamma-1)/\gamma} = (\pi_r \pi_c \pi_{tH} \pi_{tL})^{(\gamma-1)/\gamma} = \tau_r \tau_c \tau_{tH} \tau_{tL}$$

Thus
$$\boxed{\frac{T_9}{T_0} = \frac{\tau_\lambda}{\tau_r \tau_c}} \tag{5-98}$$

Step 5. From the energy balance of the ideal turbojet's burner, we have

$$f = \frac{c_p T_0}{h_{PR}} (\tau_\lambda - \tau_r \tau_c) \tag{5-25}$$

Step 6. For the high-pressure turbine, we have from the ideal turbojet analysis

$$\boxed{\tau_{tH} = 1 - \frac{\tau_r}{\tau_\lambda} (\tau_c - 1)} \tag{5-99}$$

For the low-pressure turbine (also called *free turbine*), we equate the power out of this turbine to the power into the propeller. Thus

$$\dot{m}_{4.5} c_p (T_{t4.5} - T_{t5}) = \dot{W}_{\text{prop}}$$

or
$$\boxed{C_{\text{prop}} = \frac{\eta_{\text{prop}} \dot{W}_{\text{prop}}}{\dot{m}_0 c_p T_0} = \eta_{\text{prop}} \tau_\lambda \tau_{tH} (1 - \tau_{tL})} \tag{5-100}$$

Step 7. For the turboprop engine, we consider both the specific power and the specific thrust:

$$\frac{\dot{W}}{\dot{m}_0} = C_{\text{tot}} c_p T_0 \tag{5-101a}$$

$$\frac{F}{\dot{m}_0} = \frac{C_{\text{tot}} c_p T_0}{V_0} \tag{5-101b}$$

Step 8.

$$S = \frac{f}{F/\dot{m}_0}$$

We should note here, also, that for propeller aircraft it is more usual to refer to the power specific fuel consumption in terms of S_P, where S_P is defined by

$$S_P = \frac{\dot{m}_f}{\dot{W}} = \frac{f}{\dot{W}/\dot{m}_0}$$

Thus

$$\boxed{S_P = \frac{f}{C_{\text{tot}} c_p T_0}} \tag{5-102}$$

Step 9. The thermal efficiency of the engine cycle is the same as that for the turbojet or turboprop engines. Thus

$$\eta_T = 1 - \frac{1}{\tau_r \tau_c}$$

From Eq. (1-17), the overall efficiency can be simply expressed as

$$\eta_O = \frac{\dot{W}}{\dot{m}_f h_{PR}}$$

Then with Eq. (5-25) for the fuel/air ratio and the definition of C_{tot}, the overall efficiency can be simply expressed as

$$\boxed{\eta_O = \frac{C_{\text{tot}}}{\tau_\lambda - \tau_r \tau_c}} \tag{5-103}$$

Summary of Equations—Ideal Turboprop

INPUTS: M_0, T_0(K, °R), γ, $c_p\left(\frac{\text{kJ}}{\text{kg}\cdot\text{K}}, \frac{\text{Btu}}{\text{lbm}\cdot{}^\circ\text{R}}\right)$, $h_{PR}\left(\frac{\text{kJ}}{\text{kg}}, \frac{\text{Btu}}{\text{lbm}}\right)$, T_{t4}(K, °R), π_c, π_t, η_{prop}

OUTPUTS: $\frac{F}{\dot{m}_0}\left(\frac{\text{N}}{\text{kg/sec}}, \frac{\text{lbf}}{\text{lbm/sec}}\right)$, f, $S\left(\frac{\text{mg/sec}}{\text{N}}, \frac{\text{lbm/hr}}{\text{lbf}}\right)$, η_T, η_P, η_O, C_c, C_{prop}, C_{tot}

EQUATIONS:

$$R = \frac{\gamma - 1}{\gamma} c_p \tag{5-104a}$$

$$a_0 = \sqrt{\gamma R g_c T_0} \tag{5-104b}$$

$$\tau_r = 1 + \frac{\gamma - 1}{2} M_0^2 \tag{5-104c}$$

$$\tau_\lambda = \frac{T_{t4}}{T_0} \tag{5-104d}$$

$$\tau_c = (\pi_c)^{(\gamma-1)/\gamma} \tag{5-104e}$$

$$f = \frac{c_p T_0}{h_{PR}}(\tau_\lambda - \tau_r \tau_c) \tag{5-104f}$$

$$\tau_{tH} = 1 - \frac{\tau_r}{\tau_\lambda}(\tau_c - 1) \tag{5-104g}$$

$$\tau_{tL} = \frac{\tau_t}{\tau_{tH}} \tag{5-104h}$$

$$\frac{V_9}{a_0} = \sqrt{\frac{2}{\gamma - 1}\left(\tau_\lambda \tau_t - \frac{\tau_\lambda}{\tau_r \tau_c}\right)} \tag{5-104i}$$

$$C_C = (\gamma - 1) M_0 \left(\frac{V_9}{a_0} - M_0\right) \tag{5-104j}$$

$$C_{\text{prop}} = \eta_{\text{prop}} \tau_\lambda \tau_{tH} (1 - \tau_{tL}) \tag{5-104k}$$

$$C_{\text{tot}} = C_{\text{prop}} + C_C \tag{5-104l}$$

$$\frac{F}{\dot{m}_0} = \frac{C_{\text{tot}} c_p T_0}{M_0 a_0} \tag{5-104m}$$

$$S = \frac{f}{F/\dot{m}_0} \tag{5-104n}$$

$$\eta_T = 1 - \frac{1}{\tau_r \tau_c} \tag{5-104o}$$

$$\eta_O = \frac{C_{\text{tot}}}{\tau_\lambda - \tau_r \tau_c} \tag{5-104p}$$

$$\eta_P = \frac{\eta_O}{\eta_T} \tag{5-104q}$$

Selection of Optimal Turbine Temperature Ratio

Turbopropeller or prop-fan engines will be designed primarily to be low-specific-fuel-consumption engines. Thus we select the turbine temperature ratio τ_t to make S a minimum. Equivalently, we locate the maximum of C_{tot},

$$\frac{\partial S}{\partial \tau_t} = 0 \quad \Rightarrow \quad \frac{\partial C_{\text{tot}}}{\partial \tau_t} = 0$$

where $C_{\text{tot}} = C_{\text{prop}} + C_C = \eta_{\text{prop}} \tau_\lambda (\tau_{tH} - \tau_t) + (\gamma - 1) M_0 \left(\dfrac{V_9}{a_0} - M_0\right)$

Thus
$$\frac{\partial C_{\text{tot}}}{\partial \tau_t} = -\eta_{\text{prop}} \tau_\lambda + (\gamma - 1) M_0 \frac{\partial}{\partial \tau_t}\left(\frac{V_9}{a_0}\right) = 0 \tag{i}$$

Noting $$\frac{\partial}{\partial \tau_t}\left(\frac{V_9}{a_0}\right)=\frac{1}{2V_9/a_0}\frac{\partial}{\partial \tau_t}\left[\left(\frac{V_9}{a_0}\right)^2\right]=\frac{1}{2V_9/a_0}\frac{2\tau_\lambda}{\gamma-1}$$

we see that Eq. (i) becomes

$$\frac{\partial C_{\text{tot}}}{\partial \tau_t}=-\eta_{\text{prop}}\tau_\lambda+\frac{M_0\tau_\lambda}{(V_9/a_0)_{\text{opt}}}=0$$

Thus $$\left(\frac{V_9}{a_0}\right)_{\text{opt}}=\frac{M_0}{\eta_{\text{prop}}} \quad \text{or} \quad \boxed{(V_9)_{\text{opt}}=\frac{V_0}{\eta_{\text{prop}}}} \tag{5-105}$$

Hence for a 100 percent efficient propeller, the optimum exit velocity for the core of the turboprop is equal to the flight velocity, and the propeller produces all the engine thrust.

The optimum turbine temperature ratio is obtained by equating Eq. (5-104*i*) to Eq. (5-105), giving

$$\frac{2}{\gamma-1}\frac{\tau_\lambda}{\tau_r\tau_c}(\tau_r\tau_c\tau_t^*-1)=\frac{M_0^2}{\eta_{\text{prop}}^2}$$

Thus $$\boxed{\tau_t^*=\frac{\tau_\lambda}{\tau_r\tau_c}+\frac{[(\gamma-1)/2]M_0^2}{\tau_\lambda\eta_{\text{prop}}^2}} \tag{5-106}$$

Summary of Equations—Turboprop (Optimal Work Distribution)

INPUTS: M_0, T_0(K, °R), γ, $c_p\left(\frac{\text{kJ}}{\text{kg}\cdot\text{K}},\frac{\text{Btu}}{\text{lbm}\cdot{}^\circ\text{R}}\right)$, $h_{PR}\left(\frac{\text{kJ}}{\text{kg}},\frac{\text{Btu}}{\text{lbm}}\right)$, T_{t4}(K, °R), π_c, η_{prop}

OUTPUTS: $\frac{F}{\dot{m}_0}\left(\frac{\text{N}}{\text{kg/sec}},\frac{\text{lbf}}{\text{lbm/sec}}\right)$, f, $S\left(\frac{\text{mg/sec}}{\text{N}},\frac{\text{lbm/hr}}{\text{lbf}}\right)$, η_T, η_P, η_O, C_C, C_{prop}, C_{tot}, τ_t^*

EQUATIONS: Equations (5-104*a*) through (5-104*g*), (5-106), and (5-104*h*) through (5-104*q*)

Example 5-8. With improved propeller designs, the aircraft industry is considering a turboprop business aircraft for flight at Mach 0.8. Consider an engine suitable for use in an 8- to 10-passenger business jet. The assumed altitude, gas properties, propeller efficiency, etc., are given below. The relatively high propeller efficiency has been taken from estimated propeller performance when modern transonic techniques, such as sweeping the blades, are used in the blade design. (For an example of a possible design, see Ref. 28.)

Altitude = 7.6 km (25,000 ft) $\quad \eta_{\text{prop}}=0.83 \quad T_0=240$ K $\quad T_{t4}=1370$ K

$M_0=0.8 \quad h_{PR}=42{,}800$ kJ/kg $\quad \gamma=1.4 \quad c_p=1.004$ kJ/(kg K)

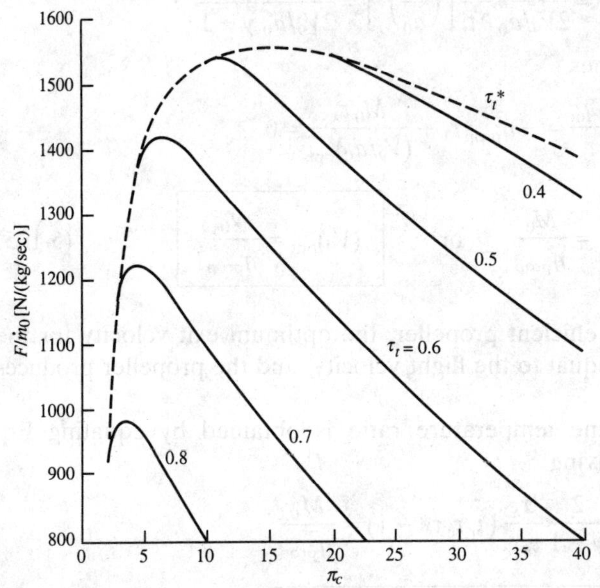

FIGURE 5-41*a*
Ideal turboprop performance versus π_c: specific thrust.

With these parameters, a range of compressor pressure ratios for both specific values and the optimum value of the turbine temperature ratios were considered. The specific thrust, thrust specific fuel consumption, cycle efficiencies, work output coefficients, and optimum turbine temperature ratio are shown in Figs. 5-41*a* through 5-41*e*. The results corresponding to the optimum turbine

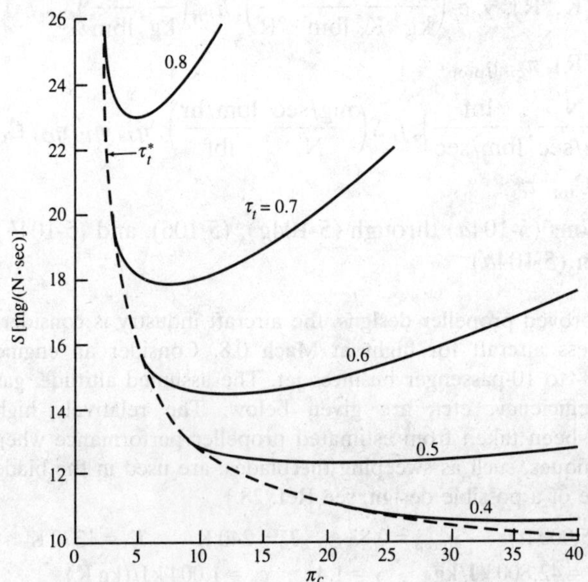

FIGURE 5-41*b*
Ideal turboprop performance versus π_c: thrust specific fuel consumption.

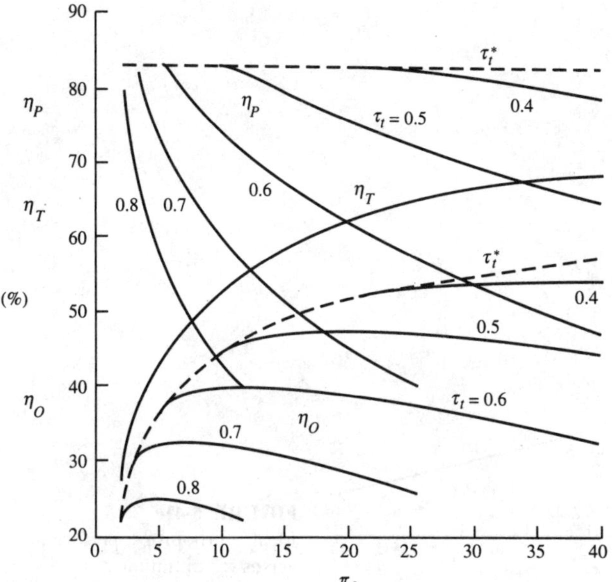

FIGURE 5-41c
Ideal turboprop performance versus π_c: efficiencies.

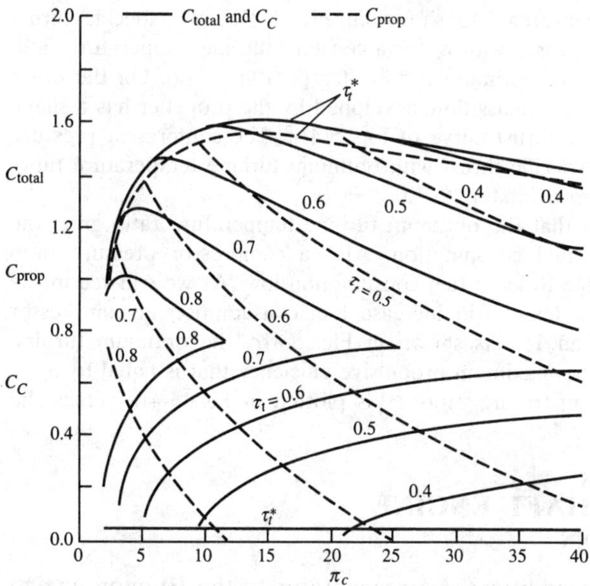

FIGURE 5-41d
Ideal turboprop performance versus π_c: work coefficients.

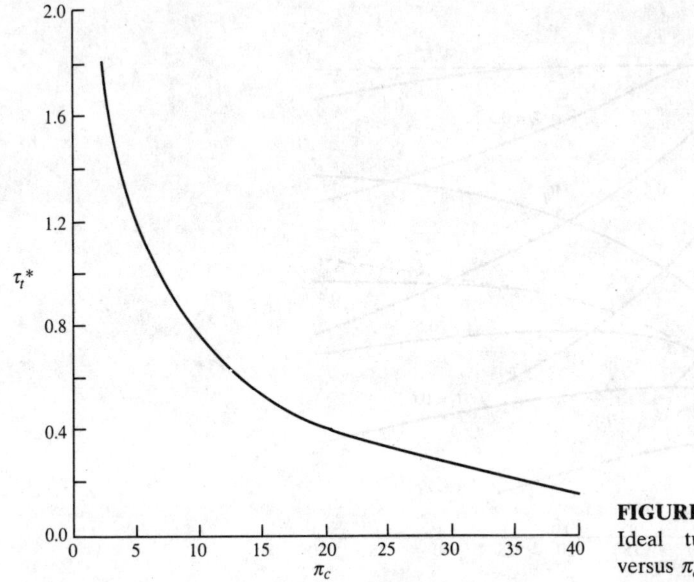

FIGURE 5-41*e*
Ideal turboprop performance versus π_c: optimum τ_t.

temperature ratio τ_t^* are drawn with dashed curves in Figs. 5-41*a* through 5-41*e*. Note the high value for specific thrust $F/\dot{m}_0$ compared to turbojets or turbofans. This is a little misleading since, here, $\dot{m}_0$ is mass flow through the core only and not through the propeller area. As shown in Fig. 5-41*d*, the specific thrust developed by the core increases with π_c for a constant turbine temperature ratio and remains constant for an optimum turbine temperature ratio. On the other hand, the thrust per unit core mass flow developed by the propeller has a shape similar to the total specific thrust curve of Fig. 5-41*a*. The compressor pressure ratio for maximum total specific thrust with optimum turbine temperature ratio, therefore, corresponds approximately to 15.

Figure 5-41*b* shows that the optimum turbine temperature ratio gives the minimum thrust specific fuel consumption. Also a compressor pressure ratio greater than 15 is desirable to keep fuel consumption low. As we will see in the next chapters, component losses will increase fuel consumption at compressor pressure ratios higher than 15. As shown in Fig. 5-41*c*, the optimum turbine temperature ratio gives the maximum propulsive efficiency that is equal to η_{prop}. The optimum turbine temperature ratio τ_t^* is plotted in Fig. 5-41*e* versus the compressor pressure ratio.

5-14 IDEAL TURBOSHAFT ENGINE WITH REGENERATION

In Chap. 4, we saw that the addition of a regenerator to the Brayton engine cycle increased the cycle's thermal efficiency when the compressor exit temperature (station 3) was below the turbine exit temperature (station 5).

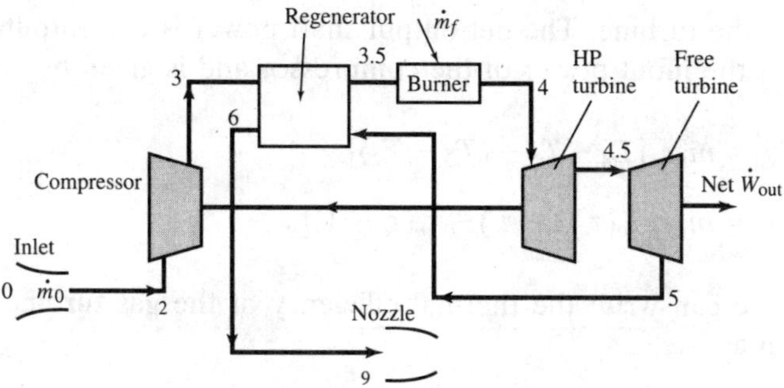

FIGURE 5-42
Station numbering of turboshaft engine with regeneration.

For analysis, we consider an ideal turboshaft engine with regeneration, as shown in Figs. 5-42 and 5-43. The low-temperature/high-pressure gas enters the regenerator at station 3 and departs at station 3.5. The high-temperature/low-pressure gas enters the regenerator at station 5 and departs at station 6.

The thermal energy added in the main combustor is given by

$$\dot{Q}_{in} = \dot{m}_0 c_p (T_{t4} - T_{t3.5})$$

By using $T_{t3.5} = T_{t5}$ (ideal regenerator) and τ's, the above equation can be rewritten as

$$\dot{Q}_{in} = \dot{m}_0 c_p (T_{t4} - T_{t5}) = \dot{m}_0 c_p T_0 \tau_\lambda (1 - \tau_t) \tag{i}$$

Thus the thermal energy added in the main burner is equal to the power

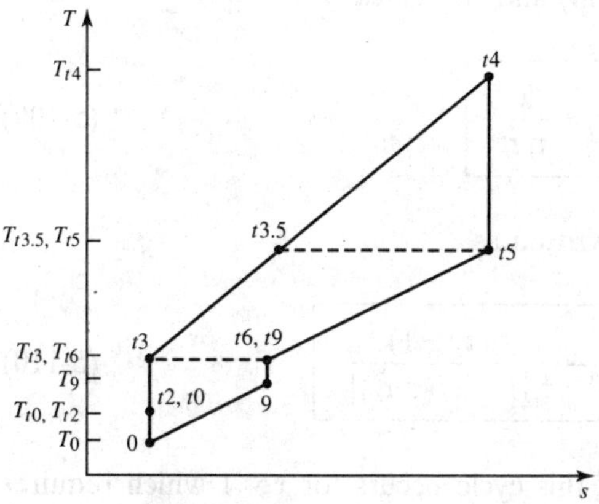

FIGURE 5-43
The T-s diagram of ideal turboshaft engine with regeneration.

removed from the gas in the turbine. The net output shaft power is the output power of the turbine less the input power of the compressor and is given by

$$\begin{aligned} \dot{W}_{out} &= \dot{m}_0 c_p [T_{t4} - T_{t5} - (T_{t3} - T_{t2})] \\ &= \dot{m}_0 c_p T_0 [\tau_\lambda (1 - \tau_t) - \tau_r (\tau_c - 1)] \end{aligned} \tag{ii}$$

From Eqs. (i) and (ii), we can write the thermal efficiency of the gas turbine engine with regeneration as

$$(\eta_T)_{regen} = \frac{\dot{W}_{out}}{\dot{Q}_{in}} = 1 - \frac{\tau_r(\tau_c - 1)}{\tau_\lambda(1 - \tau_t)} \tag{5-107}$$

For the isentropic compression process 0 to $t3$, we note that

$$\left(\frac{P_{t3}}{P_0}\right)^{(\gamma-1)/\gamma} = \tau_r \tau_c \tag{iii}$$

Also for the isentropic expansion processes $t4$ to $t5$ and $t6$ to 9, we can write

$$\left(\frac{P_{t4}}{P_9}\right)^{(\gamma-1)/\gamma} = \left(\frac{P_{t4}}{P_{t5}}\right)^{(\gamma-1)/\gamma} \left(\frac{P_{t6}}{P_9}\right)^{(\gamma-1)/\gamma} = \frac{1}{\tau_t} \frac{T_{t6}}{T_9} \tag{iv}$$

For convenience, we define

$$\boxed{x \equiv \frac{T_{t6}}{T_9}} \tag{5-108}$$

For the ideal cycle, $P_{t4} = P_{t3}$ and $P_9 = P_0$. Combining these ideal assumptions with the above definition and Eqs. (iii) and (iv) gives

$$\boxed{\tau_t = \frac{x}{\tau_r \tau_c}} \tag{5-109}$$

The thermal efficiency can now be written as

$$\boxed{(\eta_T)_{regen} = 1 - \frac{\tau_r(\tau_c - 1)}{\tau_\lambda[1 - x/(\tau_r \tau_c)]}} \tag{5-110}$$

The maximum thermal efficiency of this cycle occurs for $x = 1$ which requires an infinite exit area. A more realistic value for x would be about 1.02 (M_9 of about 0.3). Note that for a given T_{t4} and T_0, the compressor temperature ratio τ_c can be any value between unity and its maximum value, given by

$$\tau_{c\,\max} = \frac{\tau_\lambda \tau_t}{\tau_r}$$

or

$$\boxed{\tau_{c\,\max} = \frac{\sqrt{x\tau_\lambda}}{\tau_r}} \tag{5-111}$$

Cycle Analysis

It is appropriate in analyzing the turboshaft class of engine to consider the shaft work, rather than the thrust. For the output shaft power, we define its *work output coefficient*

$$\boxed{C_{\text{shaft}} = \frac{\dot{W}_{\text{shaft}}/\dot{m}_0}{h_0}} \tag{5-112}$$

Using Eq. (ii) for the shaft power, we see that this coefficient becomes

$$C_{\text{shaft}} = \tau_\lambda(1 - \tau_t) - \tau_r(\tau_c - 1)$$

The turbine temperature ratio τ_t can be replaced in the above equation by using Eq. (5-109), to give

$$\boxed{C_{\text{shaft}} = \tau_\lambda\left(1 - \frac{x}{\tau_r \tau_c}\right) - \tau_r(\tau_c - 1)} \tag{5-113}$$

The value of compressor pressure ratio π_c given by Eq. (5-111) also corresponds to that giving the maximum of Eq. (5-113). The proof is left as an exercise for the reader.

From the energy balance of the ideal burner [Eq. (i)], we have the fuel/air ratio

$$\boxed{f = \frac{c_P T_0 \tau_\lambda}{h_{PR}}\left(1 - \frac{x}{\tau_r \tau_c}\right)} \tag{5-114}$$

The specific fuel consumption of a turboshaft engine is expressed in terms of *power specific fuel consumption* S_P where S_P is defined as the fuel weight flow rate per unit of shaft output power, or

$$S_P = \frac{\dot m_f}{\dot W_{\text{shaft}}} = \frac{f}{\dot W_{\text{shaft}}/\dot m_0}$$

Thus

$$\boxed{S_P = \frac{\tau_\lambda}{C_{\text{shaft}} h_{PR}}\left(1 - \frac{x}{\tau_r \tau_c}\right)} \tag{5-115}$$

Summary of Equations—Ideal Turboshaft with Regeneration

INPUTS: $M_0,\ T_0(\text{K}, {}^\circ\text{R}),\ \gamma,\ c_p\left(\frac{\text{kJ}}{\text{kg}\cdot\text{K}}, \frac{\text{Btu}}{\text{lbm}\cdot{}^\circ\text{R}}\right),\ h_{PR}\left(\frac{\text{kJ}}{\text{kg}}, \frac{\text{Btu}}{\text{lbm}}\right),$

$T_{t4}(\text{K}, {}^\circ\text{R}),\ \pi_c,\ x$

OUTPUTS: $\frac{\dot W_{\text{shaft}}}{\dot m_0}\left(\frac{\text{kW}}{\text{kg/sec}}, \frac{\text{hp}}{\text{lbm/sec}}\right),\ f,\ S_P\left(\frac{\text{mg/sec}}{\text{kW}}, \frac{\text{lbm/hr}}{\text{hp}}\right),\ \eta_T,\ C_{\text{shaft}},\ \tau_t$

EQUATIONS:

$$\tau_r = 1 + \frac{\gamma - 1}{2} M_0^2 \tag{5-116a}$$

$$\tau_\lambda = \frac{T_{t4}}{T_0} \tag{5-116b}$$

$$\tau_c = (\pi_c)^{(\gamma-1)/\gamma} \tag{5-116c}$$

$$C_{\text{shaft}} = \tau_\lambda\left(1 - \frac{x}{\tau_r \tau_c}\right) - \tau_r(\tau_c - 1) \tag{5-116d}$$

$$\frac{\dot W_{\text{shaft}}}{\dot m_0} = c_p T_0 C_{\text{shaft}} \tag{5-116e}$$

$$f = \frac{c_p T_0 \tau_\lambda}{h_{PR}}\left(1 - \frac{x}{\tau_r \tau_c}\right) \tag{5-116f}$$

$$S_P = \frac{f}{\dot W_{\text{shaft}}/\dot m_0} \tag{5-116g}$$

$$\eta_T = 1 - \frac{\tau_r(\tau_c - 1)}{\tau_\lambda[1 - x/(\tau_r \tau_c)]} \tag{5-116h}$$

$$\tau_t = \frac{x}{\tau_r \tau_c} \tag{5-116i}$$

Example 5-9. We consider the variation in performance of a turboshaft engine with regenerator due to changes in the design compressor pressure ratio π_c and the exhaust temperature ratio x. The following input data are used:

$$T_0 = 520^\circ\text{R} \qquad T_{t4} = 2600^\circ\text{R} \qquad M_0 = 0$$

$$\gamma = 1.4 \qquad c_p = 0.24\ \text{Btu/(lbm}\cdot{}^\circ\text{R)} \qquad h_{PR} = 18{,}400\ \text{Btu/lbm}$$

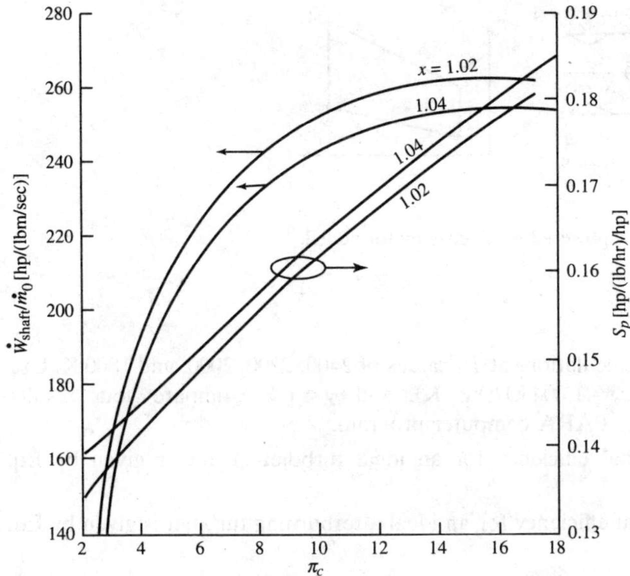

FIGURE 5-44
Variation in performance with compressor pressure ratio π_c of ideal turboshaft engine with regeneration.

For the exhaust temperature ratios of 1.02 and 1.04, the maximum compressor pressure ratios are 17.3 and 17.9, respectively. Regeneration is not possible at compressor pressure ratios above these values.

Figure 5-44 shows the variation in engine performance with compressor pressure ratio π_c and exhaust temperature ratio x. The maximum power per unit mass flow occurs at maximum π_c and lowest x. The power specific fuel consumption increases with the compressor pressure ratio because of a decrease in regeneration. A design value for the compressor pressure ratio will be a compromise between low fuel consumption S_P and high specific power $\dot{W}_{shaft}/\dot{m}_0$.

PROBLEMS

5-1. Show that the thermal and propulsive efficiencies for an ideal ramjet engine are given by Eqs. (5-17*a*) and (5-17*b*), respectively.

5-2. Calculate the variation with T_{t4} of exit Mach number, exit velocity, specific thrust, fuel/air ratio, and thrust specific fuel consumption of an ideal turbojet engine for compressor pressure ratios of 10 and 20 at a flight Mach number of 2 and $T_0 = 390°R$. Perform calculations at T_{t4} values of 4400, 4000, 3500, and 3000°R. Use $h_{PR} = 18{,}400$ Btu/lbm, $c_p = 0.24$ Btu/(lbm · °R), and $\gamma = 1.4$. Compare your results with the output of the PARA computer program.

5-3. Calculate the variation with T_{t4} of exit Mach number, exit velocity, specific thrust, fuel/air ratio, and thrust specific fuel consumption of an ideal turbojet engine for compressor pressure ratios of 10 and 20 at a flight Mach number of 2 and

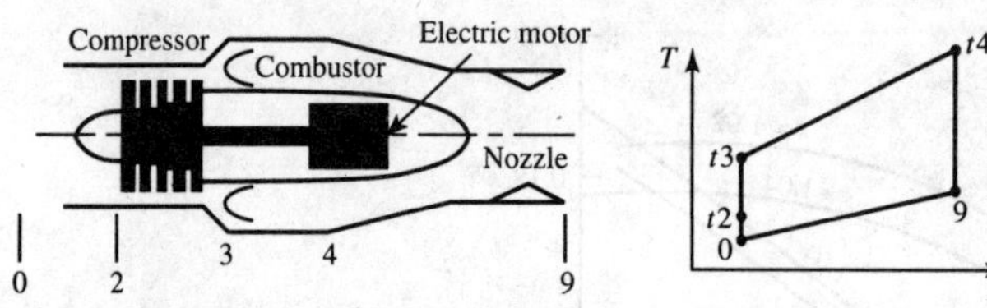

FIGURE P5-6
Ramjet engine with compressor powered by electric motor added.

$T_0 = 217$ K. Perform calculations at T_{t4} values of 2400, 2200, 2000, and 1800 K. Use $h_{PR} = 42{,}800$ kJ/kg, $c_p = 1.004$ kJ/(kg · K), and $\gamma = 1.4$. Compare your results with the output of the PARA computer program.

5-4. Show that the thermal efficiency for an ideal turbojet engine is given by Eq. (5-22).

5-5. Show that the thermal efficiency for an ideal afterburning turbojet is given by Eq. (5-42).

5-6. A major shortcoming of the ramjet engine is the lack of static thrust. To overcome this, it is proposed to add a compressor driven by an electric motor, as shown in Fig. P5-6. For this new ideal engine configuration, show the following:

a. The specific thrust is given by

$$\frac{F}{\dot{m}_0} = \frac{a_0}{g_c}\left[\sqrt{\frac{2}{\gamma - 1}\frac{\tau_\lambda}{\tau_r \tau_c}(\tau_r \tau_c - 1)} - M_0\right]$$

b. The compressor power requirement is given by

$$\dot{W}_c = \dot{m}_0 c_p T_0 \tau_r (\tau_c - 1)$$

c. Determine the static thrust of this engine at the following conditions: $T_0 = 518.7$°R, $T_{t4} = 3200$°R, $\pi_c = 4$, $c_p = 0.24$ Btu/(lbm · °R), and $\gamma = 1.4$.

5-7. Determine the optimum compressor pressure ratio, specific thrust, and thrust specific fuel consumption for an ideal turbojet engine giving the maximum specific thrust at the following conditions: $M_0 = 2.1$, $T_0 = 220$ K, $T_{t4} = 1700$ K, $h_{PR} =$ 42,800 kJ/kg, $c_p = 1.004$ kJ/(kg · K), and $\gamma = 1.4$.

5-8. Show that the thermal efficiency for an ideal turbojet engine with optimum compressor pressure ratio is given by $\eta_T = 1 - 1/\sqrt{\tau_\lambda}$.

5-9. Show that the thermal efficiency for an ideal turbofan engine is given by Eq. (5-22).

5-10. Compare the performance of three ideal turbofan engines with an ideal turbojet engine at two flight conditions by completing the following table. The first flight condition (case 1) is at a flight Mach number of 0.9 at an altitude of 40,000 ft, and the second flight condition (case 2) is at a flight Mach number of 2.6 and an altitude of 60,000 ft. Note that the fuel/air ratio need be calculated only once for each case since it is not a function of α or π_f. The following design information is given:

$\pi_c = 20$ $T_{t4} = 3000$°R $c_p = 0.24$ But/(lbm · °R) $\gamma = 1.4$ $h_{PR} = 18{,}400$ Btu/lbm

Engine	α	π_f	$\dfrac{V_9}{a_0}$	$\dfrac{V_{19}}{a_0}$	$\dfrac{F}{\dot{m}_0}$	f	S
Turbofan							
a. Case 1	1	4					
Case 2	1	4					
b. Case 1, α^*		4					
Case 2, α^*		4					
c. Case 1, π_f^*	1						
Case 2, π_f^*	1						
Turbojet							
d. Case 1	0	n/a		n/a			
Case 2	0	n/a		n/a			

5-11. Repeat Prob. 5-10 with the first flight condition (case 1) at a flight Mach number of 0.9 and altitude of 12 km and the second flight condition (case 2) at a flight Mach number of 2.6 and an altitude of 18 km. Use the following design information:

$$\pi_c = 20 \qquad T_{t4} = 1670 \qquad c_p = 1.004\ \text{kJ/(kg}\cdot\text{K)} \qquad \gamma = 1.4 \qquad h_{PR} = 42{,}800\ \text{kJ/kg}$$

5-12. Show that the propulsive efficiency for an ideal turbofan engine with optimum bypass ratio is given by Eq. (5-62).

5-13. Show that the propulsive efficiency for an ideal turbofan engine with optimum fan pressure ratio is given by Eq. (5-68).

5-14. For an ideal turbofan engine, the maximum value of the bypass ratio corresponds to $V_9 = V_0$.

a. Starting with Eq. (5-53), show that this maximum bypass ratio is given by

$$\alpha_{\max} = \frac{\tau_\lambda + 1 - \tau_r\tau_c - \tau_\lambda/(\tau_r\tau_c)}{\tau_r(\tau_f - 1)}$$

b. Show that the propulsive efficiency for this maximum bypass ratio is given by

$$\eta_P = \frac{2}{\sqrt{(\tau_r\tau_f - 1)/(\tau_r - 1)} + 1}$$

5-15. Under certain conditions, it is desirable to obtain power from the free stream. Consider the ideal air-powered turbine shown in Fig. P5-15. This cycle extracts

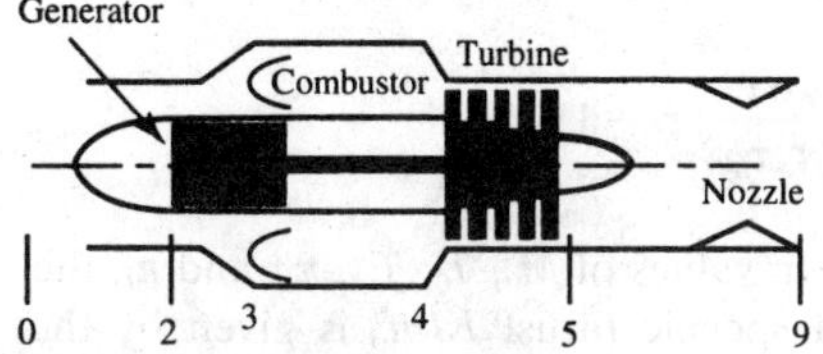

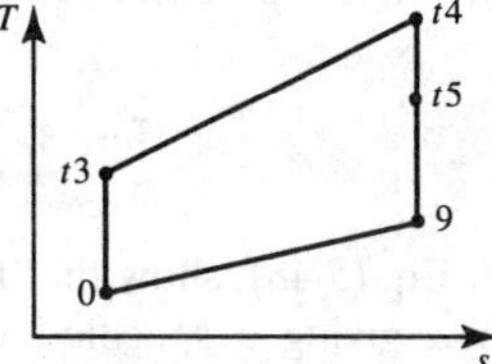

FIGURE P5-15
Ideal air-powered turbine.

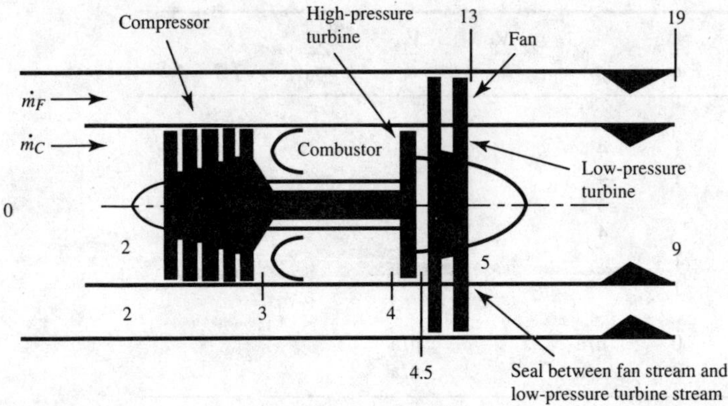

FIGURE P5-16
Turbofan engine with aft fan.

power from the incoming airstream. The incoming air is slowed down in the inlet and then heated in the combustor before going through the turbine. The cycle is designed to produce no thrust ($F = 0$), so that $V_9 = V_0$ and $P_9 = P_0$.

a. Starting with Eq. (5-29), show that

$$\tau_t = \frac{1}{\tau_r} + \frac{1}{\tau_\lambda}\frac{\gamma - 1}{2}M_0^2$$

b. Then show that the turbine output power is given by

$$\dot{W}_t = \dot{m}c_p T_0\left(\frac{\tau_\lambda}{\tau_r} - 1\right)\frac{\gamma - 1}{2}M_0^2$$

5-16. In the early development of the turbofan engine, General Electric developed a turbofan engine with an aft fan, as shown in Fig. P5-16. The compressor is driven by the high-pressure turbine, and the aft fan is directly connected to the low-pressure turbine. Consider an ideal turbofan engine with an aft fan.

a. Show that the high-pressure turbine temperature ratio is given by

$$\tau_{tH} = \frac{T_{t4.5}}{T_{t4}} = 1 - \frac{\tau_r}{\tau_\lambda}(\tau_c - 1)$$

b. Show that the low-pressure-turbine temperature ratio is given by

$$\tau_{tL} = \frac{T_{t5}}{T_{t4.5}} = 1 - \frac{\alpha\tau_r}{\tau_\lambda \tau_{tH}}(\tau_f - 1)$$

5-17. Starting with Eq. (5-48), show that for known values of M_0, T_0, T_{t4}, π_c, and π_f, the bypass ratio α giving a specified value of specific thrust $F/\dot{m}_0$ is given by the solution to the quadratic equation

$$A\alpha^2 + B\alpha + C = 0$$

where $A = \dfrac{\gamma - 1}{2} D^2$

$$B = (\gamma - 1)\left(D^2 + D\frac{V_{19}}{a_0}\right) + \tau_r(\tau_f - 1)$$

$$C = \frac{\gamma - 1}{2}\left(D^2 + 2D\frac{V_{19}}{a_0}\right) - E$$

$$D = \frac{F}{\dot{m}_0}\frac{g_c}{a_0} - \left(\frac{V_{19}}{a_0} - M_0\right)$$

$$E = \tau_\lambda - \tau_r(\tau_c - 1) - \frac{\tau_\lambda}{\tau_r \tau_c}(\tau_r \tau_f - 1)$$

$$\frac{V_{19}}{a_0} = \sqrt{\frac{2}{\gamma - 1}(\tau_r \tau_f - 1)}$$

5-18. Using the system of equations listed in Prob. 5-17, determine the bypass ratio that gives a specific thrust of 400 N/(kg/sec) for the following data:

$$T_0 = 216.7\ \text{K} \qquad T_{t4} = 1670\ \text{K} \qquad M_0 = 0.8 \qquad \pi_c = 24$$

and $\pi_f = 4$ with $\gamma = 1.4$, $c_p = 1.004\ \text{kJ/(kg} \cdot \text{K)}$, $h_{PR} = 42{,}800\ \text{kJ/kg}$

5-19. Using the system of equations listed in Prob. 5-17, determine the bypass ratio that gives a specific thrust of 40.0 lbf/(lbm/sec) for the following data:

$$T_0 = 390°\text{R} \qquad T_{t4} = 3000°\text{R} \qquad M_0 = 2 \qquad \pi_c = 16$$

and $\pi_f = 5$ with $\gamma = 1.4$, $c_p = 0.24\ \text{Btu/(lbm} \cdot °\text{R)}$, $h_{PR} = 18{,}400\ \text{Btu/lbm}$

5-20. Considerable research and development effort is going into increasing the maximum T_{t4} in gas turbine engines for fighter aircraft. For a mixed-flow turbofan engine with $\pi_c = 16$ at a flight condition of $M_0 = 2.5$ and $T_0 = 216.7$ K, use the PARA computer program to determine and plot the required engine fan pressure, specific thrust, and specific fuel consumption versus T_{t4} over a range of 1600 to 2200 K for bypass ratios of 0.5 and 1. Use $h_{PR} = 42{,}800$ kJ/kg, $c_p = 1.004$ kJ/(kg · K), and $\gamma = 1.4$. Comment on your results in general. Why do the plots of specific fuel consumption versus specific thrust for these engines all fall on one line?

5-21. Considerable research and development effort is going into increasing the maximum T_{t4} in gas turbine engines for fighter aircraft. For a mixed-flow turbofan engine with $\pi_c = 20$ at a flight condition of $M_0 = 2$ and $T_0 = 390$°R, use the PARA computer program to determine and plot the required engine bypass ratio α, specific thrust, and specific fuel consumption versus T_{t4} over a range of 3000 to 4000°R for fan pressure ratios of 2 and 5. Use $h_{PR} = 18{,}400$ Btu/lbm, $c_p = 0.24$ Btu/(lbm · °R), and $\gamma = 1.4$. Comment on your results.

5-22. Show that the thermal efficiency of the afterburning mixed-flow turbofan engine given by Eq. (5-85) can be rewritten as

$$\eta_T = \frac{c_p T_0}{f_o h_{PR}}\left[\tau_{\lambda AB}\left(1 - \frac{1}{\tau_r \tau_f}\right) - (\tau_r - 1)\right]$$

5-23. For an afterburning mixed-flow turbofan engine with $\pi_c = 16$ and $T_{t7} = 2200$ K at a flight condition of $M_0 = 2.5$ and $T_0 = 216.7$ K, use the PARA computer program to determine and plot the required engine fan pressure, specific thrust, and specific fuel consumption versus T_{t4} over a range of 1600 to 2200 K for bypass ratios of 0.5 and 1. Use $h_{PR} = 42{,}800$ kJ/kg, $c_p = 1.004$ kJ/(kg · K), and $\gamma = 1.4$. Comment on your results in general. Why do the plots of specific fuel consumption versus specific thrust for these engines all fall on one line? Compare these results to those for Prob. 5-20, and comment on the differences.

5-24. For an afterburning mixed-flow turbofan engine with $\pi_c = 20$ and $T_{t7} = 4000$°R at a flight condition of $M_0 = 2$ and $T_0 = 390$°R, use the PARA computer program to determine and plot the required engine bypass ratio α, specific thrust, and specific fuel consumption versus T_{t4} over a range of 3000 to 4000°R for fan pressure ratios of 2 and 5. Use $h_{PR} = 18{,}400$ Btu/lbm, $c_p = 0.24$ Btu/(lbm · °R), and $\gamma = 1.4$. Comment on your results. Compare these results to those for Prob. 5-21, and comment on the changes.

5-25. Use the PARA computer program to determine and plot the thrust specific fuel consumption versus specific thrust for the turboprop engine of Example 5-8 over the same range of compressor pressure ratios for turbine temperature ratios of 0.8, 0.7, 0.6, 0.5, 0.4, and optimum.

5-26. Use the PARA computer program to determine and plot the thrust specific fuel consumption versus specific thrust for the turboprop engine over the range of compressor pressure ratios from 2 to 40 at $T_0 = 425$°R, $M_0 = 0.65$, $\gamma = 1.4$, $c_p = 0.24$ Btu/(lbm · °R), $h_{PR} = 18{,}400$ Btu/lbm, $T_{t4} = 2460$°R, and $\eta_{\text{prop}} = 0.8$ for turbine temperature ratios of 0.8, 0.7, 0.6, 0.5, 0.4, and optimum.

5-27. Use the PARA computer program to determine and plot the power specific fuel consumption versus specific power for the turboshaft engine with regeneration over compressor pressure ratios of 4 to 18 at $T_0 = 290$ K, $M_0 = 0$, $\gamma = 1.4$, $c_p = 1.004$ kJ/(kg · K), $h_{PR} = 42{,}800$ kJ/kg, and $x = 1.02$ for combustor exit temperatures T_{t4} of 1300, 1400, 1500, and 1600 K.

5-28. Use the PARA computer program to determine and plot the power specific fuel consumption versus specific power for the turboshaft engine with regeneration of Example 5-9 at $x = 1.02$ over the same range of compressor ratios for combustor exit temperatures T_{t4} of 2400, 2600, 2800, and 3000°R.

5-D1 GAS TURBINE DESIGN PROBLEM 1 (HP-1 AIRCRAFT)

You are to determine the range of compressor pressure ratios and bypass ratios for ideal turbofan engines that best meet the design requirements for the hypothetical passenger aircraft, the HP-1.

Hand-Calculate Ideal Performance

Using the parametric cycle analysis equations for an ideal turbofan engine with $T_{t4} = 1560$ K, hand-calculate the specific thrust and thrust specific fuel consumption for an ideal turbofan engine with a compressor pressure ratio of 36, fan pressure ratio of 1.8, and bypass ratio of 10 at the 0.83 Mach, 11-km-altitude cruise condition. Assume $\gamma = 1.4$, $c_p = 1.004$ kJ/(kg · K), and $h_{PR} = 42{,}800$ kJ/kg. Compare your answers to results from the parametric cycle analysis program PARA.

Computer-Calculated Ideal Performance

For the 0.83 Mach, 11-km-altitude cruise condition, determine the performance available from turbofan engines. This part of the analysis is accomplished by using the PARA computer program with $T_{t4} = 1560$ K. Specifically, you are to vary the compressor pressure ratio from 20 to 40 in increments of 2. Fix the fan pressure ratio at your assigned value of _____. Evaluate bypass ratios of 4, 6, 8, 10, 12, and the optimum value. Assume $\gamma = 1.4$, $c_p = 1.004$ kJ/(kg · K), and $h_{PR} = 42{,}800$ kJ/kg.

Calculate Minimum Specific Thrust at Cruise

You can calculate the minimum uninstalled specific thrust at cruise based on the following information:

1. The thrust of the two engines must be able to offset drag at 0.83 Mach and 11-km altitude and have enough excess thrust for P_s of 1.5 m/sec. Determine the required installed thrust to attain the cruise condition using Eq. (1-28). Assuming $\phi_{\text{inlet}} + \phi_{noz} = 0.02$, determine the required uninstalled thrust.
2. Determine the maximum mass flow into the 2.2-m-diameter inlet for the 0.83 Mach, 11-km-altitude flight condition, using the equation given in the background section for this design problem in Chap. 1.
3. Using the results of steps 1 and 2, calculate the minimum uninstalled specfic thrust at cruise.
4. Perform steps 2 and 3 for inlet diameters of 2.5, 2.75, 3.0, 3.25, and 3.5 m.

Select Promising Engine Cycles

Plot thrust specific fuel consumption versus specific thrust (thrust per unit mass flow) for the engines analyzed above. Plot a curve for each bypass ratio, and cross-plot the values of the compressor pressure ratio (see Fig. 5-D1). The result is a *carpet plot* (a

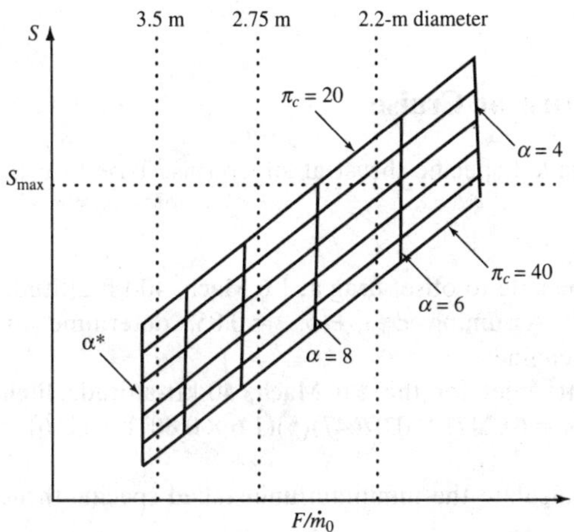

FIGURE P5-D1
Specific performance of ideal turbofan engines for HP-1 aircraft.

multivariable plot) for the cruise condition. Now draw a dashed horizontal line on the carpet plot corresponding to the maximum allowable uninstalled thrust specific fuel consumption S_{max} for the cruise condition (determined in Chap. 1 portion of this design problem). Draw a dashed vertical line for each minimum uninstalled specific thrust determined above. Your carpet plots will look similar to the example shown in Fig. 5-D1. What ranges of bypass ratio and compressor pressure ratio look most promising?

5-D2 GAS TURBINE DESIGN PROBLEM 2 (HF-1 AIRCRAFT)

You are to determine the ranges of compressor pressure ratio and bypass ratio for ideal mixed-flow turbofan engines that best meet the design requirements for the hypothetical fighter aircraft, the HF-1.

Hand-Calculate Ideal Performance

Using the parametric cycle anslysis equations for an ideal mixed-flow turbofan engine with $T_{t4} = 3250°\text{R}$, hand calculate the specific thrust and thrust specific fuel consumption for an ideal turbofan engine with a compressor pressure ratio of 25 and bypass ratio of 0.5 at the 1.6 Mach, 40-kft-altitude supercruise condition. Assume $\gamma = 1.4$, $c_p = 0.24\ \text{Btu/(lbm} \cdot °\text{R)}$, and $h_{PR} = 18{,}400\ \text{Btu/lbm}$. Compare your answers to the results from the parametric cycle analysis program PARA.

Computer-Calculated Ideal Performance

For the 1.6 Mach, 40-kft-altitude supercruise condition, determine the performance available from turbofan engines. This part of the analysis is accomplished by using the PARA computer program with $T_{t4} = 3250°\text{R}$. Specifically, you are to vary the bypass ratio from 0.1 to 1.0 in increments of 0.05. Evaluate compressor pressure ratios of 16, 18, 20, 22, 24, and 28. Assume $\gamma = 1.4$, $c_p = 0.24\ \text{Btu/(lbm} \cdot °\text{R)}$, and $h_{PR} = 18{,}400\ \text{Btu/lbm}$.

Calculate Minimum Specific Thrust at Cruise

You can calculate the minimum uninstalled specific thrust at supercruise based on the following information:

1. The thrust of the two engines must be able to offset drag at 1.6 Mach, 40-kft altitude, and 92 percent of takeoff weight. Assuming $\phi_{\text{inlet}} + \phi_{noz} = 0.05$, determine the required uninstalled thrust for each engine.
2. The maximum mass flow into a 5-ft^2 inlet for the 1.6 Mach, 40-kft-altitude flight condition is $\dot{m} = \rho AV = \sigma\rho_{\text{ref}}AMa = (0.2471 \times 0.07647)(5)(1.6 \times 0.8671 \times 1116) = 146.3\ \text{lbm/sec}$.
3. Using the results of steps 1 and 2, calculate the minimum uninstalled specific thrust at supercruise.

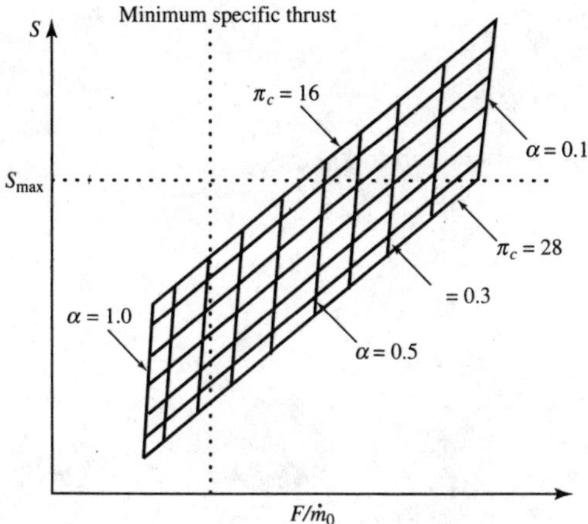

FIGURE P5-D2
Specific performance of ideal mixed-flow turbofan engines for HF-1 aircraft.

Select Promising Engine Cycles

Plot the thrust specific fuel consumption versus specific thrust (thrust per unit mass flow) for the engines analyzed above. Plot a curve for each bypass ratio, and cross-plot the values of compressor pressure ratio (see Fig. 5-D2). The result is a carpet plot (a multivariable plot) for the supercruise condition. Now draw a dashed horizontal line on the carpet plot corresponding to the maximum allowable uninstalled thrust specific fuel consumption S_{max} for the cruise condition (determined in the Chap. 1 portion of this design problem). Draw a dashed vertical line for the minimum uninstalled specific thrust determined above. Your carpet plots will look similar to the example shown in Fig. P5-D2. What ranges of bypass ratio and compressor pressure ratio look most promising?

CHAPTER 6

COMPONENT PERFORMANCE

6-1 INTRODUCTION

In Chap. 5, we idealized the engine components and assumed that the working fluid behaved as a perfect gas with constant specific heats. These idealizations and assumptions permitted the basic cycle analysis of several types of engines and the analysis of engine performance trends. In this chapter, we will develop the analytical tools that allow us to use realistic assumptions as to component losses and to include the variation of specific heats.

6-2 VARIATION IN GAS PROPERTIES

The enthalpy h and specific heat at constant pressure c_p for air (modeled as a perfect gas) are functions of temperature. Also, the enthalpy h and specific heat at constant pressure c_p for a typical hydrocarbon fuel JP-4 and air combustion products (modeled as a perfect gas) are functions of temperature and the fuel/air ratio f. The variations of properties h and c_p for fuel/air combustion products versus temperature are presented in Figs. 6-1*a* and 6-1*b*, respectively. The ratio of specific heats γ for fuel/air combustion products is also a function of temperature and of fuel/air ratio. A plot of γ is shown in Fig. 6-2. These figures are based on Eq. (2-68) and the coefficients of Table 2-3. Note that both h and c_p increase and γ decreases with temperature and the

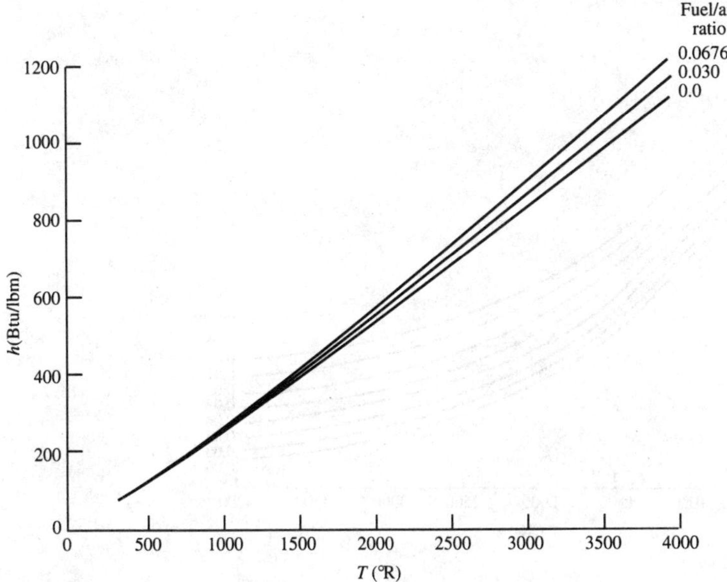

FIGURE 6-1*a*
Enthalpy versus temperature for JP-4 and air combustion products.

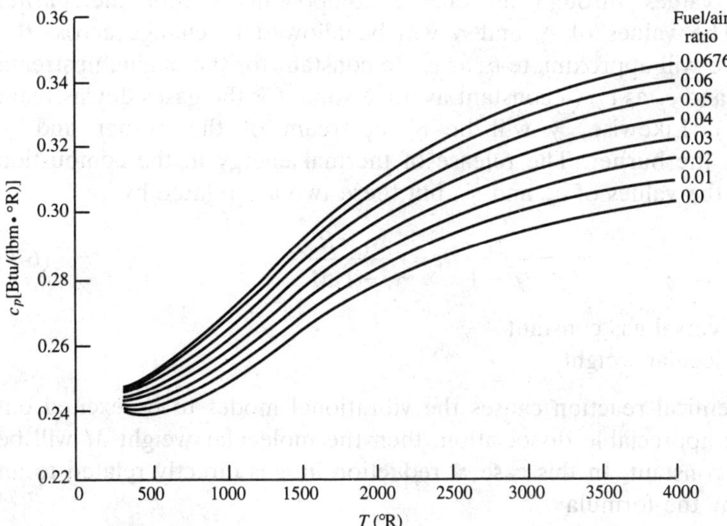

FIGURE 6-1*b*
Specific heat c_p versus temperature for JP-4 and air combustion products.

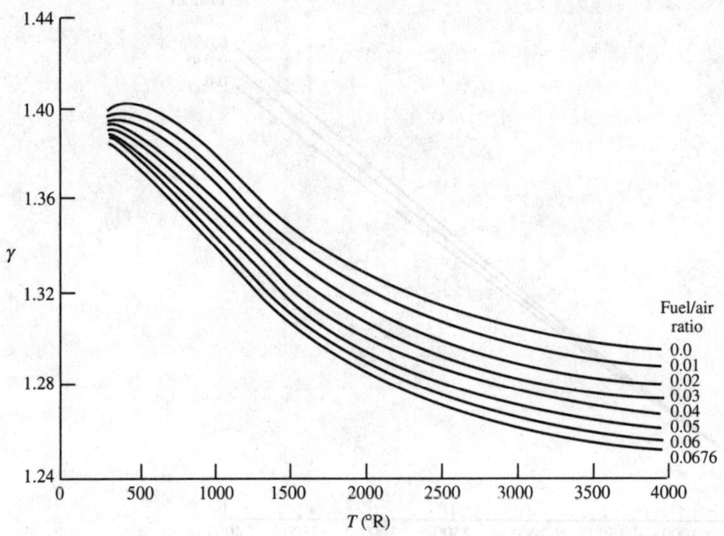

FIGURE 6-2
Ratio of specific heats γ versus temperature for JP-4 and air combustion products.

fuel/air ratio. Our models of gas properties in the engines need to include changes in both c_p and γ across components where the changes are significant.

In Chap. 7, we will include the variation in c_p and γ through the engine. To simplify the algebra, we will consider c_p and γ to have constant representative values through all engine components except the burner (combustor). The values of c_p and γ will be allowed to change across the burner. Thus we will approximate c_p as c_{pc} (a constant for the engine upstream of the burner) and c_p as c_{pt} (a constant average value for the gases downstream of the burner). Likewise, γ will be γ_c upstream of the burner and γ_t downstream of the burner. The release of thermal energy in the combustion process affects the values of c_{pt} and γ_t, but these two are related by

$$c_{pt} = \frac{\gamma_t}{\gamma_t - 1} R_t = \frac{\gamma_t}{\gamma_t - 1} \frac{R_u}{M} \tag{6-1}$$

where R_u = universal gas constant
M = molecular weight

Thus if the chemical reaction causes the vibrational modes to be excited but does not cause appreciable dissociation, then the molecular weight M will be approximately constant. In this case, a reduction in γ is directly related to an increase in c_p by the formula

$$\frac{c_{pt}}{c_{pc}} = \frac{\gamma_t}{\gamma_t - 1} \frac{\gamma_c - 1}{\gamma_c} \tag{6-2}$$

6-3 COMPONENT PERFORMANCE

In this chapter, each of the engine components will be characterized by *figures of merit* that model the component's performance and facilitate cycle analysis of real air-breathing engines. The total temperature ratio τ, the total pressure ratio π, and the interrelationship between τ and π will be used as much as possible in a component's figure of merit.

6-4 INLET AND DIFFUSER PRESSURE RECOVERY

Inlet losses arise because of the presence of wall friction and shock waves (in a supersonic inlet). Both wall friction and shock losses result in a reduction in total pressure so that $\pi_d < 1$. Inlets are adiabatic to a very high degree of approximation, so we have $\tau_d = 1$. The inlet's *figure of merit* is defined simply as π_d.

The *isentropic efficiency* η_d of the diffuser is defined as (refer to Fig. 6-3)

$$\eta_d = \frac{h_{t2s} - h_0}{h_{t0} - h_0} \cong \frac{T_{t2s} - T_0}{T_{t0} - T_0} \tag{6-3}$$

This efficiency can be related to τ_d and π_d to give

$$\boxed{\eta_d = \frac{\tau_{r}\pi_d^{(\gamma-1)/\gamma} - 1}{\tau_r - 1}} \tag{6-4}$$

Figure 6-4 gives typical values of π_d for a subsonic inlet. The diffuser efficiency η_d was calculated from π_d by using Eq. (6-4).

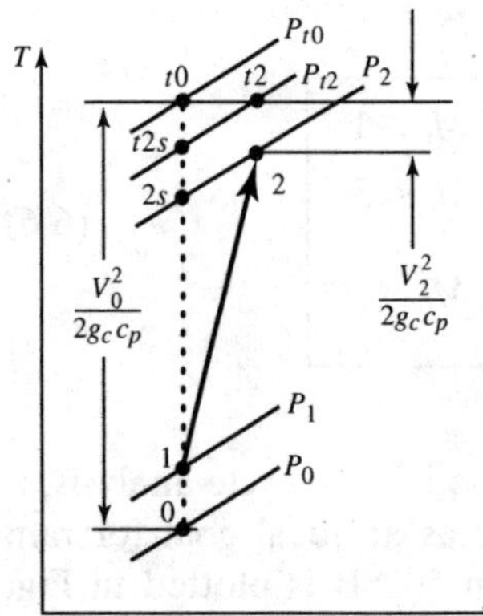

FIGURE 6-3
Definition of inlet states.

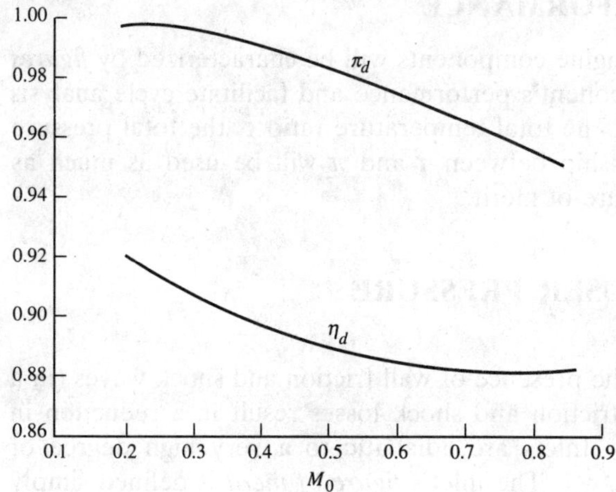

FIGURE 6-4
Typical subsonic inlet π_d and η_d.

In supersonic flight, the flow deceleration in inlets is accompanied by shock waves which can produce a total pressure loss much greater than, and in addition to, the wall friction loss. The inlet's overall pressure ratio is the product of the ram pressure ratio and the diffuser pressure ratio.

Because of shocks, only a portion of the ram total pressure can be recovered. We now define $\pi_{d\,\max}$ as that portion of π_d that is due to wall friction and define η_r as that portion of π_d due to ram recovery. Thus

$$\boxed{\pi_d = \pi_{d\,\max}\eta_r} \tag{6-5}$$

For subsonic and supersonic flow, a useful reference for the ram recovery η_r is Military Specifiction 5008B (Ref. 28), which is expressed as follows:

$$\boxed{\eta_r = \begin{cases} 1 & M_0 \leq 1 \\ 1 - 0.075(M_0 - 1)^{1.35} & 1 < M_0 < 5 \\ \dfrac{800}{M_0^4 + 935} & 5 < M_0 \end{cases}} \tag{6-6}$$

Since we often do not yet know the deatils of the inlet in cycle analysis, it is assumed that Military Specification 5008B applies as an ideal goal for ram recovery. The ram recovery of Military Specification 5008B is plotted in Fig. 6-5 versus M_0.

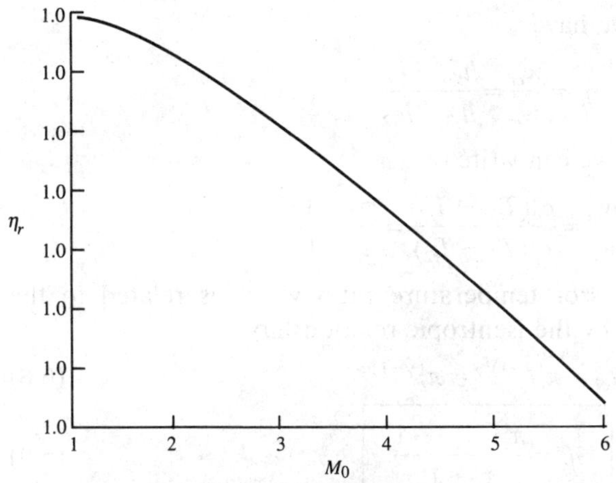

FIGURE 6-5
Inlet total pressure recovery η_r of Military Specification 5008B.

6-5 COMPRESSOR AND TURBINE EFFICIENCIES

Compressor Isentropic Efficiency

Compressors are, to a high degree of approximation, adiabatic. The overall efficiency used to measure a compressor's performance is the *isentropic efficiency* η_c, defined by

$$\eta_c = \frac{\text{ideal work of compression for given } \pi_c}{\text{actual work of compression for given } \pi_c} \tag{6-7}$$

Figure 6-6 shows both the ideal and actual compression processes for a given π_c on a T-s diagram. The actual work per unit mass w_c is $h_{t3} - h_{t2}$ $[= c_p(T_{t3} - T_{t2})]$ and the ideal work per unit mass w_{ci} is $h_{t3i} - h_{t2}$ $[= c_p(T_{t3i} - T_{t2})]$. Here, h_{t3i} is the ideal (isentropic) compressor leaving total enthalpy. Writing the isentropic efficiency of the compressor η_c in terms of the

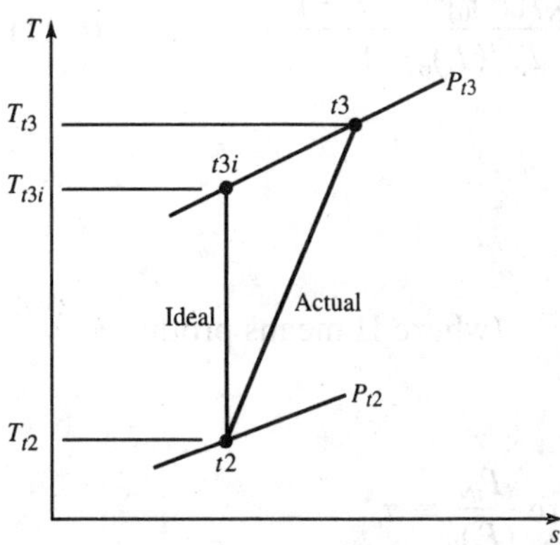

FIGURE 6-6
Actual and ideal compressor processes.

thermodynamic properties, we have

$$\eta_c = \frac{w_{ci}}{w_c} = \frac{h_{t3i} - h_{t2}}{h_{t3} - h_{t2}}$$

For a calorically perfect gas, we can write

$$\eta_c = \frac{w_{ci}}{w_c} = \frac{c_p(T_{t3i} - T_{t2})}{c_p(T_{t3} - T_{t2})} = \frac{\tau_{ci} - 1}{\tau_c - 1}$$

Here τ_{ci} is the ideal compressor temperature ratio which is related to the compressor pressure ratio π_c by the isentropic relationship

$$\tau_{ci} = \pi_{ci}^{(\gamma-1)/\gamma} = \pi_c^{(\gamma-1)/\gamma} \tag{6-8}$$

Thus we have

$$\boxed{\eta_c = \frac{\pi_c^{(\gamma-1)/\gamma} - 1}{\tau_c - 1}} \tag{6-9}$$

Compressor Stage Efficiency

For a multistage compressor, each stage (set of rotor and stator) will have an isentropic efficiency. Let η_{sj} denote the isentropic efficiency of the jth stage. Likewise, π_{sj} and τ_{sj} represent the pressure ratio and temperature ratio, respectively, for the jth stage. From Eq. (6-9), we can write for the jth stage

$$\eta_{sj} = \frac{\pi_{sj}^{(\gamma-1)/\gamma} - 1}{\tau_{sj} - 1} \tag{6-10}$$

where $\tau_{sj} = T_{tj}/T_{tj-1}$ and $\pi_{sj} = P_{tj}/P_{tj-1}$.

Figure 6-7 shows the process for a multistage compressor. Here η_{sj} can be interpreted as the vertical height from A to B divided by the vertical height from A to C. For counting purposes, subscript 0 outside the parentheses is at the inlet, and subscript N is at the outlet of the compressor. Thus $(P_t)_0 = P_{t2}$, $(T_t)_0 = T_{t2}$, $P_{tN} = P_{tN} = P_3$, and $T_{tN} = T_{t3}$. From Eq. (6-9), we have for the overall compressor isentropic efficiency

$$\eta_c = \frac{(P_{t3}/P_{t2})^{(\gamma-1)/\gamma} - 1}{T_{t3}/T_{t2} - 1} = \frac{[P_{tN}/(P_t)_0]^{(\gamma-1)/\gamma} - 1}{T_{tn}/(T_t)_0 - 1} \tag{6-11}$$

From Eq. (6-10), we have

$$\frac{T_{tj}}{T_{tj-1}} = 1 + \frac{1}{\eta_{sj}}\left[\left(\frac{P_{tj}}{P_{tj-1}}\right)^{(\gamma-1)/\gamma} - 1\right]$$

so

$$\frac{T_{tN}}{(T_t)_0} = \prod_{j=1}^{N}\left\{1 + \frac{1}{\eta_{sj}}\left[\left(\frac{P_{tj}}{P_{tj-1}}\right)^{(\gamma-1)/\gamma} - 1\right]\right\} \qquad \text{(where } \Pi \text{ means product)}$$

We note also the requirement that

$$\frac{P_{tN}}{(P_t)_0} = \prod_{j=1}^{N} \frac{P_{tj}}{P_{tj-1}} \quad \text{where } \frac{P_{tN}}{(P_t)_0} \equiv \pi_c$$

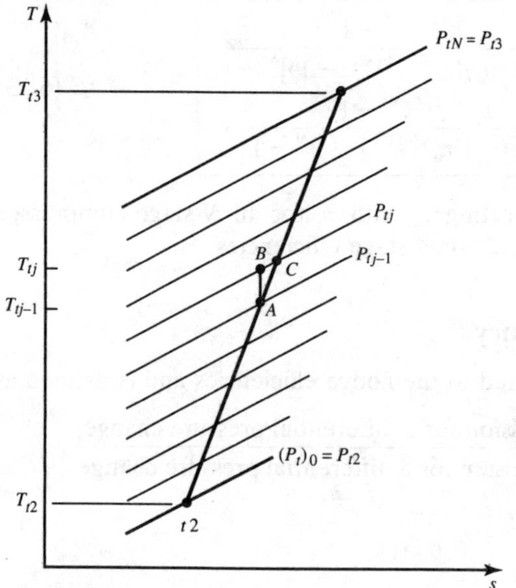

FIGURE 6-7
Multistage compressor process and nomenclature.

Thus Eq. (6-11) becomes

$$\eta_c = \frac{[P_{tN}/(P_t)_0]^{(\gamma-1)/\gamma} - 1}{\prod_{j=1}^{N} \{1 + (1/\eta_{sj})[(P_{tj}/P_{tj-1})^{(\gamma-1)/\gamma} - 1]\} - 1} \tag{6-12}$$

We can see from Eq. (6-12) that the isentropic efficiency of a compressor is a function of the compressor pressure ratio, the pressure ratio of each stage, and the isentropic efficiency of each stage. This complex functional form makes the isentropic efficiency of the compressor undesirable for use in cycle analysis. We are looking for a simpler form of the figure of merit that will allow us to vary the compression ratio and still accurately predict the variation of η_c.

Let us consider the special case when each stage pressure ratio and each stage efficiency are the same. In this case

$$\pi_c = \prod_{j=1}^{N} \left(\frac{P_{tj}}{P_{tj-1}}\right) = \pi_s{}^N$$

Here η_s is the stage pressure ratio, and π_s is the stage efficiency. Also

$$\frac{T_{tj}}{T_{tj-1}} = 1 + \frac{1}{\eta_s}(\pi_s^{(\gamma-1)/\gamma} - 1)$$

so

$$\frac{T_{tN}}{(T_t)_0} \equiv \tau_c = \left[1 + \frac{1}{\eta_s}(\pi_s^{(\gamma-1)/\gamma} - 1)\right]^N$$

or

$$\tau_c = \left[1 + \frac{1}{\eta_s}(\pi_c^{(\gamma-1)/(\gamma N)} - 1)\right]^N$$

and
$$\boxed{\begin{aligned}\eta_c &= \frac{\pi_c^{(\gamma-1)/\gamma}-1}{[1+(1/\eta_s)(\pi_c^{(\gamma-1)/(\gamma N)}-1)]^N-1}\\ &= \frac{\pi_s^{(\gamma-1)/(\gamma N)}-1}{[1+(1/\eta_s)(\pi_s^{(\gamma-1)/\gamma}-1)]^N-1}\end{aligned}} \tag{6-13}$$

Note: This is a relationship connecting η_c with η_s for an N-stage compressor with equal stage pressure ratios and equal stage efficiencies.

Compressor Polytropic Efficiency

The *polytropic efficiency* e_c is related to the above efficiencies and is defined as

$$e_c = \frac{\text{ideal work of compression for a differential pressure change}}{\text{actual work of compression for a differential pressure change}}$$

Thus $e_c = \dfrac{dw_i}{dw} = \dfrac{dh_{ti}}{dh_t} = \dfrac{dT_{ti}}{dT_t}$

Note that for an ideal compressor, the isentropic relationship gives $T_{ti} = P_{ti}^{(\gamma-1)/\gamma} \times \text{constant}$. Thus

$$\frac{dT_{ti}}{T_t} = \frac{\gamma-1}{\gamma}\frac{dP_t}{P_t}$$

and
$$e_c = \frac{dT_{ti}}{dT_t} = \frac{dT_{ti}/T_t}{dT_t/T_t} = \frac{\gamma-1}{\gamma}\frac{dP_t/P_t}{dT_t/T_t}$$

Assuming that the polytropic efficiency e_c is constant, we can obtain a simple relationship between τ_c and π_c as follows:

1. Rewrite the above equation as

$$\frac{dT_t}{T_t} = \frac{\gamma-1}{\gamma e_c}\frac{dP_t}{P_t}$$

2. Integration between states $t2$ and $t3$ gives

$$\ln\frac{T_{t3}}{T_{t2}} = \frac{\gamma-1}{\gamma e_c}\ln\frac{P_{t3}}{P_{t2}}$$

or
$$\boxed{\tau_c = \pi_c^{(\gamma-1)/(\gamma e_c)}} \tag{6-14}$$

For a state-of-the-art design, the polytropic efficiency is essentially constant. Substitution of Eq. (6-14) into Eq. (6-9) gives

$$\boxed{\eta_c = \frac{\pi_c^{(\gamma-1)/\gamma}-1}{\tau_c-1} = \frac{\pi_c^{(\gamma-1)/\gamma}-1}{\pi_c^{(\gamma-1)/(\gamma e_c)}-1}} \tag{6-15}$$

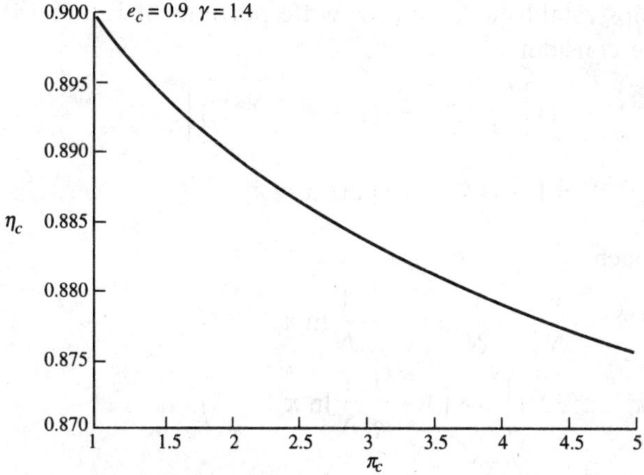

FIGURE 6-8
Isentropic efficiency versus compressor pressure ratio for constant polytropic efficiency of 0.9.

Equation (6-15) accurately predicts the relationship between the isentropic efficiency of a compressor and the compressor ratio for a given state-of-the-art polytropic efficiency. This relationship is plotted in Fig. 6-8 for a given value of e_c.

We will use the polytropic efficiency e_c as the figure of merit for the compressor. Equations (6-14) and (6-15) will be used to obtain the total temperature ratio and isentropic efficiency of the compressor, respectively, in the cycle analysis.

Relationship between Compressor Efficiencies

We have, from Eqs. (6-13) and (6-15), relationships connecting η_c, η_s, and e_c. In this section, we wish to see if η_s formally approaches e_c as we let the number of stages get very large and the pressure ratio per stage get very small. To do this, first we note the relationship

$$1 - x^{1/N} = \frac{y}{N} \qquad \text{then } x = \left(1 - \frac{y}{N}\right)^N$$

This may be expanded by the binomial expansion to give

$$x = \left(1 - \frac{y}{N}\right)^N = 1 + N\left(\frac{-y}{N}\right) + \frac{N(N-1)}{1 \cdot 2}\left(\frac{-y}{N}\right)^2 + \cdots \tag{i}$$

If N is very large, this becomes

$$x = 1 - y + \frac{y^2}{2!} - \frac{y^3}{3!} + \cdots = \exp(-y)$$

or
$$y = -\ln x \tag{ii}$$

With these basic relationships established, we now write portions of Eq. (6-13) in the form given in (i). We consider

$$\left[1+\frac{1}{\eta_s}(\pi_c^{(\gamma-1)/(\gamma N)}-1)\right]^N \equiv \left[1-\frac{1}{\eta_s}(1-\pi_c^{(\gamma-1)(\gamma N)})\right]^N$$

Then $\quad \dfrac{y}{N}=1-\pi_c^{(\gamma-1)/(\gamma N)}=1-x^{1/N} \qquad$ where $x=\pi_c^{(\gamma-1)/\gamma}$

Thus for N large, we approach

$$1-\pi_c^{(\gamma-1)/(\gamma N)} \rightarrow \frac{y}{N}=-\frac{1}{N}\ln x=-\frac{1}{N}\ln \pi_c^{(\gamma-1)/\gamma}$$

Then

$$\left[1-\frac{1}{\eta_s}(1-\pi_c^{(\gamma-1)/(\gamma N)})\right]^N \rightarrow \left(1+\frac{1}{\eta_s}\frac{1}{N}\ln \pi_c^{(\gamma-1)/\gamma}\right)^N$$

$$=\left(1+\frac{1}{N}\ln \pi_c^{(\gamma-1)/(\gamma\eta_s)}\right)^N$$

But, as above, the expansion for $(1-z/N)^N$ for large N is just e^{-z}. Here we let

$$z=-\ln \pi_c^{(\gamma-1)/(\gamma N)} \qquad \text{thus} \quad e^{-z}=\pi_c^{(\gamma-1)/(\gamma N)}$$

Hence for large N

$$\left[1-\frac{1}{\eta_s}(1-\pi_c^{(\gamma-1)/(\gamma N)})\right]^N \rightarrow \pi_c^{(\gamma-1)/(\gamma\eta_s)}$$

Thus

$$\boxed{\eta_c=\frac{\pi_c^{(\gamma-1)/\gamma}-1}{\pi_c^{(\gamma-1)/(\gamma\eta_s)}-1}} \tag{6-16}$$

for a multistage machine. This expression is identical to Eq. (6-15) with e_c replaced by η_s. Thus for very large N, η_s approaches e_c.

Example 6-1. *Compressor efficiencies.* Say we plan to construct a 16-stage compressor given $\pi_c=25$. Then we have $\pi_s=25^{1/16}=1.223$. Say η_s is measured at 0.93. Then, with Eq. (6-14) solved for e_c, we have

$$e_c=\frac{[(\gamma-1)/\gamma]\ln \pi_s}{\ln[1+(1/\eta_s)(\pi_s^{(\gamma-1)/\gamma}-1)]} \tag{6-17}$$

$$=0.9320$$

Then we get two estimates for η_c, one based on constant η_s and another based on constant e_c. From Eq. (6-13), with $\pi_s=1.223$, we obtain

$$\eta_c=\frac{\pi_c^{(\gamma-1)/\gamma}-1}{[1+(1/\eta_s)(\pi_s^{(\gamma-1)/\gamma}-1)]^N-1}$$

$$=\frac{25^{1/3.5}-1}{[1+(1/0.93)(1.223^{1/3.5}-1)]^{16}-1}$$

$$=0.8965^-$$

From Eq. (6-15) we find, for comparison,

$$\eta_c=\frac{\pi_c^{(\gamma-1)/\gamma}-1}{\pi_c^{(\gamma-1)/(\gamma e_c)}-1}=0.8965^+$$

More simply, if $e_c = \eta_s = 0.93$, then by either Eq. (6-15) or Eq. (6-16), we get $\eta_c = 0.8965$.

The point of all of this is that for a multistage machine, the simplicity and accuracy of using the polytropic efficiency make it a useful concept. Thus from now on we will use Eq. (6-15) to compute the compressor efficiency.

Compressor Stage Pressure ratio

For a multistage compressor, the energy added is divided somewhat evenly per stage, and each stage increases the total temperature of the flow about the same amount. The total temperature ratio of a stage τ_s that has a total temperature change of ΔT_t can be written as

$$\tau_s = 1 + \frac{\Delta T_t}{T_{ti}}$$

Using the polytropic efficiency e_c to relate the stage pressure ratio π_s to its temperature ratio τ_s, we have

$$\pi_s = (\tau_s)^{(\gamma e_c)/(\gamma-1)} = \left(1 + \frac{\Delta T_t}{T_{ti}}\right)^{(\gamma e_c)/(\gamma-1)}$$

This equation gives the variation of the compressor stage pressure ratio with stage inlet temperature T_{ti} and total temperature change ΔT_t. This equation shows the decrease in stage pressure ratio with increases in stage inlet temperature for stages with the same total temperature change.

Stage pressure ratio results for $\gamma = 1.4$ and $e_c = 0.9$ are plotted in Fig. 6-9

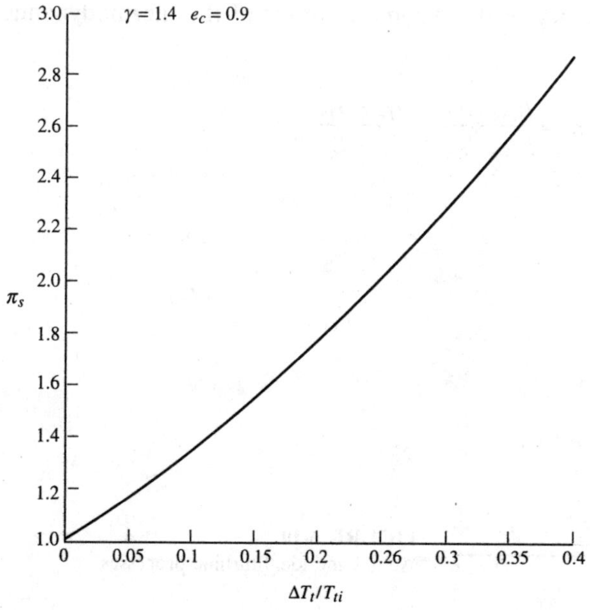

FIGURE 6-9
Variation of compressor stage pressure ratio.

versus $\Delta T_t/T_{ti}$. By using this figure, a 30 K change with 300 K inlet temperature gives a stage pressure ratio of about 1.35. Likewise, a 60°R change with 1000°R inlet temperature gives a stage pressure ratio of about 1.20.

Turbine Isentropic Efficiency

Modern turbines are cooled by air taken from the compressors, passed through vanes and rotors, and then remixed with the main flow. From the point of view of the overall flow, the flow is adiabatic; but to be correct, a multiple-stream analysis would have to be applied. Such an analysis is straightforward conceptually, but it is difficult to estimate the various mixing losses, etc., that occur. The concept of isentropic efficiency is still utilized in most such analyses (for the mainstream portion of the flow), and in any case, the isentropic efficiency gives a reasonable approximation to the turbine performance when cooling flow rates are small. Hence, in this text, we consider only the adiabatic case.

In analogy to the compressor isentropic efficiency, we define the *isentropic efficiency* of the turbine by

$$\eta_t = \frac{\text{actual turbine work for a given } \pi_t}{\text{ideal turbine work for a given } \pi_t}$$

The actual and ideal expansion processes for a given π_t are shown in Fig. 6-10 on a T-s diagram. The actual turbine work per unit mass is $h_{t4} - h_{t5}$ $[=c_p(T_{t4} - T_{t5})]$, and the ideal turbine work per unit mass is $h_{t4} - h_{t5i}$ $[=c_p(T_{t4} - T_{t5i})]$. Here, T_{t5i} is the ideal turbine leaving total temperature. Writing the isentropic efficiency of the turbine in terms of the thermodynamic properties, we have

$$\eta_t = \frac{h_{t4} - h_{t5}}{h_{t4} - h_{t5i}} = \frac{T_{t4} - T_{t5}}{T_{t4} - T_{t5i}}$$

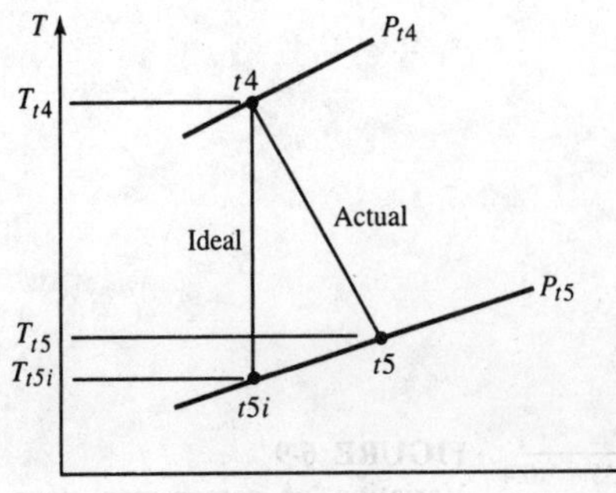

FIGURE 6-10
Actual and ideal turbine processes.

or

$$\boxed{\eta_t = \frac{1 - \tau_t}{1 - \pi_t^{(\gamma-1)/\gamma}}} \tag{6-18}$$

Turbine Stage Efficiency

In a completely similar analysis to that for the compressor, the turbine isentropic efficiency can be written in terms of η_{sj} and π_{sj}:

$$\eta_t = \frac{1 - \prod_{j=1}^{N} [1 - (1/\eta_{sj})(\pi_{sj}^{(\gamma-1)/\gamma} - 1)]}{1 - \pi_t^{(\gamma-1)/\gamma}} \tag{6-19}$$

When all stages have the same π_s and η_s, the above equation reduces to

$$\boxed{\eta_t = \frac{1 - [1 - (1/\eta_s)(1 - \pi_s^{(\gamma-1)/\gamma})]^N}{1 - \pi_t^{(\gamma-1)/\gamma}}} \tag{6-20}$$

Turbine Polytropic Efficiency

The *polytropic turbine efficiency* e_t is defined similarly to the turbine isentropic efficiency as

$$e_t = \frac{\text{actual turbine work for a differential pressure change}}{\text{ideal turbine work for a differential pressure change}}$$

Thus $$e_t = \frac{dw}{dw_i} = \frac{dh_t}{dh_{ti}} = \frac{dT_t}{dT_{ti}}$$

For the isentropic relationship, we have

$$\frac{dT_{ti}}{T_t} = \frac{\gamma - 1}{\gamma} \frac{dP_t}{P_t}$$

Thus $$e_t = \frac{dT_t}{dT_{ti}} = \frac{dT_t/T_t}{dT_{ti}/T_t} = \frac{dT_t/T_t}{[(\gamma - 1/\gamma]\, dP_t/P_t}$$

Assuming that the polytropic efficiency e_t is constant over the pressure ratio, the above equation we integrate to give

$$\boxed{\pi_t = \tau_t^{\gamma/[(\gamma-1)e_t]}} \tag{6-21}$$

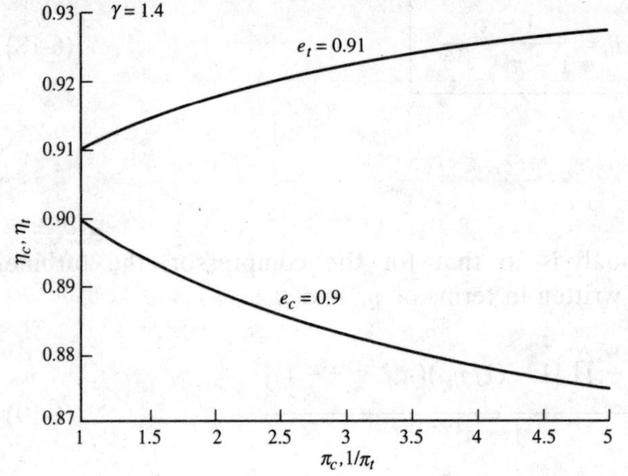

FIGURE 6-11
Compressor and turbine efficienes versus pressure ratio.

so

$$\boxed{\eta_t = \frac{1 - \tau_t}{1 - \tau_t^{1/e_t}}} \tag{6-22}$$

or

$$\boxed{\eta_t = \frac{1 - \pi_t^{(\gamma-1)/(\gamma e_t)}}{1 - \pi_t^{(\gamma-1)/\gamma}}} \tag{6-23}$$

The above relationship is plotted in Fig. 6-11 along with Eq. (6-15) for the compressor. Note that the turbine efficiency increases with the turbine expression ratio $1/\pi_t$ for a constant e_t.

In cycle analysis, τ_t is usually first obtained from the work balance. Then π_t can be calculated for a known e_t by using Eq. (6-21), and η_t can be calculated by using either Eq. (6-22) or Eq. (6-23). We will use the polytopic efficiency e_t as the figure of merit for the turbine.

6-6 BURNER EFFICIENCY AND PRESSURE LOSS

In the burner, we are concerned with two efforts: incomplete combustion of the fuel and total pressure loss. *Combustion efficiency* η_b is defined by

$$\eta_b = \frac{(\dot{m} + \dot{m}_f)h_{t4} - \dot{m}h_{t3}}{\dot{m}_f h_{PR}} = \frac{(\dot{m} + \dot{m}_f)c_{p4}T_{t4} - \dot{m}c_{p3}T_{t3}}{\dot{m}_f h_{PR}}$$

We will approximate c_{p3} as c_{pc} (a constant for the engine upstream of the burner) and c_{p4} as c_{pt} (a constant average value for the gases downstream of the burner). Thus the combustion efficiency is

$$\boxed{\eta_b = \frac{(\dot{m} + \dot{m}_f)c_{pt}T_{t4} - \dot{m}c_{pc}T_{t3}}{\dot{m}_f h_{PR}}} \tag{6-24}$$

The total pressure losses arise from two effects: the viscous losses in the combustion chamber and the total pressure loss due to combustion at finite Mach number. These effects are combined for the purpose of performance analysis in

$$\pi_b = \frac{P_{t4}}{P_{t3}} < 1$$

We will use both η_b and π_b as the figures of merit for the burner. There are similar combustion efficiencies and total pressure ratios for afterburners (augmenters) and duct burners.

6-7 EXHAUST NOZZLE LOSS

The primary loss due to the nozzle has to do with the over- or underexpansion of the nozzle. In addition, there will be a loss in total pressure from turbine to exit. Thus we may have

$$P_9 \neq P_0 \qquad \text{and} \qquad \pi_n = \frac{P_{t9}}{P_{t8}} < 1$$

We still have $\tau_n = 1$, since the nozzle is very nearly adiabatic. We will use π_n as the figure of merit for the nozzle.

6-8 SUMMARY OF COMPONENT FIGURES OF MERIT (CONSTANT c_p VALUES)

Table 6-1 summarizes the ideal and actual behaviors of gas turbine engine components with calorically perfect gases. Note that for a compressor with constant polytropic efficiency, the isentropic efficiency follows from Eq. (6-15). We will use these figures of merit in the following chapter.

At a particular level of technological development, the polytropic efficiency e_c for the compressor can be considered to be a constant, and thus the compressor pressure ratio π_c determines the compressor efficiency η_c [see Eq. (6-16)]. Similarly, the polytropic efficiency e_t for the turbine can be considered to be a constant, and thus the turbine temperature ratio τ_t determines the turbine efficiency η_t [see Eq. (6-22)]. For the analysis in the

TABLE 6-1
Summary of component figures of merit (constant c_p values)

Component	Ideal behavior	Actual behavior	Figure of merit
Inlet	Adiabatic and reversible (isentropic)	Adiabatic, not reversible	
	$\tau_d = 1,\quad \pi_d = 1$	$\tau_d = 1,\quad \pi_d < 1$	π_d
Compressor	Adiabatic and reversible (isentropic)	Adiabatic, not reversible	
	$w_c = c_p T_{t2}(\tau_c - 1)$	$w_c = c_{pc} T_{t2}(\tau_c - 1)$	
	$\pi_c = \tau_c^{\gamma/(\gamma-1)}$	$\pi_c = [1 + \eta_c(\tau_c - 1)]^{\gamma_c/(\gamma_c-1)}$	η_c
		$\tau_c = 1 + \dfrac{1}{\eta_c}(\pi_c^{(\gamma_c-1)/\gamma_c} - 1)$	
		$\tau_c = (\pi_c)^{(\gamma_c-1)/(\gamma_c e_c)}$	e_c
Burner	No total pressure loss, 100% combustion	Total pressure loss, combustion < 100%	
	$\pi_b = 1$	$\pi_b < 1$	π_b
	$\dot{m}c_p T_{t4} - \dot{m}c_p T_{t3} = \dot{m}_f h_{PR}$	$(\dot{m} + \dot{m}_f)c_{pt} T_{t4} - \dot{m}c_{pc} T_{t3} = \eta_b \dot{m}_f h_{PR}$	η_b
Turbine	Adiabatic and reversible (isentropic)	Adiabatic, not reversible	
	$w_t = c_p T_{t4}(1 - \tau_t)$	$w_t = c_{pt} T_{t4}(1 - \tau_t)$	
	$\pi_t = \tau_t^{\gamma/(\gamma-1)}$	$\pi_t = \left[1 - \dfrac{1}{\eta_t}(1 - \tau_t)\right]^{\gamma_t/(\gamma_t-1)}$	η_t
		$\tau_t = 1 - \eta_t(1 - \pi_t^{(\gamma_t-1)/\gamma_t})$	
		$\pi_t = \tau_t^{\gamma_t/[(\gamma_t-1)e_t]}$	e_t
Nozzle	Adiabatic and reversible (isentropic)	Adiabatic, not reversible	
	$\tau_n = 1,\quad \pi_n = 1$	$\tau_n = 1,\quad \pi_n < 1$	π_n

following chapter, we will use the polytropic efficiencies as input data and will calculate the resulting component efficiencies.

The values of these figures of merit have changed as technology has improved over the years. In addition, the values of the figures of merit for the diffuser and nozzle depend on the application. For example, a commercial airliner with engine nacelles and convergent, fixed-area exhaust nozzles will typically have much higher values of π_d and π_n than a supersonic fighter with its engines in the airframe and convergent-divergent, variable-area exhaust

TABLE 6-2
Component figures of merit for different technological levels

Component	Figure of merit	Type	Level of technology 1	2	3	4
		A	0.90	0.95	0.98	0.995
Diffuser	$\pi_{d\,\max}$	*B*	0.88	0.93	0.96	0.98
		C	0.85	0.90	0.94	0.96
Compressor	e_c		0.80	0.84	0.88	0.90
Fan	e_f		0.78	0.82	0.86	0.89
Burner	π_b		0.90	0.92	0.94	0.95
	η_b		0.85	0.91	0.98	0.99
Turbine	e_t	Uncooled	0.80	0.85	0.89	0.90
		Cooled		0.83	0.87	0.89
Afterburner	π_b		0.90	0.92	0.94	0.95
	η_b		0.85	0.91	0.96	0.99
		D	0.95	0.97	0.98	0.995
Nozzle	π_n	*E*	0.93	0.96	0.97	0.98
		F	0.90	0.93	0.95	0.97
Maximum T_{t4}		(K)	1110	1390	1780	2000
		(°R)	2000	2500	3200	3600
Maximum T_{t7}		(K)	1390	1670	2000	2220
		(°R)	2500	3000	3600	4000

A = subsonic aircraft with engines in nacelles
B = subsonic aircraft with engine(s) in airframe
C = supersonic aircraft with engine(s) in airframe
D = fixed-area convergent nozzle
E = variable-area convergent nozzle
F = variable-area convergent-divergent nozzle

nozzles. Table 6-2 lists typical values for the figures of merit that correspond to different periods in the evolution of engine technology (called *levels of technology*) and the application.

6-9 COMPONENT PERFORMANCE WITH VARIABLE c_p

In the section "Gas Tables" of Chap. 2, we developed the relationships [Eqs. (2-61), (2-62), and (2-65)] for the thermodynamic properties h, ϕ, and s of a perfect gas with variable specific heat. In addition, the reduced pressure P_r and reduced volume v_r were defined by Eqs. (2-63) and (2-64), respectively. We will use these properties to describe the performance of engine components when the variation of specific heat is to be included. We will use App. D or the computer program AFPROP to obtain the thermodynamic properties.

The notation π_a [see Eq. (5-3)] represents a component's total pressure ratio. However, we will use a modified definition for τ_a to represent the ratio of total enthalpies [see original definition given by Eq. (5-4)]. Thus

$$\boxed{\tau_a = \frac{\text{total enthalpy leaving component } a}{\text{total enthalpy entering component } a}} \tag{6-25}$$

Free Stream Properties

From the definition of the total enthalpy and total pressure, we can write

$$\boxed{\tau_r = \frac{h_{t0}}{h_0} = \frac{h_0 + V_0^2/(2g_c)}{h_0} \qquad \text{and} \qquad \pi_r = \frac{P_{t0}}{P_0} = \frac{P_{r\,t0}}{P_{r\,0}}} \tag{6-26}$$

Inlet

Since the inlet is assumed to be adiabatic, then

$$\boxed{\tau_d = \frac{h_{t2}}{h_{t0}} = 1} \tag{6-27}$$

By using Eq. (2-65), the inlet total pressure ratio can be expressed in terms of the entropy change as follows:

$$\boxed{\pi_d = \frac{P_{t2}}{P_{t0}} = \exp\left(-\frac{s_2 - s_0}{R}\right)} \tag{6-28}$$

Compressor

The variable τ_c represents the total enthalpy ratio of the compressor, and π_c represents its total pressure ratio, or

$$\boxed{\tau_c = \frac{h_{t3}}{h_{t2}} \qquad \text{and} \qquad \pi_c = \frac{P_{t3}}{P_{t2}}} \tag{6-29}$$

The polytropic efficiency of the compressor e_c can be written as

$$e_c = \frac{dh_{ti}}{dh_t} = \frac{dh_{ti}/T_t}{dh_t/T_t}$$

By using the Gibbs equation [Eq. (2-41)], the numerator in the above equation can be expressed as

$$\frac{dh_{ti}}{T_t} = R\frac{dP_t}{P_t}$$

Thus

$$\boxed{e_c = R\frac{dP_t/P_t}{dh_t/T_t}} \tag{6-30}$$

For a constant polytropic efficiency, integration of the above equation between states $t2$ and $t3$ gives

$$\phi_{t3} - \phi_{t2} = \frac{R}{e_c}\ln\frac{P_{t3}}{P_{t2}}$$

Thus the compressor pressure ratio π_c can be written as

$$\pi_c = \frac{P_{t3}}{P_{t2}} = \exp\left(e_c\frac{\phi_{t3} - \phi_{t2}}{R}\right)$$

or

$$\boxed{\pi_c = \left(\frac{P_{r\,t3}}{P_{r\,t2}}\right)^{e_c}} \tag{6-31}$$

The reduced pressure at state $t2$ can be obtained from App. D or the computer program AFPROP, given the temperature at state $t2$. If the values of π_c and e_c are also known, one can get the reduced pressure at state $t3$ by using

$$P_{r\,t3} = P_{r\,t2}\,\pi_c^{1/e_c} \tag{6-32}$$

Given the reduced pressure at state $t3$, the total temperature and total enthalpy can be obtained from App. D or the computer program AFPROP.

The isentropic efficiency of a compressor can be expressed as

$$\eta_c = \frac{h_{t3i} - h_{t2}}{h_{t3} - h_{t2}} \tag{6-33}$$

This equation requires that the total enthalpy be known at states $t2$, $t3$, and $t3i$.

Example 6-2. Air at 1 atm and 540°R enters a compressor whose polytropic efficiency is 0.9. If the compressor pressure ratio is 15, determine the leaving total properties and compressor isentropic efficiency. From App. D for $f = 0$, we have

$$h_{t2} = 129.02 \text{ Btu/lbm} \qquad \text{and} \qquad P_{r\,t2} = 1.384$$

The exit total pressure is 15 atm. The reduced pressures at stations $t3$ and $t3i$ are

$$P_{r\,t3} = P_{r\,t2}\pi_c^{1/e_c} = 1.384 \times 15^{1/0.9} = 28.048$$

$$P_{r\,t3i} = P_{r\,t2}\pi_c = 1.384 \times 15 = 20.76$$

Linear interpolation of App. D, with $f = 0$ and using the above reduced pressures, gives the following values of total enthalpy and total temperature:

$$h_{t3} = 304.48 \text{ Btu/lbm} \qquad \text{and} \qquad T_{t3} = 1251.92°\text{R}$$

$$h_{t3i} = 297.67 \text{ Btu/lbm} \qquad \text{and} \qquad T_{t3i} = 1154.58°\text{R}$$

The compressor isentropic efficiency is

$$\eta_c = \frac{279.67 - 129.02}{304.48 - 129.02} = 0.8586$$

Burner

The τ_b represents the total enthalpy ratio of the burner, and π_b represents its total pressure ratio, or

$$\boxed{\tau_b = \frac{h_{t4}}{h_{t3}} \qquad \text{and} \qquad \pi_b = \frac{P_{t4}}{P_{t3}}} \tag{6-34}$$

From the definition of burner efficiency, we have

$$\eta_b = \frac{(\dot{m} + \dot{m}_f)h_{t4} - \dot{m}h_{t3}}{\dot{m}_f h_{PR}}$$

or

$$\eta_b = \frac{(1 + f)h_{t4} - h_{t3}}{f h_{PR}} \tag{6-35}$$

where f is the ratio of the fuel flow rate to the airflow rate entering the burner, or $f = \dot{m}_f / \dot{m}$.

In the analysis of gas turbine engines, we determine the fuel/air ratio f and normally specify η_b, h_{PR}, and T_{t4}. The enthalpy at station $t3$ (h_{t3}) will be known from analysis of the compressor. Equation (6-35) can be solved for the fuel/air ratio f, giving

$$\boxed{f = \frac{h_{t4} - h_{t3}}{\eta_b h_{PR} - h_{t4}}} \tag{6-36}$$

Note: The value of h_{t4} is a function of the fuel/air ratio f, and thus the solution of Eq. (6-36) is iterative.

Turbine

The τ_t represents the total enthalpy ratio of the turbine, and π_t represents its total pressure ratio or

$$\boxed{\tau_t = \frac{h_{t5}}{h_{t4}} \quad \text{and} \quad \pi_t = \frac{P_{t5}}{P_{t4}}} \tag{6-37}$$

The *polytropic efficiency of a turbine* is defined as

$$e_t = \frac{dh_t}{dh_{ti}}$$

which can be written as

$$\boxed{e_t = \frac{1}{R}\frac{dh_t/T_t}{dP_t/P_t}} \tag{6-38}$$

For constant polytropic efficiency, the following relationships are obtained by integration from state $t4$ to $t5$:

$$\pi_t = \frac{P_{t5}}{P_{t4}} = \exp\frac{\phi_{t5} - \phi_{t4}}{Re_t} \tag{6-39}$$

and

$$\boxed{\pi_t = \left(\frac{P_{r\,t5}}{P_{r\,t4}}\right)^{1/e_t}} \tag{6-40}$$

The *isentropic efficiency of the turbine* is defined as

$$\eta_t = \frac{h_{t4} - h_{t5}}{h_{t4} - h_{t5i}} \tag{6-41}$$

where each total enthalpy is a function of the total temperature T_t and fuel/air ratio f.

Example 6-3. Products of combustion ($f = 0.0338$) at 20 atm and 3000°R enter a turbine whose polytropic efficiency is 0.9. If the total enthalpy of the flow through the turbine decreases 100 Btu/lbm, determine the leaving total properties and turbine isentropic efficiency. From App. D for $f = 0.0338$, we have

$$h_{t4} = 828.75 \text{ Btu/lbm} \qquad \text{and} \qquad P_{r\,t4} = 1299.6$$

The exit total enthalpy is 728.75 Btu/lbm. From linear interpolation of App. D, the total temperature and reduced pressure at station $t5$ are

$$T_{t5} = 2677.52°\text{R} \qquad \text{and} \qquad P_{rt5} = 777.39$$

From Eq. (6-40), the turbine pressure ratio is

$$\pi_t = \left(\frac{P_{rt5}}{P_{rt4}}\right)^{1/e_t} = \left(\frac{777.39}{1299.6}\right)^{1/0.9} = 0.5650$$

and the reduced pressure at state $t5i$ is

$$P_{rt5i} = P_{rt4}\,\pi_t = 1299.6 \times 0.5650 = 734.3$$

Linear interpolation of App. D, with $f = 0.0338$ and using the above reduced pressure, gives the following values of total enthalpy and total temperature for state $t5i$:

$$h_{t5i} = 718.34 \text{ Btu/lbm} \qquad \text{and} \qquad T_{t5i} = 2643.64°\text{R}$$

The turbine isentropic efficiency is

$$\eta_t = \frac{828.75 - 728.75}{828.75 - 718.34} = 0.9057$$

Nozzle

Since the nozzle is assumed to be adiabatic, then

$$\tau_n = \frac{h_{t9}}{h_{t8}} = 1 \tag{6-42}$$

By using Eq. (2-65), the inlet total pressure ratio can be expressed in terms of the entropy change as follows:

$$\pi_n = \frac{P_{t9}}{P_{t8}} = \exp\left(-\frac{s_9 - s_8}{R}\right) \tag{6-43}$$

The exit velocity is obtained from the difference between the total and static enthalpies as follows:

$$V_9 = \sqrt{2g_c(h_{t9} - h_9)} \tag{6-44}$$

where h_9 is obtained from the reduced pressure at state 9 (P_{r9}) given by

$$P_{r9} = \frac{P_{rt9}}{P_{t9}/P_9} \tag{6-45}$$

PROBLEMS

6-1. Calculate the total pressure recovery η_r, using Eq. (6-6), and the total pressure ratio across a normal shock in air for Mach numbers 1.25, 1.50, 1.75, and 2.0. How do they compare?

6-2. The isentropic efficiency for a diffuser with a calorically perfect gas can be written as

$$\eta_d = \frac{(P_{t2}/P_0)^{(\gamma-1)/\gamma} - 1}{T_{t0}/T_0 - 1}$$

Show that this equation can be rewritten in terms of τ_r and π_d as

$$\eta_d = \frac{\tau_r \pi_d^{(\gamma-1)/\gamma} - 1}{\tau_r - 1}$$

6-3. Starting from Eqs. (6-14) and (6-21), show that the polytropic efficiency for the compressor and turbine can be expressed as

$$e_c = \frac{\gamma_c - 1}{\gamma_c} \frac{\ln \pi_c}{\ln \tau_c} \qquad e_t = \frac{\gamma_t}{\gamma_t - 1} \frac{\ln \tau_t}{\ln \pi_t}$$

6-4. A J-57B afterburning turbojet engine at maximum static power on a sea-level, standard day ($P_0 = 14.696$ psia, $T_0 = 518.7$°R, and $V_0 = 0$) has the data listed in App. B.

a. Calculate the adiabatic and polytropic efficiencies of the low-pressure and high-pressure compressors. Assume $\gamma = 1.4$ for the low-pressure compressor and $\gamma = 1.39$ for the high-pressure compressor.

b. Calculate the adiabatic and polytropic efficiencies of the turbine. Assume $\gamma = 1.33$.

c. Calculate π_b, τ_b, π_{AB}, and τ_{AB}.

6-5. A J-57B afterburning turbojet engine had 167 lbm/sec of air at 167 psia and 660°F enter the combustor (station 3) and products of combustion at 158 psia and 1570°F leave the combustor (station 4). If the fuel flow into the combustor was 8520 lbm/hr, determine the combustor efficiency η_b, assuming $h_{PR} =$ 18,400 Btu/lbm, $c_{pc} = 0.25$ Btu/(lbm · °R), and $c_{pt} = 0.26$ Btu/(lbm · °R).

6-6. A J-57B afterburning turbojet engine had 169.4 lbm/sec of air at 36 psia and 1013°F enter the afterburner (station 6) and products of combustion at 31.9 psia and 2540°F leave the afterburner (station 7). If the fuel flow into the afterburner was 25,130 lbm/hr, determine the afterburner efficiency η_{AB}, assuming $h_{PR} =$ 18,400 Btu/lbm, $c_{pt} = 0.27$ Btu/(lbm · °R), and $c_{PAB} = 0.29$ Btu/(lbm · °R).

6-7. A JT9D high-bypass-ratio turbofan engine at maximum static power on a sea-level, standard day ($P_0 = 14.696$ psia, $T_0 = 518.7$°R, and $V_0 = 0$) has the data listed in App. B.

a. Calculate the adiabatic and polytropic efficiencies of the fan. Assume $\gamma = 1.4$.

b. Calculate the adiabatic and polytropic efficiencies of both the low-pressure and high-pressure compressors. Assume $\gamma = 1.4$ for the low-pressure compressor and $\gamma = 1.39$ for the high-pressure compressor.

c. Calculate the adiabatic polytropic efficiencies of the turbine. Assume $\gamma = 1.35$.

d. Calculate the power (horsepower and kilowatts) into the fan and compressors. Assume $Rg_c = 1716$ ft^2/(sec^2 · °R) and the γ of parts *b* and *c*.

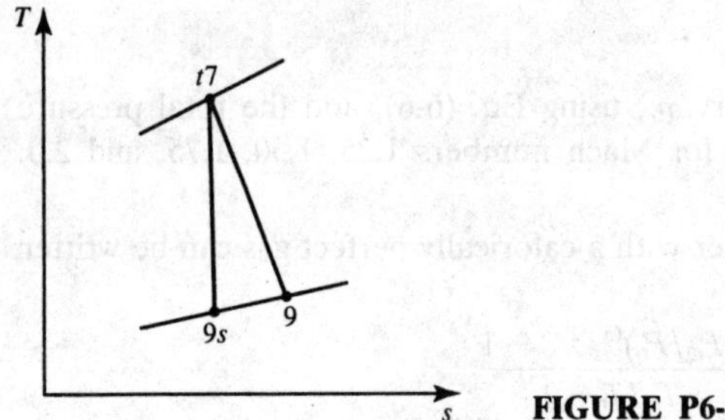

FIGURE P6-8

e. Calculate the power (horsepower and kilowatts) from the turbine for a mass flow rate of 251 lbm/sec. Assume $\gamma = 1.31$ and $Rg_c = 1716\ \text{ft}^2/(\text{sec}^2 \cdot °\text{R})$.

f. How do the results of parts *d* and *e* compare?

6-8. The *isentropic efficiency for a nozzle* η_n is defined as

$$\eta_n = \frac{h_{t7} - h_9}{h_{t7} - h_{9s}}$$

where the states $t7$, 9, and $9s$ are shown in Fig. P6-8. For $P_9 = P_0$, show that the isentropic efficiency for the nozzle in a turbojet engine can be written for a calorically perfect gas as

$$\eta_n = \frac{\text{PIT}^{(\gamma-1)/\gamma} - 1}{\text{PIT}^{(\gamma-1)/\gamma} - (\pi_n)^{(\gamma-1)/\gamma}}$$

where $\text{PIT} = \pi_r \pi_d \pi_c \pi_b \pi_t \pi_n$.

6-9. Repeat Prob. 6-4 with variable gas properties, using App. D or program AFPROP. Compare your results to those of Prob. 6-4.

6-10. Repeat Prob. 6-5 with variable gas properties, using App. D or program AFPROP. Compare your results to those of Prob. 6-5.

6-11. Repeat Prob. 6-6 with variable gas properties, using App. D or program AFPROP. Compare your results to those of Prob. 6-6.

6-12. A JT9D high-bypass-ratio turbofan engine at maximum static power on a sea-level, standard day ($P_0 = 14.696$ psia, $T_0 = 518.7$°R, and $V_0 = 0$) has the data listed in App. B. Assuming 100 percent efficient combustion and $h_{PR} =$ 18,400 Btu/lbm, calculate the fuel/air ratio, using App. D or program AFPROP and starting with an initial guess of 0.03. Now repeat Prob. 6-7 with variable gas properties, using App. D or program AFPROP. Compare your results to those of Prob. 6-7.

CHAPTER 7

PARAMETRIC CYCLE ANALYSIS OF REAL ENGINES

7-1 INTRODUCTION

In Chap. 5, we idealized the engine components and assumed that the working fluid behaved as a perfect gas with constant specific heats. These idealizations and assumptions permitted the basic parametric analysis of several types of engine cycles and the analysis of engine performance trends. In Chap. 6, we looked at the variation of specific heat with temperature and fuel/air ratio and developed component models and *figures of merit.* This allows us to use realistic assumptions as to component losses and to include the variation of specific heats in engine cycle analysis. In this chapter, we develop the cycle analysis equations for many engine cycles, analyze their performance, and determine the effects of real components by comparison with the ideal engines of Chap. 5. We begin our analysis with the turbojet engine cycle and treat the simpler ramjet engine cycle as a special case of the turbojet ($\pi_c = 1$, $\tau_c = 1$, $\pi_t = 1$, $\tau_t = 1$).

7-2 TURBOJET

We will now compute the behavior of the turbojet engine including component losses, the mass flow rate of fuel through the components, and the variation of

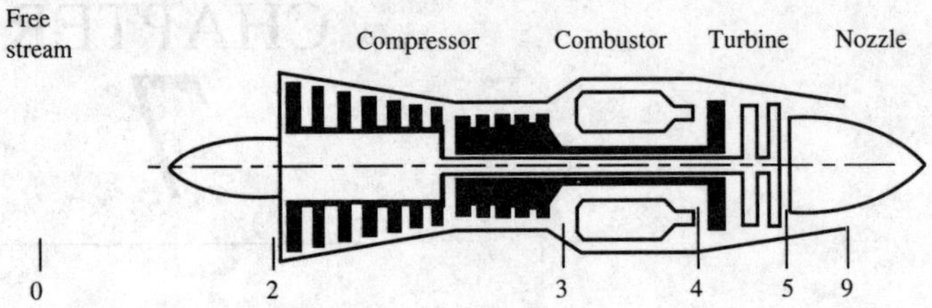

FIGURE 7-1
Station numbering of turbojet engine.

specific heats. Our analysis still assumes one-dimensional flow at the entrance and exit of each component. The variation of specific heats will be approximated by assuming a perfect gas with constant specific heat c_{pc} upstream of the main burner (combustor) and a perfect gas with different constant specific heat c_{pt} downstream of the main burner.

The turbojet engine with station numbering is shown in Fig. 7-1, and the T-s diagram for this cycle with losses is plotted in Fig. 7-2. Figure 7-2 shows the total states for all engine stations along with the static states for stations 0 and 9.

Cycle Analysis

In this section we develop a system of equations to analyze the turbojet engine cycle. The steps of cycle analysis are applied to the turbojet engine and presented below in the order listed in Sec. 5-4.

Step 1. Uninstalled thrust:

$$F = \frac{1}{g_c}(\dot{m}_9 V_9 - \dot{m}_0 V_0) + A_9(P_9 - P_0)$$

$$\boxed{\frac{F}{\dot{m}_0} = \frac{a_0}{g_c}\left(\frac{\dot{m}_9}{\dot{m}_0}\frac{V_9}{a_0} - M_0\right) + \frac{A_9 P_9}{\dot{m}_0}\left(1 - \frac{P_0}{P_9}\right)} \tag{7-1}$$

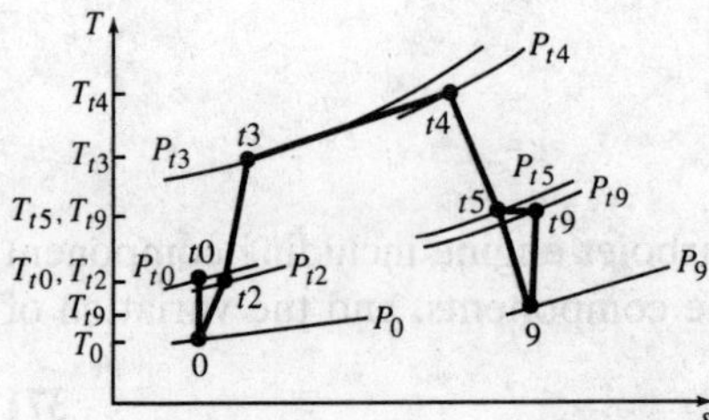

FIGURE 7-2
The T-s diagram for turbojet engine.

We note that

$$\frac{A_9 P_9}{\dot{m}_0}\left(1-\frac{P_0}{P_9}\right)=\frac{\dot{m}_9}{\dot{m}_0}\frac{A_9 P_9}{\rho_9 A_9 V_9}\left(1-\frac{P_0}{P_9}\right)$$

$$=\frac{\dot{m}_9}{\dot{m}_0}\frac{P_9}{[P_9/(R_9 T_9)]V_9}\left(1-\frac{P_0}{P_9}\right)$$

$$=\frac{\dot{m}_9}{\dot{m}_0}\frac{R_9 T_9}{V_9}\left(1-\frac{P_0}{P_9}\right)$$

$$=\frac{\dot{m}_9}{\dot{m}_0}\frac{R_9 T_9}{V_9}\frac{\gamma_0 R_0 g_c T_0}{\gamma_0 R_0 g_c T_0}\left(1-\frac{P_0}{P_9}\right)$$

$$=\frac{\dot{m}_9}{\dot{m}_0}\frac{R_9 T_9}{R_0 T_0}\frac{a_0^2}{\gamma_0 g_c V_9}\left(1-\frac{P_0}{P_9}\right)$$

$$\boxed{\frac{A_9 P_9}{\dot{m}_0}\left(1-\frac{P_0}{P_9}\right)=\frac{a_0}{g_c}\left(\frac{\dot{m}_9}{\dot{m}_0}\frac{R_9}{R_0}\frac{T_9/T_0}{V_9/a_0}\frac{1-P_0/P_9}{\gamma_0}\right)} \tag{7-2}$$

For the case of the turbojet cycle, the mass ratio can be written in terms of the fuel/air ratio f:

$$\frac{\dot{m}_9}{\dot{m}_0}=1+f$$

Using Eq. (7-2) with gas property subscripts c and t for engine stations 0 to 9, respectively, we can write Eq. (7-1) as

$$\boxed{\frac{F}{\dot{m}_0}=\frac{a_0}{g_c}\left[(1+f)\frac{V_9}{a_0}-M_0+(1+f)\frac{R_t}{R_c}\frac{T_9/T_0}{V_9/a_0}\frac{1-P_0/P_9}{\gamma_c}\right]} \tag{7-3}$$

Step 2.

$$\left(\frac{V_9}{a_0}\right)^2=\frac{a_9^2 M_9^2}{a_0^2}=\frac{\gamma_9 R_9 g_c T_9}{\gamma_0 R_0 g_c T_0}M_9^2$$

For the turbojet cycle, this equation becomes

$$\left(\frac{V_9}{a_0}\right)^2=\frac{\gamma_t R_t T_9}{\gamma_c R_c T_0}M_9^2 \tag{7-4}$$

Note: From the definition of τ_λ given in Eq. (5-7), we have

$$\boxed{\tau_\lambda=\frac{c_{pt}T_{t4}}{c_{pc}T_0}} \tag{7-5}$$

Step 3. We have

$$M_9^2 = \frac{2}{\gamma_t - 1}\left[\left(\frac{P_{t9}}{P_9}\right)^{(\gamma_t-1)/\gamma_t} - 1\right] \tag{7-6}$$

where

$$\frac{P_{t9}}{P_9} = \frac{P_0}{P_9}\pi_r\pi_d\pi_c\pi_b\pi_t\pi_n \tag{7-7}$$

Step 4. We have

$$\frac{T_9}{T_0} = \frac{T_{t9}/T_0}{(P_{t9}/P_9)^{(\gamma_t-1)/\gamma_t}}$$

where

$$\frac{T_{t9}}{T_0} = \tau_r\tau_d\tau_c\tau_b\tau_t\tau_n \tag{7-8}$$

Step 5. Application of the first law of thermodynamics to the burner gives

$$\dot{m}_0 c_{pc} T_{t3} + \eta_b \dot{m}_f h_{PR} = \dot{m}_4 c_{pt} T_{t4} \tag{7-9}$$

Dividing the above equation by $\dot{m}_0 c_{pc} T_0$ and using the definitions of temperature ratios give

$$\tau_r\tau_c + f\frac{\eta_b h_{PR}}{c_{pc}T_0} = (1+f)\tau_\lambda$$

Solving for the fuel/air ratio gives

$$\boxed{f = \frac{\tau_\lambda - \tau_r\tau_c}{\eta_b h_{PR}/(c_{pc}T_0) - \tau_\lambda}} \tag{7-10}$$

Step 6. The power balance between the turbine and compressor, with a mechanical efficiency η_m of the turbine compressor coupling, gives

$$\begin{gathered}\text{Power into compressor} = \text{net power from turbine}\\ \dot{m}_0 c_{pc}(T_{t3} - T_{t2}) = \eta_m \dot{m}_4 c_{pt}(T_{t4} - T_{t5})\end{gathered} \tag{7-11}$$

Dividing the above equation by $\dot{m}_0 c_{pc} T_{t2}$ gives

$$\tau_c - 1 = \eta_m(1+f)\frac{\tau_\lambda}{\tau_r}(1 - \tau_t)$$

Solving for the turbine temperature ratio gives

$$\boxed{\tau_t = 1 - \frac{1}{\eta_m(1+f)}\frac{\tau_r}{\tau_\lambda}(\tau_c - 1)} \tag{7-12}$$

This expression enables us to solve for τ_t, from which we then obtain

$$\boxed{\pi_t = \tau_t^{\gamma_t/[(\gamma_t-1)e_t]}} \tag{7-13}$$

We note that η_t will be given in terms of e_t by [Eq. (6-22)]

$$\eta_t = \frac{1-\tau_t}{1-\tau_t^{1/e_t}} \tag{7-14}$$

We also require the calculation of τ_c to allow determination of τ_t. Thus we note from Eq. (6-14)

$$\boxed{\tau_c = \pi_c^{(\gamma_c-1)/(\gamma_c e_c)}} \tag{7-15}$$

Then also, from Eq. (6-15),

$$\eta_c = \frac{\pi_c^{(\gamma_c-1)/\gamma_c}-1}{\tau_c-1} \tag{7-16}$$

Step 7. The equation for specific thrust cannot be simplified for this analysis.

Step 8. The equation for the thrust specific fuel consumption is

$$\boxed{S = \frac{f}{F/\dot{m}_0}} \tag{7-17}$$

Step 9. From the definitions of propulsive and thermal efficiency, one can easily show that for the turbojet engine

$$\eta_P = \frac{2g_c V_0(F/\dot{m}_0)}{a_0^2[(1+f)(V_9/a_0)^2 - M_0^2]} \tag{7-18}$$

and

$$\eta_T = \frac{a_0^2[(1+f)(V_9/a_0)^2 - M_0^2]}{2g_c f h_{PR}} \tag{7-19}$$

Now we have all the equations needed for analysis of the turbojet cycle. For convenience, this system of equations is listed (in the order of calculation) in the following section for easier calculation.

Summary of Equations—Turbojet Engine

INPUTS: M_0, T_0 (K, °R), γ_c, c_{pc} $\left(\frac{\text{kJ}}{\text{kg}\cdot\text{K}}, \frac{\text{Btu}}{\text{lbm}\cdot\text{°R}}\right)$, γ_t, c_{pt} $\left(\frac{\text{kJ}}{\text{kg}\cdot\text{K}}, \frac{\text{Btu}}{\text{lbm}\cdot\text{°R}}\right)$, h_{PR} $\left(\frac{\text{kJ}}{\text{kg}}, \frac{\text{Btu}}{\text{lbm}}\right)$, $\pi_{d\,\max}$, π_b, π_n, e_c, e_t, η_b, η_m, P_0/P_9, T_{t4} (K, °R), π_c

OUTPUTS: $\frac{F}{\dot{m}_0}\left(\frac{\text{N}}{\text{kg/sec}}, \frac{\text{lbf}}{\text{lbm/sec}}\right)$, f, $S\left(\frac{\text{mg/sec}}{\text{N}}, \frac{\text{lbm/hr}}{\text{lbf}}\right)$, η_T, η_P, η_O, η_c, η_t, etc.

EQUATIONS:

$$R_c = \frac{\gamma_c - 1}{\gamma_c} c_{pc} \tag{7-20a}$$

$$R_t = \frac{\gamma_t - 1}{\gamma_t} c_{pt} \tag{7-20b}$$

$$a_0 = \sqrt{\gamma_c R_c g_c T_0} \tag{7-20c}$$

$$V_0 = a_0 M_0 \tag{7-20d}$$

$$\tau_r = 1 + \frac{\gamma_c - 1}{2} M_0^2 \tag{7-20e}$$

$$\pi_r = \tau_r^{\gamma_c/(\gamma_c - 1)} \tag{7-20f}$$

$$\eta_r = 1 \qquad \text{for } M_0 \le 1 \tag{7-20g}$$

$$\eta_r = 1 - 0.075(M_0 - 1)^{1.35} \qquad \text{for } M_0 > 1 \tag{7-20h}$$

$$\pi_d = \pi_{d\,\max} \eta_r \tag{7-20i}$$

$$\tau_\lambda = \frac{c_{pt} T_{t4}}{c_{pc} T_0} \tag{7-20j}$$

$$\tau_c = \pi_c^{(\gamma_c - 1)/(\gamma_c e_c)} \tag{7-20k}$$

$$\eta_c = \frac{\pi_c^{(\gamma_c - 1)/\gamma_c} - 1}{\tau_c - 1} \tag{7-20l}$$

$$f = \frac{\tau_\lambda - \tau_r \tau_c}{h_{PR} \eta_b / (c_{pc} T_0) - \tau_\lambda} \tag{7-20m}$$

$$\tau_t = 1 - \frac{1}{\eta_m (1 + f)} \frac{\tau_r}{\tau_\lambda} (\tau_c - 1) \tag{7-20n}$$

$$\pi_t = \tau_t^{\gamma_t / [(\gamma_t - 1) e_t]} \tag{7-20o}$$

$$\eta_t = \frac{1 - \tau_t}{1 - \tau_t^{1/e_t}} \tag{7-20p}$$

$$\frac{P_{t9}}{P_9} = \frac{P_0}{P_9} \pi_r \pi_d \pi_c \pi_b \pi_t \pi_n \tag{7-20q}$$

$$M_9 = \sqrt{\frac{2}{\gamma_t - 1} \left[\left(\frac{P_{t9}}{P_9} \right)^{(\gamma_t - 1)/\gamma_t} - 1 \right]} \tag{7-20r}$$

$$\frac{T_9}{T_0} = \frac{\tau_\lambda \tau_t}{(P_{t9}/P_9)^{(\gamma_t - 1)/\gamma_t}} \frac{c_{pc}}{c_{pt}} \tag{7-20s}$$

$$\frac{V_9}{a_0} = M_9 \sqrt{\frac{\gamma_t R_t T_9}{\gamma_c R_c T_0}} \tag{7-20t}$$

$$\frac{F}{\dot{m}_0} = \frac{a_0}{g_c} \left[(1 + f) \frac{V_9}{a_0} - M_0 + (1 + f) \frac{R_t T_9 / T_0}{R_c V_9 / a_0} \frac{(1 - P_0/P_9)}{\gamma_c} \right] \tag{7-20u}$$

$$S = \frac{f}{F/\dot{m}_0} \tag{7-20v}$$

$$\eta_T = \frac{a_0^2 [(1 + f)(V_9/a_0)^2 - M_0^2]}{2 g_c f h_{PR}} \tag{7-20w}$$

$$\eta_P = \frac{2 g_c V_0 (F/\dot{m}_0)}{a_0^2 [(1 + f)(V_9/a_0)^2 - M_0^2]} \tag{7-20x}$$

$$\eta_O = \eta_P \eta_T \tag{7-20y}$$

Examples—Turbojet Engine

We begin this section with a single example calculation for a turbojet engine. The other examples involve multiple calculations to investigate trends in engine performance.

Example 7-1. Consider a turbojet engine operating at high speed with the following input data:

INPUTS: $M_0 = 2$, $T_0 = 216.7\text{ K}$, $\gamma_c = 1.4$, $c_{pc} = 1.004\text{ kJ/(kg}\cdot\text{K)}$, $\gamma_t = 1.3$, $c_{pt} = 1.239\text{ kJ/(kg}\cdot\text{K)}$, $h_{PR} = 42{,}800\text{ kJ/kg}$, $\pi_{d\max} = 0.95$, $\pi_b = 0.94$, $\pi_n = 0.96$, $e_c = 0.9$, $e_t = 0.9$, $\eta_b = 0.98$, $\eta_m = 0.99$, $P_0/P_9 = 0.5$, $T_{t4} = 1800\text{ K}$, $\pi_c = 10$

EQUATIONS:

$$R_c = \frac{\gamma_c - 1}{\gamma_c} c_{pc} = \frac{0.4}{1.4}(1.004) = 0.2869\text{ kJ/(kg}\cdot\text{K)}$$

$$R_t = \frac{\gamma_t - 1}{\gamma_t} c_{pt} = \frac{0.3}{1.3}(1.239) = 0.2859\text{ kJ/(kg}\cdot\text{K)}$$

$$a_0 = \sqrt{\gamma_c R_c g_c T_0} = \sqrt{1.4 \times 286.9 \times 1 \times 216.7} = 295.0\text{ m/sec}$$

$$V_0 = a_0 M_0 = 295.0 \times 2 = 590\text{ m/sec}$$

$$V_0 = a_0 M_0 = 295.0 \times 2 = 590\text{ m/sec}$$

$$\tau_r = 1 + \frac{\gamma_c - 1}{2} M_0^2 = 1 + 0.2 \times 2^2 = 1.8$$

$$\pi_r = \tau_r^{\gamma_c/(\gamma_c - 1)} = 1.8^{3.5} = 7.82445$$

$$\eta_r = 1 - 0.075(M_0 - 1)^{1.35} = 1 - 0.075(1^{1.35}) = 0.925$$

$$\pi_d = \pi_{d\max}\eta_r = 0.95 \times 0.925 = 0.87875$$

$$\tau_\lambda = \frac{c_{pt} T_{t4}}{c_{pc} T_0} = \frac{1.239 \times 1800}{1.004 \times 216.7} = 10.2506$$

$$\tau_c = \pi_c^{(\gamma_c - 1)/(\gamma_c e_c)} = 10^{1/(3.5 \times 0.9)} = 2.0771$$

$$\eta_c = \frac{\pi_c^{(\gamma_c - 1)/\gamma_c} - 1}{\tau_c - 1} = \frac{10^{1/3.5} - 1}{2.0771 - 1} = 0.8641$$

$$f = \frac{\tau_\lambda - \tau_r \tau_c}{h_{PR}\eta_b/(c_{pc}T_0) - \tau_\lambda}$$

$$= \frac{10.2506 - 1.8 \times 2.0771}{42{,}800 \times 0.98/(1.004 \times 216.7) - 10.2506} = 0.03567$$

$$\tau_t = 1 - \frac{1}{\eta_m(1 + f)} \frac{\tau_r}{\tau_\lambda}(\tau_c - 1)$$

$$= 1 - \frac{1}{0.99 \times 1.03567} \frac{1.8}{10.2506}(2.0771 - 1) = 0.8155$$

$$\pi_t = \tau_t^{\gamma_t/[(\gamma_t - 1)e_t]} = 0.8155^{1.3/(0.3 \times 0.9)} = 0.3746$$

$$\eta_t = \frac{1 - \tau_t}{1 - \tau_t^{1/e_t}} = \frac{1 - 0.8155}{1 - 0.8155^{1/0.9}} = 0.9099$$

$$\frac{P_{t9}}{P_9}=\frac{P_0}{P_9}\pi_r\pi_d\pi_c\pi_b\pi_t\pi_n$$

$$=0.5\times 7.824\times 0.8788\times 10\times 0.94\times 0.3746\times 0.96=11.621$$

$$M_9=\sqrt{\frac{2}{\gamma_t-1}\left[\left(\frac{P_{t9}}{P_9}\right)^{(\gamma_t-1)/\gamma_t}-1\right]}$$

$$=\sqrt{\frac{2}{0.3}(11.621^{0.3/1.3}-1)}=2.253$$

$$\frac{T_9}{T_0}=\frac{\tau_\lambda\tau_t}{(P_{t9}/P_9)^{(\gamma_t-1)/\gamma_t}}\frac{c_{pc}}{c_{pt}}=\frac{10.2506\times 0.8155}{11.621^{0.3/1.3}}\frac{1.004}{1.239}=3.846$$

$$\frac{V_9}{a_0}=M_9\sqrt{\frac{\gamma_t R_t T_9}{\gamma_c R_c T_0}}=2.253\sqrt{\frac{1.3\times 0.2859}{1.4\times 0.2869}(3.846)}=4.250$$

$$\frac{F}{\dot m_0}=\frac{a_0}{g_c}\left[(1+f)\frac{V_9}{a_0}-M_0+(1+f)\frac{R_t T_9/T_0}{R_c V_9/a_0}\frac{1-P_0/P_9}{\gamma_c}\right]$$

$$=\frac{295}{1}\left(1.03567\times 4.250-2+1.03567\frac{0.2859}{0.2869}\frac{3.846}{4.250}\frac{0.5}{1.4}\right)$$

$$=295(2.4016+0.3336)=806.9\text{ N/(kg/sec)}$$

$$S=\frac{f}{F/\dot m_0}=\frac{0.03567}{806.9}\times 10^6=44.21\text{ (mg/sec)/N}$$

$$\eta_T=\frac{a_0^2[(1+f)(V_9/a_0)^2-M_0^2]}{2g_c f h_{PR}}$$

$$=\frac{295.0^2[(1.03835)4.250^2)-2^2]}{2\times 1\times 0.03567\times 42{,}800\times 1000}=41.92\%$$

$$\eta_P=\frac{2g_c V_0(F/\dot m_0)}{a_0^2[(1+f)(V_9/a_0)^2-M_0^2]}$$

$$=\frac{2\times 1\times 590\times 806.9}{295^2[1.03567(4.250^2)-2^2]}=74.39\%$$

$$\eta_O=\eta_P\eta_T=0.4192\times 0.7439=31.18\%$$

Example 7-2. Now we consider the turbojet cycle with losses over the same range of Mach numbers and compressor pressure ratios as analyzed for the ideal turbojet cycle and plotted in Figs. 5-8, 5-9, and 5-10.

INPUTS: $M_0=0\rightarrow 3$, $T_0=390°\text{R}$, $\gamma_c=1.4$, $c_{pc}=0.24$ Btu/(lbm · °R), $\gamma_t=1.35$, $c_{pt}=0.262$ Btu/(lbm · °R), $h_{PR}=18{,}400$ Btu/lbm, $\pi_{d\,\max}=0.98$, $\pi_b=0.98$, $\pi_n=0.98$, $e_c=0.92$, $e_t=0.91$, $\eta_b=0.99$, $\eta_m=0.98$, $P_0/P_9=1$, $T_{t4}=3000°\text{R}$, $\pi_c=1\rightarrow 30$

The results of the analysis are plotted versus compressor pressure ratio in Figs. 7-3*a* through 7-3*d* and versus flight Mach number in Figs. 7-4*a* through 7-4*d*. When compared to the corresponding figures for the ideal turbojet cycle, the following can be concluded for the turbojet cycle with losses:

a. Specific thrust $F/\dot m_0$. Comparing Fig. 7-3*a* to Fig. 5-8*a* and Fig. 7-4*a* to Fig. 5-9*a*, one can see that the variation of specific thrust with compressor pressure ratio or Mach number is not appreciably changed and the magnitudes are

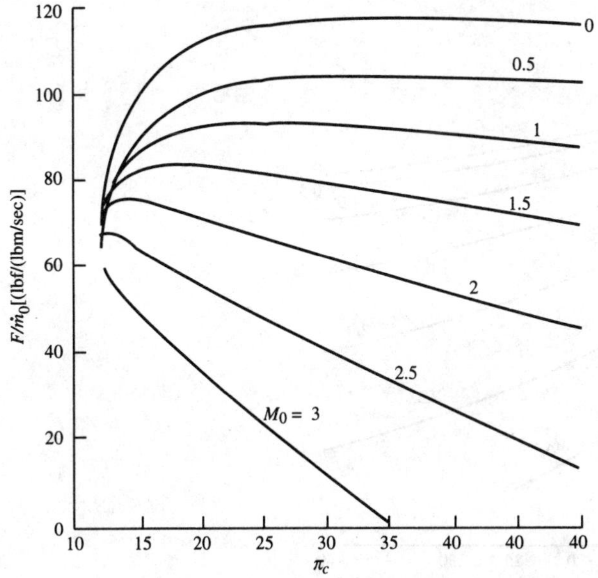

FIGURE 7-3*a*
Turbojet performance versus π_c: specific thrust.

nearly equal. At high Mach numbers, the effect of the losses causes the thrust to go to zero at a lower compressor pressure ratio. For a Mach number, the compressor pressure ratio that gives maximum specific thrust is lower than that of the ideal turbojet. Also, the ramjet cycle ($\pi_c = 1$) does not have thrust for Mach numbers less than 0.3.

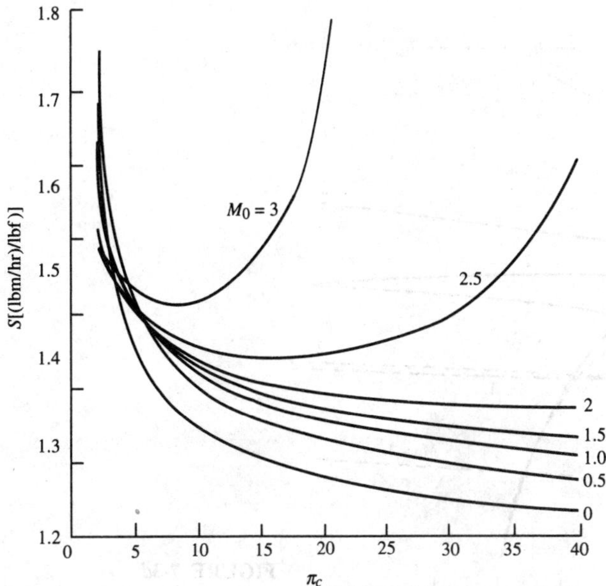

FIGURE 7-3*b*
Turbojet performance versus π_c: thrust specific fuel consumption.

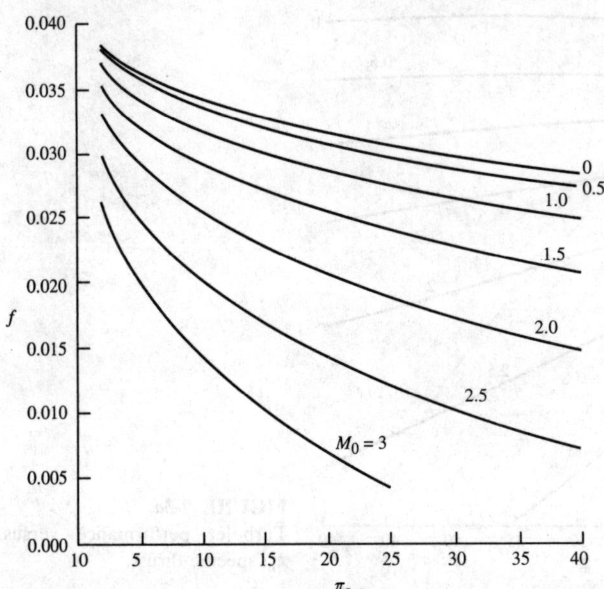

FIGURE 7-3c
Turbojet performance versus π_c: fuel/air ratio.

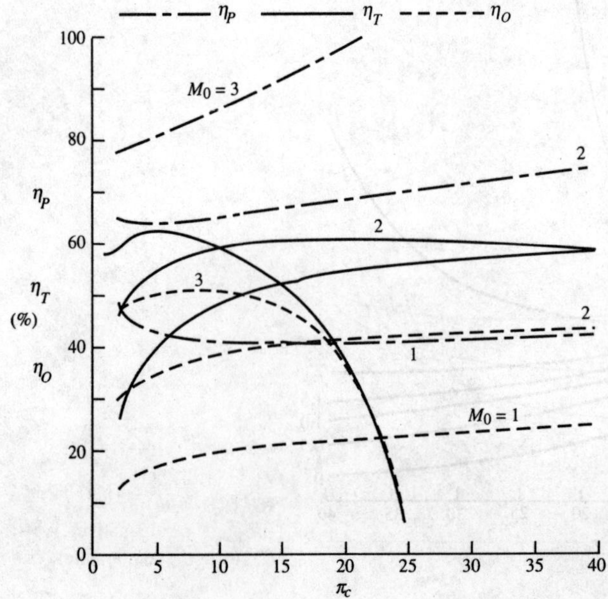

FIGURE 7-3d
Turbojet performance versus π_c: efficiencies.

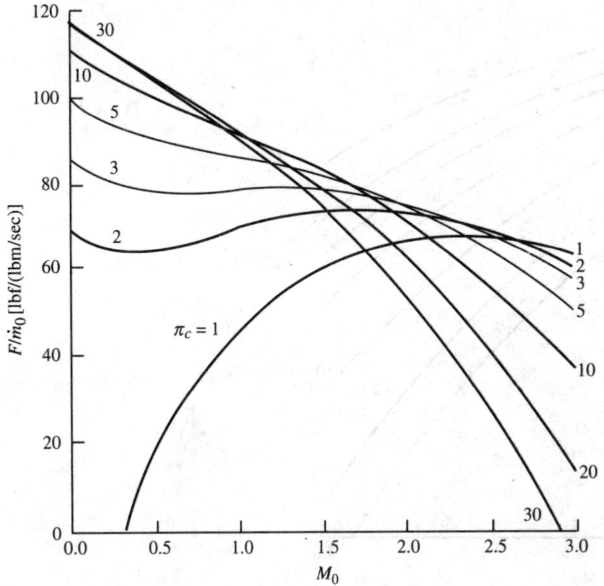

FIGURE 7-4*a*
Turbojet performance versus M_0: specific thrust.

b. Thrust specific fuel consumption S. Comparison of Fig. 7-3*b* to Fig. 5-8*b* and Fig. 7-4*b* to Fig. 5-9*b* shows that the values of fuel consumption are larger for the engine with losses. The thrust specific fuel consumption no longer continues to decrease with increasing compressor pressure ratio, and there is now a compressor pressure ratio giving minimum fuel consumption for a given Mach number.

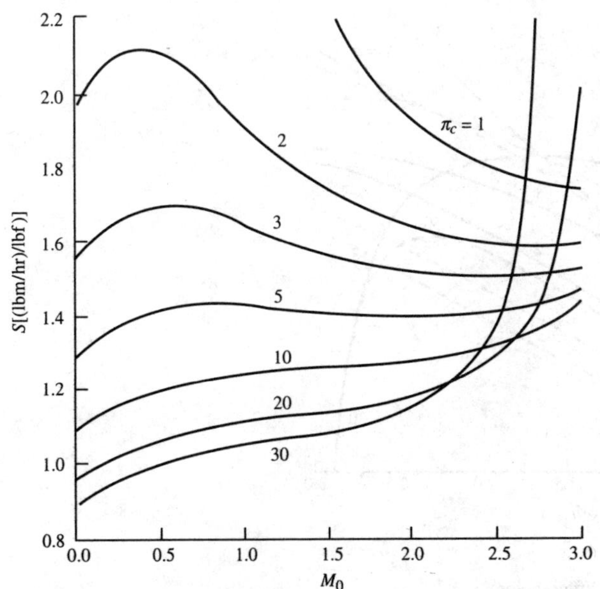

FIGURE 7-4*b*
Turbojet performance versus M_0: thrust specific fuel consumption.

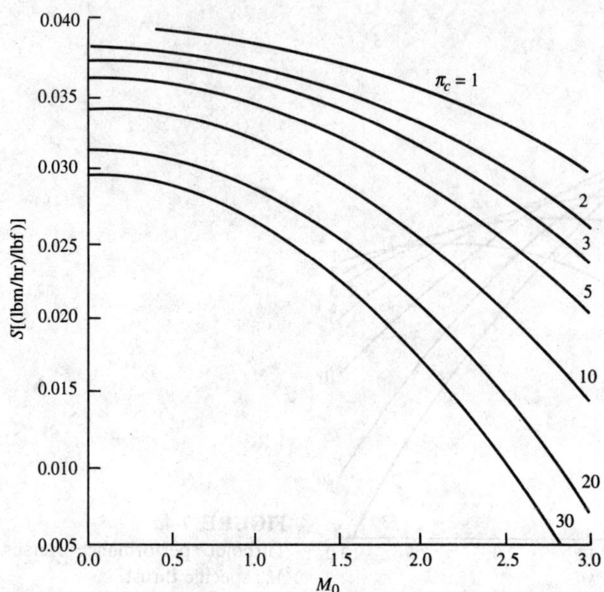

FIGURE 7-4c
Turbojet performance versus M_0: fuel/air ratio.

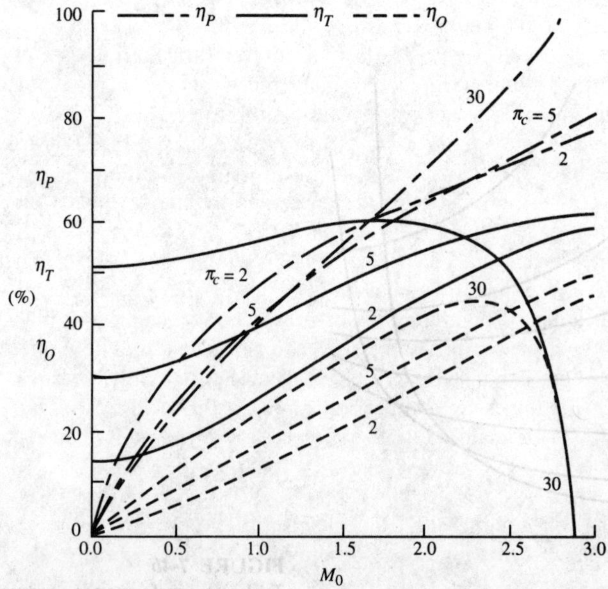

FIGURE 7-4d
Turbojet performance versus M_0: efficiencies.

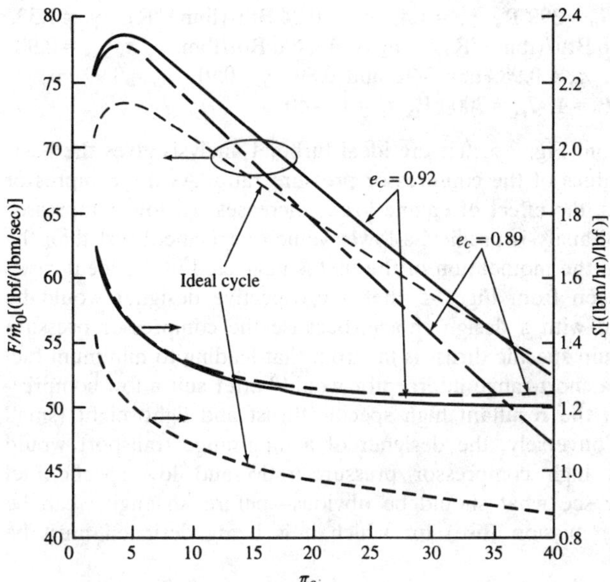

FIGURE 7-5
Effect of compressor polytropic efficiency of turbojet cycle.

c. *Fuel/Air Ratio f.* Comparing Fig. 7-3*c* to Fig. 5-8*c* and Fig. 7-4*c* to Fig. 5-9*c,* we see that the values of the fuel/air ratio are larger for the turbojet with losses. The main reasons for this increase in fuel/air ratio are the increase in specific heat across the main burner, the inefficiency of the combustion process, and the larger mass flow rate exiting the main burner.

d. *Propulsive efficiency* η_P. Comparison of Fig. 7-3*d* to Fig. 5-8*d* and Fig. 7-4*d* to Fig. 5-9*d* shows that the propulsive efficiencies are a little larger for the turbojet with losses. This is due mainly to the decrease in exhaust velocity for the engine with losses.

e. *Thermal efficiency* η_T. Comparing Fig. 7-3*d* to Fig. 5-8*d* and Fig. 7-4*d* to Fig. 5-9*d,* we can see that the engines with losses have lower thermal efficiency. Also, the thermal efficiency of high-compressor-pressure-ratio engines at high Mach go toward zero because the thrust goes to zero before the fuel flow rate.

f. *Overall efficiency* η_O. One can see that the overall efficiencies are lower for the turbojet engines with losses by comparison of Fig. 7-3*d* to Fig. 5-8*d* and Fig. 7-4*d* to Fig. 5-9*d.* This is mainly due to the decrease in thermal efficiency of the engines with losses.

Example 7-3. The effect of compressor efficiency on the performance of a turbojet engine cycle at Mach 2.0 is investigated below. The compressor pressure ratio was varied over the range of 1 to 40 for two different compressor polytropic efficiencies to give the results indicated in Fig. 7-5. Also included on this plot are the results of ideal cycle analysis. The input data for this analysis are listed over:

INPUTS: $M_0 = 2$, $T_0 = 390°\text{R}$, $\gamma_c = 1.4$, $c_{pc} = 0.24\ \text{Btu/(lbm} \cdot °\text{R)}$, $\gamma_t = 1.33$, $c_{pt} = 0.276\ \text{Btu/(lbm} \cdot °\text{R)}$, $h_{PR} = 18{,}400\ \text{Btu/lbm}$, $\pi_{d\,\max} = 0.98$, $\pi_b = 0.98$, $\pi_n = 0.98$, $e_c = 0.92$ and 0.89, $e_t = 0.91$, $\eta_b = 0.99$, $\eta_m = 0.98$, $P_0/P_9 = 1$, $T_{t4} = 3000°\text{R}$, $\pi_c = 1 \to 40$

It can be seen from Fig. 7-5 that the ideal turbojet analysis gives the basic trends for the lower values of the compressor pressure ratio. As the compressor pressure ratio increases, the effect of engine losses increases. At low compressor pressure ratio, the ideal analysis predicts a lower value of specific thrust than the engine with losses since the momentum of the fuel is neglected in the ideal case.

It can also be seen from Fig. 7-5 that a prospective designer would be immediately confronted with a design choice, because the compressor pressure ratio leading to maximum specific thrust is far from that leading to minimum fuel consumption. Clearly, a short-range interceptor would better suit a low compressor pressure ratio with the resultant high specific thrust and lightweight (small compressor) engine. Conversely, the designer of a long-range transport would favor an engine with high compressor pressure ratio and low specfic fuel consumption. Thus we see what should be obvious—before an engine can be correctly designed, the mission (use) for which it is being designed must be precisely understood.

Another aspect of the designer's dilemma becomes apparent when the curves obtained for the two different compressor polytropic efficiencies in Fig. 7-5 are compared. For example, if a designer chooses a compressor pressure ratio of 35 for use in a supersonic transport because the compressor design group has promised a compressor with $e_c = 0.92$, and then the group delivers a compressor with $e_c = 0.89$, clearly the choice $\pi_c = 35$ would be quite inappropriate. That is, such a compressor would have a higher pressure ratio than that leading to minimum fuel consumption. Thus the designer would have a compressor that was heavier (and more expensive) than that leading to a minimum specific fuel consumption, he or she would also have lower specific thrust, and finally the designer would have an acute need to change employers.

The effect of nozzle off-design conditions can be invesigated by considering the engine to have the same parameters as those indicated above, but with various values of P_0/P_9. As an example, we consider an engine with $\pi_c = 16$ and $e_c = 0.92$ to obtain the specific fuel consumption information plotted in Fig. 7-6.

It is apparent that for small exit nozzle off-design conditions ($0.8 <$

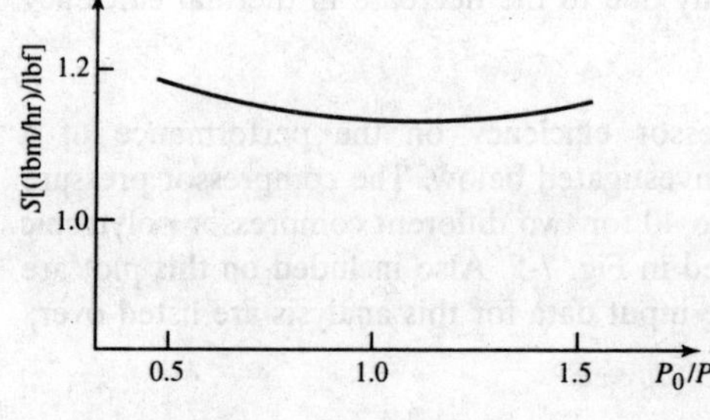

FIGURE 7-6
Effect of nozzle off-design conditions on thrust specific fuel consumption.

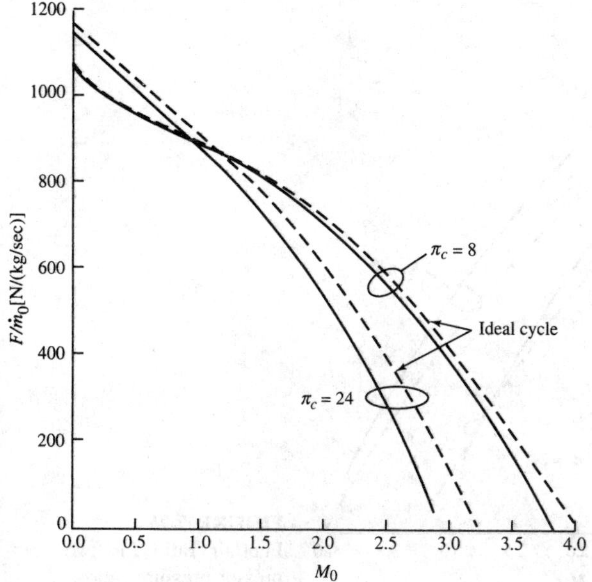

FIGURE 7-7a
Specific thrust for two compressor pressure ratios.

$P_0/P_9 < 1.2$), the thrust and specific fuel consumption vary only slowly with the exit pressure mismatch. This result indicates that the best nozzle design should be determined by considering the external flow behavior (boattail drag, etc.). Note also that for a long-range transport or passenger aircraft, a 1 percent change in specific fuel consumption is very significant.

Example 7-4. Let's consider another example in which we let the Mach number vary and see how the engine performance changes. The flight conditions, design limits, component performance figures of merit, and design choices are listed below. We will compare the turbojet engine with losses with the corresponding ideal engine. The trends that were obtained for the ideal engine are generally true for the engine with losses; exceptions are noted in the following discussion.

INPUTS: $M_0 = 1 \rightarrow 4$, $T_0 = 216.7$ K, $\gamma_c = 1.4$, $c_{pc} = 1.004$ kJ/(kg · K), $\gamma_t = 1.35$, $c_{pt} = 1.096$ kJ/(kg · K), $h_{PR} = 42{,}800$ kJ/kg, $\pi_{d\,\max} = 0.98$, $\pi_b = 0.98$, $\pi_n = 0.96$, $e_c = 0.89$, $e_t = 0.91$, $\eta_b = 0.99$, $\eta_m = 0.98$, $P_0/P_9 = 1$, $T_{t4} = 1670$ K, $\pi_c = 8$ and 24

The specific thrust versus Mach number is plotted in Fig. 7-7*a* for both compressor pressure ratios. The specific thrust is approximately the same as that for the ideal engine. While the exit velocity decreases slightly for the engine with losses, this is compensated by the extra mass flow leaving the engine due to fuel addition.

The fuel/air ratio f versus Mach number is plotted in Fig. 7-7*b* for both compressor pressure ratios. The fuel/air ratio is considerably higher for the engine with losses. There are three reasons for this:

1. The extra mass due to fuel addition, neglected in the ideal case, must be heated to the temperature of the products of combustion leaving the burner. This requires extra fuel.

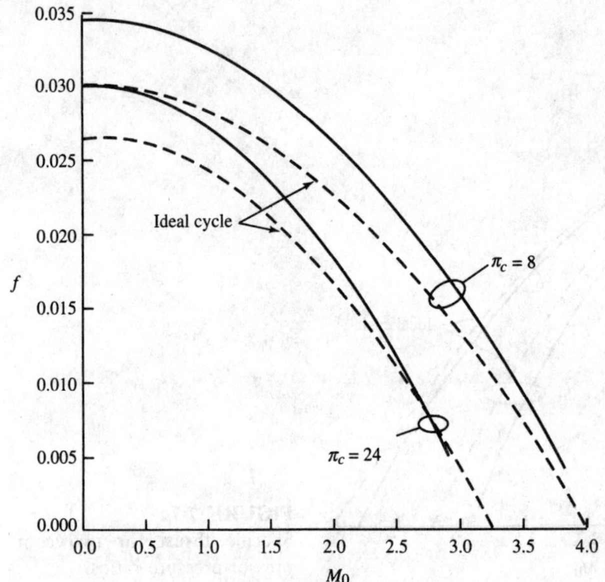

FIGURE 7-7*b*
Fuel/air ratio for two compressor pressure ratios.

2. The combustion process is not 100 percent efficient, so extra fuel is required.
3. Most important, the change in gas properties, i.e., the increase in the specific heat at constant pressure c_p, means that more energy is needed to increase the temperature of the products of combustion than if the gas remained as air with the low-temperature properties. This is true since $h_t = c_p T_t$ and the fuel burned goes to increasing h_t directly and T_t only indirectly.

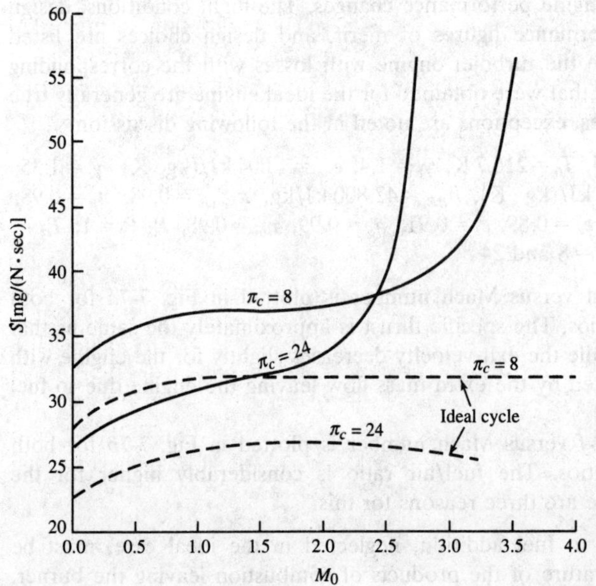

FIGURE 7-7*c*
Specific fuel consumption for two compressor pressure ratios.

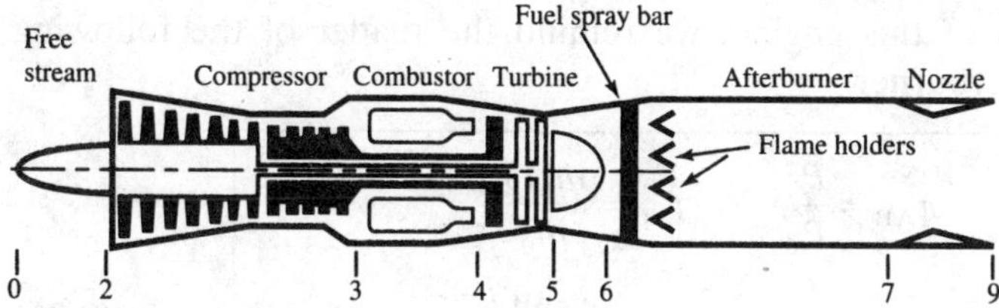

FIGURE 7-8
Ideal afterburning turbojet engine with station numbering.

The thrust specific fuel consumption S versus Mach number is plotted in Fig. 7-7*c* for both compressor pressure ratios. Because the thrust is approximately the same for the ideal engine and the corresponding engine with losses, and since the required fuel/air ratio is higher for the engine with losses, the thrust specific fuel consumption is considerably higher for the engine with losses. For the example given here, the value for the engine with losses is generally higher by 30 to 40 percent. However, the two values really diverge for high flight Mach numbers. The thrust specific fuel consumption starts increasing toward infinity at $M_0 > 2.0$ for a compressor pressure ratio of 8 and at $M_0 > 1.5$ for a compressor pressure ratio of 24. This follows from the definition of the thrust specific fuel consumption—the fuel flow rate divided by the thrust. For the engine with losses, the thrust goes to zero before the fuel flow rate does. This indicates that the thermal efficiency for the turbojet at high speeds goes to zero; i.e., there is a heat input from the fuel, but no net power output because of the component inefficiencies. This is not the case for the ideal engines where the thermal efficiency always increases with flight Mach number.

7-3 TURBOJET WITH AFTERBURNER

The turbojet engine with afterburner is shown in Fig. 7-8, and the temperature-entropy plot of this engine with losses is shown in Fig 7-9. The numbering system indicated in these figures is the industry standard.

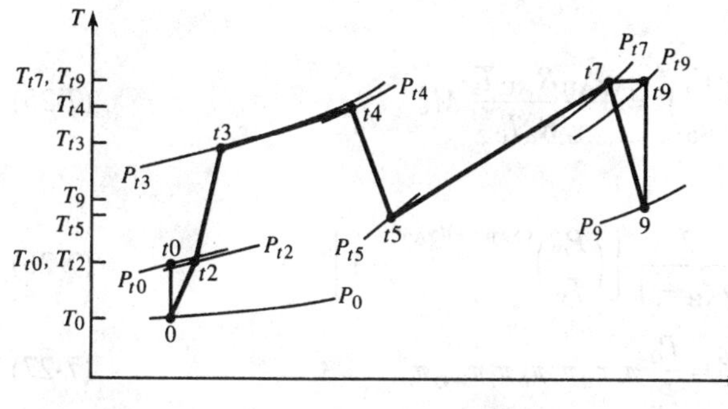

FIGURE 7-9
The T-s diagram for afterburning turbojet engine.

For the analysis of this engine, we remind the reader of the following definitions for the afterburner:

$$\pi_{AB} = \frac{P_{t7}}{P_{t6}} \qquad f_{AB} = \frac{\dot{m}_{fAB}}{\dot{m}_0}$$
$$\tau_{AB} = \frac{T_{t7}}{T_{t6}} \qquad \tau_{\lambda AB} = \frac{c_{pAB}}{c_{pc}} \frac{T_{t7}}{T_0} \tag{7-21}$$
$$\eta_{AB} = \frac{(\dot{m}_0 + \dot{m}_f + \dot{m}_{fAB})c_{pAB} T_{t7} - (\dot{m}_0 + \dot{m}_f)c_{pt} T_{t6}}{\dot{m}_{fAB} h_{PR}}$$

Note that stations 6 and 7 are used for these afterburner parameters. We assume isentropic flow from station 5 to station 6 in the following analysis. Thus Fig. 7-9 shows the afterburning process going from station 5 to 7.

We note, also, that

$$\tau_{\lambda AB} = \frac{c_{PAB}}{c_{pc}} \frac{T_{t4}}{T_0} \frac{T_{t5}}{T_{t4}} \frac{T_{t8}}{T_{t5}} = \frac{c_{pAB}}{c_{pc}} \tau_\lambda \tau_t \tau_{AB} \tag{7-22}$$

and

$$\frac{\dot{m}_9}{\dot{m}_0} = \frac{\dot{m}_0 + \dot{m}_f + \dot{m}_{fAB}}{\dot{m}_0} = 1 + f + f_{AB} \tag{7-23}$$

Cycle Analysis

The expression for the thrust will be the same as that already obtained for the turbojet without afterburning except that the effects of fuel addition in the afterburner must be included. Application of the steps of cycle analysis (see Sec. 5-4) are listed below.

Step 1. The specific thrust equation becomes

$$\frac{F}{\dot{m}_0} = \frac{a_0}{g_c}\left[(1 + f + f_{AB})\frac{V_9}{a_0} - M_0 + (1 + f + f_{AB}) \times \frac{R_{AB}}{R_c}\frac{T_9/T_0}{V_9/a_0}\frac{1 - P_0/P_9}{\gamma_c}\right] \tag{7-24}$$

Step 2. As before,

$$\left(\frac{V_9}{a_0}\right)^2 = \frac{\gamma_{AB} R_{AB} T_9}{\gamma_c R_c T_0} M_9^2 \tag{7-25}$$

Step 3. We have

$$M_9^2 = \frac{2}{\gamma_{AB} - 1}\left[\left(\frac{P_{t9}}{P_9}\right)^{(\gamma_{AB}-1)/\gamma_{AB}} - 1\right] \tag{7-26}$$

where

$$\frac{P_{t9}}{P_9} = \frac{P_0}{P_9} \pi_r \pi_d \pi_c \pi_b \pi_t \pi_{AB} \pi_n \tag{7-27}$$

Step 4. We have

$$\frac{T_9}{T_0} = \frac{T_{t9}/T_0}{(P_{t9}/P_9)^{(\gamma_{AB}-1)/\gamma_{AB}}}$$

where
$$\frac{T_{t9}}{T_0} = \tau_{\lambda AB}\frac{c_{pc}}{c_{pAB}} \tag{7-28}$$

Step 5. Application of the steady flow energy equation to the main combustor gives

$$\boxed{f = \frac{\tau_\lambda - \tau_r\tau_c}{\eta_b h_{PR}/(c_{pc}T_0) - \tau_\lambda}} \tag{7-10}$$

Application of the steady flow energy equation to the afterburner gives

$$(\dot{m}_0 + \dot{m}_f)c_{pt}T_{t6} + \eta_{AB}\dot{m}_{fAB}h_{PR} = (\dot{m}_0 + \dot{m}_f + \dot{m}_{fAB})c_{pAB}T_{t7}$$

This equation can be solved for the afterburner fuel/air ratio f_{AB}, giving

$$\boxed{f_{AB} = (1+f)\frac{\tau_{\lambda AB} - \tau_\lambda\tau_t}{\eta_{AB}h_{PR}/(c_{pc}T_0) - \tau_{\lambda AB}}} \tag{7-29}$$

Step 6. The power balance between the turbine and compressor is unaffected by the addition of the afterburner. So Eqs. (7-12) through (7-16) apply to this engine cycle.

Step 7. Not used in this analysis.

Step 8. The thrust specific fuel consumption S is expressed in terms of both the main burner and afterburner fuel/air ratios as

$$\boxed{S = \frac{f + f_{AB}}{F/\dot{m}_0}} \tag{7-30}$$

Step 9. From the definitions of propulsive and thermal efficiency, one can easily show that for the afterburning turbojet engine

$$\eta_P = \frac{2g_cV_0(F/\dot{m}_0)}{a_0^2[(1+f+f_{AB})(V_9/a_0)^2 - M_0^2]} \tag{7-31}$$

$$\eta_T = \frac{a_0^2[(1+f+f_{AB})(V_9/a_0)^2 - M_0^2]}{2g_c(f+f_{AB})h_{PR}} \tag{7-32}$$

Now we have all the equations needed for analysis of the afterburning turbojet cycle. For convenience, this system of equations is listed (in the order of calculation) in the following section for easier calculation.

Summary of Equations—Afterburning Turbojet Engine

INPUTS: M_0, T_0 (K, °R), γ_c, $c_{pc}\left(\frac{\text{kJ}}{\text{kg}\cdot\text{K}}, \frac{\text{Btu}}{\text{lbm}\cdot°\text{R}}\right)$, γ_t, $c_{pt}\left(\frac{\text{kJ}}{\text{kg}\cdot\text{K}}, \frac{\text{Btu}}{\text{lbm}\cdot°\text{R}}\right)$, $h_{PR}\left(\frac{\text{kJ}}{\text{kg}}, \frac{\text{Btu}}{\text{lbm}}\right)$, γ_{AB}, $c_{pAB}\left(\frac{\text{kJ}}{\text{kg}\cdot\text{K}}, \frac{\text{Btu}}{\text{lbm}\cdot°\text{R}}\right)$, $\pi_{d\,\max}$, π_b, π_{AB}, π_n, e_c, e_t, η_b, η_{AB}, η_m, P_0/P_9, T_{t4} (K, °R), T_{t7} (K, °R), π_c

OUTPUTS: $\frac{F}{\dot{m}_0}\left(\frac{\text{N}}{\text{kg/sec}}, \frac{\text{lbf}}{\text{lbm/sec}}\right)$, f, f_{AB}, $S\left(\frac{\text{mg/sec}}{\text{N}}, \frac{\text{lbm/hr}}{\text{lbf}}\right)$, η_T, η_P, η_O, η_c, η_t, etc.

EQUATIONS: Eqs. (7-20*a*) through (7-20*p*) and the following:

$$R_{AB} = \frac{\gamma_{AB} - 1}{\gamma_{AB}} c_{pAB} \tag{7-33a}$$

$$\tau_{\lambda AB} = \frac{c_{pAB}}{c_{pc}} \frac{T_{t7}}{T_0} \tag{7-33b}$$

$$f_{AB} = (1 + f)\frac{\tau_{\lambda AB} - \tau_\lambda \tau_t}{\eta_{AB} h_{PR}/(c_{pc} T_0) - \tau_{\lambda AB}} \tag{7-33c}$$

$$\frac{P_{t9}}{P_9} = \frac{P_0}{P_9} \pi_r \pi_d \pi_c \pi_b \pi_t \pi_{AB} \pi_n \tag{7-33d}$$

$$\frac{T_9}{T_0} = \frac{T_{t7}/T_0}{(P_{t9}/P_9)^{(\gamma_{AB}-1)/\gamma_{AB}}} \tag{7-33e}$$

$$M_9^2 = \frac{2}{\gamma_{AB} - 1}\left[\left(\frac{P_{t9}}{P_9}\right)^{(\gamma_{AB}-1)/\gamma_{AB}} - 1\right] \tag{7-33f}$$

$$\frac{V_9}{a_0} = M_9 \sqrt{\frac{\gamma_{AB} R_{AB} T_9}{\gamma_c R_c T_0}} \tag{7-33g}$$

$$\frac{F}{\dot{m}_0} = \frac{a_0}{g_c}\left[(1 + f + f_{AB})\frac{V_9}{a_0} - M_0 + (1 + f + f_{AB}) \times \frac{R_{AB}}{R_c} \frac{T_9/T_0}{V_9/a_0} \frac{1 - P_0/P_9}{\gamma_c}\right] \tag{7-33h}$$

$$S = \frac{f + f_{AB}}{F/\dot{m}_0} \tag{7-33i}$$

$$\eta_P = \frac{2 g_c V_0 (F/\dot{m}_0)}{a_0^2[(1 + f + f_{AB})(V_9/a_0)^2 - M_0^2]} \tag{7-33j}$$

$$\eta_T = \frac{a_0^2[(1 + f + f_{AB})(V_9/a_0)^2 - M_0^2]}{2 g_c (f + f_{AB}) h_{PR}} \tag{7-33k}$$

$$\eta_O = \eta_P \eta_T \tag{7-33l}$$

Example 7-5. We consider an example similar to that considered for the "dry" turbojet of Example 7-3 so that we can directly compare the effects of afterburning. Thus we have the following input data:

INPUTS: $M_0 = 2$, $T_0 = 390°\text{R}$, $\gamma_c = 1.4$, $c_{pc} = 0.24\ \text{Btu/(lbm} \cdot °\text{R)}$, $\gamma_t = 1.33$, $c_{pt} = 0.276\ \text{Btu/(lbm} \cdot °\text{R)}$, $h_{PR} = 18{,}400\ \text{Btu/lbm}$, $\gamma_{AB} = 1.30$, $c_{pAB} = 0.295\ \text{Btu/(lbm} \cdot °\text{R)}$, $\pi_{d\,\max} = 0.98$, $\pi_b = 0.98$, $\pi_{AB} = 0.98$, $\pi_n = 0.98$, $e_c = 0.89$, $e_t = 0.91$, $\eta_b = 0.99$, $\eta_{AB} = 0.96$, $\eta_m = 0.98$, $P_0/P_9 = 1$, $T_{t4} = 3000°\text{R}$, $T_{t7} = 3500°\text{R}$, $\pi_c = 2 \rightarrow 14$

In this example, we limit the maximum compressor pressure ratio to 14 because the total temperature leaving the compressor T_{t3} will exceed 1200°F (temperature limit of current compressor materials) at higher pressure ratios. For the afterburning turbojet, we take

$$\pi_n \pi_{AB} = 0.98^2 \qquad \text{afterburner on}$$

$$\pi_n \pi_{AB} = 0.98 \qquad \text{afterburner off}$$

The results are indicated in Fig. 7-10. Note that operation of the afterburner will increase both the specific thrust and the fuel consumption. The magnitude of the increases depends on the compressor pressure ratio. A compressor pressure ratio of 12 gives good specific thrust and fuel consumption for afterburner operation and reasonable performance without the afterburner.

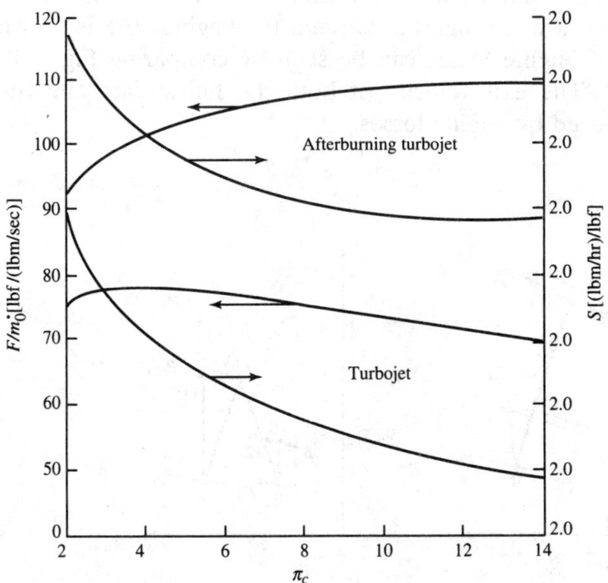

FIGURE 7-10
Performance of turbojet engine with and without afterburner.

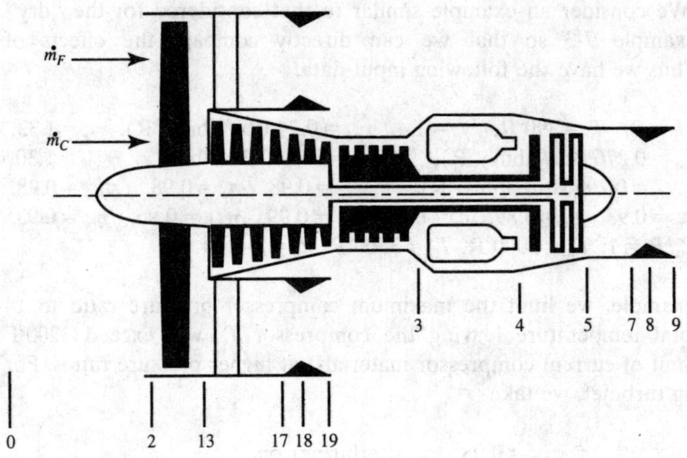

FIGURE 7-11
Station numbering of turbofan engine.

The design compressor pressure ratio will depend on the aircraft and its mission (use), which requires an in-depth analysis.

7-4 TURBOFAN—SEPARATE EXHAUST STREAMS

A turbofan engine with station numbering is shown in Fig. 7-11. A temperature versus entropy plot for the flow through the fan and the engine core is shown in Fig. 7-12. The effect of engine losses can be seen by comparing Fig. 7-12 with Figs. 5-21 and 5-22. The exit velocity of both the fan stream and the engine core stream is reduced by engine losses.

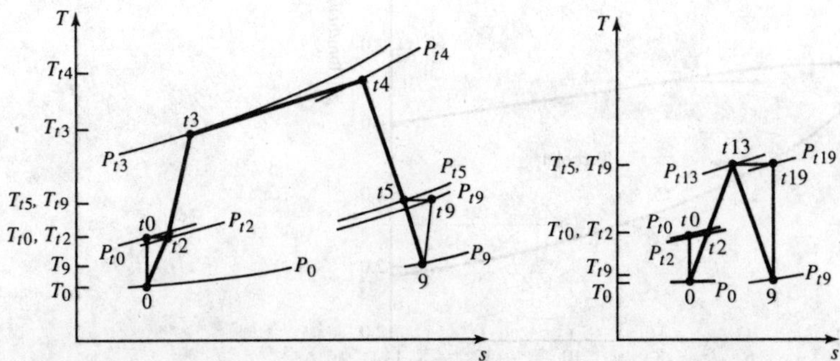

FIGURE 7-12
The T-s diagram of turbofan engine with losses (not to scale).

Cycle Analysis

The assumptions for the analysis of the turbofan engine cycle with losses are as follows:

1. Perfect gas upstream of main burner with constant properties γ_c, R_c, c_{pc}, etc.
2. Perfect gas downstream of main burner with constant properties γ_t, R_t, c_{pt}, etc.
3. All components are adiabatic (no turbine cooling).
4. The efficiencies of the compressor, fan, and turbine are described through the use of (constant) polytropic efficiencies e_c, e_f, and e_t, respectively.

The steps of cycle analysis are applied to the turbofan engine and presented below in the order listed in Sec. 5-4. We will apply the steps of cycle analysis to both the fan stream and the engine core stream.

FAN STREAM. Steps 1 through 4 are as follows:

Step 1. Uninstalled thrust of fan stream F_F:

$$F_F = \frac{\dot{m}_F}{g_c}(V_{19} - V_0) + A_{19}(P_{19} - P_0)$$

Using Eq. (7-2) for the fan stream gives

$$\boxed{\frac{F_F}{\dot{m}_F} = \frac{a_0}{g_c}\left(\frac{V_{19}}{a_0} - M_0 + \frac{T_{19}/T_0}{V_{19}/a_0}\frac{1 - P_0/P_{19}}{\gamma_c}\right)} \tag{7-34}$$

Step 2.

$$\left(\frac{V_{19}}{a_0}\right)^2 = \frac{T_{19}}{T_0} M_{19}^2 \tag{7-35}$$

Step 3. We have

$$M_{19}^2 = \frac{2}{\gamma_c - 1}\left[\left(\frac{P_{t19}}{P_{19}}\right)^{(\gamma_c - 1)/\gamma_c} - 1\right] \tag{7-36a}$$

where

$$\frac{P_{t19}}{P_{19}} = \frac{P_0}{P_{19}} \pi_r \pi_d \pi_f \pi_{fn} \tag{7-36b}$$

Step 4. We have

$$\frac{T_{19}}{T_0} = \frac{T_{t19}/T_0}{(P_{t19}/P_{19})^{(\gamma_c - 1)/\gamma_c}} \tag{7-37a}$$

where

$$\frac{T_{t19}}{T_0} = \tau_r \tau_f \tag{7-37b}$$

ENGINE CORE STREAM. Steps 1 to 5 are the same as for the turbojet engine cycle with losses.

Step 1. Uninstalled thrust:

$$F_C = \frac{1}{g_c}(\dot{m}_9 V_9 - \dot{m}_C V_0) + A_9(P_9 - P_0)$$

or
$$\frac{F_C}{\dot{m}_C} = \frac{a_0}{g_c}\left[(1+f)\frac{V_9}{a_0} - M_0 + (1+f)\frac{R_t}{R_c}\frac{T_9/T_0}{V_9/a_0}\frac{1 - P_0/P_9}{\gamma_c}\right] \tag{7-38}$$

where the fuel/air ratio for the main burner is defined as

$$f \equiv \frac{\dot{m}_f}{\dot{m}_C} \tag{7-39}$$

Step 2.
$$\left(\frac{V_9}{a_0}\right)^2 = \frac{\gamma_t R_t T_9}{\gamma_c R_c T_0} M_9^2 \tag{7-40}$$

Step 3. We have

$$M_9^2 = \frac{2}{\gamma_t - 1}\left[\left(\frac{P_{t9}}{P_9}\right)^{(\gamma_t-1)/\gamma_t} - 1\right] \tag{7-41a}$$

where
$$\frac{P_{t9}}{P_9} = \frac{P_0}{P_9}\pi_r\pi_d\pi_c\pi_b\pi_t\pi_n \tag{7-41b}$$

Step 4. We have

$$\frac{T_9}{T_0} = \frac{T_{t9}/T_0}{(P_{t9}/P_9)^{(\gamma_t-1)/\gamma_t}} \tag{7-42a}$$

where
$$\frac{T_{t9}}{T_0} = \tau_r\tau_d\tau_c\tau_b\tau_t\tau_n = \frac{c_{pc}}{c_{pt}}\tau_\lambda\tau_t \tag{7-42b}$$

Step 5. Application of the first law of thermodynamics to the burner gives

$$\dot{m}_C c_{pc} T_{t3} + \eta_b \dot{m}_f h_{PR} = \dot{m}_4 c_{pt} T_{t4}$$

By using the definitions of the temperature ratios and fuel/air ratio, the above equation becomes

$$\tau_r\tau_c + f\frac{\eta_b h_{PR}}{c_{pc}T_0} = (1+f)\tau_\lambda$$

Solving for f, we get

$$f = \frac{\tau_\lambda - \tau_r\tau_c}{\eta_b h_{PR}/(c_{pc}T_0) - \tau_\lambda} \tag{7-43}$$

Step 6. The power balance between the turbine, compressor, and fan, with a mechanical efficiency η_m of the coupling between the turbine and compressor and fan, gives

$$\underbrace{\dot{m}_C c_{pc}(T_{t3} - T_{t2})}_{\text{power into compressor}} + \underbrace{\dot{m}_F c_{pc}(T_{t13} - T_{t2})}_{\text{power into fan}} = \underbrace{\eta_m \dot{m}_4 c_{pt}(T_{t4} - T_{t5})}_{\text{net power from turbine}} \tag{7-44}$$

Dividing the above equation by $\dot{m}_C c_{pc} T_{t2}$ and using the definitions of temperature ratios, fuel/air ratio, and the bypass ratio [α, Eq. (5-46)], we obtain

$$\tau_c - 1 + \alpha(\tau_f - 1) = \eta_m(1+f)\frac{\tau_\lambda}{\tau_r}(1-\tau_t)$$

Solving for the turbine temperature ratio gives

$$\boxed{\tau_t = 1 - \frac{1}{\eta_m(1+f)}\frac{\tau_r}{\tau_\lambda}[\tau_c - 1 + \alpha(\tau_f - 1)]} \tag{7-45}$$

Equations (7-13) through (7-16) are used to obtain the unknown pressure or temperature ratio and efficiencies of the turbine and compressor. For the fan, the following equations apply:

$$\boxed{\tau_f = \pi_f^{(\gamma_c - 1)/(\gamma_c e_f)}} \tag{7-46}$$

$$\eta_f = \frac{\pi_f^{(\gamma_c-1)/\gamma_c} - 1}{\tau_f - 1} \tag{7-47}$$

Step 7. Combining the thrust equations for the fan stream and the engine core stream, we obtain

$$\boxed{\begin{aligned}\frac{F}{\dot{m}_0} = \frac{1}{1+\alpha}\frac{a_0}{g_c}\left[(1+f)\frac{V_9}{a_0} - M_0 + (1+f)\frac{R_t T_9/T_0}{R_c V_9/a_0}\frac{1-P_0/P_9}{\gamma_c}\right] \\ + \frac{\alpha}{1+\alpha}\frac{a_0}{g_c}\left(\frac{V_{19}}{a_0} - M_0 + \frac{T_{19}/T_0}{V_{19}/a_0}\frac{1-P_0/P_{19}}{\gamma_c}\right)\end{aligned}} \tag{7-48}$$

Step 8. The thrust specific fuel consumption S is

$$S = \frac{\dot{m}_f}{F} = \frac{\dot{m}_f/\dot{m}_C}{(\dot{m}_0/\dot{m}_C)F/\dot{m}_0}$$

or

$$\boxed{S = \frac{f}{(1+\alpha)\,F/\dot{m}_0}} \tag{7-49}$$

Step 9. Expressions for the propulsive efficiency η_P and thermal efficiency η_T are listed below for the case of $P_9 = P_{19} = P_0$. Development of these equations is left as an exercise for the reader.

$$\eta_P = \frac{2M_0[(1+f)(V_9/a_0) + \alpha(V_{19}/a_0) - (1+\alpha)M_0]}{(1+f)(V_9/a_0)^2 + \alpha(V_{19}/a_0)^2 - (1+\alpha)M_0^2} \tag{7-50}$$

$$\eta_T = \frac{a_0^2[(1+f)(V_9/a_0)^2 + \alpha(V_{19}/a_0)^2 - (1+\alpha)M_0^2]}{2g_c f h_{PR}} \tag{7-51}$$

Summary of Equations—Separate-Exhaust-Stream Turbofan Engine

INPUTS: M_0, T_0 (K, °R), γ_c, $c_{pc}\left(\frac{\text{kJ}}{\text{kg}\cdot\text{K}}, \frac{\text{Btu}}{\text{lbm}\cdot{}^\circ\text{R}}\right)$, γ_t, $c_{pt}\left(\frac{\text{kJ}}{\text{kg}\cdot\text{K}}, \frac{\text{Btu}}{\text{lbm}\cdot{}^\circ\text{R}}\right)$, $h_{PR}\left(\frac{\text{kJ}}{\text{kg}}, \frac{\text{Btu}}{\text{lbm}}\right)$, $\pi_{d\,\max}$, π_b, π_n, π_{fn}, e_c, e_f, e_t, η_b, η_m, P_0/P_9, P_0/P_{19}, T_{t4} (K, °R), π_c, π_f, α

OUTPUTS: $\frac{F}{\dot m_0}\left(\frac{\text{N}}{\text{kg/sec}}, \frac{\text{lbf}}{\text{lbm/sec}}\right)$, f, $S\left(\frac{\text{mg/sec}}{\text{N}}, \frac{\text{lbm/hr}}{\text{lbf}}\right)$, η_T, η_P, η_O, η_c, η_t, etc.

EQUATIONS:

$$R_c = \frac{\gamma_c - 1}{\gamma_c} c_{pc} \tag{7-52a}$$

$$R_t = \frac{\gamma_t - 1}{\gamma_t} c_{pt} \tag{7-52b}$$

$$a_0 = \sqrt{\gamma_c R_c g_c T_0} \tag{7-52c}$$

$$V_0 = a_0 M_0 \tag{7-52d}$$

$$\tau_r = 1 + \frac{\gamma_c - 1}{2} M_0^2 \tag{7-52e}$$

$$\pi_r = \tau_r^{\gamma_c/(\gamma_c - 1)} \tag{7-52f}$$

$$\eta_r = 1 \quad \text{for } M_0 \le 1 \tag{7-52g}$$

$$\eta_r = 1 - 0.075(M_0 - 1)^{1.35} \quad \text{for } M_0 > 1 \tag{7-52h}$$

$$\pi_d = \pi_{d\,\max} \eta_r \tag{7-52i}$$

$$\tau_\lambda = \frac{c_{pt} T_{t4}}{c_{pc} T_0} \tag{7-52j}$$

$$\tau_c = \pi_c^{(\gamma_c - 1)/(\gamma_c e_c)} \tag{7-52k}$$

$$\eta_c = \frac{\pi_c^{(\gamma_c - 1)/\gamma_c} - 1}{\tau_c - 1} \tag{7-52l}$$

$$\tau_f = \pi_f^{(\gamma_c - 1)/(\gamma_c e_f)} \tag{7-52m}$$

$$\eta_f = \frac{\pi_f^{(\gamma_c - 1)/\gamma_c} - 1}{\tau_f - 1} \tag{7-52n}$$

$$f = \frac{\tau_\lambda - \tau_r \tau_c}{\eta_b h_{PR}/(c_{pc} T_0) - \tau_\lambda} \tag{7-52o}$$

$$\tau_t = 1 - \frac{1}{\eta_m (1 + f)} \frac{\tau_r}{\tau_\lambda} [\tau_c - 1 + \alpha(\tau_f - 1)] \tag{7-52p}$$

$$\pi_t = \tau_t^{\gamma_t/[(\gamma_t - 1)e_t]} \tag{7-52q}$$

$$\eta_t = \frac{1 - \tau_t}{1 - \tau_t^{1/e_t}} \tag{7-52r}$$

$$\frac{P_{t9}}{P_9} = \frac{P_0}{P_9}\pi_r\pi_d\pi_c\pi_b\pi_t\pi_n \tag{7-52s}$$

$$M_9 = \sqrt{\frac{2}{\gamma_t - 1}\left[\left(\frac{P_{t9}}{P_9}\right)^{(\gamma_t-1)/\gamma_t} - 1\right]} \tag{7-52t}$$

$$\frac{T_9}{T_0} = \frac{\tau_\lambda \tau_t}{(P_{t9}/P_9)^{(\gamma_t-1)/\gamma_t}}\frac{c_{pc}}{c_{pt}} \tag{7-52u}$$

$$\frac{V_9}{a_0} = M_9\sqrt{\frac{\gamma_t R_t T_9}{\gamma_c R_c T_0}} \tag{7-52v}$$

$$\frac{P_{t19}}{P_{19}} = \frac{P_0}{P_{19}}\pi_r\pi_d\pi_f\pi_{fn} \tag{7-52w}$$

$$M_{19} = \sqrt{\frac{2}{\gamma_c - 1}\left[\left(\frac{P_{t19}}{P_{19}}\right)^{(\gamma_c-1)/\gamma_c} - 1\right]} \tag{7-52x}$$

$$\frac{T_{19}}{T_0} = \frac{\tau_r \tau_f}{(P_{t19}/P_{19})^{(\gamma_c-1)/\gamma_c}} \tag{7-52y}$$

$$\frac{V_{19}}{a_0} = M_{19}\sqrt{\frac{T_{19}}{T_0}} \tag{7-52z}$$

$$\begin{aligned}\frac{F}{\dot m_0} = \frac{1}{1+\alpha}\frac{a_0}{g_c}\bigg[(1+f)\frac{V_9}{a_0} - M_0 + (1+f)\\ \times\frac{R_t T_9/T_0}{R_c V_9/a_0}\frac{1-P_0/P_9}{\gamma_c}\bigg] + \frac{\alpha}{1+\alpha}\frac{a_0}{g_c}\\ \times\left(\frac{V_{19}}{a_0} - M_0 + \frac{T_{19}/T_0}{V_{19}/a_0}\frac{1-P_0/P_{19}}{\gamma_c}\right)\end{aligned} \tag{7-52aa}$$

$$S = \frac{f}{(1+\alpha)F/\dot m_0} \tag{7-52ab}$$

$$\mathrm{FR} = \frac{(1+f)\dfrac{V_9}{a_0} - M_0 + (1+f)\dfrac{R_t T_9/T_0}{R_c V_9/a_0}\dfrac{1-P_0/P_9}{\gamma_c}}{\dfrac{V_{19}}{a_0} - M_0 + \dfrac{T_{19}/T_0}{V_{19}/a_0}\dfrac{1-P_0/P_{19}}{\gamma_c}} \tag{7-52ac}$$

$$\eta_P = \frac{2M_0[(1+f)V_9/a_0 + \alpha(V_{19}/a_0) - (1+\alpha)M_0]}{(1+f)(V_9/a_0)^2 + \alpha(V_{19}/a_0)^2 - (1+\alpha)M_0^2} \tag{7-52ad}$$

$$\eta_T = \frac{a_0^2[(1+f)(V_9/a_0)^2 + \alpha(V_{19}/a_0)^2 - (1+\alpha)M_0^2]}{2g_c f h_{PR}} \tag{7-52ae}$$

$$\eta_O = \eta_P\eta_T \tag{7-52af}$$

Exit Pressure Conditions

Separate-stream turbofan engines are generally used with subsonic aircraft and the pressure ratio across both primary and secondary nozzles is not very large. As a result, often convergent-only nozzles are utilized. In this case, if the nozzles are choked, we have

$$\frac{P_{t19}}{P_{19}} = \left(\frac{\gamma_c + 1}{2}\right)^{\gamma_c/(\gamma_c - 1)} \quad \text{and} \quad \frac{P_{t9}}{P_9} = \left(\frac{\gamma_t + 1}{2}\right)^{\gamma_t/(\gamma_t - 1)} \tag{7-53}$$

Thus

$$\boxed{\frac{P_0}{P_{19}} = \frac{P_{t19}/P_{19}}{P_{t19}/P_0} = \frac{[(\gamma_c + 1)/2]^{\gamma_c/(\gamma_c - 1)}}{\pi_r \pi_d \pi_f \pi_{fn}}} \tag{7-54}$$

and

$$\boxed{\frac{P_0}{P_9} = \frac{P_{t9}/P_9}{P_{t9}/P_0} = \frac{[(\gamma_t + 1)/2]^{\gamma_t/(\gamma_t - 1)}}{\pi_r \pi_d \pi_c \pi_b \pi_t \pi_n}} \tag{7-55}$$

Note that these two expressions are valid only when both P_9 and P_{19} are greater than P_0. If these expressions predict P_9 and P_{19} less than P_0, the nozzles will not be choked. In this case, we take $P_{19} = P_0$ and/or $P_9 = P_0$.

Example 7-6. As our first example for the turbofan with losses, we calculate the performance of a turbofan engine cycle with the following input data.

INPUTS: $M_0 = 0.8$, $T_0 = 390°\text{R}$, $\gamma_c = 1.4$, $c_{pc} = 0.240$ Btu/(lbm · °R), $\gamma_t = 1.33$, $c_{pt} = 0.276$ Btu/(lbm · °R), $h_{PR} = 18{,}400$ Btu/lbm, $\pi_{d\,\max} = 0.99$, $\pi_b = 0.96$, $\pi_n = 0.99$, $\pi_{fn} = 0.99$, $e_c = 0.90$, $e_f = 0.89$, $e_t = 0.89$, $\eta_b = 0.99$, $\eta_m = 0.99$, $P_0/P_9 = 0.9$, $P_0/P_{19} = 0.9$, $T_{t4} = 3000°\text{R}$, $\pi_c = 36$, $\pi_f = 1.7$, $\alpha = 8$

EQUATIONS:

$$R_c = \frac{\gamma_c - 1}{\gamma_c} c_{pc} = \frac{0.4}{1.4}(0.24 \times 778.16) = 53.36 \text{ ft} \cdot \text{lbf/(lbm} \cdot °\text{R)}$$

$$R_t = \frac{\gamma_t - 1}{\gamma_t} c_{pt} = \frac{0.33}{1.33}(0.276 \times 778.16) = 53.29 \text{ ft} \cdot \text{lbf/(lbm} \cdot °\text{R)}$$

$$a_0 = \sqrt{1.4 \times 53.36 \times 32.174 \times 390} = 968.2 \text{ ft/sec}$$

$$V_0 = a_0 M_0 = 968.2 \times 0.8 = 774.6 \text{ ft/sec}$$

$$\tau_r = 1 + \frac{\gamma_c - 1}{2} M_0^2 = 1 + 0.2 \times 0.8^2 = 1.128$$

$$\pi_r = \tau_r^{\gamma_c/(\gamma_c - 1)} = 1.128^{3.5} = 1.5243$$

$$\eta_r = 1 \qquad \text{since } M_0 < 1$$

$$\pi_d = \pi_{d\,\max} \eta_r = 0.99$$

$$\tau_\lambda = \frac{c_{pt} T_{t4}}{c_{pc} T_0} = \frac{0.276 \times 3000}{0.240 \times 390} = 8.846$$

$$\tau_c = \pi_c^{(\gamma_c - 1)/(\gamma_c e_c)} = 36^{1/(3.5 \times 0.9)} = 3.119$$

$$\eta_c = \frac{\pi_c^{(\gamma_c - 1)/\gamma_c} - 1}{\tau_c - 1} = \frac{36^{1/3.5} - 1}{3.119 - 1} = \frac{1.784}{2.119} = 84.2\%$$

$$\tau_f = \pi_f^{(\gamma_c - 1)/(\gamma_c e_f)} = 1.7^{1/(3.5 \times 0.89)} = 1.1857$$

$$\eta_f = \frac{\pi_f^{(\gamma_c-1)/\gamma_c} - 1}{\tau_f - 1} = \frac{1.7^{1/3.5} - 1}{1.1857 - 1} = \frac{0.1637}{0.1857} = 88.2\%$$

$$f = \frac{\tau_\lambda - \tau_r \tau_c}{h_{PR}\eta_b/(c_p T_0) - \tau_\lambda}$$

$$= \frac{8.846 - 1.128 \times 3.119}{18{,}400 \times 0.99/(0.24 \times 390) - 8.846} = 0.02868$$

$$\tau_t = 1 - \frac{1}{\eta_m(1+f)} \frac{\tau_r}{\tau_\lambda} [\tau_c - 1 + \alpha(\tau_f - 1)]$$

$$= 1 - \frac{1}{0.99(1.02868)} \frac{1.128}{8.846} [3.119 - 1 + 8(1.1857 - 1)]$$

$$= 0.54866$$

$$\pi_t = \tau_t^{\gamma_t/[(\gamma_t-1)e_t]} = 0.54866^{1.33/(0.33\times 0.89)} = 0.06599$$

$$\eta_t = \frac{1 - \tau_t}{1 - \tau_t^{1/e_t}} = \frac{1 - 0.54866}{1 - 0.54866^{1/0.89}} = 92.0\%$$

$$\frac{P_{t9}}{P_9} = \frac{P_0}{P_9} \pi_r \pi_d \pi_c \pi_b \pi_t \pi_n$$

$$= 0.9 \times 1.5243 \times 0.99 \times 36 \times 0.96 \times 0.06599 \times 0.99 = 3.066$$

$$M_9 = \sqrt{\frac{2}{\gamma_t - 1}\left[\left(\frac{P_{t9}}{P_9}\right)^{(\gamma_t-1)/\gamma_t} - 1\right]} = \sqrt{\frac{2}{0.33}(3.066^{0.33/1.33} - 1)} = 1.394$$

$$\frac{T_9}{T_0} = \frac{8.846 \times 0.54866}{3.066^{0.33/1.33}} \frac{0.240}{0.276} = 3.196$$

$$\frac{V_9}{a_0} = M_9 \sqrt{\frac{\gamma_t R_t T_9}{\gamma_c R_c T_0}} = 1.394 \sqrt{\frac{1.33 \times 53.29}{1.40 \times 53.36}(3.196)} = 2.427$$

$$\frac{P_{t19}}{P_{19}} = \frac{P_0}{P_{19}} \pi_r \pi_d \pi_f \pi_{fn} = 0.9 \times 1.5243 \times 0.99 \times 1.7 \times 0.99 = 2.286$$

$$M_{19} = \sqrt{\frac{2}{\gamma_c - 1}\left[\left(\frac{P_{t19}}{P_{19}}\right)^{(\gamma_c-1)/\gamma_c} - 1\right]} = \sqrt{\frac{2}{0.4}(2.286^{1/3.5} - 1)} = 1.154$$

$$\frac{T_{19}}{T_0} = \frac{\tau_r \tau_f}{(P_{t19}/P_{19})^{(\gamma_c-1)/\gamma_c}} = \frac{1.128 \times 1.1857}{2.286^{1/3.5}} = 1.0561$$

$$\frac{V_{19}}{a_0} = M_{19}\sqrt{\frac{T_{19}}{T_0}} = 1.154\sqrt{1.0561} = 1.186$$

$$\frac{F}{\dot{m}_0} = \frac{1}{1+\alpha} \frac{a_0}{g_c}\left[(1+f)\frac{V_9}{a_0} - M_0 + (1+f)\frac{R_t T_9/T_0}{R_c V_9/a_0} \frac{1 - P_0/P_9}{\gamma_c}\right]$$

$$+ \frac{\alpha}{1+\alpha} \frac{a_0}{g_c}\left(\frac{V_{19}}{a_0} - M_0 + \frac{T_{19}/T_0}{V_{19}/a_0} \frac{1 - P_0/P_{19}}{\gamma_c}\right)$$

$$= \frac{968.2}{9 \times 32.174}\left(1.02868 \times 2.427 - 0.8 + 1.02868 \frac{53.29}{53.36} \frac{3.196}{2.427} \frac{0.1}{1.4}\right)$$

$$+ \frac{8 \times 968.2}{9 \times 32.174}\left(1.186 - 0.8 + \frac{1.0561}{1.186} \frac{0.1}{1.4}\right)$$

$$= 3.3436(1.79324 + 3.59684) = 18.02 \text{ lbf/(lbm/sec)}$$

$$S = \frac{f}{(1+\alpha)F/\dot{m}_0} = \frac{3600 \times 0.02868}{9 \times 18.02} = 0.6366 \text{ (lbm/hr)/lbf}$$

$$\text{FR} = \frac{1.79324}{3.59684/8} = 3.988$$

$$\eta_P = \frac{2M_0[(1+f)V_9/a_0 + \alpha V_{19}/a_0 - (1+\alpha)M_0]}{(1+f)(V_9/a_0)^2 + \alpha(V_{19}/a_0)^2 - (1+\alpha)M_0^2}$$

$$= \frac{2 \times 0.8(1.02868 \times 2.437 + 8 \times 1.86 - 9 \times 0.8)}{1.02868 \times 2.437^2 + 8 \times 1.186^2 - 9 \times 0.8^2} = 74.65\%$$

$$\eta_T = \frac{a_0^2[(1+f)(V_9/a_0)^2 + \alpha(V_{19}/a_0)^2 - (1+\alpha)M_0^2]}{2g_c f h_{PR}}$$

$$= \frac{968.2^2(1.02868 \times 2.427^2 + 8 \times 1.186^2 - 9 \times 0.8^2)}{2 \times 32.174 \times 0.02868 \times 18{,}400 \times 778.16} = 40.98\%$$

$$\eta_O = \eta_T \eta_P = 0.4098 \times 0.7465 = 30.60\%$$

Example 7-7. Since the turbofan cycle has three design variables, its performance with losses can be understood by performing a parametric analysis, plotting the results versus values of the design variables, and comparing results to the performance of the ideal turbofan. Figures 7-13 through 7-16 are plots for turbofan engines with $P_9 = P_{19} = P_0$ and the following input values. Unless shown otherwise, the Mach number, compressor pressure ratio, and fan pressure ratio are the values listed under *baseline.*

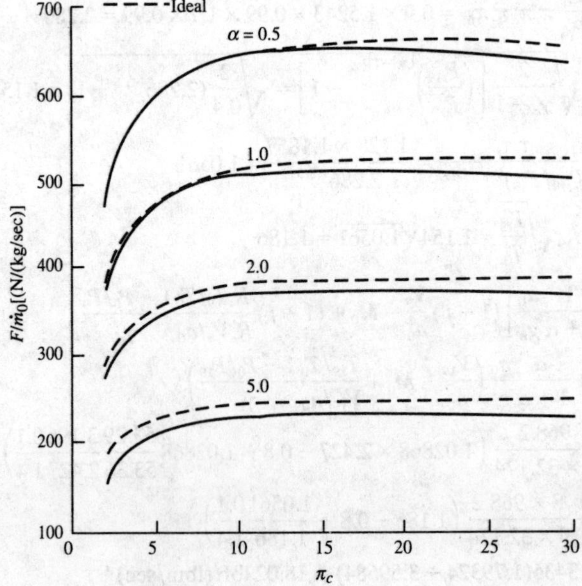

FIGURE 7-13*a*
Turbofan engine with losses versus compressor pressure ratio: specific thrust.

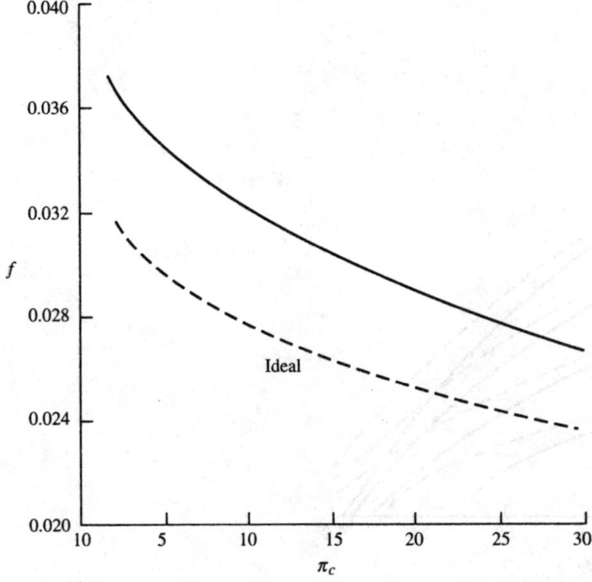

FIGURE 7-13*b*
Turbofan engine with losses versus compressor pressure ratio: fuel/air ratio.

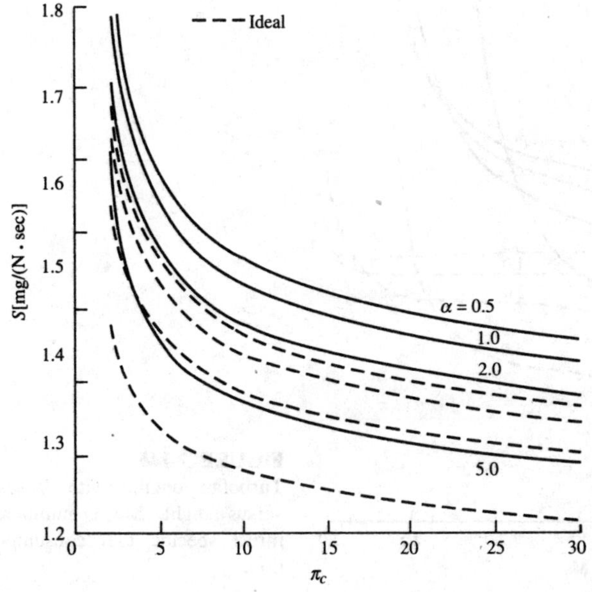

FIGURE 7-13*c*
Turbofan engine with losses versus compressor pressure ratio: thrust specific fuel consumption.

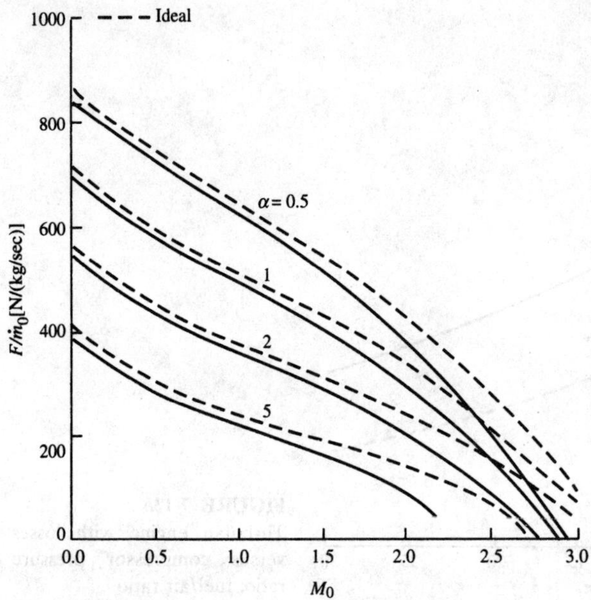

FIGURE 7-14a
Turbofan engine with losses versus flight Mach number: specific thrust.

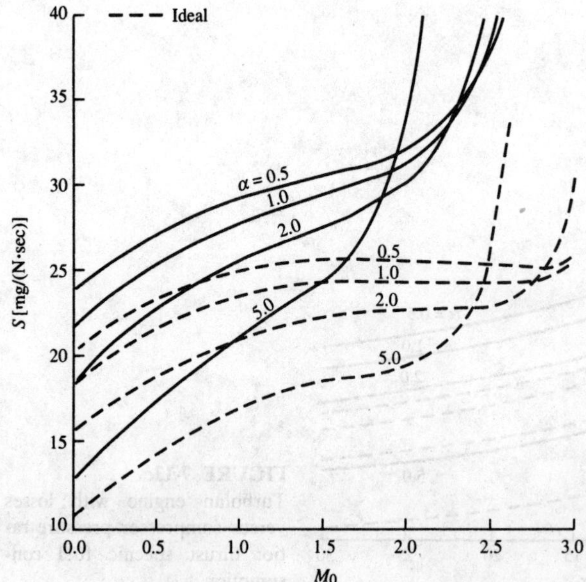

FIGURE 7-14b
Turbofan engine with losses versus flight Mach number: thrust specific fuel consumption.

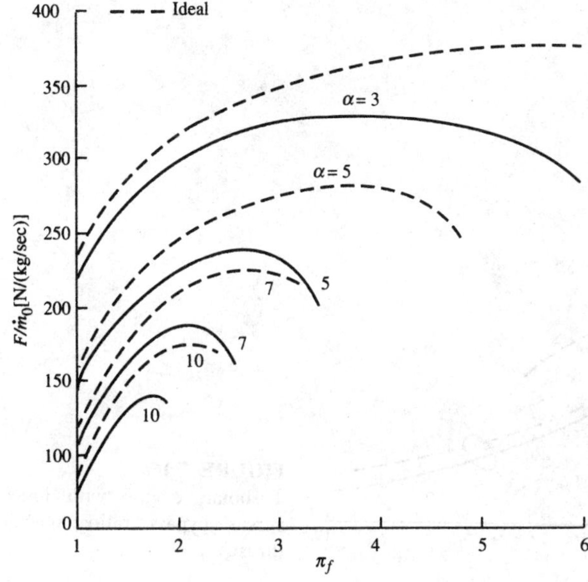

FIGURE 7-15a
Turbofan engine with losses versus fan pressure ratio: specific thrust.

$T_0 = 216.7$ K	$\pi_{d\,max} = 0.98$	$e_c = 0.90$	*Baseline*
$\gamma_c = 1.4$	$\pi_b = 0.98$	$e_t = 0.91$	$M_0 = 0.9$
$c_{pc} = 1.004$ kJ/(kg · K)	$\pi_n = \pi_{fn} = 0.98$	$e_f = 0.88$	$\pi_c = 24$
$\gamma_t = 1.35$	$\eta_b = 0.99$	$h_{PR} = 42{,}800$ kJ/kg	$\pi_f = 2$
$c_{pt} = 1.096$ kJ/(kg · K)	$\eta_m = 0.98$	$T_{t4} = 1670$ K	

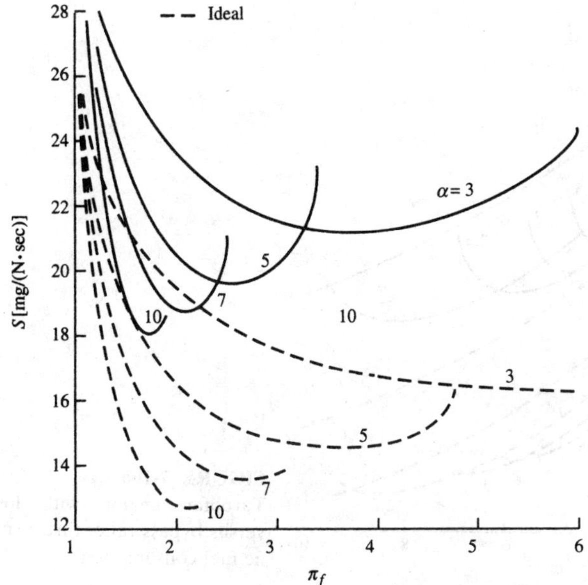

FIGURE 7-15b
Turbofan engine with losses versus fan pressure ratio: thrust specific fuel consumption.

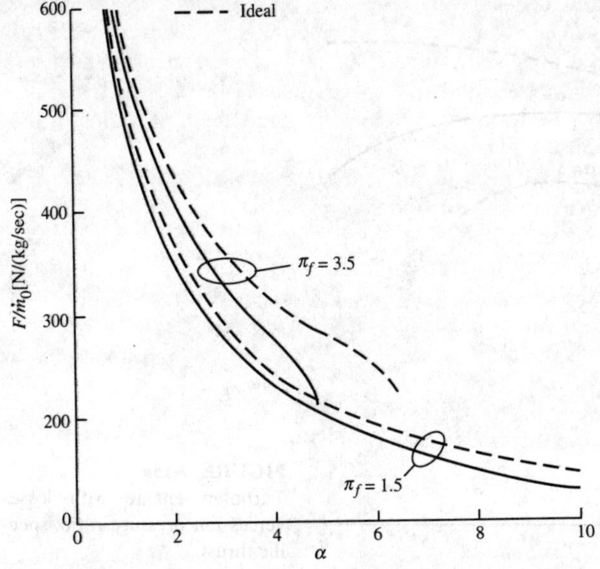

FIGURE 7-16*a*
Turbofan engine with losses versus bypass ratio: specific thrust.

Figures 7-13*a*, 7-13*b*, and 7-13*c* show the influence of compressor pressure ratio and bypass ratio on engine performance. As the bypass ratio increases, the difference in specific thrust between the engine cycle with losses and the "ideal" engine cycle increases. The major difference between the engine cycle's thrust specific fuel consumption for the two models is due to the much higher "fuel/air" ratio for the "real" engine.

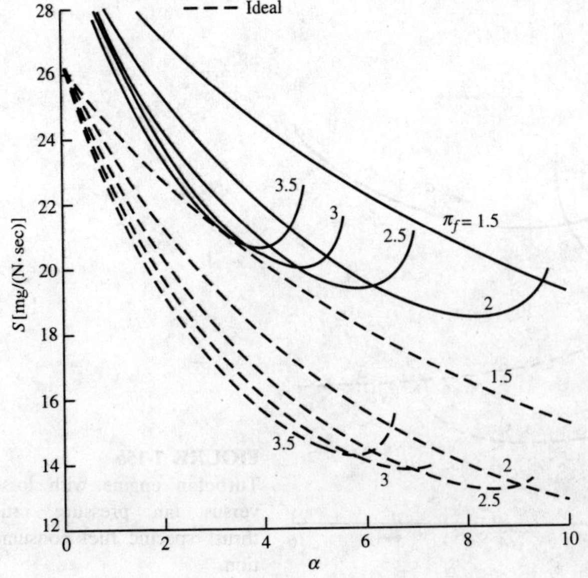

FIGURE 7-16*b*
Turbofan engine with losses versus bypass ratio: thrust specific fuel consumption.

Figures 7-14*a* and 7-14*b* show the influence of Mach number and bypass ratio on engine performance. The engine's specific thrust is reduced more than that of the ideal engine at high Mach number because of the increasing inlet total pressure loss. The limiting Mach number for economical operation of a turbofan engine with a specific bypass ratio is much lower for the engine with losses than for the ideal engine.

Figures 7-15*a* and 7-15*b* show the influence of fan pressure ratio and bypass ratio on engine performance. An optimum fan pressure ratio still exists for the turbofan with losses, and the value of the optimum fan pressure ratio is much lower than that for the ideal turbofan.

Figures 7-16*a* and 7-16*b* show the variation in specific thrust and thrust specific fuel consumption with bypass ratio and fan pressure ratio. An optimum bypass ratio still exists for the turbofan with losses, and the value of the optimum bypass ratio is much less than that for the ideal turbofan.

Optimum Bypass Ratio α^*

As was true for the turbofan with no losses, we may obtain an expression that allows us to determine the bypass ratio α^* that leads to minimum thrust specific fuel consumption. For a given set of such prescribed variables $(\tau_r, \pi_c, \pi_f, \tau_\lambda, V_0)$, we may locate the minimum S by taking the partial derivative of S with respect to the bypass ratio α. We consider the case where the exhaust pressures of both the fan stream and the core stream equal the ambient pressure $P_0 = P_9 = P_{19}$. Since the fuel/air ratio is not a function of bypass ratio, we have

$$S = \frac{f}{(1+\alpha)(F/\dot{m}_0)}$$

$$\frac{\partial S}{\partial \alpha} = \frac{\partial}{\partial \alpha}\left[\frac{f}{(1+\alpha)(F/\dot{m}_0)}\right] = 0$$

$$\frac{\partial S}{\partial \alpha} = \frac{-f}{[(1+\alpha)(F/\dot{m}_0)]^2}\frac{\partial}{\partial \alpha}\left[(1+\alpha)\left(\frac{F}{\dot{m}_0}\right)\right] = 0$$

Thus $\partial S/\partial \alpha = 0$ is satisfied by

$$\frac{\partial}{\partial \alpha}\left[\frac{g_c}{V_0}(1+\alpha)\left(\frac{F}{\dot{m}_0}\right)\right] = 0$$

where $$\frac{g_c}{V_0}(1+\alpha)\left(\frac{F}{\dot{m}_0}\right) = (1+f)\left(\frac{V_9}{V_0} - 1\right) + \alpha\left(\frac{V_{19}}{V_0} - 1\right)$$

Then the optimum bypass ratio is given by the following expression:

$$\frac{\partial}{\partial \alpha}\left[(1+f)\left(\frac{V_9}{V_0} - 1\right) + \alpha\left(\frac{V_{19}}{V_0} - 1\right)\right]$$

$$= (1+f)\frac{\partial}{\partial \alpha}\left(\frac{V_9}{V_0}\right) + \frac{V_{19}}{V_0} - 1 = 0 \qquad \text{(i)}$$

However, $\frac{1}{2V_9/V_0}\frac{\partial}{\partial\alpha}\left[\left(\frac{V_9}{V_0}\right)^2\right]=\frac{\partial}{\partial\alpha}\left(\frac{V_9}{V_0}\right)$

Thus Eq. (i) becomes

$$\left(\frac{V_9}{V_0}\right)_{\alpha^*}=-\frac{1+f}{2}\frac{\partial/\partial\alpha[(V_9/V_0)^2]}{V_{19}/V_0-1} \tag{ii}$$

Note that

$$\left(\frac{V_9}{V_0}\right)^2=\frac{1}{M_0^2}\left(\frac{V_9}{a_0}\right)^2=\frac{1}{[(\gamma_c-1)/2](\tau_r-1)}\left(\frac{V_9}{a_0}\right)^2$$
$$=\frac{1}{[(\gamma_c-1)/2](\tau_r-1)}M_9^2\frac{\gamma_t R_t T_9}{\gamma_c R_c T_0}$$

Using Eqs. (7-41) and (7-42), we have

$$\left(\frac{V_9}{V_0}\right)^2=\frac{\tau_\lambda\tau_t}{\tau_r-1}\left[1-\left(\frac{P_{t9}}{P_9}\right)^{-(\gamma_t-1)/\gamma_t}\right] \tag{iii}$$

where $$\frac{P_{t9}}{P_9}=\pi_r\pi_d\pi_c\pi_b\pi_t\pi_n \tag{iv}$$

Combining Eqs. (iii) and (iv), we obtain

$$\left(\frac{V_9}{V_0}\right)^2=\frac{\tau_\lambda\tau_t}{\tau_r-1}\left[1-\frac{1}{\Pi(\pi_t)^{(\gamma_t-1)/\gamma_t}}\right] \tag{v}$$

where $$\boxed{\Pi=(\pi_r\pi_d\pi_c\pi_b\pi_n)^{(\gamma_t-1)/\gamma_t}} \tag{7-56}$$

Noting that

$$\pi_t^{(\gamma_t-1)/\gamma_t}=\tau_t^{1/e_t}$$

we see that then Eq. (v) becomes

$$\left(\frac{V_9}{V_0}\right)^2=\frac{\tau_\lambda}{\tau_r-1}\left(\tau_t-\frac{1}{\Pi}\tau_t^{-(1-e_t)/e_t}\right) \tag{vi}$$

To evaluate the partial derivative of Eq. (ii), we apply the chain rule to Eq. (vi) as follows:

$$\frac{\partial}{\partial\alpha}\left[\left(\frac{V_9}{V_0}\right)^2\right]=\frac{\partial\tau_t}{\partial\alpha}\frac{\partial}{\partial\tau_t}\left[\left(\frac{V_9}{V_0}\right)^2\right]$$
$$=\frac{\partial\tau_t}{\partial\alpha}\frac{\tau_\lambda}{\tau_r-1}\left(1+\frac{1-e_t}{e_t}\frac{\tau_t^{-1/e_t}}{\Pi}\right) \tag{vii}$$

Since $$\tau_t = 1 - \frac{1}{\eta_m(1+f)}\frac{\tau_r}{\tau_\lambda}[\tau_c - 1 + \alpha(\tau_f - 1)]$$

then $$\frac{\partial \tau_t}{\partial \alpha} = -\frac{\tau_r(\tau_f - 1)}{\eta_m \tau_\lambda (1+f)} \tag{viii}$$

Combining Eqs. (ii), (vii), and (viii) yields

$$\left(\frac{V_9}{V_0}\right)_{\alpha*} = \frac{1}{2\eta_m(\tau_r - 1)}\frac{\tau_r(\tau_f - 1)}{V_{19}/V_0 - 1}\left(1 + \frac{1 - e_t}{e_t}\frac{\tau_t^{-1/e_t}}{\Pi}\right)$$

An expression for τ_t is obtained by squaring the above equation, substituting for $(V_9/V_0)^2$ by using Eq. (vi), and then solving for the first τ_t within parentheses on the right side of Eq. (vi). The resulting expression for the turbine temperature ratio τ_t^* corresponding to the optimum bypass ratio α^* is

$$\tau_t^* = \frac{\tau_t^{-(1-e_t)/e_t}}{\Pi} + \frac{1}{\tau_\lambda(\tau_r - 1)}\left[\frac{1}{2\eta_m}\frac{\tau_r(\tau_f - 1)}{V_{19}/V_0 - 1}\left(1 + \frac{1 - e_t}{e_t}\frac{\tau_t^{-1/e_t}}{\Pi}\right)\right]^2 \tag{7-57}$$

Since Eq. (7-57) is an equation for τ_t^* in terms of itself, in addition to other known values, an iterative solution is required. A starting value of τ_t^*, denoted by τ_{ti}^*, is obtained by solving Eq. (7-57) for the case when $e_t = 1$, which gives

$$\tau_{ti}^* = \frac{1}{\Pi} + \frac{1}{\tau_\lambda(\tau_r - 1)}\left[\frac{1}{2\eta_m}\frac{\tau_r(\tau_f - 1)}{V_{19}/V_0 - 1}\right]^2 \tag{7-58}$$

This starting value can be substituted into the right-hand side of Eq. (7-57), yielding a new value of τ_t^*. This new value of τ_t^* is then substituted into Eq. (7-57), and another new value of τ_t^* is calculated. This process continues until the change in successive calculations of τ_t^* is less than some small number (say, 0.0001). Once the solution for τ_t^* is found, the optimum bypass ratio α^* is calculated by using Eq. (7-45), solved for α:

$$\alpha^* = \frac{\eta_m(1+f)\tau_\lambda(1 - \tau_t^*) - \tau_r(\tau_c - 1)}{\tau_r(\tau_f - 1)} \tag{7-59}$$

When the optimum bypass ratio α^* is desired in calculating the parametric engine cycle performance, Eqs. (7-56), (7-57), (7-58), and (7-59) replace the equation for τ_t contained in the summary of equations and α^* is an output.

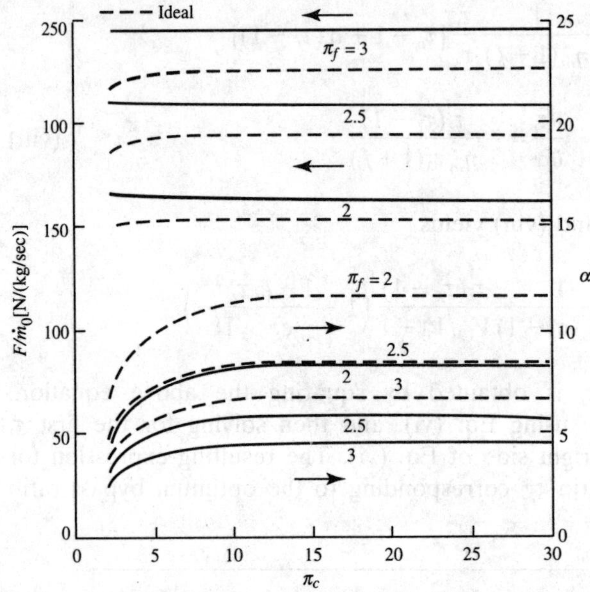

FIGURE 7-17a
Optimum-bypass-ratio turbofan engine versus π_c: specific thrust and optimum bypass ratio.

Example 7-8. Since the optimum-bypass-ratio turbofan cycle has two design variables, its performance with losses can be understood by performing a parametric analysis, plotting the results versus values of the design variables, and comparing results to the performance of the optimum-bypass-ratio ideal turbofan.

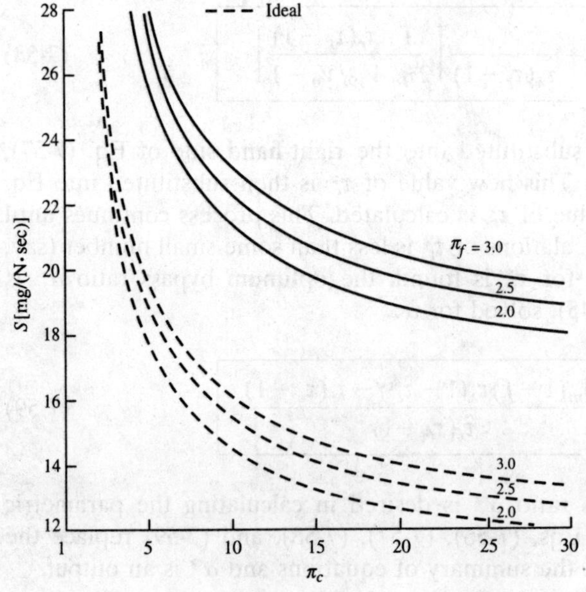

FIGURE 7-17b
Optimum-bypass-ratio turbofan engine versus π_c: thrust specific fuel consumption.

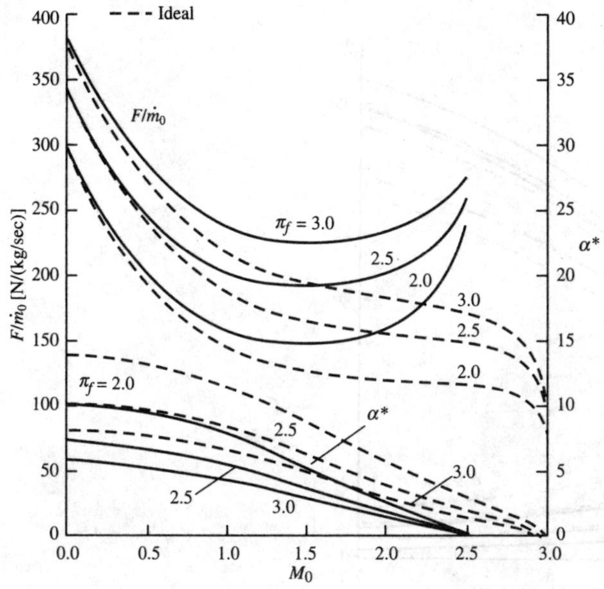

FIGURE 7-18*a*
Optimum-bypass-ratio turbofan engine versus Mach number: specific thrust and optimum bypass ratio.

Figures 7-17 through 7-19 are plots for optimum-bypass-ratio turbofan engines with the following input values (the same input used for the parametric analysis of the turbofan engine with losses in Example 7-7). The results for the ideal optimum-bypass-ratio turbofan engine cycle are shown in dashed lines. Unless

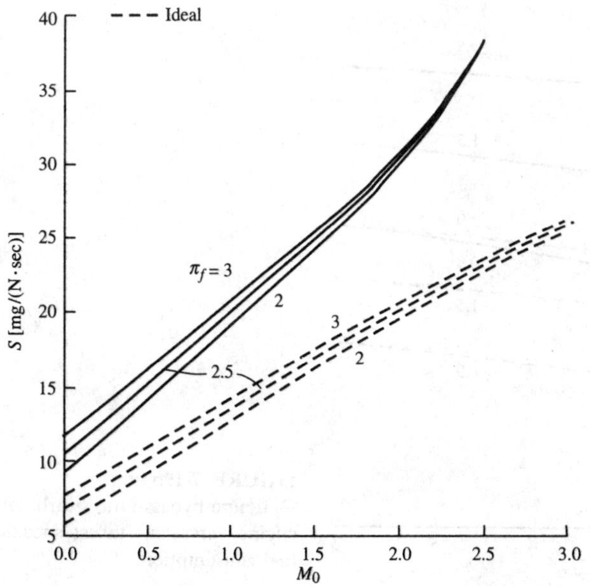

FIGURE 7-18*b*
Optimum-bypass-ratio turbofan engine versus Mach number: thrust specific fuel consumption.

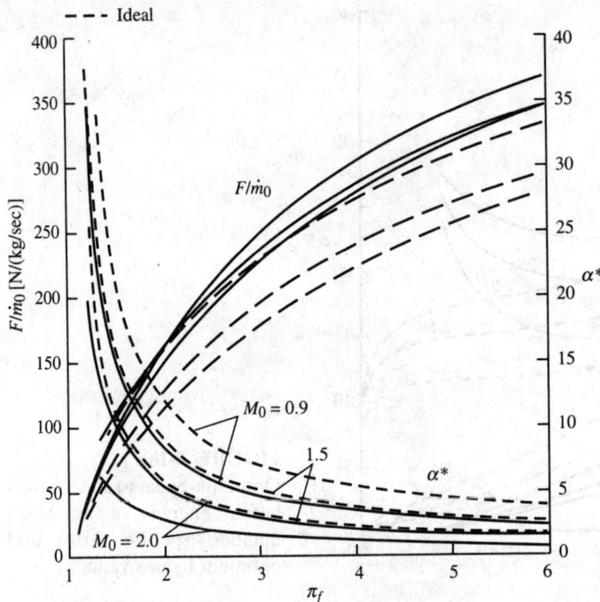

FIGURE 7-19*a*
Optimum-bypass-ratio turbofan engine versus π_f: specific thrust and optimum bypass ratio.

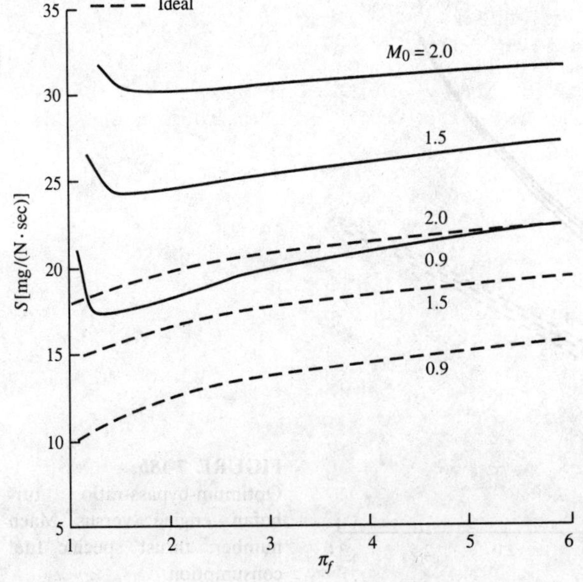

FIGURE 7-19*b*
Optimum-bypass-ratio turbofan engine versus π_f: thrust specific fuel consumption.

shown otherwise, the Mach number, compressor pressure ratio, and fan pressure ratio are the values listed under *baseline.*

$T_0 = 216.7\ \text{K}$	$\pi_{d\,\max} = 0.98$	$e_c = 0.90$	*Baseline*
$\gamma_c = 1.4$	$\pi_b = 0.98$	$e_t = 0.91$	$M_0 = 0.9$
$c_{pc} = 1.004\ \text{kJ/(kg}\cdot\text{K)}$	$\pi_n = \pi_{fn} = 0.98$	$e_f = 0.88$	$\pi_c = 24$
$\gamma_t = 1.35$	$\eta_b = 0.99$	$h_{PR} = 42{,}800\ \text{kJ/kg}$	$\pi_f = 2$
$c_{pt} = 1.096\ \text{kJ/(kg}\cdot\text{K)}$	$\eta_m = 0.98$	$T_{t4} = 1670\ \text{K}$	
$\dfrac{P_0}{P_9} = 1$	$\dfrac{P_0}{P_{19}} = 1$		

Figures 7-17*a* and 7-17*b* show the following characteristics of the optimum-bypass-ratio turbofan engine:

1. The compressor pressure ratio has very little effect on the specific thrust.
2. Increasing the fan pressure ratio increases the specific thrust.
3. The optimum bypass ratio increases with π_c and decreases with π_f.
4. Specific fuel consumption decreases with increasing π_c.
5. Specific fuel consumption increases with increasing π_f.

The effect of flight Mach number on the performance of the optimum-bypass-ratio turbofan engine as shown in Figs. 7-18*a* and 7-18*b* has the following characteristics:

1. The specific thrust decreases with Mach number up to a Mach number of about 1.5.
2. Increasing the fan pressure ratio increases the specific thrust.
3. The optimum bypass ratio decreases with increasing M_0 and π_f.
4. The optimum turbofan is a turbojet engine at a Mach number of about 2.5.
5. Specific fuel consumption increases with increasing M_0 and π_f.

Figures 7-19*a* and 7-19*b* show the following characteristics of the optimum-bypass-ratio turbofan engine with respect to fan pressure ratio and flight Mach number:

1. Increasing the fan pressure ratio increases the specific thrust.
2. Increasing the flight Mach number decreases the specific thrust.
3. The optimum bypass ratio decreases with π_f and increases with M_0.
4. Specific fuel consumption increases with increasing π_f.
5. Specific fuel consumption increases with increasing M_0.

7-5 TURBOFAN WITH AFTERBURNING—SEPARATE EXHAUST STREAMS

We now consider a turbofan engine cycle with separate exhaust streams in which afterburning may operate in the core stream and duct burning may operate in the fan stream. When both the afterburner and duct burner are in operation, this engine cycle will give substantially higher specific thrust than the basic turbofan cycle, while still providing the low fuel consumption of the basic turbofan engine cycle when both the afterburner and duct burner are turned off. A sketch of this engine and the station numbering being used are shown in Fig. 5-1.

Analogously to the turbojet with afterburning, we define for the duct burner (DB)

$$f_{\text{DB}} \equiv \frac{\dot{m}_{f\text{DB}}}{\dot{m}_F} \tag{7-60}$$

$$\eta_{\text{DB}} \equiv \frac{(\dot{m}_F + \dot{m}_{f\text{DB}})c_{p\text{DB}} T_{t17} - \dot{m}_F c_{pc} T_{t16}}{\dot{m}_{f\text{DB}} h_{PR}} \tag{7-61}$$

Cycle Analysis

The assumptions for the analysis of the turbofan engine cycle with afterburning and duct burning are as follows:

1. Perfect gas upstream of main burner with constant properties γ_c, R_c, c_{pc}, etc.
2. Perfect gas downstream of main burner with constant properties, γ_t, R_t, c_{pt}, etc.
3. Perfect gas downstream of afterburner with constant properties γ_{AB}, R_{AB}, $c_{p\text{AB}}$, etc.
4. Perfect gas downstream of duct burner with constant properties γ_{DB}, R_{DB}, $c_{p\text{DB}}$, etc.
5. All components adiabatic (no turbine cooling).
6. The efficiencies of the compressor, fan, and turbine described through the use of (constant) polytropic efficiencies e_c, e_f, and e_t, respectively.

The expression for the specific thrust of this engine cycle is

$$\begin{aligned}\frac{F}{\dot{m}_0} = \frac{1}{1+\alpha}\frac{a_0}{g_c}\bigg[&(1+f+f_{\text{AB}})\frac{V_9}{a_0} - M_0 + (1+f+f_{\text{AB}})\frac{R_{\text{AB}}}{R_c} \\ &\times \frac{T_9/T_0}{V_9/a_0}\frac{1-P_0/P_9}{\gamma_c}\bigg] + \frac{\alpha}{1+\alpha}\frac{a_0}{g_c}\bigg[(1+f_{\text{DB}})\frac{V_{19}}{a_0} \\ &- M_0 + (1+f_{\text{DB}})\frac{R_{\text{DB}}}{R_c}\frac{T_{19}/T_0}{V_{19}/a_0}\frac{1-P_0/P_{19}}{\gamma_c}\bigg]\end{aligned} \tag{7-62}$$

FAN STREAM. In a manner completely similar to the afterburning turbojet, we have

$$\frac{V_{19}}{a_0} = M_{19}\sqrt{\frac{\gamma_{\text{DB}} R_{\text{DB}} T_{19}}{\gamma_c R_c T_0}} \tag{7-63a}$$

$$M_{19}^2 = \frac{2}{\gamma_{\text{DB}} - 1}\left[\left(\frac{P_{t19}}{P_{19}}\right)^{(\gamma_{\text{DB}}-1)/\gamma_{\text{DB}}} - 1\right] \tag{7-63b}$$

$$\frac{T_{19}}{T_0} = \frac{T_{t19}/T_0}{(P_{t19}/P_{19})^{(\gamma_{\text{DB}}-1)/\gamma_{\text{DB}}}} \tag{7-63c}$$

$$\frac{P_{t19}}{P_{19}} = \frac{P_0}{P_{19}} \pi_r \pi_d \pi_f \pi_{\text{DB}} \pi_{\text{fn}} \tag{7-63d}$$

The energy balance across the duct burner gives

$$\dot{m}_F c_{pc} T_{t16} + \eta_{\text{DB}} \dot{m}_{f\text{DB}} h_{PR} = (\dot{m}_F + \dot{m}_{f\text{DB}}) c_{p\text{DB}} T_{t17}$$

Solving for the duct burner fuel/air ratio gives

$$f_{\text{DB}} = \frac{\tau_{\lambda\text{DB}} - \tau_r \tau_f}{\eta_{\text{DB}} h_{PR}/(c_{pc} T_0) - \tau_{\lambda\text{DB}}} \tag{7-64}$$

where

$$\tau_{\lambda\text{DB}} = \frac{c_{p\text{DB}} T_{t17}}{c_{pc} T_0} \tag{7-65}$$

CORE STREAM. The necessary relationships for the core stream have already been developed. Equations (7-10), (7-25), (7-26), (7-27), (7-28), and (7-29) apply to this engine cycle. The turbine temperature ratio is given by Eq. (7-45).

THRUST SPECIFIC FUEL CONSUMPTION S. Application of the definition of thrust fuel consumption to this engine cycle gives

$$S = \frac{\dot{m}_f + \dot{m}_{f\text{AB}} + \dot{m}_{f\text{DB}}}{F}$$

Dividing both numerator and denominator by the mass flow rate of air through the core gives

$$S = \frac{f + f_{\text{AB}} + \alpha f_{\text{DB}}}{(1+\alpha)(F/\dot{m}_0)} \tag{7-66}$$

Summary of Equations—Afterburning Turbofan with Separate Exhausts

INPUTS: $M_0,\ T_0\,(\mathrm{K}, °\mathrm{R}),\ \gamma_c,\ c_{pc}\left(\frac{\mathrm{kJ}}{\mathrm{kg\cdot K}}, \frac{\mathrm{Btu}}{\mathrm{lbm\cdot °R}}\right),\ \gamma_t,\ c_{pt}\left(\frac{\mathrm{kJ}}{\mathrm{kg\cdot K}}, \frac{\mathrm{Btu}}{\mathrm{lbm\cdot °R}}\right),\ h_{PR}\left(\frac{\mathrm{kJ}}{\mathrm{kg}}, \frac{\mathrm{Btu}}{\mathrm{lbm}}\right),\ \gamma_{\mathrm{AB}},\ c_{p\mathrm{AB}}\left(\frac{\mathrm{kJ}}{\mathrm{kg\cdot K}}, \frac{\mathrm{Btu}}{\mathrm{lbm\cdot °R}}\right),$
$\gamma_{\mathrm{DB}},\ c_{p\mathrm{DB}}\left(\frac{\mathrm{kJ}}{\mathrm{kg\cdot K}}, \frac{\mathrm{Btu}}{\mathrm{lbm\cdot °R}}\right),\ \pi_{d\,\max},\ \pi_b,\ \pi_{\mathrm{AB}},\ \pi_{\mathrm{DB}},\ \pi_n,\ \pi_{fn},$
$e_c,\ e_f,\ e_t,\ \eta_b,\ \eta_{\mathrm{AB}},\ \eta_{\mathrm{DB}},\ \eta_m,\ P_0/P_9,\ P_0/P_{19},\ T_{t4}(\mathrm{K}, °\mathrm{R}),$
$T_{t7}\,(\mathrm{K}, °\mathrm{R}),\ T_{t17}\,(\mathrm{K}, °\mathrm{R}),\ \pi_c,\ \pi_f,\ \alpha$

OUTPUTS: $\frac{F}{\dot m_0}\left(\frac{\mathrm{N}}{\mathrm{kg/sec}}, \frac{\mathrm{lbf}}{\mathrm{lbm/sec}}\right),\ f,\ f_{\mathrm{AB}},\ f_{\mathrm{DB}},\ S\left(\frac{\mathrm{mg/sec}}{\mathrm{N}}, \frac{\mathrm{lbm/hr}}{\mathrm{lbf}}\right),$
$\eta_T,\ \eta_P,\ \eta_O,\ \eta_c,\ \eta_t,$ etc.

EQUATIONS:

$$R_c = \frac{\gamma_c - 1}{\gamma_c} c_{pc} \tag{7-67a}$$

$$R_t = \frac{\gamma_t - 1}{\gamma_t} c_{pt} \tag{7-67b}$$

$$R_{\mathrm{AB}} = \frac{\gamma_{\mathrm{AB}} - 1}{\gamma_{\mathrm{AB}}} c_{p\mathrm{AB}} \tag{7-67c}$$

$$R_{\mathrm{DB}} = \frac{\gamma_{\mathrm{DB}} - 1}{\gamma_{\mathrm{DB}}} c_{p\mathrm{DB}} \tag{7-67d}$$

$$a_0 = \sqrt{\gamma_c R_c g_c T_0} \tag{7-67e}$$

$$V_0 = a_0 M_0 \tag{7-67f}$$

$$\tau_r = 1 + \frac{\gamma_c - 1}{2} M_0^2 \tag{7-67g}$$

$$\pi_r = \tau_r^{\gamma_c/(\gamma_c-1)} \tag{7-67h}$$

$$\eta_r = 1 \quad \text{for } M_0 \le 1 \tag{7-67i}$$

$$\eta_r = 1 - 0.075(M_0 - 1)^{1.35} \quad \text{for } M_0 > 1 \tag{7-67j}$$

$$\pi_d = \pi_{d\,\max}\eta_r \tag{7-67k}$$

$$\tau_\lambda = \frac{c_{pt} T_{t4}}{c_{pc} T_0} \tag{7-67l}$$

$$\tau_{\lambda\mathrm{AB}} = \frac{c_{p\mathrm{AB}} T_{t7}}{c_{pc} T_0} \tag{7-67m}$$

$$\tau_{\lambda\mathrm{DB}} = \frac{c_{p\mathrm{DB}} T_{t17}}{c_{pc} T_0} \tag{7-67n}$$

$$\tau_c = \pi_c^{(\gamma_c-1)/(\gamma_c e_c)} \tag{7-67o}$$

$$\eta_c = \frac{\pi_c^{(\gamma_c-1)/\gamma_c} - 1}{\tau_c - 1} \tag{7-67p}$$

$$\tau_f = \pi_f^{(\gamma_c-1)/(\gamma_c e_f)} \tag{7-67q}$$

$$\eta_f = \frac{\pi_f^{(\gamma_c-1)/\gamma_c} - 1}{\tau_f - 1} \tag{7-67r}$$

$$f = \frac{\tau_\lambda - \tau_r \tau_c}{\eta_b h_{PR}/(c_{pc}T_0) - \tau_\lambda} \tag{7-67s}$$

$$\tau_t = 1 - \frac{1}{\eta_m(1+f)} \frac{\tau_r}{\tau_\lambda}[\tau_c - 1 + \alpha(\tau_f - 1)] \tag{7-67t}$$

$$\pi_t = \tau_t^{\gamma_t/[(\gamma_t - 1)e_c]} \tag{7-67u}$$

$$\eta_t = \frac{1 - \tau_t}{1 - \tau_t^{1/e_t}} \tag{7-67v}$$

$$\frac{P_{t9}}{P_9} = \frac{P_0}{P_9} \pi_r \pi_d \pi_c \pi_b \pi_t \pi_{\text{AB}} \pi_{\text{n}} \tag{7-67w}$$

$$M_9 = \sqrt{\frac{2}{\tau_{\text{AB}} - 1}\left[\left(\frac{P_{t9}}{P_9}\right)^{(\gamma_{\text{AB}}-1)/\gamma_{\text{AB}}} - 1\right]} \tag{7-67x}$$

$$\frac{T_9}{T_0} = \frac{T_{t7}/T_0}{(P_{t9}/P_9)^{(\gamma_{\text{AB}}-1)/\gamma_{\text{AB}}}} \tag{7-67y}$$

$$\frac{V_9}{a_0} = M_9 \sqrt{\frac{\gamma_{\text{AB}} R_{\text{AB}} T_9}{\gamma_c R_c T_0}} \tag{7-67z}$$

$$\frac{P_{t19}}{P_{19}} = \frac{P_0}{P_{19}} \pi_r \pi_d \pi_f \pi_{\text{DB}} \pi_{fn} \tag{7-67aa}$$

$$M_{19} = \sqrt{\frac{2}{\gamma_{\text{DB}} - 1}\left[\left(\frac{P_{t19}}{P_{19}}\right)^{(\gamma_{\text{DB}}-1)/\gamma_{\text{DB}}} - 1\right]} \tag{7-67ab}$$

$$\frac{T_{19}}{T_0} = \frac{T_{t17}/T_0}{(P_{t19}/P_{19})^{(\gamma_{\text{DB}}-1)/\gamma_{\text{DB}}}} \tag{7-67ac}$$

$$\frac{V_{19}}{a_0} = M_{19} \sqrt{\frac{\gamma_{\text{DB}} R_{\text{DB}} T_{19}}{\gamma_c R_c T_0}} \tag{7-67ad}$$

$$f_{\text{AB}} = (1+f)\frac{\tau_{\lambda\text{AB}} - \tau_\lambda \tau_t}{\eta_{\text{AB}} h_{PR}/(c_{pc}T_0) - \tau_{\lambda\text{AB}}} \tag{7-67ae}$$

$$f_{\text{DB}} = \frac{\tau_{\lambda\text{DB}} - \tau_r \tau_f}{\eta_{\text{DB}} h_{PR}/(c_{pc}T_0) - \tau_{\lambda\text{DB}}} \tag{7-67af}$$

$$\begin{aligned}\frac{F}{\dot m_0} = {} & \frac{1}{1+\alpha}\frac{a_0}{g_c}\left[(1+f+f_{\text{AB}})\frac{V_9}{a_0} - M_0 + (1+f+f_{\text{AB}}) \right.\\ & \left. \times \frac{R_{\text{AB}}}{R_c}\frac{T_9/T_0}{V_9/a_0}\frac{1-P_0/P_9}{\gamma_c}\right]\\ & + \frac{\alpha}{1+\alpha}\frac{a_0}{g_c}\left[(1+f_{\text{DB}})\frac{V_{19}}{a_0} - M_0 + (1+f_{\text{DB}})\right.\\ & \left. \times \frac{R_{\text{DB}}}{R_c}\frac{T_{19}/T_0}{V_{19}/a_0}\frac{1-P_0/P_{19}}{\gamma_c}\right]\end{aligned} \tag{7-67ag}$$

$$S = \frac{f + f_{\text{AB}} + \alpha f_{\text{DB}}}{(1+\alpha)(F/\dot m_0)} \tag{7-67ah}$$

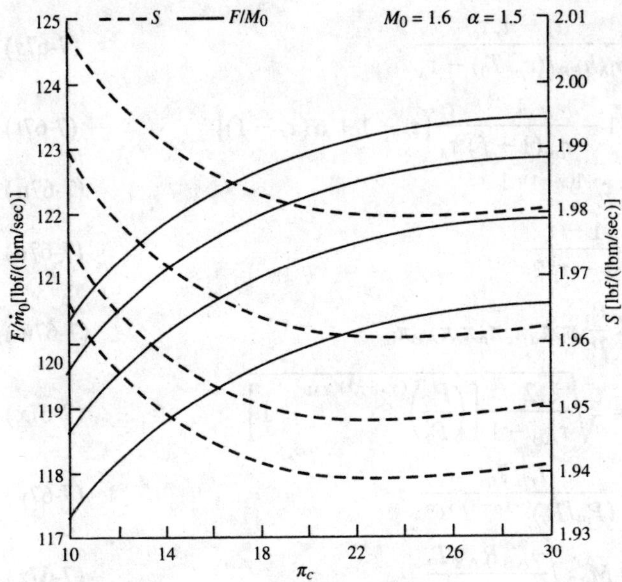

FIGURE 7-20
Specific performance of afterburning turbofan with separate exhausts versus compressor pressure ratio and fan pressure ratio.

Example 7-9. Since the turbofan cycle has three design variables (π_c, π_f, and α), its performance can be best understood by performing a parametric analysis versus values of these design variables. Figures 7-20 and 7-21 are plots for turbofan engines at $M_0 = 1.6$ with $P_9 = P_{19} = P_0$ and the following input values:

$c_{pc} = 0.240$ Btu/(lbm · °R)
$\gamma_c = 1.4$ $\quad T_0 = 390°\text{R}$ $\quad \pi_{d\,\max} = 0.98$ $\quad \eta_m = 0.99$
$h_{PR} = 18{,}400$ Btu/lbm
$e_c = 0.90$ $\quad e_f = 0.89$ $\quad e_t = 0.91$ $\quad \pi_n = \pi_{fn} = 0.98$
$c_{pt} = 0.295$ Btu/(lbm · °R)
$\gamma_t = 1.3$ $\quad \eta_b = 0.99$ $\quad \pi_b = 0.98$ $\quad T_{t4} = 3500°\text{R}$
$c_{p\text{AB}} = 0.295$ Btu/(lbm · °R)
$\gamma_{\text{AB}} = 1.3$ $\quad \eta_{\text{AB}} = 0.95$ $\quad \pi_{\text{AB}} = 0.94$ $\quad T_{t7} = 4000°\text{R}$
$c_{p\text{DB}} = 0.295$ Btu/(lbm · °R)
$\gamma_{\text{DB}} = 1.3$ $\quad \eta_{\text{DB}} = 0.95$ $\quad \pi_{\text{DB}} = 0.94$ $\quad T_{t17} = 4000°\text{R}$
$h_{PR} = 18{,}400$ Btu/lbm

The engine bypass ratio is held constant at a value of 1.5 in Fig. 7-20 while the compressor pressure ratio and fan pressure ratio vary. As shown in Fig. 7-20, specific thrust increases with both π_c and π_f. Figure 7-20 also shows that the thrust specific fuel consumption decreases with increasing π_f and decreases with increasing π_c until a value of 22 to 26 is reached. Losses in the compressor are mainly responsible for this optimum compressor pressure ratio for minimum fuel consumption.

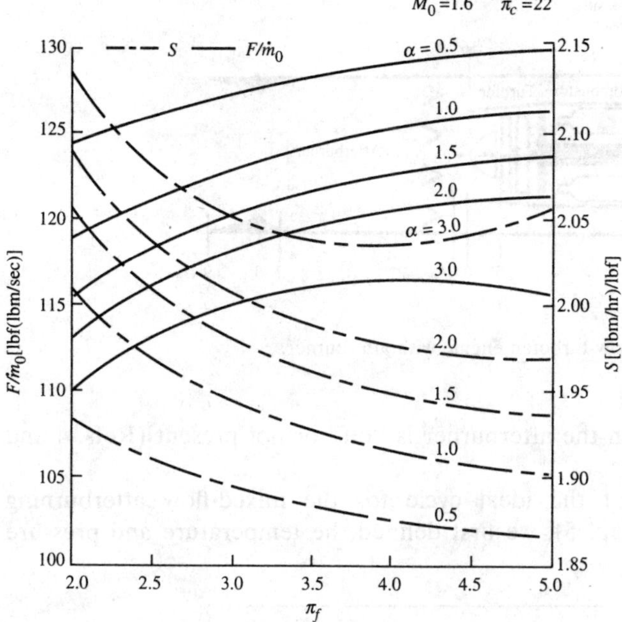

FIGURE 7-21
Specific performance of afterburning turbofan with separate exhausts versus fan pressure ratio and bypass ratio.

Figure 7-21 shows the influence of bypass ratio and fan pressure on performance while the compressor pressure ratio is held constant at a value of 22. Reducing the bypass ratio improves (reduces) the thrust specific fuel consumption for the afterburning turbofan—this is opposite the trend of the nonafterburning turbofan (see Fig. 7-16*b*). In general, increasing the fan pressure ratio will increase the specific thrust and reduce fuel consumption. As shown in Fig. 7-21, there is an optimum fan pressure ratio of about 4.0 for the engine bypass ratio α of 3.

7-6 TURBOFAN WITH AFTERBURNING—MIXED EXHAUST STREAM

Most high-speed military aircraft require an afterburner for thrust augmentation at certain flight conditions (e.g., takeoff, high-speed turns, etc.). Figure 7-22*a* shows the cross section of a mixed-flow afterburning turbofan engine. This engine cycle is used in many of these aircraft. It has several advantages over the turbofan with separate exhausts which was analyzed in the previous section: (1) one variable-area exhaust nozzle, (2) one augmenter (afterburner), and (3) cold bypass air to cool the afterburner liner. Also, mixers can improve

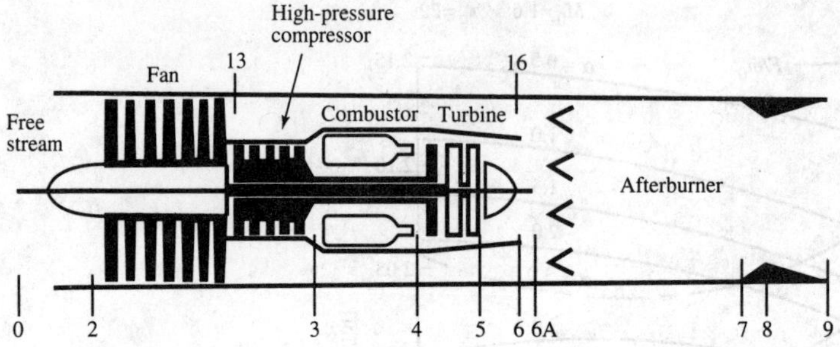

FIGURE 7-22a
Station numbering for mixed-flow turbofan engine with afterburner.

engine performance when the afterburner is "off" or not present (Refs. 4 and 30).

In our modeling of the ideal cycle for the mixed-flow afterburning turbofan engine (see Chap. 5), we first defined the temperature and pressure ratios of the mixer as

$$\tau_M = \frac{T_{t6A}}{T_{t6}} \qquad \text{and} \qquad \pi_M = \frac{P_{t6A}}{P_{t6}} \tag{5-71}$$

We also assumed that the total pressures of the two entering streams are equal ($P_{t6} = P_{t16}$) and that the mixer pressure ratio π_M was unity. The mixer temperature ratio τ_M for the ideal cycle was obtained from an energy balance of the mixer.

The mixer temperature and pressure ratios defined in Eq. (5-71) will be used in the analysis of this engine cycle with losses. The mixer temperature ratio τ_M will be obtained from an energy balance of the mixer. In addition, we assume that the mixer pressure ratio π_M is the product of the pressure ratio of

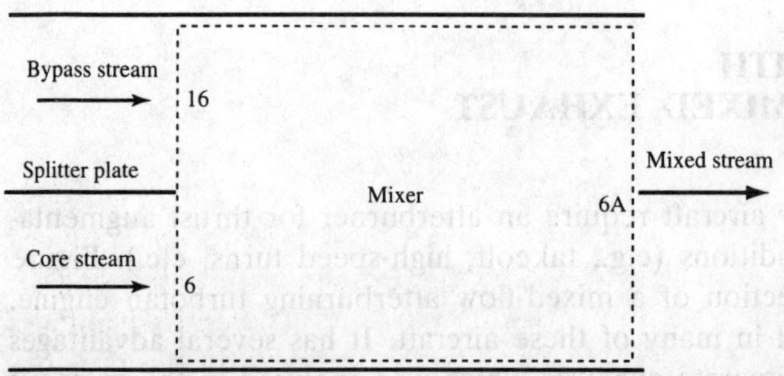

FIGURE 7-22b
Ideal constant-area mixer.

an ideal constant-area mixer ($\pi_{M\,\text{ideal}}$) times a total pressure ratio for the frictional losses ($\pi_{M\,\max}$):

$$\boxed{\pi_M = \pi_{M\,\max}\,\pi_{M\,\text{ideal}}} \tag{7-68}$$

The analysis in the following section obtains the total pressure ratio of the ideal mixer $\pi_{M\,\text{ideal}}$ and the total temperature ratio of the mixer τ_M.

Ideal Mixer Analytical Model

Consider an ideal (no wall friction) subsonic constant-area mixer (Fig. 7-22*b*) with primary and secondary streams of calorically perfect gases having different c_p and γ values. The flow is assumed to be one-dimensional, and the subscripts 6, 16, and 6*A* are used for the core, bypass, and mixed streams, respectively. We assume that the c_p and γ values of the core and bypass streams are known as well as M_6 and the following ratios:

$$\frac{T_{t16}}{T_{t6}} \qquad \frac{P_{t16}}{P_{t6}} \qquad \text{and} \qquad \alpha' \equiv \frac{\dot m_{16}}{\dot m_6} \ \text{or}\ \frac{A_{16}}{A_6}$$

The Mach number of the secondary stream M_{16} is determined by M_6 and the total pressure ratio P_{t6}/P_{t16}, as shown below. Using the Kutta condition at the splitter plate end ($P_6 = P_{16}$) and

$$P_t = P\left(1 + \frac{\gamma - 1}{2}M^2\right)^{\gamma/(\gamma-1)} \tag{3-10}$$

yields

$$\frac{P_{t16}}{P_{t6}} = \frac{\{1 + [(\gamma_{16} - 1)/2]M_{16}^2\}^{\gamma_{16}/(\gamma_{16}-1)}}{\{1 + [(\gamma_6 - 1)/2]M_6^2\}^{\gamma_6/(\gamma_{16}-1)}} \tag{7-69}$$

or

$$\boxed{M_{16} = \sqrt{\frac{2}{\gamma_{16} - 1}\left\{\left[\frac{P_{t16}}{P_{t6}}\left(1 + \frac{\gamma_6 - 1}{2}M_6^2\right)^{\gamma_6/(\gamma_6-1)}\right]^{(\gamma_{16}-1)/\gamma_{16}} - 1\right\}}} \tag{7-70}$$

A useful ratio for compressible flows in the *mass flow parameter* (MFP) is defined as

$$\frac{\dot m\sqrt{T_t}}{P_t A} \equiv \text{MFP}(M, \gamma, R) = \frac{M\sqrt{\gamma g_c/R}}{\{1 + [(\gamma - 1)/2]M^2\}^{(\gamma+1)/[2(\gamma-1)]}} \tag{3-13}$$

Combining Eqs. (3-10) an (3-13) gives

$$\frac{\dot m\sqrt{T_t}}{PA} = M\sqrt{1 + \frac{\gamma - 1}{2}M^2}\sqrt{\frac{\gamma g_c}{R}} \tag{7-71}$$

Taking the ratio of Eq. (7-71), written for the bypass stream, to the equation written for the core stream gives the following relationship between the inlet flow properties:

$$\frac{\alpha'\sqrt{T_{t16}/T_{t6}}}{A_{16}/A_6} = \frac{M_{16}}{M_6}\sqrt{\frac{\gamma_{16}R_6}{\gamma_6 R_{16}}\frac{1 + [(\gamma_{16} - 1)/2]M_{16}^2}{1 + [(\gamma_6 - 1)/2]M_6^2}} \tag{7-72}$$

This equation can be used to solve for the mass flow ratio α' given the area ratio A_{16}/A_6 or vice versa. The inlet flow characteristics of the mixer, defined by Eqs. (7-69) and (7-72), are plotted in Figs. 7-23 and 7-24, respectively. These figures can give considerable insight into the pumping characteristics of a mixer.

Figure 7-23 shows that the Mach number of the secondary stream M_{16} can be increased by increasing the total pressure ratio P_{t16}/P_{t6} at constant values of M_6. When the total pressure ratio is near unity, the Mach numbers at stations 6 and 16 are nearly equal. For a constant value of the ratio $\alpha'\sqrt{T_{t16}/T_{t6}}/(A_{16}/A_6)$, Fig. 7-24 shows the linear relationship between the Mach numbers at stations 6 and 16.

To obtain the properties of the mixed stream, we start by writing the conservation laws for the ideal constant-area mixer:

Conservation of mass

$$\dot{m}_6 + \dot{m}_{16} = \dot{m}_{6A} \tag{i}$$

Conservation of energy

$$\dot{m}_6 c_{p6} T_{t6} + \dot{m}_{16} c_{p16} T_{t16} = \dot{m}_{6A} c_{p6A} T_{t6A} \tag{ii}$$

Momentum

$$P_6 A_6 + \frac{\dot{m}_6 V_6}{g_c} + P_{16} A_{16} + \frac{\dot{m}_{16} V_{16}}{g_c} = P_{6A} A_{6A} + \frac{\dot{m}_{6A} V_{6A}}{g_c} \tag{iii}$$

Constant area

$$A_6 + A_{16} = A_{6A} \tag{iv}$$

The mixture law of perfect gases yields, for the mixed stream,

$$c_{p6A} = \frac{c_{p6} + \alpha' c_{p16}}{1 + \alpha'} \tag{7-73a}$$

$$R_{6A} = \frac{R_6 + \sigma' R_{16}}{1 + \alpha'} \tag{7-73b}$$

$$\gamma_{6A} = \frac{c_{p6A}}{c_{p6A} - R_{6A}} \tag{7-73c}$$

From Eq. (ii), the mixer total temperature ratio τ_M is

$$\boxed{\tau_M \equiv \frac{T_{t6A}}{T_{t6}} = \frac{c_{p6}}{c_{p6A}} \frac{1 + \alpha'(c_{p16}/c_{p6})(T_{t16}/T_{t6})}{1 + \alpha'}} \tag{7-74}$$

The momentum equation [Eq. (iii)] can be written as

$$I_6 + I_{16} = I_{6A} \tag{7-75}$$

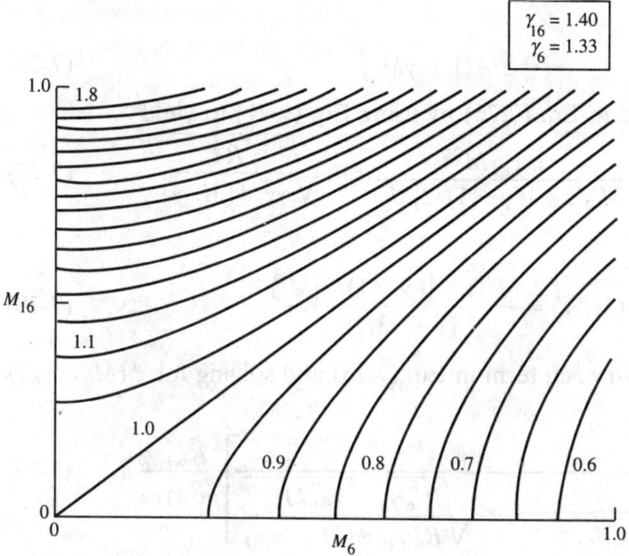

FIGURE 7-23
Contours of constant P_{t16}/P_{t6} (max = 1.8, min = 0.6, increment = 0.05).

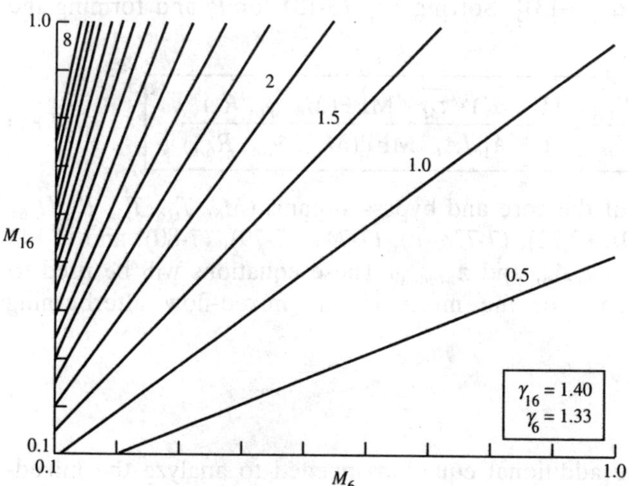

FIGURE 7-24
Contours of constant $\alpha'\sqrt{T_{t16}/T_{t6}}/(A_{16}/A_6)$ (max = 8, min = 0.5, increment = 0.5).

where, by Eq. (3-68),

$$I = PA(1 + \gamma M^2) \tag{7-76}$$

Now PA can be replaced in Eq. (7-76) by using Eq. (7-71) to yield

$$I = \dot{m}\sqrt{\frac{RT_t}{\gamma g_c}}\frac{1 + \gamma M^2}{M\sqrt{1 + [(\gamma - 1)/2]M^2}} = \dot{m}\sqrt{\frac{RT_t}{\gamma g_c \phi(M, \gamma)}} \tag{7-77}$$

where, by Eq. (3-51),

$$\phi(M, \gamma) = \frac{M^2\{1 + [(\gamma - 1)/2]M^2\}}{(1 + \gamma M^2)^2} \tag{7-78}$$

Substituting Eq. (7-77) for each term in Eq. (7-75) and solving for $\phi(M_{6A}, \gamma_{6A})$ yield

$$\phi(M_{6A}, \gamma_{6A}) = \left[\frac{1 + \alpha'}{\dfrac{1}{\sqrt{\phi(M_6, \gamma_6)}} + \alpha'\sqrt{\dfrac{R_{16}\gamma_6}{R_6\gamma_{16}}\dfrac{T_{t16}/T_{t6}}{\phi(M_{16}, \gamma_{16})}}}\right]^2 \frac{R_{6A}\gamma_6}{R_6\gamma_{6A}}\tau_M \tag{7-79}$$

For a given value of M_6 and M_{16}, Eq. (7-79) gives $\Phi \equiv \phi(M_{6A}, \gamma_{6A})$, which, when placed in Eq. (7-78), yields a quadratic equation in M_{6A}^2 with the solution [see subsonic solution of Eqs. (3-54) and (3-55)]

$$\boxed{M_{6A} = \sqrt{\frac{2\Phi}{1 - 2\gamma_{6A}\Phi + \sqrt{1 - 2(\gamma_{6A} + 1)\Phi}}}} \tag{7-80}$$

An expression for the mixer total pressure ratio π_M in terms of τ_M and the other flow properties at stations 6, 16, and 6A is obtained directly from the mass flow parameter [Eq. (3-13)]. Solving Eq. (3-13) for P_t and forming the ratio P_{t6A}/P_{t6} yields

$$\boxed{\pi_{M\,\text{ideal}} \equiv \frac{P_{t6A}}{P_{t6}} = \frac{(1 + \alpha')\sqrt{\tau_M}}{1 + A_{16}/A_6}\frac{\text{MFP}(M_6, \gamma_6, R_6)}{\text{MFP}(M_{6A}, \gamma_{6A}, R_{6A})}} \tag{7-81}$$

Given the c_p, R, and γ of the core and bypass streams (M_6, T_{t16}/T_{t6}, P_{t16}/P_{t6}, and α'), then Eqs. (7-70), (7-72), (7-73a–c), (7-74), (7-79), (7-80), and (7-81) will give M_{16}, M_{6A}, τ_M, A_{16}/A_6, and $\pi_{M\,\text{ideal}}$. These equations will be used to determine the performance of the mixer in the mixed-flow afterburning turbofan engine.

Cycle Analysis

This secton develops the additional equations needed to analyze the mixed-flow afterburning turbofan engine. Since this engine, like the turbojet, has a single inlet and exhaust, Eq. (7-1) can be used for the engine uninstalled thrust and Eq. (7-2) relates the pressure unbalance term to other flow quantities. We define the overall fuel/air ratio for this engine as the total fuel flow rate (main burner plus afterburner) divided by the inlet airflow rate, or

$$\boxed{f_O = \frac{\dot{m}_f + \dot{m}_{fAB}}{\dot{m}_0}} \tag{7-82}$$

We assume in this analysis that the mass flow rate at station 9 equals the mass flow rate at station 0 plus the fuel added in the main burner and in the afterburner. In equation form, we write

$$\dot{m}_9 = \dot{m}_0 + \dot{m}_f + \dot{m}_{fAB}$$

or

$$\frac{\dot{m}_9}{\dot{m}_0} = 1 + f_O \tag{7-83}$$

In the following, we use the steps of cycle analysis as listed in Sec. 5-4.

Step 1. Uninstalled thrust. Using Eqs. (7-1), (7-2), and (7-83), we can write

$$\boxed{\frac{F}{\dot{m}_0} = \frac{a_0}{g_c}\left[(1+f_O)\frac{V_9}{a_0} - M_0 + (1+f_O)\frac{R_9}{R_c}\frac{T_9/T_0}{V_9/a_0}\frac{1-P_0/P_9}{\gamma_c}\right]} \tag{7-84}$$

where the subscript c is used for gas properties at station 0.

Step 2.

$$\left(\frac{V_9}{a_0}\right)^2 = \frac{a_9^2 M_9^2}{a_0^2} = \frac{\gamma_9 R_9 g_c T_9}{\gamma_0 R_0 g_c T_0} M_9^2$$

Using the subscript c for the gas properties at station 0, we write

$$\left(\frac{V_9}{a_0}\right)^2 = \frac{\gamma_9 R_9 T_9}{\gamma_c R_c T_0} M_9^2 \tag{7-85}$$

Step 3. We have

$$M_9^2 = \frac{2}{\gamma_9 - 1}\left[\left(\frac{P_{t9}}{P_9}\right)^{(\gamma_9-1)/\gamma_9} - 1\right] \tag{7-86a}$$

where

$$\frac{P_{t9}}{P_9} = \frac{P_0}{P_9}\pi_r \pi_d \pi_c \pi_b \pi_t \pi_M \pi_{AB} \pi_n \tag{7-86b}$$

Step 4. We have

$$\frac{T_9}{T_0} = \frac{T_{t9}/T_0}{(P_{t9}/P_9)^{(\gamma_9-1)/\gamma_9}}$$

where

$$T_{t9} = T_{t4}\tau_t \tau_M \qquad \text{afterburner off} \tag{7-87a}$$

or

$$T_{t9} = T_{t7} \qquad \text{afterburner on} \tag{7-87b}$$

Step 5. Application of the first law of thermodynamics to the main burner and solution for the fuel/air ratio f yield Eq. (7-10), where

$$f = \frac{\dot{m}_f}{\dot{m}_C} \tag{7-88}$$

Application of the first law of thermodynamics to the afterburner gives

$$\dot{m}_{6A} c_{p6A} T_{t6A} + \eta_{AB} \dot{m}_{fAB} h_{PR} = \dot{m}_7 c_{p7} T_{t7}$$

Dividing the above equation by $\dot{m}_0 c_{pc} T_0$ and using the definitions of temperature ratios give

$$\left(1 + \frac{f}{1+\alpha}\right) \frac{c_{p6A}}{c_{pt}} \tau_\lambda \tau_t \tau_M + f_{AB} \frac{\eta_{AB} h_{PR}}{c_{pc} T_0} = \left(1 + \frac{f}{1+\alpha} + f_{AB}\right) \tau_{\lambda AB}$$

Solving for the afterburner fuel/air ratio f_{AB} gives

$$f_{AB} = \left(1 + \frac{f}{1+\alpha}\right) \frac{\tau_{\lambda AB} - (c_{p6A}/c_{pt}) \tau_\lambda \tau_t \tau_M}{\eta_{AB} h_{PR}/(c_{pc} T_0) - \tau_{\lambda AB}} \tag{7-89}$$

Step 6. The power balance between the turbine, compressor, and fan, with a mechanical efficiency η_m of the turbine shaft, gives Eq. (7-44). This equation, solved for the turbine temperature ratio, gives

$$\tau_t = 1 - \frac{1}{\eta_m (1+f)} \frac{\tau_r}{\tau_\lambda} [\tau_c - 1 + \alpha(\tau_f - 1)] \tag{7-90}$$

This expression allows solution for τ_t, from which we then obtain π_t by using Eq. (7-13) and η_t by using Eq. (7-14). Equations (7-15), (7-16), (7-46), and (7-47) are used to obtain τ_c, η_c, τ_f, and η_f, respectively, from given π_c, π_f, and polytropic efficiencies.

Normally, the fan pressure ratio or bypass ratio is selected for this engine cycle so that the total pressures at stations 6 and 16 are equal. Assuming isentropic flow in the bypass duct from 13 to 16, we can write

$$\pi_c \pi_b \pi_t = \pi_f$$

or

$$\tau_t = \pi_t^{(\gamma_t - 1)e_t/\gamma_t} = \left(\frac{\pi_f}{\pi_c \pi_b}\right)^{(\gamma_t - 1)e_t/\gamma_t} \tag{7-91}$$

Equations (7-90) and (7-91) can be solved to obtain the bypass ratio α or the fan temperature ratio τ_f in terms of known quantities. Solution for the bypass ratio gives

$$\alpha = \frac{\eta_m (1+f)(\tau_\lambda/\tau_r)\{1 - [\pi_f/(\pi_c \pi_b)]^{(\gamma_t - 1)e_t/\gamma_t}\} - (\tau_c - 1)}{\tau_f - 1} \tag{7-92}$$

Step 7. The equation for specific thrust cannot be simplified for this analysis.

Step 8. The equation for the thrust specific fuel consumption is

$$\boxed{S = \frac{f_O}{F/\dot{m}_0}} \tag{7-93}$$

Step 9. From the definitions of propulsive and thermal efficiency, one can easily show that, for this turbofan engine,

$$\eta_P = \frac{2g_c V_0(F/\dot{m}_0)}{a_0^2[(1+f_O)(V_9/a_0)^2 - M_0^2]} \tag{7-94a}$$

$$\eta_T = \frac{a_0^2[(1+f_O)(V_9/a_0)^2 - M_0^2]}{2g_c f_O h_{PR}} \tag{7-94b}$$

Now we have all the equations needed for analysis of the mixed-flow afterburning turbofan engine. For convenience, this system of equations is listed (in the order of calculation) in the following section for easier calculation.

Summary of Equations—Mixed-Flow Afterburning Turbofan Engine

INPUTS: $M_0,\ T_0\,(\text{K}, {}^\circ\text{R}),\ \gamma_c,\ c_{pc}\left(\frac{\text{kJ}}{\text{kg}\cdot\text{K}}, \frac{\text{Btu}}{\text{lbm}\cdot{}^\circ\text{R}}\right),\ \gamma_t,\ c_{pt}\left(\frac{\text{kJ}}{\text{kg}\cdot\text{K}}, \frac{\text{Btu}}{\text{lbm}\cdot{}^\circ\text{R}}\right),\ h_{PR}\left(\frac{\text{kJ}}{\text{kg}}, \frac{\text{Btu}}{\text{lbm}}\right),\ \gamma_{\text{AB}},\ c_{p\text{AB}}\left(\frac{\text{kJ}}{\text{kg}\cdot\text{K}}, \frac{\text{Btu}}{\text{lbm}\cdot{}^\circ\text{R}}\right),$ $\pi_{d\,\max},\ \pi_b,\ \pi_{\text{AB}},\ \pi_{M\,\max},\ \pi_n,\ e_c,\ e_f,\ e_t,\ \eta_b,\ \eta_{\text{AB}},\ \eta_m,\ P_0/P_9,$ $T_{t4}\,(\text{K}, {}^\circ\text{R}),\ T_{t7}\,(\text{K}, {}^\circ\text{R}),\ \pi_c,\ \pi_f$

OUTPUTS: $\frac{F}{\dot{m}_0}\left(\frac{\text{N}}{\text{kg/sec}}, \frac{\text{lbf}}{\text{lbm/sec}}\right), f, f_{\text{AB}}, f_O, S\left(\frac{\text{mg/sec}}{\text{N}}, \frac{\text{lbm/hr}}{\text{lbf}}\right), \alpha,$ $\eta_T,\ \eta_P,\ \eta_O,\ \eta_c,\ \eta_t$, etc.

EQUATIONS:

$$R_c = \frac{\gamma_c - 1}{\gamma_c} c_{pc} \tag{7-95a}$$

$$R_t = \frac{\gamma_t - 1}{\gamma_t} c_{pt} \tag{7-95b}$$

$$R_{\text{AB}} = \frac{\gamma_{\text{AB}} - 1}{\gamma_{\text{AB}}} c_{p\text{AB}} \tag{7-95c}$$

$$a_0 = \sqrt{\gamma_c R_c g_c T_0} \tag{7-95d}$$

$$V_0 = a_0 M_0 \tag{7-95e}$$

$$\tau_r = 1 + \frac{\gamma_c - 1}{2} M_0^2 \tag{7-95f}$$

$$\pi_r = \tau_r^{\gamma_c/(\gamma_c - 1)} \tag{7-95g}$$

$$\eta_r = 1 \qquad \text{for } M_0 \leq 1 \tag{7-95h}$$

$$\eta_r = 1 - 0.075(M_0 - 1)^{1.35} \qquad \text{for } M_0 > 1 \tag{7-95i}$$

$$\pi_d = \pi_{d\,\max}\eta_r \tag{7-95j}$$

$$\tau_\lambda = \frac{c_{pt} T_{t4}}{c_{pc} T_0} \tag{7-95k}$$

$$\tau_{\lambda \mathrm{AB}} = \frac{c_{p\mathrm{AB}} T_{t7}}{c_{pc} T_0} \tag{7-95l}$$

$$\tau_c = \pi_c^{(\gamma_c - 1)/(\gamma_c e_c)} \tag{7-95m}$$

$$\eta_c = \frac{\pi_c^{(\gamma_c - 1)/\gamma_c} - 1}{\tau_c - 1} \tag{7-95n}$$

$$f = \frac{\tau_\lambda - \tau_r \tau_c}{\eta_b h_{PR}/(c_{pc} T_0) - \tau_\lambda} \tag{7-95o}$$

$$\tau_f = \pi_f^{(\gamma_c - 1)/(\gamma_c e_f)} \tag{7-95p}$$

$$\eta_f = \frac{\pi_f^{(\gamma_c - 1)/\gamma_c} - 1}{\tau_f - 1} \tag{7-95q}$$

$$\alpha = \frac{\eta_m (1 + f)(\tau_\lambda/\tau_r)\{1 - [\pi_f/(\pi_c \pi_b)]^{(\gamma_t - 1)e_t/\gamma_t}\} - (\tau_c - 1)}{\tau_f - 1} \tag{7-95r}$$

$$\tau_t = 1 - \frac{1}{\eta_m (1 + f)} \frac{\tau_r}{\tau_\lambda} [\tau_c - 1 + \alpha(\tau_f - 1)] \tag{7-95s}$$

$$\pi_t = \tau_t^{\gamma_t/[(\gamma_t - 1)e_t]} \tag{7-95t}$$

$$\eta_t = \frac{1 - \tau_t}{1 - \tau_t^{1/e_t}} \tag{7-95u}$$

$$\frac{P_{t16}}{P_{t6}} = \frac{\pi_f}{\pi_c \pi_b \pi_t} \tag{7-95v}$$

$$M_{16} = \sqrt{\frac{2}{\gamma_c - 1}\left\{\left[\frac{P_{t16}}{P_{t6}}\left(1 + \frac{\gamma_t - 1}{2} M_6^2\right)^{\gamma_t/(\gamma_t - 1)}\right]^{(\gamma_c - 1)/\gamma_c} - 1\right\}} \tag{7-95w}$$

$$\alpha' = \frac{\alpha}{1+f} \tag{7-95x}$$

$$c_{p6A} = \frac{c_{pt} + \alpha' c_{pc}}{1+\alpha'} \tag{7-95y}$$

$$R_{6A} = \frac{R_t + \alpha' R_c}{1+\alpha'} \tag{7-95z}$$

$$\gamma_{6A} = \frac{c_{p6A}}{c_{p6A} - R_{6A}} \tag{7-95aa}$$

$$\frac{T_{t16}}{T_{t6}} = \frac{T_0 \tau_r \tau_f}{T_{t4} \tau_t} \tag{7-95ab}$$

$$\tau_M = \frac{c_{pt}}{c_{p6A}} \frac{1 + \alpha'(c_{pc}/c_{pt})(T_{t16}/T_{t6})}{1+\alpha'} \tag{7-95ac}$$

$$\phi(M_6, \gamma_6) = \frac{M_6^2\{1 + [(\gamma_t - 1)/2]M_6^2\}}{(1 + \gamma_t M_6^2)^2} \tag{7-95ad}$$

$$\phi(M_{16}, \gamma_{16}) = \frac{M_{16}^2\{1 + [(\gamma_c - 1)/2]M_{16}^2\}}{(1 + \gamma_c M_{16}^2)^2} \tag{7-95ae}$$

$$\Phi = \left[\frac{1+\alpha'}{\dfrac{1}{\sqrt{\phi(M_6, \gamma_6)}} + \alpha' \sqrt{\dfrac{R_c \gamma_t}{R_t \gamma_c} \dfrac{T_{t16}/T_{t6}}{\phi(M_{16}, \gamma_{16})}}} \right]^2 \frac{R_{6A}\gamma_t}{R_t \gamma_{6A}} \tau_M \tag{7-95af}$$

$$M_{6A} = \sqrt{\frac{2\Phi}{1 - 2\gamma_{6A}\Phi + \sqrt{1 - 2(\gamma_{6A}+1)\Phi}}} \tag{7-95ag}$$

$$\frac{A_{16}}{A_6} = \frac{\alpha' \sqrt{T_{t16}/T_{t6}}}{\dfrac{M_{16}}{M_6} \sqrt{\dfrac{\gamma_c R_t}{\gamma_t R_c} \dfrac{1 + [(\gamma_c - 1)/2]M_{16}^2}{1 + [(\gamma_t - 1)/2]M_6^2}}} \tag{7-95ah}$$

$$\pi_{M\,\text{ideal}} = \frac{(1+\alpha')\sqrt{\tau_M}}{1 + A_{16}/A_6} \frac{\text{MFP}(M_6, \gamma_t, R_t)}{\text{MFP}(M_{6A}, \gamma_{6A}, R_{6A})} \tag{7-95ai}$$

$$\pi_M = \pi_{M\,\max} \pi_{M\,\text{ideal}} \tag{7-95aj}$$

$$\frac{P_{t9}}{P_9} = \frac{P_0}{P_9} \pi_r \pi_d \pi_c \pi_b \pi_t \pi_M \pi_{\text{AB}} \pi_n \tag{7-95ak}$$

Afterburner off

$$c_{p9} = c_{p6A} \qquad R_9 = R_{6A} \qquad \gamma_9 = \gamma_{6A} \qquad f_{AB} = 0 \tag{7-95al}$$

$$\frac{T_9}{T_0} = \frac{T_{t4}\tau_t\tau_M/T_0}{(P_{t9}/P_9)^{(\gamma_9-1)/\gamma_9}} \tag{7-95am}$$

Afterburner on

$$c_{p9} = c_{pAB} \qquad R_9 = R_{AB} \qquad \gamma_9 = \gamma_{AB} \tag{7-95an}$$

$$f_{AB} = \left(1 + \frac{f}{1+\alpha}\right)\frac{\tau_{\lambda AB} - (c_{p6A}/c_{pt})\tau_\lambda\tau_t\tau_M}{\eta_{AB}h_{PR}/(c_{pc}T_0) - \tau_{\lambda AB}} \tag{7-95ao}$$

$$\frac{T_9}{T_0} = \frac{T_{t7}/T_0}{(P_{t9}/P_9)^{(\gamma_9-1)/\gamma_9}} \tag{7-95ap}$$

Continue

$$M_9 = \sqrt{\frac{2}{\gamma_9 - 1}\left[\left(\frac{P_{t9}}{P_9}\right)^{(\gamma_9-1)/\gamma_9} - 1\right]} \tag{7-95aq}$$

$$\frac{V_9}{a_0} = M_9\sqrt{\frac{\gamma_9 R_9 T_9}{\gamma_c R_c T_0}} \tag{7-95ar}$$

$$f_O = \frac{f}{1+\alpha} + f_{AB} \tag{7-95as}$$

$$\frac{F}{\dot{m}_0} = \frac{a_0}{g_c}\left[(1+f_O)\frac{V_9}{a_0} - M_0 + (1+f_O)\frac{R_9}{R_c}\frac{T_9/T_0}{V_9/a_0}\frac{1-P_0/P_9}{\gamma_c}\right] \tag{7-95at}$$

$$S = \frac{f_O}{F/\dot{m}_0} \tag{7-95au}$$

$$\eta_P = \frac{2g_c V_0(F/\dot{m}_0)}{a_0^2[(1+f_O)(V_9/a_0)^2 - M_0^2]} \tag{7-95av}$$

$$\eta_T = \frac{a_0^2[(1+f_O)(V_9/a_0)^2 - M_0^2]}{2g_c f_o h_{PR}} \tag{7-95aw}$$

$$\eta_O = \eta_P\eta_T \tag{7-95ax}$$

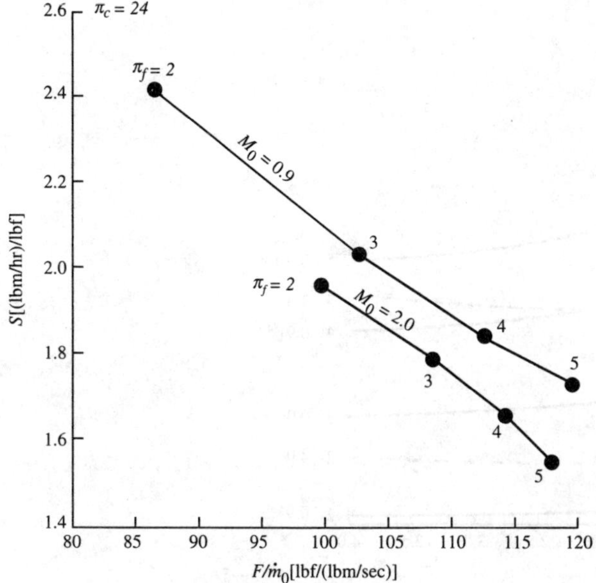

FIGURE 7-25
Performance of mixed-flow afterburning turbofan engine.

Example 7-10. The afterburning and nonafterburning performance of the mixed-flow turbofans with losses are plotted in Figs. 7-25 through 7-27 vesus compressor pressure ratio π_c and fan pressure ratio π_f at two flight Mach numbers. Figure 7-28 plots the required bypass ratio α versus compressor pressure ratio π_c for the different values of fan pressure ratio π_f at flight Mach numbers of 0.9 and 2. Calculations were performed for the following input data:

$$c_{pc} = 0.240 \text{ Btu/(lbm} \cdot {}^\circ\text{R)}$$

$$\gamma_c = 1.4 \qquad T_0 = 390^\circ\text{R} \qquad \pi_{d\,\max} = 0.98 \qquad \pi_{M\,\max} = 0.98$$

$$h_{PR} = 18{,}400 \text{ Btu/lbm}$$

$$e_c = 0.90 \qquad e_f = 0.89 \qquad e_t = 0.91 \qquad \pi_n = 0.98$$

$$c_{pt} = 0.295 \text{ Btu/(lbm} \cdot {}^\circ\text{R)}$$

$$\gamma_t = 1.3 \qquad \eta_b = 0.99 \qquad \pi_b = 0.96 \qquad T_{t4} = 3000^\circ\text{R}$$

$$c_{p\text{AB}} = 0.295 \text{ Btu/(lbm} \cdot {}^\circ\text{R)}$$

$$\gamma_{\text{AB}} = 1.3 \qquad \eta_{\text{AB}} = 0.95 \qquad \pi_{\text{AB}} = 0.94 \qquad T_{t7} = 3600^\circ\text{R}$$

$$h_{PR} = 18{,}400 \text{ Btu/lbm}$$

$$M_6 = 0.4 \qquad \eta_m = 0.99 \qquad \frac{P_0}{P_9} = 1$$

$$\pi_c = 10 \rightarrow 40$$

$$\pi_f = 2 \rightarrow 5 \qquad M_0 = 0.9,\ 2$$

Since the compressor pressure ratio has very little effect on the performance of an afterburning turbofan engine, only the compressor pressure ratio of

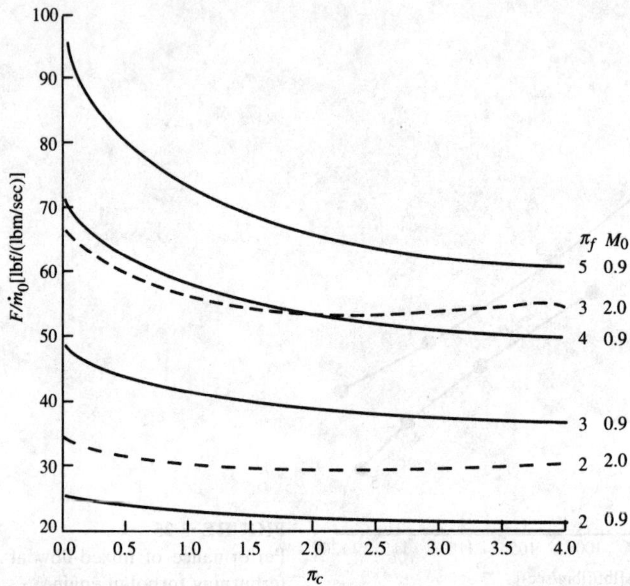

FIGURE 7-26
Specific thrust of mixed-flow turbofan engine (no afterburner).

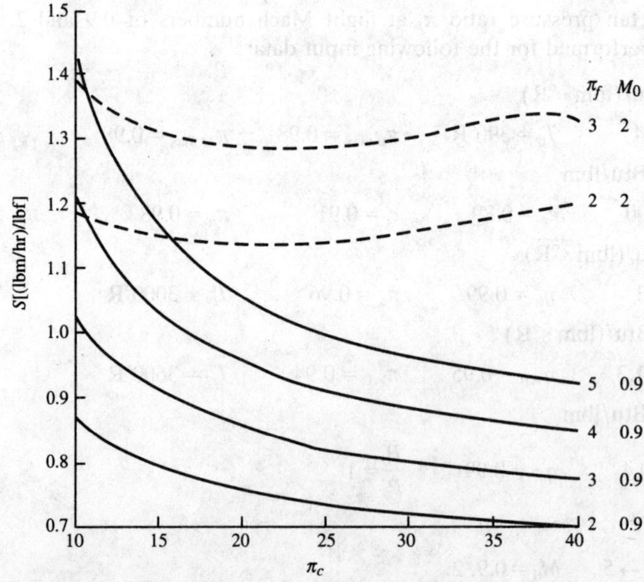

FIGURE 7-27
Thrust specific fuel consumption of mixed-flow turbofan engine (no afterburner).

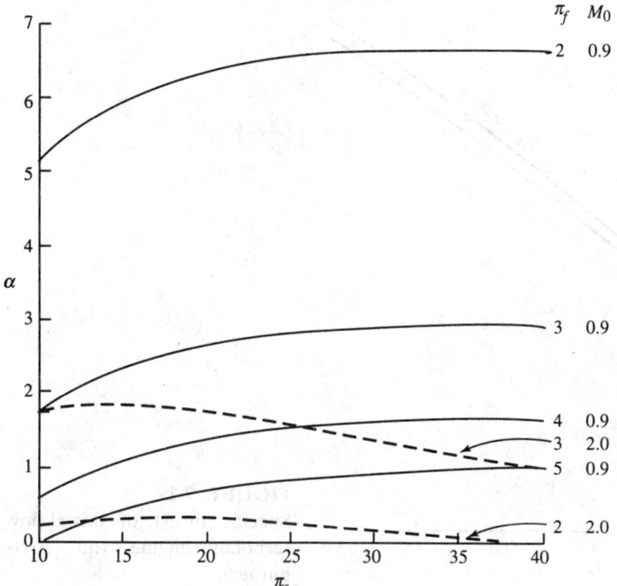

FIGURE 7-28
Bypass ratio of mixed-flow turbofan engine.

24 was used for the data presented in Fig. 7-25. Figure 7-25 is a composite performance plot of fuel consumption versus specific thrust with different fan pressure ratios and Mach numbers—this is sometimes called a *carpet plot.* This figure shows that increasing the fan pressure ratio reduces fuel consumption and increases specific thrust—both desirable.

Figures 7-26 and 7-27 show that increasing the fan pressure ratio of the nonafterburning mixed-flow turbofan engine will increase both the specific thrust and fuel consumption. Figure 7-28 shows the corresponding engine bypass ratios. Note that the bypass ratio decreases with increasing fan pressure ratio and Mach number.

Figures 7-25 through 7-28 can be compared to the results for the ideal mixed-flow turbofan engine presented in Figs. 5-40 through 5-44. The trends are the same.

Example 7-11. In this example, we look at the effect of increasing T_{t4} on the performance of the mixed-flow turbofan engine without afterburning. The fan pressure ratio π_f was varied from 2 to 5 for values of T_{t4} from 3000 to 4000°R with $M_0 = 0$, $\pi_c = 24$, and the other data of Example 7-10. The results are plotted in Figs. 7-29 through 7-31. The results show the following for increasing T_{t4} from 3000 to 4000°R while keeping the fan pressure ratio at 3.5:

1. About a 3 percent increase in specific thrust (this could translate to a physically smaller engine)
2. Dramatic increases in engine bypass ratio (from about 1.3 to 3.1) resulting in reduced fuel consumption [from about 0.74 to 0.67 (lbm/hr)/lbf, a 10 percent decrease]

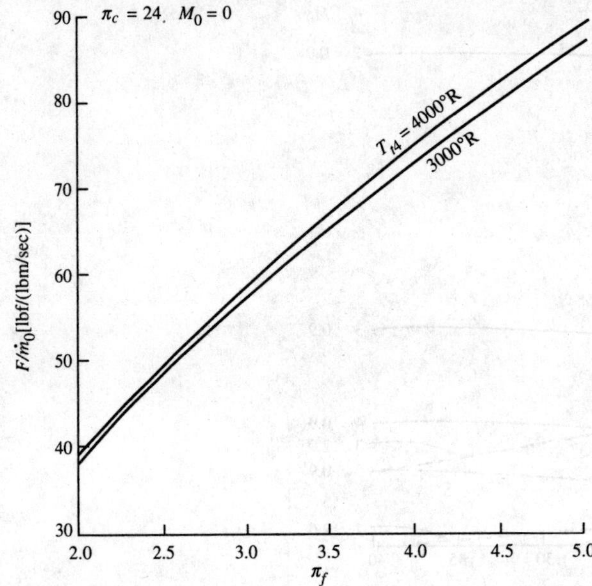

FIGURE 7-29
Specific thrust of mixed-flow turbofan engine (no afterburner).

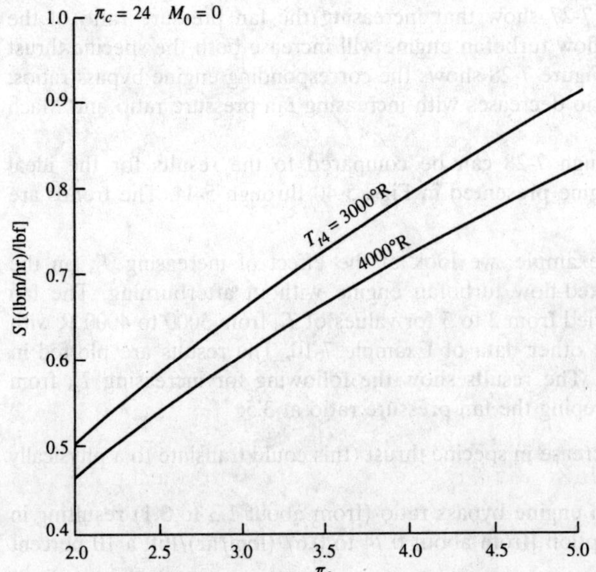

FIGURE 7-30
Thrust specific fuel consumption of mixed-flow turbofan engine (no afterburner).

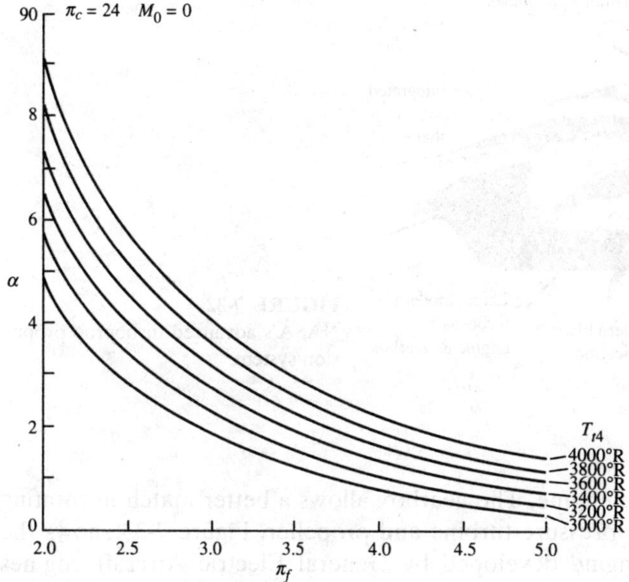

FIGURE 7-31
Bypass ratio of mixed-flow turbofan engine.

If the engine bypass ratio is held constant at 1.5, increasing T_{t4} from 3000 to 4000°R results in the following:

1. Dramatic increase in fan pressure ratio from about 3.3 to 4.9.
2. Increase in fuel consumption from about 0.7 to 0.83 (lbm/hr)/lbf (about a 19 percent increase).
3. Dramatic increase in specific thrust from about 62 to 88 lbf/(lbm/sec). This is about a 42 percent increase which could translate to an engine that is physically much smaller.

7-7 TURBOPROP ENGINE

There continues to be interest in the development of advanced turboprop engines that will improve the installed propulsive efficiency for Mach 0.8 flight above current high-bypass-ratio turbofan engines. Two particular research and development efforts have led to the advancement of turboprop technology, as shown in Figs. 7-32 and 7-33. Figure 7-32 shows a sketch of the NASA-sponsored Advanced Turboprop Propulsion System program which included highly swept propeller blades connected by an advanced gearbox to a

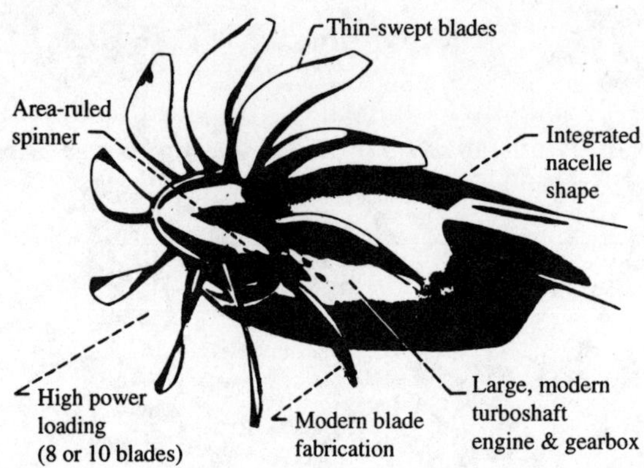

FIGURE 7-32
NASA's advanced turboprop propulsion system.

conventional gas turbine engine. The gearbox allows a better match in rotating speeds between the low-pressure turbine and propeller. Figure 7-33 shows the *unducted fan* (UDF) engine developed by General Electric Aircraft engines which has two counterrotating rows of highly swept propeller blades that are directly driven by stages of the low-pressure turbine. Lack of a gearbox reduces engine weight, increases engine reliability, and compromises the speed match of the propeller and low-pressure turbine.

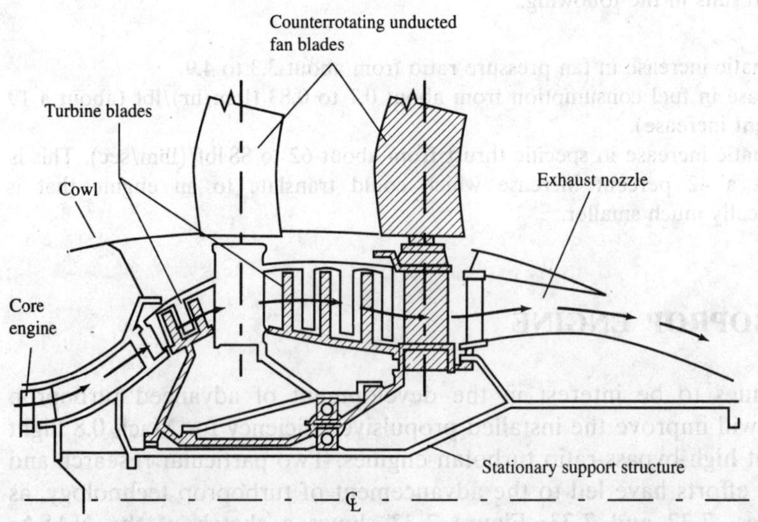

FIGURE 7-33
General Electric's unducted fan (UDF) engine.

Cycle Analysis

The analysis of the turboprop engine cycle builds on the ideal analysis developed in Chap. 5 and on the previous analysis in this chapter. We use the dimensionless *work output coefficient C,* defined by

$$C = \frac{\text{power interaction/mass flow of air through engine core}}{h_0} \tag{5-99}$$

For the thrust of the core stream, we have its work output coefficient

$$C_C = \frac{F_C V_0}{\dot{m}_0 c_p T_0} \tag{5-100}$$

Thus the work output coefficient for the total turboprop engine is

$$C_{\text{tot}} = C_{\text{prop}} + C_C \tag{5-101}$$

and the corresponding thrust is

$$F = F_{\text{prop}} + F_C = \frac{C_{\text{tot}} \dot{m}_0 c_p T_0}{V_0} \tag{5-102}$$

It is usual with turboprop engines to have the core stream exit nozzles unchoked, so the pressure imbalance term will not contribute in the expression for the thrust. We consider the numbering stations indicated in Fig. 5-46 with station 4.5 being the exit from the high-pressure turbine and the entrance to the low-pressure or power turbine. For a turboprop engine, we have two design variables: the compressor pressure ratio and the low-pressure (free or power) turbine temperature ratio. We want to develop the cycle equations in terms of the pressure and temperature ratios across both the high-pressure turbine (drives the compressor) and the low-pressure turbine.

Step 1. Using Eq. (7-3), we have for the engine core

$$\frac{F_C}{\dot{m}_0} = \frac{a_0}{g_c}\left[(1+f)\frac{V_9}{a_0} - M_0 + (1+f)\frac{R_t}{R_c}\frac{T_9/T_0}{V_9/a_0}\frac{1-P_0/P_9}{\gamma_c}\right]$$

Then $$C_C = \frac{V_0}{c_p T_0}\frac{a_0}{g_c}\left[(1+f)\frac{V_9}{a_0} - M_0 + (1+f)\frac{R_t}{R_c}\frac{T_9/T_0}{V_9/a_0}\frac{1-P_0/P_9}{\gamma_c}\right]$$

Thus
$$C_C = (\gamma_c - 1)M_0\left[(1+f)\frac{V_9}{a_0} - M_0 + (1+f)\frac{R_t}{R_c}\frac{T_9/T_0}{V_9/a_0}\frac{1-P_0/P_9}{\gamma_c}\right] \tag{7-96}$$

Step 2.
$$\left(\frac{V_9}{a_0}\right)^2 = \frac{\gamma_t R_t T_9}{\gamma_c R_c T_0} M_9^2 \tag{7-40}$$

Step 3. We have

$$M_9^2 = \frac{2}{\gamma_t - 1}\left[\left(\frac{P_{t9}}{P_9}\right)^{(\gamma_t-1)/\gamma_t} - 1\right] \tag{7-41a}$$

where
$$\frac{P_{t9}}{P_9} = \frac{P_0}{P_9}\pi_r\pi_d\pi_c\pi_b\pi_{tH}\pi_{tL}\pi_n \tag{7-97a}$$

Two flow regimes exist for flow through the convergent exhaust nozzle: unchoked flow and choked flow. For unchoked flow, the exit static pressure P_9 is equal to the ambient pressure P_0, and the exit Mach number is less than or equal to 1. Unchoked flow will exist when

$$\frac{P_{t9}}{P_0} \le \left(\frac{\gamma_t + 1}{2}\right)^{\gamma_t/(\gamma_t-1)} \tag{7-97b}$$

and the exit Mach number is given by Eqs. (7-41*a*) and (7-97*a*) with $P_9 = P_0$. On the other hand, choked flow will exist when

$$\frac{P_{t9}}{P_0} > \left(\frac{\gamma_t + 1}{2}\right)^{\gamma_t/(\gamma_t-1)} \tag{7-97c}$$

thus
$$M_9 = 1 \qquad \frac{P_{t9}}{P_9} = \left(\frac{\gamma_t + 1}{2}\right)^{\gamma_t/(\gamma_t-1)} \qquad \text{and} \qquad \frac{P_0}{P_9} = \frac{P_{t9}/P_9}{P_{t9}/P_0} \tag{7-97d}$$

Step 4. We have

$$\frac{T_9}{T_0} = \frac{T_{t9}/T_0}{(P_{t9}/P_9)^{(\gamma_t-1)/\gamma_t}} \tag{7-98a}$$

where
$$\frac{T_{t9}}{T_0} = \frac{T_{t4}}{T_0}\tau_{tH}\tau_{tL} \tag{7-98b}$$

Combining Eqs. (7-41*a*), (7-98*a*), and (7-98*b*) gives

$$\frac{V_9}{a_0} = \sqrt{\frac{2\tau_\lambda\tau_{tH}\tau_{tL}}{\gamma_c - 1}\left[1 - \left(\frac{P_{t9}}{P_9}\right)^{(\gamma_t-1)/\gamma_t}\right]} \tag{7-99}$$

Step 5. From the energy balance of the ideal turbojet's burner, we have

$$f = \frac{\tau_\lambda - \tau_r\tau_c}{\eta_b h_{PR}/(c_{pc}T_0) - \tau_\lambda} \tag{7-10}$$

Step 6. For the high-pressure turbine, we have from Eq. (7-11) of the turbojet analysis

$$\boxed{\tau_{tH} = 1 - \frac{1}{\eta_{mH}(1+f)}\frac{\tau_r}{\tau_\lambda}(\tau_c - 1)} \tag{7-100}$$

where η_{mH} is the mechanical efficiency of the high-pressure shaft. For the low-pressure turbine (also called the *free turbine*), we equate the power out of this turbine to the power into the propeller. Thus

$$\eta_{mL}\dot{m}_{4.5}c_{pt}(T_{t4.5} - T_{t5}) = \frac{\dot{W}_{\text{prop}}}{\eta_g}$$

or

$$\boxed{C_{\text{prop}} = \frac{\eta_{\text{prop}}\dot{W}_{\text{prop}}}{\dot{m}_0 c_p T_0} = \eta_{\text{prop}}\eta_g\eta_{mL}(1+f)\tau_\lambda\tau_{tH}(1-\tau_{tL})} \tag{7-101}$$

Step 7. For the turboprop engine, we consider both the specific power and the specific thrust:

$$\frac{\dot{W}}{\dot{m}_0} = C_{\text{tot}}c_{pc}T_0 \tag{7-102a}$$

$$\frac{F}{\dot{m}_0} = \frac{C_{\text{tot}}c_{pc}T_0}{V_0} \tag{7-102b}$$

Step 8.

$$S = \frac{f}{F/\dot{m}_0}$$

We should note here, also, that it is more usual when we refer to propeller aircraft to refer to the power specific fuel consumption in terms of S_P, where S_P is defined by

$$S_P = \frac{\dot{m}_f}{\dot{W}} = \frac{f}{\dot{W}/\dot{m}_0}$$

Thus

$$\boxed{S_P = \frac{f}{C_{\text{tot}}c_{pc}T_0}} \tag{7-103}$$

Step 9. The thermal efficiency of the turboprop engine cycle is defined as the ratio of the total power produced by the engine to the energy contained in the fuel. Thus

$$\eta_T = \frac{\dot{m}_0 c_{pc}T_0 C_{\text{tot}}}{\dot{m}_f h_{PR}}$$

or

$$\boxed{\eta_T = \frac{C_{\text{tot}}}{f h_{PR}/(c_{pc}T_0)}} \tag{7-104}$$

The propulsive efficiency of the turboprop engine is defined as the ratio of the total power interaction with the vehicle producing propulsive power to the total energy available for producing propulsive power. Thus,

$$\eta_P = \frac{\dot{m}_0 c_{pc} T_0 C_{tot}}{\dot{W}_{prop}(\dot{m}_9 V_9^2 - \dot{m}_0 V_0^2)/(2g_c)}$$

or

$$\boxed{\eta_P = \frac{C_{tot}}{C_{prop}/\eta_{prop} + [(\gamma_c - 1)/2][(1+f)(V_9/a_0)^2 - M_0^2]}} \tag{7-105}$$

Selection of Optimal Turbine Expansion Ratio τ_{tL}^*

Turboprop or prop-fan engines are designed primarily to be low-specific-fuel-consumption engines. Thus we select τ_{tL} to make S_P a minimum. From Eq. (7-103), this is equivalent to locating the maximum of C_{tot}. We will obtain an expression for the optimum low-pressure turbine temperature ratio τ_{tL}^* that gives maximum C_{tot} with all other variables constant and when $P_9 = P_0$. We have

$$C_{tot} = C_{prop} + C_C$$

with

$$C_{prop} = \eta_{prop}\eta_g\eta_{mL}(1+f)\tau_\lambda\tau_{tH}(1-\tau_{tL})$$

and for the case $P_9 = P_0$

$$C_C = (\gamma_c - 1)M_0\left[(1+f)\frac{V_9}{a_0} - M_0\right]$$

Thus the total temperature ratio of the low-pressure turbine corresponding to minimum fuel consumption is obtained by finding the maximum of C_{tot} with respect to τ_{tL}. Taking the partial derivative of C_{tot} with respect to τ_{tL} (noting that only τ_{tL} is a variable in the equation for C_{prop} and that V_9/a_0 is a function of τ_{tL} in the equation for C_C) and setting the result equal to zero gives

$$\frac{\partial C_{tot}}{\partial \tau_{tL}} = -\eta_{prop}\eta_g\eta_{mL}(1+f)\tau_\lambda\tau_{tH} + (\gamma_c - 1)(1+f)M_0 \times \frac{\partial}{\partial \tau_{tL}}\left(\frac{V_9}{a_0}\right) = 0$$

or

$$\frac{\partial}{\partial \tau_{tL}}\left(\frac{V_9}{a_0}\right) = \eta_{prop}\eta_g\eta_{mL}\frac{\tau_\lambda\tau_{tH}}{(\gamma_c - 1)M_0} \tag{7-106}$$

By the chain rule, the partial derivative of the velocity ratio can be expressed as

$$\frac{\partial}{\partial \tau_{tL}}\left(\frac{V_9}{a_0}\right) = \frac{\partial(V_9/a_0)}{\partial[(V_9/a_0)^2]}\,\frac{\partial[(V_9/a_0)^2]}{\partial \tau_{tL}} \tag{7-107}$$

where

$$\frac{\partial(V_9/a_0)}{\partial[(V_9/a_0)^2]} = \frac{1}{2V_9/a_0} \tag{7-108}$$

The velocity ratio $(V_9/a_0)^2$ is given by

$$\left(\frac{V_9}{a_0}\right)^2 = \frac{2\tau_\lambda\tau_{tH}\tau_{tL}}{\gamma_c - 1}\left[1 - \left(\frac{P_{t9}}{P_9}\right)^{-(\gamma_t - 1)/\gamma_t}\right] \tag{7-99}$$

where $$\frac{P_{t9}}{P_9} = \pi_r \pi_d \pi_c \pi_b \pi_{tH} \pi_{tL} \pi_n$$

Thus $$\left(\frac{V_9}{a_0}\right)^2 = \frac{2\tau_\lambda \tau_{tH}}{\gamma_c - 1}\left[\tau_{tL} - \frac{\tau_{tL}}{\Pi(\pi_{tH}\pi_{tL})^{(\gamma_t-1)/\gamma_t}}\right] \tag{7-109}$$

where $$\Pi = (\pi_r \pi_d \pi_c \pi_b \pi_n)^{(\gamma_t-1)/\gamma_t}$$

Using different polytropic efficiencies for the high- and low-pressure turbines, we can write

$$\pi_{tH}^{(\gamma_t-1)/\gamma_t} = \tau_{tH}^{1/e_{tH}} \qquad \text{and} \qquad \pi_{tL}^{(\gamma_t-1)/\gamma_t} = \tau_{tL}^{1/e_{tL}}$$

then Eq. (7-109) becomes

$$\left(\frac{V_9}{a_0}\right)^2 = \frac{2\tau_\lambda \tau_{tH}}{\gamma_c - 1}\left(\tau_{tL} - \frac{\tau_{tH}^{-1/e_{tH}}}{\Pi}\tau_{tL}^{-(1-e_{tL})/e_{tL}}\right)$$

and thus $$\frac{\partial[(V_9/a_0)^2]}{\partial \tau_{tL}} = \frac{2\tau_\lambda \tau_{tH}}{\gamma_c - 1}\left(1 + \frac{1-e_{tL}}{e_{tL}}\frac{\tau_{tH}^{-1/e_{tH}}\tau_{tL}^{-1/e_{tL}}}{\Pi}\right) \tag{7-110}$$

Substitution of Eqs. (7-107), (7-108), (7-109), and (7-110) into Eq. (7-106) gives

$$\frac{\tau_\lambda \tau_{tH}}{(\gamma_c - 1)(V_9/a_0)}\left(1 + \frac{1-e_{tL}}{e_{tL}}\frac{\tau_{tH}^{-1/e_{tH}}\tau_{tL}^{-1/e_{tL}}}{\Pi}\right) = \eta_{\text{prop}}\eta_g\eta_{mL}\frac{\tau_\lambda \tau_{tH}}{(\gamma_c - 1)M_0}$$

and solving for the velocity ratio gives

$$\frac{V_9}{a_0} = \frac{M_0}{\eta_{\text{prop}}\eta_g\eta_{mL}}\left(1 + \frac{1-e_{tL}}{e_{tL}}\frac{\tau_{tH}^{-1/e_{tH}}\tau_{tL}^{-1/e_{tL}}}{\Pi}\right) \tag{7-111}$$

Equation (7-111) can be most easily solved for τ_{tL}^* by squaring this equation and then equating it to Eq. (7-109). Thus

$$\left(\frac{V_9}{a_0}\right)^2 = \frac{M_0^2}{(\eta_{\text{prop}}\eta_g\eta_{mL})^2}\left(1 + \frac{1-e_{tL}}{e_{tL}}\frac{\tau_{tH}^{-1/e_{tH}}\tau_{tL}^{-1/e_{tL}}}{\Pi}\right)^2$$

$$= \frac{2\tau_\lambda \tau_{tH}}{\gamma_c - 1}\left(\tau_{tL} - \frac{\tau_{tH}^{-1/e_{tH}}}{\Pi}\tau_{tL}^{-(1-e_{tL})/e_{tL}}\right)$$

or $$\tau_{tL} - \frac{\tau_{tH}^{-1/e_{tH}}}{\Pi}\tau_{tL}^{-(1-e_{tL})/e_{tL}}$$

$$= \frac{[(\gamma_c - 1)/2][M_0^2/(\tau_\lambda \tau_{tH})]}{(\eta_{\text{prop}}\eta_g\eta_{mL})^2}\left(1 + \frac{1-e_{tL}}{e_{tL}}\frac{\tau_{tH}^{-1/e_{tH}}\tau_{tL}^{-1/e_{tL}}}{\pi}\right)^2$$

Solving for the first τ_{tL} gives

$$\boxed{\tau_{tL}^* = \frac{\tau_{tH}^{-1/e_{tH}}}{\Pi}\tau_{tL}^{-(1-e_{tL})/e_{tL}} + A\left(1 + \frac{1-e_{tL}}{e_{tL}}\frac{\tau_{tH}^{-1/e_{tH}}\tau_{tL}^{-1/e_{tL}}}{\Pi}\right)^2} \tag{7-112a}$$

where $$A = \frac{[(\gamma_c - 1)/2][M_0^2/(\tau_\lambda \tau_{tH})]}{(\eta_{prop}\eta_g \eta_{mL})^2} \tag{7-112b}$$

Since Eq. (7-112*a*) is an equation for τ_{tL}^* in terms of itself, an iterative solution is required. A starting value of τ_{tL}^*, denoted by $\tau_{tL\,i}^*$, is obtained by solving Eq. (7-112*a*) for the case when $e_{tL} = 1$:

$$\tau_{tL\,i}^* = \frac{\tau_{tH}^{-1/e_{tH}}}{\Pi} + A \tag{7-113}$$

This starting value can be substituted into Eq. (7-112*a*) and another new value of τ_{tL}^* calculated. This process continues until the change in successive calculations of τ_{tL}^* is less than some small number (say, 0.0001).

Summary of Equations—Turboprop Engine

INPUTS: M_0, T_0 (K, °R), γ_c, $c_{pc}\left(\frac{\text{kJ}}{\text{kg}\cdot\text{K}}, \frac{\text{Btu}}{\text{lbm}\cdot{}^\circ\text{R}}\right)$, γ_t, $c_{pt}\left(\frac{\text{kJ}}{\text{kg}\cdot\text{K}}, \frac{\text{Btu}}{\text{lbm}\cdot{}^\circ\text{R}}\right)$, $h_{PR}\left(\frac{\text{kJ}}{\text{kg}}, \frac{\text{Btu}}{\text{lbm}}\right)$, $\pi_{d\,\max}$, π_b, π_n, e_c, e_{tH}, e_{tL}, η_b, η_g, η_{mH}, η_{mL}, η_{prop}, T_{t4} (K, °R), π_c, and τ_t (if known)

OUTPUTS $\frac{F}{\dot m_0}\left(\frac{\text{N}}{\text{kg/sec}}, \frac{\text{lbf}}{\text{lbm/sec}}\right)$, $\frac{\dot W}{\dot m_0}\left(\frac{\text{W}}{\text{kg/sec}}, \frac{\text{hp}}{\text{lbm/sec}}\right)$, f, $S\left(\frac{\text{mg/sec}}{\text{N}}, \frac{\text{lbm/hr}}{\text{lbf}}\right)$, $S_P\left(\frac{\text{mg/sec}}{\text{W}}, \frac{\text{lbm/hr}}{\text{hp}}\right)$, η_T, η_P, η_O, C_C, C_{prop}, C_{tot}, τ_{tL}^* (if desired), etc.

EQUATIONS:

$$R_c = \frac{\gamma_c - 1}{\gamma_c} c_{pc} \tag{7-114a}$$

$$R_t = \frac{\gamma_t - 1}{\gamma_t} c_{pt} \tag{7-114b}$$

$$a_0 = \sqrt{\gamma_c R_c g_c T_0} \tag{7-114c}$$

$$V_0 = a_0 M_0 \tag{7-114d}$$

$$\tau_r = 1 + \frac{\gamma_c - 1}{2} M_0^2 \tag{7-114e}$$

$$\pi_r = \tau_r^{\gamma_c/(\gamma_c - 1)} \tag{7-114f}$$

$$\eta_r = 1 \qquad \text{for } M_0 \le 1 \tag{7-114g}$$

$$\eta_r = 1 - 0.0075(M_0 - 1)^{1.35} \qquad \text{for } M_0 > 1 \tag{7-114h}$$

$$\pi_d = \pi_{d\,\max}\eta_r \tag{7-114i}$$

$$\tau_\lambda = \frac{c_{pt} T_{t4}}{c_{pc} T_0} \tag{7-114j}$$

$$\tau_c = \pi_c^{(\gamma_c-1)/(\gamma_c e_c)} \tag{7-114k}$$

$$\eta_c = \frac{\pi_c^{(\gamma_c-1)/\gamma_c} - 1}{\tau_c - 1} \tag{7-114l}$$

$$f = \frac{\tau_\lambda - \tau_r \tau_c}{\eta_b h_{PR}/(c_{pc} T_0) - \tau_\lambda} \tag{7-114m}$$

$$\tau_{tH} = 1 - \frac{\tau_r(\tau_c - 1)}{\eta_{mH}(1+f)\tau_\lambda} \tag{7-114n}$$

$$\pi_{tH} = \tau_{tH}^{\gamma_t/[(\gamma_t-1)e_{tH}]} \tag{7-114o}$$

$$\eta_{tH} = \frac{1 - \tau_{tH}}{1 - \tau_{tH}^{1/e_{tH}}} \tag{7-114p}$$

If the optimum turbine temperature ratio τ_{tL}^* is desired,

$$A = \frac{[(\gamma_c - 1)/2][M_0^2/(\tau_\lambda \tau_{tH})]}{\eta_{\text{prop}} \eta_g \eta_{mL})^2} \tag{7-114q}$$

$$\Pi = (\pi_r \pi_d \pi_c \pi_b \pi_n)^{(\gamma_t-1)/\gamma_t} \tag{7-114r}$$

$$\tau_{tL\,i}^* = \frac{\tau_{tH}^{-1/e_{tH}}}{\Pi} + A \tag{7-114s}$$

$$\tau_{tL}^* = \frac{\tau_{tH}^{-1/e_{tH}}}{\Pi} \tau_{tL}^{-(1-e_{tL})/e_{tL}} + A\left(1 + \frac{1-e_{tL}}{e_{tL}} \frac{\tau_{tH}^{-1/e_{tH}} \tau_{tL}^{-1/e_{tL}}}{\Pi}\right)^2 \tag{7-114t}$$

Repeat calculations, using Eq. (7-114t) until successive values are within 0.0001.

Else, turbine temperature τ_t has been specified:

$$\tau_{tL} = \frac{\tau_t}{\tau_{tH}} \tag{7-114u}$$

Continue

$$\pi_{tL} = \tau_{tL}^{\gamma_t/[(\gamma_t-1)e_{tL}]} \tag{7-114v}$$

$$\eta_{tL} = \frac{1 - \tau_{tL}}{1 - \tau_{tL}^{1/e_{tL}}} \tag{7-114w}$$

$$\frac{P_{t9}}{P_0} = \pi_r \pi_d \pi_c \pi_b \pi_{tH} \pi_{tL} \pi_n \tag{7-114x}$$

$$\text{If} \quad \frac{P_{t9}}{P_0} > \left(\frac{\gamma_t + 1}{2}\right)^{\gamma_t/(\gamma_t-1)} \tag{7-114y}$$

$$\text{then} \quad M_9 = 1, \quad \frac{P_{t9}}{P_9} = \left(\frac{\gamma_t + 1}{2}\right)^{\gamma_t/(\gamma_t-1)},$$

$$\text{and} \quad \frac{P_0}{P_9} = \frac{P_{t9}/P_9}{P_{t9}/P_0} \tag{7-114z}$$

$$\text{else} \quad M_9 = \sqrt{\frac{2}{\gamma_t - 1}\left[\left(\frac{P_{t9}}{P_0}\right)^{(\gamma_t-1)/\gamma_t} - 1\right]}, \quad \frac{P_{t9}}{P_9} = \frac{P_{t9}}{P_0},$$

$$\text{and} \quad \frac{P_0}{P_9} = 1 \tag{7-114aa}$$

$$\frac{V_9}{a_0} = \sqrt{\frac{2\tau_\lambda \tau_{tH} \tau_{tL}}{\gamma_c - 1}\left[1 - \left(\frac{P_{t9}}{P_9}\right)^{-(\gamma_t - 1)/\gamma_t}\right]} \tag{7-114ab}$$

$$C_{\text{prop}} = \eta_{\text{prop}} \eta_g \eta_{mL}(1+f)\tau_\lambda \tau_{tH}(1-\tau_{tL}) \tag{7-114ac}$$

$$C_C = (\gamma_c - 1)M_0\left[(1+f)\frac{V_9}{a_0} - M_0 + (1+f)\frac{R_t}{R_c}\frac{T_9/T_0}{V_9/a_0}\frac{1 - P_0/P_9}{\gamma_c}\right] \tag{7-114ad}$$

$$C_{\text{tot}} = C_{\text{prop}} + C_C \tag{7-114ae}$$

$$\frac{F}{\dot{m}_0} = \frac{C_{\text{tot}} c_{pc} T_0}{V_0} \tag{7-114af}$$

$$S = \frac{f}{F/\dot{m}_0} \tag{7-114ag}$$

$$\frac{\dot{W}}{\dot{m}_0} = C_{\text{tot}} c_{pc} T_0 \tag{7-114ah}$$

$$S_P = \frac{f}{C_{\text{tot}} c_{pc} T_0} \tag{7-114ai}$$

$$\eta_T = \frac{C_{\text{tot}}}{f h_{PR}/(c_{pc} T_0)} \tag{7-114aj}$$

$$\eta_P = \frac{C_{\text{tot}}}{\dfrac{C_{\text{prop}}}{\eta_{\text{prop}}} + \dfrac{\gamma_c - 1}{2}\left[(1+f)\left(\dfrac{V_9}{a_0}\right)^2 - M_0^2\right]} \tag{7-114ak}$$

Example 7-12. For comparison with the ideal turboprop analysis of Chap. 5, we consider the performance of a turboprop engine for use at Mach 0.8. The input data are as follows:

INPUTS: $M_0 = 0.8$, $T_0 = 240$ K, $\gamma_c = 1.4$, $c_{pc} = 1.004$ kJ/(kg · K), $\gamma_t = 1.35$, $c_{pt} = 1.108$ kJ/(kg · K), $h_{PR} = 42{,}800$ kJ/kg, $e_c = 0.90$, $e_{tH} = 0.89$, $e_{tL} = 0.91$, $\pi_d = 0.98$, $\pi_b = 0.96$, $\pi_n = 0.99$, $\eta_b = 0.99$, $\eta_{mH} = 0.99$, $\eta_{mL} = 0.99$, $\eta_{\text{prop}} = 0.83$, $\eta_g = 0.99$, $T_{t4} = 1370$ K

Figures 7-34*a* through 7-34*d* show the variation in performance of a turboprop engine with compressor pressure ratio π_c and turbine temperature ratio τ_t. These figures for the engine cycle with losses can be compared with the performance of ideal turboprop engines (Figs. 5-41*a* through 5-41*e*) to see the effects of

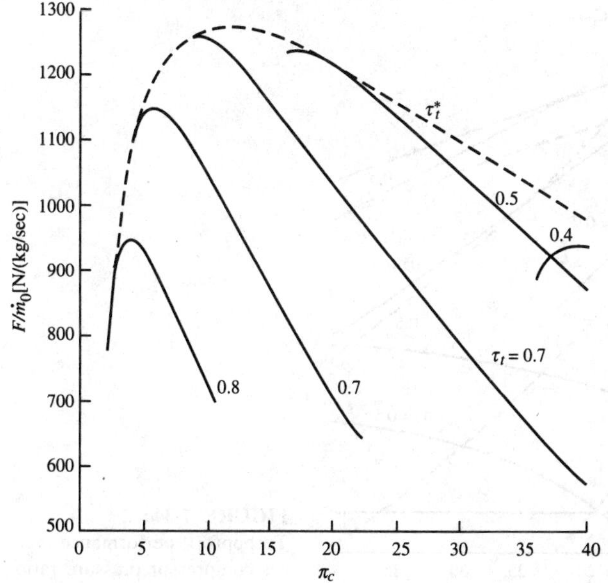

FIGURE 7-34a
Turboprop performance versus compressor pressure ratio: specific thrust.

component performance on the overall cycle. The general trends are the same as for the ideal cycle. The engine with losses that gives minimum fuel consumption has a compressor pressure ratio of $\pi_c = 30$ (see Fig. 7-34b) and corresponding optimum turbine temperature ratio of $\tau_t^* = 0.45$.

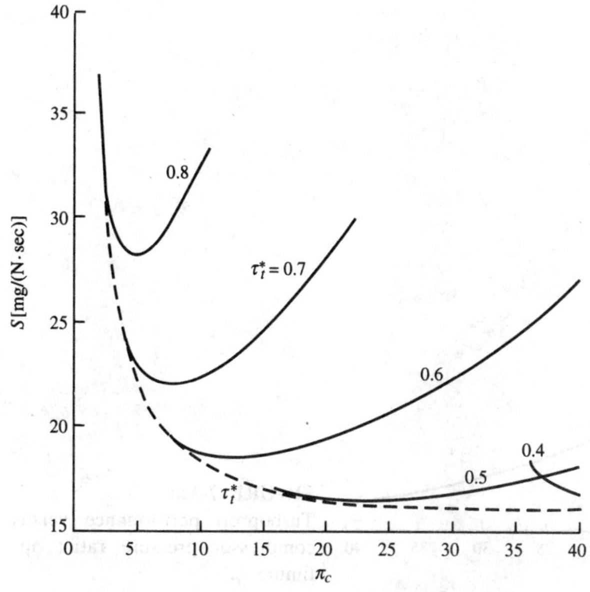

FIGURE 7-34b
Turboprop performance versus compressor pressure ratio: thrust specific fuel consumption.

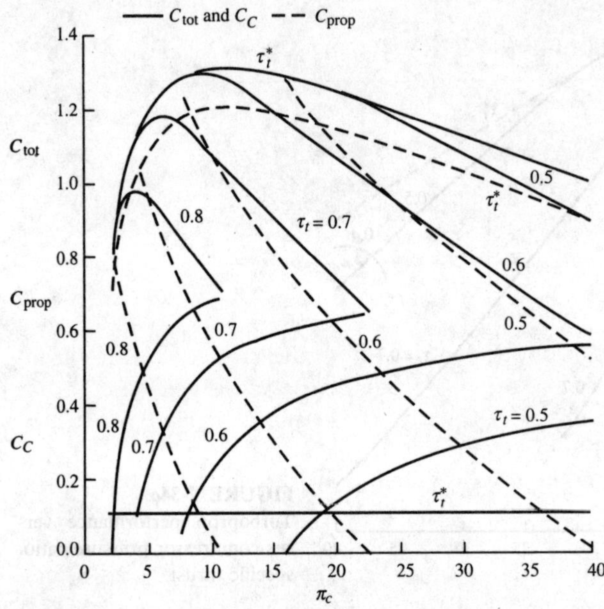

FIGURE 7-34c
Turboprop performance versus compressor pressure ratio: work coefficients.

7-8 VARIABLE GAS PROPERTIES

The effect of variable gas properties can be easily included in the computer analysis of gas turbine engine cycles. One first needs a subroutine that can calculate the thermodynamic state of the gas given the fuel/air ratio f and two

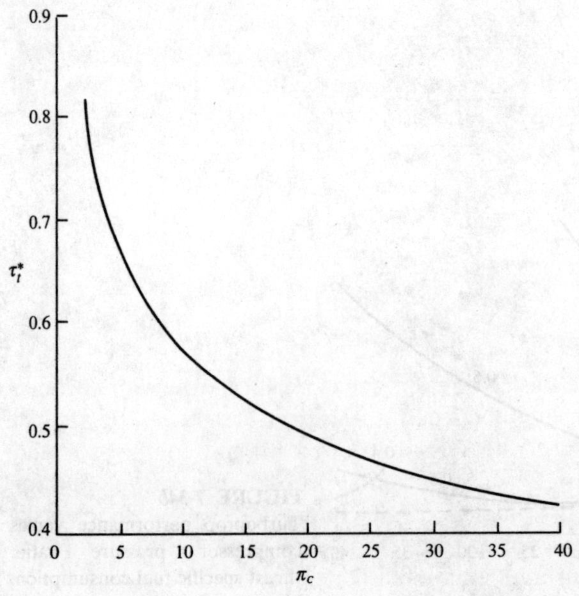

FIGURE 7-34d
Turboprop performance versus compressor pressure ratio: optimum τ_t.

TABLE 7-1
Calling nomenclature for subroutine FAIR

Symbol	Knowns	Unknowns
FAIR(1, $T, h, P_r, \phi, c_p, R, \gamma, a, f$)	T, f	$h, c_p, P_r, \phi, R, \gamma, a$
FAIR(2, $T, h, P_r, \phi, c_p, R, \gamma, a, f$)	h, f	$T, c_p, P_r, \phi, R, \gamma, a$
FAIR(3, $T, h, P_r, \phi, c_p, R, \gamma, a, f$)	P_r, f	$T, h, c_p, \phi, R, \gamma, a$
FAIR(4, $T, h, P_r, \phi, c_p, R, \gamma, a, f$)	ϕ, f	$T, h, c_p, P_r, R, \gamma, a$

independent properties. A subroutine for air and products of combustion from air and hydrocarbon fuels of the type $(CH_2)_n$ was developed for use in the program AFPROP first introduced in Chap. 2 and mentioned again in Chap. 6. This subroutine is called *FAIR*.

The subroutine FAIR contains Eqs. (2-68) through (2-70), (2-72*a*) through (2-72*d*), and (2-63) and the constants of Table 2-3. This information gives direct calculation of h, c_p, ϕ, and P_r given the fuel/air ratio f and temperature T. Calculation of the temperature T given the fuel/air ratio f and one of h, P_r, or ϕ is made possible by the addition of simple iteration algorithms. In addition, the subroutine FAIR determines c_p, the gas constant R, the ratio of specfiic heats γ, and the speed of sound a.

For convenience, we will use the following nomenclature for the subroutine FAIR. The primary input of FAIR (T, h, P_r, or ϕ) is indicated by first listing a corresponding number from 1 to 4, followed by a list of the variables. Table 7-1 identifies the four sets of knowns for the subroutine FAIR. The subroutine FAIR with the first three sets of unknowns is used extensively in the list of equations on page 447 for the turbojet engine with afterburner.

An additional property such as pressure (P), density (ρ), or entropy (s) is needed to completely define the thermodynamic state of the gas. We will normally use pressure or entropy as the additional property and Eqs. (2-30) and (2-65) to obtain the remaining unknowns:

$$\rho = \frac{P}{RT} \tag{2-30}$$

$$s_2 - s_1 = \phi_2 - \phi_1 - R \ln \frac{P_2}{P_1} \tag{2-65}$$

Section 6-8 develops the basics of component performance with variable gas properties. The relationships between total pressure ratio, polytropic efficiency, and reduced pressure ratio are developed for the compressor and turbine. The relationships between static and total properties are developed for the inlet and nozzle. The energy balance of the combustor gives an expression for the fuel/air ratio f. These basics and others are used in the following section for the analysis of a turbojet engine with afterburning.

Cycle Analysis—Turbojet with Afterburning

Figure 7-8 shows a cross-sectional drawing of the turbojet engine with afterburning and its station numbering. The uninstalled specfic thrust is given in Eqs. (7-1) and (7-2) and is written in terms of the engine stations, or

$$\boxed{\frac{F}{\dot{m}_0}=\frac{a_0}{g_c}\left[(1+f_O)\frac{V_9}{a_0}-M+(1+f_O)\frac{R_9}{R_0}\frac{T_9/T_0}{V_9/a_0}\frac{1-P_0/P_9}{\gamma_0}\right]} \tag{7-115}$$

where f_O is the overall fuel/air ratio, defined by Eq. (5-82) as

$$f_O=\frac{\dot{m}_f+\dot{m}_{f\mathrm{AB}}}{\dot{m}_0} \tag{5-82}$$

The exit velocity V_9 is determined from the total and static enthalpies at station 9 by using

$$\boxed{V_9=\sqrt{2g_c(h_{t9}-h_9)}} \tag{6-44}$$

The total enthalpy at station 9 is obtained from application of the first law of thermodynamics to the engine and from tracking the changes in energy from the engine's inlet to its exit. The static state at station 9 (h_9, T_9, etc.) is obtained by using the following relationship between the reduced pressure at the static state P_{r9}, the reduced pressure at the total state P_{rt9}, and the nozzle pressure ratio P_{t9}/P_9:

$$\boxed{P_{r9}=\frac{P_{rt9}}{P_{t9}/P_9}} \tag{6-45}$$

The nozzle pressure ratio is obtained by using Eq. (7-27), which tracks the ratios of total pressure from engine inlet to exit:

$$\frac{P_{t9}}{P_9}=\frac{P_0}{P_9}\pi_r\pi_d\pi_c\pi_b\pi_t\pi_{\mathrm{AB}}\pi_n \tag{7-27}$$

The enthalpy leaving the compressor h_{t3} is obtained by first determining the reduced pressure leaving the compressor P_{rt3}. From a rewrite of Eq. (6-31), we have

$$\boxed{P_{rt3}=P_{rt2}\pi_c^{1/e_c}} \tag{7-116}$$

Application of the first law of thermodynamics to the compressor and turbine gives the required turbine exit enthalpy. Equating the required compressor power to the net output power from the turbine, we have

$$\dot{W}_c=\eta_m\dot{W}_t$$

Rewriting in terms of mass flow rates and total enthalpies gives

$$\dot{m}_0(h_{t3} - h_{t2}) = \eta_m(\dot{m}_0 + \dot{m}_f)(h_{t4} - h_{t5}) = \eta_m \dot{m}_0(1+f)(h_{t4} - h_{t5})$$

Solving for h_{t5} gives

$$\boxed{h_{t5} = h_{t4} - \frac{h_{t3} - h_{t2}}{(1+f)\eta_m}} \tag{7-117}$$

where both h_{t4} and h_{t5} are functions of the fuel/air ratio. The turbine pressure ratio π_t is obtained from Eq. (6-40).

The fuel/air ratio for the main burner is given by Eq. (6-36), where h_{t4} is a function of f:

$$f = \frac{h_{t4} - h_{t3}}{\eta_b h_{PR} - h_{t4}} \tag{6-36}$$

Application of the first law to the afterburner gives the following equation for its fuel/air ratio f_{AB}, where h_{t6} is a function of the entering fuel/air ratio and h_{t7} is a function of the leaving fuel/air ratio ($f_O = f + f_{AB}$):

$$\boxed{f_{AB} = \frac{h_{t7} - h_{t6}}{\eta_{AB} h_{PR} - h_{t7}}} \tag{7-118}$$

Summary of Equations—Afterburning Turbojet with Variable Specific Heats

INPUTS: M_0, T_0 (K, °R), h_{PR} (kJ/kg, Btu/lbm), $\pi_{d\,\max}$, π_b, π_{AB}, π_n, e_c, e_t, η_b, η_{AB}, η_m, P_0/P_9, T_{t4} (K, °R), T_{t7} (K, °R), π_c

OUTPUTS: $\dfrac{F}{\dot{m}_0}\left(\dfrac{\text{N}}{\text{kg/sec}}, \dfrac{\text{lbf}}{\text{lbm/sec}}\right)$, f, f_{AB}, f_O, $S\left(\dfrac{\text{mg/sec}}{\text{N}}, \dfrac{\text{lbm/hr}}{\text{lbf}}\right)$, η_T, η_P, η_O, η_c, η_t, etc.

EQUATIONS:

FAIR(1, T_0, h_0, P_{r0}, ϕ_0, c_{p0}, R_0, γ_0, a_0, 0)

$$V_0 = M_0 a_0 \tag{7-119a}$$

$$h_{t0} = h_0 + \frac{V_0^2}{2g_c} \tag{7-119b}$$

FAIR(2, T_{t0}, h_{t0}, $P_{r\,t0}$, ϕ_0, $c_{p\,t0}$, R_{t0}, γ_{t0}, a_{t0}, 0)

$$\tau_r = \frac{h_{t0}}{h_0} \tag{7-119c}$$

$$\pi_r = \frac{P_{r\,t0}}{P_{r\,0}} \tag{7-119d}$$

$$\eta_r = 1 \qquad \text{for } M_0 \le 1 \tag{7-119e}$$

$$\eta_r = 1 - 0.075(M_0 - 1)^{1.35} \qquad \text{for } M_0 > 1 \tag{7-119f}$$

$$\pi_d = \pi_{d\,\max}\eta_r \tag{7-119g}$$

$$h_{t2} = h_{t0} \tag{7-119h}$$

$$P_{r\,t2} = P_{r\,t0} \tag{7-119i}$$

$$P_{r\,t3} = P_{r\,t2}\pi_c^{\ 1/e_c} \tag{7-119j}$$

FAIR(3, T_{t3}, h_{t3}, $P_{r\,t3}$, ϕ_{t3}, $c_{p\,t3}$, R_{t3}, γ_{t3}, a_{t3}, 0)

$$\tau_c = \frac{h_{t3}}{h_{t2}} \tag{7-119k}$$

$$P_{r\,t3i} = P_{r\,t2}\pi_c \tag{7-119l}$$

FAIR(3, T_{t3i}, h_{t3i}, $P_{r\,t3i}$, ϕ_{t3i}, $c_{p\,t3i}$, R_{t3i}, γ_{t3i}, a_{t3i}, 0)

$$\eta_c = \frac{h_{t3i} - h_{t2}}{h_{t3} - h_{t2}} \tag{7-119m}$$

Set initial value of fuel/air ratio = f_i.

A FAIR(1, T_{t4}, h_{t4}, $P_{r\,t4}$, ϕ_{t4}, $c_{p\,t4}$, R_{t4}, γ_{t4}, γ_{t4}, a_{t4}, f_i)

$$f = \frac{h_{t4} - h_{t3}}{\eta_b h_{PR} - h_{t4}} \tag{7-119n}$$

If $|f - f_i| > 0.0001$, then $f_i = f$ and go to A; else continue.

$$\tau_\lambda = \frac{h_{t4}}{h_0} \tag{7-119o}$$

$$h_{t5} = h_{t4} - \frac{h_{t3} - h_{t2}}{(1+f)\eta_m} \tag{7-119p}$$

FAIR(2, T_{t5}, h_{t5}, $P_{r\,t5}$, ϕ_{t5}, $c_{p\,t5}$, R_{t5}, γ_{t5}, a_{t5}, f)

$$\pi_t = \left(\frac{P_{r\,t5}}{P_{r\,t4}}\right)^{1/e_t} \tag{7-119q}$$

$$P_{r\,t5i} = \pi_r P_{r\,t4} \tag{7-119r}$$

FAIR(3, T_{t5i}, h_{t5i}, $P_{r\,t5i}$, ϕ_{t5i}, $c_{p\,t5i}$, R_{t5i}, γ_{t5i}, a_{t5i}, f)

$$\eta_t = \frac{h_{t4} - h_{t5}}{h_{t4} - h_{t5i}} \tag{7-119s}$$

Set initial value of AB fuel/air ratio = f_{ABi}.

B $f_O = f + f_{ABi}$ (7-119t)

FAIR(1, T_{t8}, h_{t8}, $P_{r\,t8}$, ϕ_{t8}, $c_{p\,t8}$, R_{t8}, γ_{t8}, a_{t8}, f_O)

$$f_{AB} = \frac{h_{t8} - h_{t5}}{\eta_{AB} h_{PR} - h_{t8}} \tag{7-119u}$$

If $|f_{AB} - f_{ABi}| > 0.0001$, then $f_{ABi} = f_{AB}$ and go to B; else continue.

$$\tau_{\lambda AB} = \frac{h_{t8}}{h_0} \tag{7-119v}$$

$$h_{t9} = h_{t8} \tag{7-119w}$$

$$P_{r\,t9} = P_{r\,t8} \tag{7-119x}$$

$$\frac{P_{t9}}{P_9} = \frac{P_0}{P_9}\pi_r \pi_d \pi_c \pi_b \pi_t \pi_{AB} \pi_n \tag{7-119y}$$

$$P_{r\,9} = \frac{P_{r\,t9}}{P_{t9}/P_9} \tag{7-119z}$$

FAIR(3, T_9, h_9, $P_{r\,9}$, ϕ_9, $c_{p\,9}$, R_9, γ_9, a_9, f_O)

$$V_9 = \sqrt{2g_c(h_{t9} - h_9)} \tag{7-119aa}$$

$$\frac{F}{\dot{m}_0} = \frac{a_0}{g_c}\left[(1 + f_O)\frac{V_9}{a_0} - M_0 + (1 + f_O)\frac{R_9}{R_0}\frac{T_9/T_0}{V_9/a_0}\frac{1 - P_0/P_9}{\gamma_0}\right] \tag{7-119ab}$$

$$S = \frac{f_O}{F/\dot{m}_0} \tag{7-119ac}$$

$$\eta_T = \frac{a_0^2[(1 + f_O)(V_9/a_0)^2 - M_0^2]}{2g_c f_O h_{PR}} \tag{7-119ad}$$

$$\eta_P = \frac{2g_c V_0(F/\dot{m}_0)}{a_0^2[(1 + f_O)(V_9/a_0)^2 - M_0^2]} \tag{7-119ae}$$

$$\eta_O = \eta_P \eta_T \tag{7-119af}$$

Example 7-13. We consider an example with the same input data as those considered for the afterburning turbojet in Example 7-5. Thus we have variable specific heats and the following input data:

INPUTS: $M_0 = 2$, $T_0 = 390°\text{R}$, $h_{PR} = 18{,}400$ Btu/lbm, $\pi_{d\,\max} = 0.98$, $\pi_b = 0.98$, $\pi_{AB} = 0.98$, $\pi_n = 0.98$, $e_c = 0.89$, $e_t = 0.91$, $\eta_b = 0.99$, $\eta_{AB} = 0.96$, $\eta_m = 0.98$, $P_0/P_9 = 1$, $T_{t4} = 3000°\text{R}$, $T_{t7} = 3500°\text{R}$, $\pi_c = 2 \to 14$

The results for the engine with variable specific heats are indicated in Fig. 7-35 with solid lines, along with the data for the engine with constant specific heats (Fig. 7-10), shown in dashed lines. The trends are the same: Operation of the afterburner increases both the specific thrust and the thrust specific fuel consumption; the fuel consumption is lower for the engine with variable specific heats than that of the engine with constant specific heats; and the specific thrusts

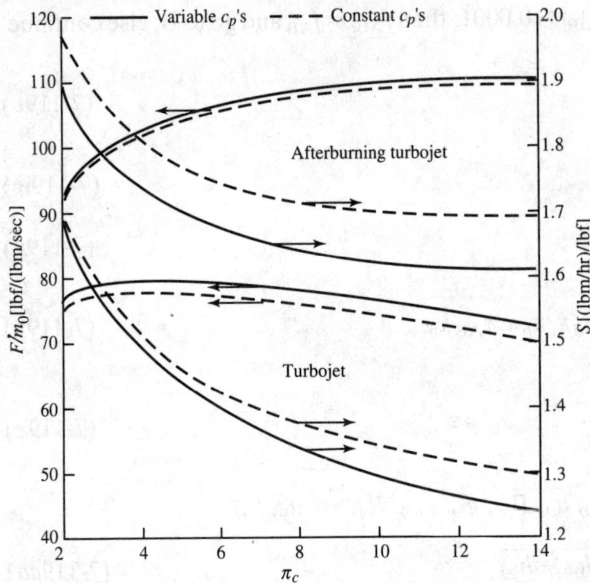

FIGURE 7-35
Performance of afterburning turbojet engine with variable gas properties.

are very close. The difference between the two models increases with the compressor pressure ratio. The computations for this engine model with variable heats require about 10 times longer than those for the engine model with constant specific heats.

The specific thrusts of both the afterburning and nonafterburning engines with constant specific heats are very close to those with variable specific heats because of the selected values for the ratio of specific heats. Note that the ratio of specific heats for the flow through the exhaust nozzle was selected to be 1.3 for the afterburning case and 1.33 for the nonafterburning case.

As shown by Oates in Ref. 4, one can obtain equivalent constant gas properties and simplify the analysis by selecting the ratio of specific heats that matches the exit velocity of the two cases (equal specific thrusts). The resulting equivalent gas properties can be used in the analytical tools developed while using constant gas properties and obtain trends very rapidly.

An expression for the equivalent ratio of specific heats γ_e can be obtained for the case of the turbojet engine by equating the exit velocity of Eq. (7-119*aa*) to that given for an engine cycle with constant specific heats. For expansion of a gas with constant specific heats, we can write

$$V_9^2 = 2g_c h_{t9e}\left[1 - \left(\frac{P_9}{P_{t9e}}\right)^{(\gamma_e - 1)/\gamma_e}\right] \tag{7-120}$$

where the subscript e is used to represent the equivalent value. Setting this equation equal to Eq. (7-119*aa*) gives

$$h_{t9e}\left[1-\left(\frac{P_9}{P_{t9e}}\right)^{(\gamma_e-1)/\gamma_e}\right]=h_{t9}\left(1-\frac{h_9}{h_{t9}}\right)$$

or

$$\boxed{\gamma_e=\left\{1+\frac{\ln[1-(h_{t9}/h_{t9e})(1-h_9/h_{t9})]}{\ln(P_9/P_{t9e})}\right\}^{-1}} \tag{7-121}$$

For the simple turbojet cycle, we could compare engines with the same values of h_{t4}. In the case of the afterburning turbojet, we would have $h_{t9}=h_{t9e}$ and Eq. (7-120) simplifies. The easiest method to find the equivalent ratio of specific heats γ_e is to first calculate the performance with variable specific heats and then calculate the performance with constant specific heats for several values of γ.

The system of engine cycle analysis equations for constant specific heats predicts higher thrust specific fuel consumption S than that predicted by using variable specific heats. This higher value of S is due to the higher enthalpy rise predicted by the model equations for the combustor. There are two methodsto improve the predicted fuel consumption for the engine models with constant specific heats:

1. One could obtain an equivalent fuel heating value (h_{PRe}) that would give a better match between the two predicted fuel consumptions.

2. One could calculate the fuel burned in a combustion process by using variable specific heats.

The next section outlines this latter method and compares its results to those of an engine cycle with variable specific heats.

Afterburning Turbojet with Modified Combustion Model

We consider the afterburning turbojet engine of Sec. 7-3 with constant specific heats for all engine components except the main burner and afterburner. We use the subroutine FAIR to evaluate the enthalpy at engine stations 3, 4, 6, and 7. The following equations give the fuel/air ratios for the main burner and afterburner, respectively:

$$f = \frac{h_{t4} - h_{t3}}{\eta_b h_{PR} - h_{t4}} \tag{7-122}$$

$$f_{\text{AB}} = \frac{h_{t7} - h_{t6}}{\eta_{\text{AB}} h_{PR} - h_{t7}} \tag{7-118}$$

where h_{t4} and h_{t6} are a function of the main burner's fuel/air ratio f, and h_{t7} is a function of the overall fuel/air ratio $f_O = f + f_{\text{AB}}$. Because of these functional relationships, calculation of these fuel/air ratios (f and f_{AB}) requires iteration, as do those outlined in the summary of equations for the afterburning turbojet with variable specific heats. And h_{t3} and h_{t6} are evaluated at their total temperature as predicted by the basic analysis:

$$T_{t3} = T_0 \tau_r \tau_c \tag{7-123a}$$

$$T_{t6} = T_{t4} \tau_t \tag{7-123b}$$

where τ_r, τ_c, and τ_t are calculated from Eqs. (7-20e), (7-20k), and (7-20n), respectively.

Example 7-14. We consider an example with the same input data as for the afterburning turbojet in Example 7-5. Thus we have the following input data:

INPUTS: $M_0 = 2$, $T_0 = 390°\text{R}$, $\gamma_c = 1.4$, $c_{pc} = 0.24$ Btu/(lbm · °R), $\gamma_t = 1.33$, $c_{pt} = 0.276$ Btu/(lbm · °R), $h_{PR} = 18{,}400$ Btu/lbm, $\gamma_{\text{AB}} = 1.30$, $c_{p\text{AB}} = 0.295$ Btu/(lbm · °R), $\pi_{d\,\max} = 0.98$, $\pi_b = 0.98$, $\pi_{\text{AB}} = 0.98$, $\pi_n = 0.98$, $e_c = 0.89$, $e_t = 0.91$, $\eta_b = 0.99$, $\eta_{\text{AB}} = 0.96$, $\eta_m = 0.98$, $P_0/P_9 = 1$, $T_{t4} = 3000°\text{R}$, $T_{t7} = 3500°\text{R}$, $\pi_c = 2 \rightarrow 14$

The results of this analysis with the fuel consumption calculated by using the subroutine FAIR and Eqs. (7-118) and (7-122) are shown with dashed lines in Fig. 7-36. The solid lines are the results of Example 7-13 for the variable-specific-heat engine model. For the afterburning case, the fuel consumptions are nearly equal to those predicted by using the more complex variable-specific-heat engine model. For the nonafterburning case, the modified combustion model predicts fuel consumptions that are about 2 percent lower than those of the variable-specific-heat engine model. The modified combustion model gives much better results than those shown with dashed lines in Fig. 7-35 (constant specific heat model of Example 7-5) while requiring only double the computer time.

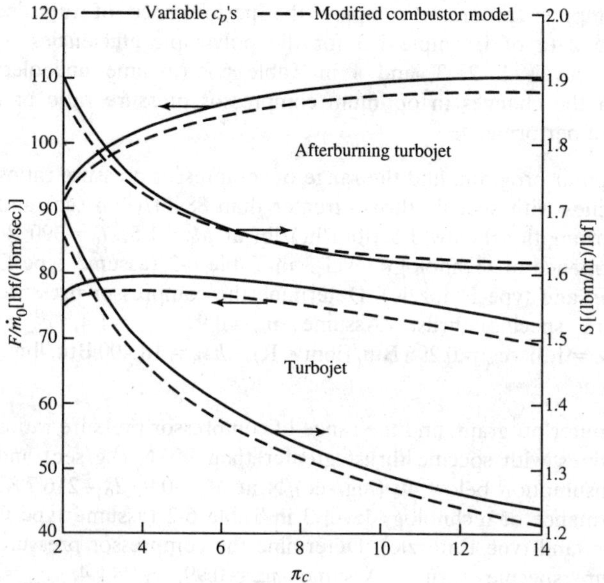

FIGURE 7-36
Performance of afterburning turbojet engine with modified combustion model.

PROBLEMS

7-1. Develop a set of equations for parametric analysis of a ramjet engine with losses. Calculate the performance of a ramjet with losses over a Mach number range of 1 to 3 for the following input data:

$\pi_{d\,\max} = 0.95$	$T_0 = 217\text{ K}$	$\gamma_c = 1.4$	$c_{pc} = 1.004\text{ kJ/(kg}\cdot\text{K)}$
$\pi_b = 0.94$	$\eta_b = 0.96$	$\gamma_t = 1.3$	$c_{pt} = 1.235\text{ kJ/(kg}\cdot\text{K)}$
$\pi_n = 0.95$	$\dfrac{P_0}{P_9} = 1$	$T_{t4} = 1800\text{ K}$	$h_{PR} = 42{,}800\text{ kJ/kg}$

Compare your results to those obtained from PARA.

7-2. Why are the polytropic efficiencies used for the fans, compressors, and turbines in parametric engine cycle analysis rather than the isentropic efficiencies?

7-3. Calculate and compare the performance of turbojet engines with the basic data of Example 7-1 for components with technology level 2 values in Table 6-2 (assume cooled turbine and the same diffuser and nozzle values as in Example 7-1). Comment on the changes in engine performance.

7-4. Using the PARA computer program, compare the performance of turbojet engines with the basic data of Example 7-1 for the polytropic efficiencies of component technology levels 1, 2, 3, and 4 in Table 6-2 (assume uncooled turbine). Comment on the improvements in engine performance.

7-5. Using the PARA computer program, compare the performance of turbojet engines with the basic data of Example 7-3 for the polytropic efficiencies of component technology levels 1, 2, 3, and 4 in Table 6-2 (assume uncooled turbine). Comment on the changes in optimum compressor pressure ratio and improvements in engine performance.

7-6. Using the PARA computer program, find the range of compressor pressure ratios that give turbojet engines with specific thrust greater than 88 lbf/(lbm/sec) and thrust specific fuel consumption below 1.5 (lbm/hr)/lbf at $M_0 = 1.5$, $T_0 = 390°\text{R}$, and component performance of technology level 3 in Table 6-2 (assume type C diffuser, cooled turbine, and type F nozzle). Determine the compressor pressure ratio giving maximum specific thrust. Assume $\eta_m = 0.99$, $\gamma_c = 1.4$, $c_{pc} = 0.24\ \text{Btu/(lbm}\cdot°\text{R)}$, $\gamma_t = 1.3$, $c_{pt} = 0.296\ \text{Btu/(lbm}\cdot°\text{R)}$, $h_{PR} = 18{,}400\ \text{Btu/lbm}$, and $P_0/P_9 = 1$.

7-7. Using the PARA computer program, find the range of compressor pressure ratios that give turbojet engines with specific thrust greater than 950 N/(kg/sec) and thrust specific fuel consumption below 40 (mg/sec)/N at $M_0 = 0.9$, $T_0 = 216.7\ \text{K}$, and component performance of technology level 3 in Table 6-2 (assume type C diffuser, cooled turbine, and type F nozzle). Determine the compressor pressure ratio giving maximum specific thrust. Assume $\eta_m = 0.99$, $\gamma_c = 1.4$, $c_{pc} = 1.004\ \text{kJ/(kg}\cdot\text{K)}$, $\gamma_t = 1.3$, $c_{pt} = 1.239\ \text{kJ/(kg}\cdot\text{K)}$, $h_{PR} = 42{,}800\ \text{kJ/kg}$, and $P_0/P_9 = 1$.

7-8. For a single-spool turbojet engine with losses, determine the compressor exit T_t and P_t, the turbine exit T_t and P_t, and the nozzle exit Mach number M_9 for the following input data:

$M_0 = 0.8$	$\pi_c = 9$	$T_{t4} = 1780\ \text{K}$	$h_{PR} = 42{,}800\ \text{kJ/kg}$
$P_0 = 29.92\ \text{kPa}$	$T_0 = 229\ \text{K}$	$\gamma_c = 1.4$	$c_{pc} = 1.004\ \text{kJ/(kg}\cdot\text{K)}$
$\pi_{d\,\max} = 0.95$	$\pi_b = 0.94$	$\gamma_t = 1.3$	$c_{pt} = 1.239\ \text{kJ/(kg}\cdot\text{K)}$
$e_c = 0.85$	$e_t = 0.88$	$\eta_b = 0.99$	$\eta_m = 0.98$
$\pi_n = 0.98$	$\dfrac{P_0}{P_9} = 0.8$		

Compare your results with those obtained from PARA.

7-9. Products of combustion enter the afterburner (station 6) at a rate of 230 lbm/sec with the following properties: $T_{t6} = 1830°\text{R}$, $P_{t6} = 38\ \text{psia}$, $M_6 = 0.4$, $\gamma = 1.33$, $c_p = 0.276\ \text{Btu/(lbm}\cdot°\text{R)}$, and $R = 53.34\ \text{ft}\cdot\text{lbf/(lbm}\cdot°\text{R)}$. Assume a calorically perfect gas and $\eta_{AB} = 0.95$.

a. Determine the flow area at station 6 in square feet.

b. With the afterburner off, determine the area (ft^2) of the exhaust nozzle's choked throat (station 8) for $P_{t8}/P_{t6} = 0.97$.

c. With the afterburner on, determine the afterburner fuel flow rate (lbm/sec) and the area (ft^2) of the exhaust nozzle's choked throat (station 8) for $P_{t8}/P_{t6} = 0.94$ and $T_{t8} = 3660°\text{R}$. *Assume* that the gas leaving the operating afterburner (part *c*) is a calorically perfect gas with $\gamma = 1.3$, $c_p = 0.297\ \text{Btu/(lbm}\cdot°\text{R)}$, and the same gas constant. Also assume the properties at station 6 do not change and $h_{PR} = 18{,}400\ \text{Btu/lbm}$.

7-10. Calculate and compare the performance of afterburning turbojet engines with the basic data of Example 7-5 but with combustion temperatures of level 4 in Table 6-2 for compressor pressure ratios of 4, 8, and 12. Comment on the improvements in engine performance.

7-11. Using the PARA computer program, find the range of compressor pressure ratios that give afterburning turbojet engines with specific thrust greater than 118 lbf/(lbm/sec) and thrust specific fuel consumption below 1.7 (lbm/hr)/lbf at $M_0 = 1.5$, $T_0 = 390°\text{R}$, and component performance of technology level 3 in Table 6-2 (assume type C diffuser, cooled turbine, and type F nozzle). Determine the compressor pressure ratio giving maximum specific thrust. Assume $\eta_m = 0.99$, $\gamma_c = 1.4$, $c_{pc} = 0.24$ Btu/(lbm · °R), $\gamma_t = 1.3$, $c_{pt} = 0.296$ Btu/(lbm · °R), $\gamma_{AB} = 1.3$, $c_{pAB} = 0.296$ Btu/(lbm · °R), $h_{PR} = 18{,}400$ Btu/lbm, and $P_0/P_9 = 1$.

7-12. Using the PARA computer program, find the range of compressor pressure ratios that give afterburning turbojet engines with specific thrust greater than 1250 N/(kg/sec) and thrust specific fuel consumption below 45 (mg/sec)/N at $M_0 = 0.9$, $T_0 = 216.7$ K, and component performance of technology level 3 in Table 6-2 (assume type C diffuser, cooled turbine, and type F nozzle). Determine the compressor pressure ratio giving maximum specific thrust. Assume $\eta_m = 0.99$, $\gamma_c = 1.4$, $c_{pc} = 1.004$ kJ/(kg · K), $\gamma_t = 1.3$, $c_{pt} = 1.239$ kJ/(kg · K), $\gamma_{AB} = 1.3$, $c_{pAB} = 0.239$ kJ/(kg · K), $h_{PR} = 42{,}800$ kJ/kg, and $P_0/P_9 = 1$.

7-13. Using the PARA computer program, calculate and compare the performance of afterburning turbojet engines with the basic data of Example 7-5 for the different combustion temperatures and component technologies of levels 2, 3, and 4 in Table 6-2 (assume cooled turbine, type B diffuser, and type F nozzle). Comment on the improvements in engine performance.

7-14. Show that the propulsive efficiency and thermal efficiency of a turbofan engine with separate exhausts are given by Eqs. (7-50) and (7-51), respectively.

7-15. Calculate the performance of a turbofan engine with the basic data of Example 7-6 but with a fan pressure ratio of 1.65 and a bypass ratio of 10. Comment on the improvement in engine performance. Compare your results to those of PARA.

7-16. Using PARA, compare the performance of turbofan engines with the basic data of Example 7-6 for the polytropic efficiencies of component technology levels 2, 3, and 4 in Table 6-2 (assume cooled turbine, type A diffuser, and type D nozzle). Comment on the improvement in engine performance.

7-17. Using PARA, find the range of compressor pressure ratios and fan pressure ratios that give optimum-bypass-ratio, separate-exhaust turbofan engines with specific thrust greater than 13 lbf/(lbm/sec) and thrust specific fuel consumption below 1.0 (lbm/hr)/lbf at $M_0 = 0.9$, $T_0 = 390°\text{R}$, and component performance of technology level 2 in Table 6-2 (assume type A diffuser, uncooled turbine, and type D nozzle). Assume $\eta_m = 0.99$, $\gamma_c = 1.4$, $c_{pc} = 0.24$ Btu/(lbm · °R), $\gamma_t = 1.3$, $c_{pt} =$ 0.296 Btu/(lbm · °R), $h_{PR} = 18{,}400$ Btu/lbm, and $P_0/P_9 = 1$.

7-18. Using PARA, find the range of compressor pressure ratios and fan pressure ratios that give optimum-bypass-ratio, separate-exhaust turbofan engines with specific thrust greater than 130 N/(kg/sec) and thrust specific fuel consumption below 28 (mg/sec)/N at $M_0 = 0.8$, $T_0 = 216.7$ K, and component performance of technology level 2 in Table 6-2 (assume type A diffuser, uncooled turbine, and type D nozzle). Assume $\eta_m = 0.99$, $\gamma_c = 1.4$, $c_{pc} = 1.004$ kJ/(kg · K), $\gamma_t = 1.3$, $c_{pt} =$ 1.239 kJ/(kg · K), $h_{PR} = 42{,}800$ kJ/kg, and $P_0/P_9 = 1$.

7-19. Calculate the performance of an optimum-bypass-ratio turbofan engine with the basic data of Example 7-8 but with a compressor pressure ratio of 30 and fan pressure ratio of 1.7. Compare your results to those of PARA.

7-20. Using PARA, compare the performance of optimum-bypass-ratio turbofan engines with the basic data of Example 7-8 for the polytropic efficiencies of component technology levels 2, 3, and 4 in Table 6-2 (assume cooled turbine, type A diffuser, and type D nozzle). Comment on the improvement in engine performance.

7-21. Calculate the performance of an afterburning mixed-flow turbofan engine with the basic data of Example 7-10 at $M_0 = 0.9$ for a compressor pressure ratio of 30 and a fan pressure ratio of 4. Compare your results to those of PARA.

7-22. Using PARA, find the range of compressor pressure ratios and corresponding fan pressure ratios that give mixed-flow turbofan engines of 0.5 bypass ratio a specific thrust greater than 55 lbf/(lbm/sec) and thrust specific fuel consumption below 1.3 (lbm/hr)/lbf at $M_0 = 1.8$, $T_0 = 390°\text{R}$, and component performance of technology level 3 in Table 6-2 (assume type C diffuser, cooled turbine, and type F nozzle). Assume $\eta_m = 0.99$, $\gamma_c = 1.4$, $c_{pc} = 0.24$ Btu/(lbm · °R), $\gamma_t = 1.3$, $c_{pt} =$ 0.296 Btu/(lbm · °R), $M_6 = 0.5$, $\pi_{M\,\max} = 0.95$, $h_{PR} = 18{,}400$ Btu/lbm, and $P_0/P_9 = 1$.

7-23. Using PARA, find the range of compressor pressure ratios and corresponding fan pressure ratios that give mixed-flow turbofan engines of 0.4 bypass ratio a specific thrust greater than 550 N/(kg/sec) and thrust specific fuel consumption below 39 (mg/sec)/N at $M_0 = 2.0$, $T_0 = 216.7$ K, and component performance of technology level 3 in Table 6-2 (assume type C diffuser, cooled turbine, and type F nozzle). Assume $\eta_m = 0.99$, $\gamma_c = 1.4$, $c_{pc} = 1.004$ kJ/(kg · K), $\gamma_t = 1.3$, $c_{pt} =$ 1.239 kJ/(kg · K), $M_6 = 0.5$, $\pi_{M\,\max} = 0.95$, $h_{PR} = 42{,}800$ kJ/kg, and $P_0/P_9 = 1$.

7-24. Using PARA, find the range of compressor pressure ratios and corresponding fan pressure ratios that give afterburning mixed-flow turbofan engines of 0.5 bypass ratio a specific thrust greater than 105 lbf/(lbm/sec) and thrust specific fuel consumption below 1.845 (lbm/hr)/lbf at $M_0 = 1.8$, $T_0 = 390°\text{R}$, and component performance of technology level 3 in Table 6-2 (assume type C diffuser, cooled turbine, and type F nozzle). Assume $\eta_m = 0.99$, $\gamma_c = 1.4$, $c_{pc} =$ 0.24 Btu/(lbm · °R), $\gamma_t = 1.3$, $c_{pt} = 0.296$ Btu/(lbm · °R), $\gamma_{\text{AB}} = 1.3$, $c_{p\text{AB}} =$ 0.296 Btu/(lbm · °R), $M_6 = 0.5$, $\pi_{M\,\max} = 0.95$, $h_{PR} = 18{,}400$ Btu/lbm, and $P_0/P_9 = 1$.

7-25. Using PARA, find the range of compressor pressure ratios and corresponding fan pressure ratios that give afterburning mixed-flow turbofan engines of 0.4 bypass ratio a specific thrust greater than 1000 N/(kg/sec) and thrust specific fuel consumption below 52.25 (mg/sec)/N at $M_0 = 2.0$, $T_0 = 216.7$ K, and component performance of technology level 3 in Table 6-2 (assume type C diffuser, cooled turbine, and type F nozzle). Assume $\eta_m = 0.99$, $\gamma_c = 1.4$, $c_{pc} = 1.004$ kJ/(kg · K), $\gamma_t = 1.3$, $c_{pt} = 1.239$ kJ/(kg · K), $\gamma_{\text{AB}} = 1.3$, $c_{p\text{AB}} = 1.239$ kJ/(kg · K), $M_6 = 0.5$, $\pi_{M\,\max} = 0.95$, $h_{PR} = 42{,}800$ kJ/kg, $M_6 = 0.5$, and $P_0/P_9 = 1$.

7-26. Using PARA, compare the performance of afterburning mixed-flow turbofan engines with the basic data of Example 7-10 at $M_0 = 0.9$, $\pi_c = 24$, and $\pi_f = 3.5$ for the different combustion temperatures and component technologies of levels 2, 3, and 4 in Table 6-2 (assume cooled turbine, type C diffuser, and type F nozzle). Also assume the same γ's, c_p's, η_m, and $\pi_{M\,\max}$. Comment on the improvement in engine performance.

7-27. For the mixed-flow turbofan engine with the bypass ratio specified, show that the following functional iteration equation for the fan temperature ratio with matched total pressures entering the mixer can be obtained from Eqs. (7-90) and (7-91):

$$(\tau_f)_{i+1} = \frac{\tau_r[\alpha - (\tau_c - 1)] + \eta_m(1+f)\tau_\lambda}{\tau_r\alpha + [\eta_m(1+f)\tau_\lambda/(\pi_c\pi_b)^{(\gamma_t-1)e_t/\gamma_t}](\tau_f)_i^{(\gamma_t-1)/(\gamma_c-1)(\gamma_c/\gamma_t)e_t e_f - 1}}$$

with the first value of the fan temperature ratio given by

$$(\tau_f)_1 = \frac{\tau_r[\alpha - (\tau_c - 1)] + \eta_m(1+f)\tau_\lambda}{\tau_r\alpha + \eta_m(1+f)\tau_\lambda/(\pi_c\pi_b)^{(\gamma_t-1)e_t/\gamma_t}}$$

7-28. Calculate the performance of a turboprop engine with the basic data of Example 7-12 at a compressor pressure ratio of 20 and turbine temperature ratio of 0.5. Compare your results to those of Example 7-12 and the PARA computer program.

7-29. Using PARA, find the range of compressor pressure ratios that give turboprop engines with optimum turbine temperature ratio τ_t^* a specific thrust greater than 120 lbf/(lbm/sec) and thrust specific fuel consumption below 0.8 (lbm/hr)/lbf at $M_0 = 0.7$, $T_0 = 447°\text{R}$, and component performance of technology level 2 in Table 6-2 (assume type A diffuser, uncooled turbine, and type D nozzle). Assume $\eta_{\text{prop}} = 0.83$, $\eta_g = 0.99$, $\eta_{mH} = 0.99$, $\eta_{mL} = 0.99$, $\gamma_c = 1.4$, $c_{pc} = 0.24$ Btu/(lbm · °R), $\gamma_t = 1.35$, $c_{pt} = 0.265$ Btu/(lbm · °R), and $h_{PR} = 18{,}400$ Btu/lbm.

7-30. Using PARA, find the range of compressor pressure ratios that give turboprop engines with optimum turbine temperature ratio τ_t^* a specific thrust greater than 1300 N/(kg/sec) and thrust specific fuel consumption below 18 (mg/sec)/N at $M_0 = 0.6$, $T_0 = 250$ K, and component performance of technology level 2 in Table 6-2 (assume type A diffuser, uncooled turbine, and type D nozzle). Assume $\eta_{\text{prop}} = 0.83$, $\eta_g = 0.99$, $\eta_{mH} = 0.995$, $\eta_{mL} = 0.995$, $\gamma_c = 1.4$, $c_{pc} = 1.004$ kJ/(kg · K), $\gamma_t = 1.35$, $c_{pt} = 1.108$ kJ/(kg · K), and $h_{PR} = 42{,}800$ kJ/kg.

7-31. Using PARA, compare the performance of turboprop engines with the basic data of Example 7-12 with component technologies of levels 1, 2, 3, and 4 in Table 6-2. Comment on the improvement in engine performance.

7-32. A stationary gas turbine engine with regeneration is shown in Fig. P7-32. The effectiveness of a regenerator η_{rg} is defined by

$$\eta_{\text{rg}} = \frac{T_{t3.5} - T_{t3}}{T_{t5} - T_{t3}}$$

The total pressure ratios across the cold and hot gas paths of the regenerator are defined by

$$\pi_{\text{rg cold}} = \frac{P_{t3.5}}{P_{t3}} \qquad \pi_{\text{rg hot}} = \frac{P_{t6}}{P_{t5}}$$

Using these definitions and others, develop a set of equations for parametric analysis of this turboshaft engine with regeneration and losses.

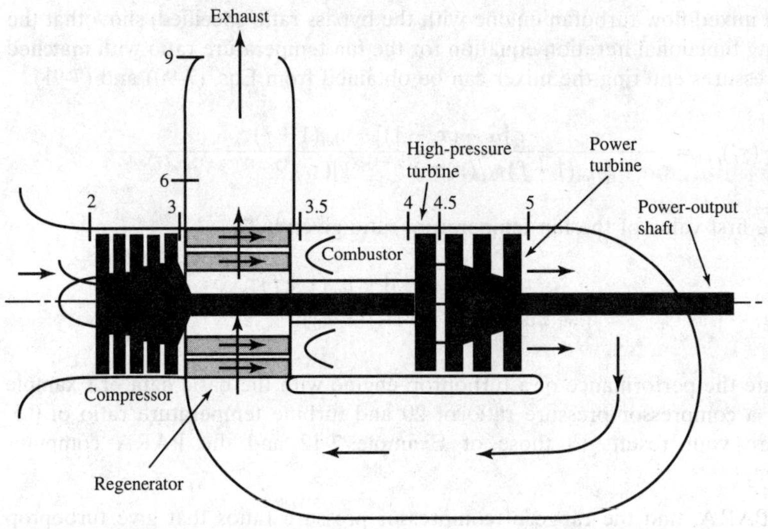

FIGURE 7-P7-32
Stationary gas turbine engine with regeneration.

7-D1 GAS TURBINE DESIGN PROBLEM 1 (HP-1 AIRCRAFT)

You are to determine the range of compressor pressure ratios and bypass ratios for turbofan engines with losses that best meets the design requirements for the hypothetical passenger aircraft HP-1.

Hand-Calculate Performance with Losses

Using the parametric cycle analysis equations for a turbofan engine with losses and component technology level 4 in Table 6-2 (assume cooled turbine, type A diffuser, and type D nozzle) with $T_{t4} = 1560$ K, hand-calculate the specific thrust and thrust specific fuel consumption for a turbofan engine with a compressor pressure ratio of 36, fan pressure ratio of 1.8, and bypass ratio of 10 at the 0.83 Mach and 11-km altitude cruise condition. Assume $\gamma_c = 1.4$, $c_{pc} = 1.004$ kJ/(kg · K), $\gamma_t = 1.3$, $c_{pt} = 1.235$ kJ/(kg · K), $h_{PR} = 42{,}800$ kJ/kg, and $\eta_m = 0.99$. Compare your answers to results from the parametric cycle analysis program PARA and Design Problem 5-D1.

Computer-Calculated Performance with Losses

For the 0.83 Mach and 11-km altitude cruise condition, determine the performance available from turbofan engines with losses. This part of the analysis is accomplished by using PARA with component technology level 4 in Table 6-2 (assume cooled turbine, type A diffuser, and type D nozzle) and $T_{t4} = 1560$ K. Specifically, you are to vary the compressor pressure ratio from 20 to 40 in increments of 2. Fix the fan pressure ratio at your assigned value of _____. Evaluate bypass ratios of 4, 6, 8, 10, 12, and the optimum value. Assume $\gamma_c = 1.4$, $c_{pc} = 1.004$ kg/(kg · K), $\gamma_t = 1.3$, $c_{pt} = 1.235$ kJ/(kg · K), $h_{PR} =$ 42,800 kJ/kg, and $\eta_m = 0.99$.

Calculate Minimum Specific Thrust at Cruise

You can calculate the minimum uninstalled specific thrust at cruise based on the following information:

1. The thrust of the two engines must be able to offset drag at 0.83 Mach and 11-km altitude and have enough excess thrust for P_s of 1.5 m/sec. Determine the required installed thrust to attain the cruise condition, using Eq. (1-28). Assuming $\phi_{\text{inlet}} + \phi_{noz} = 0.02$, determine the required uninstalled thrust.
2. Determine the maximum mass flow into the 2.2-m-diameter inlet for the 0.83 Mach and 11-km altitude flight condition, using the equation given in the background section for this design problem in Chapt. 1.
3. Using the results of steps 1 and 2, calculate the minimum uninstalled specific thrust at cruise.
4. Perform steps 2 and 3 for inlet diameters of 2.5, 2.75, 3.0, 3.25, and 3.5 m.

Select Promising Engine Cycles

Plot thrust specific fuel consumption versus specific thrust (thrust per unit mass flow) for the engines analyzed above. Plot a curve for each bypass ratio and cross-plot the values of the compressor pressure ratio (see Fig. P5-D1). The result is a carpet plot (a multivariable plot) for the cruise condition. Now draw a dashed horizontal line on the carpet plot corresponding to the maximum allowable uninstalled thrust specific consumption ($S_{\max}$) for the cruise condition (determined in the Chap. 1 portion of this design problem). Draw a dashed vertical line for each minimum uninstalled specific thrust determined above. Your carpet plots will look similar to the example shown in Fig. P5-D1. What ranges of bypass ratio and compressor pressure ratio look most promising? Compare to the results of Design Problem 5-D1.

7-D2 GAS TURBINE DESIGN PROBLEM 2 (HF-1 AIRCRAFT)

You are to determine the ranges of compressor pressure ratio and bypass ratio for mixed-flow turbofan engines with losses that best meet the design requirements for the hypothetical fighter aircraft HF-1.

Hand-Calculate Performance with Losses

Using the parametric cycle analysis equations for a mixed-flow turbofan engine with losses and component technology level 4 in Table 6-2 (assume cooled turbine, type C diffuser, and type F nozzle) with $T_{t4} = 3250$°R, hand-calculate the specific thrust and thrust specific fuel consumption for an ideal turbofan engine with a compressor pressure ratio of 25 and bypass ratio of 0.5 at the 1.6-Mach and 40-kft altitude supercruise condition. Since the bypass ratio is given, you will need to use the system of equations given in Prob. 7-27 to calculate the temperature ratio of the fan. Assume $\gamma_c = 1.4$, $c_{pc} = 0.240$ Btu/(lbm · °R), $\gamma_t = 1.3$, $c_{pt} = 0.296$ Btu/(lbm · °R), $h_{PR} = 18{,}400$ Btu/lbm, $M_6 = 0.4$, $\pi_{M\,\max} = 0.96$, and $\eta_m = 0.99$. Compare your answers to results from the parametric cycle analysis program PARA and Design Problem 5-D2.

Computer-Calculated Performance with Losses

For the 1.6-Mach and 40-kft altitude supercruise condition, determine the performance available from mixed-flow turbofan engines with losses. This part of the analysis is accomplished by using PARA with component technology level 4 in Table 6-2 (assume cooled turbine, type C diffuser, and type F nozzle) and $T_{t4} = 3250$°R. Specifically, you are to vary the bypass ratio from 0.1 to 1.0 in increments of 0.05. Evaluate compressor pressure ratios of 16, 18, 20, 22, 24, and 28. Assume $\gamma_c = 1.4$, $c_{pc} = 0.240$ Btu/(lbm · °R), $\gamma_t = 1.3$, $c_{pt} = 0.296$ Btu/(lbm · °R), $h_{PR} = 18{,}400$ Btu/lbm, $M_6 = 0.4$, $\pi_{M\,\max} = 0.96$, and $\eta_m = 0.99$.

Calculate Minimum Specific Thrust at Cruise

You can calculate the minimum uninstalled specific thrust at supercruise based on the following information:

1. The thrust of the two engines must be able to offset drag at 1.6-Mach number and 40-kft altitude and 92 percent of takeoff weight. Assuming $\phi_{\text{inlet}} + \phi_{noz} = 0.05$, determine the required uninstalled thrust for each engine.

2. The maximum mass flow into a 5-ft² inlet for the 1.6 Mach number and 40-kft altitude flight condition is $\dot{m} = \rho AV = \sigma \rho_{\text{ref}} AMa = (0.2471 \times 0.07647)(5)(1.6 \times 0.8671) \times 1116) = 146.3$ lbm/sec.

3. Using the results of steps 1 and 2, calculate the minimum uninstalled specific thrust at supercruise.

Select Promising Engine Cycles

Plot thrust specific fuel consumption versus specific thrust (thrust per unit mass flow) for the engines analyzed above. Plot a curve for each bypass ratio, and cross-plot the values of compressor pressure ratio (see Fig. P5-D2). The result is a carpet plot (a multivariable plot) for the supercruise condition. Now draw a dashed horizontal line on the carpet plot corresponding to the maximum allowable uninstalled thrust specific fuel consumption ($S_{\max}$) for the cruise condition (determined in the Chap. 1 portion of this design problem). Draw a dashed vertical line for the minimum uninstalled specific thrust determined above. Your carpet plots will look similar to the example shown in Fig. P5-D2. What ranges of bypass ratio and compressor pressure ratio look most promising? Compare to the results of Design Problem 5-D2.

CHAPTER

8

ENGINE PERFORMANCE ANALYSIS

8-1 INTRODUCTION

This chapter is concerned with predicting the performance of a gas turbine engine and obtaining performance data similar to Figs. 1-14*a* through 1-14*e*, 1-15*a*, and 1-15*b* and the data contained in App. B. The analysis required to obtain engine performance is related to, but very different from, the parametric cycle analysis of Chaps. 5 and 7. In parametric cycle analysis of a turbojet engine, we independently selected values of the compressor pressure ratio, main burner exit temperature, flight condition, etc. The analysis determined the turbine temperature ratio—it is dependent on the choices of compressor pressure ratio, main burner exit temperature, and flight condition, as shown by Eq. (7-12). In engine performance analysis, we consider the performance of an engine that was built (constructed physically or created mathematically) with a selected compressor pressure ratio and its corresponding turbine temperature ratio. As will be shown in this chapter, the turbine temperature ratio remains essentially constant for a turbojet engine (and many other engine cycles), and its compressor pressure ratio is dependent on the throttle setting (main burner exit temperature T_{t4}) and flight condition (M_0 and T_0). The basic independent and dependent variables of the turbojet engine are listed in Table 8-1 for both parametric cycle analysis and engine performance analysis.

In parametric cycle analysis, we looked at the variation of gas turbine engine cycles where the main burner exit temperature and aircraft flight

TABLE 8-1
Comparison of analysis variables

Variable	Parametric cycle	Engine performance
Flight condition (M_0, T_0, and P_0)	Independent	Independent
Compressor pressure ratio π_c	Independent	Dependent
Main burner exit temperature T_{t4}	Independent	Independent
Turbine temperature ratio τ_t	Dependent	Constant

conditions were specified via the design inputs: T_{t4}, M_0, T_0, and P_0. In addition, the engine cycle was selected along with the compressor pressure atio, the polytropic efficiency of turbomachinery components, etc. For the combination of design input values, the resulting calculations yielded the specific performance of the engine (specific thrust and thrust specific fuel consumption), required turbine temperature ratio, and the efficiencies of the turbomachinery (fan, compressor, and turbine). The specific combination or design input values is referred to as the engine *design point* or *reference point.* The resulting specific engine thrust and fuel consumption are valid only for the given engine cycle and values of T_{t4}, M_0, T_0, π_c, τ_t, η_c, etc. When we changed any of these values in parametric cycle analysis, we were studying a "rubber" engine, i.e., one which changes its shape and component design to meet the thermodynamic, fluid dynamic, etc., requirements.

When a gas turbine engine is designed and built, the degree of variability of an engine depends upon available technology, the needs of the principal application for the engine, and the desires of the designers. Most gas turbine engines have constant-area flow passages and limited variability (variable T_{t4}; *and sometimes variable* T_{t7} and exhaust nozzle throat area). In a simple constant-flow-area turbojet engine, the performance (pressure ratio and mass flow rate) of its compressor depends upon the power from the turbine and the inlet conditions to the compressor. As we will see in this chapter, a simple analytical expression can be used to express the relationship between the compressor performance and the independent variables: throttle setting (T_{t4}) and flight condition (M_0, T_0, P_0).

When a gas turbine engine is installed in an aircraft, its performance varies with flight conditions and throttle setting and is limited by the engine control system. In flight, the pilot controls the operation of the engine directly through the throttle and indirectly by changing flight conditions. The thrust and fuel consumption will thereby change. In this chapter, we will look at how specific engine cycles perform at conditions other than their design (or reference) point.

There are several ways to obtain this engine performance. One way is to look at the interaction and performance of the compressor-burner-turbine combination, known as the *pumping characteristics* of the gas generator. In this case, the performance of the components is known since the gas generator exists. However, in a preliminary design, the gas generator has not been built,

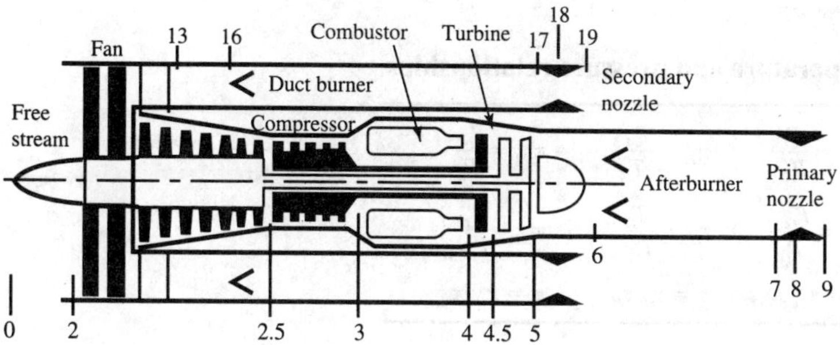

FIGURE 8-1
Station numbering for two-spool gas turbine engine.

and the pumping characteristics are not available. In such a case, the gas generator performance can be estimated by using first principles and estimates of the variations in component efficiencies. In reality, the principal effects of engine performance occur because of the changes in propulsive efficiency and thermal efficiency (rather than because of changes in component efficiency). Thus a good approximation of an engine's performance can be obtained by simply assuming that the component efficiencies remain constant.

The analysis of engine performance requires a model for the behavior of each engine component over its actual range of operation. The more accurate and complete the model, the more reliable the computed results. Even though the approach (constant efficiency of rotating components and constant total pressure ratio of the other components) used in this textbook gives answers that are perfectly adequate for preliminary design, it is important to know that the usual industrial practice is to use data or correlations having greater accuracy and definition in the form of component "maps." The principal values of the maps are to improve the understanding of component behavior and to slightly increase the accuracy of the results.

Nomenclature

The station numbering used for the performance analysis of the turbojet and turbofan is shown in Fig. 8-1. Note that the turbine is divided into a high-pressure turbine (station 4 to 4.5) and a low-pressure turbine (station 4.5 to 5). The high-pressure turbine drives the high-pressure compressor (station 2.5 to 3), and the low-pressure turbine drives the fan (station 2 to 13) and low-pressure compressor (station 2 to 2.5).

The assembly containing the high-pressure turbine, high-pressure compressor, and connecting shaft is called the *high-pressure spool.* That containing the low-pressure turbine, fan or low-pressure compressor, and connecting shaft is called the *low-pressure spool.* In addition to the τ and π values defined in Table 5-1, the component total temperature ratios and total pressure ratios listed in Table 8-2 are required for analysis of the above gas turbine engine with high- and low-pressure spools.

TABLE 8-2
Additional temperature and pressure relationships

$\tau_{cH} = \dfrac{T_{t3}}{T_{t2.5}}$	$\pi_{cH} = \dfrac{P_{t3}}{P_{t2.5}}$	$\tau_{tH} = \dfrac{T_{t4.5}}{T_{t4}}$	$\pi_{tH} = \dfrac{P_{t4.5}}{P_{t4}}$
$\tau_{cL} = \dfrac{T_{t2.5}}{T_{t2}}$	$\pi_{cL} = \dfrac{P_{t2.5}}{P_{t2}}$	$\tau_{tL} = \dfrac{T_{t5}}{T_{t4.5}}$	$\pi_{tL} = \dfrac{P_{t5}}{P_{t4.5}}$
$\tau_c = \tau_{cL}\tau_{cH}$	$\pi_c = \pi_{cL}\pi_{cH}$	$\tau_t = \tau_{tH}\tau_{tL}$	$\pi_t = \pi_{tH}\pi_{tL}$

Reference Values and Engine Performance Analysis Assumptions

Functional relationships are used to predict the performance of a gas turbine engine at different flight conditions and throttle settings. These relationships are based on the application of mass, energy, momentum, and entropy considerations to the one-dimensional steady flow of a perfect gas at an engine steady-state operating point. Thus, if

$$f(\tau, \pi) = \text{constant}$$

represents a relationship between the two engine variables τ and π at a steady-state operating point, then the constant can be evaluated at a reference condition (subscript R) so that

$$f(\tau, \pi) = f(\tau_R, \pi_r) = \text{constant}$$

since $f(\tau, \pi)$ applies to the engine at all operating points. *Sea-level static* (*SLS*) *is the normal reference condition* (*design point*) *for the value of the gas turbine engine variables.* This technique for replacing constants with reference conditions is frequently used in the analysis to follow.

For conventional turbojet, turbofan, and turboprop engines, we will consider the simple case where the high-pressure turbine entrance nozzle, low-pressure turbine entrance nozzle, and primary exit nozzle (and bypass duct nozzle for the separate-exhaust turbofan) are choked. In addition, we assume that the throat areas where choking occurs in the high-pressure turbine entrance nozzle and the low-pressure turbine entrance nozzle are constant. This type of turbine is known as a *fixed-area turbine* (FAT) engine. These assumptions are true over a wide operating range for modern gas turbine engines. The following performance analyses also include the case(s) of unchoked engine exit nozzle(s).

The following assumptions will be made in the turbojet and turbofan performance analysis:

1. The flow is choked at the high-pressure turbine entrance nozzle, low-pressure turbine entrance nozzle, and the primary exit nozzle. Also the bypass duct nozzle for the turbofan is choked.

2. The total pressure ratios of the main burner, primary exit nozzle, and bypass stream exit nozzle (π_b, π_n, and π_{fn}) do not change from their reference values.
3. The component efficiencies (η_c, η_f, η_b, η_{tH}, η_{tL}, η_{mH}, and η_{mL}) do not change from their reference values.
4. Turbine cooling and leakage effects are neglected.
5. No power is removed from the turbine to drive accessories (or alternately, η_{mH} or η_{mL} includes the power removed but is still constant).
6. Gases will be assumed to be calorically perfect both upstream and downstream of the main burner, and γ_t and c_{pt} do not vary with the power setting (T_{t4}).
7. The term unity plus the fuel/air ratio $(1+f)$ will be considered as a constant.

Assumptions 4 and 5 are made to simplify the analysis and increase understanding. Reference 12 includes turbine cooling air, compressor bleed air, and power takeoff in the performance analysis. Assumptions 6 and 7 permit easy analysis which results in a set of algebraic expressions for an engine's performance. The performance analysis of an engine with variable gas properties is covered in Sec. 8-8.

Dimensionless and Corrected Component Performance Parameters

Dimensional analysis identifies correlating parameters that allow data taken under one set of conditions to be extended to other conditions. These parameters are useful and necessary because it is always impractical to accumulate experimental data for the bewildering number of possible operating conditions, and because it is often impossible to reach many of the operating conditions in a single, affordable facility.

The quantities of pressure and temperature are normally made dimensionless by dividing each by its respective standard sea-level static values. The dimensionless pressure and temperature are represented by δ and θ, respectively. When total (stagnation) properties are nondimensionalized, a subscript is used to indicate the station number of that property. The only static properties made dimensionless are free stream, the symbols for which carry no subscripts. Thus

$$\boxed{\delta_i \equiv \frac{P_{ti}}{P_{\text{ref}}}} \tag{8-1a}$$

and

$$\boxed{\theta_i \equiv \frac{T_{ti}}{T_{\text{ref}}}} \tag{8-1b}$$

where $P_{\text{ref}} = 14.696$ psia (101,300 Pa) and $T_{\text{ref}} = 518.69°\text{R}$ (288.2 K).

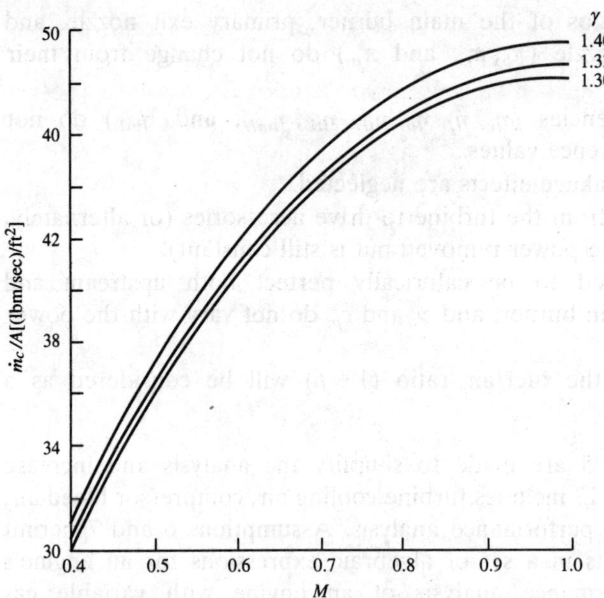

FIGURE 8-2
Variation of corrected mass flow per area.

Dimensionless analysis of engine components yields many useful dimensionless and/or modified component performance parameters. Some examples of these are the compressor pressure ratio, adiabatic efficiency, Mach number at the compressor face, ratio of blade (tip) speed to the speed of sound, and the Reynolds number.

The *corrected mass flow rate* at engine station i used in this analysis is defined as

$$\boxed{\dot{m}_{ci} \equiv \frac{\dot{m}_i \sqrt{\theta_i}}{\delta_i}} \tag{8-2}$$

and is related to the Mach number at station i as shown below. From the definition of the mass flow parameter [Eq. (3-12)], we can write the mass flow at station i as

$$\dot{m}_i = \frac{P_{ti}}{\sqrt{T_{ti}}} A_i \times \text{MFP}(M_i)$$

Then

$$\boxed{\frac{\dot{m}_{ci}}{A_i} = \frac{\dot{m}_i \sqrt{T_{ti}}}{P_{ti}} \frac{P_{\text{ref}}}{\sqrt{T_{\text{ref}}}} = \frac{P_{\text{ref}}}{\sqrt{T_{\text{ref}}}} \text{MFP}(M_i)} \tag{8-3}$$

and the corrected mass flow rate per unit area is a function of the Mach number alone for a gas. Equation (8-3) is plotted versus Mach number in Fig. 8-2 for three different γ values. Aircraft gas turbine engines need high thrust or power per unit weight which requires high corrected mass flow rates per unit area.

At the entrance to the fan or compressor (station 2), the design Mach number is about 0.56 which corresponds to a corrected mass flow rate per unit area of about 40 lbm/(sec · ft^2). A reduction in engine power will lower the corrected mass flow rate and the corresponding Mach number into the fan or compressor.

The flow is normally choked at the entrance to the turbine (station 4) and the throat of the exhaust nozzle (station 8) for most steady-state operating conditions of interest (the flow is typically unchoked at these stations during engine start-up). When the flow is choked at station 4, the corrected mass flow rate per unit area entering the turbine is constant, which helps define the pumping characteristics of the gas generator. As shown later in this chapter, choked flow at both stations 4 and 8 limits the turbine operation. Even if the flow unchokes at a station and the Mach number drops from 1.0 to 0.9, the corrected mass flow rate is reduced less than 1 percent. Thus the corrected mass flow rate is considered constant when the flow is near or at choking conditions.

Choked flow at station 8 is desired in convergent-only exhaust nozzles to obtain high exit velocity and is required in a convergent-divergent exhaust nozzle to reach supersonic exit velocities. When the afterburner is operated on a turbojet or turbofan engine with choked exhaust nozzle, T_{t8} increases—this requires an increase in the nozzle throat area A_8 to maintain the correct mass flow rate/area ratio corresponding to choked conditions. If the nozzle throat is not increased, the pressure increases and the mass flow rate decreases, which can adversely impact the upstream engine components.

The *corrected engine speed* at engine station i used in this analysis is defined as

$$\boxed{N_{ci} \equiv \frac{N}{\sqrt{\theta_i}}} \tag{8-4}$$

and is related to the *blade* Mach number.

These four parameters represent a first approximation of the complete set necessary to reproduce nature for the turbomachinery. These extremely useful parameters have become a standard in the gas turbine industry and are summarized in Table 8-3.

Three additional corrected quantities have found common acceptance for describing the performance of gas turbine engines: corrected thrust F_c, corrected thrust specific fuel consumption S_c, and correct fuel mass flow rate $\dot{m}_{fc}$.

The *corrected thrust* is defined as

$$\boxed{F_c \equiv \frac{F}{\delta_0}} \tag{8-5}$$

TABLE 8-3
Corrected parameters

Parameter	Symbol	Corrected parameter
Total pressure	P_{ti}	$\delta_i = \dfrac{P_{ti}}{P_{\text{ref}}}$
Total temperature	T_{ti}	$\theta_i = \dfrac{T_{ti}}{T_{\text{ref}}}$
Rotational speed	$N = \text{RPM}$	$N_{ci} = \dfrac{N}{\sqrt{\theta_i}}$
Mass flow rate	$\dot{m}_i$	$\dot{m}_{ci} = \dfrac{\dot{m}_i\sqrt{\theta_i}}{\delta_i}$
Thrust	F	$F_c = \dfrac{F}{\delta_0}$
Thrust specific fuel consumption	S	$S_c = \dfrac{S}{\sqrt{\theta_0}}$
Fuel mass flow rate	$\dot{m}_f$	$\dot{m}_{fc} = \dfrac{\dot{m}_f}{\delta_2\sqrt{\theta_2}}$

For many gas turbine engines operating at maximum T_{t4}, the corrected thrust is essentially a function of only the corrected free-stream total temperature θ_0.

The *corrected thrust specific fuel consumption* is defined as

$$\boxed{S_c \equiv \frac{S}{\sqrt{\theta_0}}} \tag{8-6}$$

and the *corrected fuel mass flow rate* is defined as

$$\boxed{\dot{m}_{fc} \equiv \frac{\dot{m}_f}{\delta_2\sqrt{\theta_2}}} \tag{8-7}$$

Like the corrected thrust, these two corrected quantities collapse the variation in fuel consumption with flight condition and throttle setting.

These three corrected quantities are closely related. By using the equation for thrust specific fuel consumption

$$S = \frac{\dot{m}_f}{F}$$

$\pi_d = P_{t2}/P_{t0}$, and the fact that $\theta_2 = \theta_0$, the following relationship results between these corrected quantities:

$$\boxed{S_c = \pi_d \frac{\dot{m}_{fc}}{F_c}} \tag{8-8}$$

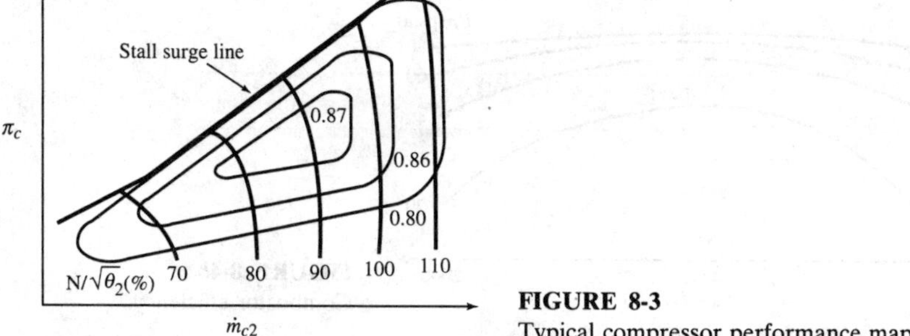

FIGURE 8-3
Typical compressor performance map.

These extremely useful corrected engine performance parameters have also become a standard in the gas turbine industry and are included in Table 8-3.

Component Performance Maps

COMPRESSOR AND FAN PERFORMANCE MAPS. The performance of a compressor or fan is normally shown by using the total pressure ratio, corrected mass flow rate, corrected engine speed, and component efficiency. Most often this performance is presented in one map showing the interrelationship of all four parameters, like that depicted in Fig. 8-3. Sometimes, for clarity, two maps are used, with one showing the pressure ratio versus corrected mass flow rate/corrected speed and the other showing compressor efficiency versus corrected mass flow rate/corrected speed.

A limitation on fan and compressor performance of special concern is the *stall* or *surge line*. Steady operation above the line is impossible, and entering the region even momentarily is dangerous to the gas turbine engine.

MAIN BURNER MAPS. The performance of the main burner is normally presented in terms of its performance parameters that are most important to engine performance: total pressure ratio of the main burner π_b and its combustion efficiency η_b. The total pressure ratio of the main burner is normally plotted versus the corrected mass flow rate through the burner $(\dot{m}_3\sqrt{\theta_3}/\delta_3)$ for different fuel/air ratios f, as shown in Fig. 8-4*a*. The efficiency of the main burner can be represented as a plot versus the temperature rise in the main burner $T_{t4} - T_{t3}$ or fuel/air ratio f for various values of inlet pressures P_{t3}, as shown in Fig. 8-4*b*.

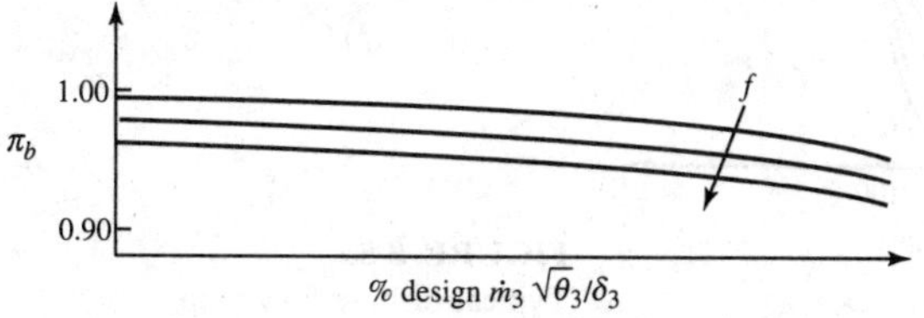

FIGURE 8-4*a*
Combustor pressure ratio.

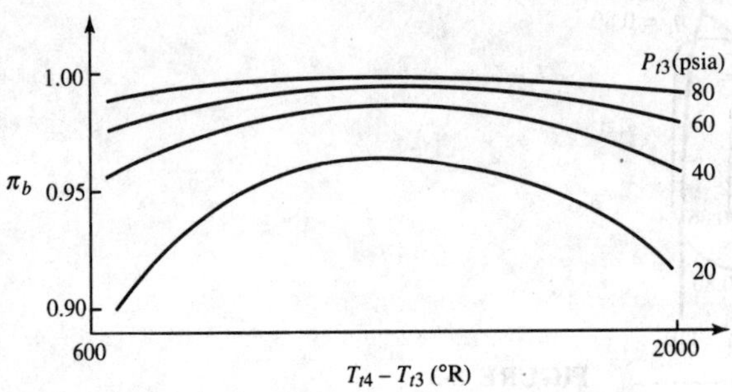

FIGURE 8-4b
Combustor efficiency.

TURBINE MAPS. The flow through a turbine first passes through stationary airfoils (often called *inlet guide vanes* or *nozzles*) which turn and accelerate the fluid, increasing its tangential momentum. The flow then passes through rotating airfoils (called *rotor blades*) that remove energy from the fluid as they change its tangential momentum. Successive pairs of stationary airfoils followed by rotating airfoils remove additional energy from the fluid. To obtain a high output power/weight ratio from a turbine, the flow entering the first-stage turbine rotor is normally supersonic which requires the flow to pass through sonic conditions at the minimum passage area in the inlet guide vanes (nozzles). By using Eq. (8-3), the corrected inlet mass flow rate based on this minimum passage area (throat) will be constant for fixed-inlet-area turbines. This flow characteristic is shown in the typical turbine flow map (Fig. 8-5a) when the expansion ratio across the turbine $[(P_{t4}/P_{t5}) = 1/\pi_t)]$ is greater than about 2 and the flow at the throat is choked.

The performance of a turbine is normally shown by using the total pressure ratio, corrected mass flow rate, corrected turbine speed, and component efficiency. This performance can be presented in two maps or a combined map (similar to that shown for the compressor in Fig. 8-3). When two maps are used, one map shows the interrelationship of the total pressure

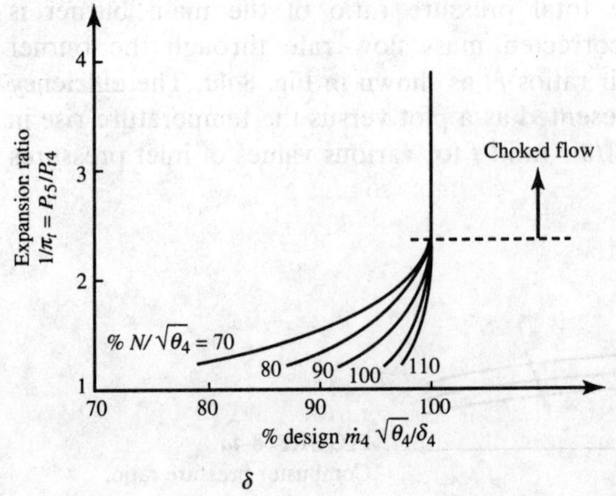

FIGURE 8-5a
Typical turbine flow map.

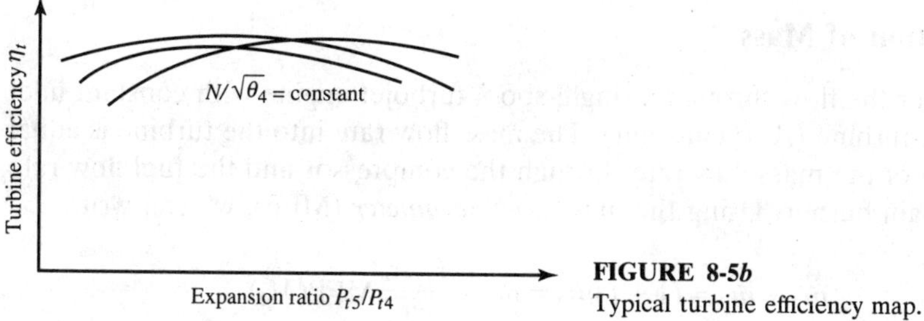

FIGURE 8-5*b*
Typical turbine efficiency map.

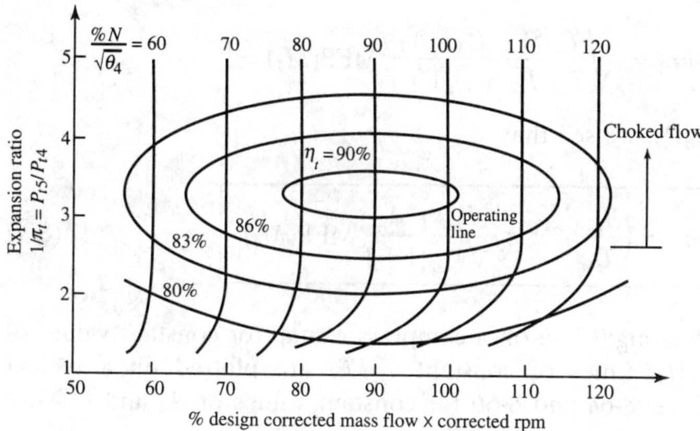

FIGURE 8-5*c*
Combined turbine performance map.

ratio, corrected mass flow rate, and corrected turbine speed, like that depicted in Fig. 8-5*a*. The other map shows the interrelationship of turbine efficiency versus corrected mass flow rate/expansion ratio, like that shown in Fig. 8-5*b*. When a combined map is used, the total pressure ratio of the turbine is plotted versus the product of corrected mass flow rate and the corrected speed, as shown in Fig. 8-5*c*. This spreads out the lines of constant corrected speed from those shown in Fig. 8-5*a*, and the turbine efficiency can now be shown. If we tried to add these lines of constant turbine efficiency to Fig. 8-5*a*, many would coincide with the line for choked flow.

For the majority of aircraft gas turbine engine operation, the turbine efficiency varies very little. In the analysis of this chapter, we consider that the turbine efficiency is constant.

8-2 GAS GENERATOR

The performance of a gas turbine engine depends on the operation of its gas generator. In this section, algebraic expressions for the pumping characteristics of a simple gas turbine engine are developed.

Conservation of Mass

We consider the flow through a single-spool turbojet engine with constant inlet area to the turbine (A_4 = constant). The mass flow rate into the turbine is equal to the sum of the mass flow rate through the compressor and the fuel flow rate into the main burner. Using the *mass flow parameter* (MFP), we can write

$$\dot{m}_2 + \dot{m}_f = (1+f)\dot{m}_2 = \dot{m}_4 = \frac{P_{t4}A_4}{\sqrt{T_{t4}}}\text{MFP}(M_4)$$

With the help of Eq. (8-3), the above equation yields the following expression for the compressor corrected mass flow rate:

$$\dot{m}_{c2} = \sqrt{\frac{T_{t2}}{T_{\text{ref}}}}\frac{P_{\text{ref}}}{P_{t2}}\frac{P_{t4}}{\sqrt{T_{t4}}}\frac{A_4}{1+f}\text{MFP}(M_4)$$

Noting that $P_{t4} = \pi_c\pi_b P_{t2}$, we see that

$$\boxed{\dot{m}_{c2} = \left(\frac{T_{t2}}{T_{t4}}\right)^{1/2}\pi_c\pi_b\frac{P_{\text{ref}}}{\sqrt{T_{\text{ref}}}}\frac{A_4}{1+f}\text{MFP}(M_4)} \tag{8-9}$$

Equation (8-9) is a straight line on a compressor map for constant values of T_{t4}/T_{t2}, A_4, f, and M_4. Lines of constant T_{t2}/T_{t4} are plotted on a typical compressor map in Figs. 8-6*a* and 8-6*b* for constant values of A_4 and f. Note

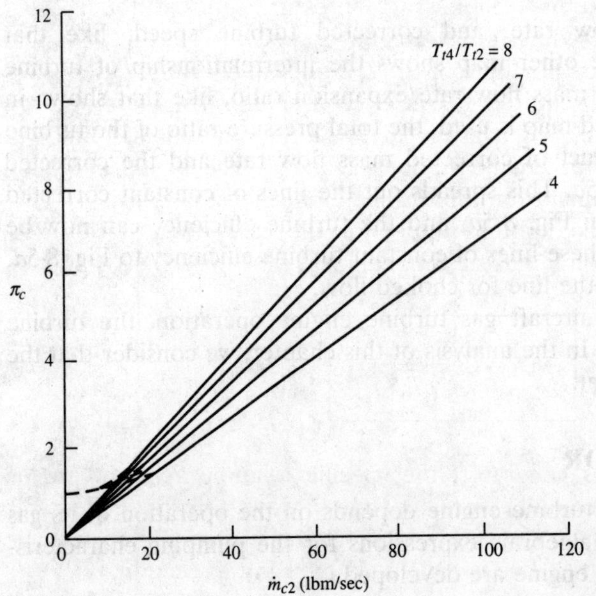

FIGURE 8-6*a*
Compressor map with lines of constant T_{t4}/T_{t2}.

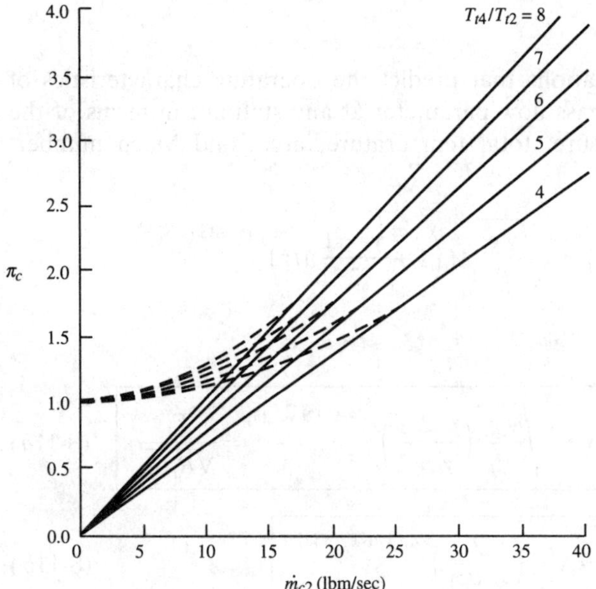

FIGURE 8-6*b*
Compressor map origin with lines of constant T_{t4}/T_{t2}.

that these lines start at a pressure ratio of 1 and corrected mass flow rate of 0 and are curved for low compressor pressure ratios (see Fig. 8-6*b*) because station 4 is unchoked. Station 4 chokes at a pressure ratio of about 2. At pressure ratios above 2, these lines are straight and appear to start at the origin (pressure ratio of 0 and mass flow rate of 0). The lines of constant T_{t2}/T_{t4} show the general characteristics required to satisfy conservation of mass and are independent of the turbine. For a given T_{t4}/T_{t2}, any point on that line will satisfy mass conservation for engine stations 2 and 4. The actual operating point of the compressor depends on the turbine and exhaust nozzle.

Equation (8-9) can be written simply for the case when station 4 is choked (the normal situation in gas turbine engines) as

$$\boxed{\dot{m}_{c2} = C_1 \frac{\pi_c}{\sqrt{T_{t4}/T_{t2}}}} \tag{8-10}$$

For an engine or gas generator, the specific relationship between the compressor pressure ratio and corrected mass flow rate is called the *compressor operating line* and depends on the characteristics of the turbine. The equation for the operating line is developed later in this section.

Turbine Characteristics

Before developing the equations that predict the operating characteristics of the turbine, we write the mass flow parameter at any station i in terms of the mass flow rate, total pressure, total temperature, area, and Mach number. Since

$$\frac{\dot{m}_i\sqrt{T_{ti}}}{P_{ti}A_i} = \text{MFP}(M_i) = \sqrt{\frac{\gamma_i g_c}{R_i}}\, M_i\left(1+\frac{\gamma_i-1}{2}M_i^2\right)^{-(\gamma_i+1)/[2(\gamma_i-1)]}$$

Then, for $M_i = 1$,

$$\boxed{\frac{\dot{m}_i\sqrt{T_{ti}}}{P_{ti}A_i} = \text{MFP}(M_i=1) = \sqrt{\frac{\gamma_i g_c}{R_i}}\left(\frac{2}{\gamma_i+1}\right)^{(\gamma_i+1)/[2(\gamma_i-1)]} = \frac{\Gamma_i}{\sqrt{R_i/g_c}}} \tag{8-11a}$$

where

$$\boxed{\Gamma_i \equiv \sqrt{\gamma_i}\left(\frac{2}{\gamma_i+1}\right)^{(\gamma_i+1)/[2(\gamma_i-1)]}} \tag{8-11b}$$

For a turbojet engine, the flow is choked ($M = 1$) in the turbine inlet guide vanes (station 4) and nearly at the throat of the exhaust nozzle (station 8). Thus the corrected mass flow rate per unit area is constant at station 4 and

$$\dot{m}_4 = \frac{P_{t4}A_4}{\sqrt{T_{t4}}}\frac{\Gamma_4}{\sqrt{R_4}} \qquad \dot{m}_8 = \frac{P_{t8}A_8}{\sqrt{T_{t8}}}\text{MFP}(M_8) \tag{i}$$

For a simple turbojet engine, the mass flow rate through the turbine is equal to that through the exhaust nozzle, or

$$\boxed{\dot{m}_8 = \dot{m}_4}$$

Using Eq. (i), then, we have

$$\frac{\sqrt{T_{t8}/T_{t4}}}{P_{t8}/P_{t4}} = \frac{A_8}{A_4}\frac{\text{MFP}(M_8)}{\Gamma_4/\sqrt{R_4}}$$

or

$$\boxed{\frac{\sqrt{\tau_t}}{\pi_t} = \frac{A_8}{A_4}\frac{\text{MFP}(M_8)}{\Gamma_4/\sqrt{R_4}}} \tag{8-12a}$$

where

$$\boxed{\pi_t = \left(1-\frac{1-\tau_t}{\eta_t}\right)^{\gamma_t/(\gamma_t-1)}} \tag{8-12b}$$

For constant turbine efficiency η_t, constant values of R and Γ, constant areas at stations 4 and 8, and choked flow at station 8, Eqs. (8-12a) and (8-12b) can be satisfied only by constant values of the turbine temperature ratio τ_t and the turbine pressure ratio π_t. Thus we have

$$\boxed{\tau_t, \pi_t \text{ constant} \qquad \text{for } M_8 = 1 \text{ and constant } A_4 \text{ and } A_8}$$

If the exhaust nozzle unchokes and/or its throat area is changed, then both τ_t and π_t will change. Consider a turbine with reference values of $\eta_t = 0.90$ and $\tau_t = 0.80$ when the exhaust nozzle is choked and the gas has $\gamma = 1.33$. From Eqs. (8-12a) and (8-12b), $\pi_t = 0.363174$ and $A_8/A_4 = 2.46281$ at reference conditions. Figure 8-7a shows plots of Eq. (8-12a) for different values of the area ratio A_8/A_4 times the mass flow parameter at station 8 [MFP(M_8)] and Eq. (8-12b). Because of the relative slopes of these equations, the changes of both τ_t and π_t with A_8 and M_8 can be found by using the following functional

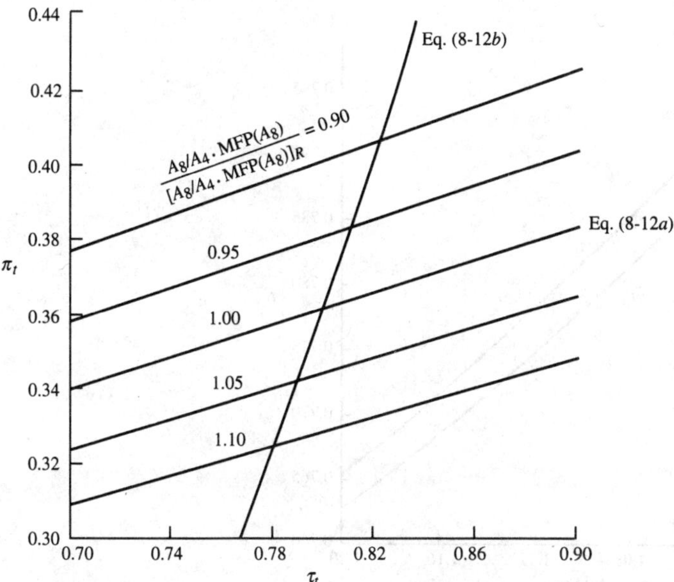

FIGURE 8-7*a*
Plot of turbine performance Eqs. (8-12a) and (8-12b).

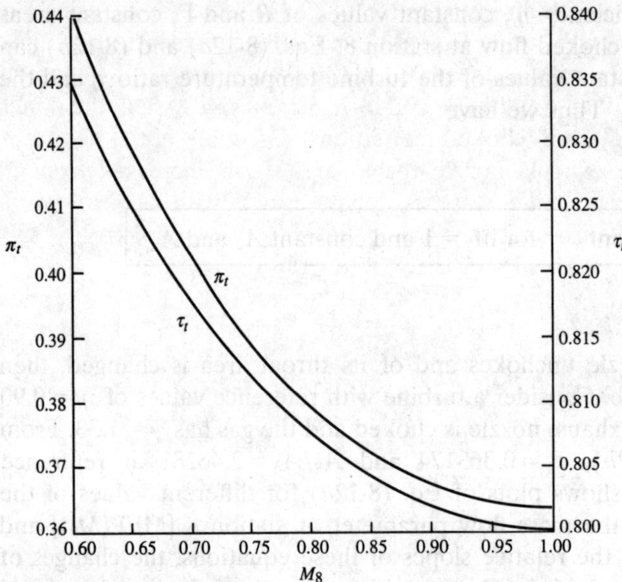

FIGURE 8-7*b*
Variation of turbine performance with exhaust nozzle Mach number.

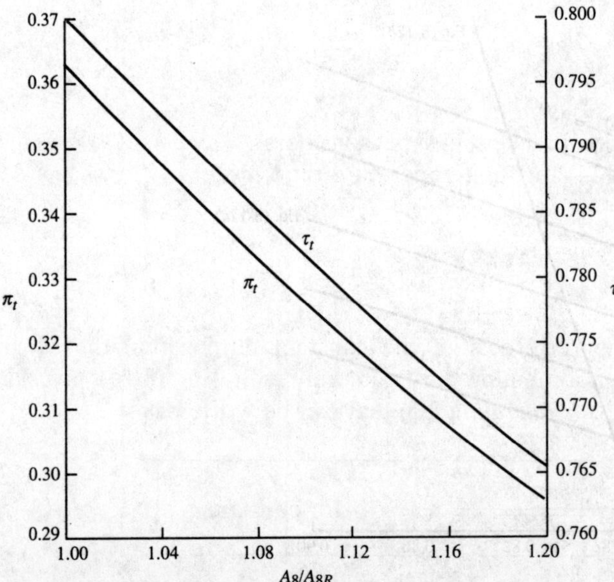

FIGURE 8-7*c*
Variation of turbine performance with exhaust nozzle area.

iteration scheme, starting with an initial value of τ_t: (1) solve for π_t, using Eq. (8-12*a*); (2) calculate a new τ_t, using Eq. (8-12*b*); (3) repeat steps 1 and 2 until successive values of τ_t are within a specified range (say, ±0.0001). The results of this iteration, plotted in Figs. 8-7*b* and 8-7*c*, show that when the Mach number M_8 is reduced from choked conditions ($M_8 = 1$), both τ_t and π_t increase; and when the exhaust nozzle throat area A_8 is increased from its reference value, both τ_t and π_t decrease. A decrease in τ_t, with its corresponding decrease in π_t, will increase the turbine power per unit mass flow and change the pumping characteristics of the gas generator.

Compressor Operating Line

From a work balance between the compressor and turbine, we write

$$\dot{m}_2 c_{pc}(T_{t3} - T_{t2}) = \eta_m \dot{m}_2(1+f)c_{pt}(T_{t4} - T_{t5})$$

or

$$\tau_c = 1 + \frac{T_{t4}}{T_{t2}}\frac{c_{pt}}{c_{pc}}\eta_m(1+f)(1-\tau_t) \tag{8-13}$$

where

$$\pi_c = [1 + \eta_c(\tau_c - 1)]^{\gamma_c/(\gamma_c - 1)} \tag{ii}$$

Combining Eqs. (8-13) and (ii) gives

$$\pi_c = \left\{1 + \frac{T_{t4}}{T_{t2}}\left[\frac{c_{pt}}{c_{pc}}\eta_c\eta_m(1+f)(1-\tau_t)\right]\right\}^{\gamma_c/(\gamma_c-1)} \tag{8-14}$$

where the term in square brackets can be considered a constant when τ_t is constant. Solving Eq. (8-14) for the temperature ratio gives

$$\frac{T_{t4}}{T_{t2}} = C_2[(\pi_c)^{(\gamma_c-1)/\gamma_c} - 1]$$

where C_2 represents the reciprocal of the constant term within the square brackets of Eq. (8-14). Combining this equation with Eq. (8-10) gives an equation for the *compressor operating line* that can be written as

$$\boxed{\dot{m}_{c2} = \frac{\pi_c}{\sqrt{\pi_c^{(\gamma_c-1)/\gamma_c} - 1}}\frac{C_1}{\sqrt{C_2}} \quad \text{for constant } \tau_t} \tag{8-15}$$

We can plot the *compressor operating line*, using Eq. (8-15), on the compressor map of Fig. 8-6*a*, giving the compressor map with operating line shown in Fig. 8-8. This compressor operating line shows that for each value of the temperature ratio T_{t2}/T_{t4} there is one value of compressor pressure ratio and corrected mass flow rate. One can also see that for a constant value of T_{t2}, both the compressor pressure ratio and the corrected mass flow rate will increase with increases in throttle setting (increases in T_{t4}). In addition, when at constant T_{t4}, the compressor pressure ratio and corrected mass flow rate will decrease with increases in T_{t2} due to higher speed and/or lower altitude (*note*: $T_{t2} = T_{t0} = T_0\tau_r$). The curving of the operating line in Fig. 8-8 at pressure ratios below 4 is due to the exhaust nozzle being unchoked ($M_8 < 1$), which increases the value of τ_t (see Fig. 8-7*b*).

The compressor operating line defines the pumping characteristics of the gas generator. As mentioned earlier, changing the throat area of the exhaust nozzle A_8 will change these characteristics. It achieves this change by shifting the compressor operating line. Increasing A_8 will decrease τ_t (see Fig. 8-7*c*). This decrease in τ_t will increase the term within the square brackets of Eq. (8-14) which corresponds to the reciprocal of constant C_2 in Eq. (8-15). Thus an increase in A_8 will decrease the constant C_2 in Eq. (8-15). For a constant T_{t4}/T_{t2}, this shift in the operating line will increase both the corrected mass flow rate and the pressure ratio of the compressor, as shown in Fig. 8-9 for a 20 percent increase in A_8. For some compressors, an increase in the exhaust nozzle throat area A_8 can keep engine operation away from the surge.

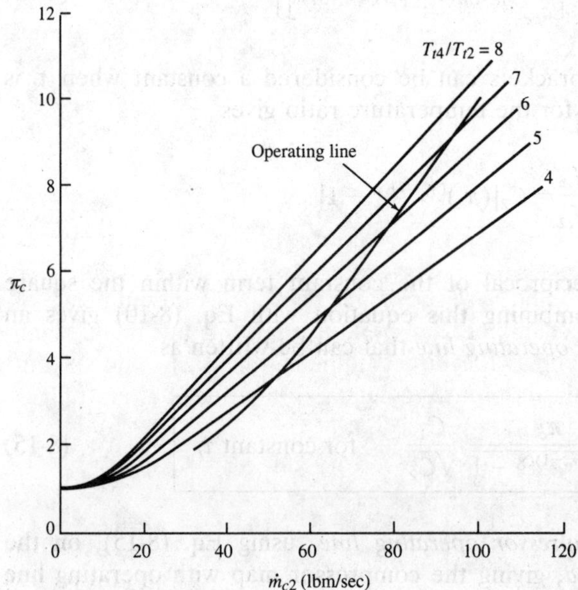

FIGURE 8-8
Compressor map with operating line.

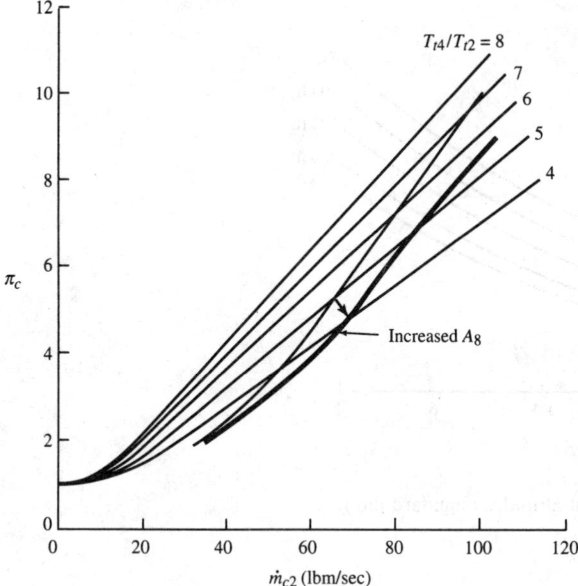

FIGURE 8-9
Effect of exhaust nozzle area on compressor operating line.

Engine Controls

The engine control system will control the gas generator operation to keep the main burner exit temperature T_{t4} and the compressor's pressure ratio π_c, rotational speed N, exit total pressure T_{t3}, and exit total pressure P_{t3} from exceeding specific maximum values. An understanding of the influence of the engine control system on compressor performance during changing flight conditions and throttle settings can be gained by recasting Eqs. (8-10) and (8-14) in terms of the dimensionless total temperature at station 0 (θ_0). We note that

$$T_{t0} = T_{\text{ref}} \frac{T_{t0}}{T_{\text{ref}}} = T_{\text{ref}} \theta_0$$

and

$$\theta_0 = \frac{T_0}{T_{\text{ref}}} \tau_r = \frac{T_0}{T_{\text{ref}}} \left(1 + \frac{\gamma - 1}{2} M_0^2\right) \tag{8-16}$$

Equation (8-16) and Figs. 8-10 and 8-11 show that θ_0 includes the influence of both the altitude (through the ambient temperature T_0) and the flight Mach number. Although Fig. 8-10 shows the direct influence of Mach number and altitude on θ_0, Fig. 8-11 is an easier plot to understand in terms of aircraft flight conditions (Mach number and altitude).

Using Eq. (8-16) and the fact that $T_{t2} = T_{t0}$, we can write Eq. (8-14) as

$$\boxed{\pi_c = \left(1 + \frac{T_{t4}}{\theta_0} K_1\right)^{\gamma_c/(\gamma_c - 1)}} \tag{8-17}$$

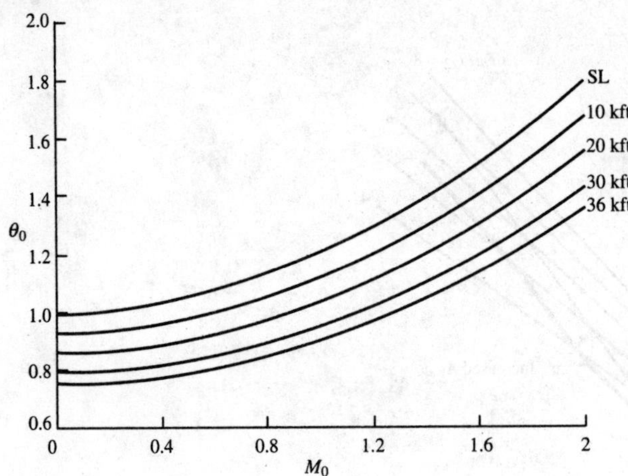

FIGURE 8-10
θ_0 versus Mach number at different altitudes (standard day).

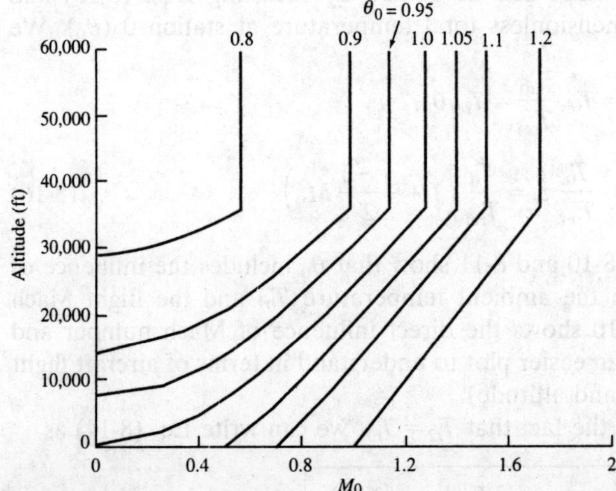

FIGURE 8-11
θ_0 versus Mach number and altitude (standard day).

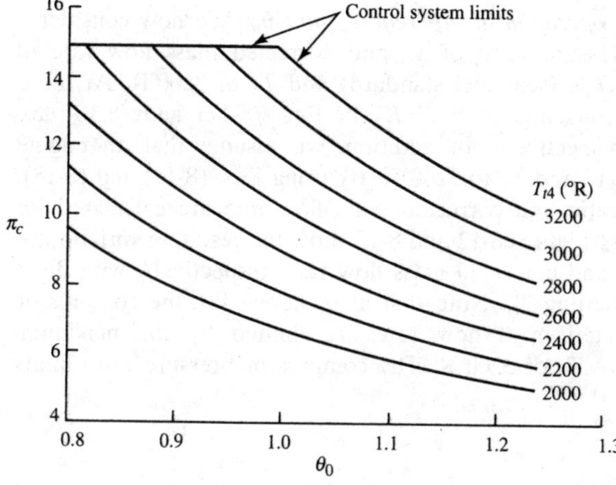

FIGURE 8-12
Compressor pressure ratio versus θ_0 and T_{t4}.

where K_1 is a constant. Equation (8-17) is plotted in Fig. 8-12 for the turbojet engine of Example 8-1.

By using Eqs. (8-17) and (8-10), the corrected mass flow rate through the compressor can be expressed as

$$\boxed{\dot{m}_{c2} = \left(\frac{\theta_0}{T_{t4}}\right)^{1/2}\left(1 + \frac{T_{t4}}{\theta_0}K_1\right)^{\gamma_c/(\gamma_c-1)} K_2} \tag{8-18}$$

where K_2 is a constant. Equation (8–18) is plotted in Fig. 8-13 for the turbojet engine of Example 8-1.

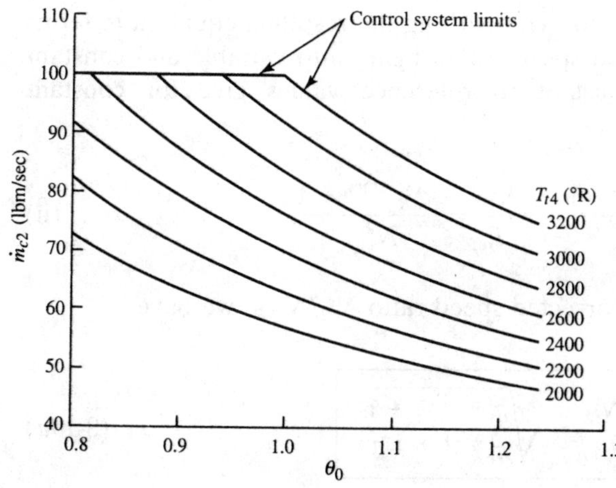

FIGURE 8-13
Compressor corrected mass flow rate versus θ_0 and T_{t4}.

Example 8-1. *Compressor operation at different T_{t4} and θ_0.* We now consider a compressor that has a pressure ratio of 15 and corrected mass flow rate of 100 lbm/sec for T_{t2} of 518.7°R (sea-level standard) and T_{t4} of 3200°R. At these conditions, θ_0 is 1, and constants K_1 and K_2 in Eqs. (8-17) and (8-18) are 3.649×10^{-4} and 377-1, respectively. In addition, we assume that an engine control system limits π_c to 15 and T_{t4} to 3200°R. By using Eqs. (8-17) and (8-18), the compressor pressure ratio and corrected mass flow rate are calculated for various values of T_{t4} and θ_0. Figures 8-12 and 8-13 show the resulting variation of compressor pressure ratio and corrected mass flow rate, respectively, with flight condition θ_0 and throttle setting T_{t4}. Note that at θ_0 above 1.0, the compressor pressure ratio and corrected mass flow rate are limited by the maximum combustor exit temperature T_{t4} of 3200°R. The compressor pressure ratio limits performance at θ_0 below 1.0.

Variation in Engine Speed

As will be shown in Chap. 9, the change in total enthalpy across a fan or compressor is proportional to the rotational speed N squared. For a calorically perfect gas, we can write

$$T_{t3} - T_{t2} = K_1 N^2$$

or

$$\tau_c - 1 = \frac{K_1}{T_{\text{ref}}} N_{c2}^2 \tag{i}$$

where N_{c2} is the compressor corrected speed. The compressor temperature ratio is related to the compressor pressure ratio through the efficiency, or

$$\tau_c - 1 = \eta_c(\pi_c^{(\gamma_c-1)/\gamma_c} - 1)$$

Combining this equation with Eq. (i), rewriting the resulting equation in terms of pressure ratio and corrected speed, rearranging into variable and constant terms, and equating the constant to reference values give for constant compressor efficiency

$$\frac{\pi_c^{(\gamma_c-1)/\gamma_c} - 1}{N_{c2}^2} = \frac{K_1}{\eta_c T_{\text{ref}}} = \frac{\pi_{cR}^{(\gamma_c-1)/\gamma_c} - 1}{N_{c2R}^2} \tag{ii}$$

Solving Eq. (ii) for the corrected speed ratio N_{c2}/N_{c2R}, we have

$$\boxed{\frac{N_{c2}}{N_{c2R}} = \sqrt{\frac{\pi_c^{(\gamma_c-1)/\gamma_c} - 1}{\pi_{cR}^{(\gamma_c-1)/\gamma_c} - 1}}} \tag{8-19a}$$

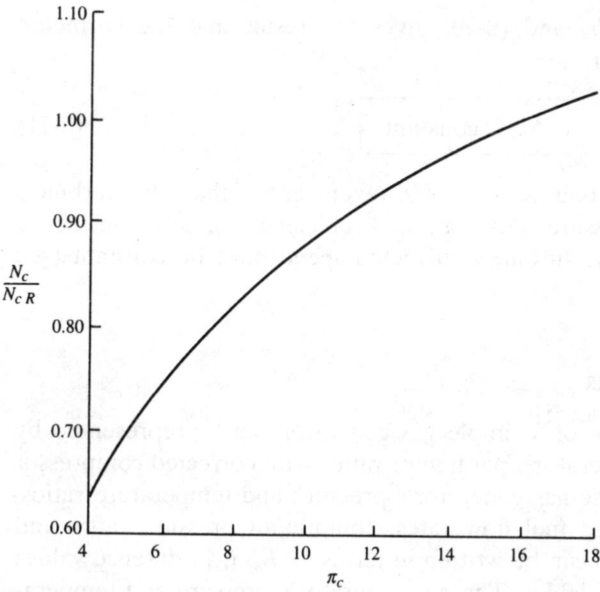

FIGURE 8-14
Variation in corrected speed with compressor pressure ratio.

This equation can also be used to estimate the variation in engine speed (N) with flight condition. Equation (8-19a) is plotted in Fig. 8-14 for a reference compressor pressure ratio of 16. Note that a reduction in compressor pressure ratio from 16 to 11 requires only a 10 percent reduction in corrected speed N_c. Equation (8-19a) can be written in terms of T_{t4}/θ_0 by using Eq. (8-17), yielding

$$\boxed{\frac{N_{c2}}{N_{c2R}} = \sqrt{\frac{T_{t4}/\theta_0}{(T_{t4}/\theta_0)_R}}} \tag{8-19b}$$

Since the compressor and turbine are connected to the same shaft, they have the same rotational speed N, and we can write the following relationship between their corrected speeds:

$$\boxed{N_{c2} = \frac{1}{\sqrt{T_{\text{ref}}}}\sqrt{\frac{T_{t4}}{\theta_0}}\, N_{c4}} \tag{8-20}$$

Comparison of Eqs. (8-19*b*) and (8-20) gives the result that the corrected turbine speed is constant, or

$$\boxed{N_{c4} = \text{constant}} \tag{8-21}$$

This result may surprise one at first. However, given that the turbine's temperature ratio τ_t, pressure ratio π_t, and efficiency η_t are considered constant in this analysis, the turbine's corrected speed must be constant (see Fig. 8-5*c*).

Gas Generator Equations

The pumping characteristics of a simple gas generator can be represented by the variation of the gas generator's parameter ratios with corrected compressor speed. The equations for the gas generator's pressure and temperature ratios, corrected air mass flow and fuel flow rates, compressor pressure ratio, and corrected compressor speed can be written in terms of T_{t4}/T_{t2}, reference values (subscript R), and other variables. The gas generator's pressure and temperature ratios are given simply by

$$\frac{P_{t6}}{P_{t2}} = \pi_c \pi_b \pi_t \tag{8-22}$$

$$\frac{T_{t6}}{T_{t2}} = \frac{T_{t4}}{T_{t2}} \tau_t \tag{8-23}$$

From Eq. (8-10) and referencing, the corrected mass flow rate can be written as

$$\frac{\dot{m}_{c2}}{\dot{m}_{c2R}} = \frac{\pi_c}{\pi_{cR}} \sqrt{\frac{(T_{t4}/T_{t2})_R}{T_{t4}/T_{t2}}} \tag{8-24}$$

where the compressor pressure ratio is given by Eq. (8-17), rewritten in terms of T_{t4}/T_{t2}, or

$$\pi_c = \left[1 + \frac{T_{t4}/T_{t2}}{(T_{t4}/T_{t3})_R} (\pi_{cR}^{(\gamma_c - 1)/\gamma_c} - 1)\right]^{\gamma_c/(\gamma_c - 1)} \tag{8-25}$$

Equation (8-19*b*) for the corrected speed can be rewritten in terms of T_{t4}/T_{t2} as

$$\frac{N_{c2}}{N_{c2R}} = \sqrt{\frac{T_{t4}/T_{t2}}{(T_{t4}/T_{t2})_R}} \tag{8-26}$$

An expression for the corrected fuel flow rate results from Eqs. (7-9), (8-2), and (8-7) as follows: Solving Eq. (7-9) for the fuel flow rate gives

$$\dot{m}_f = \dot{m}_0 \frac{c_{pt} T_{t4} - c_{pc} T_{t3}}{\eta_b h_{PR} - c_{pt} T_{t4}}$$

From Eqs. (8-2) and (8-7), this equation becomes

$$\dot{m}_{fc} = \frac{\dot{m}_{c2}}{\theta_2} \frac{c_{pt} T_{t4} - c_{pc} T_{t3}}{\eta_b h_{PR} - c_{pt} T_{t4}}$$

or

$$\boxed{\dot{m}_{fc} = \dot{m}_{c2} \frac{T_{t4}/T_{t2} - \tau_c (c_{pc}/c_{pt})}{\eta_b h_{PR}/(c_{pt} T_{\text{ref}}) - T_{t4}/T_{\text{ref}}}} \tag{8-27}$$

where by using Eq. (8-13) and referencing, τ_c is given by

$$\tau_c = 1 + (\tau_{cR} - 1) \frac{T_{t4}/T_{t2}}{(T_{t4}/T_{t2})_R} \tag{8-28}$$

Equations (8-22) through (8-28) constitute a set of equations for the pumping characteristics of a simple gas generator in terms of T_{t4}/T_{t2} and reference values. Only Eq. (8-27) for the corrected fuel flow rate has the term T_{t4}/T_{ref} that is not strictly a function of T_{t4}/T_{t2}. The first term in the denominator of Eq. (8-27) has a magnitude of about 130, and T_{t4}/T_{ref} has a value of about 6 or smaller. Thus the denominator of Eq. (8-28) does not vary appreciably, and the corrected fuel flow rate is a function of T_{t4}/T_{t2} and reference values. In summary, the pumping characteristics of the gas generator are a function of only the temperature ratio T_{t4}/T_{t2}.

Example 8-2. *Gas generator.* We want to determine the characteristics of a gas generator with a maximum compressor pressure ratio of 15, a compressor corrected mass flow rate of 100 lbm/sec at T_{t2} of 518.7°R (sea-level standard), and a maximum T_{t4} of 3200°R. This is the same compressor we considered in Example 8-1 (see Figs. 8-12 and 8-13). We assume the compressor has an efficiency η_c of 0.8572 ($e_c = 0.9$), and the burner has an efficiency η_b of 0.995 and a pressure ratio π_b of 0.96. In addition, we assume the following gas constants: $\gamma_c = 1.4$, $c_{pc} = 0.24$ Btu/(lbm · °R), $\gamma_t = 1.33$, and $c_{pt} = 0.276$ Btu/(lbm · °R).

By using Eq. (7-10), the reference fuel/air ratio f_R is 0.03381 for $h_{PR} = 18{,}400$ Btu/lbm, and the corrected fuel flow rate is 12,170 lb/hr. From Eq. (7-12), the turbine temperature ratio τ_t is 0.8124. Assuming $e_t = 0.9$, Eqs. (7-13) and (7-14) give the turbine pressure ratio π_t as 0.3943 and the turbine efficiency η_t as 0.910. The reference compressor temperature ratio τ_{cR} is 2.3624.

Calculations were done over a range of T_{t4} with $T_{t2} = 518.7$°R and using Eqs. (8-22) through (8-28). The resulting gas generator pumping characteristics are plotted in Fig. 8-15. We can see that the compressor pressure ratio and corrected fuel flow rate decrease more rapidly with decreasing corrected speed than corrected airflow rate. As discussed above, the gas generator's pumping characteristics are a function of only T_{t4}/T_{t2}, and Fig. 8-15 shows this most important relationship in graphical form.

Since the maximum T_{t4} is 3200°R and the maximum pressure ratio is 15, the operation of the gas generator at different inlet conditions (T_{t2}, P_{t2}) and/or different throttle setting (T_{t4}) can be obtained from Fig. 8-15. For example, consider a 100°F day (T_{t2}) at sea level with maximum power. Here $T_{t2} = 560$°R, $P_{t2} = 14.7$ psia, and $T_{t4} = 3200$°R; thus $T_{t4}/T_{t2} = 5.71$, and Fig. 8-15 gives the

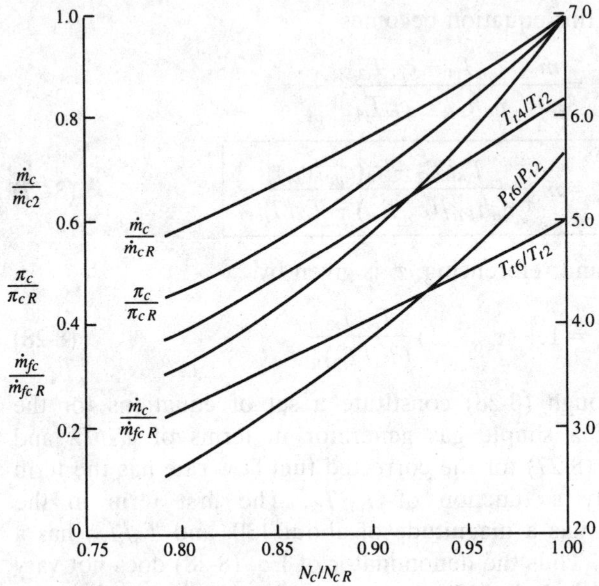

FIGURE 8-15
Gas generator pumping characteristics.

following data: $N_c/N_{cR} = 0.96$, $\dot{m}_c/\dot{m}_{cR} = 0.88$, $\pi_c/\pi_{cR} = 0.84$, $\dot{m}_{fc}/\dot{m}_{fcR} = 0.78$, $T_{t6}/T_{t2} = 4.6$, and $P_{t6}/P_{t2} = 4.8$. With these data, the pressures, temperatures, and flow rates can be calculated as follows:

$$\dot{m} = \left(\frac{P_{t2}}{P_{t2R}}\sqrt{\frac{T_{t2R}}{T_{t2}}}\right)\left(\frac{\dot{m}_c}{\dot{m}_{cR}}\right)\dot{m}_{cR} = 1 \times \sqrt{\frac{518.7}{560}}(0.88)(100) = 84.7 \text{ lbm/sec}$$

$$\dot{m}_f = \frac{P_{t2}}{P_{t2R}}\sqrt{\frac{T_{t2}}{T_{t2R}}}\frac{\dot{m}_{cf}}{\dot{m}_{cfR}}\dot{m}_{cfR} = 1 \times \sqrt{\frac{560}{518.6}}(0.78)(12{,}170) = 9860 \text{ lbm/hr}$$

$$T_{t6} = \frac{T_{t6}}{T_{t2}}T_{t2} = 4.6(560) = 2576°\text{R}$$

$$P_{t6} = \frac{P_{t6}}{P_{t2}}P_{t2} = 4.8(14.7) = 70.6 \text{ psia}$$

$$\pi_c = \frac{\pi_c}{\pi_{cR}}\pi_{cR} = 0.84(15) = 12.6$$

As another example, consider flight at Mach 0.6 and 40 kft ($\theta = 0.7519$, $\delta = 0.1858$) with maximum throttle. Since T_{t2} (=418.1°R) is less than T_{t2R}, the maximum value for T_{t4} is 2579.4°R (=3200 × 418.1/518.7), and the compressor has a pressure ratio of 15 and corrected mass flow rate of 100 lbm/sec. The air mass flow rate is reduced to 20.7 lbm/sec, and the mass fuel flow rate is reduced to 2030 lbm/hr.

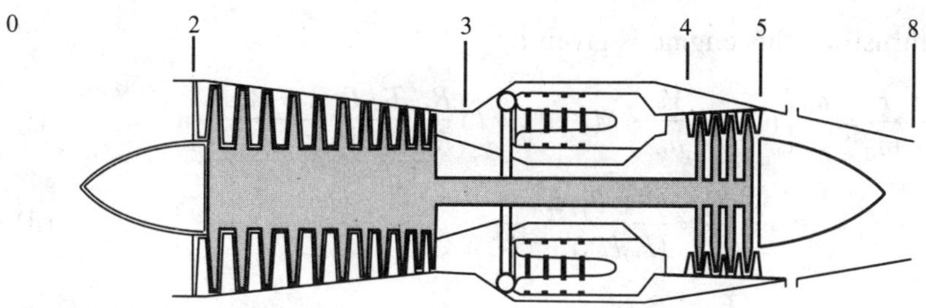

FIGURE 8-16
Single-spool turbojet engine. (*Courtesy of Pratt & Whitney.*)

8-3 TURBOJET ENGINE

In this section, the performance equations of the single-spool turbojet engine, shown in Fig. 8-16, are developed and the results are studied. We assume choked flow at stations 4 and 8. In addition, the throttle (T_{t4}), flight conditions (M_0, T_0, and P_0), and the ambient pressure/exhaust pressure ratio P_0/P_9 can be independently varied for this engine. The performance equations for this turbojet can be obtained easily by adding inlet and exhaust nozzle losses to the single-spool gas generator studied in the previous section.

This engine has five independent variables (T_{t4}, M_0, T_0, P_0, and P_0/P_9). The performance analysis develops analytical expressions for component performance in terms of these independent variables. We have six dependent variables for the single-spool turbojet engine: engine mass flow rate, compressor pressure ratio, compressor temperature ratio, burner fuel/air ratio, exit temperature ratio T_9/T_0, and exit Mach number. A summary of the independent variables, dependent variables, and constants or knowns for this engine is given in Table 8-4.

TABLE 8-4
Performance analysis variables for single-spool turbojet engine

	Variables		
Component	**Independent**	**Constant or known**	**Dependent**
Engine	M_0, T_0, P_0		$\dot{m}_0$
Diffuser		$\pi_d = f(M_0)$	
Compressor		η_c	π_c, τ_c
Burner	T_{t4}	π_b, η_b	f
Turbine		π_t, τ_t	
Nozzle	$\dfrac{P_9}{P_0}$	π_n	M_9, $\dfrac{T_9}{T_0}$
Total number	5		6

The thrust for this engine is given by

$$\frac{F}{\dot{m}_0}=\frac{a_0}{g_c}\left[(1+f)\frac{V_9}{a_0}-M_0+(1+f)\frac{R_t}{R_c}\frac{T_9/T_0}{V_9/A_0}\frac{1-P_0/P_9}{\gamma_c}\right] \tag{i}$$

where

$$\frac{T_9}{T_0}=\frac{T_{t4}\tau_t}{(P_{t9}/P_9)^{(\gamma_t-1)/\gamma_t}} \tag{ii}$$

$$\frac{P_{t9}}{P_9}=\frac{P_0}{P_9}\pi_r\pi_d\pi_c\pi_b\pi_t\pi_n \tag{iii}$$

$$M_9=\sqrt{\frac{2}{\gamma_t-1}\left[\left(\frac{P_{t9}}{P_9}\right)^{(\gamma_t-1/\gamma_t}-1\right]} \tag{iv}$$

and

$$\frac{V_9}{a_0}=M_9\sqrt{\frac{\gamma_t R_t T_9}{\gamma_c R_c T_0}} \tag{v}$$

The thrust specific fuel consumption for this engine is given by

$$S=\frac{f}{F/\dot{m}_0} \tag{vi}$$

where

$$f=\frac{\tau_\lambda-\tau_r\tau_c}{h_{PR}\eta_b/(c_pT_0)-\tau_\lambda} \tag{vii}$$

Equations (i) through (vii) can be solved for given T_{t4}, M_0, T_0, P_0, P_0/P_9, and gas properties with expressions for τ_λ, π_r, τ_r, π_d, π_c, τ_c, and engine mass flow rate in terms of the five independent variables and other dependent variables. In the previous section, we developed Eq. (8-28), repeated here, for the compressor's temperature ratios in terms of T_{t4}/T_{t2} and reference values.

$$\tau_c=1+(\tau_{cR}-1)\frac{T_{t4}/T_{t2}}{(T_{t4}/T_{t2})_R} \tag{8-28}$$

The compressor pressure ratio is related to its temperature ratio by its efficiency.

An equation for the engine mass flow rate follows from the mass flow parameter (MFP) written for station 4 with choked flow and the definitions of component π values. We write

$$\dot{m}_0=\frac{P_{t4}}{\sqrt{T_{t4}}}\frac{A_4}{1+f}\text{MFP}(1)=\frac{P_0\pi_r\pi_d\pi_c}{\sqrt{T_{t4}}}\left[\frac{\pi_bA_4}{1+f}\text{MFP}(1)\right]$$

Since the terms within the square brackets are considered constant, we move the variable terms to the left side of the equation, and, using referencing, equate the constant to reference values:

$$\frac{\dot{m}_0\sqrt{T_{t4}}}{P_0\pi_r\pi_d\pi_c}=\frac{\pi_bA_4}{1+f}\text{MFP}(1)=\left(\frac{\dot{m}_0\sqrt{T_{t4}}}{P_0\pi_r\pi_d\pi_c}\right)_R$$

Solving for the engine mass flow rate, we get

$$\boxed{\dot{m}_0 = \dot{m}_{0R} \frac{P_0 \pi_r \pi_d \pi_c}{(P_0 \pi_r \pi_d \pi_c)_R} \sqrt{\frac{T_{t4R}}{T_{t4}}}} \tag{8-29}$$

Relationships for τ_λ, π_r, τ_r, and π_d follow from their equations in Chap. 7.

EXHAUST NOZZLE EXIT AREA. The throat area of the exhaust nozzle is assumed to be constant. With P_0/P_9 an independent variable, the exit area of the exhaust nozzle A_9 must correspond to the nozzle pressure ratio P_{t9}/P_9. An expression for the exhaust nozzle exit area follows from the mass flow parameter and other compressible flow properties. The subscript t is used in the following equations for the gas properties (γ, R, and Γ) at stations 8 and 9. Using Eq. (8-11) for choked flow at station 8 gives

$$\dot{m}_8 = \frac{P_{t9} A_8}{\sqrt{T_{t8}}} \frac{\Gamma_t}{\sqrt{R_t/g_c}} \tag{i}$$

From the equation for the mass flow parameter [Eq. (3-13)], the mass flow rate at station 9 is

$$\dot{m}_9 = \frac{P_{t9} A_9}{\sqrt{T_{t9}}} \frac{\sqrt{\gamma_t}}{\sqrt{R_t/g_c}} M_9 \left(1 + \frac{\gamma_t - 1}{2} M_9^2\right)^{-(\gamma_t+1)/[2(\gamma_t-1)]} \tag{ii}$$

Using the nozzle relationships $T_{t8} = T_{t9}$ and $\pi_n = P_{t9}/P_{t9}$ and equating the mass flow rate at station 8 [Eq. (i)] to that at station 9 [Eq. (ii)] give

$$\frac{A_9}{A_8} = \frac{\Gamma_t}{\sqrt{\gamma_t}} \frac{1}{\pi_n} \frac{1}{M_9} \left(1 + \frac{\gamma_t - 1}{2} M_9^2\right)^{(\gamma_t+1)/[2(\gamma_t-1)]}$$

Replacing the Mach number at station 9 by using

$$M_9 = \sqrt{\frac{2}{\gamma_t - 1}[(P_{t9}/P_9)^{(\gamma_t-1)/\gamma_t} - 1]}$$

gives

$$\boxed{\frac{A_9}{A_8} = \Gamma_t \sqrt{\frac{\gamma_t - 1}{2\gamma_t}} \frac{1}{\pi_n} \frac{(P_{t9}/P_9)^{(\gamma_t+1)/(2\gamma_t)}}{\sqrt{(P_{t9}/P_9)^{(\gamma_t-1)/\gamma_t} - 1}}} \tag{8-30}$$

Since the throat area A_8 is constant, Eq. (8-30) can be used to obtain the ratio of the exit area A_9 to a reference exit area A_{9R} that can be written as

$$\boxed{\frac{A_9}{A_{9R}} = \left[\frac{P_{t9}/P_9}{(P_{t9}/P_9)_R}\right]^{(\gamma_t+1)/(2\gamma_t)} \sqrt{\frac{(P_{t9}/P_9)_R^{(\gamma_t-1)/\gamma_t} - 1}{(P_{t9}/P_9)^{(\gamma_t-1)/\gamma_t} - 1}}} \tag{8-31}$$

Summary of Performance Equations—Single-Spool Turbojet without Afterburner

INPUTS:

Choices

Flight parameters:	M_0, T_0 (K, °R), P_0 (kPa, psia)
Throttle setting:	T_{t4} (K, °R)
Exhaust nozzle setting:	P_0/P_9

Design constants

π's:	$\pi_{d\,\max}$, π_b, π_t, π_n
τ's:	τ_t
η's:	η_c, η_b, η_m
Gas properties:	γ_c, γ_t, c_{pc}, c_{pt} [kJ/(kg · K), Btu/(lbm · °R)]
Fuel:	h_{PR} (kJ/kg, Btu/lbm)

Reference conditions

Flight parameters:	M_{0R}, T_{0R} (K, °R), P_{0R} (kPa, psia), τ_{rR}, π_{rR}
Throttle setting:	T_{t4R} (K, °R)
Component behavior:	π_{dR}, π_{cR}, τ_{cR}

OUTPUTS:

Overall performance:	F (N, lbf), $\dot{m}_0$ (kg/sec, lbm/sec), f, $S\left(\dfrac{\text{mg/s}}{\text{N}}, \dfrac{\text{lbm/hr}}{\text{lbf}}\right)$, η_P, η_T, η_O
Component behavior:	π_d, π_c, τ_c, f, M_9, N/N_R

EQUATIONS:

$$R_c = \frac{\gamma_c - 1}{\gamma_c} c_{pc} \tag{8-32a}$$

$$R_t = \frac{\gamma_t - 1}{\gamma_t} c_{pt} \tag{8-32b}$$

$$a_0 = \sqrt{\gamma_c R_c g_c T_0} \tag{8-32c}$$

$$V_0 = a_0 M_0 \tag{8-32d}$$

$$\tau_r = 1 + \frac{\gamma_c - 1}{2} M_0^2 \tag{8-32e}$$

$$\pi_r = \tau^{\gamma_c/(\gamma_c - 1)} \tag{8-32f}$$

$$\eta_r = 1 \qquad \text{for } M_0 \le 1 \tag{8-32g}$$

$$\eta_r = 1 - 0.075(M_0 - 1)^{1.35} \qquad \text{for } M_0 > 1 \tag{8-32h}$$

$$\pi_d = \pi_{d\,\max} \eta_r \tag{8-32i}$$

$$T_{t2} = T_0 \tau_r \tag{8-32j}$$

$$\tau_c = 1 + (\tau_{cR} - 1)\frac{T_{t4}/T_{t2}}{(T_{t4}/T_{t2})_R} \tag{8-32k}$$

$$\pi_c = [1 + \eta_c(\tau_c - 1)]^{\gamma_c/(\gamma_c - 1)} \tag{8-32l}$$

$$\tau_\lambda = \frac{c_{pt}T_{t4}}{c_{pc}T_0} \tag{8-32m}$$

$$f = \frac{\tau_\lambda - \tau_r\tau_c}{h_{PR}\eta_b/(c_pT_0) - \tau_\lambda} \tag{8-32n}$$

$$\dot{m}_0 = \dot{m}_{0R}\frac{P_0\pi_r\pi_d\pi_c}{(P_0\pi_r\pi_d\pi_c)_R}\sqrt{\frac{T_{t4R}}{T_{t4}}} \tag{8-32o}$$

$$\frac{P_{t9}}{P_9} = \frac{P_0}{P_9}\pi_r\pi_d\pi_c\pi_b\pi_t\pi_n \tag{8-32p}$$

$$M_9 = \sqrt{\frac{2}{\gamma_t - 1}\left[\left(\frac{P_{t9}}{P_9}\right)^{(\gamma_t - 1/\tau_t} - 1\right]} \tag{8-32q}$$

$$\frac{T_9}{T_0} = \frac{T_{t4}\tau_t}{(P_{t9}/P_9)^{(\gamma_t - 1)/\gamma_t}} \tag{8-32r}$$

$$\frac{V_0}{a_0} = M_9\sqrt{\frac{\gamma_tR_t}{\gamma_cR_c}\frac{T_9}{T_0}} \tag{8-32s}$$

$$\frac{F}{\dot{m}_0} = \frac{a_0}{g_c}\left[(1+f)\frac{V_9}{a_0} - M_0 + (1+f)\frac{R_t}{R_c}\frac{T_9/T_0}{V_9/a_0}\frac{1 - P_0/P_9}{\gamma_c}\right] \tag{8-32t}$$

$$F = \dot{m}_0\left(\frac{F}{\dot{m}_0}\right) \tag{8-32u}$$

$$S = \frac{f}{F/\dot{m}_0} \tag{8-32v}$$

$$\eta_T = \frac{a_0^2[(1+f)(V_9/a_0)^2 - M_0^2]}{2g_cfh_{PR}} \tag{8-32w}$$

$$\eta_P = \frac{2g_cV_0(F/\dot{m}_0)}{a_0^2[(1+f)(V_0/a_0)^2 - M_0^2]} \tag{8-32x}$$

$$\eta_P = \eta_P\eta_T \tag{8-32y}$$

$$\frac{N}{N_R} = \sqrt{\frac{T_0\tau_r}{T_{0R}\tau_{rR}}\frac{\pi_c^{(\gamma_c - 1)/\gamma_c} - 1}{\pi_{cR}^{(\gamma_c - 1)/\gamma_c} - 1}} \tag{8-32z}$$

$$\frac{A_9}{A_{9R}} = \left[\frac{P_{t9}/P_9}{(P_{t9}/P_9)_R}\right]^{(\gamma_t + 1)/(2\gamma_t)}\sqrt{\frac{(P_{t9}/P_9)_R^{(\gamma_t - 1)/\gamma_t} - 1}{(P_{t9}/P_9)^{(\gamma_t - 1)/\gamma_t} - 1}} \tag{8-32aa}$$

Example 8-3. We consider the performance of the turbojet engine of Example 7-1 sized for a mass flow rate of 50 kg/sec at the reference condition and altitude of 12 km. We are to determine this engine's performance at an altitude of 9 km, Mach number of 1.5, reduced throttle setting ($T_{t4} = 1670°\text{R}$), and exit to ambient pressure ratio (P_0/P_9) of 0.955.

REFERENCE: $T_0 = 216.7$ K, $\gamma_c = 1.4$, $c_{pc} = 1.004$ kJ/(kg · K), $\gamma_t = 1.3$, $c_{pt} = 1.239$ kJ/(kg · K), $T_{t4} = 1800$ K, $M_0 = 2$, $\pi_c = 10$, $\tau_c = 2.0771$, $\eta_c = 0.8641$, $\tau_t = 0.8155$, $\pi_t = 0.3746$, $\pi_{d\,\max} = 0.95$, $\pi_d = 0.8788$, $\pi_b = 0.94$, $\pi_n = 0.96$, $\eta_b = 0.98$, $\eta_m = 0.99$, $P_0/P_9 = 0.5$, $h_{PR} = 42{,}800$ kJ/kg, $f = 0.03567$, $P_{t9}/P_9 = 11.62$, $F/\dot{m}_0 = 806.9$ N/(kg/sec), $S = 44.21$ (mg/sec)/N, $P_0 = 19.40$ kPa (12 km), $\dot{m}_0 = 50$ kg/sec, $F = \dot{m}_0 \times (F/\dot{m}_0) = 50 \times 806.9 = 40{,}345$ N

OFF-DESIGN CONDITION:
$T_0 = 229.8$ K, $P_0 = 30.8$ kPa (9 km), $M_0 = 1.5$, $P_0/P_9 = 0.955$, $T_{t4} = 1670$ K

EQUATIONS:

$$R_c = \frac{\gamma_c - 1}{\gamma_c} c_{pc} = \frac{0.4}{1.4}(1.004) = 0.2869 \text{ kJ/(kg} \cdot \text{K)}$$

$$R_t = \frac{\gamma_t - 1}{\gamma_t} c_{pt} = \frac{0.3}{1.3}(1.239) = 0.2859 \text{ kJ/(kg} \cdot \text{K)}$$

$$a_0 = \sqrt{\gamma_c R_c g_c T_0} = \sqrt{1.4 \times 286.9 \times 1 \times 229.8} = 303.8 \text{ m/sec}$$

$$V_0 = a_0 M_0 = 303.8 \times 1.5 = 455.7 \text{ m/sec}$$

$$\tau_r = 1 + \frac{\gamma_c - 1}{2} M_0^2 = 1 + 0.2 \times 1.5^2 = 1.45$$

$$\pi_r = \tau^{\gamma_c/(\gamma_c - 1)} = 1.45^{3.5} = 3.671$$

$$\eta_r = 1 - 0.075(M_0 - 1)^{1.35} = 1 - 0.075(0.5)^{1.35} = 0.9706$$

$$\pi_d = \pi_{d\,\max} \eta_r = 0.95 \times 0.9706 = 0.9220$$

$$\tau_\lambda = \frac{c_{pt} T_{t4}}{c_{pc} T_0} = \frac{1.2329 \times 1670}{1.004 \times 229.8} = 8.9682$$

$$T_{t2} = T_0 \tau_r = 229.8 \times 1.45 = 333.2 \text{ K}$$

$$\tau_{rR} = 1 + \frac{\gamma_c - 1}{2} M_{0R}^2 = 1 + 0.2 \times 2^2 = 1.80$$

$$T_{t2R} = T_{0R} \tau_{rR} = 216.7 \times 1.8 = 390.1 \text{ K}$$

$$\pi_{rR} = \tau_{rR}^{\gamma_c/(\gamma_c - 1)} = 1.8^{3.5} = 7.824$$

$$\tau_c = 1 + (\tau_{cR} - 1) \frac{T_{t4}/T_{t2}}{(T_{t4}/T_{t2})_R}$$

$$= 1 + (2.0771 - 1) \frac{1670/333.2}{1800/390.1} = 2.170$$

$$\pi_c = [1 + \eta_c(\tau_c + 1)]^{\gamma_c/(\gamma_c - 1)} = [1 + 0.8641(2.170 - 1)]^{3.5} = 11.53$$

$$f = \frac{\tau_\lambda - \tau_r \tau_c}{h_{PR}\eta_b/(c_{pc}T_0) - \tau_\lambda} = \frac{8.9682 - 1.45 \times 2.170}{42{,}800 \times 0.98/(1.004 \times 229.8) - 8.9682} = 0.03368$$

$$\frac{P_{t9}}{P_9} = \frac{P_0}{P_9}\pi_r \pi_d \pi_c \pi_b \pi_t \pi_n$$

$$= 0.955 \times 3.671 \times 0.9220 \times 11.53 \times 0.94 \times 0.3746 \times 0.96 = 12.60$$

$$M_9 = \sqrt{\frac{2}{\gamma_t - 1}[(P_{t9}/P_9)^{(\gamma_t-1)/\gamma_t} - 1]} = \sqrt{\frac{2}{0.3}(12.60^{0.3/1.3} - 1)} = 2.301$$

$$\frac{T_9}{T_0} = \frac{\tau_\lambda \tau_t}{(P_{t9}/P_9)^{(\gamma_t-1)/\gamma_t}}\frac{c_{pc}}{c_{pt}} = \frac{8.9682 \times 0.8155}{12.60^{0.3/1.3}}\frac{1.004}{1.239} = 3.303$$

$$\frac{V_9}{a_0} = M_9\sqrt{\frac{\gamma_t R_t T_9}{\gamma_c R_c T_0}} = 2.301\sqrt{\frac{1.3 \times 285.9}{1.4 \times 286.9}(3.303)} = 4.023$$

$$\frac{F}{\dot{m}_0} = \frac{a_0}{g_c}\left[(1+f)\frac{V_9}{a_0} - M_0 + (1+f)\frac{R_t}{R_c}\frac{T_9/T_0}{V_9/a_0}\frac{1 - P_0/P_9}{\gamma_c}\right]$$

$$= 303.8\left(1.03368 \times 4.023 - 1.5 + 1.03368\frac{285.9}{286.9}\frac{3.303}{4.023}\frac{0.045}{1.4}\right)$$

$$= 303.8(2.6585 + 0.0272) = 815.9 \text{ N/(kg/sec)}$$

$$S = \frac{f}{F/\dot{m}_0} = \frac{0.03368 \times 10^6}{815.9} = 41.28 \text{ (mg/sec)/N}$$

$$\dot{m}_0 = \dot{m}_{0R}\frac{P_0\pi_r\pi_d\pi_c}{(P_0\pi_r\pi_d\pi_c)_R}\sqrt{\frac{T_{t4R}}{T_{t4}}}$$

$$\dot{m}_0 = 50\frac{30.8 \times 3.671 \times 0.9220 \times 11.53}{19.4 \times 7.824 \times 0.8788 \times 10}\sqrt{\frac{1800}{1670}} = 46.78 \text{ kg/sec}$$

$$F = \dot{m}_0\frac{F}{\dot{m}_0} = 46.78 \times 815.9 = 38{,}170 \text{ N}$$

$$\eta_T = \frac{a_0^2[(1+f)(V_9/a_0)^2 - M_0^2]}{2g_c f h_{PR}} = \frac{303.8^2[(1.03368)(4.023^2) - 1.5^2]}{2 \times 1 \times 0.03368 \times 42{,}800 \times {,}000} = 46.36\%$$

$$\eta_P = \frac{2g_c V_0(F/\dot{m}_0)}{a_0^2[(1+f)(V_9/a_0)^2 - M_0^2]} = \frac{2 \times 1 \times 455.7 \times 815.9}{303.8^2[(1.03368)(4.023^2) - 1.5^2]} = 55.64\%$$

$$\eta_O = \eta_P\eta_T = 0.4635 \times 0.5564 = 25.79\%$$

$$\frac{N}{N_R} = \sqrt{\frac{T_0\pi_r}{T_{0R}\tau_{rR}}\frac{\pi^{(\gamma_c-1)/\gamma_c} - 1}{\pi_{cR}^{(\gamma_c-1)/\gamma_c} - 1}} = \sqrt{\frac{229.8 \times 1.45}{216.7 \times 1.8}\frac{11.53^{0.4/1.4} - 1}{10^{0.4/1.4} - 1}} = 0.9278$$

$$\frac{\dot{m}_{c2}}{\dot{m}_{c2R}} = \frac{\pi_c}{\pi_{cR}}\sqrt{\frac{(T_{t4}/t_{t2})_R}{T_{t4}/T_{t2}}} = \frac{11.53}{10}\sqrt{\frac{1800/390.1}{1670/333.2}} = 1.106$$

$$\frac{A_9}{A_{9R}} = \left[\frac{P_{t9}/P_9}{(P_{t9}/P_9)_R}\right]^{(\gamma_t+1)/(2\gamma_t)} \sqrt{\frac{(P_{t9}/P_9)_R^{(\gamma_t-1)/\gamma_t} - 1}{(P_{t9}/P_9)^{(\gamma_t-1)/\gamma_t} - 1}}$$

$$\frac{A_9}{A_{9R}} = \left(\frac{12.60}{11.62}\right)^{2.3/1.3} \sqrt{\frac{11.62^{0.3/1.3} - 1}{12.60^{0.3/1.3} - 1}} = 1.052$$

Example 8-4. Consider a turbojet engine composed of the gas generator of Example 8-2, an inlet with $\pi_{d\,\max} = 0.99$, and an exhaust nozzle with $\pi_n = 0.99$ and $P_0/P_9 = 1$. The reference engine has the following values:

REFERENCE: $T_0 = 518.7°R$, $\gamma_c = 1.4$, $c_{pc} = 0.24$ Btu/(lbm · °R), $\gamma_t = 1.33$, $c_{pt} = 0.276$ Btu/(lbm · °R), $T_{t4} = 3200°R$, $M_0 = 0$, $\pi_c = 15$, $\eta_c = 0.8572$, $\tau_t = 0.8124$, $\pi_t = 0.3943$, $\pi_{d\,\max} = 0.99$, $\pi_b = 0.96$, $\pi_n = 0.99$, $\eta_b = 0.995$, $\eta_m = 0.99$, $P_0/P_9 = 1$, $P_0 = 14.696$ psia (sea level), $P_{t9}/P_9 = 5.5653$, $\dot{m}_0 = 100$ lbm/sec, $F/\dot{m}_0 = 113.42$ lbf/(lbm/sec), $F = \dot{m}_0 \times (F/\dot{m}_0) = 100 \times 113.42 = 11{,}342$ lbf

This engine has a control system that limits the compressor pressure ratio π_c to 15 and the combustor exit total temperature T_{t4} to 3200°R. Calculation of engine performance using Eqs. (8-32*a*) through (8-32*aa*) with full throttle at altitudes of sea level, 20 kft, and 40 kft over a range of flight Mach numbers gives the results shown in Figs. 8-17 through 8-22. Note the breaks in the plots of thrust, engine mass flow rate, compressor pressure ratio, and station 2 corrected mass flow rate at a Mach/altitude combination of about 0.9/20 kft and 1.3/40 kft. To the left of these breaks, the combustor exit temperature T_{t4} is below its maximum of 3200°R, and the compressor pressure ratio π_c is at its maximum of 15. To the right of these breaks, the combustor exit temperature T_{t4} is at its maximum of 3200°R, and the compressor pressure ratio π_c is below its maximum of 15. At the break, both the compressor pressure ratio and combustor exit temperature are at their maximum values.

The designer of a gas generator's turbomachinery needs to know the maximum power requirements of the compressor and turbine. Since the turbine drives the compressor, the maximum requirements of both occur at the same conditions. Consider the following power balance between the compressor and turbine:

$$\dot{W}_c = \eta_m \dot{W}_t$$

Rewriting turbine power in terms of its mass flow rate, total temperatures, etc., gives

$$\dot{W}_c = \eta_m \dot{m}_0 (1+f) c_{pt} (T_{t4} - T_{t5})$$

or

$$\dot{W}_c = \dot{m}_0 T_{t4} [\eta_m (1+f) c_{pt} (1-\tau_t)]$$

Since the terms within the square braces of the above equation are considered constant, the maximum compressor power will be at the flight condition having maximum engine mass flow rate at maximum T_{t4}. From Fig. 8-19, the maximum compressor or turbine power corresponds to the maximum engine mass flow rate at sea level and Mach 1.4.

At an altitude of 20 kft and a Mach number of 0.8, engine performance calculations at reduced throttle (T_{t4}) using Eqs. (8-32*a*) through (8-32*aa*) were performed, and some of these results are given in Fig. 8-23. The typical variation

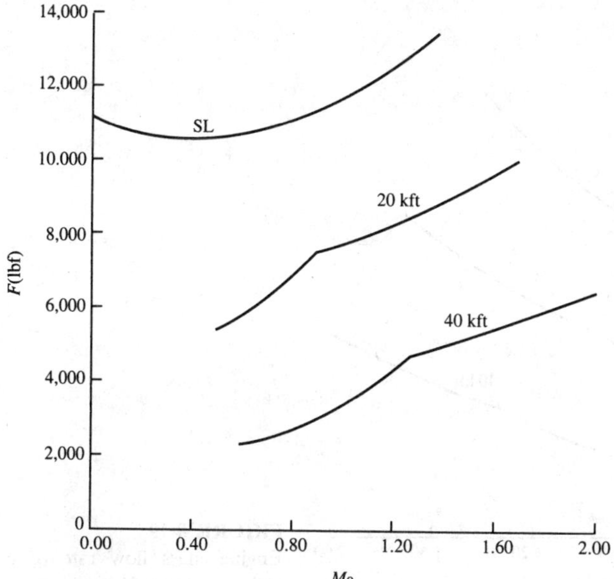

FIGURE 8-17
Maximum thrust F of a turbojet versus M_0.

in thrust specific fuel consumption S with thrust F is shown in this figure. As the throttle is reduced, the thrust specific fuel consumption first reduces before increasing. This plot of thrust specific fuel consumption S versus thrust F is commonly called the *throttle hook* because of its shape.

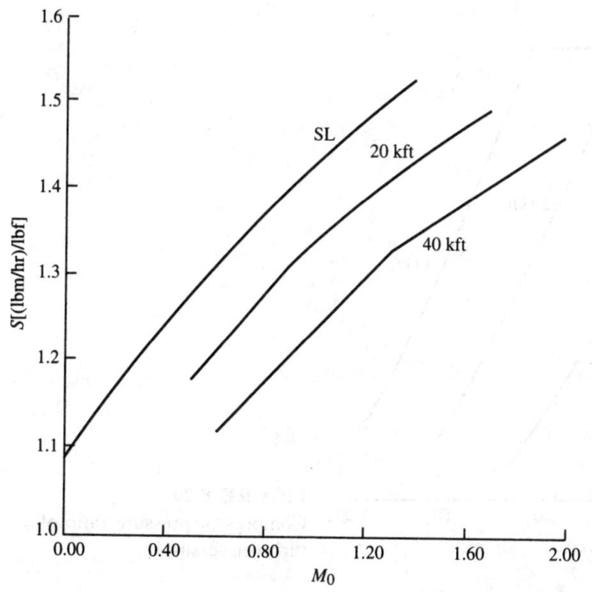

FIGURE 8-18
Thrust specific fuel consumption S of a turbojet versus M_0.

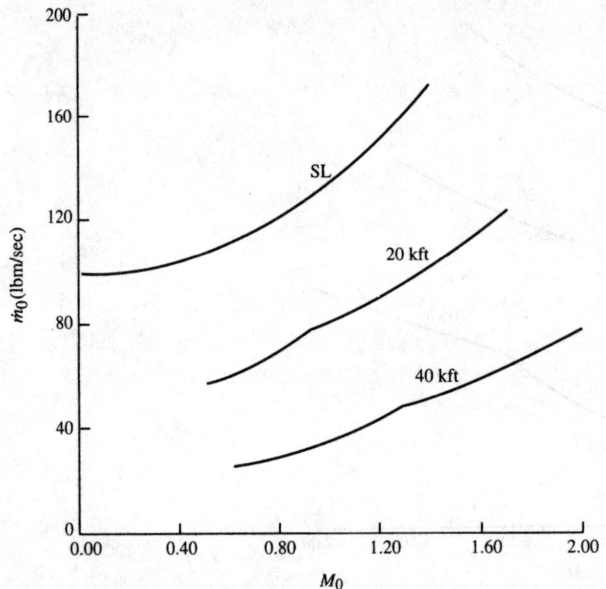

FIGURE 8-19
Engine mass flow rate of a turbojet versus M_0.

We stated at the beginning of this chapter that the principal efficiencies that affect engine performance are the thermal efficiency and the propulsive efficiency. Figure 8-23 shows the very large changes in both propulsive and thermal efficiency with engine thrust. Note that as thrust is reduced from its maximum, the increase in propulsive efficiency more than offsets the decrease in

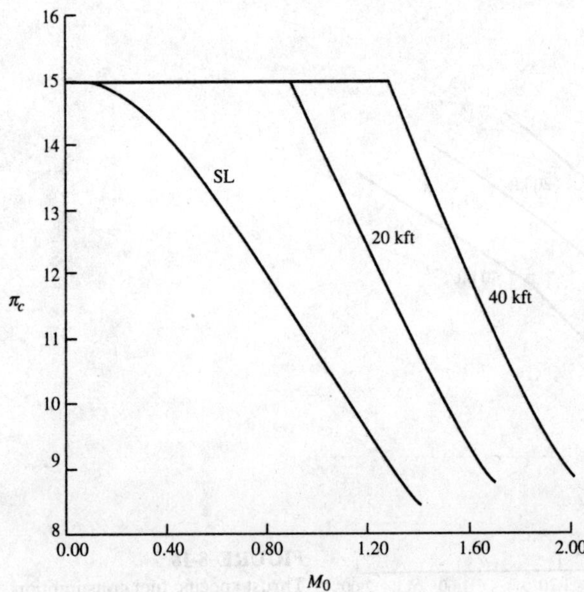

FIGURE 8-20
Compressor pressure ratio of a turbojet versus M_0.

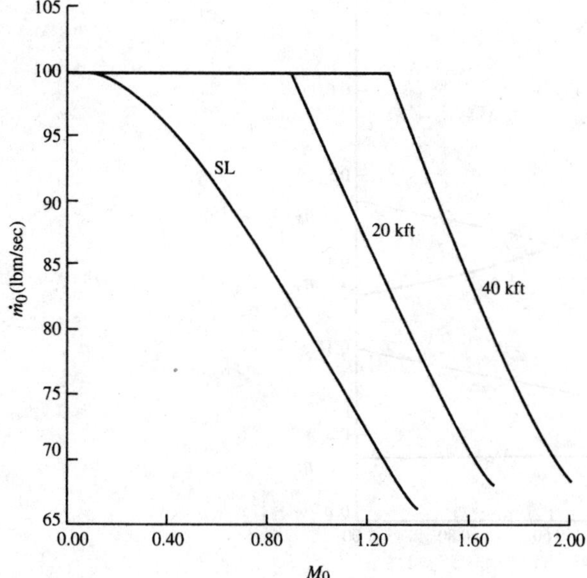

FIGURE 8-21
Compressor corrected mass flow rate of a turbojet versus M_0.

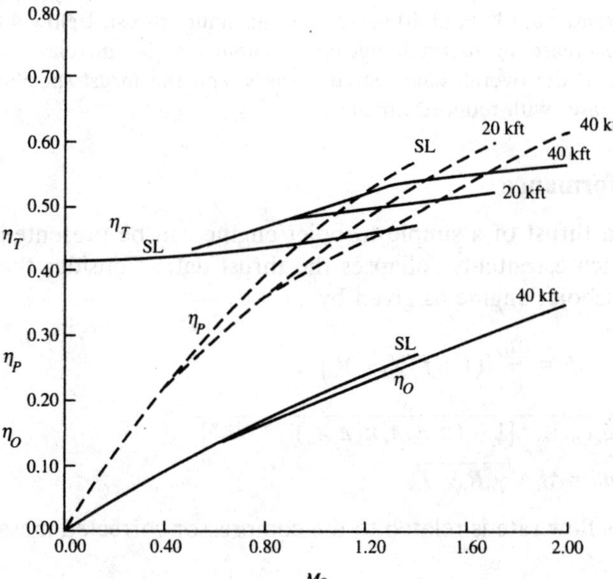

FIGURE 8-22
Turbojet efficiencies versus M_0.

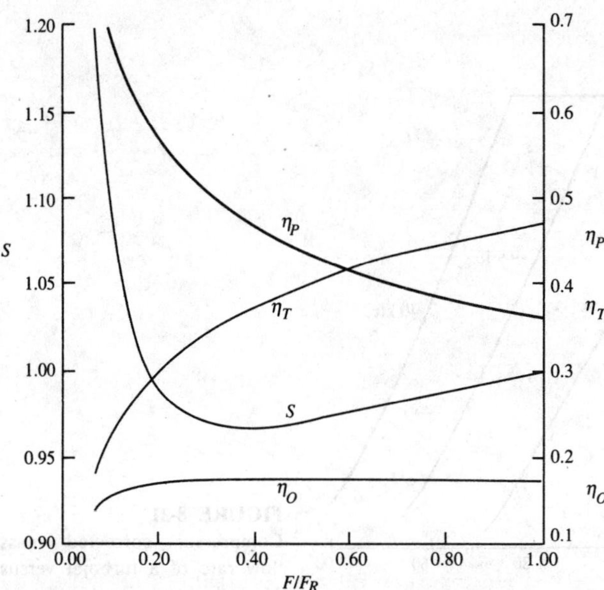

FIGURE 8-23
Turbojet performance at partial throttle.

thermal efficiency such that the overall efficiency increases and the thrust specific fuel consumption decreases until about 40 percent of maximum thrust. Below 40 percent thrust, the decrease in thermal efficiency dominates the increase in propulsive efficiency and the overall efficiency decreases, and the thrust specific fuel consumption increases with reduced thrust.

Corrected Engine Performance

The changes in maximum thrust of a simple turbojet engine can be presented in a corrected format which essentially collapses the thrust data. Consider the thrust equation for the turbojet engine as given by

$$F = \frac{\dot{m}_0}{g_c}[(1+f)V_9 - V_0]$$

where $$V_9 = \sqrt{2g_c c_{pt} T_{t4} \tau_t [1 - (\pi_r \pi_d \pi_c \pi_b \pi_t \pi_n)^{-(\gamma_t - 1)/\gamma_t}]}$$

and $$V_0 = M_0 a_0 = M_0 \sqrt{\gamma_c R_c g_c T_0}$$

Note that the engine mass flow rate is related to the compressor corrected mass flow rate by

$$\dot{m}_0 = \dot{m}_{c0} \frac{\delta_0}{\sqrt{\theta_0}} = \dot{m}_{c2} \frac{\delta_2}{\sqrt{\theta_2}} = \dot{m}_{c2} \frac{\pi_d \delta_0}{\sqrt{\theta_0}}$$

The engine thrust can now be written as

$$F = \frac{\dot{m}_{c2}}{g_c}\frac{\pi_d \delta_0}{\sqrt{\theta_0}}[(1+f)V_9 - V_0]$$

Dividing the thrust by the dimensionless total pressure at station 0 gives

$$\boxed{\frac{F}{\delta_0} = \frac{\dot{m}_{c2}\pi_d}{g_c}\left[(1+f)\frac{V_9}{\sqrt{\theta_0}} - \frac{V_0}{\sqrt{\theta_0}}\right]} \tag{8-33a}$$

where
$$\frac{V_9}{\sqrt{\theta_0}} = \sqrt{\frac{T_{t4}}{T_{t2}}}\sqrt{2g_c c_{pt} T_{SL}\tau_t[1 - (\pi_r \pi_d \pi_c \pi_b \pi_t \pi_n)^{-(\gamma_t - 1)/\gamma_t}]} \tag{8-33b}$$

and
$$\frac{V_0}{\sqrt{\theta_0}} = \frac{M_0}{\sqrt{\tau_r}} a_{SL} \tag{8-33c}$$

The maximum thrust for the turbojet engine of Example 8-4 can be determined by using the above equations. Figures 8-17, 8-20, and 8-21 show the variation of the maximum thrust F, compressor pressure ratio, and corrected mass flow rate from this turbojet engine at full throttle versus flight Mach number M_0. The corrected thrust F/δ_0 of this engine is plotted versus flight condition θ_0 in Fig. 8-24. The variation of T_{t4}/T_{t2}, compressor pressure ratio, corrected mass flow rate, and corrected fuel flow rate are plotted versus θ_0 in

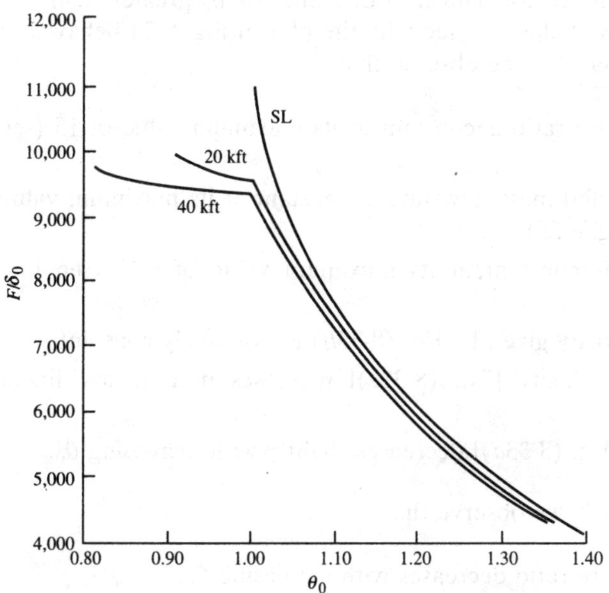

FIGURE 8-24
Maximum corrected thrust (F/δ_0) of a turbojet versus θ_0.

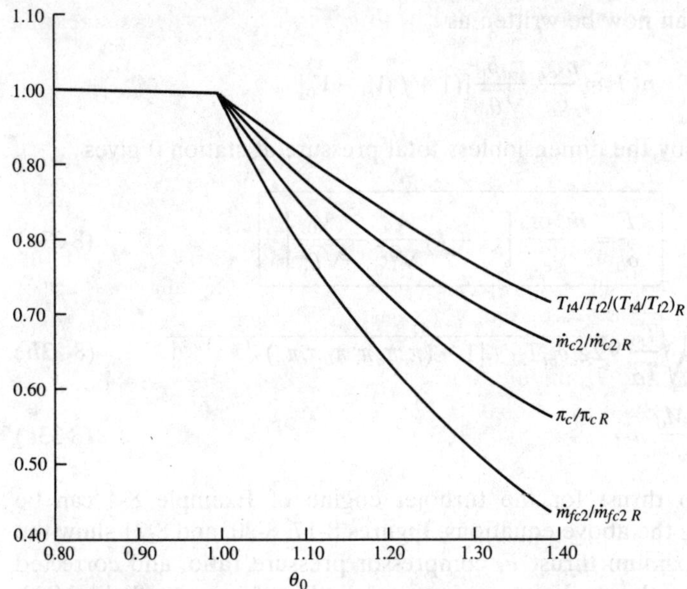

FIGURE 8-25
Maximum throttle characteristics of a turbojet versus θ_0.

Fig. 8-25. The representation of the engine thrust, as corrected thrust versus θ_0, essentially collapses the thrust data into one line for θ_0 greater than 1.0. The discussion that follows helps one see why the plot in Fig. 8-24 behaves as shown. When θ_0 is less than 1.0, we observe that

1. The compressor pressure ratio is constant at its maximum value of 15 (see Fig. 8-25).
2. The compressor corrected mass flow rate is constant at its maximum value of 100 lbm/sec (see Fig. 8-25).
3. The value of T_{t4}/T_{t2} is constant at its maximum value of 6.17 (see Fig. 8-15).
4. The corrected exit velocity given by Eq. (8-33*b*) is essentially constant.
5. The corrected flight velocity [Eq. (8-33*c*)] increases in a nearly linear manner with M_0.
6. The corrected thrust [Eq. (8-33*a*)] decreases slightly with increasing θ_0.

When θ_0 is greater than 1.0, we observe that

1. The compressor pressure ratio decreases with increasing θ_0.
2. The compressor corrected mass flow rate decreases with increasing θ_0.
3. The value of T_{t4} is constant at its maximum value of 3200°R.

4. The corrected exit velocity given by Eq. (8-33*b*) decreases with increasing θ_0.
5. The corrected flight velocity [Eq. (8-33*c*)] increases in a nearly linear manner with M_0.
6. The corrected thrust [Eq. (8-33*a*)] decreases substantially with increasing θ_0.

As shown in Fig. 8-24, the trend in maximum corrected thrust F/δ_0 of this turbojet dramatically changes at the θ_0 value of 1.0. Both the compressor pressure ratio π_c and combustor exit temperature T_{t4} are at their maximum values when θ_0 is 1.0. The engine control system varies the fuel flow to the combustor to keep π_c and T_{t4} under control. The control system maintains π_c at its maximum for θ_0 values less than 1.0, and T_{t4} at its maximum for θ_0 values greater than 1.0. These same kinds of trends are observed for many other gas turbine aircraft engines.

The thrust specific fuel consumption S of this turbojet at maximum thrust is plotted versus Mach number in Fig. 8-18. If the values of S are divided by the square root of the corrected ambient temperature, then the curves for higher altitudes are shifted up and we get Fig. 8-26. Note that these curves could be estimated by a straight line. Equations (1-36*a*) through (1-36*f*) are based on this nearly linear relationship with flight Mach number M_0. When the

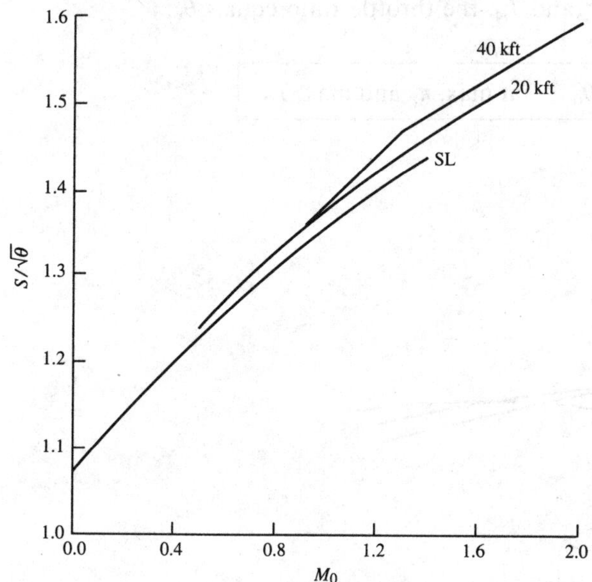

FIGURE 8-26
$S/\sqrt{\theta}$ of a turbojet versus M_0.

corrected thrust specific fuel consumption [S_c, see Eq. (8-8)] is plotted versus θ_0, the spread in fuel consumption data is substantially reduced, as shown in Fig. 8-27. One could estimate that the corrected thrust specific fuel consumption has a value of about 1.24 for most flight conditions.

Throttle Ratio

The *throttle ratio* (TR) is defined as the ratio of the maximum value of T_{t4} to the value of T_{t4} at sea-level static (SLS) conditions. In equation form, the throttle ratio is

$$\boxed{\mathrm{TR} \equiv \frac{(T_{t4})_{\max}}{(T_{t4})_{\mathrm{SLS}}}} \tag{8-34}$$

The throttle ratio for the simple turbojet engine and compressor of Figs. 8-17 through 8-27 has a value of 1.0. Both the compressor performance and engine performance curves change shape at a θ_0 value of 1.0. This change in shape of the performance curves occurs at the simultaneous maximum of π_c and T_{t4}. The fact that both the throttle ratio and dimensionless total temperature θ_0 have a value of 1.0 at the simultaneous maximum is not a coincidence but is a direct result of compressor-turbine power balance given by Eq. (8-17). At the simultaneous maximum of π_c and T_{t4}, the throttle ratio equals θ_0:

$$\boxed{\mathrm{TR} = \theta_0 \qquad \text{at max. } \pi_c \text{ and max. } T_{t4}}$$

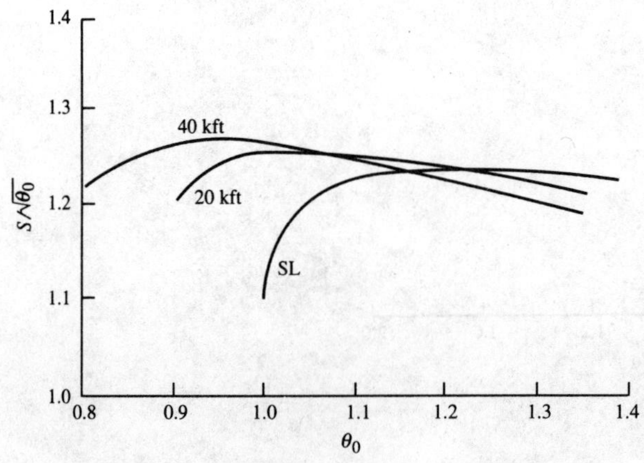

FIGURE 8-27
$S/\sqrt{\theta_0}$ of a turbojet versus θ_0.

High-performance fighters want gas turbine engines whose thrust does not drop off as fast with increasing θ_0 as that of Fig. 8-24. The value of θ_0, where the corrected maximum thrust F/δ_0 curves change slope, can be increased by increasing the maximum T_{t4} of the above example turbojet engine.

Example 8-5. Again, we consider the example turbojet engine with a compressor that has a compressor pressure ratio of 15 and corrected mass flow rate of 100 lbm/sec for T_{t2} of 518.7°R and T_{t4} of 3200°R. The maximum π_c is maintained at 15, and the maximum T_{t4} is increased from 3200 to 3360°R (TR = 1.05). The variation in thrust, thrust specific fuel consumption, compressor pressure ratio, and corrected mass flow rate of this turbojet engine at full throttle are plotted versus flight Mach number M_0 in Figs. 8-28, 8-29, 8-30, and 8-31, respectively. Figure 8-32 shows the corrected thrust F/δ_0 plotted versus θ_0. Comparing Figs. 8-17 and 8-28, we note that the thrust of both engines are the same at sea level static, and the engine with a throttle ratio of 1.05 has higher thrust at high Mach numbers. Figures 8-24 and 8-32 show that changing the throttle ratio from 1.0 to 1.05 changes the θ_0 value at which the curves change shape and increases the corrected thrust at θ_0 values greater than 1.0.

Since the compressor and turbine are connected to the same shaft, they have the same rotational speed N, and we can write the following relationship between their corrected speeds:

$$N_{c2} = 1/\sqrt{T_{\text{ref}}}\sqrt{T_{t4}/\theta_0}\,N_{c4} \tag{8-35}$$

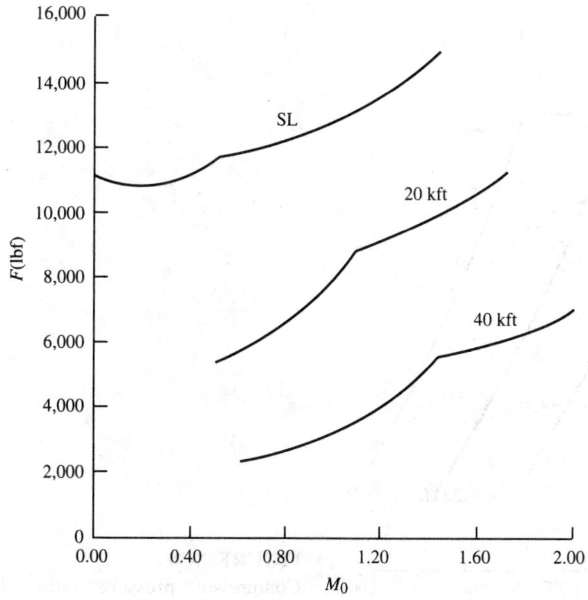

FIGURE 8-28
Maximum thrust F of improved turbojet versus M_0.

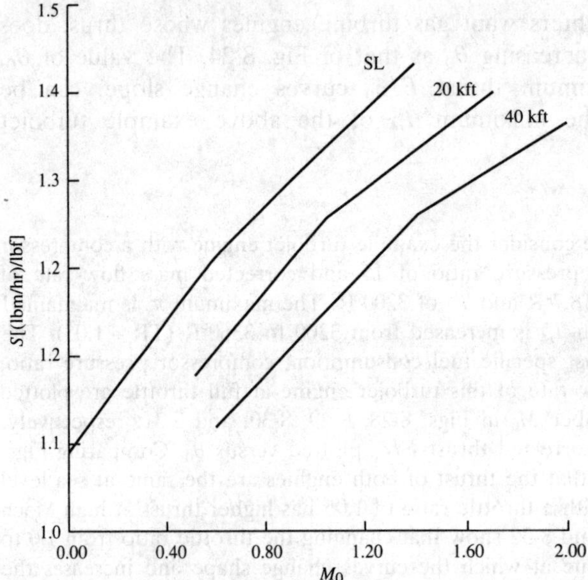

FIGURE 8-29
Thrust specific fuel consumption S of improved turbojet versus M_0.

Recall that for constant turbine efficiency and choked flow at stations 4 and 8, the correct turbine speed N_{c4} was found to be constant. For maximum thrust engine conditions where θ_0 is less than the throttle ratio, the corrected rotational speed of the compressor N_{c2} and the ratio T_{t4}/θ_0 are constant. Equation (8-35) shows that the corrected speed of the turbine N_{c4} must also be constant at these engine conditions. At $\theta_0 = \text{TR}$, T_{t4} is maximum, the corrected rotational speed of the

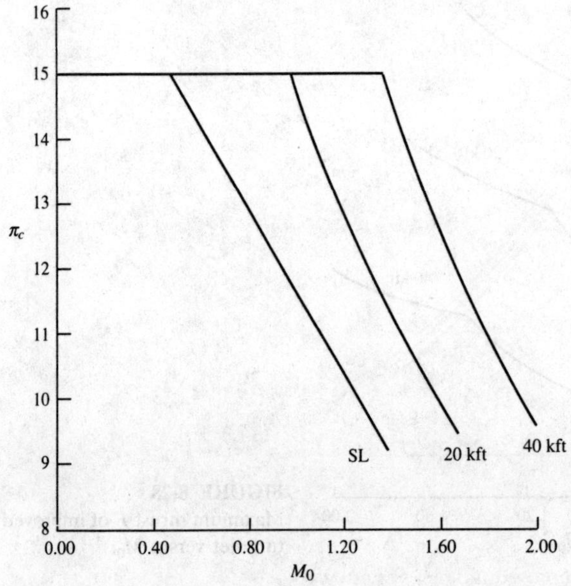

FIGURE 8-30
Compressor pressure ratio of improved turbojet versus M_0.

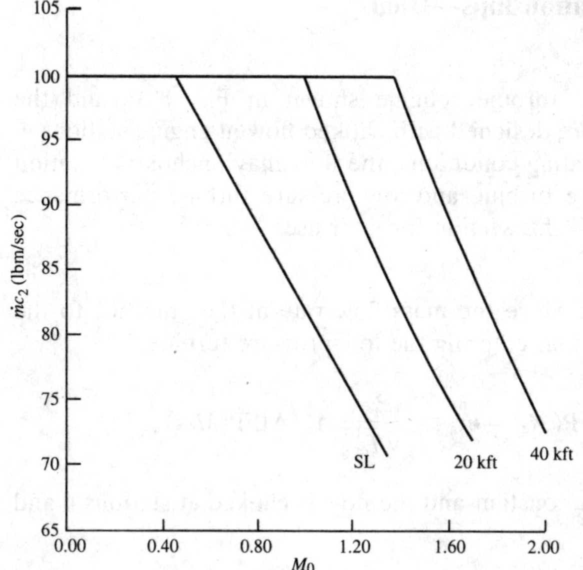

FIGURE 8-31
Compressor corrected mass flow rate of improved turbojet versus M_0.

compressor N_{c2} is constant, and the shaft rotational speed N increases by the square root of θ_0. Thus an engine with a throttle ratio of 1.05 can have a shaft rotational speed at $\theta_0 = \text{TR}$ that is 1.0247 times the maximum speed at sea-level static conditions. This is commonly referred to as an *overspeed* of 2.47 percent.

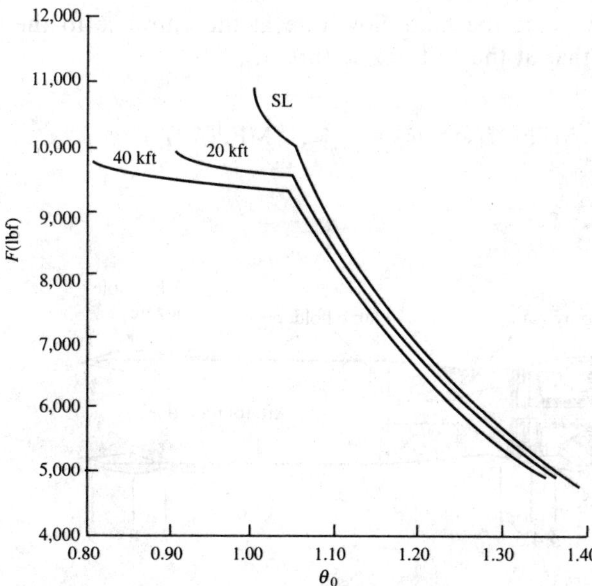

FIGURE 8-32
Maximum corrected thrust F/δ_0 of improved turbojet versus θ_0.

Turbine Performance Relationships—Dual-Spool Engines

Two-spool engines, like the turbojet engine shown in Fig. 8-33 and the turbofan engine of Fig. 8-1, are designed with choked flow at engine stations 4, 4.5, and 8. Under some operating conditions, the flow may unchoke at station 8. The resulting high-pressure turbine and low-pressure turbine performance relationships are developed in this section for later use.

HIGH-PRESSURE TURBINE. Since the mass flow rate at the entrance to the high-pressure turbine equals that entering the low-pressure turbine,

$$\dot{m}_4 = \frac{P_{t4}}{\sqrt{T_{t4}}} A_4 \,\text{MFP}(M_4) = \dot{m}_{4.5} = \frac{P_{t4.5}}{\sqrt{T_{t4.5}}} A_{4.5} \,\text{MFP}(M_{4.5})$$

We assume that the areas are constant and the flow is choked at stations 4 and 4.5. Then

$$\frac{P_{t4}/P_{t4.5}}{\sqrt{T_{t4}/T_{t4.5}}} = \frac{\pi_{tH}}{\sqrt{\tau_{tH}}} = \text{const}$$

Thus for constant η_{tH}, we have

$$\boxed{\text{Constant values of } \pi_{tH},\ \tau_{tH},\ \dot{m}_{c4},\ \text{and } \dot{m}_{c4.5}} \qquad (8\text{-}36)$$

LOW-PRESSURE TURBINE. Since the mass flow rate at the entrance to the low-pressure turbine equals that at the exit nozzle throat,

$$\dot{m}_{4.5} = \frac{P_{t4.5}}{\sqrt{T_{t4.5}}} A_{4.5} \,\text{MFP}(M_{4.5}) = \dot{m}_8 = \frac{P_{t8}}{\sqrt{T_{t8}}} A_8 \,\text{MFP}(M_8)$$

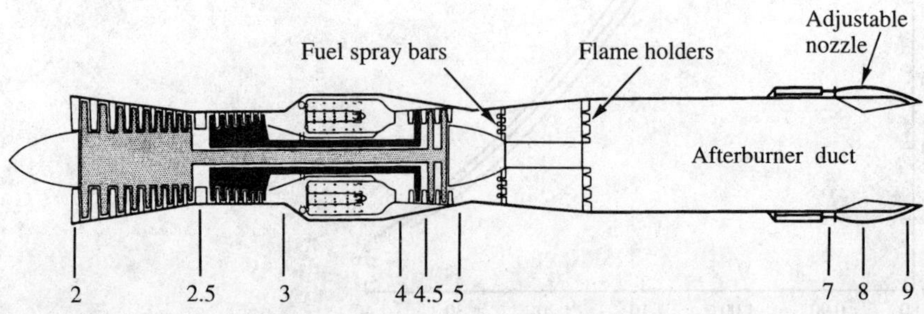

FIGURE 8-33
Dual-spool afterburning turbojet engine. (*Courtesy of Pratt & Whitney.*)

We assume that the areas are constant at stations 4.5 and 8 and the flow is choked at station 4.5, so

$$\frac{P_{t4.5}/P_{t5}}{\sqrt{T_{t4.5}/T_{t8}}}\frac{1}{\text{MFP}(M_8)}=\frac{\pi_{tL}/\sqrt{\tau_{tL}}}{\text{MFP}(M_8)}=\frac{A_8\pi_{\text{AB}}}{A_{4.5}\,\text{MFP}(M_{4.5})}$$

Using the reference condition to evaluate the constant on the right-hand side of the above equation gives

$$\boxed{\pi_{tL}=\pi_{tL\,R}\sqrt{\frac{\tau_{tL}}{\tau_{tL\,R}}}\frac{\text{MFP}(M_{8\,R})}{\text{MFP}(M_8)}} \tag{8-37}$$

where

$$\boxed{\tau_{tL}=1-\eta_{tL}(1-\pi_{tL}^{(\gamma_t-1)/\gamma_t})} \tag{8-38}$$

If station 8 is choked at the reference condition and at the current operating point, then π_{tL} and τ_{tL} are constant.

8-4 TURBOJET ENGINE WITH AFTERBURNING

The dual-spool afterburning turbojet engine (Fig. 8-33) is normally designed with choked flow at stations 4, 4.5, and 8. For the afterburning turbojet engine, the variable-area exhaust nozzle is controlled by the engine control system so that the upstream turbomachinery is unaffected by the afterburner operation. In other words, the exhaust nozzle throat area A_8 is controlled during afterburner operation such that the turbine exit conditions (P_{t5}, T_{t5}, and M_5) remain constant. Since the exhaust nozzle has choked flow at its throat at all operating conditions of interest, Eqs. (8-37) and (8-38) for constant efficiency of the low-pressure turbine require that π_{tL} and τ_{tL} be constant:

$$\boxed{\text{Constant values of } \pi_{tL} \text{ and } \tau_{tL}} \tag{8-39}$$

This engine has six independent variables (T_{t4}, T_{t7}, M_0, T_0, P_0, and P_0/P_9) and nine dependent variables. These performance analysis variables are summarized in Table 8-5.

HIGH-PRESSURE COMPRESSOR (τ_{cH}, π_{cH}). The power balance between the high-pressure turbine and the high-pressure compressor (high-pressure spool) gives

$$\eta_{mH}\dot{m}_4c_{pt}(T_{t4}-T_{t4.5})=\dot{m}_2c_{pc}(T_{t3}-T_{t2.5})$$

TABLE 8-5
Performance analysis variables for dual-spool afterburning turbojet engine

Component	Variables		
	Independent	Constant or known	Dependent
Engine	M_0, T_0, P_0		$\dot{m}_0$
Diffuser		$\pi_d = f(M_0)$	
Fan		η_{cL}	π_{cL}, τ_{cL}
High-pressure compressor		η_{cH}	π_{cH}, τ_{cH}
Burner	T_{t4}	π_b, η_b	f
High-pressure turbine		π_{tH}, τ_{tH}	
Low-pressure turbine		π_{tL}, τ_{tL}	
Afterburner	T_{t7}	π_{AB}, η_{AB}	f_{AB}
Nozzle	$\dfrac{P_9}{P_0}$	π_n	M_9, $\dfrac{T_9}{T_0}$
Total number	6		9

Rewriting this equation in terms of temperature ratios, rearranging into variable and constant terms, and equating the constant to reference values give

$$\frac{\tau_r \tau_{cL}(\tau_{cH} - 1)}{T_{t4}/T_0} = \eta_{mH}(1+f)(1-\tau_{tH}) = \left[\frac{\tau_r \tau_{cL}(\tau_{cH} - 1)}{T_{t4}/T_0}\right]_R$$

Solving for τ_{cH} gives

$$\boxed{\tau_{cH} = 1 + \frac{T_{t4}/T_0}{(T_{t4}/T_0)_R} \frac{(\tau_r \tau_{cL})_R}{\tau_r \tau_{cL}} (\tau_{cH} - 1)_R} \tag{8-40}$$

From the definition of compressor efficiency, π_{cH} is given by

$$\boxed{\pi_{cH} = [1 + \eta_{cH}(\tau_{cH} - 1)]^{\gamma_c/(\gamma_c - 1)}} \tag{8-41}$$

LOW-PRESSURE COMPRESSOR (τ_{cL}, π_{cL}). From a power balance between the low-pressure compressor and low-pressure turbine, we get

$$\eta_{mL}\dot{m}_{4.5}c_{pt}(T_{t4.5} - T_{t5}) = \dot{m}_2 c_{pc}(T_{t2.5} - T_{t2})$$

Rewriting this equation in terms of temperature ratios, rearranging into variable and constant terms, and equating the constant to reference values give

$$\frac{\tau_r(\tau_{cL} - 1)}{T_{t4}/T_0} = \eta_{mL}(1+f)\tau_{tH}(1-\tau_{tL}) = \left[\frac{\tau_r(\tau_{cl} - 1)}{T_{t4}/T_0}\right]_R$$

Solving for τ_{cL} gives

$$\tau_{cL} = 1 + \frac{T_{t4}/T_0}{(T_{t4}/T_0)_R} \frac{(\tau_r)_R}{\tau_r} (\tau_{cL} - 1)_R \tag{8-42}$$

where

$$\pi_{cL} = [1 + \eta_{cL}(\tau_{cL} - 1)]^{\gamma_c/(\gamma_c - 1)} \tag{8-43}$$

Mass Flow Rate

Since

$$\dot{m}_4 = \dot{m}_0 + \dot{m}_f = \dot{m}_0(1 + f)$$

and

$$\dot{m}_4 = \frac{P_{t4}}{\sqrt{T_{t4}}} A_4 \,\text{MFP}(M_4)$$

thus

$$\dot{m}_0 = \frac{P_{t4}}{\sqrt{T_{t4}}} \frac{A_4 \,\text{MFP}(M_4)}{1 + f} = \frac{P_0 \pi_r \pi_d \pi_{cL} \pi_{cH} \pi_b}{\sqrt{T_{t4}}} \frac{A_4 \,\text{MFP}(M_4)}{1 + f}$$

For A_4, M_4, $1 + f$, and π_b essentially constant, the above expression can be rewritten as

$$\frac{\dot{m}_0 \sqrt{T_{t4}}}{P_0 \pi_r \pi_d \pi_{cL} \pi_{cH}} = \frac{\pi_b A_4 \,\text{MFP}(M_4)}{1 + f} = \left(\frac{\dot{m}_0 \sqrt{T_{t4}}}{P_0 \pi_r \pi_d \pi_{cL} \pi_{cH}}\right)_R$$

or

$$\frac{\dot{m}_0}{\dot{m}_{0R}} = \frac{P_0 \pi_r \pi_d \pi_{cL} \pi_{cH}}{(P_0 \pi_r \pi_d \pi_{cl} \pi_{cH})_R} \sqrt{\frac{T_{t4R}}{T_{t4}}} \tag{8-44}$$

Summary of Performance Equations—Turbojet with and without Afterburner

INPUTS:

Choices

Flight parameters:	M_0, T_0 (K, °R), P_0 (kPa, psia)
Throttle setting:	T_{t4} (K, °R), T_{t7} (K, °R)
Exhaust nozzle setting:	P_0/P_9

Design constants

π's:	$\pi_{d\,\max}$, π_b, π_{tH}, π_{tL}, π_{AB}, π_n
τ's:	τ_{tH}, τ_{tL}
η's:	η_{cL}, η_{cH}, η_b, η_{AB}, η_{mH}, η_{mL}
Gas properties:	γ_c, γ_t, γ_{AB}, c_{pc}, c_{pt}, c_{pAB} [kJ/(kg · K), Btu/(lbm · °R)]
Fuel:	h_{PR} (kJ/kg, Btu/lbm)

Reference conditions

Flight parameters:	M_{0R}, T_{0R} (K, °R), P_{0R} (kPa, psia) τ_{rR}, π_{rR}
Throttle setting:	τ_{t4R} (K, °R)
Component behavior:	τ_{dR}, π_{cLR}, π_{cHR}, τ_{cLR}, τ_{cHR}

OUTPUTS:

Overall performance:	F (N, lbf), $\dot{m}_0$ (kg/sec, lbm/sec), f_O, $S\left(\frac{\text{mg/sec}}{\text{N}}, \frac{\text{lbm/hr}}{\text{lbf}}\right)$, η_P, η_T, η_O
Component behavior:	π_{cL}, π_{cH}, τ_{cL}, τ_{cH}, f, f_{AB}, M_9, $(N/N_R)_{\text{LPspool}}$, $(N/N_r)_{\text{HPspool}}$

EQUATIONS:

$$R_c = \frac{\gamma_c - 1}{\gamma_c} c_{pc} \tag{8-45a}$$

$$R_t = \frac{\gamma_t - 1}{\gamma_t} c_{pt} \tag{8-45b}$$

$$a_0 = \sqrt{\gamma_c R_c g_c T_0} \tag{8-45c}$$

$$V_0 = a_0 M_0 \tag{8-45d}$$

$$\tau_r = 1 + \frac{\gamma_c - 1}{2} M_0^2 \tag{8-45e}$$

$$\pi_r = \tau_r^{\gamma_c/(\gamma_c - 1)} \tag{8-45f}$$

$$\eta_r = 1 \qquad \text{for } M_0 \leq 1 \tag{8-45g}$$

$$\eta_r = 1 - 0.075(M_0 - 1)^{1.35} \qquad \text{for } M_0 > 1 \tag{8-45h}$$

$$\pi_d = \tau_{d\,\max} \eta_r \tag{8-45i}$$

$$\tau_{cL} = 1 + \frac{T_{t4}/T_0}{(T_{t4}/T_0)_R} \frac{(\tau_r)_R}{\tau_r} (\tau_{cL} - 1)_R \tag{8-45j}$$

$$\pi_{cL} = [1 + \eta_{cL}(\tau_{cL} - 1)]^{\gamma_c/(\gamma_c - 1)} \tag{8-45k}$$

$$\tau_{cH} = 1 + \frac{T_{t4}/T_0}{(T_{t4}/t_0)_R} \frac{(\tau_r \tau_{cL})_R}{\tau_r \tau_{cL}} (\tau_{cH} - 1)_R \tag{8-45l}$$

$$\pi_{cH} = [1 + \eta_{cH}(\tau_{cH} - 1)]^{\gamma_c/(\gamma_c - 1)} \tag{8-45m}$$

$$\tau_\lambda = \frac{c_{pt} T_{t4}}{c_{pc} T_0} \tag{8-45n}$$

$$f = \frac{\tau_\lambda - \tau_r \tau_{cL} \tau_{cH}}{h_{PR} \eta_b / (c_{pc} T_0) - \tau_\lambda} \tag{8-45o}$$

$$\dot{m}_0 = \dot{m}_{0R} \frac{P_0 \pi_r \pi_d \pi_{cL} \pi_{cH}}{(P_0 \pi_r \pi_d \pi_{cL} \pi_{cH})_R} \sqrt{\frac{T_{t4R}}{T_{t4}}} \tag{8-45p}$$

Without afterburner:

$$R_{AB} = R_t \qquad c_{pAB} = c_{pt} \qquad \gamma_{AB} = \gamma_t \qquad T_{t7} = T_{t4} \tau_{tH} \tau_{tL} \qquad \pi_{AB} = 1 \qquad f_{AB} = 0 \tag{8-45q}$$

With afterburner:

$$R_{AB} = \frac{\gamma_{AB} - 1}{\gamma_{AB}} c_{pAB} \tag{8-45r}$$

$$\tau_{\lambda AB} = \frac{c_{pAB} T_{t7}}{c_{pc} T_0} \tag{8-45s}$$

$$f_{AB} = \frac{\tau_{\lambda AB} - \tau_\lambda \tau_{tH} \tau_{tL}}{h_{PR} \eta_{AB} — (c_{pc} T_0) - \tau_{\lambda AB}} \tag{8-45t}$$

Remainder of equations:

$$\frac{P_{t9}}{P_9} = \frac{P_0}{P_9} \pi_r \pi_d \pi_{cL} \pi_{cH} \pi_b \pi_{tH} \pi_{tL} \pi_{AB} \pi_n \tag{8-45u}$$

$$M_9 = \sqrt{\frac{2}{\gamma_{AB} - 1}\left[\left(\frac{P_{t9}}{P_9}\right)^{(\gamma_{AB}-1)/\gamma_{AB}} - 1\right]} \tag{8-45v}$$

$$\frac{T_9}{T_0} = \frac{T_{t7}/T_0}{(P_{t9}/P_9)^{(\gamma_{AB}-1)\gamma_{AB}}} \tag{8-45w}$$

$$\frac{V_9}{a_0} = M_9 \sqrt{\frac{\gamma_{AB} R_{AB}}{\gamma_c R_c} \frac{T_9}{T_0}} \tag{8-45x}$$

$$f_O = f + f_{AB} \tag{8-45y}$$

$$\frac{F}{\dot{m}_0} = \frac{a_0}{g_c}\left[(1 + f_O)\frac{V_9}{a_0} - M_0 + (1 + f_O)\frac{R_{AB}}{R_c} \frac{T_9/T_0}{V_9/a_0} \frac{1 - P_0/P_9}{\gamma_c}\right] \tag{8-45z}$$

$$F = \dot{m}_0\left(\frac{F}{\dot{m}_0}\right) \tag{8-45aa}$$

$$S = \frac{f_O}{F/\dot{m}_0} \tag{8-45ab}$$

$$\eta_T = \frac{a_0^2[(1 + f_O)(V_0/a_0)^2 - M_0^2]}{2 g_c f_O h_{PR}} \tag{8-45ac}$$

$$\eta_P = \frac{2 g_c V_0 (F/\dot{m}_0)}{a_0^2[(1 + f_O)(V_9/a_0)^2 - M_0^2]} \tag{8-45ad}$$

$$\eta_O = \eta_P \eta_T \tag{8-45ae}$$

$$\left(\frac{N}{N_R}\right)_{\text{LP spool}} = \sqrt{\frac{T_0 \tau_r}{T_{0R} \tau_{rR}} \frac{\pi_{cL}^{(\gamma-1)/\gamma} - 1}{\pi_{cLR}^{(\gamma-1)/\gamma} - 1}} \tag{8-45af}$$

$$\left(\frac{N}{N_R}\right)_{\text{HP spool}} = \sqrt{\frac{T_0 \tau_r \tau_{cL}}{T_{0R} \tau_{rR} \tau_{cLR}} \frac{\pi_{cH}^{(\gamma-1)/\gamma} - 1}{\pi_{cHR}^{(\gamma-1)/\gamma} - 1}} \tag{8-45ag}$$

$$\frac{A_9}{A_{9R}} = \left[\frac{P_{t9}/P_9}{(P_{t9}/P_9)_R}\right]^{(\gamma_t+1)/(2\gamma_t)} \sqrt{\frac{(P_{t9}/P_9)_R^{(\gamma_t-1)/\gamma_t} - 1}{(P_{t9}/P_9)^{(\gamma_t-1)/\gamma_t} - 1}} \tag{8-45ah}$$

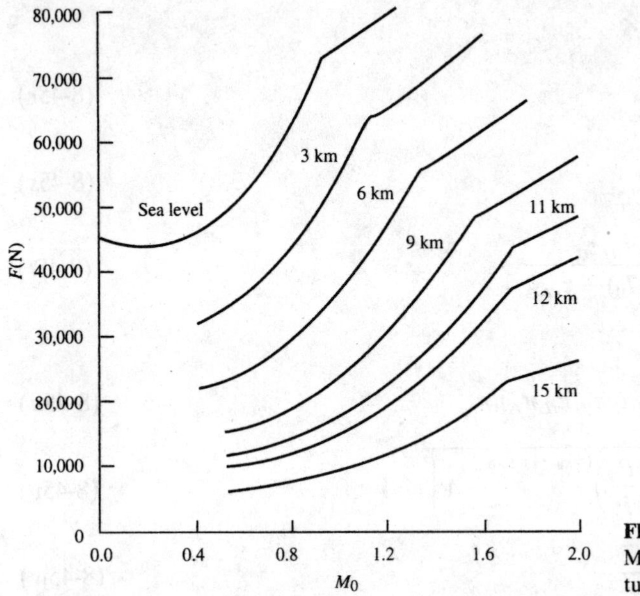

FIGURE 8-34
Maximum thrust of dry turbojet.

Example 8-6. In this example, we consider the variation in engine performance of the dry turbojet in Example 8-3 with Mach number M_0, altitude, ambient temperature T_0, ambient pressure P_0, and throttle setting T_{t4}. The compressor pressure ratio is limited to 12.3, and the combustor exit temperature T_{t4} is limited to 1800 K. Figures 8-34, 8-35, 8-36, 8-37, and 8-38 show the variations of thrust,

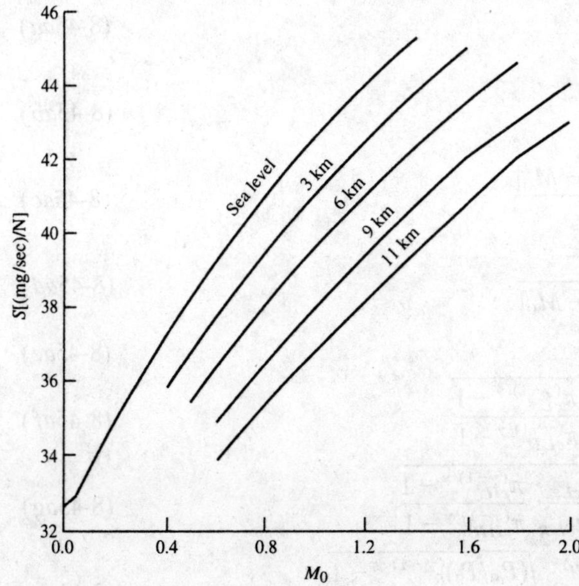

FIGURE 8-35
Thrust specific fuel consumption of dry turbojet at maximum thrust.

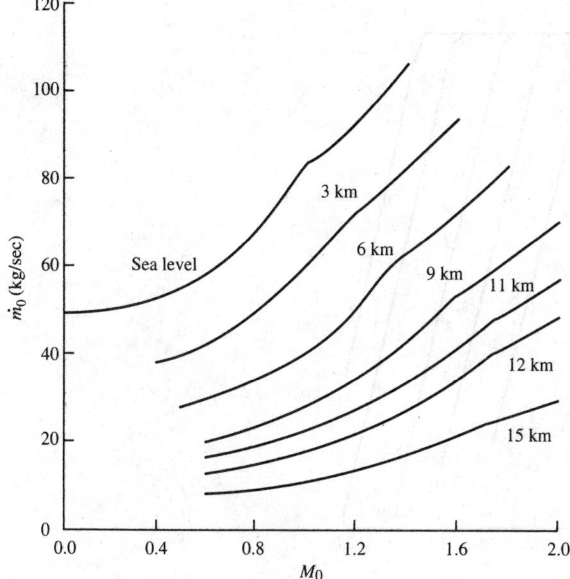

FIGURE 8-36
Mass flow rate of dry turbojet at maximum thrust.

thrust specific fuel consumption S, engine mass flow, engine corrected mass flow, and compressor pressure ratio with Mach number, respectively.

At θ_0 values below 1.2, the engine is at the maximum compressor pressure ratio of 12.3 and T_{t4} is below its maximum value of 1800 K. At θ_0 values above

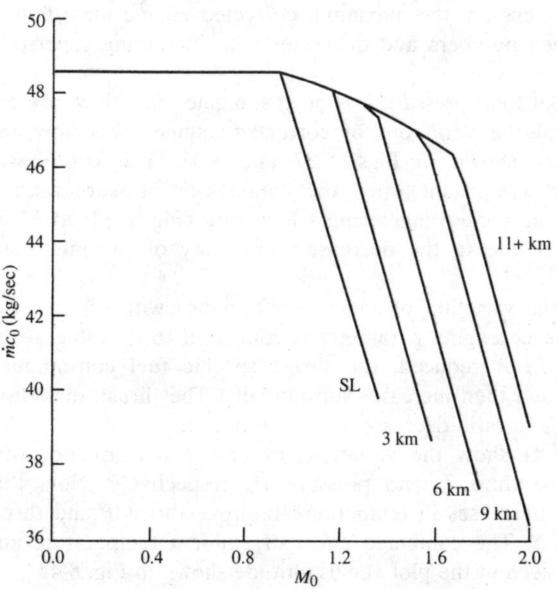

FIGURE 8-37
Corrected mass flow rate of dry turbojet at maximum thrust.

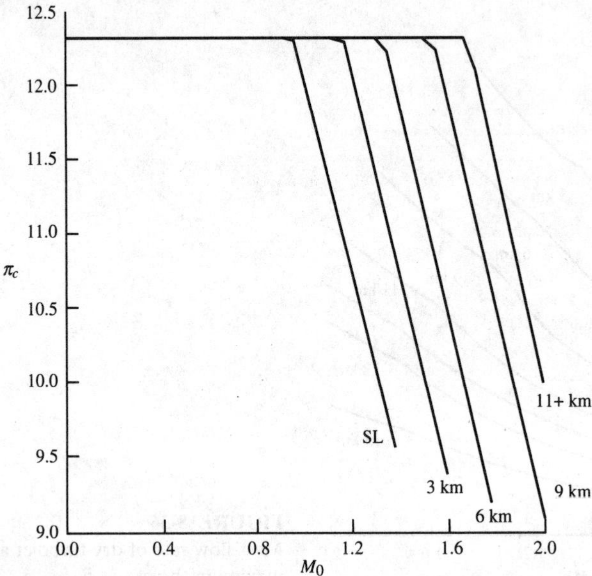

FIGURE 8-38
Compressor pressure ratio of dry turbojet at maximum thrust.

1.2, the engine is at its maximum T_{t4} value of 1800 K and the compressor pressure ratio is below its maximum value of 12. This engine has a throttle ratio of 1.2.

The corrected engine mass flow, shown in Fig. 8-37, is used in sizing the engine inlet area. For this engine, the maximum corrected engine mass flow is constant for subsonic Mach numbers and decreases with increasing supersonic Mach numbers.

The effect of the inlet total pressure loss on the engine mass flow rate can be seen by comparison of the variations of corrected engine mass flow and compressor pressure ratio, shown in Figs. 8-37 and 8-38. The compressor corrected mass flow rate is constant when the compressor pressure ratio is constant. The drop-off in corrected engine mass flow rate (Fig. 8-37) at Mach numbers greater than 1 is due to the decrease from unity of the inlet total pressure recovery.

Figure 8-39 shows the variation of engine performance with reduction in engine throttle T_{t4}. Here each engine parameter is compared to its value at the reference condition. As T_{t4} is reduced, the thrust specific fuel consumption initially decreases a little and then increases substantially. The thrust, mass flow rate, and compressor pressure ratio decrease as T_{t4} is reduced.

Figures 8-40 and 8-41 show the variations of engine performance with changes in ambient temperature T_0 and pressure P_0, respectively. Note that increases in pressure and decreases in temperaure improve thrust F and thrust specific fuel consumption S. The combined effect of ambient temperature and pressure T_0 and P_0 can be seen in the plot versus altitude shown in Fig. 8-42.

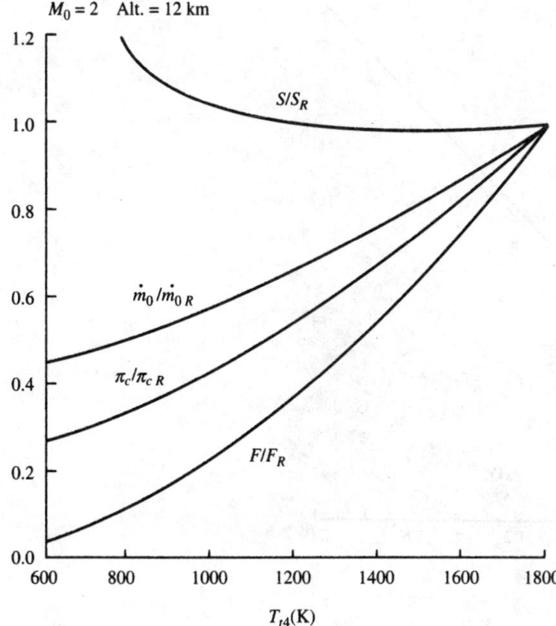

FIGURE 8-39
Performance of dry turbojet at partial throttle.

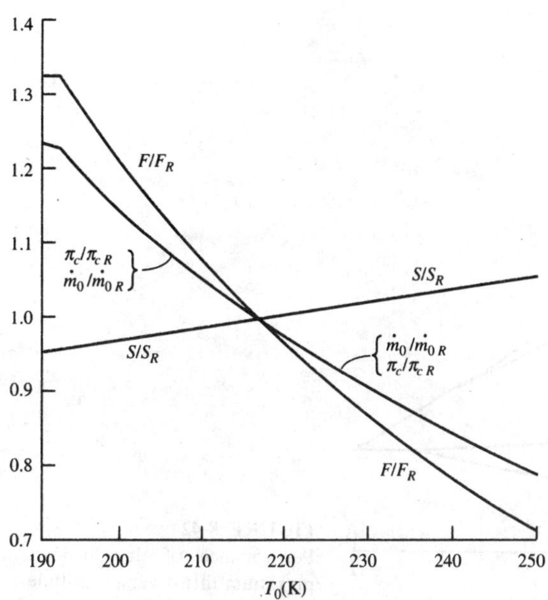

FIGURE 8-40
Performance of dry turbojet at maximum thrust versus T_0.

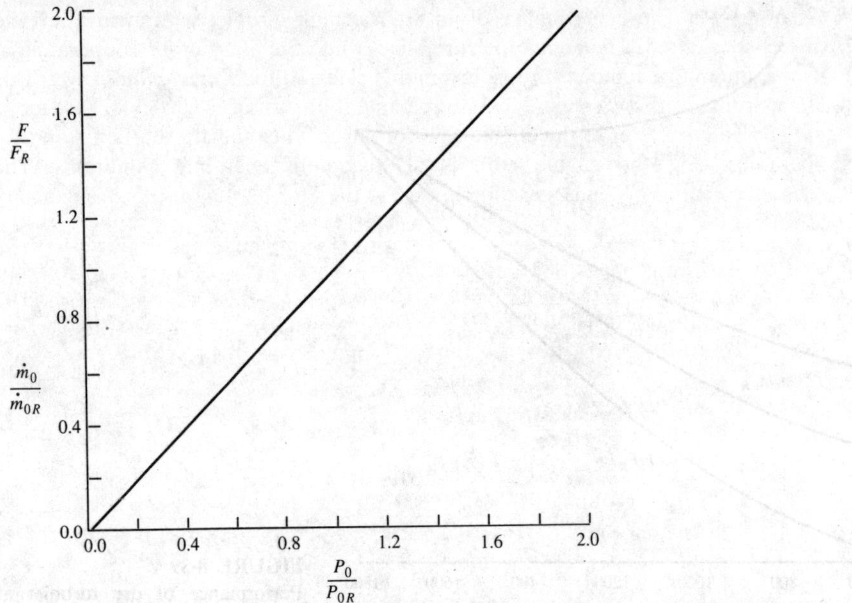

FIGURE 8-41
Performance of dry turbojet at maximum thrust versus P_0.

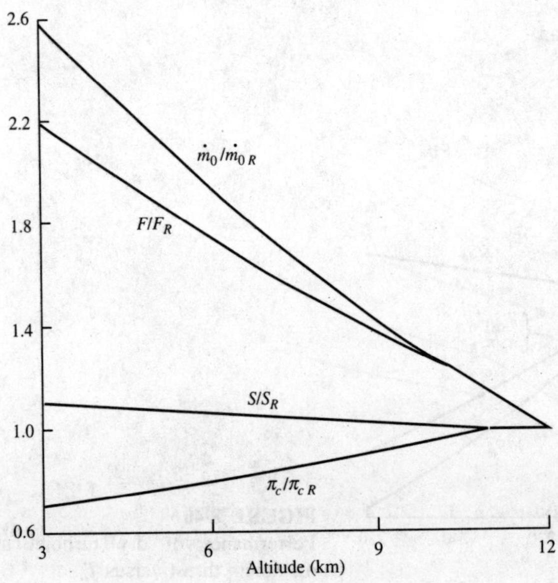

FIGURE 8-42
Performance of dry turbojet at maximum thrust versus altitude.

Example 8-7. The performance of an afterburning turbojet with a throttle ratio of 1 is considered. The engine performance, when the afterburner is operating at its maximum exit temperature, is commonly referred to as *maximum* or *wet*. This afterburning turbojet engine has a maximum thrust of 25,000 lbf. The terms *military* and *dry* refer to the engine's performance when the afterburner is off (not operating) and the engine core is at maximum operating conditions. The reference conditions and operating limits for the afterburning turbojet engine are as follows:

REFERENCE: Sea level static ($T_0 = 518.7$°R, $P_0 = 14.696$ psia), $\pi_c = 20$, $\pi_{cL} = 5$, $\pi_{cH} = 4$, $e_{cL} = 0.9$, $e_{cH} = 0.9$, $e_{tH} = 0.9$, $e_{tL} = 0.9$, $\pi_{d\max} = 0.98$, $\pi_b = 0.96$, $\pi_n = 0.98$, $T_{t4} = 3200$°R, $c_{pc} =$ 0.24 Btu/(lbm · °R), $\gamma_c = 1.4$, $c_{pt} = 0.295$ Btu/(lbm · °R), $\gamma_t =$ 1.3, $\eta_b = 0.995$, $\eta_{mL} = 0.995$, $\eta_{mH} = 0.995$, $h_{PR} =$ 18,400 Btu/lbm, $T_{t7} = 3600$°R, $c_{p\text{AB}} = 0.295$ Btu/(lbm · °R), $\gamma_{\text{AB}} = 1.3$, $\pi_{\text{AB}} = 0.94$, $\eta_{\text{AB}} = 0.95$, $\eta_{cL} = 0.8755$, $\eta_{cH} = 0.8791$, $\eta_{tH} = 0.9062$, $\eta_{tL} = 0.9050$, $\pi_{tH} = 0.5466$, $\tau_{tH} = 0.8821$, $\pi_{tL} =$ 0.6127, $\tau_{tL} = 0.9033$, $M_8 = 1$, $M_9 = 1.85$, $f = 0.0358$, $f_{\text{AB}} =$ 0.0195, $f_O = 0.0554$, $F = 25{,}000$ lbf, $S = 1.4473$ (lbm/hr)/lbf, $\dot{m}_0 = 181.57$ lbm/sec

OPERATION: Maximum $T_{t4} = 3200$°R Maximum $T_{t7} = 3600$°R
Mach number: 0 to 2 Altitudes (kft): 0, 20, and 40

The wet and dry performances of this afterburning turbojet are compared in Figs. 8-43 and 8-44. Note that the wet thrust is about 20 percent greater than the dry thrust, and the thrust at 40-kft altitude is about 25 percent of its sea-level

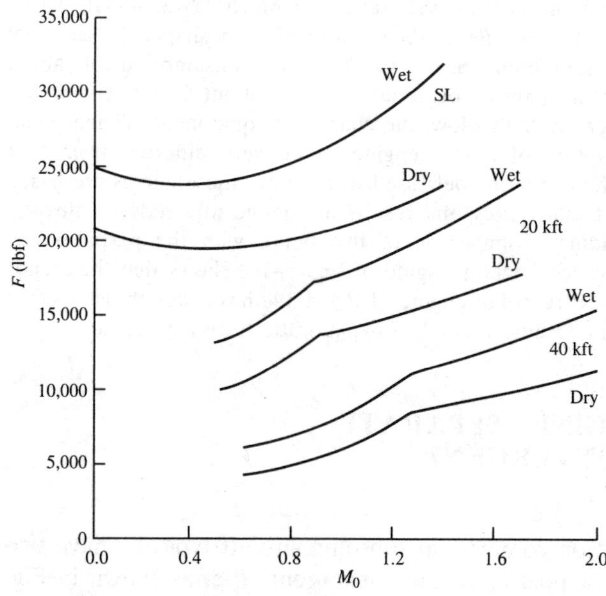

FIGURE 8-43
Maximum wet and dry thrust of afterburning turbojet.

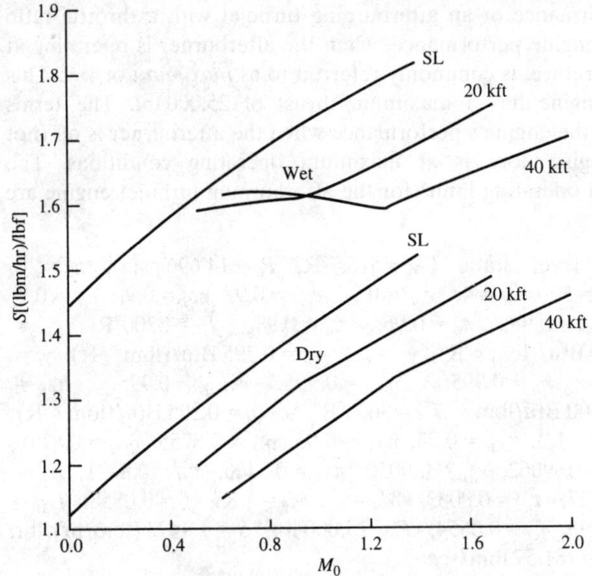

FIGURE 8-44
Maximum wet and dry thrust specific fuel consumption of afterburning turbojet.

value. The thrust specific fuel consumption at 40-kft altitude is much higher than expected for Mach numbers below about 1.3. This high S is due to the reduction in T_{t4} below maximum for $\theta_0 < \text{TR}$, which lowers the temperature of the gas entering the afterburner and increases the temperature rise across the afterburner.

The partial-throttle performance of the afterburning turbjoet is shown in Fig. 8-45 at flight conditions of sea-level static and Mach 1.5 at 40 kft. These curves are commonly called *throttle hooks* because of their shape. At sea level static conditions, the minimum thrust specific fuel consumption of about 1.02 (lbm/hr)/lbf occurs at a thrust of about 4300 lbf (about 20 percent of dry thrust). At partial-power levels this low, the change in component efficiency can cause the fuel consumption of a real engine to be very different from that predicted here. Since the engine models used to generate these curves are based on constant component efficiencies, the results at significantly reduced throttle settings can be misleading. Comparison of this figure with the partial-power performance of the advanced fighter engine of Fig. 1–14*e* shows that the trends are correct. The advanced turbofan engine of Fig. 1-14*e* has lower thrust specific fuel consumption mainly because it is a low-bypass-ratio turbofan engine.

8-5 TURBOFAN ENGINE—SEPARATE EXHAUSTS AND CONVERGENT NOZZLES

The turbofan engines used on commercial subsonic aircraft typically have two spools and separate exhaust nozzles of the convergent type, as shown in Fig.

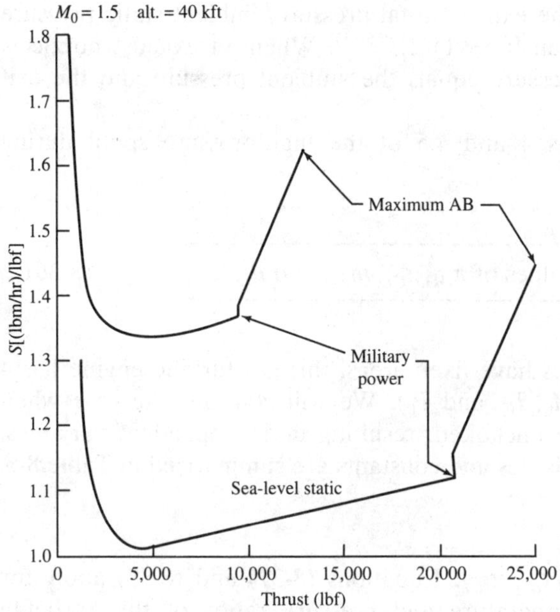

FIGURE 8-45
Partial-throttle performance of afterburning turbojet.

8-46. For ease of analysis, we will consider a turbofan engine whose fan exit state (13) is the same as the low-pressure compressor exit state (2.5). Thus

$$\tau_f = \tau_{cL} \quad \text{and} \quad \pi_f = \pi_{cL}$$

The exhaust nozzles of these turbofan engines have fixed throat areas

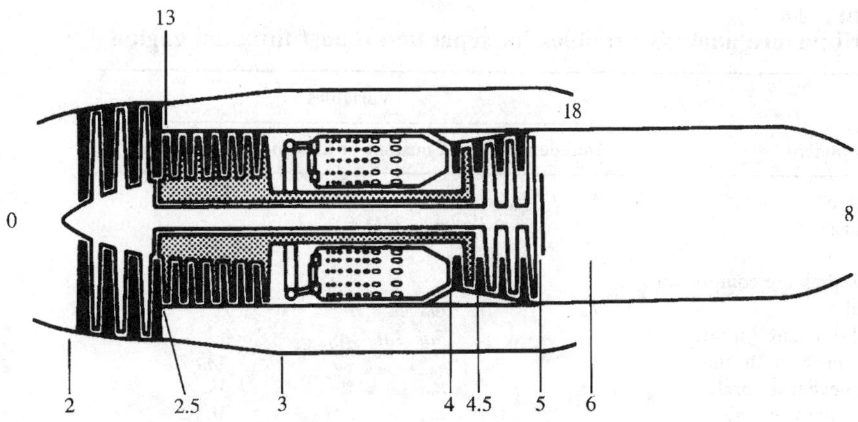

FIGURE 8-46
Turbofan engine with separate exhausts. (*Courtesy of Pratt & Whitney.*)

which will be choked when the exhaust total pressure/ambient static pressure ratio is equal to or larger than $[(\gamma+1)/2]^{\gamma/(\gamma-1)}$. When an exhaust nozzle is unchoked, the nozzle exit pressure equals the ambient pressure and the exit Mach number is subsonic.

Choked flow at stations 4 and 4.5 of the high-pressure spool during engine operation requires

$$\boxed{\text{Constant values of } \pi_{tH},\ \tau_{tH},\ \dot{m}_{c4},\ \text{and } \dot{m}_{c4.5}} \tag{8-36}$$

Since the exhaust nozzles have fixed areas, this gas turbine engine has 4 independent variables (T_{t4}, M_0, T_0, and P_0). We will consider the case when both exhaust nozzles may be unchoked, resulting in 11 dependent variables. The performance analysis variables and constants are summarized in Table 8-6.

LOW-PRESSURE TURBINE (τ_{tL}, π_{tL}). Equations (8-37) and (8-38) apply for the low-pressure turbine temperature and pressure ratios of this turbofan engine.

$$\boxed{\pi_{tL} = \pi_{tL\,R}\sqrt{\frac{\tau_{tL}}{\tau_{tL\,R}}\,\frac{\text{MFP}(M_{9\,R})}{\text{MFP}(M_9)}}} \tag{8-37}$$

TABLE 8-6
Performance analysis variables for separate-exhaust turbofan engine

	Variables		
Component	**Independent**	**Constant or known**	**Dependent**
Engine	M_0, T_0, P_0		$\dot{m}_0$, α
Diffuser		$\pi_d = f(M_0)$	
Fan			π_f, τ_f
High-pressure compressor			π_{cH}, τ_{cH}
Burner	T_{t4}	π_b, η_b	f
High-pressure turbine		π_{tH}, τ_{tH}	
Low-pressure turbine			π_{tL}, τ_{tL}
Core exhaust nozzle		π_n	M_9
Fan exhaust nozzle		π_{fn}	M_{19}
Total number	4		11

where
$$\tau_{tL} = 1 - \eta_{tL}(1 - \pi_{tL}^{(\gamma_t - 1)/\gamma_t}) \tag{8-38}$$

If station 9 is choked at the reference condition and at off-design conditions, then π_{tL} and τ_{tL} are constant.

BYPASS RATIO α. An expression for the engine bypass ratio at any operating condition is obtained by first relating the mass flow rates of the core and fan streams to their reference values. For the engine core, we have

$$\dot{m}_C = \frac{\dot{m}_4}{1+f} = \frac{P_{t4}A_4}{\sqrt{T_{t4}}} \frac{\text{MFP}(M_4)}{1+f}$$

Thus
$$\frac{\dot{m}_C}{\dot{m}_{CR}} = \frac{P_{t4}}{P_{t4R}} \sqrt{\frac{T_{t4R}}{T_{t4}}} \tag{i}$$

For the fan stream, we have

$$\dot{m}_F = \frac{P_{t19}A_{19}}{\sqrt{T_{t19}}} \text{MFP}(M_{19})$$

Thus
$$\frac{\dot{m}_F}{\dot{m}_{FR}} = \frac{P_{t19}}{P_{t19R}} \sqrt{\frac{T_{t19R}}{T_{t19}}} \frac{\text{MFP}(M_{19})}{\text{MFP}(M_{19R})} \tag{ii}$$

Combining Eqs. (i) and (ii) to obtain the equation for the bypass ratio α yields

$$\alpha = \alpha_R \frac{\pi_{cHR}}{\pi_{cH}} \sqrt{\frac{\tau_\lambda/(\tau_r\tau_f)}{[\tau_\lambda/(\tau_r\tau_f)]_R}} \frac{\text{MFP}(M_{19})}{\text{MFP}(M_{19}R)} \tag{8-46}$$

ENGINE MASS FLOW $\dot{m}_0$. The engine mass flow rate can be written simply as

$$\dot{m}_0 = (1+\alpha)\dot{m}_C$$

Then from Eq. (i), we have

$$\dot{m}_0 = \dot{m}_{0R} \frac{1+\alpha}{1+\alpha_R} \frac{P_0\pi_r\pi_d\pi_f\pi_{cH}}{(P_0\pi_r\pi_d\pi_f\pi_{cH})_R} \sqrt{\frac{T_{t4R}}{T_{t4}}} \tag{8-47}$$

HIGH-PRESSURE COMPRESSOR (τ_{cH}, π_{cH}). The power balance between the high-pressure turbine and the high-pressure compressor [*high-pressure* (HP) spool] gives

$$\eta_{mH}\dot{m}_4 c_{pt}(T_{t4} - T_{t4.5}) = \dot{m}_{2.5}c_{pc}(T_{t4} - T_{t2.5})$$

Rewriting this equation in terms of temperature ratios, rearranging into variable and constant terms, and equating the constant to reference values give

$$\frac{\tau_r \tau_f(\tau_{cH}-1)}{T_{t4}/T_0} = \eta_{mH}(1+f)(1-\tau_{tH}) = \left[\frac{\tau_r \tau_f(\tau_{cH}-1)}{T_{t4}/T_0}\right]_R$$

Solving for τ_{cH} gives

$$\tau_{cH} = 1 + \frac{T_{t4}/T_0}{(T_{t4}/T_0)_R}\frac{(\tau_r\tau_f)_R}{\tau_r\tau_f}(\tau_{cH}-1)_R \tag{8–48}$$

From the definition of compressor efficiency, π_{cH} is given by

$$\pi_{cH} = [1+\eta_{cH}(\tau_{cH}-1)]^{\gamma_c/(\gamma_c-1)} \tag{8-49}$$

FAN (τ_f, π_f). From a power balance between the fan and low-pressure turbine, we get

$$\eta_{mL}\dot{m}_{4.5}c_{pt}(T_{t4.5}-T_{t5}) = (\dot{m}_C + \dot{m}_F)c_{pc}(T_{t13}-T_{t2})$$

Rewriting this equation in terms of temperature ratios, rearranging into variable and constant terms, and equating the constant to reference values give

$$(1+\alpha)\frac{\tau_r(\tau_f-1)}{T_{t4}/T_0} = \eta_{mL}(1+f)\tau_{tH}(1-\tau_{tL}) = \left[(1+\alpha)\frac{\tau_r(\tau_f-1)}{T_{t4}/T_0}\right]_R$$

Solving for τ_f gives

$$\tau_f = 1 + \frac{1-\tau_{tL}}{(1+\tau_{tL})_R}\frac{\tau_\lambda/\tau_r}{(\tau_\lambda/\tau_r)_R}\frac{1+\alpha_R}{1+\alpha}(\tau_{fR}-1) \tag{8-50}$$

where

$$\pi_f = [1+(\tau_f+1)\eta_f]^{\gamma_c/(\gamma_c-1)} \tag{8-51}$$

Solution Scheme

The principal dependent variables for the turbofan engine are π_{tL}, τ_{tL}, α, τ_{cH}, π_{cH}, τ_f, π_f, M_9, and M_{19}. These variables are dependent on each other plus the engine's independent variables—throttle setting and flight condition. The functional interrelationship of the dependent variables can be written as

$$\begin{aligned}
\tau_{cH} &= f_1(\tau_f) & M_9 &= f_6(\pi_f, \pi_{cH}, \pi_{tL})\\
\pi_{cH} &= f_2(\tau_{cH}) & \pi_{tL} &= f_7(\tau_{tL}, M_9)\\
\tau_f &= f_3(\tau_{tL}, \alpha) & \tau_{tL} &= f_8(\pi_{tL})\\
\pi_f &= f_4(\tau_f) & \alpha &= f_9(\tau_f, \pi_{cH}, M_{19})\\
M_{19} &= f_5(\pi_f)
\end{aligned}$$

This system of nine equations is solved by functional iteration, starting with reference quantities as initial values for π_{tL}, τ_{tL}, and τ_f. The following equations are calculated for the nine dependent variables in the order listed until successive values of τ_{tL} do not change more than a specified amount (say, 0.0001):

$$\tau_{cH} = 1 + \frac{T_{t4}/T_0}{(T_{t4}/T_0)_R} \frac{(\tau_r \tau_f)_R}{\tau_r \tau_f} (\tau_{cH} - 1)_R \tag{i}$$

$$\pi_{cH} = [1 + \eta_{cH}(\tau_{cH} - 1)]^{\gamma_c/(\gamma_c - 1)} \tag{ii}$$

$$\pi_f = [1 + (\tau_f - 1)\eta_f]^{\gamma_c/(\gamma_c - 1)} \tag{iii}$$

$$P_{t19}/P_0 = \pi_r \pi_d \pi_f \pi_{fn} \tag{iv}$$

$$\text{If} \quad \frac{P_{t19}}{P_0} < \left(\frac{\gamma_c + 1}{2}\right)^{\gamma_c/(\gamma_c - 1)} \quad \text{then} \quad \frac{P_{t19}}{P_{19}} = \frac{P_{t19}}{P_0} \qquad \text{else} \quad \frac{P_{t19}}{P_{19}} = \left(\frac{\gamma_c + 1}{2}\right)^{\gamma_c/(\gamma_c - 1)} \tag{v}$$

$$M_{10} = \sqrt{\frac{2}{\gamma_c - 1}\left[\left(\frac{P_{t19}}{P_{19}}\right)^{(\gamma_c - 1)/\gamma_c} - 1\right]} \tag{vi}$$

$$\frac{P_{t9}}{P_0} = \pi_r \pi_d \pi_f \pi_{cH} \pi_b \pi_{tH} \pi_{tL} \pi_n \tag{vii}$$

$$\text{If} \quad \frac{P_{t9}}{P_0} < \left(\frac{\gamma_t + 1}{2}\right)^{\gamma_t/(\gamma_t - 1)} \quad \text{then} \quad \frac{P_{t9}}{P_9} = \frac{P_{t9}}{P_0} \qquad \text{else} \quad \frac{P_{t9}}{P_9} = \left(\frac{\gamma_t + 1}{2}\right)^{\gamma_t/(\gamma_t - 1)} \tag{viii}$$

$$M_9 = \sqrt{\frac{2}{\gamma_t - 1}\left[\left(\frac{P_{t9}}{P_9}\right)^{(\gamma_t - 1)/\gamma_t} - 1\right]} \tag{ix}$$

$$\alpha = \alpha_R \frac{\pi_{cHR}}{\pi_{cH}} \sqrt{\frac{\tau_\lambda/(\tau_r \tau_f)}{[\tau_\lambda/(\tau_r \tau_f)]_R}} \frac{\text{MFP}(M_{19})}{\text{MFP}(M_{19R})} \tag{x}$$

$$\tau_f = 1 + \frac{1 - \tau_{tL}}{(1 + \tau_{tL})_R} \frac{\tau_\lambda/\tau_r}{(\tau_\lambda/\tau_r)_R} \frac{1 + \alpha_R}{1 + \alpha} (\tau_{fR} - 1) \tag{xi}$$

$$\tau_{tL} = 1 - \eta_{tL}(1 - \pi_{tL}^{(\gamma_t - 1)/\gamma_t}) \tag{xii}$$

$$\pi_{tL} = \pi_{tLR} \sqrt{\frac{\tau_{tL}}{\tau_{tLR}}} \frac{\text{MFP}(M_{9R})}{\text{MFP}(M_9)} \tag{xiii}$$

Summary of Performance Equations—Turbofan Engine with Separate Exhausts and Convergent Nozzles

INPUTS:

Choices

Flight parameters:	M_0, T_0 (K, °R), P_0 (kPa, psia)
Throttle setting:	T_{t4} (K, °R)

Design constants

π's:	$\pi_{d\max}, \pi_b, \pi_{tH}, \pi_n, \pi_{fn}$
τ's:	τ_{tH}
η's:	$\eta_f, \eta_{cH}, \eta_b, \eta_{mH}, \eta_{mL}$
Gas properties:	$\gamma_c, \gamma_t, c_{pc}, c_{pt}$ [kJ/(kg · K), Btu/(lbm · °R)]
Fuel:	h_{PR} (kJ/kg, Btu/lbm)

Reference conditions

Flight parameters:	M_{0R}, T_{0R} (K, °R), P_{0R} (kPa, psia), τ_{rR}, π_{rR}
Throttle setting:	T_{t4R} (K, °R)
Component behavior:	$\pi_{dR}, \pi_{fR}, \pi_{cHR}, \pi_{tL}, \tau_{fR}, \tau_{cHR}, \tau_{tLR}, \alpha_R, M_{9R}, M_{19R}$

OUTPUTS:

Overall performance:	F (N, lbf), $\dot{m}_0$ (kg/sec, lbm/sec), f, $S\left(\dfrac{\text{mg/sec}}{\text{N}}, \dfrac{\text{lbm/hr}}{\text{lbf}}\right)$, η_P, η_T, η_O
Component behavior:	$\alpha, \pi_f, \pi_{cH}, \pi_{tL}, \tau_f, \tau_{cH}, \tau_{tL}, f, M_9, M_{19}, N_{\text{fan}}, N_{\text{HPspool}}$
Exhaust nozzle pressure:	P_0/P_9, P_0/P_{19}

EQUATIONS:

$$R_c = \frac{\gamma_c - 1}{\gamma_c} c_{pc} \tag{8-52a}$$

$$R_t = \frac{\gamma_t - 1}{\gamma_t} c_{pt} \tag{8-52b}$$

$$a_0 = \sqrt{\gamma_c R_c g_c T_0} \tag{8-52c}$$

$$V_0 = a_0 M_0 \tag{8-52d}$$

$$\tau_r = 1 + \frac{\gamma_c - 1}{2} M_0^2 \tag{8-52e}$$

$$\pi_r = \tau_r^{\gamma_c/(\gamma_c - 1)} \tag{8-52f}$$

$$\eta_r = 1 \qquad \text{for } M_0 \le 1 \tag{8-52g}$$

$$\eta_r = 1 - 0.075(M_0 - 1)^{1.35} \qquad \text{for } M_0 > 1 \tag{8-52h}$$

$$\pi_d = \pi_{d\max} \eta_r \tag{8-52i}$$

$$\tau_\lambda = \frac{c_{pt} T_{t4}}{c_{pc} T_0} \tag{8-52j}$$

Initial values:

$$\tau_{tL} = \tau_{tLR} \qquad \tau_f = \tau_{fR} \qquad \tau_{tLR}$$

$$\tau_{cH} = 1 + \frac{\tau_\lambda/\tau_r}{(\tau_\lambda/\tau_r)_R} \frac{\tau_{fR}}{\tau_f} (\tau_{cHR} - 1) \tag{8-52k}$$

$$\pi_{cH} = [1 + (\tau_{cH} - 1)\eta_{cH}]^{\gamma_c/(\gamma_c - 1)} \tag{8-52l}$$

$$\pi_f = [1 + (\tau_f - 1)\eta_f]^{\gamma_c/(\gamma_c - 1)} \tag{8-52m}$$

Exhaust nozzles:

$$\frac{P_{t19}}{P_0} = \pi_r \pi_d \pi_f \pi_{fn} \tag{8-52n}$$

$$\text{If} \quad \frac{P_{t19}}{P_0} < \left(\frac{\gamma_c + 1}{2}\right)^{\gamma_c/(\gamma_c - 1)} \quad \text{then} \quad \frac{P_{t19}}{P_{19}} = \frac{P_{t19}}{P_0}$$

$$\text{else} \quad \frac{P_{t19}}{P_{19}} = \left(\frac{\gamma_c + 1}{2}\right)^{\gamma_c/(\gamma_c - 1)} \tag{8-52o}$$

$$M_{19} = \sqrt{\frac{2}{\gamma_c - 1}\left[\left(\frac{P_{t19}}{P_{19}}\right)^{(\gamma_c - 1)/\gamma_c} - 1\right]} \tag{8-52p}$$

$$\frac{P_{t9}}{P_0} = \pi_r \pi_d \pi_f \pi_{cH} \pi_b \pi_{tH} \pi_{tL} \pi_n \tag{8-52q}$$

$$\text{If} \quad \frac{P_{t9}}{P_0} < \left(\frac{\gamma_t + 1}{2}\right)^{\gamma_t/(\gamma_t - 1)} \quad \text{then} \quad \frac{P_{t9}}{P_9} = \frac{P_{t9}}{P_0}$$

$$\text{else} \quad \frac{P_{t9}}{P_9} = \left(\frac{\gamma_t + 1}{2}\right)^{\gamma_t/(\gamma_t - 1)} \tag{8-52r}$$

$$M_9 = \sqrt{\frac{2}{\gamma_t - 1}\left[\left(\frac{P_{t9}}{P_9}\right)^{(\gamma_t - 1)/\gamma_t} - 1\right]} \tag{8-52s}$$

$$\alpha = \alpha_R \frac{\pi_{cHR}}{\pi_{cH}} \sqrt{\frac{\tau_\lambda/(\tau_r \tau_f)}{[\tau_\lambda/(\tau_r \tau_f)]_R}} \frac{\text{MFP}(M_{19})}{\text{MFP}(M_{19R})} \tag{8-52t}$$

$$\tau_f = 1 + \frac{1 - \tau_{tL}}{(1 - \tau_{tL})_R} \frac{\tau_\lambda/\tau_r}{(\tau_\lambda/\tau_r)_R} \frac{1 + \alpha_R}{1 + \alpha}(\tau_{fR} - 1) \tag{8-52u}$$

$$\tau_{tL} = 1 - \eta_{tL}(1 - \pi_{tL}^{(\gamma_t - 1)/\gamma_t}) \tag{8-52v}$$

$$\pi_{tL} = \pi_{tLR} \sqrt{\frac{\tau_{tL}}{\tau_{tLR}}} \frac{\text{MFP}(M_{9R})}{\text{MFP}(M_9)} \tag{8-52w}$$

If τ_{tL} is not within 0.0001 of its previous value, return to Eq. (8-52*k*) and perform another iteration.

Remainder of calculations:

$$\dot{m}_0 = \dot{m}_{0R} \frac{1 + \alpha}{1 + \alpha_R} \frac{P_0 \pi_r \pi_d \pi_f \pi_{cH}}{(P_0 \pi_r \pi_d \pi_f \pi_{cH})_R} \sqrt{\frac{T_{t4R}}{T_{t4}}} \tag{8-52x}$$

$$f = \frac{\tau_\lambda - \tau_r \tau_f \tau_{cH}}{h_{PR}\eta_b/(c_p T_0) - \tau_\lambda} \tag{8-52y}$$

$$\frac{T_9}{T_0} = \frac{\tau_\lambda \tau_{tH} \tau_{tL}}{(P_{t9}/P_9)^{(\gamma_t - 1)/\gamma_t}} \frac{c_{pc}}{c_{pt}} \tag{8-52z}$$

$$\frac{V_9}{a_0} = M_9 \sqrt{\frac{\gamma_t R_t T_9}{\gamma_c R_c T_0}} \tag{8-52aa}$$

$$\frac{T_{19}}{T_0} = \frac{\tau_r \tau_f}{(P_{t19}/P_{19})^{(\gamma_c - 1)/\gamma_c}} \tag{8-52ab}$$

$$\frac{V_{19}}{a_0} = M_{19} \sqrt{\frac{T_{19}}{T_0}} \tag{8-52ac}$$

$$\frac{F}{\dot{m}_0} = \frac{1}{1+\alpha}\,\frac{a_0}{g_c}\left[(1+f)\frac{V_9}{a_0} - M_0 + (1+f)\frac{R_t}{R_c}\,\frac{T_9/t_0}{V_9/a_0}\,\frac{1-P_0/P_9}{\gamma_c}\right]$$

$$+\frac{\alpha}{1+\alpha}\,\frac{a_0}{g_c}\left[\frac{V_{19}}{a_0} - M_0 + \frac{T_{19}/T_0}{V_{19}/a_0}\,\frac{1-P_0/P_{19}}{\gamma_c}\right] \tag{8-52ad}$$

$$S = \frac{f}{(1+\alpha)(F/\dot{m}_0)} \tag{8-52ae}$$

$$F = \dot{m}_0\left(\frac{F}{\dot{m}_0}\right) \tag{8-52af}$$

$$\left(\frac{N}{N_R}\right)_{\text{fan}} = \sqrt{\frac{T_0\tau_r}{T_{0R}\tau_{rR}}\,\frac{\pi_f^{(\gamma_c-1)/\gamma_c}-1}{\pi_{fR}^{(\gamma_c-1)/\gamma_c}-1}} \tag{8-52ag}$$

$$\left(\frac{N}{N_R}\right)_{\text{HP spool}} = \sqrt{\frac{T_0\tau_r\tau_f}{(T_0\tau_r\tau_f)_R}\,\frac{\pi_{cH}^{(\gamma_c-1)/\gamma_c}-1}{\pi_{cHR}^{(\gamma_c-1)/\gamma_c}-1}} \tag{8-52ah}$$

$$\eta_T = \frac{a_0^2[(1+f)(V_0/a_0)^2 + \alpha(V_{19}/a_0)^2 - (1+\alpha)m_0^2]}{2g_c f h_{PR}} \tag{8-52ai}$$

$$\eta_P = \frac{2g_c V_0(1+\alpha)(F/\dot{m}_0)}{a_0^2[(1+f)(V_9/a_0)^2 + \alpha(V_{19}/a_0)^2 - (1+\alpha)M_0^2]} \tag{8-52aj}$$

$$\eta_O = \eta_P\eta_T \tag{8-52ak}$$

Example 8-8. Given the reference engine (see data) sized for a mass flow rate of 600 lbm/sec at 40 kft and Mach 0.8, determine the performance at sea-level static conditions with $T_{t4} = 3000°\text{R}$.

REFERENCE: $T_0 = 390°\text{R}$, $\gamma_c = 1.4$, $c_{pc} = 0.24$ Btu/(lbm · °R), $\gamma_t = 1.33$, $c_{pt} = 0.276$ Btu/(lbm · °R), $T_{t4} = 3000°\text{R}$, $M_0 = 0.8$, $\pi_c = 36$, $\pi_f = 1.7$, $\alpha = 8$, $\eta_f = 0.8815$, $\eta_{cH} = 0.8512$, $\tau_{tH} = 0.7580$, $\pi_{tH} = 0.2851$, $\tau_{tL} = 0.7262$, $\pi_{tL} = 0.2349$, $\eta_{tL} = 0.9068$, $\eta_b = 0.99$, $\pi_{d\max} = 0.99$, $\pi_b = 0.96$, $\pi_n = 0.99$, $\pi_{fn} = 0.99$, $\eta_{mH} = 0.9915$, $\eta_{mL} = 0.997$, $P_0 = 2.730$ psia (40 kft), $\dot{m}_0 = 600$ lbm/sec, $F/\dot{m}_0 = 17.92$ lbf/(lbm/sec), $F = 10{,}750$ lbf

PERFORMANCE CONDITIONS:
$T_0 = 518.7°\text{R}$ $P_0 = 14.696$ psia (sea level) $T_{t4} = 3000°\text{R}$ $M_0 = 0$

EQUATIONS:

$$R_c = \frac{\gamma_c - 1}{\gamma_c}c_{pc} = \frac{0.4}{1.4}(0.24\times 778.16) = 53.36 \text{ ft}\cdot\text{lbf/(lbm}\cdot°\text{R)}$$

$$R_t = \frac{\gamma_t - 1}{\gamma_t}c_{pt} = \frac{0.33}{1.33}(0.276\times 778.16) = 53.29 \text{ ft}\cdot\text{lbf/(lbm}\cdot°\text{R)}$$

$$a_0 = \sqrt{\gamma_c R_c g_c T_0} = \sqrt{1.4\times 53.36\times 32.174\times 518.7} = 1116.6 \text{ ft/sec}$$

$$V_0 = a_0 M_0 = 1116.6 \times 0 = 0 \text{ ft/sec}$$

$$\tau_r = 1 \quad \text{and} \quad \pi_r = 1$$

$$\pi_d = \pi_{d\max}\eta_r = 0.99 \times 1 = 0.99$$

$$\tau_\lambda = \frac{c_{pt}T_{t4}}{c_{pc}T_0} = \frac{0.276 \times 3000}{0.240 \times 518.7} = 6.651$$

Initial values:

$$\tau_{tL} = \tau_{tL\,R} = 0.7262 \qquad \tau_f = \tau_{fR} = 1.1857 \qquad \pi_{tL} = \pi_{tL\,R} = 0.2349$$

$$\text{Eq. (A)} \quad \tau_{cH} = 1 + \frac{\tau_\lambda/\tau_r}{(\tau_\lambda/\tau_r)_R}\frac{\tau_{fR}}{\tau_f}(\tau_{cH\,R} - 1)$$

$$= 1 + \frac{6.651/1.0}{8.846/1.128}\frac{1.1857}{1.1857}(2.636 - 1) = 2.3875$$

$$\pi_{cH} = [1 - (\tau_{cH} - 1)\eta_{cH}]^{\gamma_c/(\gamma_c - 1)}$$
$$= [1 + (2.3875 - 1)(0.8512)]^{3.5} = 15.286$$

$$\pi_f = [1 + (\tau_f - 1)\eta_f]^{\gamma_c/(\gamma_c - 1)}$$
$$= [1 + (1.1857 - 1)(0.8815)]^{3.5} = 1.70$$

Exhaust nozzles:

$$\frac{P_{t19}}{P_0} = \pi_r\pi_d\pi_f\pi_{fn} = 1 \times 0.99 \times 1.70 \times 0.99 = 1.6662$$

$$\text{Since} \quad \frac{P_{t19}}{P_0} < 1.893 \quad \text{then} \quad P_{19} = P_0$$

$$M_{19} = \sqrt{\frac{2}{\gamma_c - 1}\left[\left(\frac{P_{t19}}{P_{19}}\right)^{(\gamma_c - 1)/\gamma_c} - 1\right]} = \sqrt{\frac{2}{0.4}(1.6662^{1/3.5} - 1)} = 0.8861$$

$$\frac{P_{t9}}{P_0} = \pi_r\pi_d\pi_f\pi_{cH}\pi_b\pi_{tH}\pi_{tL}\pi_n$$

$$= 1 \times 0.99 \times 1.70 \times 15.322 \times 0.96 \times 0.2851 \times 0.2349 \times 0.99 = 1.6413$$

$$\text{Since} \quad \frac{P_{t9}}{P_0} < 1.851 \quad \text{then} \quad P_9 = P_0$$

$$M_9 = \sqrt{\frac{2}{\gamma_t - 1}\left[\left(\frac{P_{t9}}{P_9}\right)^{(\gamma_t - 1)/\gamma_t} - 1\right]} = \sqrt{\frac{2}{0.33}(1.6413^{0.33/1.33} - 1)} = 0.8904$$

$$\alpha = \alpha_R \frac{\pi_{cH\,R}}{\pi_{cH}}\sqrt{\frac{\tau_\lambda/(\tau_r\tau_f)}{[\tau_\lambda/(\tau_r\tau_f)]_R}}\frac{\text{MFP}(M_{19})}{\text{MFP}(M_{19R})}$$

$$= 8\frac{21.177}{15.322}\sqrt{\frac{6.651/1.1857}{8.846/(1.128 \times 1.1857)}}\left(\frac{0.5257}{0.5318}\right) = 10.066$$

TABLE 8-7
Summary of internal iterations

i	τ_{cH}	π_{cH}	π_f	M_{19}	M_9	α	τ_f	τ_{tL}	π_{tL}
1	2.3875	15.322	1.7000	0.8861	0.8904	10.07	1.1281	0.7262	0.2375
2	2.4584	16.857	1.4542	0.7299	0.8419	8.833	1.1441	0.7279	0.2408
3	2.4379	16.403	1.5199	0.7766	0.8719	9.233	1.1376	0.7301	0.2391
4	2.4461	16.585	1.4930	0.7580	0.8586	9.077	1.1387	0.7290	0.2398
5	2.4448	16.556	1.4972	0.7609	0.8623	9.102	1.1389	0.7294	0.2396
...	...	...	...	...	...	...	...	...	...
10	2.4448	16.555	1.4973	0.7610	0.8617	9.103	1.1387	0.7293	0.2396

$$\tau_f = 1 + \frac{1-\tau_{tL}}{(1-\tau_{tL})_R}\,\frac{\tau_\lambda/\tau_r}{(\tau_\lambda/\tau_r)_R}\,\frac{1+\alpha_R}{1+\alpha}(\tau_{fR}-1)$$

$$= 1 + \frac{1-0.7262}{1-0.7262}\,\frac{6.651/1}{8.846/1.128}\,\frac{1+8}{1+10.066}(1.1857-1) = 1.1281$$

$$\tau_{tL} = 1 - \eta_{tL}(1-\pi_{tL}^{(\gamma_t-1)/\gamma_t}) = 1 - 0.9068(1-0.2349^{0.33/1.33}) = 0.7262$$

$$\pi_{tL} = \pi_{tL\,R}\sqrt{\frac{\tau_{tL}}{\tau_{tL\,R}}\,\frac{\text{MFP}(M_{9R})}{\text{MFP}(M_9)}} = 0.2349\sqrt{\frac{0.7262}{0.7262}\,\frac{0.5224}{0.5167}} = 0.2375$$

Since τ_{tL} is not within 0.0001 of its previous value, return to Eq. (A) and do another iteration. These data required 10 iterations, which are summarized in Table 8-7.

Remainder of calculations:

$$\dot{m}_0 = \dot{m}_{0R}\frac{1+\alpha}{1+\alpha_R}\,\frac{P_0\pi_r\pi_d\pi_f\pi_{cH}}{(P_0\pi_r\pi_d\pi_f\pi_{cH})_R}\sqrt{\frac{T_{t4R}}{T_{t4}}}$$

$$= 600\,\frac{1+9.103}{1+8}\,\frac{14.696\times 1.0\times 0.99\times 1.4973\times 16.555}{2.730\times 1.524\times 0.99\times 1.7\times 21.176}\sqrt{\frac{3000}{3000}} = 1638\text{ lbm}$$

$$f = \frac{\tau_\lambda - \tau_r\tau_f\tau_{cH}}{h_{PR}\eta_b/(c_pT_0) - \tau_\lambda}$$

$$= \frac{6.651 - 1\times 1.1387\times 2.448}{18{,}400\times 0.99/(0.24\times 518.7) - 6.651} = 0.02769$$

$$\frac{T_9}{T_0} = \frac{\tau_\lambda\tau_{tH}\tau_{tL}}{(P_{t9}/P_9)^{(\gamma_t-1)/\gamma_t}}\,\frac{c_{pc}}{c_{pt}}$$

$$= \frac{6.651\times 0.7580\times 0.7293}{1.5932^{0.33/1.33}}\,\frac{0.240}{0.276} = 2.848$$

$$\frac{V_9}{a_0} = M_9\sqrt{\frac{\gamma_tR_tT_9}{\gamma_cR_cT_0}} = 0.8617\sqrt{\frac{1.33\times 53.29}{1.40\times 53.36}(2.848)} = 1.4165$$

$$\frac{T_{19}}{T_0} = \frac{\tau_r \tau_f}{(P_{t19}/P_{19})^{(\gamma_c - 1)/\gamma_c}} = \frac{1.0 \times 1.1387}{1.4675^{1/3.5}} = 1.0205$$

$$\frac{V_{19}}{a_0} = M_{19}\sqrt{\frac{T_{19}}{T_0}} = 0.7610\sqrt{1.0205} = 0.7688$$

$$\frac{F}{\dot{m}_0} = \frac{a_0}{(1+\alpha)g_c}\left[(1+f)\frac{V_9}{a_0} - M_0 + \alpha\left(\frac{V_{19}}{a_0} - M_0\right)\right]$$

$$= \frac{1116.6/32.174}{1 + 9.1039}[1.02769(1.4165) + 9.103(0.7688)] = 29.04 \text{ lbf/(lbm/sec)}$$

$$S = \frac{3600 \times 0.02769}{10.103 \times 29.04}\,\frac{32.174}{32.174} = 0.3398 \text{ (lbm/hr)/lbf}$$

$$F = 1639 \times 29.04 = 47{,}570 \text{ lbf}$$

$$\left(\frac{N}{N_R}\right)_{\text{fan}} = \sqrt{\frac{T_0 \tau_r}{T_{0R}\tau_{rR}}\,\frac{\pi_f^{(\gamma-1)/\gamma} - 1}{\pi_{fR}^{(\gamma-1)/\gamma} - 1}}$$

$$= \sqrt{\frac{518.7 \times 1.0}{390 \times 1.128}\,\frac{1.4973^{0.4/1.4} - 1}{1.7^{0.4/1.4} - 1}} = 0.938$$

$$\left(\frac{N}{N_R}\right)_{\text{HPspool}} = \sqrt{\frac{T_0 \tau_r \tau_f}{(T_0 \tau_r \tau_f)_R}\,\frac{\pi_{cH}^{(\gamma-1)/\gamma} - 1}{\pi_{cHR}^{(\gamma-1)/\gamma} - 1}}$$

$$= \sqrt{\frac{518.7 \times 1.0 \times 1.1387}{390 \times 1.128 \times 1.1857}\,\frac{16.555^{0.4/1.4} - 1}{21.176^{0.4/1.4} - 1}} = 1.00$$

Example 8-9. In this example, we consider the variation in engine performance of a 270,000-N thrust, high-bypass-ratio turbofan engine with Mach number M_0, altitude, ambient temperature T_0, and throttle setting T_{t4}. The engine reference flight condition is sea-level static with the following values:

$$\alpha = 8 \qquad \pi_f = 1.77 \qquad \pi_{cH} = 20.34 \qquad T_{t4} = 1890 \text{ K} \qquad \dot{m}_0 = 760 \text{ kg/sec}$$

For the performance curves drawn in solid lines, the compressor pressure ratio was limited to 36, the combustor exit temperature T_{t4} was limited to 1890 K, and the compressor exit temperature T_{t3} was limited to 920 K. This engine has a throttle ratio TR of 1. At θ_0 values below 1.0, the engine is at the maximum compressor pressure ratio of 36 and T_{t4} is below its maximum value of 1890 K. For these conditions, the flow in the bypass stream is unchoked at sea level and does not choke at altitude until a Mach number of 0.34.

Figures 8-47 through 8-53 show the variations of thrust, thrust specific fuel consumption S, engine mass flow, corrected engine mass flow, bypass ratio, fan pressure ratio π_f, and high-pressure (HP) compressor pressure ratio π_{cH} with Mach number and altitude, respectively. The dashed lines in these figures show the engine performance with the combustor exit temperature T_{t4} limited to 1940 K.

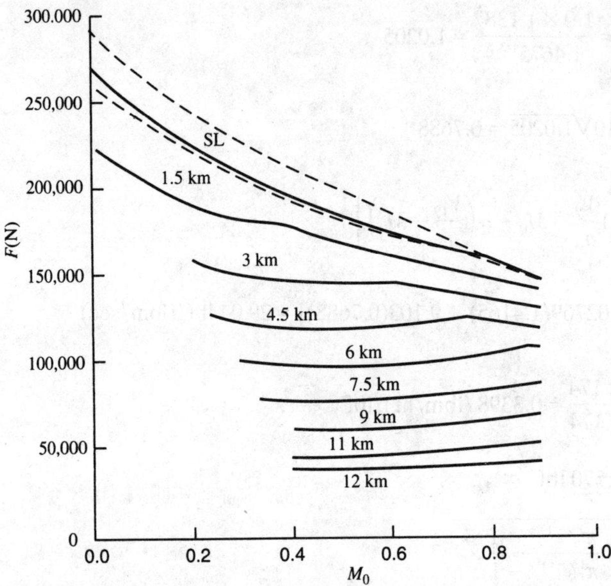

FIGURE 8-47
Maximum thrust of high-bypass-ratio turbofan.

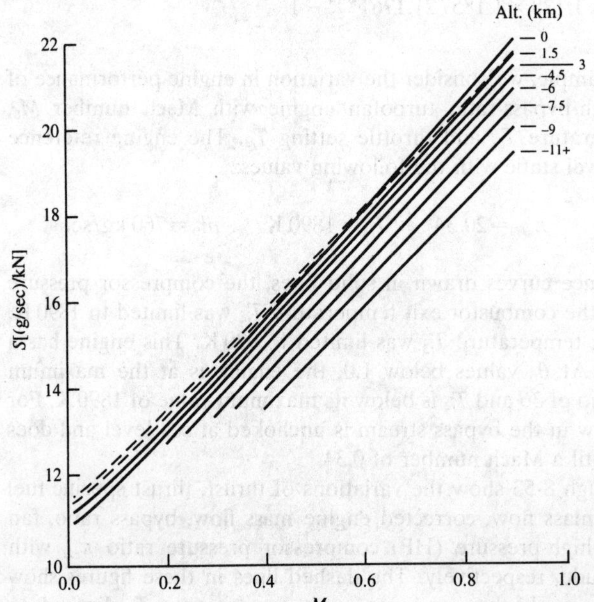

FIGURE 8-48
Thrust specific fuel consumption of high-bypass-ratio turbofan at maximum thrust.

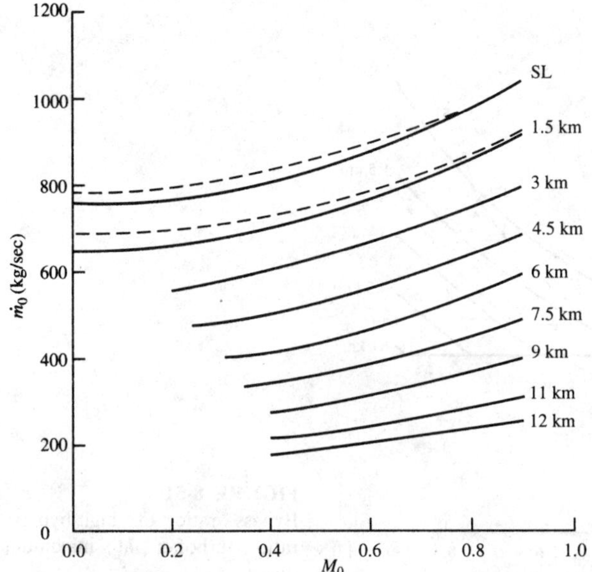

FIGURE 8-49
Mass flow rate of high-bypass-ratio turbofan at maximum thrust.

The corrected engine mass flow rate of Fig. 8-50 has the same trend with Mach number and altitude as the fan pressure ratio of Fig. 8-52 and the HP compressor pressure ratio of Fig. 8-53. Both the corrected mass flow rate and the HP compressor pressure ratio reach their maximum values when the bypass

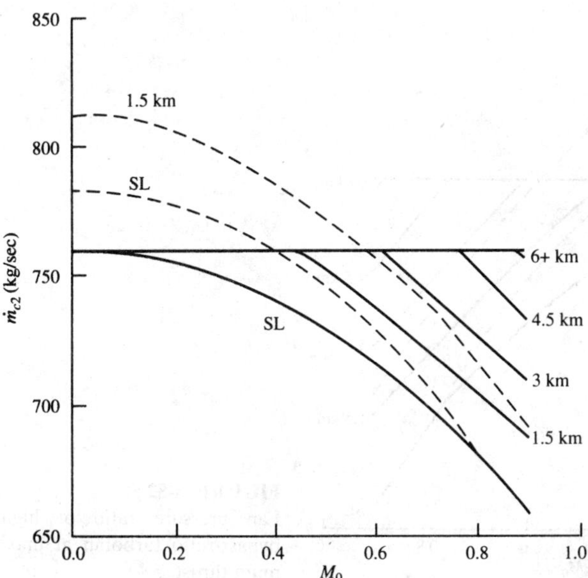

FIGURE 8-50
Corrected mass flow rate of high-bypass-ratio turbofan at maximum thrust.

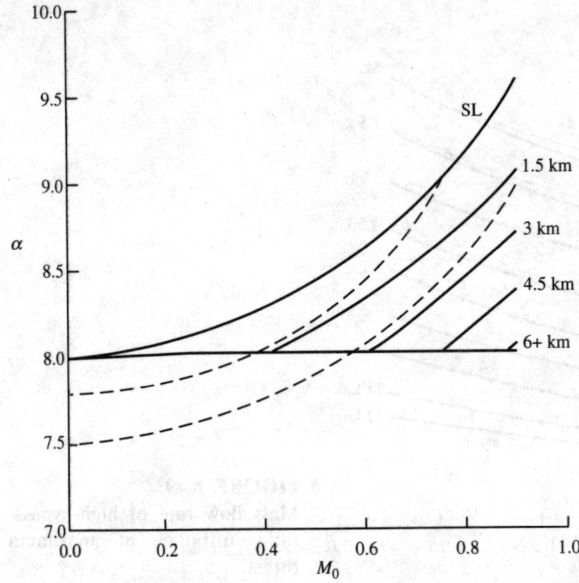

FIGURE 8-51
Bypass ratio of high-bypass-ratio turbofan at maximum thrust.

stream chokes (flight Mach of 0.34). Figure 8-51 shows that the engine bypass ratio at maximum thrust has a constant minimum value of about 8 when the bypass stream is choked.

The effects of ambient temperature T_0 and altitude on engine performance

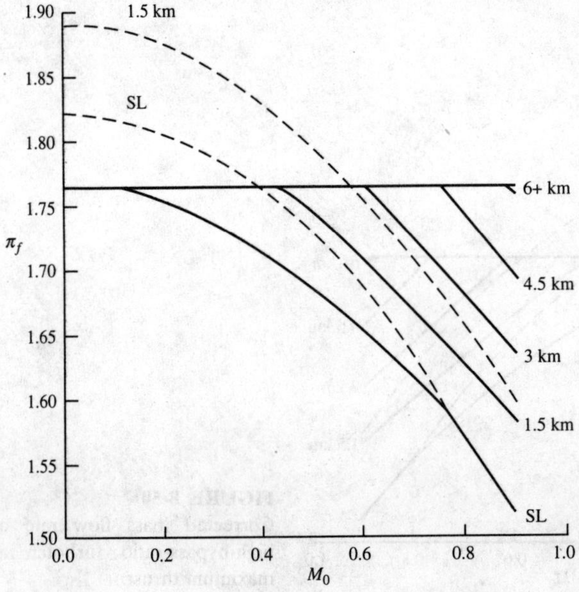

FIGURE 8-52
Fan pressure ratio of high-bypass-ratio turbofan at maximum thrust.

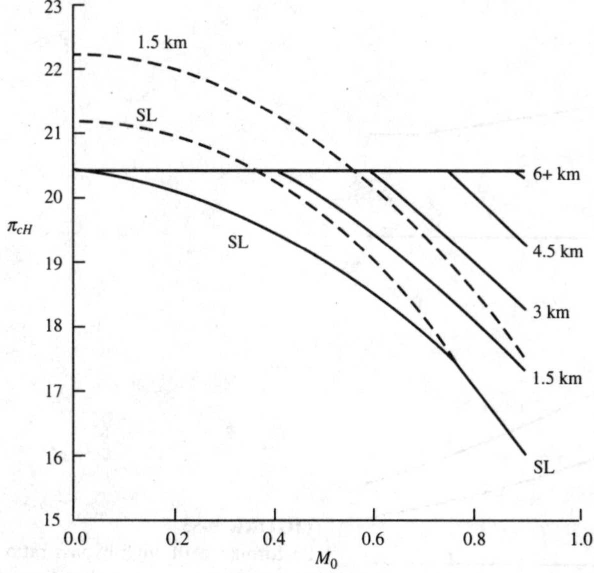

FIGURE 8-53
High-pressure compressor pressure ratio of high-bypass-ratio turbofan at maximum thrust.

at maximum thrust are shown in Figs. 8-54 and 8-55, respectively. For ambient temperatures below the reference value of 288.2 K ($\theta_0 < 1.0$), Fig. 8-54 shows that the limit of 36 for the compressor pressure ratio ($\pi_c = \pi_f \pi_{cH}$) holds the engine thrust, bypass ratio, and fan pressure ratio constant. Engine thrust drops off

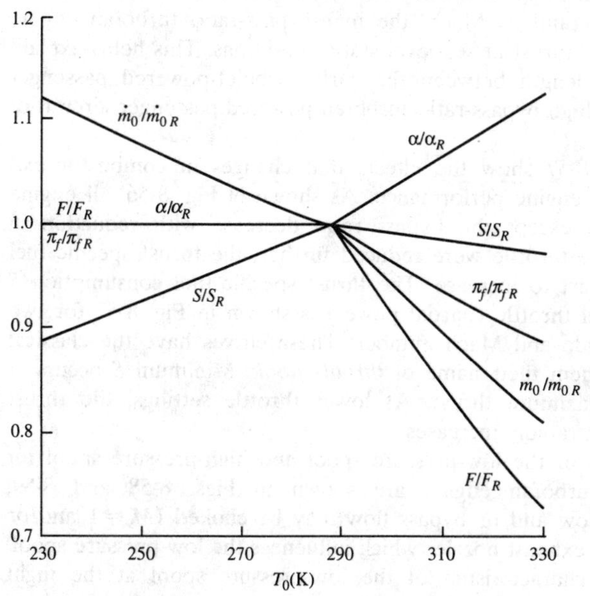

FIGURE 8-54
Performance of high-bypass-ratio turbofan versus T_0 at sea-level static, maximum thrust.

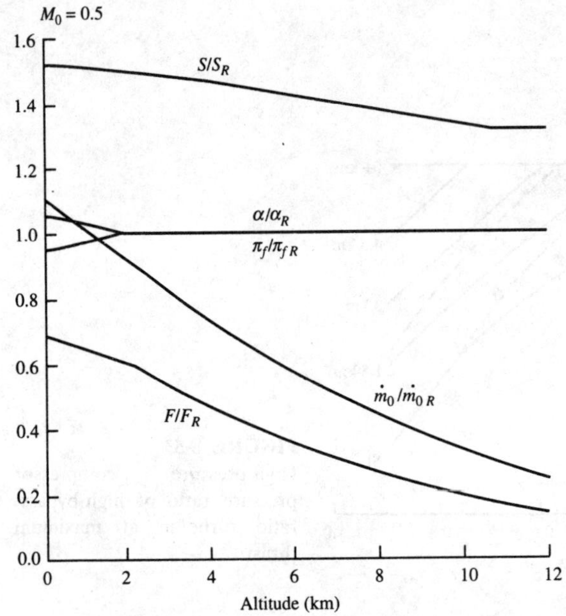

FIGURE 8-55
Performance of high-bypass-ratio turbofan at maximum thrust versus altitude.

rapidly with T_0 for $\theta_0 > 1.0$. The decreases in engine thrust, fuel consumption, and air mass flow rate with altitude are shown in Fig. 8-55 for a flight Mach number of 0.5. The decrease in engine thrust with altitude for the high-bypass-ratio turbofan engine is much greater than that of the dry turbojet (see Fig. 8-42). If both a high-bypass-ratio turbofan engine and a dry turbojet engine were sized to produce the same thrust at 9 km and 0.8 Mach, the high-bypass-ratio turbofan engine would have much greater thrust at sea-level static conditions. This helps explain the decrease in takeoff length between the early turbojet-powered passenger aircraft and the modern high-bypass-ratio turbofan-powered passenger aircraft of today.

Figures 8-56 and 8-57 show the effects that changes in combustor exit temperature T_{t4} have on engine performance. As shown in Fig. 8-56, all engine performance parameters except the bypass ratio decrease with reduction in engine throttle T_{t4}. If the throttle were reduced further, the thrust specific fuel consumption S would start to increase. The thrust specific fuel consumption S versus thrust F at partial throttle (partial power) is shown in Fig. 8-57 for two different values of altitude and Mach number. These curves have the classical hook shape that gives them their name of *throttle hook.* Minimum S occurs at about 50 percent of maximum thrust. At lower throttle settings, the thrust specific fuel consumption rapidly increases.

The characteristics of the low-pressure spool and high-pressure spool for this high-bypass-ratio turbofan engine are shown in Figs. 8-58 and 8-59, respectively. The core flow and/or bypass flow may be choked ($M_9 = 1$ and/or $M_{19} = 1$) at its respective exhaust nozzles which influences the low-pressure spool. Figure 8-58 shows the characteristics of the low-pressure spool at the flight

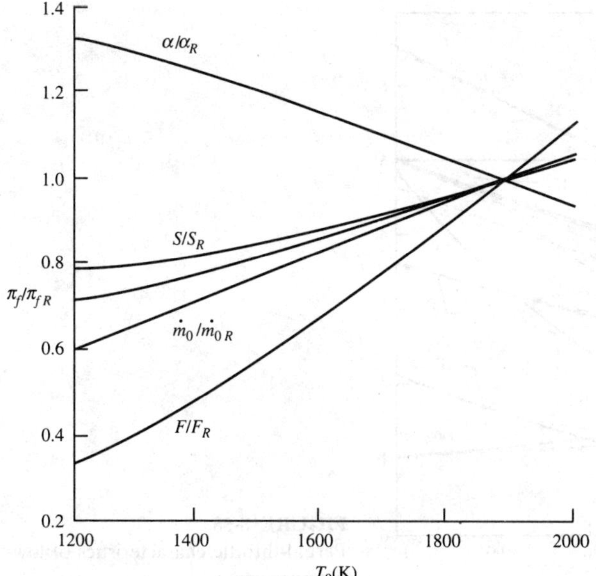

FIGURE 8-56
Performance of high-bypass-ratio turbofan versus T_{t4} at sea-level static conditions.

condition of 9 km and $M_0 = 0.8$ with solid lines, and at the sea-level static flight condition with dashed lines. At sea-level static conditions, the bypass stream is unchoked for all operating conditions of the low-pressure spool, and the core exhaust nozzle unchokes at about 95 percent of N_{cL}. However, at 9 km and

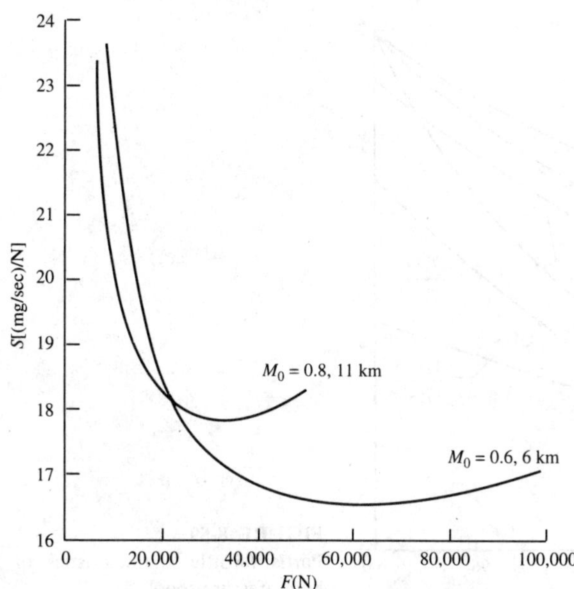

FIGURE 8-57
Partial-throttle performance of high-bypass-ratio turbofan.

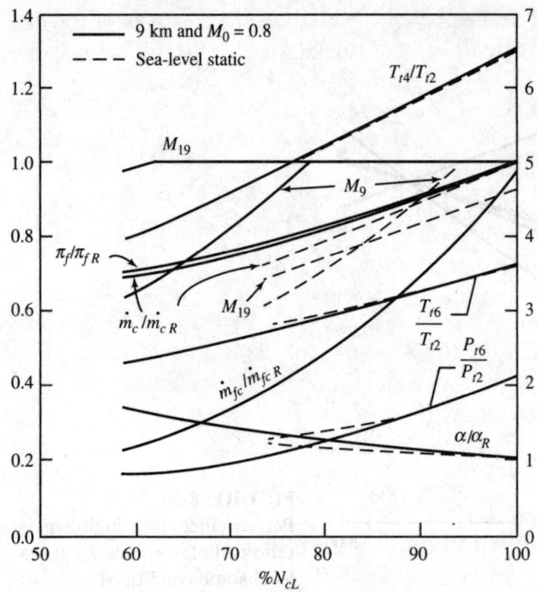

FIGURE 8-58
Partial-throttle characteristics of low-pressure spool.

$M_0 = 0.8$, the core exhaust nozzle unchokes at about 78 percent of N_{cL}, and the bypass stream unchokes at about 61 percent of N_{cL}. The variation of fan pressure ratio and corrected fuel flow with the corrected speed of the low-pressure spool is unaffected by the flight condition. The variations in T_{t6}/T_{t2}, P_{t6}/P_{t2}, and α/α_R with

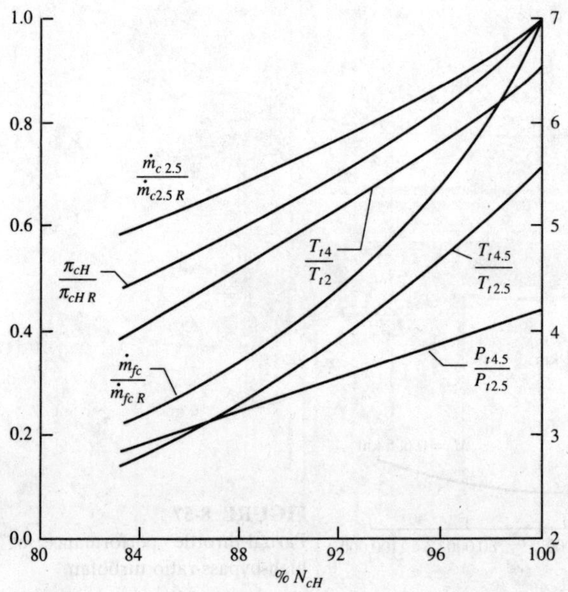

FIGURE 8-59
Partial-throttle characteristics of high-pressure spool.

corrected speed are small above 80 percent of N_{cL}. As in the single-spool engine, there is a one-to-one correspondence of the temperature ratio T_{t4}/T_{t2} with the corrected speed of the spool.

The pumping characteristics of the high-pressure spool are shown in Fig. 8-59. These are the same characteristic curves that we found for the gas generator of the single-spool turbojet (Fig. 8-15).

Compressor Stages on Low-Pressure Spool

Modern high-bypass-ratio turbofan engines and other turbofan engines are constructed with compressor stages on the low-pressure spool as shown in Fig. 8-60. This addition of compressor stages to the spool that powers the fan gives a better balance between the high- and low-pressure turbines. This change in engine layout also adds two dependent variables to the nine we had for the performance analysis of the turbofan engine in the previous section. These two new variables are the low-pressure compressor's total temperature ratio τ_{cL} and total pressure ratio π_{cL}.

Since the low-pressure compressor and the fan are on the same shaft, the enthalpy rise across the low-pressure compressor will be proportional to the enthalpy rise across the fan during normal operation. For a calorically perfect gas, we can write

$$T_{t2.5} - T_{t2} = K(T_{t13} - T_{t2})$$

or

$$\tau_{cL} - 1 = K(\tau_f - 1)$$

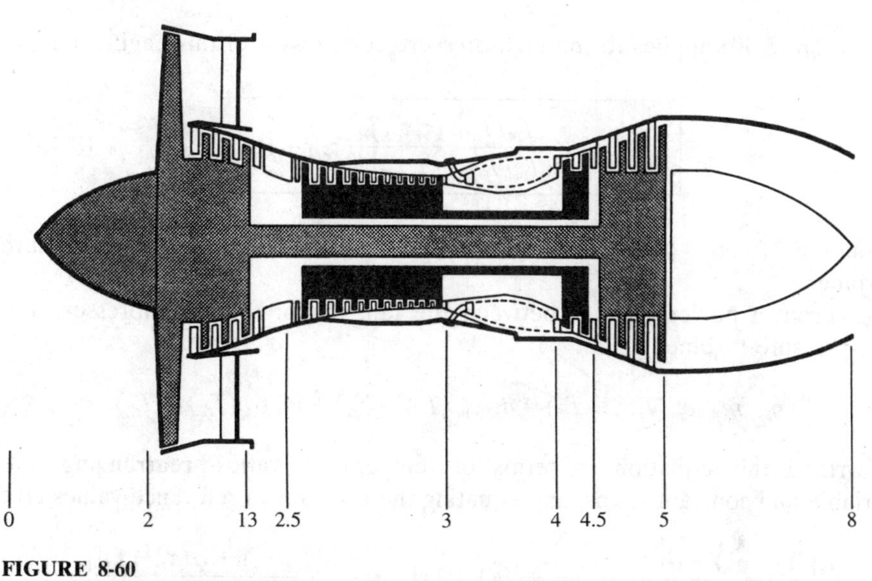

FIGURE 8-60
Turbofan engine with compressor stages on low-pressure spool. (*Courtesy of Pratt & Whitney.*)

Using reference conditions to replace the constant K, we can solve the above equation for τ_{cL} as

$$\tau_{cL} = 1 + (\tau_f - 1)\frac{\tau_{cL\,R} - 1}{\tau_{fR} - 1} \tag{8-53}$$

The pressure ratio for the low-pressure compressor is given by Eq. (8–43):

$$\pi_{cL} = [1 + \eta_{cL}(\tau_{cL} - 1)]^{\gamma_c/(\gamma_c - 1)} \tag{8-43}$$

In a manner like that used to obtain Eq. (8-46), the following equation for the bypass ratio results:

$$\alpha = \alpha_R \frac{\pi_{cL\,R}\pi_{cH\,R}/\pi_{fR}}{\pi_{cL}\pi_{cH}/\pi_f}\sqrt{\frac{\tau_\lambda/(\tau_r\tau_f)}{[\tau_\lambda/(\tau_r\tau_f)]_R}}\frac{\mathrm{MFP}(M_{19})}{\mathrm{MFP}(M_{19\,R})} \tag{8-54}$$

By rewriting Eq. (8-47) for this engine configuration, the engine mass flow rate is given by

$$\dot{m}_0 = \dot{m}_{0\,R}\frac{1+\alpha}{1+\alpha_R}\frac{P_0\pi_r\pi_d\pi_{cL}\pi_{cH}}{(P_0\pi_r\pi_d\pi_{cL}\pi_{cH})_R}\sqrt{\frac{T_{t4\,R}}{T_{t4}}} \tag{8-55}$$

Equation (8-40) applies to the high-pressure compressor of this engine and is

$$\tau_{cH} = 1 + \frac{T_{t4}/T_0}{(T_{t4}/T_0)_R}\frac{(\tau_r\tau_{cL})_R}{\tau_r\tau_{cL}}(\tau_{cH} - 1)_R \tag{8-40}$$

Equations (8-36), (8-37), and (8-38) apply to the high- and low-pressure turbines.

From a power balance between the fan, low-pressure compressor, and low-pressure turbine, we get

$$\eta_{mL}\dot{m}_{4.5}c_{pt}(T_{t4.5} - T_{t5}) = \dot{m}_F c_{pc}(T_{t13} - T_{t2}) + \dot{m}_C c_{pc}(T_{t2.5} - T_{t2})$$

Rewriting this equation in terms of temperature ratios, rearranging into variable and constant terms, and equating the constant to reference values give

$$\frac{\tau_r[(\tau_{cL} - 1) + \alpha(\tau_f - 1)]}{(T_{t4}/T_0)(1 - \tau_{tL})} = \eta_{mL}(1 + f)\tau_{tH} = \left\{\frac{\tau_r[\tau_{cL} - 1 + \alpha(\tau_f - 1)]}{(T_{t4}/T_0)(1 - \tau_{tL})}\right\}_R$$

Using Eq. (8-53), we substitute for τ_{cL} on the left side of the above equation, solve for τ_f, and get

$$\boxed{\tau_f = 1 + (\tau_{fR} - 1)\left[\frac{1-\tau_{tL}}{(1-\tau_{tL})_R}\,\frac{\tau_\lambda/\tau_r}{(\tau_\lambda/\tau_r)_R}\,\frac{\tau_{cL\,R} - 1 + \alpha_R(\tau_{fR}-1)}{\tau_{cL\,R} - 1 + \alpha(\tau_{fR}-1)}\right]} \tag{8-56}$$

Solution Scheme

The principal dependent variables for the turbofan engine are π_{tL}, τ_{tL}, α, τ_{cL}, π_{cL}, τ_{cH}, π_{cH}, τ_f, π_f, M_9, and M_{19}. These variables are dependent on each other plus the engine's independent variables—throttle setting and flight condition. The functional interrelationship of the dependent variables can be written as

$$\tau_{cH} = f_1(\tau_{cL}) \qquad M_{19} = f_7(\pi_f)$$

$$\pi_{cH} = f_2(\tau_{ch}) \qquad M_9 = f_8(\pi_f, \pi_{cH}, \pi_{tL})$$

$$\tau_f = f_3(\tau_{tL}, \alpha) \qquad \pi_{tL} = f_9(\tau_{tL}, M_9)$$

$$\pi_f = f_4(\tau_f) \qquad \tau_{tL} = f_{10}(\pi_{tL})$$

$$\tau_{cL} = f_5(\tau_f) \qquad \alpha = f_{11}(\tau_f, \pi_{cH}, M_{19})$$

$$\pi_{cL} = f_6(\tau_{cL})$$

This system of 11 equations is solved by functional iteration, starting with reference quantities as initial values for π_{tL}, τ_{tL}, and τ_f. The following equations are calculated for the 11 dependent variables in the order listed until successive values of τ_{tL} do not change more than a specified amount (say, 0.0001):

$$\tau_{cH} = 1 + \frac{T_{t4}/T_0}{(T_{t4}/T_0)_R}\,\frac{(\tau_r\tau_{cL})_R}{\tau_r\tau_{cL}}(\tau_{cH}-1)_R \tag{8-57a}$$

$$\pi_{cH} = [1 + \eta_{cH}(\tau_{cH}-1)]^{\gamma_c/(\gamma_c-1)} \tag{8-57b}$$

$$\pi_f = [1 + (\tau_f - 1)\eta_f]^{\gamma_c/(\gamma_c-1)} \tag{8-57c}$$

$$\frac{P_{t19}}{P_0} = \pi_r\pi_d\pi_f\pi_{fn} \tag{8-57d}$$

$$\text{If} \quad \frac{P_{t19}}{P_0} < \left(\frac{\gamma_c+1}{2}\right)^{\gamma_c/(\gamma_c-1)} \quad \text{then} \quad \frac{P_{t19}}{P_{19}} = \frac{P_{t19}}{P_0}$$

$$\text{else} \quad \frac{P_{t19}}{P_{19}} = \left(\frac{\gamma_c+1}{2}\right)^{\gamma_c/(\gamma_c-1)} \tag{8-57e}$$

$$M_{19} = \sqrt{\frac{2}{\gamma_c - 1}\left[\left(\frac{P_{t19}}{P_{19}}\right)^{(\gamma_c-1)/\gamma_c} - 1\right]} \tag{8-57f}$$

$$\frac{P_{t9}}{P_0} = \pi_r \pi_d \pi_{cL} \pi_{cH} \pi_b \pi_{th} \pi_{tL} \pi_n \tag{8-57g}$$

$$\text{If} \quad \frac{P_{t9}}{P_0} < \left(\frac{\gamma_t + 1}{2}\right)^{\gamma_t/(\gamma_t - 1)} \quad \text{then} \quad \frac{P_{t9}}{P_9} = \frac{P_{t9}}{P_0} \tag{8-57h}$$

$$\text{else} \quad \frac{P_{t9}}{P_9} = \left(\frac{\gamma_t + 1}{2}\right)^{\gamma_t/(\gamma_t - 1)}$$

$$M_9 = \sqrt{\frac{2}{\gamma_t - 1}\left[\left(\frac{P_{t9}}{P_9}\right)^{(\gamma_t - 1)/\gamma_t} - 1\right]} \tag{8-57i}$$

$$\alpha = \alpha_R \frac{\pi_{cLR}\pi_{cHR}/\pi_{fR}}{\pi_{cL}\pi_{cH}/\pi_f} \sqrt{\frac{\tau_\lambda/(\tau_r \tau_f)}{[\tau_\lambda/(\tau_r \tau_f)]_R} \frac{\text{MFP}(M_{19})}{\text{MFP}(M_{19R})}} \tag{8-57j}$$

$$\tau_f = 1 + (\tau_{fR} - 1)\left[\frac{1 - \tau_{tL}}{(1 - \tau_{tL})_R} \frac{\tau_\lambda/\tau_r}{(\tau_\lambda/\tau_r)_R} \frac{\tau_{cLR} - 1 + \alpha_R(\tau_{fR} - 1)}{\tau_{cLR} - 1 + \alpha(\tau_{fR} - 1)}\right] \tag{8-57k}$$

$$\tau_{cL} = 1 + (\tau_f - 1)\frac{\tau_{cLR} - 1}{\tau_{fR} - 1} \tag{8-57l}$$

$$\pi_{cL} = [1 + \eta_{cL}(\tau_{cL} - 1)]^{\gamma_c/(\gamma_c - 1)} \tag{8-57m}$$

$$\tau_{tL} = 1 - \eta_{tL}(1 - \pi_{tL}^{(\gamma_t - 1)/\gamma_t}) \tag{8-57n}$$

$$\pi_{tL} = \pi_{tLR}\sqrt{\frac{\tau_{tL}}{\tau_{tLR}}} \frac{\text{MFP}(M_{9R})}{\text{MFP}(M_9)} \tag{8-57o}$$

Summary of Performance Equations—Turbofan Engine with Compressor Stages on Low-Pressure Spool

INPUTS:

Choices

Flight parameters:	M_0, T_0 (K, °R), P_0 (kPa, psia)
Throttle setting:	T_{t4} (K, °R)

Design constants

π's:	$\pi_{d\,\max}$, π_b, π_{tH}, π_{AB}, π_n, π_{fn}
τ's:	τ_{tH}
η's:	η_f, η_{cL}, η_{cH}, η_b, η_{AB}, η_{mH}, η_{mL}
Gas properties:	γ_c, γ_t, c_{pc}, c_{pt} [kJ/(kg · K), Btu/(lbm · °R)]
Fuel:	h_{PR} (kJ/kg, Btu/lbm)

Reference conditions

Flight parameters:	M_{0R}, T_{0R} (K, °R), P_{0R} (kPa, psia), τ_{rR}, π_{rR}
Throttle setting:	T_{t4R} (K, °R)
Component behavior:	π_{dR}, π_{fR}, π_{cLR}, π_{cHR}, π_{tL}, τ_{fR}, τ_{cHR}, τ_{tLR}, α_R, m_{9R}, M_{19R}

OUTPUTS:

Overall performance:	F (N, lbf), $\dot{m}_0$ (kg/sec, lbm/sec), f, $S\left(\frac{\text{mg/sec}}{\text{N}}, \frac{\text{lbm/hr}}{\text{lbf}}\right)$, η_P, η_T, η_O
Component behavior:	α, π_f, π_{cL}, π_{cH}, π_{tL}, τ_f, τ_{cH}, τ_{tL}, f, M_9, M_{19}, N_{fan}, N_{HPspool}
Exhaust nozzle pressure:	P_0/P_9, P_0/P_{19}

Equations in order of calculation:

Equations (8-52*a*) through (8-52*j*)

Set initial values: $\tau_{tL} = \tau_{tL\,R}$ $\quad \tau_f = \tau_{fR}$ $\quad \tau_{cL} = \tau_{cL\,R}$ $\quad \pi_{tL} = \pi_{tL\,R}$

Equations (8-57*a*) through (8-57*o*)

$$\dot{m}_0 = \dot{m}_{0R}\frac{1+\alpha}{1+\alpha_R}\frac{P_0\pi_r\pi_d\pi_{cL}\pi_{cH}}{(P_0\pi_r\pi_d\pi_{cL}\pi_{cH})_R}\sqrt{\frac{T_{t4R}}{T_{t4}}} \tag{8-57p}$$

$$f = \frac{\tau_\lambda - \tau_r\tau_{cL}\tau_{cH}}{h_{PR}\eta_b/(c_pT_0) - \tau_\lambda} \tag{8-57q}$$

Equations (8-52*z*) through (8-52*ag*)

$$\left(\frac{N}{N_R}\right)_{\text{HPspool}} = \sqrt{\frac{T_0\tau_r\tau_{cL}}{(T_0\tau_r\tau_{cL})_R}\frac{\pi_{cH}^{(\gamma-1)/\gamma}-1}{\pi_{cHR}^{(\gamma-1)/\gamma}-1}} \tag{8-57r}$$

Equations (8-52*ai*) through (8-52*ak*)

8-6 TURBOFAN WITH AFTERBURNING—MIXED-FLOW EXHAUST STREAM

Modern fighter aircraft and advanced bombers use the mixed-flow exhaust turbofan engine with afterburning like that shown in Fig. 8-61. These engines

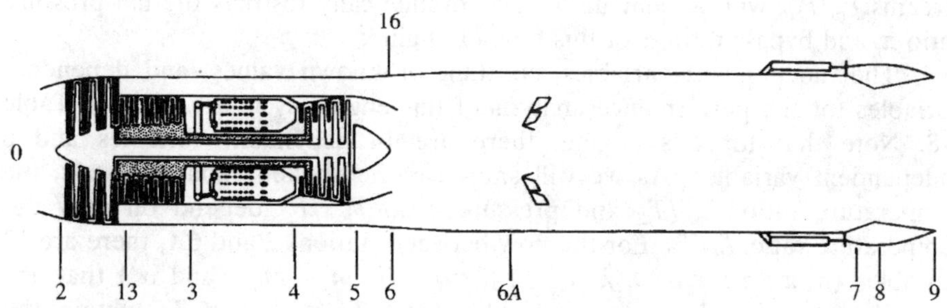

FIGURE 8-61
Mixed-flow exhaust turbofan engine with afterburning. (*Courtesy of Pratt & Whitney.*)

TABLE 8-8
Performance analysis variables for mixed-flow exhaust turbofan engine

	Variables		
Component	**Independent**	**Constant or known**	**Dependent**
Engine	M_0, T_0, P_0		$\dot{m}_0$, α
Diffuser		$\pi_d = f(M_0)$, τ_d	
Fan			π_f, τ_f
High-pressure compressor			π_{cH}, τ_{cH}
Burner	T_{t4}	π_b	
High-pressure turbine		π_{tH}, τ_{tH}	
Low-pressure turbine			π_{tL}, τ_{tL}
Mixer		$\pi_{M\,\max}$	π_M, τ_M, M_6, M_{16}, α', M_{6A}
Afterburner	T_{t7}		
		π_{AB}	
Nozzle	$\dfrac{P_0}{P_9}$ or $\dfrac{A_9}{A_8}$	π_n, τ_n	
Total number	6		14

have good fuel consumption when operated dry (afterburner off) and high specific thrust when the afterburner is turned on. This type of engine is normally designed with choked flow at stations 4, 4.5, and 8. The variable-area exhaust nozzle is controlled by the engine control system so that the upstream turbomachinery is unaffected by the afterburner operation.

The mixing of the core stream and bypass stream in the fixed-area mixer adds six additional dependent variables to the performance analysis (π_M, τ_M, M_6, M_{16}, M_{6A}, and α'). Since the static pressures at stations 6 and 16 must be equal for operating conditions ($P_6 = P_{16}$), the total pressure ratio of the two streams P_{t6}/P_{t16} will be near unity. This dramatically restricts the fan pressure ratio π_f and bypass ratio α of this type of engine.

The independent variables, constant or known values, and dependent variables for the performance analysis of this engine cycle are listed in Table 8-8. Note that for this engine, there are 14 dependent variables and 6 independent variables. As we will show for the choked exhaust nozzle, the temperature ratio T_{t6A}/T_{t2} and pressure ratio P_{t6A}/P_{t2} depend on only the temperature ratio T_{t4}/T_{t2}. For the flow between stations 2 and 6A, there are 13 variables (α, π_f, τ_f, π_{cH}, τ_{cH}, π_{tL}, π_M, τ_M, M_6, M_{16}, M_{6A}, and α') that are dependent on 3 independent variables (M_0, T_0, and T_{t4}). To obtain the performance of this engine, we need to write an equation for each dependent variable in terms of the independent variables and other dependent variables.

The equations for the performance analysis of the mixed-flow turbofan engine with afterburner are developed by making the assumptions and using the methods for both the turbojet engine and separate-exhaust turbofan engine. The goal is to obtain independent equations relating the dependent variables of Table 8-8. The equations to be developed are represented in turn by the following 14 functional relationships between the 14 dependent variables of interest:

$\tau_{tL} = f_1(\tau_f, M_6, M_{16}, \alpha')$ $\qquad \pi_{tL} = f_2(\tau_{tL})$

$\tau_f = f_3(\tau_{tL}, \alpha)$ $\qquad \pi_f = f_4(\tau_f)$

$\tau_{cH} = f_5(\tau_f)$ $\qquad \pi_{cH} = f_6(\tau_{cH})$

$\alpha = f_7(\alpha')$ $\qquad M_6 = f_8(\tau_{tL}, \pi_{tL})$

$M_{16} = f_9(\pi_{cH}, \pi_{tL}, M_6)$ $\qquad \tau_M = f_{10}(\tau_f, \tau_{tL})$

$M_{6A} = f_{11}(M_6, M_{16}, \tau_M)$ $\qquad \pi_M = f_{12}(\alpha', \tau_M, M_6, M_{6A})$

$\alpha' = f_{13}(\pi_{tL}, \pi_M, \tau_{tL}, \tau_M)$ $\qquad$ choked exhaust nozzle

$\alpha' = f_{13}(\pi_f, \pi_{cH}, \pi_{tL}, \pi_M, \tau_{tL}, \tau_M)$ $\qquad$ unchoked exhaust nozzle

$\dot{m}_0 = f_{14}(\pi_f, \pi_{cH}, \alpha)$

Please notice that each equation can be solved, in principle, in the order listed for given initial estimates of the two component performance variables τ_{tL} and α'. As the solution progresses, these estimates are compared with the newly computed values and iterated, if necessary, until convergence is obtained. We start the analysis with the turbomachinery.

High-Pressure and Low-Pressure Turbines

The flow is assumed to be choked at stations 4 and 4.5. Thus Eq. (8-36) applies for the high-pressure turbine, or

$$\boxed{\text{Constant values of } \pi_{tH},\ \tau_{tH},\ \dot{m}_{c4},\ \text{and } \dot{m}_{c4.5}} \tag{8-36}$$

From Eq. (7-17), we can write

$$T_t = \left(\frac{PAM}{\dot{m}}\right)^2 \frac{\gamma g_c}{R}\left(1 + \frac{\gamma - 1}{2} M^2\right)$$

There follows, with $P_6 = P_{16}$ and $\alpha' = \dot{m}_{16}/\dot{m}_6$,

$$\frac{T_{t6}}{T_{t16}} = \left(\frac{A_6}{A_{16}}\frac{M_6}{M_{16}}\alpha'\right)^2 \frac{\gamma_6}{\gamma_{16}}\frac{R_{16}}{R_6}\frac{1 + [(\gamma_6 - 1)/2]M_6^2}{1 + [(\gamma_{16} - 1)/2]M_{16}^2}$$

The ratio T_{t6}/T_{t16} can also be written in terms of τ_{tL} as

$$\frac{T_{t6}}{T_{t16}} = \frac{T_{t4}}{T_{t2}}\frac{\tau_{tH}\tau_{tL}}{\tau_f}$$

Equating the last two equations and solving for τ_{tL} gives

$$\tau_{tL} = \frac{T_{t2}}{T_{t4}} \frac{\tau_f}{\tau_{tH}} \left(\frac{A_6}{A_{16}} \frac{M_6}{M_{16}} \alpha' \right)^2 \frac{\gamma_6}{\gamma_{16}} \frac{R_{16}}{R_6} \frac{1 + [(\gamma_6 - 1)/2] M_6^2}{1 + [(\gamma_{16} - 1)/2] M_{16}^2} \tag{8-58}$$

From the definition of the turbine efficiency, we write

$$\pi_{tL} = \left(1 - \frac{1 - \tau_{tL}}{\eta_{tL}} \right)^{(\gamma_t - 1)/\gamma_t} \tag{8-59}$$

FAN TEMPERATURE AND PRESSURE RATIO (τ_f, π_f). Since the low-pressure turbine drives only the fan, Eqs. (8-50) and (8-51) both apply for the mixed-flow turbofan engine:

$$\tau_f = 1 + \frac{1 - \tau_{tL}}{(1 - \tau_{tL})_R} \frac{\tau_\lambda/\tau_r}{(\tau_\lambda/\tau_r)_R} \frac{1 + \alpha_R}{1 + \alpha} (\tau_{fR} - 1) \tag{8-50}$$

where

$$\pi_f = [1 + (\tau_f - 1)\eta_f]^{\gamma_c/(\gamma_c - 1)} \tag{8-51}$$

HIGH-PRESSURE COMPRESSOR (τ_{cH}, π_{cH}). The power balance between the high-pressure turbine and the high-pressure compressor (high-pressure spool) for the separate-exahust turbofan engine also applies to the mixed-flow turbofan engine. Thus

$$\tau_{cH} = 1 + \frac{T_{t4}/T_0}{(T_{t4}/T_0)_R} \frac{(\tau_r \tau_f)_R}{\tau_r \tau_f} (\tau_{cH} - 1)_R \tag{8-48}$$

From the definition of compressor efficiency, π_{cH} is given by

$$\pi_{cH} = [1 + \eta_{cH}(\tau_{cH} - 1)]^{\gamma_c/(\gamma_c - 1)} \tag{8-49}$$

ENGINE BYPASS RATIO α. The bypass ratio of the engine α is related to the bypass ratio of the mixer α' by

$$\alpha' = \frac{\alpha}{1 + f} \tag{8-60}$$

Solution for Mixer Performance

MACH NUMBER AT STATION 6 M_6**.** Since the mass flow rate at the entrance to the low-pressure turbine (station 4.5) equals that at the core entrance to the mixer (station 6),

$$\dot{m}_{4.5} = \frac{P_{t4.5}}{\sqrt{T_{t4.5}}} A_{4.5}\,\text{MFP}(M_{4.5}) = \dot{m}_6 = \frac{P_{t6}}{\sqrt{T_{t6}}} A_6\,\text{MFP}(M_6)$$

We assume that the areas are constant at stations 4.5 and 6, there is isentropic flow from station 5 to 6, and the flow is choked at station 4.5. Then

$$\frac{P_{t4.5}/P_{t6}}{\sqrt{T_{t4.5}/T_{t6}}}\frac{1}{\text{MFP}(M_6)} = \frac{\pi_{tL}/\sqrt{\tau_{tL}}}{\text{MFP}(M_6)} = \frac{A_6}{A_{4.5}\,\text{MFP}(M_{4.5})}$$

Using the reference condition to evaluate the constant on the right-hand side of the above equation and solving for $\text{MFP}(M_6)$ gives

$$\boxed{\text{MFP}(M_6) = \text{MFP}(M_{6R})\sqrt{\frac{\tau_{tL}}{\tau_{tL\,r}}\frac{\pi_{tL\,R}}{\pi_{tL}}}} \tag{8-61}$$

The Mach number at station 6 follows directly from the mass flow parameter MFP.

MACH NUMBER AT STATION 16 M_{16}**.** The definition of the total pressure yields M_{16} once P_{t16}/P_{16} is evaluated. Since $P_6 = P_{16}$,

$$\frac{P_{t16}}{P_{16}} = \frac{P_{t16}}{P_{t6}}\frac{P_{t6}}{P_6} = \frac{P_{t16}}{P_{t6}}\left(1 + \frac{\gamma_6 - 1}{2}M_6^2\right)^{\gamma_6/(\gamma_6-1)}.$$

where, by referencing and assuming both $P_{t13} = P_{t2.5}$ and isentropic flow from station 13 to 16,

$$\frac{P_{t16}}{P_{t6}} = \frac{P_{t13}}{P_{t2.5}\pi_{cH}\pi_b\pi_{tH}\pi_{tL}} = \frac{(\pi_{ch}\pi_{tL})_R}{\pi_{cH}\pi_{tL}}\left(\frac{P_{t16}}{P_{t6}}\right)_R$$

so that

$$\boxed{\frac{P_{t16}}{P_{16}} = \frac{(\tau_{cH}\pi_{tL})_R}{\pi_{cH}\pi_{tL}}\left(\frac{P_{t16}}{P_{t6}}\right)_R\left(1 + \frac{\gamma_6 - 1}{2}M_6^2\right)^{\gamma_6/(\gamma_6-1)}} \tag{8-62a}$$

For the flow to be possible, $P_{t16} > P_{16}$.

With P_{t16}/P_{16} known, then

$$\boxed{M_{16} = \left\{\frac{2}{\gamma_{16} - 1}\left[\left(\frac{P_{t16}}{P_{16}}\right)^{(\gamma_{16}-1)/\gamma_{16}} - 1\right]\right\}^{1/2}} \tag{8-62b}$$

where, for the flow to be subsonic, $M_{16} < 1.0$.

MIXER TEMPERATURE RATIO τ_M. From Eq. (7-74), we have

$$\tau_M \equiv \frac{T_{t6A}}{T_{t6}} = \frac{c_{p6}}{c_{p6A}} \frac{1 + \alpha'(c_{p16}/c_{p6})(T_{t16}/T_{t6})}{1 + \alpha'} \tag{8-63a}$$

where

$$\frac{T_{t16}}{T_{t6}} = \frac{T_{t2}}{T_{t4}} \frac{\tau_f}{\tau_{tH}\tau_{tL}} \tag{8-63b}$$

MACH NUMBER AT STATION 6A M_{6A} AND MIXER PRESSURE RATIO π_M. The Mach number at station 6A is given by

$$M_{6A} = \sqrt{\frac{2\Phi}{1 - 2\gamma_{6A}\Phi + \sqrt{1 - 2(\gamma_{6A} + 1)\Phi}}} \tag{8-64}$$

with Φ and ϕ given by Eqs. (7-79) and (7-78), respectively. Using Eqs. (7-68) and (7-81), we see that the total pressure ratio of the mixer π_M is given by

$$\pi_M = \pi_{M\max} \frac{(1 + \alpha')\sqrt{\tau_M}}{1 + A_{16}/A_6} \frac{\text{MFP}(M_6, \gamma_6, R_6)}{\text{MFP}(M_{6A}, \gamma_{6A}, R_{6A})} \tag{8-65}$$

MIXER BYPASS RATIO α'. The engine exhaust nozzle normally operates in the choked condition but may become unchoked at reduced throttle settings, flight Mach numbers, and altitudes. Each of these operating conditions must be considered separately in determining α'. However, since α' is unaffected by afterburning, it is not necessary to consider the afterburning case separately. This follows from the facts that the afterburner is not used in the unchoked exhaust nozzle condition and that, during choked afterburner operation, A_8 is modulated to keep $A_8\pi_{AB}\sqrt{\tau_{AB}}$ constant so that the upstream flow remains uninfluenced by afterburning. The development to follow, therefore, is based on no afterburning, but applies equally well to the choked-exhaust-nozzle afterburning case.

From the conservation of mass and the definition of α'

$$1 + \alpha' = \frac{\dot{m}_8}{\dot{m}_{4.5}} = \frac{\dot{m}_9}{\dot{m}_{4.5}}$$

For choked exhaust nozzle and low-pressure turbine inlet nozzles, Eq. (8-11*a*) yields

$$1 + \alpha' = \frac{\dot{m}_8}{\dot{m}_{4.5}} = \frac{P_{t8}A_8}{\sqrt{T_{t8}}} \frac{\sqrt{T_{t4.5}}}{P_{t4.5}A_{4.5}} \frac{\Gamma_8}{\sqrt{R_8}} \frac{\sqrt{R_{4.5}}}{\Gamma_{4.5}}$$

The exhaust nozzle control system holds the throat area of the exhaust nozzle A_8 constant when the nozzle is choked, or

$$\frac{P_{t9}}{P_0} \geq \left(\frac{\gamma_8 + 1}{2}\right)^{\gamma_8/(\gamma_8 - 1)}$$

In addition, the choked area at station 4.5 $A_{4.5}$ is constant, and the gas properties ($R_{4.5}$ and $\Gamma_{4.5}$) are considered constant. Rewriting in terms of τ's and π's and separating out the constant terms give

$$1 + \alpha' = \frac{\dot{m}_8}{\dot{m}_{4.5}} = \frac{\pi_{tL}\pi_M}{\sqrt{\tau_{tL}\tau_M}} \frac{\Gamma_8}{\sqrt{R_8}} \left(\frac{A_8}{A_{4.5}} \frac{\sqrt{R_{4.5}}}{\Gamma_{4.5}}\right)$$

Replacing the constant term within the parentheses with reference conditions and solving for α' give, for the *choked* exhaust nozzle,

$$\boxed{\alpha' = (1 + \alpha'_R)\frac{\pi_{tL}\pi_M}{(\pi_{tL}\pi_M)_R} \sqrt{\frac{(\tau_{tL}\tau_M)_R}{\tau_{tL}\tau_M}} \frac{\Gamma_8}{(\Gamma_8)_R} - 1} \tag{8-66a}$$

For an unchoked exhaust nozzle and choked low-pressure turbine inlet nozzle at station 4.5, the mass flow parameter at station 8 and Eq. (8-11*a*) give

$$1 + \alpha' = \frac{\dot{m}_8}{\dot{m}_{4.5}} = \frac{\pi_{tl}\pi_M}{\sqrt{\tau_{tL}\tau_M}} A_8 \,\text{MFP}(M_8, \gamma_8, R_8)\left(\frac{P_{t8}}{P_{t6}} \frac{1}{A_{4.5}} \frac{\sqrt{R_{4.5}/g_c}}{\Gamma_{4.5}}\right)$$

For engine operation when the exhaust nozzle is unchoked, it is advantageous to adjust A_8 so that $M_8 = M_9$. This requires that $A_8 = A_9\pi_n$. Using $M_8 = M_9$, replacing the constant term within the parentheses above with reference conditions, and solving for α' give, for the *unchoked* exhaust nozzle,

$$\boxed{\begin{aligned}\alpha' = (1 + \alpha'_R)&\frac{\pi_{tL}\pi_M}{(\pi_{tL}\pi_M)_R} \sqrt{\frac{(\tau_{tL}\tau_M)_R}{\tau_{tL}\tau_M}} \frac{A_8}{(A_8)_R} \\ &\times \frac{\text{MFP}(M_8, \gamma_8, R_8)}{\text{MFP}(M_8, \gamma_8, R_8)_R} - 1\end{aligned}} \tag{8-66b}$$

The Mach number at station 9 in Eq. (8-66*b*) follows from the definition of the total pressure

$$M_9 = \left\{\frac{2}{\gamma_9 - 1}\left[\left(\frac{P_{t9}}{P_9}\right)^{(\gamma_9 - 1)/\gamma_9} - 1\right]\right\}^{1/2}$$

where, since $P_9 = P_0$,

$$\frac{P_{t9}}{P_9} = \pi_r \pi_d \pi_f \pi_{cH} \pi_b \pi_{tH} \pi_{tL} \pi_M \pi_{AB} \pi_n$$

Engine Mass Flow and Exhaust Nozzle Areas

ENGINE MASS FLOW $\dot{m}_0$. The engine mass flow rate can be written simply as

$$\dot{m}_0 = (1 + \alpha)\dot{m}_C$$

Thus Eq. (8-47) applies:

$$\dot{m}_0 = \dot{m}_{0R} \frac{1+\alpha}{1+\alpha_R} \frac{P_0 \pi_r \pi_d \pi_f \pi_{cH}}{(P_0 \pi_r \pi_d \pi_f \pi_{cH})_R} \sqrt{\frac{T_{t4R}}{T_{t4}}} \tag{8-47}$$

The corrected mass flow at station 2 (fan entrance) can be obtained from the above equation and Eq. (8-2), yielding

$$\dot{m}_{c2} = \dot{m}_{c2R} \frac{1+\alpha}{1+\alpha_R} \frac{\pi_f \pi_{cH}}{(\pi_f \pi_{ch})_R} \sqrt{\frac{(T_{t4}/T_{t2})_R}{T_{t4}/T_{t2}}} \tag{8-67}$$

EXHAUST NOZZLE THROAT AREA A_9. Increasing the exhaust nozzle throat area A_8 moves the operating line to the right on a compressor or fan map (see Fig. 10-53), and decreasing the throat area moves this line to the left. For variable-area exhaust nozzles, the throat area is increased during engine start-up and low thrust settings to reduce the turbine backpressure, increase the corrected mass flow rate, and thus keep the compressor from stall or surge. Once the engine operation has reached high corrected mass flow rates (this normally corresponds to sufficient nozzle pressure to choke its flow), the throat area is reduced to its nominal value which shifts the compressor operating line to the left—a region of improved efficiency (see Fig. 10-53). For analysis of engine operation, we limit ourselves to the steady-state conditions when sufficient nozzle total pressure exists to choke the flow.

The throat area of the choked exhaust nozzle depends on the operation of the afterburner. With the *afterburner off* (dry), we assume that the engine control system maintains a constant throat area, or

$$A_8 = A_{8R} \tag{8-68a}$$

This will keep the operating line on the fan and high-pressure compressor maps constant.

When the afterburner is in operation (wet), the engine control system increases the throat area of the exhaust nozzle to keep the flow properties at station 6*A* constant (P_{t6A}, T_{t6A}, and M_{6A}). In this way, the turbomachinery (fan, high-pressure compressor, high-pressure turbine, and low-pressure turbine) is not affected by afterburner operation—a highly desirable situation. If the engine control system allows P_{t6A} to vary during afterburning operation, the flow through the turbomachinery is affected, which, in the extreme, could lead to compressor stall or engine overspeed.

An expression for the ratio of exhaust nozzle throat area with the afterburner on to its area when the afterburner is off will now be developed. Using conservation of mass between stations $6A$ and 8 and the mass flow parameter with the afterburner on gives

$$\dot{m}_8 = \dot{m}_{6A} + \dot{m}_{f\text{AB}}$$

or

$$\left[\frac{P_{t8}A_8}{\sqrt{T_{t8}}}\text{MFP}(\gamma_8, R_8, M_8 = 1)\right]_{\text{AB}} = \left(1 + \frac{\dot{m}_{f\text{AB}}}{\dot{m}_{6A}}\right)\left[\frac{P_{t6A}A_{6A}}{\sqrt{T_{t6A}}}\text{MFP}(\gamma_{6A}, R_{6A}, M_{6A})\right]$$

Likewise, conservation of mass with the afterburner off gives

$$\left[\frac{P_{t8}A_8}{\sqrt{T_{t8}}}\text{MFP}(\gamma_8, R_8, M_8 = 1)\right]_{\text{no AB}} = \left[\frac{P_{t6A}A_{6A}}{\sqrt{T_{t6A}}}\text{MFP}(\gamma_{6A}, R_{6A}, M_{6A})\right]$$

Since the flow at station $6A$ is unaffected by the operation of the afterburner, the terms inside square brackets on the right-hand sides of both equations written above are equal. In addition, the γ, R, and T_t at station 8 with the afterburner off are the same as those at station $6A$. Thus

$$\frac{A_{8\,\text{AB on}}}{A_{8\,\text{AB off}}} = \frac{\pi_{\text{AB dry}}}{\pi_{\text{AB wet}}}\sqrt{\frac{T_{t8}}{T_{t6A}}}\left(1 + \frac{\dot{m}_{f\text{AB}}}{\dot{m}_{6A}}\right)\frac{\Gamma_{6A}}{\Gamma_{8\,\text{AB on}}}$$

Neglecting the afterburner fuel flow rate and differences in Γ, we can write

$$\boxed{\frac{A_{8\,\text{AB on}}}{A_{8\,\text{AB off}}} \approx \frac{\pi_{\text{AB dry}}}{\pi_{\text{AB wet}}}\sqrt{\frac{T_{t7}}{T_{t6A}}}} \tag{8-68b}$$

Iteration Scheme

The solution of the 13 dependent variables between stations 2 and $6A$ is found by using the iteration scheme described in this section. Initial values are needed for τ_{tL} and α' to start the solution. The initial value of τ_{tL} is selected to be its reference value, $\tau_{tL\,R}$. When θ_0 is less than TR, the initial value of α' is selected to be equal to its reference value, α'_R. However, when θ_0 is greater than TR, the initial value of α' is calculated by using the following relationship, which accounts for its variation with Mach number and altitude:

$$\boxed{\alpha' = \alpha'_R \frac{\theta_0}{\theta_{0\,R}}} \tag{8-69}$$

For repeated calculations where one of the independent variables is changed, the initial values of τ_{tL} and α' for subsequent calculations are taken to be their previously calculated values.

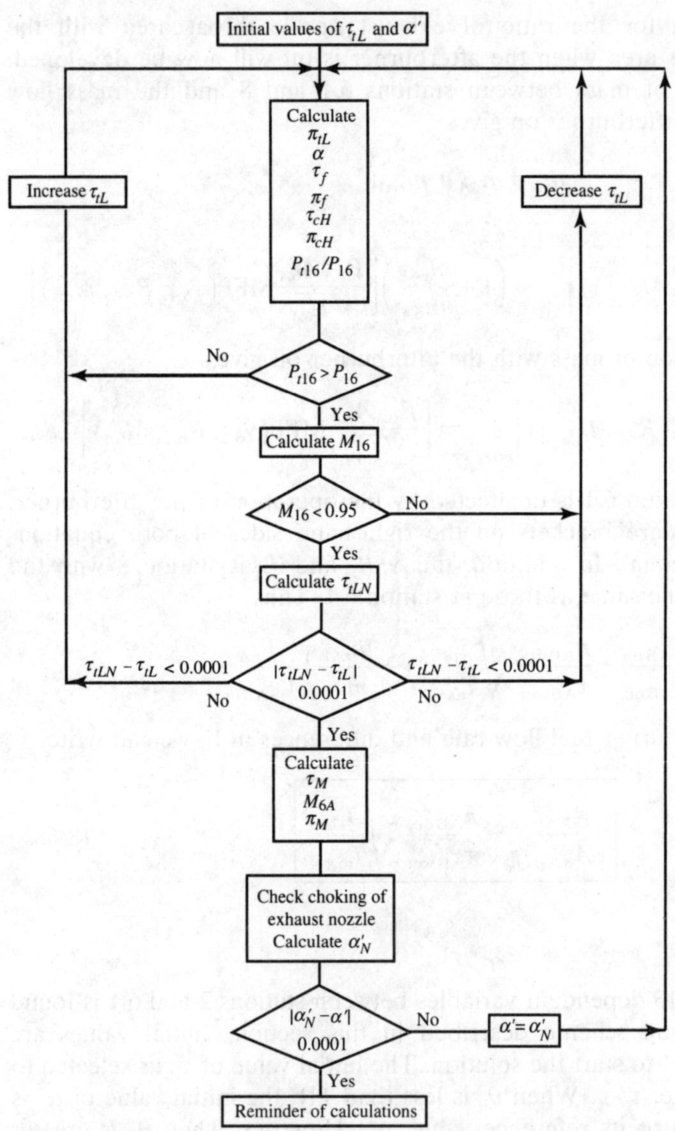

FIGURE 8-62
Flow-chart of iterative solution scheme.

A flowchart of the iteration scheme is shown in Fig. 8-62. Certain features of the programmed iteration methods used in the engine performance computer program PERF deserve highlighting:

1. If either the pressure ratio of the bypass stream entering the mixer P_{t16}/P_{16}

or the Mach number M_{16} is out of limits, the low-pressure turbine temperature ratio τ_{tL} is incremented by 0.0001.

2. If the new value of the low-pressure turbine temperature ratio calculated by Eq. (8-58) is not within 0.0001 of the previous value, newtonian iteration is used to converge to a solution.
3. Functional iteration is used for the mixer bypass ratio (α').

Summary of Performance Equations—Turbofan with Afterburning Mixed-Flow Exhaust

INPUTS:

Choices

Flight parameters:	M_0, T_0 (K, °R), P_0 (kPa, psia)
Throttle setting:	T_{t4} (K, °R), T_{t7} (K, °R)
Exhaust nozzle:	P_0/P_9 or A_9/A_8
Engine control:	TR

Design constants

π's:	$\pi_{d\,\max}$, π_b, π_{tH}, π_{AB}, π_n, $\pi_{M\,\max}$
τ's:	τ_{tH}
η's:	η_f, η_{cH}, η_b, η_{aB}, η_{mH}, η_{mL}
Gas properties:	γ_c, γ_t, γ_{AB}, c_{pc}, c_{pt}, c_{pAB} [kJ/(kg · K), Btu/(lbm · °R)]
Fuel:	h_{PR} (kJ/kg, Btu/lbm)

Reference conditions

Flight parameters:	M_{0R}, T_{0R} (K, °R), P_{0R} (kPa, psia), τ_{rR}, π_{rR}, θ_{0R}
Throttle setting:	T_{t4R} (K, °R), T_{t7R} (K, °R)
Component behavior:	π_{dR}, π_{fR}, π_{cHR}, π_{tLR}, τ_{fR}, τ_{cHR}, τ_{tLR}, α_R, M_{6R}, M_{9R}, A_6/A_{16}

OUTPUTS:

Overall performance:	F (N, lbf), $\dot{m}_0$ (kg/sec, lbm/sec), f_O, $S\left(\dfrac{\text{mg/sec}}{\text{N}}, \dfrac{\text{lbm/hr}}{\text{lbf}}\right)$, η_P, η_T, η_O
Component behavior:	α, π_d, π_f, π_{cH}, π_{tL}, τ_f, τ_{cH}, τ_{tL}, f, f_{AB}, M_9, N_{LPspool}, N_{HPspool}
Exhaust nozzle:	A_9/A_8 or P_0/P_9

EQUATIONS IN ORDER OF CALCULATION:

$$R_c = \frac{\gamma_c - 1}{\gamma_c} c_{pc} \tag{8-70a}$$

$$R_t = \frac{\gamma_t - 1}{\gamma_t} c_{pt} \tag{8-70b}$$

$$a_0 = \sqrt{\gamma_c R_c g_c T_0} \tag{8-70c}$$

$$\tau_r = 1 + \frac{\gamma_c - 1}{2} M_0^2 \tag{8-70d}$$

$$\pi_r = \tau_r^{\gamma_c/(\gamma_c - 1)} \tag{8-70e}$$

$$T_{t2} = T_0 \tau_r \tag{8-70f}$$

$$\eta_r = 1 \qquad \text{for } M_0 \leq 1 \tag{8-70g}$$

$$\eta_r = 1 - 0.075(M_0 - 1)^{1.35} \qquad \text{for } M_0 > 1 \tag{8-70h}$$

$$\pi_d = \pi_{d\max} \eta_r \tag{8-70i}$$

$$\theta_{0R} = \tau_{rR} \frac{T_{0R}}{T_{\text{ref}}} \tag{8-70j}$$

$$\alpha'_R = \frac{\alpha_R}{1 + f_R} \tag{8-70k}$$

$$\text{If} \quad \theta_{0R} \geq \text{TR} \quad \text{then} \quad T_{t4\max} = T_{t4R} \tag{8-70l}$$

$$\text{else} \quad T_{t4\max} = T_{t4R} \left(\frac{\text{TR}}{\theta_{0R}} \right) \tag{8-70m}$$

$$\theta_0 = \tau_r \frac{T_0}{T_{\text{ref}}} \tag{8-70n}$$

$$\text{If} \quad \theta_0 \geq \text{TR} \quad \text{then} \quad T_{t4\lim} = T_{t4\max} \tag{8-70o}$$

$$\text{else} \quad T_{t4\lim} = T_{t4\max} \frac{\theta_0}{\text{TR}} \tag{8-70p}$$

$$\text{If} \quad \text{TR} \geq 1 \quad \text{and} \quad T_{t4} > T_{t4\lim} \quad \text{then} \quad T_{t4} = T_{t4\lim} \quad \text{and} \quad \alpha' = \alpha'_R \tag{8-70q}$$

$$\text{else} \quad \alpha' = \alpha'_R \frac{\theta_0}{\theta_{0R}} \tag{8-70r}$$

$$\tau_\lambda = \frac{c_{pt} T_{t4}}{c_{pc} T_0} \tag{8-70s}$$

Set initial values:

$$\tau_{tL} = \tau_{tLR} \qquad \tau_f = \tau_{fR} \qquad \pi_{tL} = \pi_{tLR} \tag{8-70t}$$

$$\pi_{tL} = \left(1 - \frac{1 - \tau_{tL}}{\eta_{tL}} \right)^{(\gamma_t - 1)/\gamma_t} \tag{8-70u}$$

$$\alpha = \alpha_R \frac{\alpha'}{\alpha'_R} \tag{8-70v}$$

$$\tau_f = 1 + \frac{1 - \tau_{tL}}{(1 - \tau_{tL})_R} \frac{\tau_\lambda / \tau_r}{(\tau_\lambda / \tau_r)_R} \frac{1 + \alpha_R}{1 + \alpha} (\tau_{fR} - 1) \tag{8-70w}$$

$$\pi_f = [1 + (\tau_f - 1)\eta_f]^{\gamma_c/(\gamma_c - 1)} \tag{8-70x}$$

$$\tau_{cH} = 1 + \frac{T_{t4}/T_0}{(T_{t4}/T_0)_R} \frac{(\tau_r \tau_f)_R}{\tau_r \tau_f} (\tau_{cH} - 1)_R \tag{8-70y}$$

$$\pi_{cH} = [1 + \eta_{cH}(\tau_{cH} - 1)]^{\gamma_c/(\gamma_c - 1)} \tag{8-70z}$$

Set mixer entrance gas properties:

$$R_6 = R_t \qquad R_{16} = R_c \qquad c_{p6} = c_{pt} \qquad c_{p16} = c_{pc} \qquad \gamma_6 = \gamma_t \qquad \gamma_{16} = \gamma_c$$

$$\text{MFP}(M_6) = \text{MFP}(M_{6R})\sqrt{\frac{\tau_{tL}}{\tau_{tL\,R}}\,\frac{\pi_{tL\,R}}{\pi_{tL}}} \tag{8-70aa}$$

$$\frac{P_{t16}}{P_{16}} = \frac{(\pi_{cH}\pi_{tL})_R}{\pi_{cH}\pi_{tL}}\left(\frac{P_{t16}}{P_{t6}}\right)_R\left(1+\frac{\gamma_6-1}{2}M_6^2\right)^{\gamma_6/(\gamma_6-1)} \tag{8-70ab}$$

$$M_{16} = \left\{\frac{2}{\gamma_{16}-1}\left[\left(\frac{P_{t16}}{P_{16}}\right)^{(\gamma_{16}-1)/\gamma_{16}} - 1\right]\right\}^{1/2} \tag{8-70ac}$$

$$\tau_{tL\,N} = \frac{T_{t2}}{T_{t4}}\,\frac{\tau_f}{\tau_{tH}}\left(\frac{A_6}{A_{16}}\,\frac{M_6}{M_{16}}\,\alpha'\right)^2\frac{\gamma_6}{\gamma_{16}}\,\frac{R_{16}}{R_6}\,\frac{1+\dfrac{\gamma_6-1}{2}M_6^2}{1+\dfrac{\gamma_{16}-1}{2}M_{16}^2} \tag{8-70ad}$$

If $|\tau_{tL\,N} - \tau_{tL}| > 0.0001$, then

if $\tau_{tL\,N} - \tau_{tL} > 0.0001$, increase τ_{tL} and go to Eq. (8-70*t*)

if $\tau_{tL\,N} - \tau_{tL} < -0.0001$, decrease τ_{tL} and go to Eq. (8-70*t*) (8-70*ae*)

End if

$$c_{p6A} = \frac{c_{p6} + \alpha' c_{p16}}{1+\alpha'} \qquad R_{6A} = \frac{R_6 + \alpha' R_{16}}{1+\alpha'} \qquad \gamma_{6A} = \frac{c_{p6A}}{c_{p6A} - R_{6A}} \tag{8-70af}$$

$$\frac{T_{t16}}{T_{t6}} = \frac{T_{t2}}{T_{t4}}\,\frac{\tau_f}{\tau_{tH}\tau_{tL}} \tag{8-70ag}$$

$$\tau_M = \frac{c_{p6}}{c_{p6A}}\,\frac{1+\alpha'(c_{p16}/c_{p6})(T_{t16}/T_{t6})}{1+\alpha'} \tag{8-70ah}$$

$$\phi(M_6, \gamma_6) = \frac{M_6^2\left(1+\dfrac{\gamma_6-1}{2}M_6^2\right)}{(1+\gamma_6 M_6^2)^2}$$

$$\phi(M_{16}, \gamma_{16}) = \frac{M_{16}^2\left(1+\dfrac{\gamma_{16}-1}{2}M_{16}^2\right)}{(1+\gamma_{16} M_{16}^2)^2} \tag{8-70ai}$$

$$\Phi = \left[\frac{1+\alpha'}{\dfrac{1}{\sqrt{\phi(M_6, \gamma_6)}} + \alpha'\sqrt{\dfrac{R_{16}\gamma_6}{R_5\gamma_{16}}\,\dfrac{T_{t6}/T_{16}}{\phi(M_{16}, \gamma_{16})}}}\right]^2\frac{R_{6A}\gamma_6}{R_6\gamma_{6A}}\,\tau_M \tag{8-70aj}$$

$$M_{6A} = \sqrt{\frac{2\Phi}{1-2\gamma_{6A}\Phi + \sqrt{1-2(\gamma_{6A}+1)\Phi}}} \tag{8-70ak}$$

$$\pi_{M\,\text{ideal}} = \frac{(1+\alpha')\sqrt{\tau_M}}{1+A_{16}/A_6}\frac{\text{MFP}(M_6, \gamma_6, R_6)}{\text{MFP}(M_{6A}, \gamma_{6A}, R_{6A})} \tag{8-70al}$$

$$\pi_M = \tau_{M\,\text{max}}\pi_{M\,\text{ideal}} \tag{8-70am}$$

$$\pi_{\text{AB dry}} = 1 - \frac{1}{2}(1-\pi_{\text{AB}}) \tag{8-70an}$$

$$\left(\frac{P_{t9}}{P_9}\right)_{\text{dry}} = \frac{P_0}{P_9}\pi_r\pi_d\pi_f\pi_{cH}\pi_b\pi_{tH}\pi_{tL}\pi_M\pi_{\text{AB dry}}\pi_n \tag{8-70ao}$$

Is

$$\left(\frac{P_{t9}}{P_9}\right)_{\text{dry}} \geq \left(\frac{\gamma_{6A}+1}{2}\right)^{\gamma_{6A}/(\gamma_{6A}-1)} \tag{8-70ap}$$

true? If so, then exhaust nozzle is choked and $M_{8\,\text{dry}} = 1$. If not, then exhaust nozzle is unchoked and

$$M_{8\,\text{dry}} = \sqrt{\frac{2}{\gamma_{6A}-1}\left[\left(\frac{P_{t9}}{P_9}\right)_{\text{dry}}^{(\gamma_{6A}-1)/\gamma_{6A}} - 1\right]} \tag{8-70aq}$$

$$\alpha'_N = (1+\alpha'_R)\frac{\pi_{tL}\pi_M}{(\pi_{tL}\pi_M)_R}\sqrt{\frac{(\tau_{tL}\tau_M)_R}{\tau_{tL}\tau_M}}\frac{\text{MFP}(M_{8\,\text{dry}}, \gamma_{6A}, R_{6A})}{\text{MFP}(M_{8\,\text{dry}}, \gamma_{6A}, R_{6A})_R} - 1 \tag{8-70ar}$$

If $|\alpha'_N - \alpha'| > 0.0001$, then set $\alpha' = \alpha'_N$ and return to Eq. (8-70*u*).

$$\alpha = \alpha_R\frac{\alpha'}{\alpha'_R} \tag{8-70as}$$

$$\dot{m}_0 = \dot{m}_{0R}\frac{1+\alpha}{1+\alpha_R}\frac{P_0\pi_r\pi_d\pi_f\pi_{cH}}{(P_0\pi_r\pi_d\pi_f\pi_{cH})_R}\sqrt{\frac{T_{t4R}}{T_{t4}}} \tag{8-70at}$$

$$f = \frac{\tau_\lambda - \tau_r\tau_f\tau_{cH}}{h_{PR}\eta_b/(c_pT_0) - \tau_\lambda} \tag{8-70au}$$

Is $T_{t7} \geq T_{t7R}$? If so, then $c_{p\text{AB}}$, R_{AB}, and γ_{AB} are equal to their reference values, $x = 1$, and go to Eq. (8-70*az*). Else, calculate the ratio

$$x = \frac{T_{t7} - T_{t6A}}{T_{t7R} - T_{t6A}} \tag{8-70av}$$

and then determine revised values of $c_{p\text{AB}}$, R_{AB}, and γ_{AB}, using

$$c_{pa\text{B}} = c_{p6A} + x(c_{p\text{AB}R} - c_{p6A}) \tag{8-70aw}$$

$$R_{\mathrm{AB}} = R_{6A} + x(R_{\mathrm{AB}\,R} - R_{6a}) \tag{8-70ax}$$

$$\gamma_{\mathrm{AB}} = \frac{c_{p\mathrm{AB}}}{c_{p\mathrm{AB}} - R_{\mathrm{AB}}} \tag{8-70ay}$$

$$\pi_{\mathrm{AB}} = 1 - (1+x)(1 - \pi_{\mathrm{AB\,dry}}) \tag{8-70az}$$

$$\tau_{\lambda\mathrm{AB}} = \frac{c_{p\mathrm{AB}} T_{t7}}{c_{pc} T_0} \tag{8-70ba}$$

$$f_{\mathrm{AB}} = \left(1 + \frac{f}{1+\alpha}\right) \frac{\tau_{\lambda\mathrm{AB}} - (c_{p6A}/c_{pt})\tau_\lambda \tau_{tH} \tau_{tL} \tau_M}{\eta_{\mathrm{AB}} h_{PR}/(c_{pc} T_0) - \tau_{\lambda\mathrm{AB}}} \tag{8-70bb}$$

$$f_O = \frac{f}{1+\alpha} + f_{\mathrm{AB}} \tag{8-70bc}$$

$$\frac{P_{t9}}{P_9} = \frac{P_0}{P_9} \pi_r \pi_d \pi_f \pi_{cH} \pi_b \pi_{tH} \pi_{tL} \pi_M \pi_{\mathrm{AB}} \pi_n \tag{8-70bd}$$

$$M_9 = \sqrt{\frac{2}{\gamma_9 - 1}\left[\left(\frac{P_{t9}}{P_9}\right)^{(\gamma_9-1)/\gamma_9} - 1\right]} \tag{8-70be}$$

$$\frac{T_9}{T_0} = \frac{T_{t7}/T_0}{(P_{t9}/P_9)^{(\gamma_9-1)/\gamma_9}} \tag{8-70bf}$$

$$\frac{V_9}{a_0} = M_9 \sqrt{\frac{\gamma_9 R_9}{\gamma_c r_c} \frac{T_9}{T_0}} \tag{8-70bg}$$

$$\frac{E}{\dot{m}_0} = \frac{a_0}{g_c}\left[(1+f_O)\frac{V_9}{a_0} - M_0 + (1+f_O)\frac{R_9}{R_c}\frac{T_9/T_0}{V_9/a_0}\frac{1 - P_0/P_9}{\gamma_c}\right] \tag{8-70bh}$$

$$S = \frac{f_O}{F/\dot{m}_0} \tag{8-70bi}$$

$$\eta_P = \frac{2g_c V_0 (F/\dot{m}_0)}{a_0^2[(1+f_O)(V_9/a_0)^2 - M_0^2]} \tag{8-70bj}$$

$$\eta_T = \frac{a_0^2[(1+f_O)(V_9/a_0)^2 - M_0^2]}{2g_c f_o h_{PR}} \tag{8-70bk}$$

$$\eta_O = \eta_P \eta_T \tag{8-70bl}$$

$$\dot{m}_{c2} = \dot{m}_{c2\,R} \frac{1+\alpha}{1+\alpha_R} \frac{\pi_f \pi_{cH}}{(\pi_f \pi_{cH})_R} \sqrt{\frac{(T_{t4}/T_{t2})_R}{T_{t4}/T_{t2}}} \tag{8-70bm}$$

$$\left(\frac{N}{N_R}\right)_{\mathrm{LP\,spool}} = \sqrt{\frac{T_0 \tau_r}{(T_0 \tau_r)_R} \frac{\pi_f^{(\gamma_c-1)/\gamma_c} - 1}{\pi_{fR}^{(\gamma_c-1)/\gamma_c} - 1}} \tag{8-70bn}$$

$$\left(\frac{N}{N_R}\right)_{\text{NP spool}} = \sqrt{\frac{T_0\tau_r\tau_f}{(T_0\tau_r\tau_f)_R}\,\frac{\pi_{cH}^{(\gamma_c-1)/\gamma_c}-1}{\pi_{cHR}^{(\gamma_c-1)/\gamma_c}-1}} \tag{8-70bo}$$

If exhaust nozzle is choked, then

$$\frac{A_9}{A_8} = \frac{\Gamma_8}{\pi_n}\sqrt{\frac{\gamma_8-1}{2\gamma_8}}\,\frac{(P_{t9}/P_9)^{(\gamma_8+1)/(2\gamma_8)}}{\sqrt{(P_{t9}/P_9)^{(\gamma_8-1)/\gamma_8}-1}} \tag{8-70bp}$$

Else

$$\frac{A_9}{A_8} = \frac{1}{\pi_n} \tag{8-70bq}$$

End if

Example 8-10. *Turbofan with afterburning and mixed exhaust.* In this example, we consider the performance of a low-bypass-ratio, mixed-flow, two-spool, afterburning turbofan engine with an uninstalled thrust of 25,000 lbf, π_c of 20, and α of 0.5 at sea-level static (SLS) conditions. A sea-level static reference is selected with the resulting data listed below. The engine has a $T_{t4\,\max}$ of 3200°R and a T_{t4} at SLS conditions of 2909°R—these give an engine throttle ratio of 1.10.

The performance of the engine between station 2 and station 6*A* is considered first. This is followed by the full-throttle performance maps for the engine with and without afterburning. This section is concluded with a discussion of several partial-throttle performance curves.

REFERENCE: $T_0 = 518.7$°R, $\gamma_c = 1.4$, $c_{pc} = 0.24$ Btu/(lbm · °R), $\gamma_t = 1.3$, $c_{pt} = 0.295$ Btu/(lbm · °R), $M_0 = 0$, $T_{t4} = 2909$°R, $\gamma_{AB} = 1.3$, $c_{pAB} = 0.295$ Btu/(lbm · °R), $T_{t7} = 3600$°R, $\pi_c = 20$, $\pi_f = 4.16$, $\alpha = 0.5$, $M_6 = 0.4$, $M_{16} = 0.386$, $\eta_f = 0.8663$, $\eta_{cH} = 0.8761$, $\tau_{tH} = 0.8548$, $\pi_{tH} = 0.46591$, $\tau_{tL} = 0.8552$, $\pi_{tL} = 0.4749$, $\eta_{tL} = 0.9169$, $\eta_b = 0.99$, $\pi_{d\,\max} = 0.97$, $\pi_b = 0.94$, $\pi_{M\,\max} = 0.96$, $\pi_{AB} = 0.94$, $\pi_n = 0.98$, $\eta_{AB} = 0.95$, $\eta_{mH} = 0.99$, $\eta_{mL} = 0.99$, $P_9/P_0 = 1$, $P_0 = 14.696$ psia, $h_{PR} = 18{,}400$ Btu/lbm, $\dot{m}_0 = 207.65$ lbm/sec, $F/\dot{m}_0 = 120.4$ lbf/(lbm/sec), $f = 0.0308$, $f_{AB} = 0.0358$, $F = 25{,}000$ lbf, $S = 1.683$ (lbm/hr)/lbf

For flight conditions where $\theta_0 < \text{TR}$, the maximum value of T_{t4} is given by the following equation:

$$\boxed{T_{t4} = \frac{\theta_0}{\text{TR}}\,T_{t4\,\max}} \tag{8-71}$$

When the engine operates at the value of T_{t4} given by the above equation, the ratio T_{t4}/T_{t2} is constant at its maximum value and the corrected speeds N_c of both the low-pressure spool and the high-pressure spool are constant at their maximum. For flight conditions where $\theta_0 > \text{TR}$, the maximum value of T_{t4} is $T_{t4\,\max}$, the ratio T_{t4}/T_{t2} is less than its maximum value, and the corrected speeds

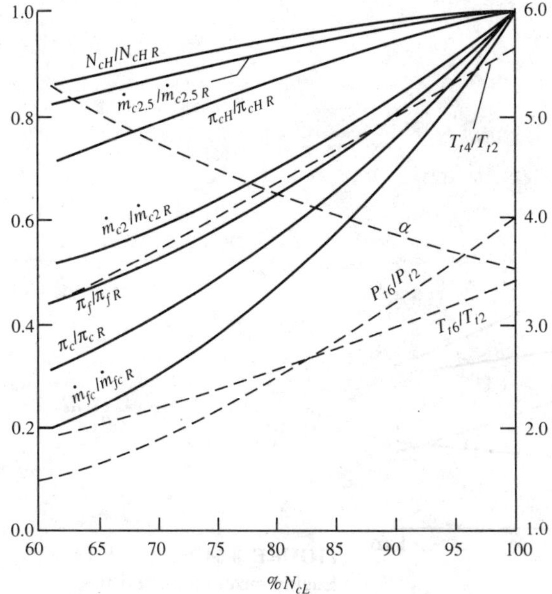

FIGURE 8-63
Pumping characteristics of mixed-flow turbofan engine.

of both the low-pressure spool and the high-pressure spool are less than their maximum.

The pumping characteristics of the engine are plotted in Fig. 8-63 versus the corrected speed of the low-pressure spool. Note that at reduced corrected speeds of the low-pressure spool, all the quantities plotted, except the bypass ratio α, are less than their maximum values. Also note that the variations of the high-pressure spool's corrected quantities are much less than those of the low-pressure spool. Even for a cycle as complex as the mixed-flow turbofan engine, *there is a one-to-one correspondence between the temperature ratio* T_{t4}/T_{t2} *and the engine's pumping characteristics between station* 2 *and station* 6.

The characteristics of the engine's mixer are plotted in Fig. 8-64 versus corrected speed of the low-pressure spool. One notes that, at reduced corrected speed, the Mach numbers M_6 and M_{16} are significantly different from their values at 100 percent corrected speed. Also noted from this figure is the increase in the pressure ratio of the low-pressure turbine π_{tL} with reduction in corrected speed. Depending on the design of the low-pressure turbine, the increased value of π_{tL} may correspond to unchoking of the inlet nozzle (station 4.5) of the low-pressure turbine (we assume that this nozzle stays choked). Comparison of Figs. 8-63 and 8-64 shows that the mixer bypass ratio α' varies directly with the engine bypass ratio α.

The uninstalled thrust F and uninstalled thrust specific fuel consumption S performance of the mixed-flow turbofan engine at full throttle with afterburner on are plotted versus flight Mach number and altitude in Figs. 8-65 and 8-66, respectively. The F and S performances of this engine with the afterburner off are plotted in Figs. 8-67 and 8-68, respectively. One notes from these figures the change in slope of the curves at a combination of Mach number and altitude that

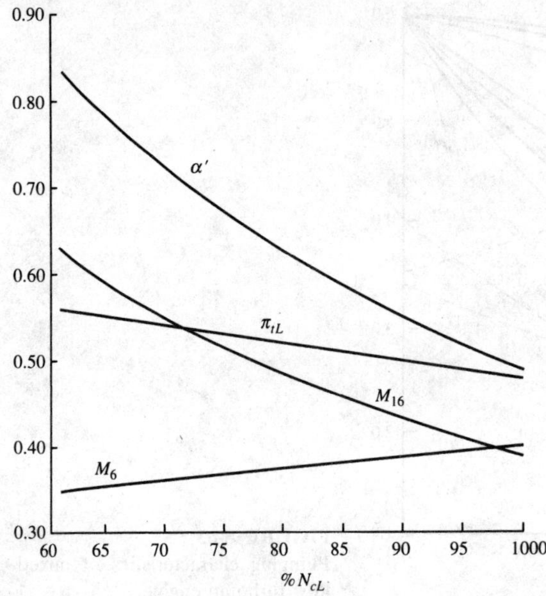

FIGURE 8-64
Engine mixer characteristics.

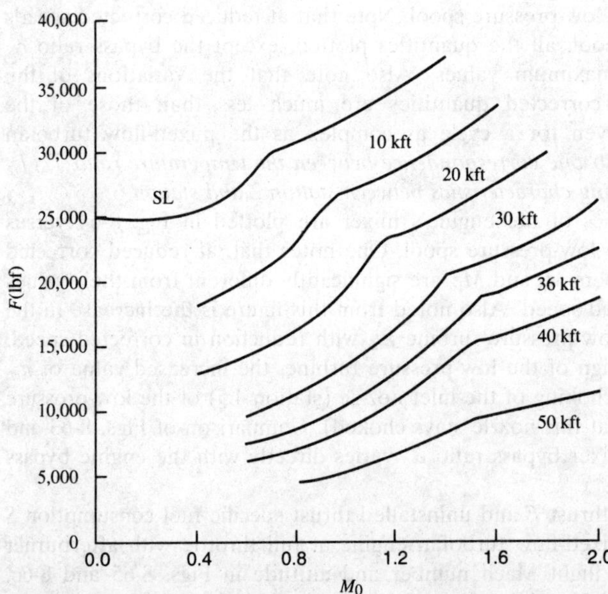

FIGURE 8-65
Uninstalled thrust F of mixed-flow turbofan engine at maximum power setting (afterburner on).

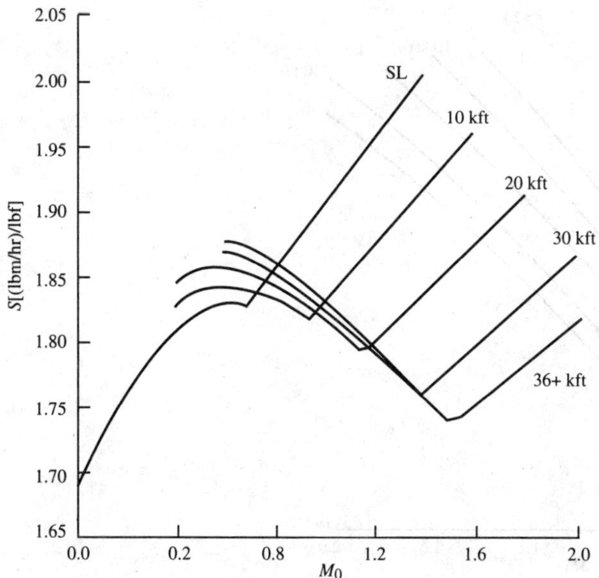

FIGURE 8-66
Uninstalled fuel consumption S of mixed-flow turbofan engine at maximum power setting (afterburner on).

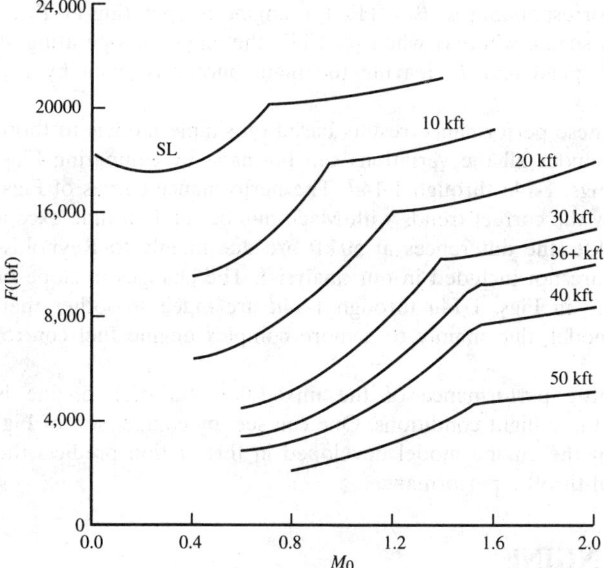

FIGURE 8-67
Uninstalled thrust F of mixed-flow turbofan engine at military power setting (afterburner off).

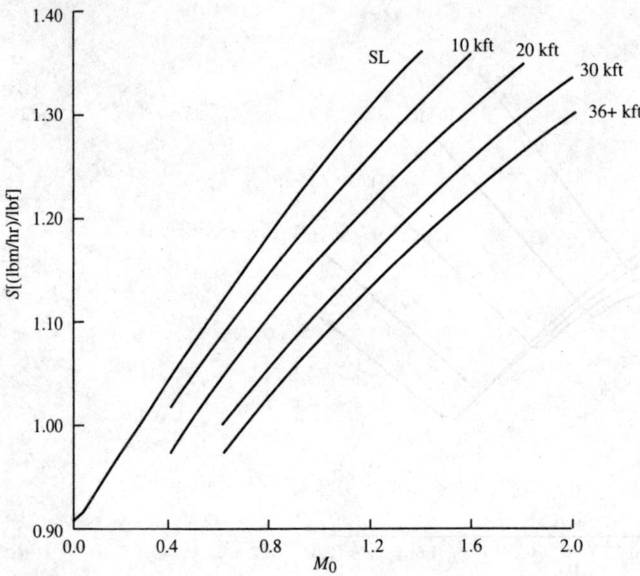

FIGURE 8-68
Uninstalled fuel consumption S of mixed-flow turbofan engine at military power setting (afterburner off).

corresponds to a θ_0 of 1.1 (the throttle ratio of this engine). At flight conditions (Mach and altitude) corresponding to $\theta_0 > \mathrm{TR}$, the engine is operating at $T_{t4\,\max}$ and reduced corrected speed, whereas when $\theta_0 < \mathrm{TR}$, the engine is operating at 100 percent corrected speed and T_{t4} leaving the main burner is given by Eq. (8-71).

Comparison of these performance results based on simple models to those of an engine which includes all the variations can be made by comparing Figs. 8-65 through 8-68 to Figs. 1-14*a* through 1-14*d*. The performance curves of Figs. 8-65 through 8-68 show the correct trends with Mach number and altitude except for the altitude of 50 kft (the differences at 50 kft are due mainly to Reynolds-number effects which are not included in our analysis). The changes in slope of the performance curves in Figs. 1-14*a* through 1-14*d* are much smoother than those of our engine model, due mainly to a more complex engine fuel control algorithm.

The partial-throttle performance of the mixed-flow turbofan engine is plotted in Fig. 8-69 at three flight conditions. One can see, by comparison of Fig. 8-69 to Fig. 1-14*e*, that the engine model developed in this section predicts the proper trends in partial-throttle performance.

8-7 TURBOPROP ENGINE

The turboprop engine used on many small commercial subsonic aircraft is shown in Fig. 8-70. This engine typically has two spools: the core engine spool

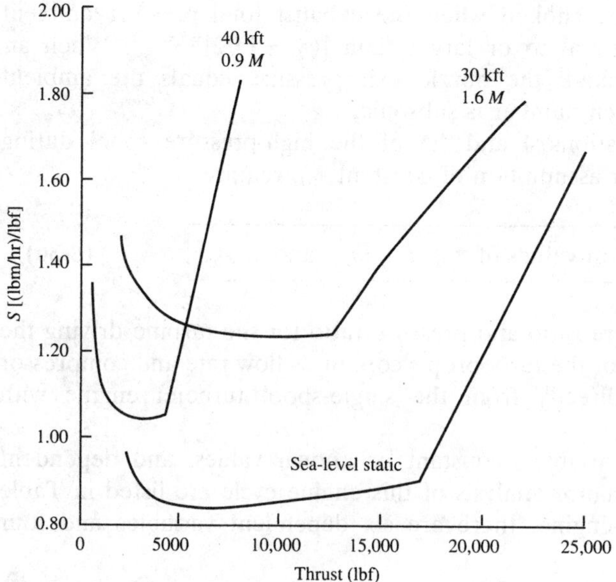

FIGURE 8-69
Partial-throttle performance of mixed-flow turbofan engine.

and the power spool. The pressure ratios across the high-pressure turbine and power turbine are normally high enough to have choked flow in that turbine's inlet nozzle (station 4 and station 4.5, respectively) for most operating conditions of interest.

The convergent exhaust nozzle of these turboprop engines has a fixed

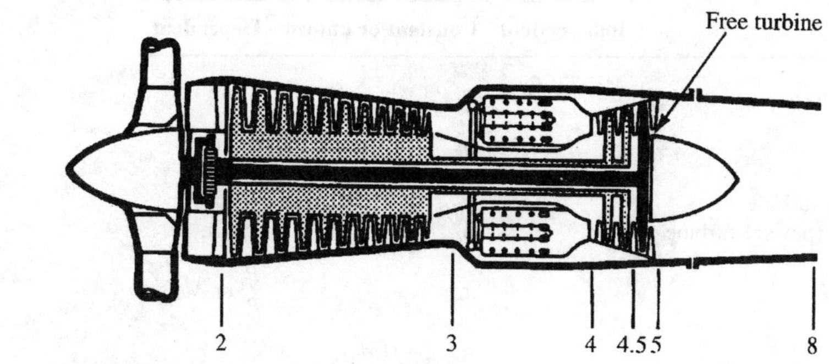

FIGURE 8-70
Turboprop engine. (*Courtesy of Pratt & Whitney.*)

throat area which will be choked when the exhaust total pressure/ambient static pressure ratio is equal to or larger than $[(\gamma_t+1)/2]^{\gamma_t/(\gamma_t-1)}$. When an exhaust nozzle is unchoked, the nozzle exit pressure equals the ambient pressure and the exit Mach number is subsonic.

Choked flow at stations 4 and 4.5 of the high-pressure spool during engine operation and our assumption of constant η_{tH} require

$$\boxed{\text{Constant values of } \pi_{tH},\ \tau_{tH},\ \dot{m}_{c4}, \text{ and } \dot{m}_{c4.5}} \tag{8-36}$$

With constant temperature ratio and pressure ratio for the turbine driving the compressor, the analysis of the turboprop's core mass flow rate and compressor pressure ratio follows directly from the single-spool turbojet engine with choked exhaust nozzle.

The independent variables, constant or known values, and dependent variables for the performance analysis of this engine cycle are listed in Table 8-9. Note that for this engine, there are six dependent variables and four independent variables.

Engine Mass Flow $\dot{m}_0$

Using the mass flow parameter and conservation of mass, we can write for the turboprop engine

$$\dot{m}_2 + \dot{m}_f = \dot{m}_2(1+f) = \dot{m}_4 = \frac{P_{t4}A_4}{\sqrt{T_{t4}}}\text{MFP}(M_4)$$

TABLE 8-9
Performance analysis variables for turboprop engine

Component	Variables: Independent	Constant or known	Dependent
Engine	M_0, T_0, P_0		$\dot{m}_0$
Diffuser		$\pi_d = f(M_0)$	
Compressor		η_c	π_c, τ_c
Burner	T_{t4}	π_b, η_b	
High-pressure turbine		π_{tH}, τ_{tH}	
Low-pressure (power) turbine		η_{tL}	π_{tL}, τ_{tL}
Nozzle		π_n	$\dfrac{P_9}{P_0}$ or M_9
Propeller		$\eta_{\text{prop}} = f(M_0)$	
Total number	4		6

Since the flow is choked ($M_4 = 1$) and the area is constant (A_4 = constant) at station 4, the above equation can be rewritten for the core mass flow rate in terms of component pressure ratios as

$$\dot{m}_0 = \frac{P_0 \pi_r \pi_d \pi_c}{\sqrt{T_{t4}}} \left[\pi_b A_4 \frac{\text{MFP}(M_4)}{1+f} \right]$$

where the terms within the square brackets are considered constant. Equating the constants to reference values gives

$$\boxed{\dot{m}_0 = \dot{m}_{0R} \frac{P_0 \pi_r \pi_d \pi_c}{(P_0 \pi_r \pi_d \pi_c)_R} \sqrt{\frac{T_{t4R}}{T_{t4}}}} \tag{8-72}$$

Compressor (τ_c, π_c)

The power balance of the core spool between the high-pressure turbine and the compressor gives

$$\eta_m \dot{m}_4 c_{pt}(T_{t4} - T_{t4.5}) = \dot{m}_2 c_{pc}(T_{t3} - T_{t2})$$

Rewriting this equation in terms of temperature ratios, rearranging into variable and constant terms, and equating the constant to reference values give

$$\frac{\tau_r(\tau_c - 1)}{T_{t4}/T_0} = \eta_m(1+f)(1-\tau_{tH}) = \left[\frac{\tau_r(\tau_c - 1)}{T_{t4}/T_0} \right]_R$$

Solving for τ_c gives

$$\boxed{\tau_c = 1 + \frac{T_{t4}/T_0}{(T_{t4}/T_0)_R} \frac{(\tau_r)_R}{\tau_r} (\tau_c - 1)_R} \tag{8-73}$$

From the definition of compressor efficiency, π_c is given by

$$\boxed{\pi_c = [1 + \eta_c(\tau_c - 1)]^{\gamma_c/(\gamma_c - 1)}} \tag{8-74}$$

Core Work Coefficient C_C

The expression for the core work coefficient C_C developed in Chap. 7 still applies and is given by Eq. (7-96)

$$\boxed{C_C = (\gamma_c - 1) M_0 \left[(1+f)\frac{V_9}{a_0} - M_0 + (1+f)\frac{R_t}{R_c} \frac{T_9/T_0}{V_9/a_0} \frac{1 - P_0/P_9}{\gamma_c} \right]} \tag{7-96}$$

where V_9/a_0 is given by Eq. (7-99) and T_9/T_0 is given by Eqs. (7-98*a*) and (7-98*b*).

Power (Low-Pressure) Turbine (τ_{tL}, π_{tL})

Equations (7-37) and (8-38) apply for the power (low-pressure) turbine temperature and pressure ratios of this turboprop engine. We write Eq. (8-37) in terms of the Mach number at station 9 as

$$\boxed{\pi_{tL} = \pi_{tL\,R}\sqrt{\frac{\tau_{tL}}{\tau_{tL\,R}}}\frac{\text{MFP}(M_{9\,R})}{\text{MFP}(M_9)}} \tag{8-75}$$

where

$$\boxed{\tau_{tL} = 1 - \eta_{tL}(1 - \pi_{tL}^{(\gamma_t-1)/\gamma_t})} \tag{8-38}$$

If station 9 is choked at the reference condition and at all performance conditions of interest, then π_{tL} and τ_{tL} are constant.

The power balance of this spool was found in Chap. 7. It still applies, and Eq. (7-101) gives the propeller work coefficient C_{prop}:

$$\boxed{C_{\text{prop}} = \frac{\eta_{\text{prop}}\dot{W}_{\text{prop}}}{\dot{m}_0 c_{pc} T_0} = \eta_{\text{prop}}\eta_g\eta_{mL}(1+f)\tau_\lambda\tau_{tH}(1-\tau_{tL})} \tag{7-101}$$

Exhaust Nozzle

Two flow regimes exist for flow through the convergent exhaust nozzle (unchoked flow and choked flow). Unchoked flow will exist when

$$\frac{P_{t9}}{P_0} = \pi_r\pi_d\pi_c\pi_b\pi_{tH}\pi_{tL}\pi_n < \left(\frac{\gamma_t+1}{2}\right)^{\gamma_t/(\gamma_t-1)}$$

and choked flow will exist when

$$\frac{P_{t9}}{P_0} = \pi_r\pi_d\pi_c\pi_b\pi_{tH}\pi_{tL}\pi_n \geq \left(\frac{\gamma_t+1}{2}\right)^{\gamma_t/(\gamma_t-1)}$$

For unchoked flow, the exit static pressure P_9 is equal to the ambient pressure P_0, and the subsonic exit Mach number M_9 is given by

$$M_9 = \sqrt{\frac{2}{\gamma_t-1}\left[\left(\frac{P_{t9}}{P_0}\right)^{(\gamma_t-1)/\gamma_t} - 1\right]}$$

When the flow is choked, then

$$M_9 = 1, \qquad \frac{P_{t9}}{P_9} = \left(\frac{\gamma_t + 1}{2}\right)^{\gamma_t/(\gamma_t - 1)}, \qquad \text{and} \qquad \frac{P_0}{P_9} = \frac{P_{t9}/P_9}{P_{t9}/P_0}$$

Iteration Scheme for τ_{tL}, π_{tL}, and M_9

Determination of the conditions downstream of station 4.5 requires an iterative solution. The method used is as follows:

1. Initially assume that π_{tL} equals its reference value $\pi_{tL\,R}$.
2. Calculate τ_{tL}, using Eq. (8-38).
3. Calculate P_{t9}/P_0 and conditions at exit including M_9.
4. Calculate the new π_{tL}, using Eq. (8-75).
5. Compare the new π_{tL} to the previous value. If the difference is greater than 0.0001, then go to step 2.

Propeller Performance

The performance of the propeller can be simply modeled as a function of the flight Mach number (Ref. 12); one such model, which is used in the PERF computer program of this textbook, is shown in Fig. 8-71 and expressed

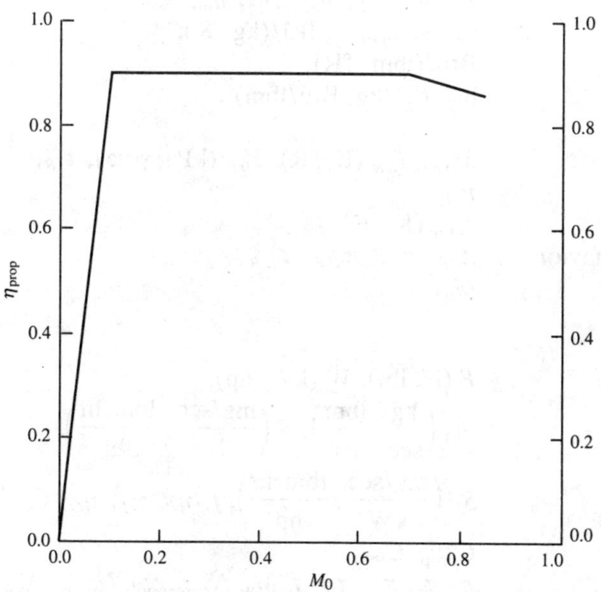

FIGURE 8-71
Variation in propeller efficiency with Mach number.

algebraically as

$$\eta_{\text{prop}} = \begin{cases} 10M_0\eta_{\text{prop max}} & M_0 \le 0.1 \\ \eta_{\text{prop max}} & 0.1 < M_0 \le 0.7 \\ \left(1 - \dfrac{M_0 - 0.7}{3}\right)\eta_{\text{prop max}} & 0.7 < M_0 < 0.85 \end{cases}$$

This equation for the Mach range of 0.7 to 0.85, given above, models the drop in η_{prop} experienced in this flight regime due to transonic flow losses in the tip region of the propeller.

The following section presents the performance equations for the turboprop engine in the order of calculation.

Summary of Performance Equations—Turboprop

INPUTS:

Choices

Flight parameters:	M_0, T_0 (K, °R), P_0 (kPa, psia)
Throttle setting:	T_{t4} (K, °R)

Design constants

π's:	$\pi_{d\,\max}$, π_b, π_{tH}, π_n
τ's:	τ_{tH}
η's:	η_c, η_b, η_{tL}, η_{mL}, η_g, $\eta_{\text{prop max}}$
Gas properties:	γ_c, γ_t, c_{pc}, c_{pt} [kJ/(kg · K), Btu/(lbm · °R)]
Fuel:	h_{PR} (kJ/kg, Btu/lbm)

Reference conditions

Flight parameters:	M_{0R}, T_{0R} (K, °R), P_{0R} (kPa, psia), τ_{rR}, π_{rR}
Throttle setting:	T_{t4R} (K, °R)
Component behavior:	π_{dR}, π_{cR}, π_{tLR}, τ_{tLR}
Exhaust nozzle:	M_{9R}

OUTPUTS:

Overall performance:	F (N, lbf), $\dot{W}$ (kW, hp), $\dot{m}_0\left(\dfrac{\text{kg}}{\text{sec}}, \dfrac{\text{lbm}}{\text{sec}}\right)$, $S\left(\dfrac{\text{mg/sec}}{\text{N}}, \dfrac{\text{lbm/hr}}{\text{lbf}}\right)$, $S_P\left(\dfrac{\text{mg/sec}}{\text{kW}}, \dfrac{\text{lbm/hr}}{\text{hp}}\right)$, f, η_P, η_T, η_O, C_C, C_{prop}, C_{tot}
Component behavior:	π_c, τ_c, π_{tL}, τ_{tL}, f, M_9, $N_{\text{core spool}}$, $N_{\text{power spool}}$

EQUATIONS:

$$R_c = \frac{\gamma_c - 1}{\gamma_c} c_{pc} \tag{8-76a}$$

$$R_t = \frac{\gamma_t - 1}{\gamma_t} c_{pt} \tag{8-76b}$$

$$a_0 = \sqrt{\gamma_c R_c g_c T_0} \tag{8-76c}$$

$$V_0 = a_0 M_0 \tag{8-76d}$$

$$\tau_r = 1 + \frac{\gamma_c - 1}{2} M_0^2 \tag{8-76e}$$

$$\pi_r = \tau_r^{\gamma_c/(\gamma_c-1)} \tag{8-76f}$$

$$\eta_r = 1 \tag{8-76g}$$

$$\pi_d = \pi_{d\max}\eta_r \tag{8-76h}$$

$$\tau_c = 1 + \frac{T_{t4}/T_0}{(T_{t4}/T_0)_R}\frac{(\tau_r)_R}{\tau_r}(\tau_c - 1)_R \tag{8-76i}$$

$$\pi_c = [1 + \eta_c(\tau_c - 1)]^{\gamma_c/(\gamma_c-1)} \tag{8-76j}$$

$$\tau_\lambda = \frac{c_{pt}T_{t4}}{c_{pc}T_0} \tag{8-76k}$$

$$f = \frac{\tau_\lambda - \tau_r\tau_c}{h_{PR}\eta_b/(c_p T_0) - \tau_\lambda} \tag{8-76l}$$

$$\dot{m}_0 = \dot{m}_{0R}\frac{P_0\pi_r\pi_d\pi_c}{(P_0\pi_r\pi_d\pi_c)_R}\sqrt{\frac{T_{t4R}}{T_{t4}}} \tag{8-76m}$$

Initial value of π_{tL}:

$$\pi_{tL} = \pi_{tLR} \tag{8-76n}$$

Low-pressure turbine and exhaust nozzle:

$$\tau_{tL} = 1 - \eta_{tL}(1 - \pi_{tL}^{(\gamma_t-1)/\gamma_t}) \tag{8-76o}$$

$$\frac{P_{t9}}{P_0} = \pi_r\pi_d\pi_c\pi_b\pi_{tH}\pi_{tL}\pi_n \tag{8-76p}$$

If $\quad \dfrac{P_{t9}}{P_0} \geq \left(\dfrac{\gamma_t + 1}{2}\right)^{\gamma_t/(\gamma_t-1)}$

$$\text{then} \quad M_9 = 1 \quad \frac{P_{t9}}{P_9} = \left(\frac{\gamma_t + 1}{2}\right)^{\gamma_t/(\gamma_t-1)} \quad \text{and} \quad \frac{P_0}{P_9} = \frac{P_{t9}/P_9}{P_{t9}/P_0} \tag{8-76q}$$

$$\text{else} \quad \frac{P_0}{P_9} = 1 \quad \frac{P_{t9}}{P_9} = \frac{P_{t9}}{P_0} \quad \text{and} \quad M_9 = \sqrt{\frac{2}{\gamma_t - 1}\left[\left(\frac{P_{t9}}{P_0}\right)^{(\gamma_t-1)/\gamma_t} - 1\right]} \tag{8-76r}$$

$$\pi_{tLN} = \pi_{tLR}\sqrt{\frac{\tau_{tL}}{\tau_{tLR}}}\frac{\text{MFP}(M_{9R})}{\text{MFP}(M_9)} \tag{8-76s}$$

Is $|\tau_{tL\,N} - \pi_{tL}| \le 0.0001$? If so, then continue. If not, set $\pi_{tL} = \pi_{tL\,N}$ and return to Eq. (8-76*o*).

$$\frac{T_9}{T_0} = \frac{T_{t4}\tau_{tH}\tau_{tL}}{(P_{t9}/P_9)^{(\gamma_t-1)/\gamma_t}} \tag{8-76t}$$

$$\frac{V_9}{a_0} = M_9\sqrt{\frac{\gamma_t R_t T_9}{\gamma_c R_c T_0}} \tag{8-76u}$$

$$C_C = (\gamma_c - 1)M_0\left[(1+f)\frac{V_9}{a_0} - M_0 + (1+f)\frac{R_t}{R_c}\frac{T_9/T_0}{V_9/a_0}\frac{1-P_0/P_9}{\gamma_c}\right] \tag{8-76v}$$

$$C_{\text{prop}} = \eta_{\text{prop}}\eta_g\eta_{mL}(1+f)\tau_\lambda\tau_{tH}(1-\tau_{tL}) \tag{8-76w}$$

$$C_{\text{tot}} = C_{\text{prop}} + C_C \tag{8-76x}$$

$$\frac{F}{\dot m_0} = \frac{C_{\text{tot}}c_{pc}T_0}{V_0} \tag{8-76y}$$

$$S = \frac{f}{F/\dot m_0} \tag{8-76z}$$

$$\frac{\dot W}{\dot m_0} = C_{\text{tot}}c_{pc}T_0 \tag{8-76aa}$$

$$S_P = \frac{f}{C_{\text{tot}}c_{pc}T_0} \tag{8-76ab}$$

$$F = \dot m_0\left(\frac{F}{\dot m_0}\right) \tag{8-76ac}$$

$$\dot W = \dot m_0\left(\frac{\dot W}{\dot m_0}\right) \tag{8-76ad}$$

$$\eta_P = \frac{C_{\text{tot}}}{C_{\text{prop}}/\eta_{\text{prop}} + ([\gamma_c - 1)/2][(1+f)(V_9/a_0)^2 - M_0^2]} \tag{8-76ae}$$

$$\eta_T = \frac{C_{\text{tot}}c_{pc}T_0}{fh_{PR}} \tag{8-76af}$$

$$\eta_O = \eta_P\eta_T \tag{8-76ag}$$

$$\left(\frac{N}{N_R}\right)_{\text{core spool}} = \sqrt{\frac{T_0\tau_r}{T_{0R}\tau_{rR}}\frac{\tau_c - 1}{\tau_{cR} - 1}} \tag{8-76ah}$$

$$\left(\frac{N}{N_R}\right)_{\text{power spool}} = \sqrt{\frac{T_{t4}}{T_{t4R}}\frac{1-\tau_{tL}}{1-\tau_{tLR}}} \tag{8-76ai}$$

Example 8-11. *Turboprop engine.* In this example, we consider the performance of a turboprop engine with an uninstalled thrust of 140,000 N, π_c of 30, and τ_t of 0.55 at sea level, and $M_0 = 0.1$. Mach 0.1 is selected for reference because the propeller efficiency falls off very rapidly below this Mach number. The resulting reference data are listed below. The engine has a $T_{t4\,\text{max}}$ of 1670 K and an engine throttle ratio TR of 1.0.

The full-throttle performance for this turboprop engine is considered first. This section is followed by a discussion of several partial-throttle performance

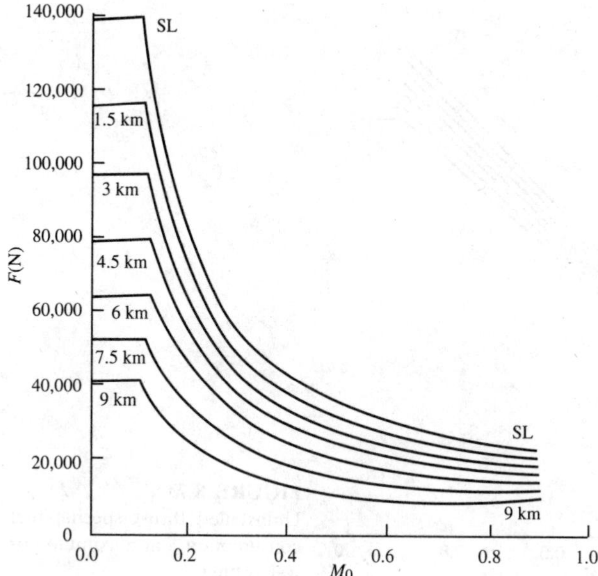

FIGURE 8-72
Uninstalled thrust F at maximum power setting.

curves. This section is concluded with discussion of gas generator performance curves.

REFERENCE: $T_0 = 288.2$ K, $\gamma_c = 1.4$, $c_{pc} = 1.004$ kJ/(kg · K), $\gamma_t = 1.3$, $c_{pt} = 1.235$ kJ/(kg · K), $M_0 = 0.1$, $T_{t4} = 1670$ K, $\pi_c = 30$, $\eta_c = 0.8450$, $\tau_{tH} = 0.7336$, $\pi_{tH} = 0.2212$, $\tau_{tL} = 0.7497$, $\pi_{tL} = 0.2537$, $\eta_{tL} = 0.9224$, $\eta_b = 0.995$, $\pi_{d\,\max} = 0.98$, $\pi_b = 0.94$, $f = 0.0299$, $\pi_n = 0.98$, $\eta_m = 0.99$, $\eta_{\text{prop}} = 0.812$, $\eta_g = 0.99$, $P_9/P_0 = 1$, $P_0 = 101.3$ kPa, $h_{PR} = 42{,}800$ kJ/kg, $\dot{m}_0 = 14.55$ kg/sec, $F/\dot{m}_0 = 9260$ N/(kg/sec), $F = 140{,}000$ N, $S = 3.105$ (mg/sec)/N, Power $= 4764$ kW

The uninstalled thrust and thrust specific fuel consumption of the turboprop engine at full throttle are shown in Figs. 8-72 and 8-73, respectively. Note that both the thrust and fuel consumption curves are flat between Mach numbers of 0 and 0.1. This is due to the constant engine output power in the Mach range and the linear variation of propeller efficiency shown in Fig. 8-71. The thrust of the turboprop engine falls off rapidly with flight Mach number.

Figures 8-74*a* and 8-74*b* show the variation with Mach number and altitude of the engine's air mass flow rate and corrected air mass flow rate, respectively, for maximum throttle. Since this engine has a TR of 1.0, the corrected air mass flow rate drops off with Mach number when $\theta_0 > 1.0$.

The partial-throttle performance of this turboprop engine is given at sea level and 6-km altitude in Figs. 8-75*a* and 8-75*b*, respectively. Note that the minimum thrust specific fuel consumption for this engine occurs at maximum throttle, and not at a reduced throttle setting as it did for the turbojet and

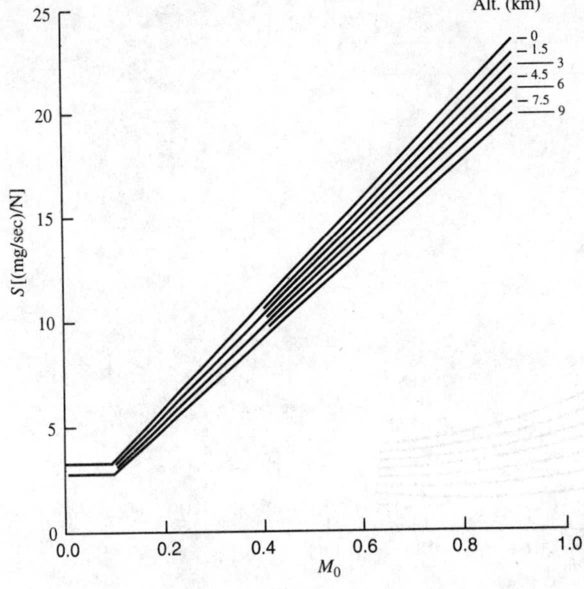

FIGURE 8-73
Uninstalled thrust specific fuel consumption S at maximum power setting.

turbofan engines. This characteristic occurs because the turboprop engine has a high propulsive efficiency and the reduction in the engine's thermal efficiency at partial throttle is not offset by its increase in propulsive efficiency at partial throttle.

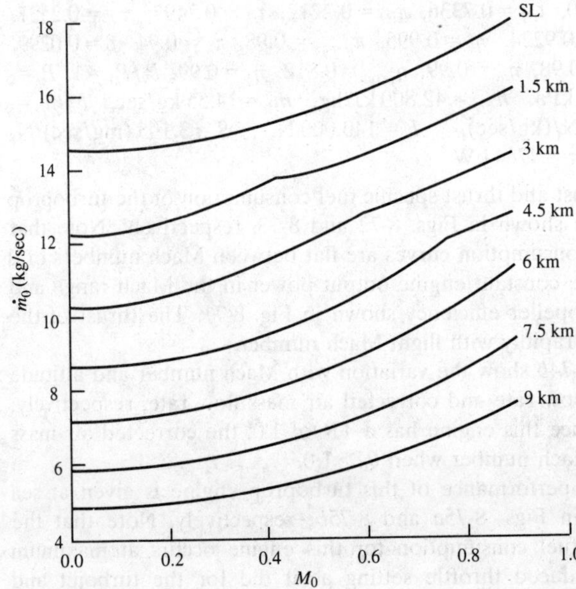

FIGURE 8-74*a*
Engine mass flow rate at maximum power setting.

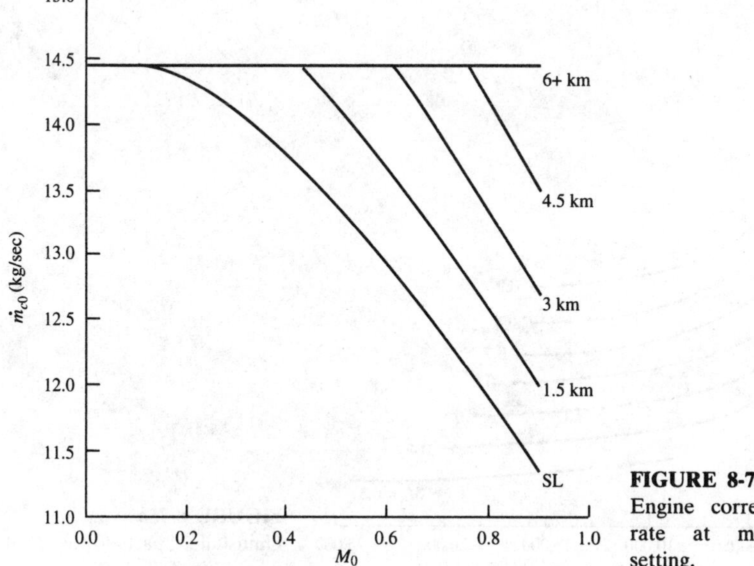

FIGURE 8-74*b*
Engine corrected mass flow rate at maximum power setting.

The variation in the pumping characteristics of the turboprop engine's gas generator are shown in Fig. 8-76. These are the same trends that we observed for the gas generators of the turbojet engine (Fig. 8-15) and mixed-flow turbofan engine (Fig. 8-63).

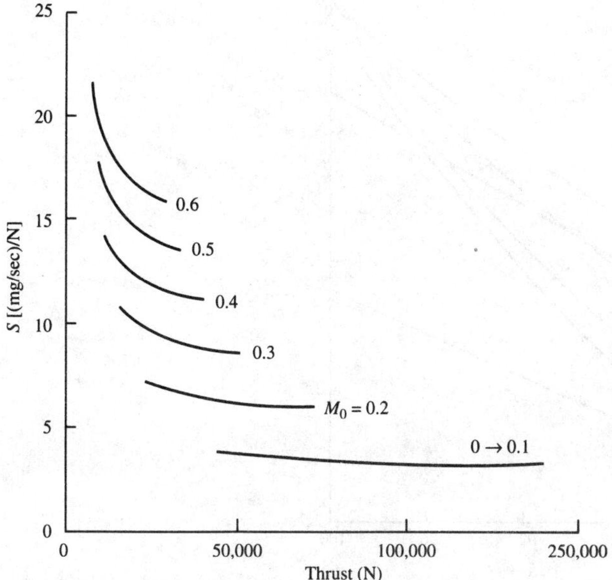

FIGURE 8-75*a*
Uninstalled partial power at sea level.

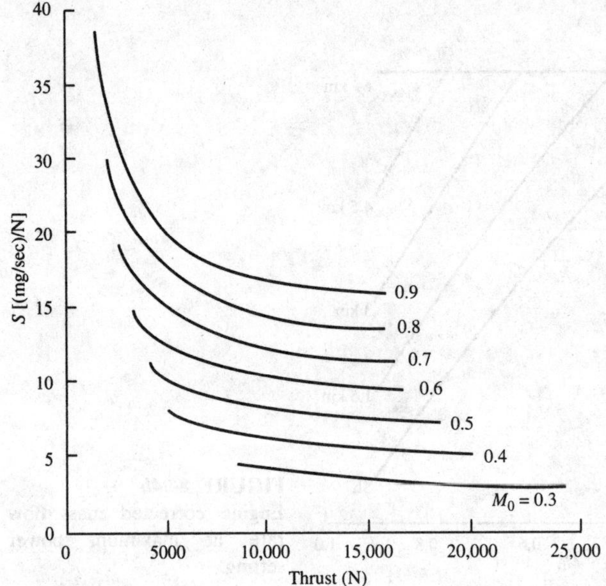

FIGURE 8-75b
Uninstalled partial power at 6-km altitude.

The variations in the pumping characteristics of the turboprop engine's gas generator are shown in Fig. 8-76. These are the same trends that we observed for the gas generators of the turbojet engine (Fig. 8-15) and mixed-flow turbofan engine (Fig. 8-49).

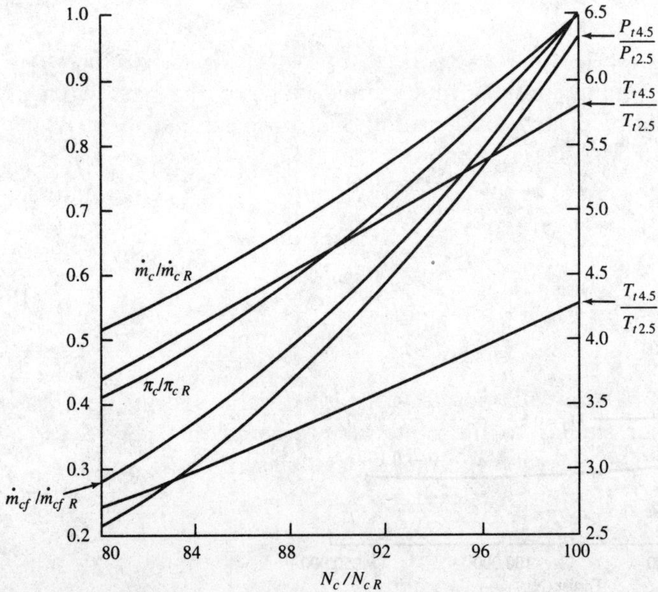

FIGURE 8-76
Gas generator pumping characteristics.

8-8 VARIABLE GAS PROPERTIES

The effect of variable gas properties can be included in the analysis of gas turbine engine performance. One first needs a method to calculate the thermodynamic state of the gas, given the fuel/air ratio f and two independent properties. Equations (2-68) through (2-70), Eqs. (2-72a) through (2-72d), Eq. (2-63), and the constants of Table 2-3 permit direct calculation of h, c_p, ϕ, and P_r given the fuel/air ratio f and temperature T. Calculation of the temperature T given the fuel/air ratio f and one of h, P_r, or ϕ requires iteration. The methods developed in this section can be used to hand-calculate the performance of a gas turbine engine by using App. D. However, use of a computer is recommended due to the iterative nature of the calculations.

The subroutine FAIR [for products of combustion from air and hydrocarbon fuels of the type $(CH_2)_n$] was developed for use in the program AFPROP, first introduced in Chap. 2 and mentioned again in Chaps. 6 and 7. It contains Eqs. (2-68) through (2-70), Eqs. (2-72a) through (2-72d), Eq. (2-63), and the constants of Table 2-3; and it gives direct calculation of h, c_p, ϕ, γ, P_r, R, and the speed of sound a for given value of the fuel/air ratio f and temperature T. Given the fuel/air ratio f and one of h, P_r, or ϕ, the temperature T can be found by the addition of simple iteration algorithms.

For convenience, we use the nomenclature for the subroutine FAIR first introduced in Chap. 7. The primary input of FAIR (one of T, h, P_r or ϕ) is indicated by first listing a corresponding number from 1 to 4, followed by a list of the variables. Table 7-1 identifies the four sets of knowns for the subroutine FAIR. The subroutine FAIR with the first three sets of unknowns is used extensively in this section.

An additional property such as pressure P, density ρ, or entropy s is needed to completely define the thermodynamic state of the gas. We will normally use pressure or entropy as the additional property and Eqs. (2-30) and (2-65) to obtain the remaining unknowns:

$$\rho = \frac{P}{RT} \tag{2-30}$$

$$s_2 - s_1 = \phi_2 - \phi_1 - R \ln \frac{P_2}{P_1} \tag{2-65}$$

The one-dimensional flow of a perfect gas with variable specific heats can be studied in a manner similar to the material presented in Chap. 3 for a calorically perfect gas. The mass flow parameter can be written as

$$\text{MFP} = \frac{\dot{m}\sqrt{T_t}}{P_t A} = \rho V \frac{\sqrt{T_t}}{P_t} = \frac{M\sqrt{\gamma g_c RT}}{RT} \frac{\sqrt{T_t}}{P_t/P} = M\sqrt{\frac{\gamma g_c}{R}} \frac{\sqrt{T_t/T}}{P_t/P}$$

where R is a function of the fuel/air ratio f and the terms γ, T_t/T, and P_t/P are functions of the Mach number M, the static or total temperature T or T_t, and

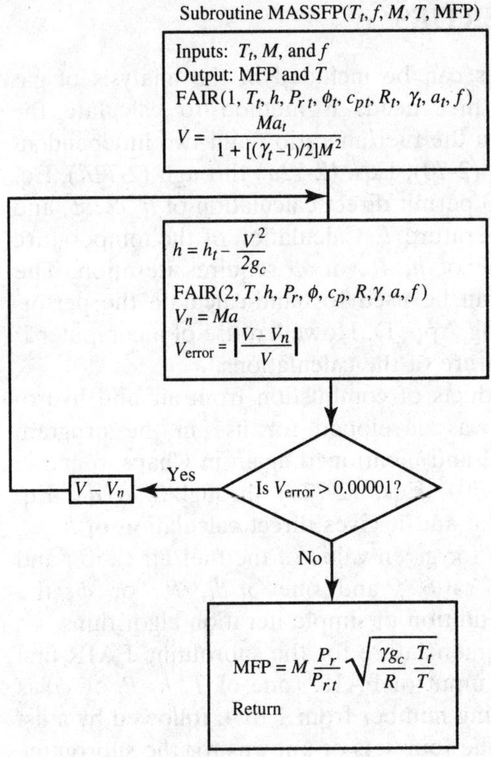

Subroutine MASSFP(T_t, f, M, T, MFP)
Inputs: T_t, M, and f
Output: MFP and T
FAIR(1, T_t, h, Pr_t, ϕ_t, c_{pt}, R_t, γ_t, a_t, f)
$V = \frac{Ma_t}{1+[(\gamma_t-1)/2]M^2}$
$h = h_t - \frac{V^2}{2g_c}$
FAIR(2, T, h, P_r, ϕ, c_p, R, γ, a, f)
$V_n = Ma$
$V_{error} = \left|\frac{V-V_n}{V}\right|$
Is $V_{error} > 0.00001$?
Yes
$V = V_n$
No
$\text{MFP} = M\frac{P_r}{P_{rt}}\sqrt{\frac{\gamma g_c}{R}\frac{T_t}{T}}$
Return

FIGURE 8-77
Flowchart of subroutine MASSFP.

the fuel/air ratio f. For convenience, we choose the total temperature T_t for expressing the mass flow parameter in its functional form, and we write

$$\text{MFP} \equiv \frac{\dot{m}\sqrt{T_t}}{P_t A} = M\sqrt{\frac{\gamma g_c}{R}}\frac{\sqrt{T_t/T}}{P_t/P} = \text{MFP}(M, T_t, f) \tag{8-77}$$

The mass flow parameter can be calculated for given values of M, T_t, and f by using functional iteration and the subroutine FAIR as outlined in Fig. 8-77 for the subroutine MASSFP. It starts with an initial guess for the velocity V based on an approximate speed of sound a. Then the velocity is used in a functional iteration loop to obtain the static state.

For the performance analysis of gas turbine engines, two important characteristics of a perfect gas with variable specific heats are the following:

1. The variations of the mass flow parameter, T/T_t, and P/P_t with Mach number, total temperature T_t, and fuel/air ratio f
2. The variation of the mass flow parameter for choked flow with total temperature T_t and fuel/air ratio f

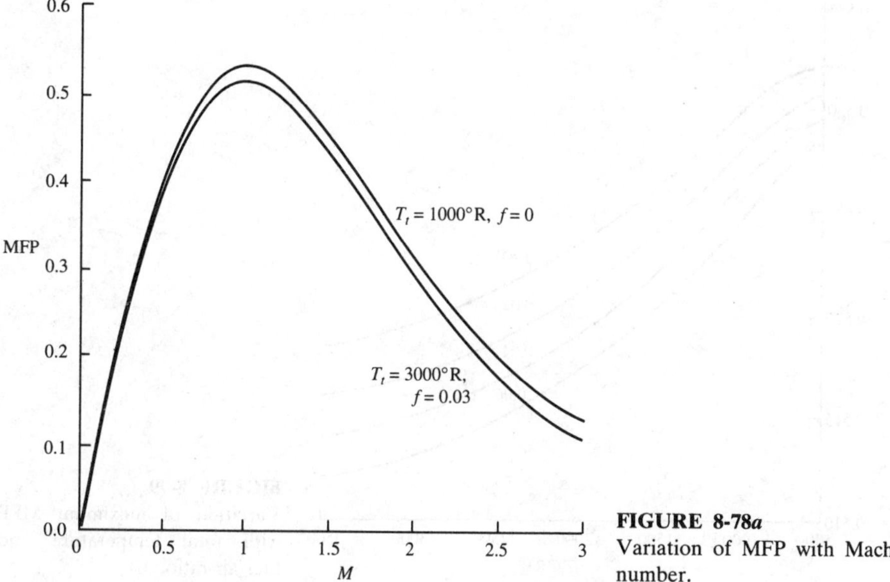

FIGURE 8-78*a*
Variation of MFP with Mach number.

Figure 8-78*a* shows the variation of MFP with Mach number for two cases: air alone ($f = 0$) with a total temperature of 1000°R, and products of combustion for a fuel/air ratio of 0.03 with a total temperature of 3000°R. The MFP peaks at Mach 1.0 (this corresponds to choked flow) for both cases, and

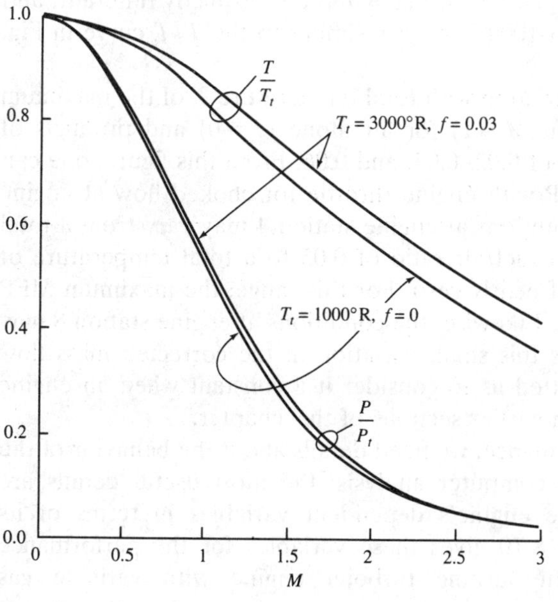

FIGURE 8-78*b*
Variation of P/P_t and T/T_t with Mach number.

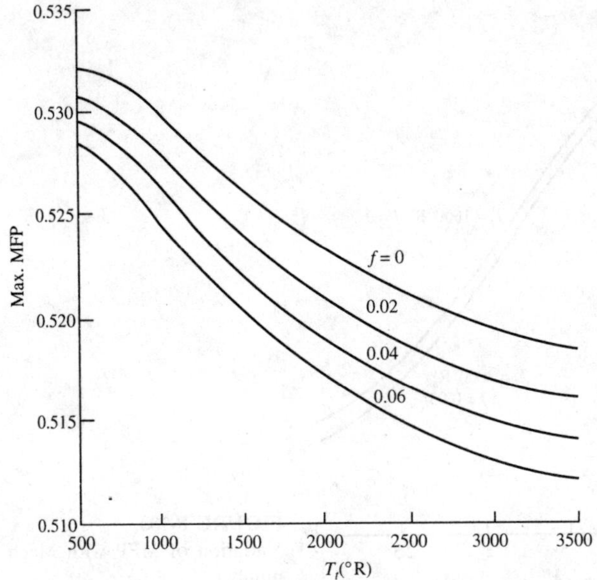

FIGURE 8-79
Variation of maximum MFP with total temperature and fuel/air ratio.

these curves are very similar to those of Fig. 3-9. Figure 8-78*b* gives the variations of T/T_t and P/P_t with Mach number for the same two cases as Fig. 8-78*a*: air alone ($f = 0$) with a total temperature of 1000°R, and products of combustion for a fuel/air ratio of 0.03 with a total temperature of 3000°R. The P/P_t curves in Fig. 8-78*b* are about the same and are similar to the P/P_t curve in Fig. 3-7. However, the T/T_t curves in Fig. 8-78*b* are distinctly different, and the T/T_t curve for air alone at 1000°R is very similar to the T/T_t curve in Fig. 3-7.

Figure 8-79 shows the variation with total temperature T_t of the maximum mass flow parameter (MFP at $M = 1$) for air alone ($f = 0$) and products of combustion for fuel/air ratios of 0.02, 0.04, and 0.06. From this figure, one can estimate the variation of MFP with engine throttle for choked flow at engine stations 4, 4.5, and 8. The conditions at engine station 4 may vary from a total temperature of 3500°R with a fuel/air ratio of 0.05 to a total temperature of 1000°R with a fuel/air ratio of nearly zero. For this range, the maximum MFP will vary only about 3 percent. Likewise, the conditions at engine station 8 may vary over similar ranges. It is this small variation in the corrected mass flow rate per unit area that permitted us to consider it a constant when an engine station was choked ($M = 1$) in earlier sections of this chapter.

To predict engine performance, we need details about the behavior of the engine components. For our computer analysis, the most useful details are analytical expressions for the engine's dependent variables in terms of its independent variables. Table 8-10 gives these variables for the performance analysis of a dual-spool afterburning turbojet engine with variable gas

TABLE 8-10
Performance analysis variables for afterburning turbojet engine with variable gas properties

Component	Variables: Independent	Constant or known	Dependent
Engine	M_0, T_0, P_0		$\dot{m}_0$
Diffuser		$\pi_d = f(M_0)$, τ_d	
Low-pressure compressor		η_{cL}	π_{cL}, τ_{cL}
High-pressure compressor		η_{cH}	π_{cH}, τ_{cH}
Burner	T_{t4}	π_b, η_b	f
High-pressure turbine		η_{tH}, $\dfrac{A_4}{A_{4.5}}$	π_{tH}, τ_{tH}
Low-pressure turbine		η_{tL}, $\dfrac{A_{4.5}}{A_{8\,\mathrm{dry}}}$	π_{tL}, τ_{tL}
Afterburner	T_{t7}	π_{AB}, η_{AB}	f_{AB}
Nozzle	$\dfrac{P_9}{P_0}$ (choked), $\dfrac{A_9}{A_8}$ (choked), *or* $\dfrac{A_8}{A_{8R}}$ (unchoked)	π_n, τ_n	M_9
Total number	6		12

properties. Note that the fuel/air ratios (f and f_{AB}) show up as dependent variables for the first time.

Section 6-8 develops some of the basics for component performance with variable gas properties. The efficiency relationships between actual and ideal total enthalpy changes are given for the compressor and turbine in Eqs. (6-33) and (6-41), respectively. The relationships between static and total properties are developed and given for the inlet and nozzle in Eqs. (6-26), (6-44), and (6-45). The energy balance of the combustor gives Eq. (6-36) for the fuel/air ratio. These relationships and others will be used in the following section to develop a system of equations that predict the performance of a gas turbine engine.

Turbine Characteristics

We analyze the turbine performance in a gas turbine engine by first considering the high-pressure turbine. Typically, the flow entering both the high-pressure turbine and low-pressure turbine is choked. However, we will consider the general case when the Mach number at stations 4 and 4.5 can be any known value.

Since the mass flows entering and leaving the high-pressure turbine are equal, we can write

$$\dot{m}_4 = \dot{m}_{4.5}$$

Writing this in terms of the mass flow parameter at stations 4 and 4.5 gives

$$\mathrm{MFP}_4 = \frac{\dot{m}_3\sqrt{T_{t4}}}{P_{t4}A_4} = \frac{\dot{m}_{4.5}\sqrt{T_{t4.5}}}{P_{t4.5}A_{4.5}}\frac{P_{t4.5}}{P_{t4}}\frac{A_{4.5}}{A_4}\sqrt{\frac{T_{t4}}{T_{t4.5}}}$$

$$= \mathrm{MFP}_{4.5}\frac{P_{t4.5}}{P_{t4}}\frac{A_{4.5}}{A_4}\sqrt{\frac{T_{t4}}{T_{t4.5}}}$$

Since the fuel/air ratio f is constant for the gas flowing through the high-pressure turbine, this equation can be rewritten as

$$\boxed{\frac{\pi_{tH}}{\sqrt{T_{t4.5}/T_{t4}}}\frac{\mathrm{MFP}_{4.5}}{\mathrm{MFP}_4} = \frac{A_4}{A_{4.5}} = \text{const}} \tag{8-78}$$

where the area ratio $A_4/A_{4.5}$ is constant and the mass flow parameters MFP_4 and $\mathrm{MFP}_{4.5}$ are functions of T_{t4}, $T_{t4.5}$, the fuel/air ratio f, and Mach numbers M_4 and $M_{4.5}$.

From Eq. (6-41), the efficiency of the high-pressure turbine is given by

$$\boxed{\eta_{tH} = \frac{h_{t4} - h_{t4.5}}{h_{t4} - h_{t4.5i}}} \tag{8-79}$$

Solving this equation for the high-pressure turbine's ideal exit enthalpy $h_{t4.5i}$ gives

$$\boxed{h_{t4.5i} = h_{t4} - \frac{h_{t4} - h_{t4.5}}{\eta_{tH}}} \tag{8-80}$$

where the total enthalpies are functions of T_{t4}, $T_{t4.5}$, and the fuel/air ratio f. During normal engine operation, the efficiency of the high-pressure turbine η_{tH} does not vary much. Thus we will consider η_{tH} to be constant in our analysis.

The pressure ratio of the high-pressure turbine π_{tH} is a function of T_{t4}, $T_{t4.5i}$, and the fuel/air ratio f, which can be written in terms of the reduced pressure as

$$\boxed{\pi_{tH} = \frac{P_{t4.5}}{P_{t4}} = \frac{P_r @ T_{t4.5i}}{P_r @ T_{t4}} = \frac{P_{rt4.5i}}{P_{rt4}}} \tag{8-81}$$

In summary, the performance of the high-pressure turbine is a function of the variables T_{t4} and f; known values for the Mach numbers M_4 and $M_{4.5}$; the area ratio $A_4/A_{4.5}$; and the turbine efficiency η_{tH}. Equations (8-78), (8-81), and (8-80) can be written in their functional forms as

$$\pi_{tH} = f_1\left(f,\ T_{t4},\ T_{t4},\ M_4,\ M_{4.5},\ \frac{A_4}{A_{4.5}}\right)$$

$$T_{t4.5i} = f_2(f,\ T_{t4},\ \pi_{tH})$$

$$h_{t4.5} = f_3(f,\ h_{t4},\ h_{t4.5i},\ \eta_{tH})$$

For known values of M_4, $M_{4.5}$, $A_4/A_{4.5}$, and η_{tH}, the above three functional relationships can be solved for values of T_{t4} and f by using functional iteration [this is the same iteration procedure used to solve Eqs. (8-12a) and (8-12b)].

The performance of the low-pressure turbine depends on the same set of equations as the high-pressure turbine with the subscripts 4, 4.5, and H replaced by 4.5, 5, and L, respectively. Performance calculations for both the high- and low-pressure turbines can be done by using a single subroutine which we call *TURB*. A flowchart of subroutine TURB is shown in Fig. 8-80, which

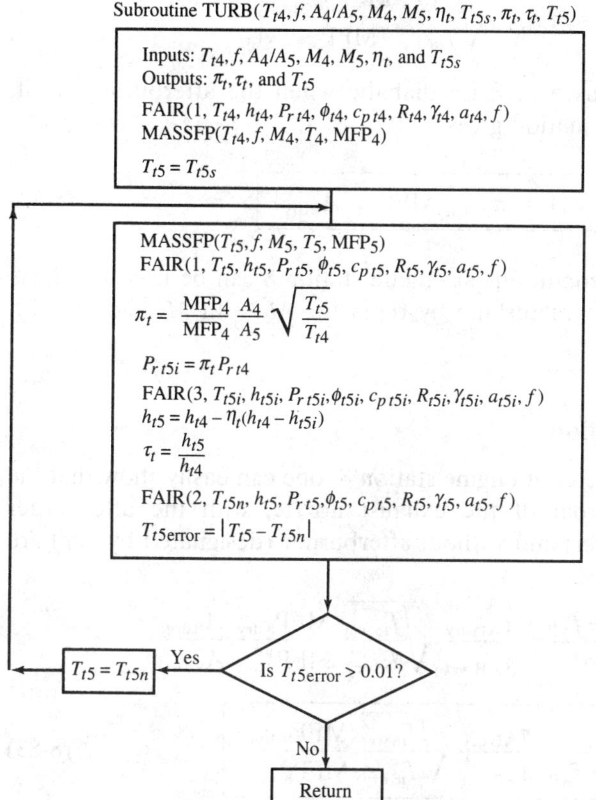

FIGURE 8-80
Flowchart of subroutine TURB.

uses the general subscripts 4 and 5 for the turbine inlet and exit, respectively. A starting value for the total temperature leaving the turbine T_{t5} is required to initiate calculations. A good starting value for T_{t5} is its value at the reference conditions T_{t5R} or a previously calculated value. The starting value is designated by the variable T_{t5S} in subroutine TURB.

The performance calculations for the low-pressure turbine use engine station 8 (the throat of the exhaust nozzle) to represent the exit conditions from the low-pressure turbine for several reasons. First, the Mach number and flow area at the exit of the low-pressure turbine (M_5 and A_5) are usually unknown since they depend on more detailed design of the turbine. Second, the Mach number and flow area at the throat of the exhaust nozzle (M_8 and A_8) are directly related to those at station 5. Finally, M_8 and A_8 are known or easily determined. For an afterburning engine, the flow area at the throat of the exhaust nozzle is varied during afterburner operation to maintain the same flow conditions at the exit of the low-pressure turbine. Thus only variations at the throat of the exhaust nozzle when the afterburner is off (designated by *dry*) will affect the operation of the low-pressure turbine. From conservation of mass between engine station 5 and engine station 8 with the afterburner off, we have

$$\frac{\dot{m}_{8\,\mathrm{dry}}}{\dot{m}_5} = 1 = \pi_{\mathrm{AB\,dry}} \sqrt{\frac{T_{t5}}{T_{t8\,\mathrm{dry}}}} \frac{\mathrm{MFP}_{8\,\mathrm{dry}}}{\mathrm{MFP}_5} \frac{A_{8\,\mathrm{dry}}}{A_5}$$

Since the flow from stations 5 to 8 is adiabatic when the afterburner is off, $T_{t5} = T_{t8\,\mathrm{dry}}$ and the above equation gives

$$\boxed{\mathrm{MFP}_5 A_5 = \pi_{\mathrm{AB\,dry}} \mathrm{MFP}_{8\,\mathrm{dry}} A_{8\,\mathrm{dry}}} \tag{8-82}$$

From Eq. (8-82), the flow conditions at engine station 8 can be used for those at the exit of the low-pressure turbine by replacing M_5 with M_8 and A_5 with $(\pi_{\mathrm{AB}} A_8)_{\mathrm{dry}}$.

Afterburner Area Variation

Using the mass flow parameter at engine station 8, one can easily show that the flow conditions at the throat of the exhaust nozzle, with the afterburner operating (designated by *wet*) and without afterburner (designated by *dry*) are related by

$$\frac{\dot{m}_{8\,\mathrm{wet}}}{\dot{m}_{8\,\mathrm{dry}}} = \frac{1+f+f_{\mathrm{AB}}}{1+f} = \frac{\tau_{\mathrm{AB\,dry}}}{\pi_{\mathrm{AB\,wet}}} \sqrt{\frac{T_{t8\,\mathrm{wet}}}{T_{t8\,\mathrm{dry}}}} \frac{\mathrm{MFP}_{8\,\mathrm{dry}}}{\mathrm{MFP}_{8\,\mathrm{wet}}} \frac{A_{8\,\mathrm{dry}}}{A_{8\,\mathrm{wet}}}$$

or

$$\boxed{\frac{A_{8\,\mathrm{wet}}}{A_{8\,\mathrm{dry}}} = \frac{1+f}{1+f+f_{\mathrm{AB}}} \frac{\pi_{\mathrm{AB\,dry}}}{\pi_{\mathrm{AB\,wet}}} \sqrt{\frac{T_{t8\,\mathrm{wet}}}{T_{t8\,\mathrm{dry}}}} \frac{\mathrm{MFP}_{8\,\mathrm{dry}}}{\mathrm{MFP}_{8\,\mathrm{wet}}}} \tag{8-83}$$

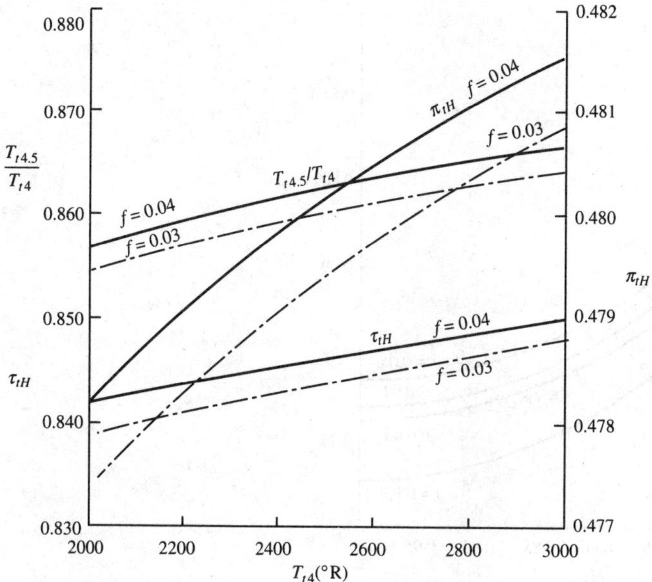

FIGURE 8-81
Variation of high-pressure turbine performance with total temperature.

Example 8-12. We consider the performance of a high-pressure turbine with choked flow at both inlet and exit ($M_4 = 1$ and $M_{4.5} = 1$) as our first example of turbine performance. The reference values are

$$T_{t4\,R} = 3000°\text{R} \qquad T_{t4.5\,R} = 2600°\text{R} \qquad \eta_{tH} = 0.9 \qquad f_R = 0.03 \qquad \frac{A_4}{A_{4.5}} = 0.5183883$$

With subroutine TURB, calculation of the high-pressure turbine performance over the range of T_{t4} from 2000 to 3000°R for fuel/air ratios f of 0.03 and 0.04 gives the results shown in Fig. 8-81. One can see that τ_{tH}, π_{tH}, and $T_{t4.5}/T_{t4}$ vary little over the range of input data. The changes in τ_{tH}, π_{tH}, and $T_{t4.5}/T_{t4}$ for a change in T_{t4}/f from 2000°R/0.03 to 3000°R/0.04 are 1.22, 0.82, and 1.40 percent, respectively. This is a very small change which helps justify the assumption of constant τ_{tH} and π_{tH} used in earlier sections of this chapter.

Example 8-13. We now consider the performance of a low-pressure turbine with choked flow at its inlet ($M_{4.5} = 1$). Two cases are considered: The Mach number at the throat of the exhaust nozzle M_8 is varied with the area A_8 held constant: and the throat area A_8 is increased with the throat choked ($M_8 = 1$). The reference values are

$$T_{t4.5\,R} = 2600°\text{R} \qquad T_{t5\,R} = 2080°\text{R} \qquad \eta_{tL} = 0.9 \qquad f_R = 0.04$$

$$\pi_{\text{AB dry}} = 1 \qquad \frac{A_{4.5}}{A_8} = 0.3686362$$

With subroutine TURB, calculation of the low-pressure turbine performance

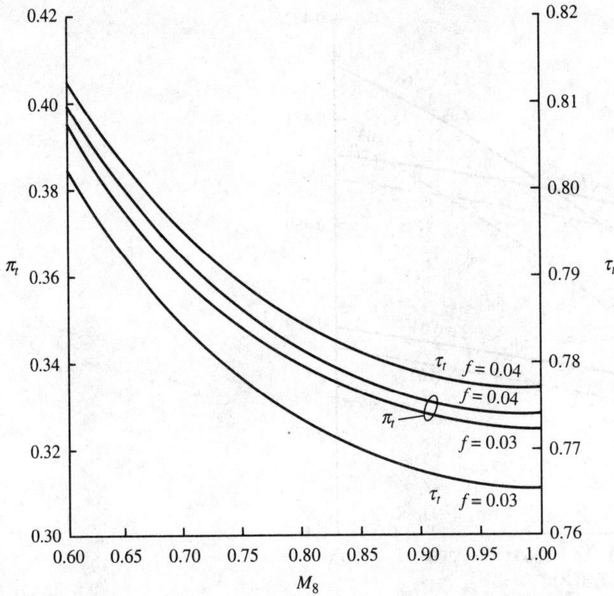

FIGURE 8-82*a*
Variation of low-pressure turbine performance with exhaust nozzle Mach number.

over the range of exhaust nozzle throat Mach numbers M_8 from 0.6 and 1.0 at fuel/air ratios f of 0.03 and 0.04 gives the results shown in Fig. 8-82*a*. Reducing M_8 increases τ_{tL} and π_{tL}. These are the same trends as shown in Fig. 8-7*b* for our basic engine performance model.

Calculation of the low-pressure turbine performance over the range of exhaust nozzle throat areas A_8/A_{8R} from 1.0 to 1.2 at fuel/air ratios f of 0.03 and 0.04 gives the results shown in Fig. 8-82*b*. Increasing A_8 increases τ_{tL} and π_{tL}. Again, these are the same trends shown in Fig. 8-7*c* for our basic engine performance model.

Gas Generator Pumping Characteristics

The gas generator pressure ratio P_{t6}/P_{t2} is obtained by multiplying the ratios of total pressure from gas generator inlet to exit, which yields

$$\frac{P_{t6}}{P_{t2}} = \pi_{cL}\pi_{cH}\pi_b\pi_{tH}\pi_{tH} \tag{8-84}$$

Similarly, the total temperature ratio of the gas generator T_{t6}/T_{t2} is obtained by multiplying the total temperature ratios, which yields

$$\frac{T_{t6}}{T_{t2}} = \frac{T_{t4}}{T_{t2}}\frac{T_{t4.5}}{T_{t4}}\frac{T_{t5}}{T_{t4.5}} \tag{8-85}$$

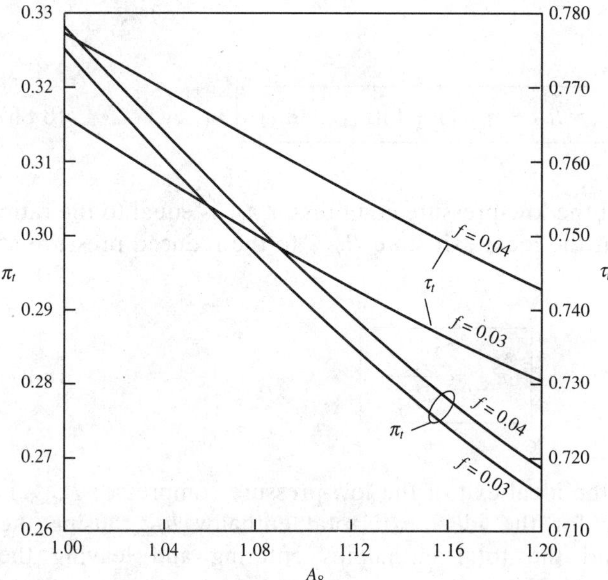

FIGURE 8-82*b*
Variation of low-pressure turbine performance with exhaust nozzle area.

We consider the case where the inlet flows to the high- and low-pressure turbines are choked ($M_4 = 1$ and $M_{4.5} = 1$) and the flow areas are constant at stations 4, 4.5, 5, 6, and 8. From our previous analysis, the total pressure and total temperature ratios for the high- and low-pressure turbines (π_{tH}, $T_{t4}/T_{t4.5}$, π_{tL}, and $T_{t4.5}/T_{t5}$) are dependent on T_{t4}, f, and exhaust nozzle Mach number M_8.

As shall be shown, the total pressure ratio of the low-pressure compressor π_{cL} and that of the high-pressure compressor π_{cH} are dependent on T_{t2}, T_{t4}, f, and the enthalpy changes across the turbines. We start the compressor analysis with the low-pressure compressor.

LOW-PRESSURE COMPRESSOR. Application of the first law of thermodynamics to the low-pressure compressor and low-pressure turbine gives the exit enthalpy of the low-pressure compressor. Equating the required compressor power to the net output power from the turbine, we have

$$\dot{W}_{cL} = \eta_{mL} \dot{W}_{tL}$$

Rewriting in terms of mass flow rates and total enthalpies gives

$$\dot{m}_0(h_{t2.5} - h_{t2}) = \eta_{mL}(\dot{m}_0 + \dot{m}_f)(h_{t4.5} - h_{t5}) = \eta_{mL}\dot{m}_0(1 + f)(h_{t4.5} - h_{t5})$$

Solving for $h_{t2.5}$ gives

$$h_{t2.5} = h_{t2} - \eta_{mL}(1+f)(h_{t4.5} - h_{t5}) \tag{8-86}$$

The total pressure ratio of the low-pressure compressor π_{cL} is equal to the ratio of the reduced pressure at the ideal exit state $P_{rt2.5i}$ to the reduced pressure at the inlet P_{rt2}, or

$$\pi_{cL} = \frac{P_{rt2.5i}}{P_{rt2}} \tag{8-87}$$

The reduced pressure at the ideal exit of the low-pressure compressor $P_{rt2.5i}$ is obtained by first solving for the ideal exit total enthalpy $h_{t2.5i}$, using the compressor efficiency and the total enthalpies entering and leaving the compressor. Rewriting Eq. (6-33) gives

$$h_{t2.5i} = h_{t2} + \eta_{cL}(h_{t2.5} - h_{t2}) \tag{8-88}$$

The reduced pressure for the ideal exit of the low-pressure compressor $P_{rt2.5i}$ follows directly from the value of $h_{t2.5i}$ and the subroutine FAIR.

HIGH-PRESSURE COMPRESSOR. Application of the first law of thermodynamics to the high-pressure compressor and high-pressure turbine gives the exit enthalpy of the high-pressure compressor, or

$$h_{t3} = h_{t2.5} - \eta_{mH}(1+f)(h_{t4} - h_{t4.5}) \tag{8-89}$$

The total pressure ratio of the high-pressure compressor π_{cH} is equal to the ratio of the reduced pressure at the ideal exit state P_{rt3i} to the reduced pressure at the inlet $P_{rt2.5}$, or

$$\pi_{cH} = \frac{P_{rt3i}}{P_{rt2.5}} \tag{8-90}$$

The reduced pressure at the ideal exit of the high-pressure compressor P_{rt3i} is obtained by first solving for the ideal exit total enthalpy h_{t3i}, using the compressor efficiency and the total enthalpies entering and leaving the compressor. Rewriting Eq. (6-33) gives

$$h_{t3i} = h_{t2.5} + \eta_{cH}(h_{t3} - h_{t2.5}) \tag{8-91}$$

The reduced pressure for the ideal exit of the high-pressure compressor P_{rt3i} follows directly from the value of h_{t3i} and the subroutine FAIR.

MAIN BURNER. The fuel/air ratio for the main burner f is given by Eq. (6-36), where h_{t4} is a function of f:

$$f = \frac{h_{t4} - h_{t3}}{\eta_b h_{PR} - h_{t4}} \tag{6-36}$$

ENGINE SPEED. As will be shown in Chap. 9, the change in total enthalpy across a fan or compressor is proportional to the rotational speed N squared. For the low-pressure compressor, we write

$$h_{t2.5} - h_{t2} = K_1 N_{cL}^2$$

where N_{cL} is the speed of the low-pressure spool. By using Eq. (8-4), this equation can be rewritten in terms of the corrected speed N_{cL} based on the total temperature at engine station 2 as

$$h_{t2.5} - h_{t2} = K_1 \frac{T_{t2}}{T_{\text{ref}}} N_{cL}^2$$

Evaluating the constant K_1 at reference conditions and solving the above equation for the corrected speed give

$$\frac{N_{cL}}{N_{cL\,R}} = \sqrt{\frac{T_{t2\,R}}{T_{t2}} \frac{h_{t2.5} - h_{t2}}{(h_{t2.5} - h_{t2})_R}} \tag{8-92a}$$

Similarly, for the high-pressure compressor, we have

$$\frac{N_{cH}}{N_{cH\,R}} = \sqrt{\frac{T_{t2.5\,R}}{T_{t2.5}} \frac{h_{t3} - h_{t2.5}}{(h_{t3} - h_{t2.5})_R}} \tag{8-92b}$$

SOLUTION PROCEDURE. All the equations required to calculate the pumping characteristics of a dual-spool gas generator with variable gas properties have now been developed. Figure 8-83 gives a flowchart showing the order of calculation of dependent variables to obtain the gas generator pumping characteristics. The subroutine TURB (see Fig. 8-80) is used to calculate the performance of both the high- and low-pressure turbines. Note that initial values of the fuel/air ratio f, $T_{t4.5}$, and T_{t5} are needed to start the calculations. Calculations continue until successive values of the fuel/air ratio f are within 0.0001 of each other.

Example 8-14. We now consider a dual-spool gas generator with the following reference conditions:

$T_{t2} = 518.7°\text{R}$ $\quad T_{t4} = 3200°\text{R}$ $\quad f = 0.03272$ $\quad M_4 = 1$

$\pi_{cL} = 5$ $\quad \eta_{cL} = 0.875724$ $\quad \pi_{cH} = 4$ $\quad \eta_{cH} = 0.880186$

$\tau_{tH} = 0.876058$ $\quad \pi_{tH} = 0.553469$ $\quad \tau_{tL} = 0.896517$ $\quad \pi_{tL} = 0.617798$

$\dfrac{A_4}{A_{4.5}} = 0.587805$ $\quad M_{4.5} = 1$ $\quad \left(\dfrac{\pi_{AB} A_{4.5}}{A_8}\right)_{dry} = 0.587805$ $\quad M_8 = 1$

The performance of this gas generator was calculated by using the procedure flowcharted in Fig. 8-83 for the following three cases:

a. Varied T_{t4} with T_{t2} and $(\pi_{AB} A_{4.5}/A_8)_{dry}$ equal to their reference values.
b. Varied T_{t2} with T_{t4} and $(\pi_{AB} A_{4.5}/A_8)_{dry}$ equal to their reference values.
c. Varied T_{t4} with T_{t2} equal to its reference values and $A_{8\,dry} = 1.4 A_{8\,dry\,R}$.

The pumping characteristics of the gas generator are plotted in Fig. 8-84 versus the corrected speed of the low-pressure spool for cases a and b with solid and dashed lines, respectively. Note that at reduced corrected speeds of the low-pressure spool, all the quantities plotted are less than their maximum values. Also note that the variations of the high-pressure spool's corrected quantities are much less that those of the low-pressure spool. These general trends (see Fig. 8-84) are the same as those we obtained with the basic performance model (see Fig. 8-15). Only the corrected fuel flow rate, T_{t4}/T_{t2}, and P_{t6}/P_{t2} seem to be impacted by which variable is varied—T_{t2} or T_{t4}. Even for engine cycle performance calculations as complex as these, *there is essentially a one-to-one correspondence between the temperature ratio* T_{t4}/T_{t2} *and the gas generator's pumping characteristics between station* 2 *and station* 6.

Figure 8-85 presents the variation of the compressor pressure ratio π_c versus the corrected mass flow rate for cases a and c. With T_{t4}/T_{t2} held constant, increasing A_8 will increase both the compressor pressure ratio and the corrected mass flow rate, which shifts the compressor operating line to the right and up. These are the same trends that we obtained with the basic performance model (see Fig. 8-9).

Inputs: T_{t4}, T_{t2}, and A_8/A_{8R}

Constants: η_{cL}, η_{cH}, π_b, η_b, η_{tH}, M_4, $A_4/A_{4.5}$, η_{tL}, $M_{4.5}$, and h_{PR}

Reference: T_{t4}, T_{t2}, $T_{t4.5}$, T_{t5}, π_{cL}, π_{cH}, $A_{4.5}/A_8$, M_8, and f

Outputs: $\dfrac{\pi_{cL}}{\pi_{cLR}}, \dfrac{N_{cL}}{N_{cLR}}, \dfrac{\pi_{cH}}{\pi_{cHR}}, \dfrac{N_{cH}}{N_{cHR}}, \dfrac{\pi_c}{\pi_{cR}}, \dfrac{\dot{m}_{c2}}{\dot{m}_{c2R}}, \dfrac{\dot{m}_{cf}}{\dot{m}_{cfR}}, \dfrac{T_{t4}}{T_{t2}}, \dfrac{P_{t6}}{P_{t2}}$, and $\dfrac{T_{t6}}{T_{t2}}$

Calculations:

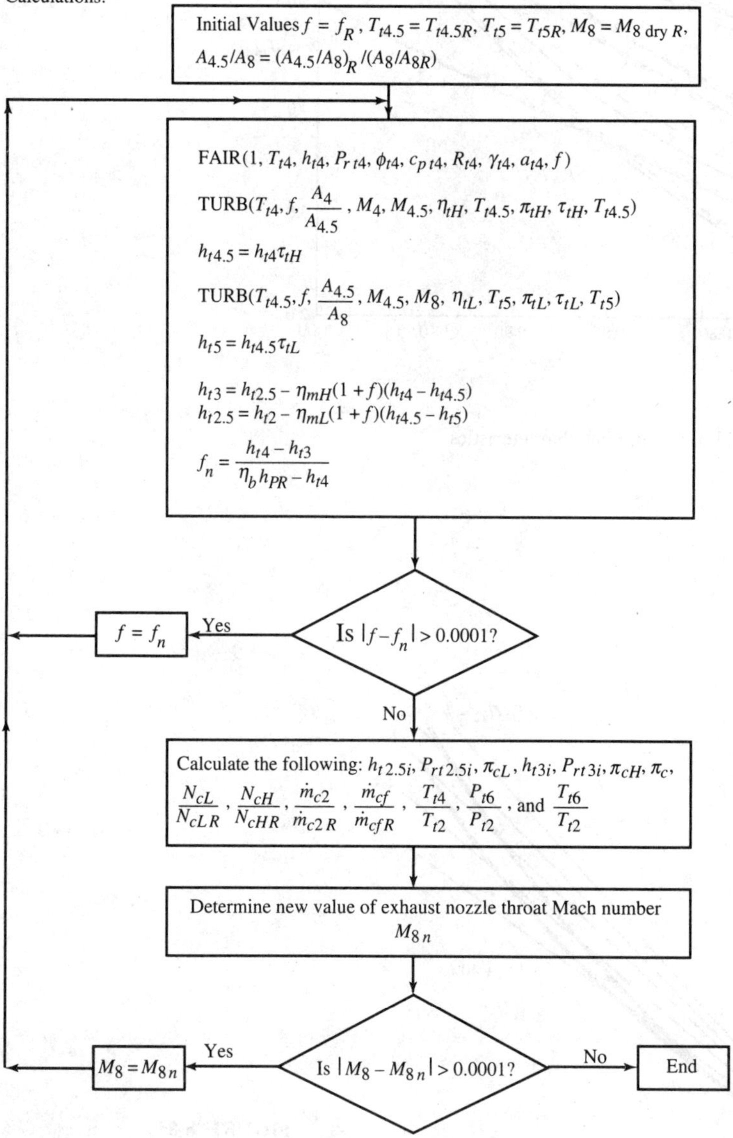

Initial Values $f = f_R$, $T_{t4.5} = T_{t4.5R}$, $T_{t5} = T_{t5R}$, $M_8 = M_{8\text{ dry }R}$, $A_{4.5}/A_8 = (A_{4.5}/A_8)_R/(A_8/A_{8R})$

FAIR(1, T_{t4}, h_{t4}, $P_{r\,t4}$, ϕ_{t4}, $c_{p\,t4}$, R_{t4}, γ_{t4}, a_{t4}, f)

TURB(T_{t4}, f, $\dfrac{A_4}{A_{4.5}}$, M_4, $M_{4.5}$, η_{tH}, $T_{t4.5}$, π_{tH}, τ_{tH}, $T_{t4.5}$)

$h_{t4.5} = h_{t4}\tau_{tH}$

TURB($T_{t4.5}$, f, $\dfrac{A_{4.5}}{A_8}$, $M_{4.5}$, M_8, η_{tL}, T_{t5}, π_{tL}, τ_{tL}, T_{t5})

$h_{t5} = h_{t4.5}\tau_{tL}$

$h_{t3} = h_{t2.5} - \eta_{mH}(1+f)(h_{t4} - h_{t4.5})$
$h_{t2.5} = h_{t2} - \eta_{mL}(1+f)(h_{t4.5} - h_{t5})$

$$f_n = \frac{h_{t4} - h_{t3}}{\eta_b h_{PR} - h_{t4}}$$

Is $|f - f_n| > 0.0001$? Yes → $f = f_n$ (return to loop start). No ↓

Calculate the following: $h_{t2.5i}$, $P_{rt2.5i}$, π_{cL}, h_{t3i}, P_{rt3i}, π_{cH}, π_c, $\dfrac{N_{cL}}{N_{cLR}}, \dfrac{N_{cH}}{N_{cHR}}, \dfrac{\dot{m}_{c2}}{\dot{m}_{c2R}}, \dfrac{\dot{m}_{cf}}{\dot{m}_{cfR}}, \dfrac{T_{t4}}{T_{t2}}, \dfrac{P_{t6}}{P_{t2}}$, and $\dfrac{T_{t6}}{T_{t2}}$

Determine new value of exhaust nozzle throat Mach number M_{8n}

Is $|M_8 - M_{8n}| > 0.0001$? Yes → $M_8 = M_{8n}$ (return to loop start). No → End

FIGURE 8-83
Flow chart of calculations for gas generator performance.

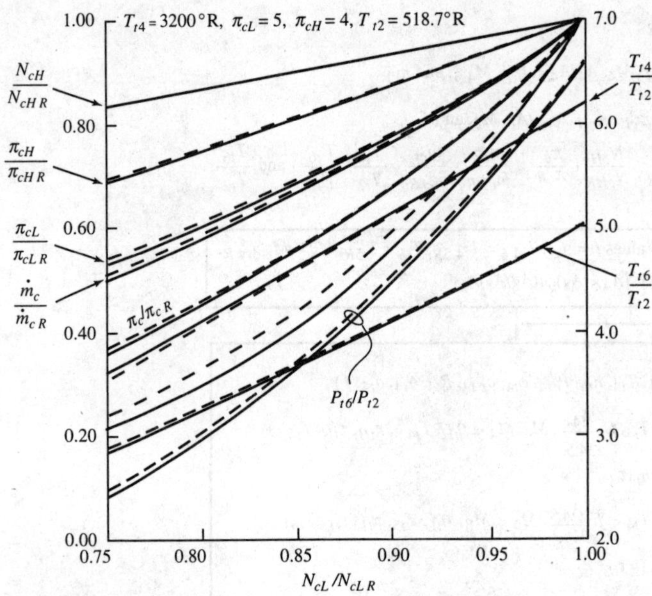

FIGURE 8-84
Dual-spool gas generator pumping characteristics.

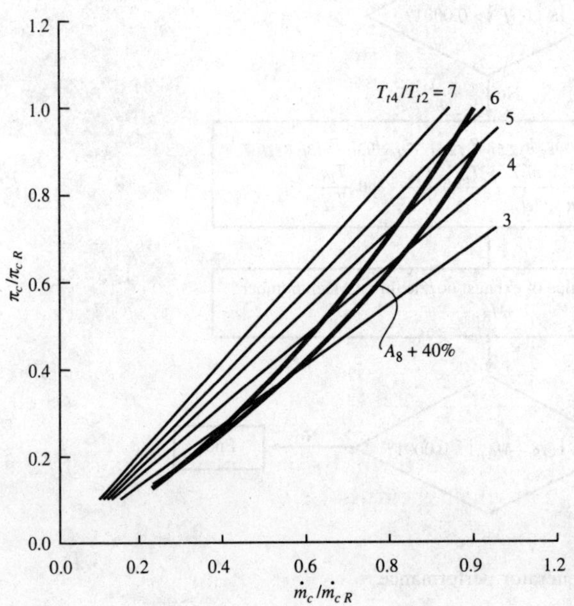

FIGURE 8-85
Compressor map with operating lines and lines of constant T_{t4}/T_{t2}.

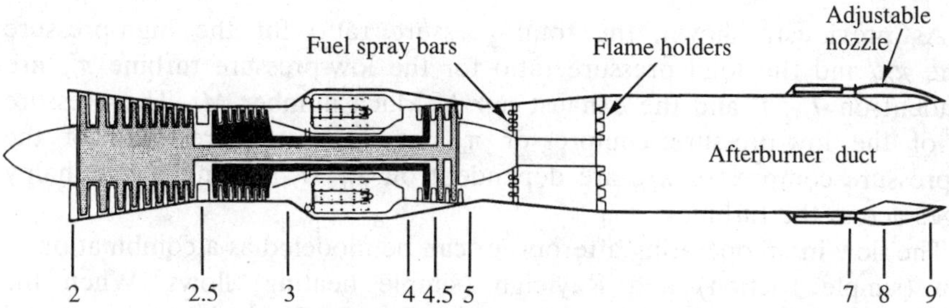

FIGURE 8-86
Station numbering for dual-spool turbojet engine. (*Courtesy of Pratt & Whitney.*)

Performance Analysis—Dual-Spool Afterburning Turbojet Engine

Figure 8-86 shows a cross-sectional drawing of the dual-spool afterburning turbojet engine and its station numbering. The uninstalled thrust is given by

$$F = \frac{\dot{m}_0 a_0}{g_c}\left[(1+f_O)\frac{V_9}{a_0} - M_0 + (1+f_O)\frac{R_9}{R_0}\frac{T_9/T_0}{V_9/a_0}\frac{1-P_0/P_9}{\gamma_0}\right] \tag{8-93}$$

The exit velocity V_9 is determined from the total and static enthalpies at station 9 by using

$$V_9 = \sqrt{2g_c(h_{t9} - h_9)} \tag{6-44}$$

The total enthalpy at station 9 is obtained from application of the first law to the engine and tracking the changes in energy from the engine's inlet to its exit. The static state at station 9 (h_9, T_9, etc.) is obtained by using the following relationship between the reduced pressure at the static state P_{r9}, the reduced pressure at the total state P_{rt9}, and the nozzle pressure ratio P_{t9}/P_9:

$$P_{r9} = \frac{P_{rt9}}{P_{t9}/P_9} \tag{6-45}$$

The nozzle pressure ratio P_{t9}/P_9 is obtained by multiplying the ratios of pressure from engine inlet to exit which yields

$$\frac{P_{t9}}{P_9} = \frac{P_0}{P_9}\pi_r\pi_d\pi_{cL}\pi_{cH}\pi_b\pi_{tH}\pi_{tH}\pi_{AB}\pi_n \tag{8-94}$$

As previously shown, the total pressure ratio for the high-pressure turbine π_{tH} and the total pressure ratio for the low-pressure turbine π_{tL} are dependent on T_{t4}, f, and the exhaust nozzle Mach number M_8. The pressure ratio of the low-pressure compressor π_{cL} and the pressure ratio of the high-pressure compressor π_{cH} are dependent on T_{t2}, T_{t4}, f, and the enthalpy changes across the turbines.

The flow in an operating afterburner can be modeled as a combination of Fanno (simple friction) and Rayleigh (simple heating) flows. When the afterburner is off (dry operation with $T_{t7} = T_{t5}$), only Fanno losses occur and the total pressure losses are about 50 percent of the losses when it is operating. When the afterburner is on (wet operation), the Rayleigh losses are proportional to the rise in total temperature across the afterburner ($T_{t7} - T_{t5}$). Thus we approximate the total pressure ratio of an afterburner as

$$\boxed{\pi_{\text{AB}} = 1 - 0.5\left[1 + \frac{T_{t7} - T_{t5}}{(T_{t7} - T_{t5})_R}\right](1 - \pi_{\text{AB}\,R})} \qquad (8\text{-}95)$$

The static pressure ratio P_0/P_9 is required to obtain the uninstalled thrust equation [Eq. (8-93)] and the exhaust nozzle pressure ratio [Eq. (8-94)]. The exhaust nozzle area ratio A_9/A_8 is an alternative input to the static pressure ratio P_0/P_9. And A_9/A_8 is directly related to the mass flow parameter at station 9 by

$$\boxed{\text{MFP}_9 = \frac{\text{MFP}_8}{\pi_n A_9/A_8}} \qquad (8\text{-}96)$$

For a given value of the mass flow parameter and total temperature T_t, there are two Mach numbers: a subsonic one and a supersonic one. The total/static pressure ratio determines which Mach number is appropriate. The Mach number M at a station can be obtained by a computer subroutine from the corresponding values of the mass flow parameter, total temperature, and fuel/air ratio at that station. The subroutine MACH was written to do just this, and its flowchart is sketched in Fig. 8-87. An initial Mach number M_i is input and used to indicate which solution is desired ($M_i > 1$ for supersonic, $M_i < 1$ for subsonic). This subroutine uses a modified newtonian iteration and the subroutine MASSFP (see Fig. 8-83) to obtain successive values of the Mach number and mass flow parameter, respectively. This process is repeated until the calculated value of the mass flow parameter is within 0.00001 of the specified value. The subroutine MACH also gives the static temperature T which, together with the total temperature T_t, defines the total/static pressure ratio P_t/P.

Given the exhaust nozzle area ratio A_9/A_8 and Mach region, Eqs. (8-96) and (8-94) and subroutines MACH, MASSFP, and FAIR will give the exit

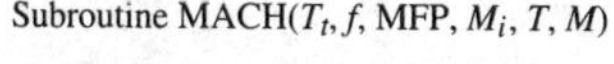

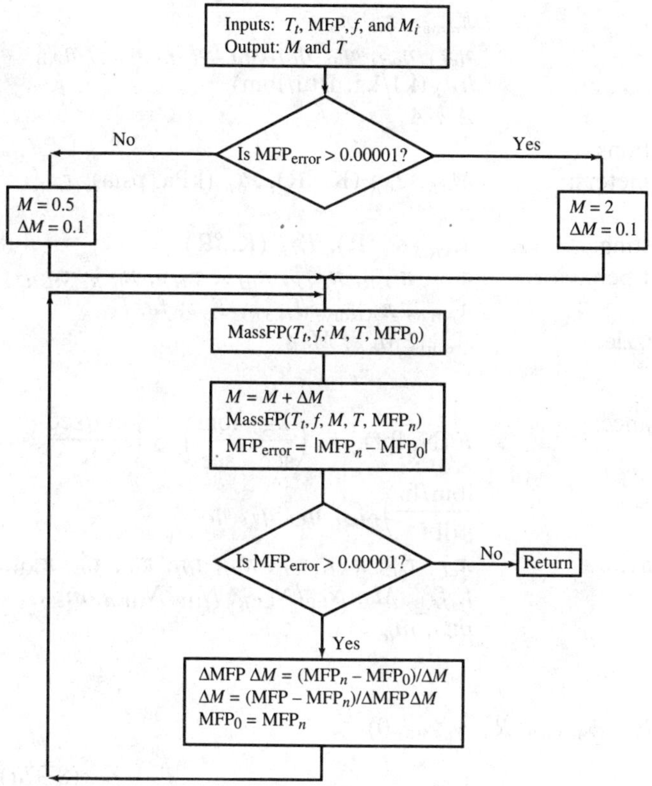

FIGURE 8-87
Flow chart of subroutine MACH.

Mach number M_9 and the static pressure ratio P_0/P_9. Thus the exhaust nozzle area ratio A_9/A_8 is an alternative input to P_0/P_9 with the static pressure ratio P_0/P_9 determined by using Eq. (8-94), P_{t9}/P_9, and the component π's.

Summary of Equations—Dual-Spool Afterburning Turbojet Engine with Variable Gas Properties

INPUTS:

Choices

Flight parameters:	M_0, T_0 (K, °R), P_0 (kPa, psia)
Throttle setting:	T_{t4} (K, °R), T_{t7} (K, °R)
Exhaust nozzle:	P_0/P_9 or A_9/A_8 (nozzle choked); $A_{8\,\text{dry}}/A_{8\,\text{dry}\,R}$ (nozzle unchoked)

Design constants

π's:	$\pi_{d\,\max}$, π_b, π_n
η's:	η_{cL}, η_{cH}, η_b, η_{tH}, η_{tL}, η_{mL}, η_{mH}, η_{AB}
Fuel:	h_{PR} (kJ/kg, Btu/lbm)
Areas:	A_4, $A_{4.5}$

Reference conditions

Flight parameters:	M_{0R}, T_{0R} (K, °R), P_{0R} (kPa, psia), τ_{rR}, $\pi_{r,R}$
Throttle setting:	T_{t4R} (K, °R), T_{t7R} (K, °R)
Component behavior:	π_{dR}, π_{cLR}, π_{cHR}, π_{tHR}, τ_{tHR}, π_{tLR}, τ_{tLR}, π_{ABR}, $\pi_{AB\,dry}$, $T_{t4.5R}$, T_{t5R}, f_R, f_{ABR}
Exhaust nozzle:	$A_{8\,dry}$, M_{8R}, M_{9R}

OUTPUTS:

Overall performance:	F (N, lbf), $\dot{m}_0\left(\dfrac{\text{kg}}{\text{sec}}, \dfrac{\text{lbm}}{\text{sec}}\right)$, $S\left(\dfrac{\text{mg/sec}}{\text{N}}, \dfrac{\text{lbm/hr}}{\text{lbf}}\right)$, f_O, η_P, η_T, η_O
Component behavior:	π_{cL}, τ_{cL}, π_{cH}, τ_{cH}, π_{tH}, τ_{tH}, π_{tL}, τ_{tL}, π_{AB}, f, f_{AB}, M_9, N_{LP}/N_{LPR}, N_{HP}/N_{HPR}, $\dot{m}_{c0}$, $\dot{m}_{c2}$, $\dot{m}_{fc}$

EQUATIONS:

FAIR(1, T_0, h_0, P_{r0}, ϕ_0, c_{p0}, R_0, γ_0, a_0, 0)

$$V_0 = M_0 a_0 \tag{8-97a}$$

$$h_{t0} = h_0 + \frac{V_0^2}{2g_c} \tag{8-97b}$$

FAIR(2, T_{t0}, h_{t0}, p_{rt0}, ϕ_{t0}, c_{pt0}, R_{t0}, γ_{t0}, a_{t0}, 0)

$$\tau_r = \frac{h_{t0}}{h_0} \tag{8-97c}$$

$$\pi_r = \frac{P_{rt0}}{P_{r0}} \tag{8-97d}$$

$$\eta_r = 1 \qquad \text{for } M_0 \le 1 \tag{8-97e}$$

$$\eta_r = 1 - 0.075(M_0 - 1)^{1.35} \qquad \text{for } M_0 > 1 \tag{8-97f}$$

$$\pi_d = \pi_{d\,\max}\eta_r \tag{8-97g}$$

$$h_{t2} = h_{t0} \tag{8-97h}$$

$$P_{rt2} = P_{rt0} \tag{8-97i}$$

$$T_{t2} = T_{t0} \tag{8-97j}$$

Set initial values:

$$f = f_R \qquad T_{t4.5} = T_{t4.5\,R} \qquad T_{t5} = T_{t5\,R} \qquad M_4 = 1 \qquad M_{4.5} = 1 \qquad M_8 = M_{8\,R}$$

$$(\pi_{AB} A_8)_{dry} = (\pi_{AB} A_8)_{dry\,R} \qquad M_{9o} = M_{9\,R}$$

A FAIR$(1, T_{t4}, h_{t4}, P_{rt4}, \phi_{t4}, c_{pt4}, R_{t4}, \gamma_{t4}, a_{t4}, f)$

$$\text{TURB}\left(T_{t4}, f, \frac{A_4}{A_{4.5}}, M_4, M_{4.5}, \eta_{tH}, T_{t4.5}, \pi_{tH}, \tau_{tH}, T_{t4.5}\right)$$

B FAIR$(1, T_{t4.5}, h_{t4.5}, P_{rt4.5}, \phi_{t4.5}, c_{pt4.5}, R_{t4.5}, \gamma_{t4.5}, a_{t4.5}, f)$

$$\text{TURB}\left(T_{t4.5}, f, \frac{A_{4.5}}{(\pi_{AB} A_8)_{dry}}, M_{4.5}, M_8, \eta_{tL}, T_{t5}, \pi_{tL}, \tau_{tL}, T_{t5}\right)$$

$$h_{t25} = h_{t2} + (h_{t45} - h_{t5})(1+f)\eta_{mL} \tag{8-97k}$$

$$h_{t3} = h_{t25} + (h_{t4} - h_{t45})(1+f)\eta_{mH} \tag{8-97l}$$

$$f_n = \frac{h_{t4} - h_{t3}}{\eta_b h_{PR} - h_{t4}} \tag{8-97m}$$

If $|f - f_n| > 0.0001$ then $f = f_n$ go to A

$$h_{t25i} = h_{t2} + (h_{t25} - h_{t2})\eta_{cL} \tag{8-97n}$$

FAIR$(2, T_{t25i}, h_{t25i}, P_{rt25i}, \phi_{t25i}, c_{pt25i}, R_{t25i}, \gamma_{t25i}, a_{t25i}, f)$

$$\pi_{cL} = \frac{P_{rt25i}}{P_{rt2}} \tag{8-97o}$$

$$\tau_{cL} = \frac{h_{t25}}{h_{t2}} \tag{8-97p}$$

$$h_{t3i} = h_{t25} + (h_{t3} - h_{t25})\eta_{cH} \tag{8-97q}$$

FAIR$(2, T_{t3i}, h_{t3i}, P_{rt3i}, \phi_{t3i}, c_{pt3i}, R_{t3i}, \gamma_{t3i}, a_{t3i}, f)$

$$\pi_{cH} = \frac{P_{rt3i}}{P_{rt25}} \tag{8-97r}$$

$$\tau_{cH} = \frac{h_{t3}}{h_{t25}} \tag{8-97s}$$

$$\pi_c = \pi_{cL}\pi_{cH} \tag{8-97t}$$

If the afterburner is off, then

$$T_{t7} = T_{t5} \tag{8-97u}$$

$$f_O = f \tag{8-97v}$$

Else

$$f_{ABi} = f_{AB\,R} \tag{8-97w}$$

C $f_O = f + f_{ABi}$ (8-97x)

FAIR(1, T_{t7}, h_{t7}, P_{rt7}, ϕ_{t7}, c_{pt7}, R_{t7}, γ_{t7}, a_{t7}, f_O)

$$f_{AB} = \frac{h_{t7} - h_{t5}}{\eta_{AB} h_{PR} - h_{t7}} \tag{8-97y}$$

If $|f_{AB} - f_{ABi}| > 0.0001$, then $f_{ABi} = f_{AB}$, go to C

End if

$$\pi_{AB} = 1 - 0.5\left[1 + \frac{T_{t7} - T_{t5}}{(T_{t7} - T_{t5})_R}\right](1 - \pi_{AB\,R}) \tag{8-97z}$$

$$T_{t9} = T_{t7} \tag{8-97aa}$$

FAIR(1, T_{t9}, h_{t9}, P_{rt9}, ϕ_{t9}, c_{pt9}, R_{t9}, γ_{t9}, f_O)

If P_0/P_9 is given for exhaust nozzle, then

$$\frac{P_{t9}}{P_9} = \frac{P_0}{P_9}\pi_r \pi_d \pi_{cL} \pi_{cH} \pi_b \pi_{tH} \pi_{tH} \pi_{AB} \pi_n \tag{8-97ab}$$

$$P_{r9} = \frac{P_{rt9}}{P_{t9}/P_9} \tag{8-97ac}$$

FAIR(3, T_9, h_9, P_{r9}, ϕ_9, c_{p9}, R_9, γ_9, a_9, f_O)

$$V_9 = \sqrt{2g_c(h_{t9} - h_9)} \tag{8-97ad}$$

$$M_9 = \frac{V_9}{a_9} \tag{8-97ae}$$

If $M_9 < 1$ then

$M_8 = M_9$

Get value of $A_{8\,\text{dry}}/A_{8\,\text{dry}\,R}$ from user

$$(\pi_{AB} A_8)_{\text{dry}} = (\pi_{AB} A_8)_{\text{dry}\,R}\left(\frac{A_{8\,\text{dry}}}{A_{8\,\text{dry}\,R}}\right) \tag{8-97af}$$

If $M_8 = M_{8R}$, then

$M_{9o} = M_9$

Else

If $|M_9 - M_{9o}| > 0.0001$, then go to B

End if

Go to D

Else

$M_8 = 1$

IF $|M_9 - M_{9o}| > 0.0001$, then $M_{9o} = M_9$, go to B

End if

MASSFP(T_{t9}, f_O, M_8, T_8, MFP$_8$)

MASSFT(T_{t9}, f_O, M_9, T_9, MFP$_9$)

$$\frac{A_9}{A_8} = \frac{\text{MFP}_8}{\pi_n \text{MFP}_9} \tag{8-97ag}$$

End if

If A_9/A_8 is given for exhaust nozzle, then

$$\frac{P_{t9}}{P_0} = \pi_r \pi_d \pi_{cL} \pi_{cH} \pi_b \pi_{tH} \pi_{tH} \pi_{\text{AB}} \pi_n \tag{8-97ah}$$

$$P_{r9i} = \frac{P_{rt9}}{P_{t9}/P_9} \tag{8-97ai}$$

FAIR(3, $T_{9i}, h_{9i}, P_{r9i}, \phi_{9i}, c_{p9i}, R_{9i}, \gamma_{9i}, a_{9i}, f_O$)

$$M_{9i} = \frac{\sqrt{2g_c(h_{t9} - h_{9i})}}{a_{9i}} \tag{8-97aj}$$

If $M_{9i} > 1$, then

$M_8 = 1$

Else

$M_8 = M_{9i}$

Get value of $A_{8\,\text{dry}}/A_{8\,\text{dry}\,R}$ from user

$$(\pi_{\text{AB}} A_8)_{\text{dry}} = (\pi_{\text{AB}} A_8)_{\text{dry}\,R} \frac{A_{8\,\text{dry}}}{A_{8\,\text{dry}\,R}} \tag{8-97ak}$$

If $M_8 = M_{8R}$, then

$M_{9o} = M_9$

Else

If $|M_9 - M_{9o}| > 0.0001$, then go to B

End if

End if

MASSFP($T_{t9}, f_O, M_8, T_8, \text{MFP}_8$)

$$\text{MFP}_9 = \frac{\text{MFP}_8}{\pi_n(A_9/A_8)} \tag{8-97al}$$

MACH($T_{t9}, f_O, \text{MFP}_9, M_{9i}, T_9, M_9$)

FAIR($1, T_9, h_9, P_{r9}, \phi_9, c_{p\,9}, R_9, \gamma_9, a_9, f_O$)

$$V_9 = M_9 a_9 \tag{8-97am}$$

$$\frac{P_{t9}}{P_9} = \frac{P_{rt9}}{P_{r9}} \tag{8-97an}$$

$$\frac{P_0}{P_9} = \frac{P_{t9}/P_9}{P_{t9}/P_0} \tag{8-97ao}$$

End if

D MASSFP($T_{t4}, f, M_4, T_4, \text{MFP}_4$)

$$\dot{m}_0 = \frac{P_0 \pi_r \pi_d \pi_{cL} \pi_{cH} \pi_b A_4 \,\text{MFP}_4}{(1+f)\sqrt{T_{t4}}} \tag{8-97ap}$$

$$F = \frac{\dot{m}_0 a_0}{g_c}\left[(1+f_O)\frac{V_9}{a_0} - M_0 + (1+f_O)\frac{R_9}{R_0}\frac{T_9/T_0}{V_9/a_0}\frac{1-P_0/P_9}{\gamma_0}\right] \tag{8-97aq}$$

$$S = \frac{f_O}{F/\dot{m}_0} \tag{8-97ar}$$

$$\eta_T = \frac{a_0^2[(1+f_O)(V_9/a_0)^2 - M_0^2]}{2g_c f_o h_{PR}} \tag{8-97as}$$

$$\eta_P = \frac{2g_c V_0(F/\dot{m}_0)}{a_0^2[(1+f_O)(V_9/a_0)^2 - M_0^2]} \tag{8-97at}$$

$$\eta_O = \eta_P \eta_T \tag{8-97au}$$

$$\frac{N_{cL}}{N_{cL\,R}} = \sqrt{\frac{T_{t2\,R}}{T_{t2}}\,\frac{h_{t2.5} - h_{t2}}{(h_{t2.5} - h_{t2})_R}} \tag{8-97av}$$

$$\frac{N_{cH}}{N_{cH\,R}} = \sqrt{\frac{T_{t2.5\,R}}{T_{t2.5}}\,\frac{h_{t3} - h_{t2.5}}{(h_{t3} - h_{t2.5})_R}} \tag{8-97aw}$$

$$\theta_0 = \frac{T_{t0}}{T_{\text{ref}}} \tag{8-97ax}$$

$$\delta_0 = \frac{P_{t0}}{P_{\text{ref}}} \tag{8-97ay}$$

$$\delta_2 = \pi_d \delta_0 \tag{8-97az}$$

$$\dot{m}_{c0} = \frac{\dot{m}_0 \sqrt{\theta_0}}{\delta_0} \tag{8-97ba}$$

$$\dot{m}_{c2} = \frac{\dot{m}_0 \sqrt{\theta_0}}{\delta_2} \tag{8-97bb}$$

$$\dot{m}_{fc} = \frac{f \dot{m}_0}{\sqrt{\theta_0}\, \delta_2} \tag{8-97bc}$$

Example 8-15. We consider an afterburning turbojet engine with the same input data as those considered for the afterburning turbojet in Example 8-7. Thus we have variable specific heats and the following reference data and operating conditions:

REFERENCE: Sea-level static ($T_0 = 518.7°\text{R}$, $P_0 = 14.696$ psia), $\pi_c = 20$, $\pi_{cL} = 5$, $\pi_{cH} = 4$, $e_{cL} = 0.9$, $e_{cH} = 0.9$, $e_{tH} = 0.9$, $e_{tL} = 0.9$, $\pi_{d\,\max} = 0.98$, $\pi_b = 0.96$, $\pi_n = 0.98$, $T_{t4} = 3200°\text{R}$, $\eta_b = 0.995$, $\eta_{mL} = 0.995$, $\eta_{mH} = 0.995$, $h_{PR} = 18{,}400$ Btu/lbm, $T_{t7} = 3600°\text{R}$, $\pi_{\text{AB}} = 0.94$, $\eta_{\text{AB}} = 0.95$, $\eta_{cL} = 0.8757$, $\eta_{cH} = 0.8801$, $\eta_{tH} = 0.9058$, $\eta_{tL} = 0.9048$, $\pi_{tH} = 0.5535$, $\tau_{tH} = 0.8761$, $\pi_{tL} = 0.6178$, $\tau_{tL} = 0.8965$, $M_8 = 1$, $M_9 = 1.84$, $f = 0.0327$, $f_{\text{AB}} = 0.0207$, $f_O = 0.0533$, $F = 25{,}000$ lbf, $S = 1.3688$ (lbm/hr)/lbf, $\dot{m}_0 = 178.18$ lbm/sec

OPERATION:

Maximum $T_{t4} = 3200°\text{R}$	Maximum $T_{t7} = 3600°\text{R}$
Maximum $\pi_c = 20$	
Mach number: 0 to 2	Altitudes (kft): 0, 20, and 40

Comparison of these reference data to those of Example 8-7 shows the following:

1. The efficiencies of the low- and high-pressure compressors are a little higher and the efficiencies of the high- and low-pressure turbines are a little lower.
2. The fuel/air ratio of the main burner is lower, and that of the afterburner is higher.
3. The engine mass flow rate is about 2 percent lower due to the higher specific thrust.
4. The thrust specific fuel consumption is about 6 percent lower.

These results agree with those found in Sec. 7-8.

To calculate the performance of the afterburning turbojet with variable gas properties, Eqs. (8-97*a*) through (8-97*bc*) and subroutines FAIR, MASSFP, and TURB were used to write a short computer program. Due to its numerous iteration loops, the calculations of this engine's performance took about 80 times longer than those for the afterburning turbojet with constant gas properties. For

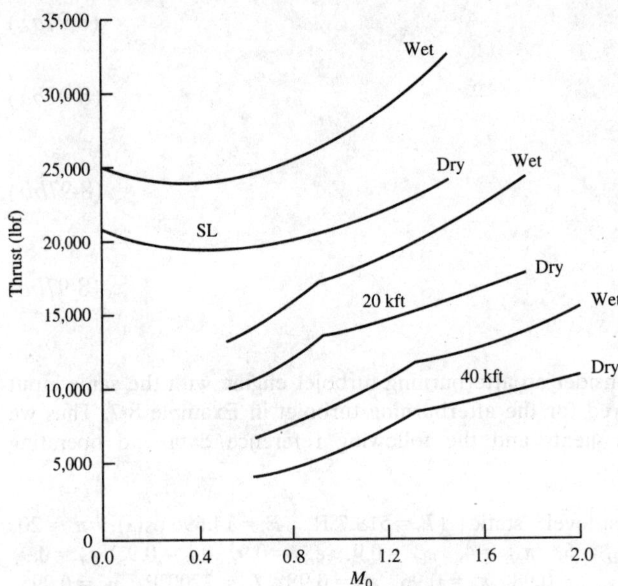

FIGURE 8-88*a*
Variation of thrust with flight Mach number and altitude.

some, this larger calculation time is prohibitive, and faster, less accurate results may be appropriate.

The maximum thrust results (wet and dry) for this engine are shown in Fig. 8-88*a*. Comparison with the maximum thrust results of Example 8-7 (see Fig. 8-43) shows the following:

1. The maximum thrusts predicted for the two engine models are nearly equal for most operating conditions.
2. There are very small differences in thrust between the models at high Mach numbers.

The thrust specific fuel consumption results (wet and dry) for this engine are shown in Fig. 8-88*b*. Comparison with the fuel consumption results of Example 8-7 (see Fig. 8-44) shows that the trends with variations in Mach number and altitude are the same; however, the basic engine model predicts fuel consumptions that are 6 to 11 percent higher. This difference in predicted fuel consumption between the two engine models is due to the following:

1. The basic performance model uses specific-heat values for the air entering and leaving the main burner that are too low. As a result, the predicted fuel consumptions are about 11 percent higher for this model.
2. The basic performance model uses a specific-heat value for the air entering the afterburner that is too high and a specific-heat value for the air leaving the afterburner that is too low. The predicted fuel consumptions of the afterburner are lower for this model. The combined effects of both combustion processes

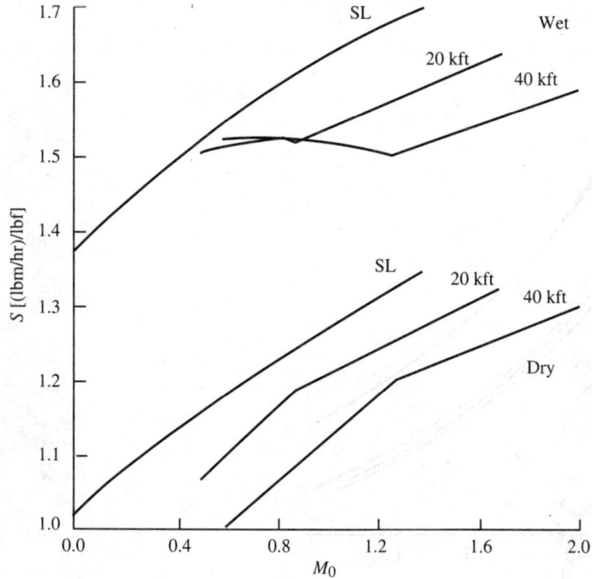

FIGURE 8-88*b*
Variation of thrust specific fuel consumption with flight Mach number and altitude.

(main burner and afterburner) are fuel consumptions that are about 6 percent higher for the constant specific heat engine model.

As will be shown, more accurate fuel consumption results can be obtained from the basic performance model by using the FAIR subroutine to compute the fuel burned in both the main burner and the afterburner.

Figure 8-89*a* shows the variation of maximum corrected thrust (wet and dry) with dimensionless total temperature θ_0. These are the same trends that we obtained with the basic engine performance model (see Fig. 8-24). The change in maximum total temperature leaving the main burner T_{t4} with θ_0 is shown by a solid line in Fig. 8-89*b* for engine model with variable gas properties and by a dashed line for the constant specific heat engine model [Eqs. (8-70*n*) and (8-70*o*)].

Figure 8-89*c* shows the variations of the maximum compressor corrected mass flow rate and pressure ratio with dimensionless total temperature (θ_0). At flight conditions where θ_0 is greater than unity, both the maximum compressor corrected mass flow rate and the pressure ratio fall off with increasing Mach number. At flight conditions where θ_0 is less than unity, the maximum compressor pressure ratio is constant and the maximum corrected mass flow rate increases slightly. These are the same fundamental trends that we obtained with the basic engine performance model (see Figs. 8-20, 8-21, 8-30, and 8-31). The slight increase in the maximum corrected mass flow rate, when $\theta_0 < 1.0$, is primarily due to the increased corrected mass flow rate at engine station 4 that results from the reductions in both fuel-to-air ratio f and total temperature T_t at this engine station (see Fig. 8-78*a*).

The partial-throttle performance of this afterburning turbojet is shown in Fig. 8-90*a* at two operating conditions: sea-level static and Mach 1.5 at 40 kft.

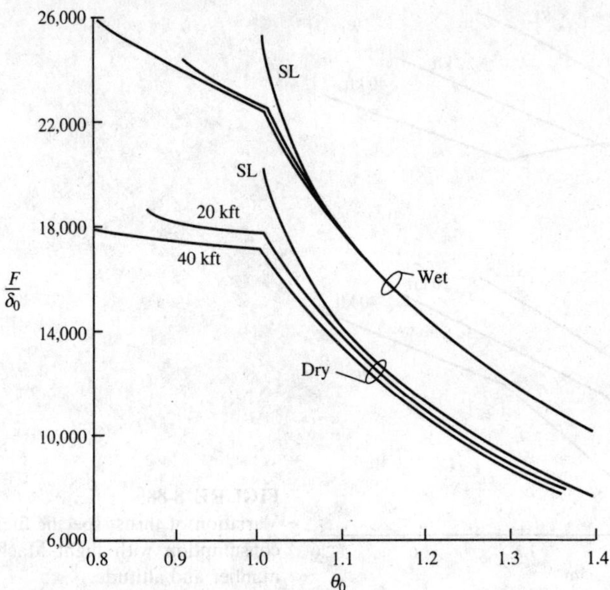

FIGURE 8-89*a*
Variation of corrected thrust with θ_0 and altitude.

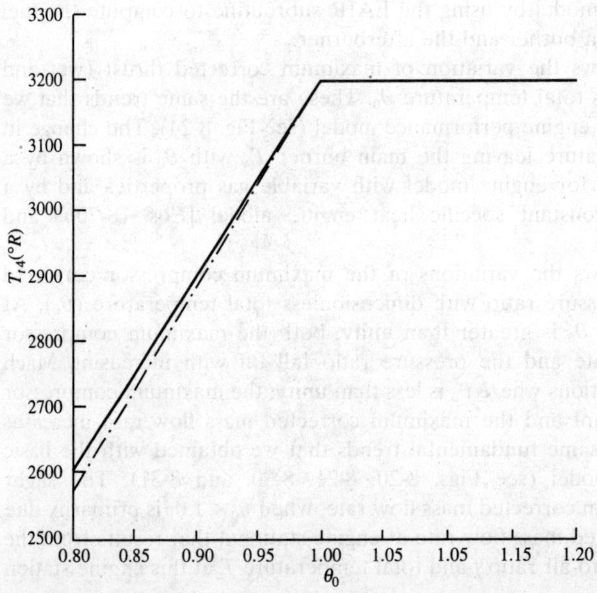

FIGURE 8-89*b*
Variation of maximum T_{t4} with θ_0.

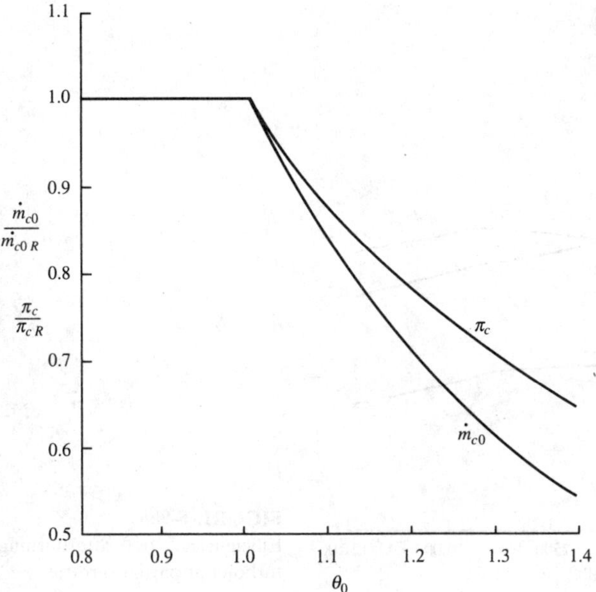

FIGURE 8-89*c*
Variation of corrected mass flow and compressor pressure ratio with θ_0.

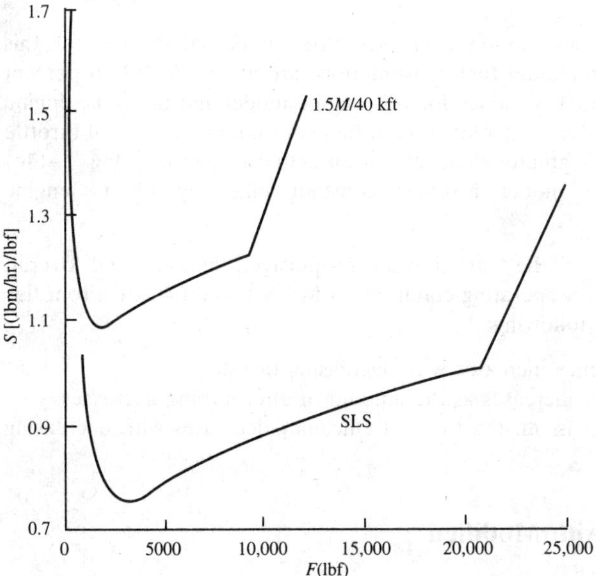

FIGURE 8-90*a*
Partial-throttle performance of afterburning turbojet.

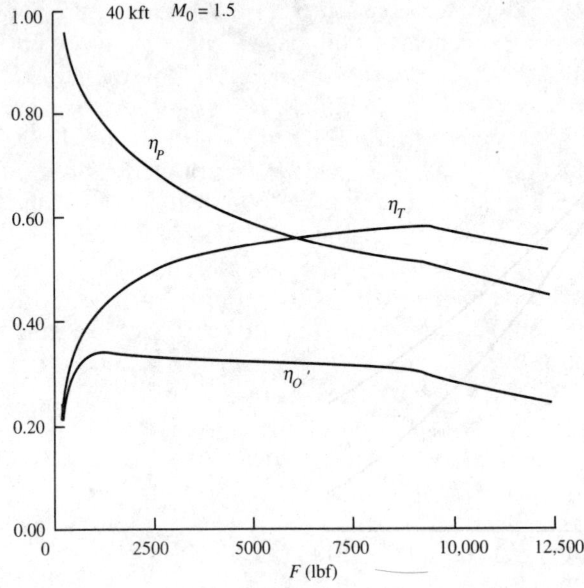

FIGURE 8-90*b*
Efficiencies of afterburning turbojet at partial throttle.

Comparison of these partial-throttle curves to those of Example 8-7 (see Fig. 8-45) shows the following:

1. The predicted fuel consumptions are lower for this engine model at all thrust levels.
2. The predicted fuel consumption decreases more at partial throttle for this engine model. The minimum fuel consumptions are about 75 and 90 percent of their sea-level static dry values for this engine model and the basic engine model, respectively. The large reduction in fuel consumption at partial throttle shown in Fig. 8-90*a* is greater than that of an actual engine (see Fig. 1–14*e*) because this engine model assumes constant efficiency of all engine components.

Figure 8-90*b* shows the variation in propulsive, thermal, and overall efficiency with thrust at an operating condition of Mach 1.5 and 40 kft. From this figure, one can note the following:

1. The propulsive efficiency increases with decreasing thrust.
2. The thermal efficiency increases as the amount of afterburning decreases.
3. When the afterburner is off, the thermal efficiency decreases with decreasing thrust.

Afterburning Turbojet with Modified Combustion Model

More accurate fuel consumption predictions can be obtained without the complexities and time of the full variable gas properties calculations given by

Eqs. (8-97*a*) through (8-97*bc*). Here we consider the afterburning turbojet engine of Sec. 8-4 with constant specific heats for all engine components except the main burner and afterburner. We use the subroutine FAIR to evaluate the enthalpy at engine stations 3, 4, 6, and 7. The fuel/air ratios for the main burner and afterburner are given by Eqs. (7-122) and (7-118), respectively. Note that the enthalpies at stations 4 and 6 (h_{t4} and h_{t6}) are functions of the main burner's fuel/air ratio f, and that at station 7 h_{t7} is a function of the overall fuel/air ratio ($f_O = f + f_{\text{AB}}$). Because of these functional relationships, calculation of these fuel/air ratios (f and f_{AB}) requires iteration like those outlined in the summary of equations for the afterburning turbojet with variable specific heats. And h_{t3} and h_{t6} are evaluated at their total temperature as predicted by the basic analysis in Sec. 8-4.

Example 8-16. We consider an example with the same input data as those considered for the afterburning turbojet in Example 8-7. Thus we have the following reference data and operating conditions:

REFERENCE: Sea-level static ($T_0 = 518.7°\text{R}$, $P_0 = 14.696$ psia), $\pi_c = 20$, $\pi_{cL} = 5$, $\pi_{cH} = 4$, $e_{cL} = 0.9$, $e_{cH} = 0.9$, $e_{tH} = 0.9$, $e_{tL} = 0.9$, $\pi_{d\,\max} = 0.98$, $\pi_b = 0.96$, $\pi_n = 0.98$, $T_{t4} = 3200°\text{R}$, $\eta_b = 0.995$, $\eta_{mL} = 0.995$, $\eta_{mH} = 0.995$, $h_{PR} = 18{,}400$ Btu/lbm, $T_{t7} = 3600°\text{R}$, $\pi_{\text{AB}} = 0.94$, $\eta_{\text{AB}} = 0.95$, $\eta_{cL} = 0.8755$, $\eta_{cH} = 0.8791$, $\eta_{tH} = 0.9062$, $\eta_{tL} = 0.9050$, $\pi_{tH} = 0.5454$, $\tau_{tH} = 0.8817$, $\pi_{tL} = 0.6115$, $\tau_{tL} = 0.9029$, $M_8 = 1$, $M_9 = 1.82$, $f = 0.0323$, $f_{\text{AB}} = 0.0194$, $f_O = 0.0517$, $F = 25{,}000$ lbf, $S = 1.3566$ (lbm/hr)/lbf, $\dot{m}_0 = 182.40$ lbm/sec

OPERATION:

Maximum $T_{t4} = 3200°\text{R}$	Maximum $T_{t7} = 3600°\text{R}$
Maximum $\pi_c = 20$	
Mach number: 0 to 2	Altitudes (kft): 0, 20, and 40

The results of this analysis with the fuel consumption calculated by using the subroutine FAIR and Eqs. (8-45*a*) through (8-45*ab*) are shown with dashed lines in Figs. 8-91*a*, 8-91*b*, and 8-91*c*. The solid lines are the results of Example 8-15 for the variable specific heat engine model. For the nonafterburning case in Figs. 8-91*a* and 8-91*b*, the thrusts and fuel consumptions are nearly equal to those predicted by using the more complicated variable specific heat engine model. At maximum power (full afterburning) in Figs. 8-81*a* and 8-81*b*, the thrusts are nearly equal and the modified combustion model predicts fuel consumptions that are about 1 percent lower than those of the variable specific heat engine model.

Figure 8-91*c* compares the throttle hooks of these two performance models at two operating conditions. At partial power, the fuel consumptions predicted by the modified combustion model (solid lines) are lower than those predicted by the variable specific heat model (dashed lines).

In general, the modified combustion model gives much better results than those of the constant specific heat model shown in Figs. 8-43, 8-44, and 8-45 for Example 8-7, while requiring only double the computer time.

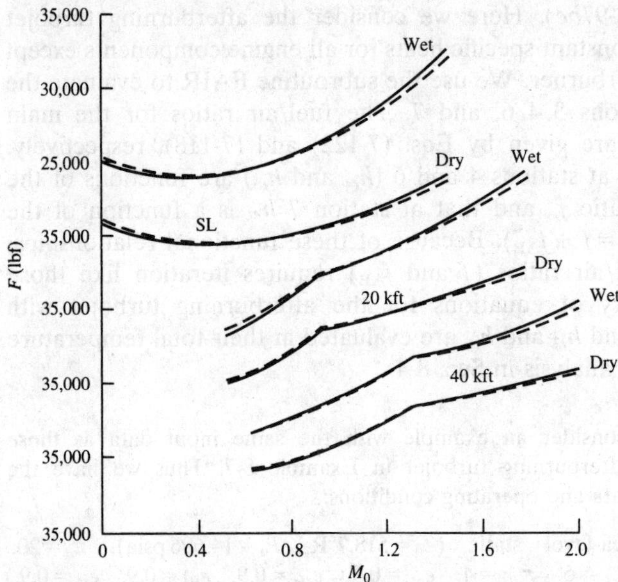

FIGURE 8-91*a*
Variation of thrust with flight Mach number and altitude for two engine models.

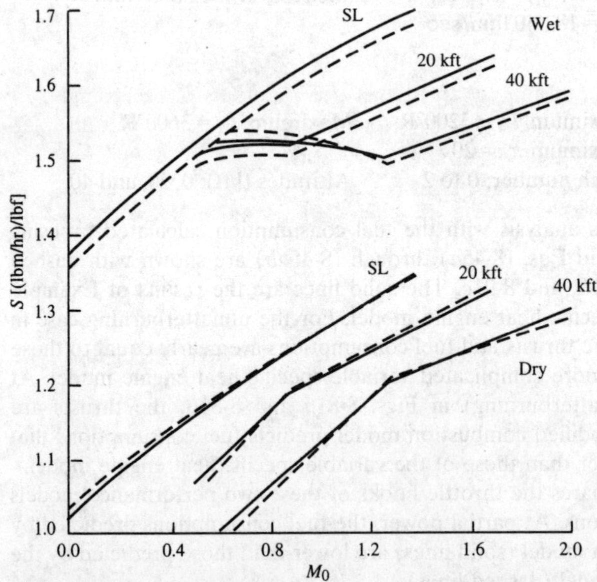

FIGURE 8-91*b*
Variation of thrust specific fuel consumption with flight Mach number and altitude for two engine models.

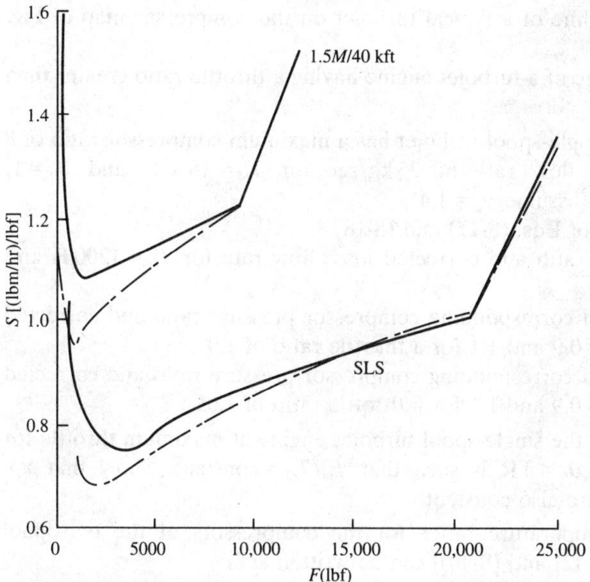

FIGURE 8-91*c*
Partial-throttle performance for two engine models.

PROBLEMS

8-1. The flow in a typical single-spool turbojet engine is choked in two locations. This fact is used in performance analysis to predict the variations of the compressor and turbine with changes in T_{t4} and T_{t2}. As a result, the turbine temperature and pressure ratios are constant for all operating conditions.

a. Identify the two locations where the flow is choked in the engine.

b. Describe the basic engineering principle that gives the equation for the lines of constant T_{t4}/T_{t2}, sketched in Fig. P8-1 and in Figs. 8-6*a* and 8-6*b*.

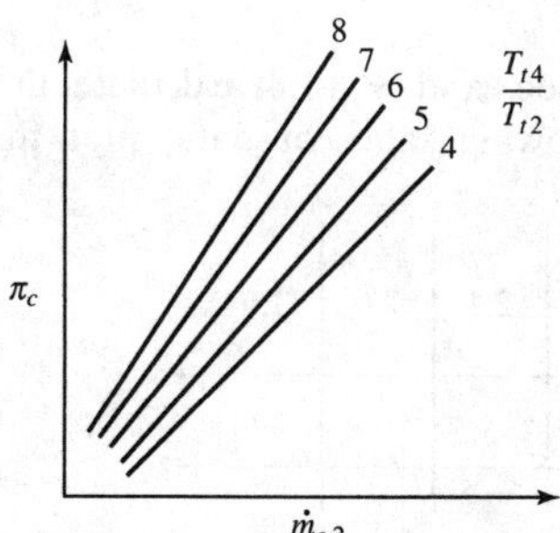

FIGURE P8-1
Compressor map with lines of constant T_{t4}/T_{t2}.

c. Sketch the operating line of a typical turbojet on the compressor map of Fig. P8-1.
d. Describe the advantage of a turbojet engine having a throttle ratio greater than 1.

8-2. If the compressor of a single-spool turbojet has a maximum compressor ratio of 8 with a corrected mass flow rate of 25 kg/sec for $T_{t4} = 1800$ K and $\theta_0 = 1$, determine the following (assume $\gamma_c = 1.4$):
a. Constants K_1 and K_2 of Eqs. (8-17) and (8-18)
b. Compressor pressure ratio and corrected mass flow rate for $T_{t4} = 1200$ K and $\theta_0 = 1.1$
c. The maximum T_{t4} and corresponding compressor pressure ratio and corrected mass flow rate at $\theta_0 = 0.9$ and 1.1 for a throttle ratio of 1.0
d. The maximum T_{t4} and corresponding compressor pressure ratio and corrected mass flow rate at $\theta_0 = 0.9$ and 1.1 for a throttle ratio of 1.05

8-3. The typical operation of the single-spool turbojet engine at maximum throttle for flight conditions where $\theta_0 < \text{TR}$ is such that $T_{t4}/T_{t2} = \text{constant}$. Show that π_c, T_{t5}/T_{t2}, P_{t5}/P_{t2}, and $\dot{m}_{c2}$ are also constant.

8-4. Show that the total temperature ratios for the compressors of the two-spool turbojet engine [Eqs. (8-42) and (8-40)] can be written as

$$\tau_{cL} = 1 + \frac{T_{t4}/\theta_0}{(T_{t4}/\theta_0)_R}(\tau_{cL} - 1)_R$$

$$\tau_{cH} = 1 + \frac{T_{t4}/\theta_0}{(T_{t4}/\theta_0)_R}\frac{\tau_{cL\,R}}{\tau_{cL}}(\tau_{cH} - 1)_R$$

8-5. In terms of reference conditions (subscript R), show that the following equations apply for the operation of an *ideal* single-spool turbojet engine.
a. The compressor pressure ratio is given by

$$\pi_c = \left\{1 + [(\pi_{cR})^{(\gamma-1)/\gamma} - 1]\frac{T_{t4}/T_{t2}}{(T_{t4}/T_{t2})_R}\right\}^{\gamma/(\gamma-1)}$$

b. The engine mass flow rate is given by

$$\dot{m}_0 = \dot{m}_{0R}\frac{P_{t2}}{P_{t2R}}\frac{\pi_c}{\pi_{cR}}\sqrt{\frac{T_{t4R}}{T_{t4}}}$$

c. The corrected mass flow rate at station 2 is given by

$$\dot{m}_{c2} = \dot{m}_{c2R}\frac{\pi_c}{\pi_{cR}}\sqrt{\frac{(T_{t4}/T_{t2})_R}{T_{t4}/T_{t2}}}$$

d. Given $(T_{t4}/T_{t2})_R = 4$, $\pi_{cR} = 12$, $\dot{m}_{cR} = 200$ lbm/sec, and $\gamma = 1.4$, calculate the engine operating line by completing the following table of data; plot the results.

$\frac{T_{t4}}{T_{t2}}$	4.0	3.6	3.2	2.8	2.4	2.0	1.6
π_c	12						
$\dot{m}_c$ (lbm/sec)	200						

8-6. For a ramjet engine with a constant nozzle throat area A_8, develop the performance equations and calculate the performance of the ramjet with the reference data of Prob. 7-1.

a. Show that the engine mass flow rate can be written as

$$\dot{m}_0 = \dot{m}_{0R} \frac{P_0 \pi_r \pi_d}{(P_0 \pi_r \pi_d)_R} \sqrt{\frac{T_{t4R}}{T_{t4}}} \frac{\text{MFP}(M_8)}{\text{MFP}(M_{8R})}$$

where the Mach number at station 8 is determined by the value of P_{t8}/P_0

b. Show that the remainder of the performance equations are given by those developed to answer Prob. 7-1.

c. If the ramjet of Prob. 7-1 has a reference mass flow rate of 20 kg/sec at 15 km and $M_0 = 2$, determine its performance at 20 km, $M_0 = 3$, and $T_{t4} = 1600$ K. Assume $P_9 = P_0$.

8-7. A turbojet engine operated at a flight Mach number of 2.0 and an altitude of 15 km has the following compressor performance with $T_{t4} = 1860$ K: $\pi_c = 8$, $\tau_c = 1.9$, and $\eta_c = 0.9$. Determine τ_c, π_c, and $\dot{m}_2/\dot{m}_{2R}$ for $M_0 = 0.8$, 11-km altitude, and $T_{t4} = 1640$ K. Assume that $\pi_d = 0.88$ at $M_0 = 2$, $\pi_d = 0.98$ at $M_0 = 0.8$, and $\gamma_c = 1.4$.

8-8. Calculate the thrust of the turbojet engine in Example 7-1 at $M_0 = 0.8$, 9-km altitude, reduced throttle ($T_{t4} = 1100$ K), and $P_0/P_9 = 1$ for a reference air mass flow rate of 50 kg/sec at a reference altitude of 12 km.

8-9. Given a single-spool turbojet engine which has the following reference values:

REFERENCE: $\dot{m}_{c2} = 100$ lbm/sec, $\pi_c = 6$, $M_0 = 0$, $T_{t2} = 518.7$°R, $T_{t4} = 3200$°R, $P_0 = 1$ atm, $\pi_d = 0.97$, $\pi_b = 0.96$, $\pi_n = 0.98$, $\eta_b = 0.995$, $\eta_m = 0.99$, $P_0/P_9 = 1$, $\eta_c = 0.8725$, $\pi_t = 0.6098$, $\tau_t = 0.9024$, $\eta_t = 0.9051$, $f = 0.041895$, $V_9/a_0 = 2.8876$, $P_{t9}/P_9 = 3.3390$, $M_9 = 1.4624$, $F/\dot{m}_0 = 104.41$ lbf/(lbm/sec), $\gamma_c = 1.4$, $c_{pc} = 0.24$ Btu/(lbm · °R), $\gamma_t = 1.3$, $c_{pt} = 0.296$ Btu/(lbm · °R), $h_{PR} = 18{,}400$ Btu/lbm

a. Determine $\dot{m}_0$, P_{t5}/P_{t2}, T_{t5}/T_{t2}, V_9, F, and S at the reference condition.

b. If this engine has a throttle ratio of 1.0 and is operating at maximum T_{t4} at a flight condition where $\theta_0 = 1.2$, determine π_c, $\dot{m}_{c2}$, P_{t5}/P_{t2}, T_{t5}/T_{t2}, and N_c/N_{cR} at this operating point.

c. If this engine has a throttle ratio of 1.1 and is operating at maximum T_{t4} at a flight condition where $\theta_0 = 1.2$, determine π_c, $\dot{m}_{c2}$, P_{t5}/P_{t2}, T_{t5}/T_{t2}, and N_c/N_{cR} at this operating point.

d. Determine the percentage change in performance parameters between parts *b* and *c*.

8-10. Given a single-spool turbojet engine which has the following reference values:

REFERENCE: $\dot{m}_{c2} = 50$ kg/sec, $\pi_c = 8$, $M_0 = 0$, $T_{t2} = 288.2$ K, $T_{t4} = 1780$ K, $P_0 = 1$ atm, $\pi_d = 0.97$, $\pi_b = 0.96$, $\pi_n = 0.98$, $\eta_b = 0.995$, $\eta_m = 0.99$, $P_0/P_9 = 1$, $\eta_c = 0.8678$, $\pi_t = 0.5434$, $\tau_t = 0.8810$, $\eta_t = 0.9062$, $f = 0.040796$, $V_9/a_0 = 3.0256$, $P_{t9}/P_9 = 3.9674$, $M_9 = 1.5799$, $F/\dot{m}_0 = 1071$ N/(kg/sec), $\gamma_c = 1.4$, $c_{pc} = 1.004$ kJ/(kg · K), $\gamma_t = 1.3$, $c_{pt} = 1.24$ kJ/(kg · K), $h_{PR} = 42{,}800$ kJ/kg

a. Determine $\dot{m}_0$, P_{t5}/P_{t2}, T_{t5}/T_{t2}, V_9, F, and S at the reference condition.
b. If this engine has a throttle ratio of 1.0 and is operating at maximum T_{t4} at a flight condition where $\theta_0 = 1.4$, determine π_c, $\dot{m}_{c2}$, P_{t5}/P_{t2}, T_{t5}/T_{t2}, and N_c/N_{cR} at this operating point.
c. If this engine has a throttle ratio of 1.15 and is operating at maximum T_{t4} at a flight condition where $\theta_0 = 1.4$, determine π_c, $\dot{m}_{c2}$, P_{t5}/P_{t2}, T_{t5}/T_{t2}, and N_c/N_{cR} at this operating point.
d. Determine the percentage change in performance parameters between parts *b* and *c*.

8-11. Calculate the thrust of the afterburning turbojet engine in Example 8-7 at $M_0 = 2.0$, 40-kft altitude, maximum afterburner ($T_{t7} = 3600°\text{R}$), and $P_0/P_9 = 1$ for throttle ratios of 1.0, 1.05, 1.1, 1.15, and 1.2. Comment on the variation in performance with throttle ratio.

8-12. Calculate the thrust and fuel consumption of the afterburning turbojet engine in Example 8-7 at $M_0 = 0.8$, 40-kft altitude, $P_0/P_9 = 1$, a throttle ratio of unity, and a range of T_{t7} from 3600°R down to T_{t5}. Compare your results to those of the PERF computer program.

8-13. Using PERF, find the performance of the afterburning turbojet engine in Example 8-7 for throttle ratios of 1.1 and 1.2 over the same range of Mach numbers and altitudes. Compare these results to those of Example 8-7.

8-14. Calculate the thrust of the high-bypass-ratio turbofan engine in Example 8-8 at $M_0 = 0.8$, 40-kft altitude, and partial throttle ($T_{t4} = 2600°\text{R}$). Assume convergent-only exhaust nozzles. Compare your results to those of PERF.

8-15. Calculate the thrust of the high-bypass-ratio turbofan engine in Example 8-8 at $M_0 = 0$, sea-level altitude, and increased throttle ($T_{t4} = 3500°\text{R}$). Assume convergent-only exhaust nozzles. Compare your results to those of PERF.

8-16. Using PERF, find the performance of the high-bypass-ratio turbofan engine in Example 8-8 for a throttle ratio of 1.0 over the range of Mach numbers from 0 to 0.8 and altitudes of sea level, 20 kft, and 40 kft. Use 3200°R for maximum T_{t4}.

8-17. Early jet aircraft for passenger service used turbojet engines (e.g., Boeing 707) and the newer aircraft use high-bypass-ratio turbofan engines (e.g., Boeing 767). The early turbojets required a much longer takeoff distance than the newer turbofan-powered aircraft. This difference is due mainly to the variation in thrust of these different engine types with Mach number and altitude. To get a better understanding, use the PERF computer program to design two engines and determine their variations in thrust with Mach number and altitude. Consider a turbojet with the component performance of technology level 3 in Table 6-2 (assume type A diffuser, uncooled turbine, and type D nozzle), $T_{t4} = 2500°\text{R}$, compressor pressure ratio of 12, and sea-level static thrust of 10,000 lbf. Determine the turbojet's performance for TR = 1 at maximum T_{t4}, Mach 0.8, and 30-kft altitude. Now consider a high-bypass-ratio turbofan with the component performance of technology level 3 in Table 6-2 (assume type A diffuser, uncooled turbine, and type D nozzle), $T_{t4} = 3000°\text{R}$, compressor pressure ratio of 22, fan pressure ratio of 1.54, bypass ratio of 5, and sea-level static thrust of 56,000 lbf. Determine the turbofan's performance for TR = 1 at maximum T_{t4}, Mach 0.8, and 30-kft altitude, and compare to the turbojet.

8-18. Calculate the maximum thrust of the afterburning mixed-flow exhaust turbofan engine in Example 8-10 at $M_0 = 2$ and 40-kft altitude for throttle ratios of 1.1 and 1.2 using the PERF computer program.

8-19. Using PERF, find the performance of the afterburning mixed-flow exhaust turbofan engine in Example 8-10 for throttle ratios of 1.0 and 1.2 over the range of Mach numbers from 0 to 2 and altitude of sea level, 10 kft, 20 kft, 30 kft, 36 kft, 40 kft, and 50 kft. Compare your results to those of Example 8-10 for a throttle ratio of 1.1.

8-20. Calculate the thrust and fuel consumption of the turboprop engine in Example 8-11 at $M_0 = 0.5$, a 6-km altitude, and reduced throttle ($T_{t4} = 1400$ K). Assume a convergent-only exhaust nozzle. Compare your results to those of PERF.

8-21. Using PERF, find the performance of the turboprop engine in Example 8-11 at partial throttle at $M_0 = 0.5$ and altitudes of sea level, 3 km, and 6 km. Compare these results to those of Example 8-11.

8-22. Develop a set of performance equations for the stationary gas turbine engine with regeneration (see Problem 7-32) depicted in Fig. P8-22 based on the following assumptions:

a. Flow is choked at engine stations 4 and 4.5.
b. Constant component efficiencies (η_c, η_b, η_t, η_{rg}, etc.).
c. Exit pressure equals the ambient pressure ($P_9 = P_0$).
d. Constant specific heat c_{pc} and ratio of specific heats γ_c from stations 0 to 3.5.
e. Constant specific heat c_{pt} and ratio of specific heats γ_t from stations 4 to 9.

8-23. Calculate the corrected fuel flow rate [see Eq. (8-7)] and corrected thrust specific fuel consumption [see Eq. (8-6)] for the turbojet engine of Example 8-4 at an

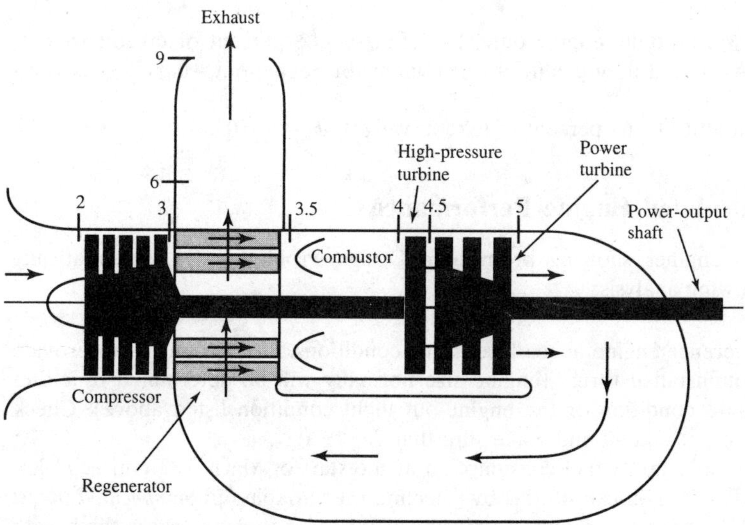

FIGURE P8-22
Stationary gas turbine engine with regeneration.

altitude of 40 kft and Mach numbers of 0.6, 0.8, 1.0, and 1.2 with maximum T_{t4}. Comment on your results.

8-24. For a single-spool turbojet engine, show that the maximum corrected fuel flow rate is essentially constant for $\theta_0 \leq \text{TR}$. See Eq. (8-27) for a starting point.

8-D1 GAS TURBINE DESIGN PROBLEM 1 (HP-1 AIRCRAFT)

Find the best high-bypass-ratio turbofan engine for the HP-1 aircraft from those engines showing promise in design problem 7-D1. Your are to determine the best engine, sized to meet the required engine thrust at takeoff and/or single engine out (0.45 Mach at 16 kft), and whose fuel consumption is minimum.

Hand-Calculate Engine Performance

Using the performance analysis equations for a high-bypass-ratio turbofan engine, hand-calculate the performance of the turbofan engine hand-calculated in Design Problem 7-D1 at the flight condition of 0.83 Mach and 11-km altitude at $T_{t4} = 1500$ K.

Required Thrust at Different Flight Conditions

Determine both the required installed thrust and the required uninstalled engine thrust for each of the following flight conditions (assume $\phi_{\text{noz}} = 0.01$):

1. Uninstalled thrust of 267 kN for each engine at sea-level static while at takeoff power setting ($T_{t4} = 1890$ K). Assume $\phi_{\text{inlet}} = 0.05$.
2. Start of Mach 0.83 cruise, 11-km altitude, $P_s = 1.5$ m/sec, 95.95 percent of takeoff weight; $\phi_{\text{inlet}} = 0.01$.
3. Mach 0.45, 5-km altitude, engine out, $P_s = 1.5$ m/sec, 88 percent of takeoff weight; $\phi_{\text{inlet}} = 0.02$. Assume a drag coefficient increment for engine out = 0.0035 (based on wing area).
4. Loiter at 9-km altitude, 64 percent of takeoff weight; $\phi_{\text{inlet}} = 0.03$.

Computer-Calculated Engine Performance

For each of the engines showing promise in Design Problem 7-D1, systematically perform the following analysis:

1. Design the reference engine at sea-level static conditions. Size the engine to provide the required uninstalled thrust (engine size normally will be determined by either the takeoff flight condition or the engine-out flight condition listed above). Check engine operation at takeoff and make sure that $T_{t3} < 920$ K.
2. Determine the uninstalled fuel consumption at the start of Mach 0.83 cruise, 11-km altitude, and $P_s = 0$. You can do this by selecting the variable option *specified thrust* in PERF and entering the required uninstalled thrust. Assuming cruise climb with constant range factor (RF), calculate the weight at the end of the Mach 0.83 cruise, using the Breguet range equation, Eq. (1-45*a* or *b*).

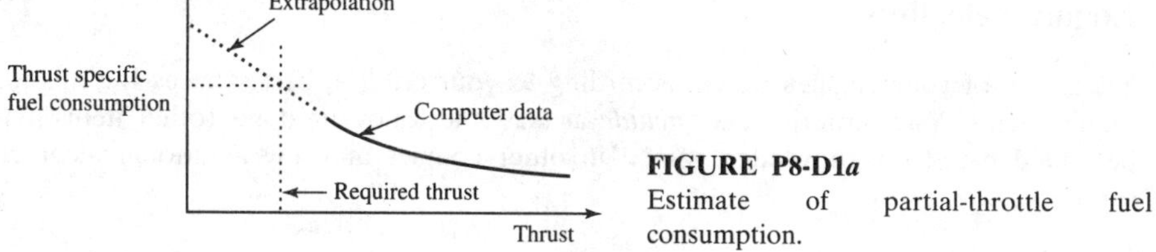

FIGURE P8-D1*a*
Estimate of partial-throttle fuel consumption.

3. Determine the loiter Mach number at 9-km altitude for the current aircraft weight at the start of loiter. Find the engine fuel consumption at start of loiter. Assuming a constant endurance factor (EF), calculate the weight at the end of the 9-km loiter.

   Some engines may not throttle down to the required uninstalled thrust due to the model used in the computer program, and the uninstalled thrust specific fuel consumption will have to be obtained by *extrapolation.* To extrapolate, use the performance analysis computer program and iterate on T_{t4} in steps of 25 K to the lowest value giving results. Then plot S versus F as shown in Fig. P8-D1a, and draw a tangent line to obtain the extrapolated value of S at the desired uninstalled thrust.

Fuel Consumption

During this preliminary analysis, you can assume that the fuel consumption changes only for the Mach 0.83 cruise and 9-km loiter. For every one of the engines you investigate, you must determine whether it can satisfy the fuel consumption requirements by calculating the amount of fuel consumed during the Mach 0.83 cruise climb and 9-km loiter and adding these to that consumed for other parts of the flight. During your analysis of the engines, make a plot of fuel consumed versus the reference bypass ratio like that shown in Fig. P8-D1b. Starting with one compressor pressure ratio π_{c1} and a low-bypass-ratio engine, calculate the total fuel consumed for the flight. Now increase the bypass ratio, size the engine, and determine this engine's performance.

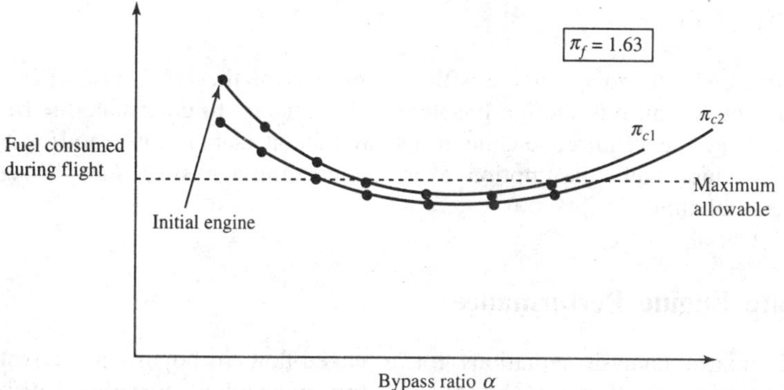

FIGURE P8-D1*b*
Graphical search for best fuel consumption.

Engine Selection

Select one of your engines which, according to your criteria, best satisfies the mission requirements. Your criteria *must include* at least the following items (other items may be added based on knowledge gained in other courses and any additional technical sources):

Thrust requirement
Fuel consumption
Aircraft performance
Operating cost (assume 10,000-hr engine life and fuel cost of $0.40 per pound)
First cost
Size and weight
Complexity

Determine Engine Thrust versus Mach Number and Altitude

For the engine you select, determine and plot the uninstalled thrust F at maximum power versus Mach number at sea level, 5-km altitude, and 11-km altitude and at takeoff power at sea level (see Fig. 8-47). Use $T_{t4} = 1780$ K for maximum power and $T_{t4} = 1890$ K for takeoff power.

Summary

Summarize the final choice for the selected engine incuding a list of design conditions and choices, performance during the mission, and overall mission performance. Include suggestions, if necessary, for overcoming any of the performance shortcomings which may exist in any of the mission legs. In addition, make meaningful comments about the feasibility of building such an engine.

8-D2 GAS TURBINE DESIGN PROBLEM 2 (HF-1 AIRCRAFT)

Find the best mixed-flow turbofan engine with afterburner for the HF-1 aircraft from those engines showing promise in Design Problem 7-D2. You are to determine the best engine, sized to meet the required engine thrust at takeoff, supercruise, and/or 5g turns, and whose cruise fuel consumption over the maximum mission (see Design Problem 1-D2) is minimum.

Hand-Calculate Engine Performance

Using the performance analysis equations for a mixed-flow turbofan engine with afterburner, hand-calculate the performance of the mixed-flow turbofan engine hand-calculated in Design Problem 7-D2 at the flight condition of 1.6 Mach and 40-kft altitude at $T_{t4} = 3200$°R with the afterburner turned off.

Required Thrust at Different Flight Conditions

Determine both the required installed thrust and the required uninstalled engine thrust for each of the following flight conditions (assume $\phi_{noz} = 0.01$):

1. For takeoff, an installed thrust of 23,500 lbf for each engine at sea level, 0.1 Mach while at maximum power setting (afterburner on with $T_{t7} = 3600°R$). Assume $\phi_{inlet} = 0.10$.
2. Start of Mach 1.6 supercruise, 40-kft altitude, 92 percent of takeoff weight W_{TO}; $\phi_{inlet} = 0.04$.
3. Start of 5*g* turn at Mach 1.6, 30-kft altitude, 88 percent of W_{TO}; $\phi_{inlet} = 0.04$.
4. Start of 5*g* turn at Mach 0.9, 30-kft altitude, 88 percent of W_{TO}; $\phi_{inlet} = 0.04$.

Computer-Calculated Engine Performance

Develop a reference mixed-flow turbofan engine with afterburner based on the data used in Design Problem 7-D2. For the afterburner, use $\gamma_{AB} = 1.3$, $c_{pAB} = 0.296$ Btu/(lbm · °R), $\pi_{AB} = 0.96$, $\eta_{AB} = 0.97$, and $T_{t7} = 3600°R$. For each of the engines showing promise in Design Problem 7-D2, systematically perform the following analysis:

1. Design the reference engine at sea-level static conditions. Size the engine to provide the required uninstalled thrust (engine size will normally be determined by the takeoff flight condition, by the start of supercruise flight condition, or by the 5*g* turn at Mach 1.6 listed above). Check engine operation at takeoff, and make sure that $T_{t3} < 1600°R$ and that the compressor pressure is within a specified limit.
2. Determine uninstalled fuel consumption at the start of the Mach 1.6 supercruise, 40-kft altitude. You can do this by selecting the variable option *specified thrust* in PERF and entering the required uninstalled thrust. Your engine should be able to deliver the required thrust with the afterburner off. Assuming cruise climb with constant range factor (RF), calculate the weight at the end of the Mach 1.6 supercruise, using the Breguet range equation, Eq. (1-45*a* or *b*).
3. Calculate the aircraft weight at the start of the Mach 0.9 cruise and the corresponding best cruise altitude (maximum C_L/C_D) and aircraft drag. Calculate the uninstalled required thrust at start of Mach 0.9 cruise, assuming $\phi_{inlet} = 0.05$ and $\phi_{noz} = 0.01$. Now determine the uninstalled fuel consumption at the start of Mach 0.9 cruise. Assuming cruise climb with constant range factor (RF), calculate the weight at the end of the Mach 0.9 cruise, using the Breguet range equation, Eq. (1-45*a*/*b*).
4. Determine the loiter Mach number at 30-kft altitude for the current aircraft weight at the start of loiter. Find the engine fuel consumption at the start of loiter. Assuming constant endurance factor (EF), calculate the weight at the end of the 30-kft loiter.

   Some engines may not throttle down to the required uninstalled thrust due to the model used in the computer program, and the uninstalled thrust specific fuel consumption will have to be obtained by *extrapolation.* To extrapolate, use the performance analysis computer program and iterate on T_{t4} in steps of 50°R to the lowest value giving results. Then plot S versus F as shown in Fig. P8-D1*a*, and draw a tangent line to obtain the extrapolated value of S at the desired uninstalled thrust.

Fuel Consumption

During this preliminary analysis, you can assume that the fuel consumption changes only for the Mach 1.6 supercruise, Mach 0.9 cruise, and 30-kft loiter. For every one of the engines you investigate, you must determine whether it can satisfy the fuel consumption requirements by calculating the amount of fuel consumed during the Mach 1.6 supercruise, Mach 0.9 cruise, and 30-kft loiter and adding these values to that consumed for other parts of the maximum mission. During your analysis of the engines, make a plot of fuel consumed versus the reference bypass ratio like that shown in Fig. P8-D1*b*. Starting with one compressor pressure ratio π_{c1} and a low-bypass-ratio engine, calculate the total fuel consumed for the mission. Now increase the bypass ratio, size the engine, and determine this engine's performance.

Engine Selection

Select one of your engines which, according to your criteria, best satisfies the mission requirements. Your criteria *must include* at least the following items (other items may be added based on knowledge gained in other courses and any additional technical sources):

Thrust required
Fuel consumption
Aircraft performance
Operating cost (assume 10,000-hr engine life and fuel cost of $0.40 per pound)
First cost
Size and weight
Complexity

Determine Engine Thrust versus Mach Number and Altitude

For the engine you select, determine and plot the uninstalled thrust F and thrust specific fuel consumption at both maximum power (afterburner on) and military power (afterburner off) versus Mach number at altitudes of sea level, 10 kft, 20 kft, 30 kft, 36 kft, and 40 kft (see Figs. 8-65, 8-66, 8-67, and 8-68). Use $T_{t4\,\max} = 3250°\text{R}$ and the throttle ratio TR for your engine. Also determine and plot the partial-throttle performance (see Fig. 8-69) of your engine at sea-level static, 1.6 Mach and 40 kft, 1.6 Mach and 30 kft, and 0.9 Mach and 30 kft.

Summary

Summarize the final choice for the selected engine including a list of design conditions and choices, performance during the mission, and overall mission performance. Include suggestions, if necessary, for overcoming any of the performance shortcomings which may exist in any of the mission legs. In addition, make meaningful comments about the feasibility of building such an engine.

CHAPTER

9

TURBOMACHINERY

9-1 INTRODUCTION

In general, turbomachinery is classified as all those devices in which energy is transferred either to or from a continuously flowing fluid by the dynamic action of one or more moving blade rows (Ref. 31). The word *turbo* or *turbinis* is of Latin origin and implies that which spins or whirls around. Essentially, a rotating blade row or rotor changes the total enthalpy of the fluid moving through it by either doing work on the fluid or having work done on it by the fluid, depending upon the effect required of the machine. These enthalpy changes are intimately linked with the pressure changes occurring simultaneously in the fluid.

The above definition of turbomachinery embraces both open and enclosed turbomachines (Ref. 31). Open turbomachinery (such as propellers, windmills, and unshrouded fans) influence an indeterminate quantity of fluid. In enclosed turbomachinery (such as centrifugal compressors, axial-flow turbines, etc.), a finite quantity of fluid passes through a casing in unit time. In this chapter, we will focus on the enclosed turbomachinery used in gas turbine engines: fans, compressors, and turbines. There are many excellent references on enclosed turbomachinery such as Refs. 4, 12, 26, and 31 through 42. Open turbomachines are covered in aeronautics textbooks such as Refs. 43, 44, and 45.

Turbomachines are further categorized according to the nature of the flow path through the passages of the rotor. When the path of the throughflow is wholly or mainly parallel to the axis of rotation, the device is termed an *axial-flow turbomachine.* When the path of the throughflow is wholly or mainly in a plane perpendicular to the rotation axis, the device is termed a *radial-flow turbomachine.* When the direction of the throughflow at the rotor outlet has both radial and axial velocity components present in significant amounts, the device is termed a *mixed-flow turbomachine.*

9-2 EULER'S TURBOMACHINERY EQUATIONS

In turbomachinery, power is added to or removed from the fluid by the rotating components. These rotating components exert forces on the fluid which change both the energy and the tangential momentum of the fluid. In this section, we will develop Euler's equations for turbomachinery that relate the change in energy to the change in tangential momentum.

Consider the adiabatic flow of a fluid as shown in Fig. 9-1. The fluid in a stream tube enters a control volume at radius r_i with tangential velocity v_i and exits at r_e with tangential velocity v_e. For a compressor or pump with steady flow, the applied torque τ_A is equal to the change in angular momentum of the fluid, or

$$\tau_A = \frac{\dot{m}}{g_c}(r_e v_e - r_i v_i)$$

The input power is $\dot{W}_c = \omega \tau_A$, or

$$\boxed{\dot{W}_c = \frac{\dot{m}\omega}{g_c}(r_e v_e - r_i v_i)} \tag{9-1}$$

This equation is often referred to as the *Euler pump equation.* Application of the first law of thermodynamics to the flow through the control volume gives

$$\dot{W}_c = \dot{m}(h_{te} - h_{ti})$$

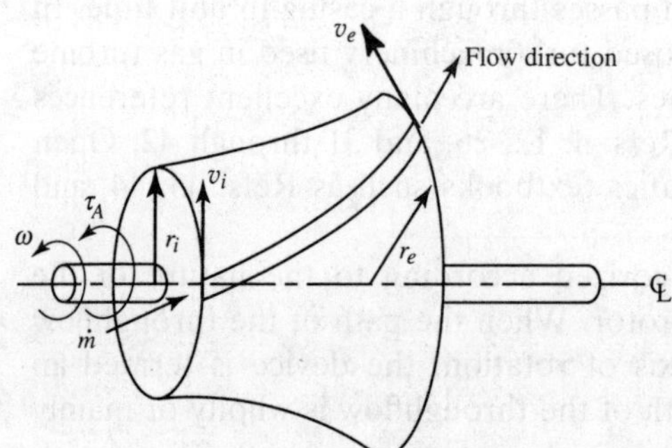

FIGURE 9-1
Control volume for a general turbomachine.

Combining this expression with Eq. (9-1) gives

$$h_{te} - h_{ti} = \frac{\omega}{g_c}(r_e v_e - r_i v_i) \tag{9-2}$$

Likewise, for a steady-flow turbine, the output torque τ_O is equal to the change in angular momentum of the fluid, or

$$\tau_O = \frac{\dot{m}}{g_c}(r_i v_i - r_e v_e)$$

The output power is

$$\dot{W}_t = \omega \tau_O$$

or

$$\dot{W}_t = \frac{\dot{m}\omega}{g_c}(r_i v_i - r_e v_e) \tag{9-3}$$

This equation is often referred to as the *Euler turbine equation.* Application of the first law of thermodynamics to the flow through the control volume gives

$$\dot{W}_t = \dot{m} = (h_{ti} - h_{te})$$

Combining this expression with Eq. (9-3) gives

$$h_{ti} - h_{te} = \frac{\omega}{g_c}(r_i v_i - r_e v_e) \tag{9-4}$$

which is the same as Eq. (9-2).

Calorically Perfect Gas

In the design of turbomachinery for a compressible gas, the gas is often modeled as having constant specific heats. For this case, we can write Eq. (9-4) as

$$c_p(T_{ti} - T_{te}) = \frac{\omega}{g_c}(r_i v_i - r_e v_e) \tag{9-5}$$

This equation is also referred to as the *Euler turbine equation.* We will be using this equation throughout the analysis of turbomachinery for a compressible gas. Component efficiencies and the isentropic relationships will be used to relate total temperature changes to total pressure changes.

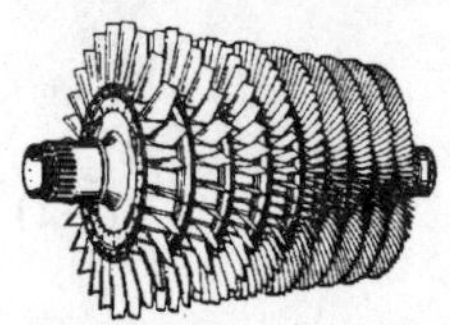
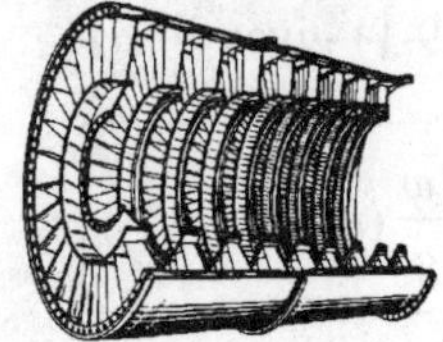
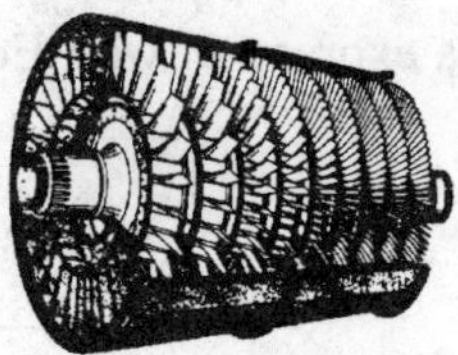

FIGURE 9-2
(a) Axial-flow compressor assembly (Ref. 46); complete assembly. (b) Axial-flow compressor assembly (Ref. 46); rotor with blades. (c) Axial-flow compressor assembly (Ref. 46); case with stators.

9-3 AXIAL-FLOW COMPRESSOR ANALYSIS

The axial-flow compressor is one of the most common compressor types in use today. It finds its major application in large gas turbine engines like those that power today's jet aircraft. A cutaway view of an axial-flow compressor is shown in Fig. 9-2*a*. The compressor is made up of two major assemblies: the rotor with its blades, as shown in Fig. 9-2*b*, and the casing with its stationary blades (called *stators*), as shown in Fig. 9-2*c*.

This chapter investigates the relationships of the desired performance parameters to the related blade loading and resultant fluid flow angles. Since the flow is inherently three-dimensional, the problem of analysis seems almost incomprehensible. *Do not fear*! This most complex flow can be understood by dividing the three-dimensional flow field into three two-dimensional flow fields. The complete flow field will be the "sum" of these less complex two-dimensional flows. The two-dimensional flow fields are normally called the *throughflow field*, the *cascade field* (or *blade-to-blade field*), and the *secondary flow field*. Each of these fields is described in more detail in the following sections.

THE THROUGHFLOW FIELD. The throughflow field is concerned with the variation in fluid properties in only the radial r and axial z directions (see Fig. 9-3). No variations in the θ direction occur. A row of blades is modeled as a thin disk which affects the flow field uniformly in the θ direction. If you imagine that the forces of the blades had been distributed among an infinite number of very thin blades, then you can begin to see the throughflow field model. As a result of throughflow field analysis, one will obtain the axial, tangential, and radial velocities as a function of r and z. Typical axial velocity profiles as a result of throughflow analysis are shown in Fig. 9-4*a*.

When the axial velocity changes, like that shown in Fig. 9-4*a*, conservation of mass requires that a downward flow of the fluid occur between stations 1 and 2. This downward flow could be shown by the stream surface as drawn in Fig. 9-4*b*.

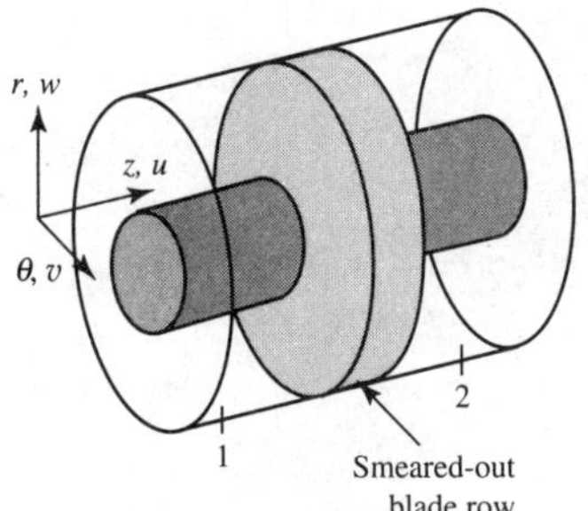

FIGURE 9-3
Coordinate system and throughflow representation.

THE CASCADE FIELD. The cascade field considers the flow behavior along stream surfaces (s coordinate) and tangentially through blade rows. Unwrapping the stream surface (like that shown in Fig. 9-5) gives the meridional projection of blade profiles, as shown in Fig. 9-6—a two-dimensional flow field in the θ and the meridional (almost z) coordinates. If the curvature of the stream surfaces in the throughflow field is not too great, the flow at a radial location may be modeled as a meridional projection and a suitable blade profile determined for the flow conditions. By considering a number of such projections, the blade profiles for selected radial locations on the blade are determined. The complete blade shape necessary to describe the full three-dimensional blade can be obtained by blending in the desired blade profiles.

The most common method of obtaining performance data for different blade profiles is to run cascade tests. A set of airfoils of the desired blade shape is mounted in a conditioned flow stream, and the performance is experimentally measured. Figure 9-7 shows the complete flow field about a typical cascade with the blades spaced a distance s apart.

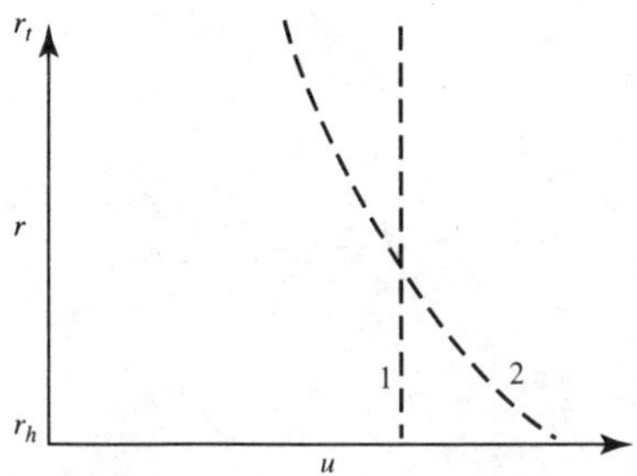

FIGURE 9-4*a*
Typical axial velocity profiles.

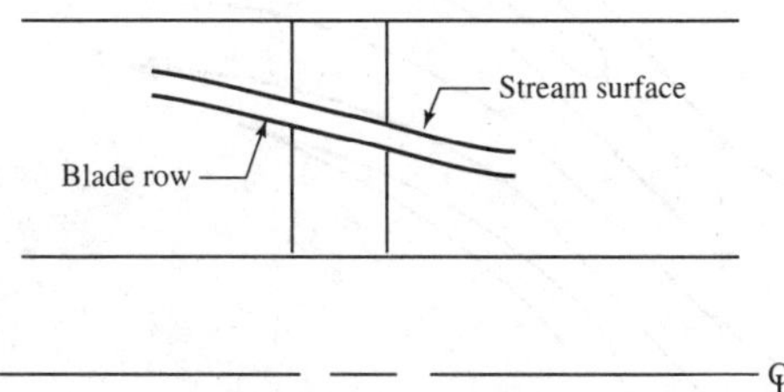

FIGURE 9-4*b*
Typical stream surface.

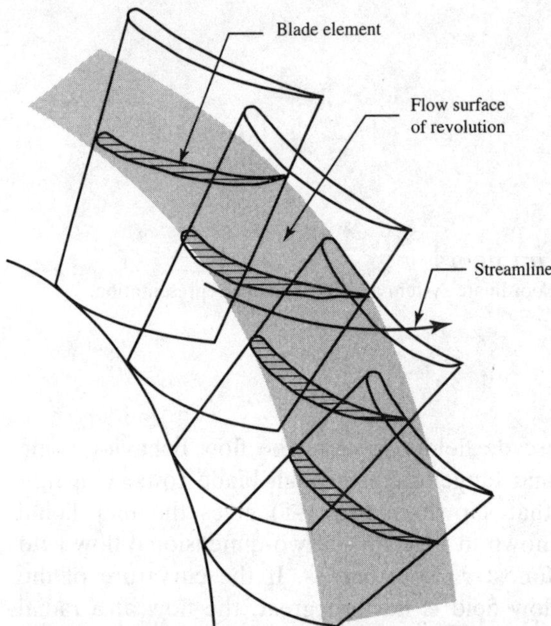

FIGURE 9-5
Stream surface and streamlines.

THE SECONDARY FIELD. The secondary flow field exists because the fluid near the solid surfaces (in the boundary layer) of the blades and passage walls has a lower velocity than that in the *free stream* (external to the boundary layer). The pressure gradients imposed by the free stream will cause the fluid in the boundary layers to flow from regions of higher pressure to regions of lower pressure. Figure 9-8 shows the possible secondary flow field within a stator row.

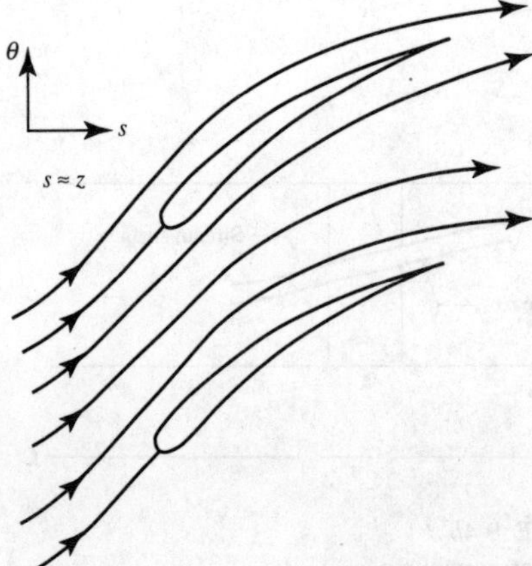

FIGURE 9-6
Meridional projections of blade profiles.

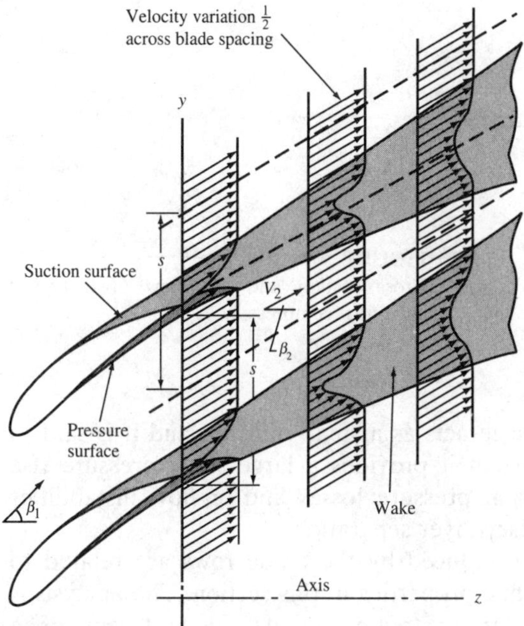

FIGURE 9-7
Flow field about cascade.

Two-Dimensional Flow through Blade Rows

A cross section and a top view of a typical axial-flow compressor are shown in Fig. 9-9. Depending on the design, an inlet guide vane (IGV) may be used to deflect the incoming airflow to a predetermined angle toward the direction of rotation of the rotor. The rotor increases the angular velocity of the fluid, resulting in increases in total temperature, total pressure, and static pressure. The following stator decreases the angular velocity of the fluid, resulting in an increase in the static pressure, and sets the flow up for the following rotor. A compressor stage is made up of a rotor and a stator.

The basic building block of the aerodynamic design of axial-flow compressors is the *cascade,* an endless repeating array of airfoils (Fig. 9-10) that results from the "unwrapping" of the stationary (stators) and rotating

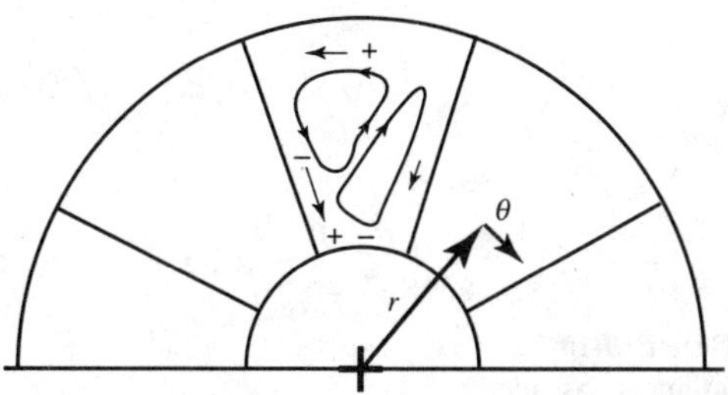

FIGURE 9-8
Secondary flow field within a stator row.

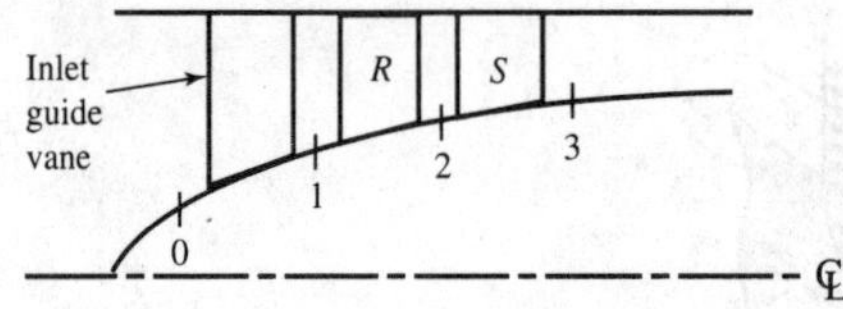

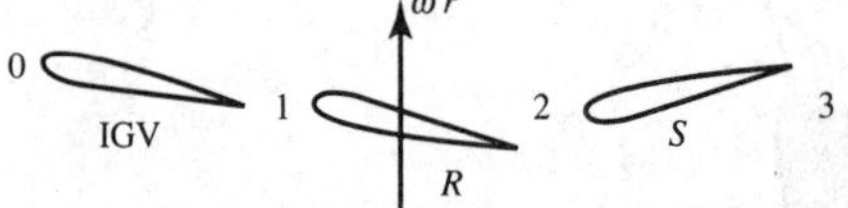

FIGURE 9-9
Cross section and top view of a typical axial-flow compressor.

(rotor) airfoils. Each cascade passage acts as a small diffuser, and it is said to be well designed or "behaved" when it provides a large static pressure rise without incurring unacceptable total pressure losses and/or flow instabilities due to shock waves and/or boundary layer separation.

The changes in fluid velocity induced by the blade rows are related to changes in the fluid's thermodynamic properties in this section. The analysis is concerned with only the flow far upstream and far downstream of a cascade—the regions where the flow fields are uniform. In this manner, the details about the flow field are not needed, and performance can be related to just the changes in fluid properties across a blade row.

In the analysis that follows, two different coordinate systems are used: one fixed to the compressor housing (absolute) and the other fixed to the rotating blades (relative). The static (thermodynamic) properties *do not* depend on the reference frame. However, the *total properties do depend on the*

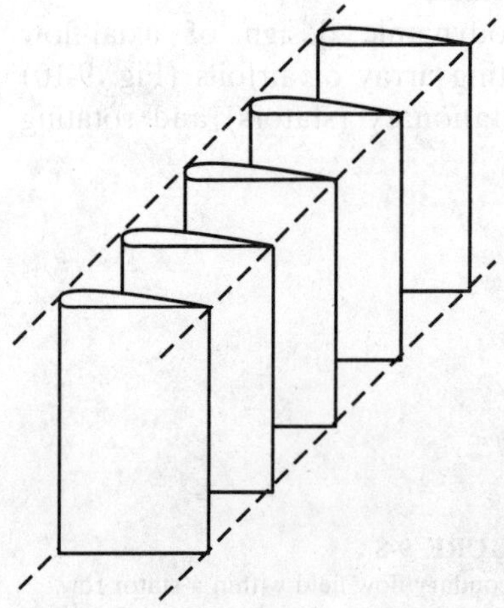

FIGURE 9-10
Rectilinear cascade.

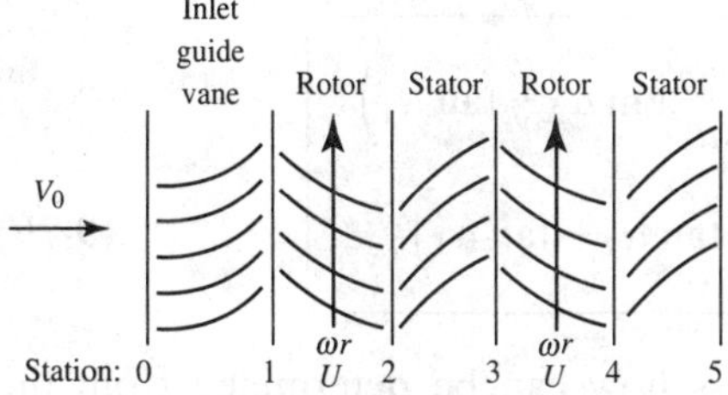

FIGURE 9-11
Two repeating compressor stages with inlet guide vane.

reference frame. The velocity of a fluid in one reference frame is easily converted to the other frame by the following equation:

$$\boxed{\mathbf{V} = \mathbf{V}_R + \mathbf{U}} \tag{9-6}$$

where $\mathbf{V}$ = velocity in stationary coordinate system
$\mathbf{V}_R$ = velocity in moving coordinate system
$\mathbf{U}$ = velocity of moving coordinate system ($=\omega r$)

Consider the compressor stage made up of a rotor followed by a stator as shown in Fig. 9-11. The flow enters the rotor with velocity V_1 (relative velocity V_{1R}) and leaves with velocity V_2 (relative velocity V_{2R}). The rotor is moving upward at velocity ωr (the symbol U is also used). The flow enters the stator with velocity V_2 and leaves with velocity V_3. Rather than keep the axial velocity constant, as is done in many textbooks, the following analysis permits variation in axial velocity from station to station.

EULER'S EQUATION

$$c_p(T_{t2} - T_{t1}) = \frac{\omega}{g_c}(r_2 v_2 - r_1 v_1)$$

For $r_2 \cong r_1$,

$$c_p(T_{t2} - T_{t1}) = \frac{\omega r}{g_c}(v_2 - v_1) = \frac{U}{g_c}(v_2 - v_1)$$

Since

$$v_2 = \omega r - v_{2R} = \omega r - u_2 \tan\beta_2 = u_2 \tan\alpha_2$$

and

$$v_1 = \omega r - v_{1R} = \omega r - u_1 \tan\beta_1 = u_1 \tan\alpha_1$$

Then

$$\boxed{\begin{aligned} c_p(T_{t2} - T_{t1}) &= \frac{(\omega r)^2}{g_c}\frac{u_1}{\omega r}\left(\tan\beta_1 - \frac{u_2}{u_1}\tan\beta_2\right) \\ &= \frac{U^2}{g_c}\frac{u_1}{U}\left(\tan\beta_1 - \frac{u_2}{u_1}\tan\beta_2\right) \end{aligned}} \tag{9-7a}$$

or

$$c_p(T_{t2} - T_{t1}) = \frac{(\omega r)^2}{g_c} \frac{u_1}{\omega r} \left(\frac{u_2}{u_1} \tan \alpha_2 - \tan \alpha_1 \right)$$
$$= \frac{U^2}{g_c} \frac{u_1}{U} \left(\frac{u_2}{u_1} \tan \alpha_2 - \tan \alpha_1 \right) \tag{9-7b}$$

Hence the work done per unit mass flow can be determined from the rotor speed ($U = \omega r$), the velocity ratios (u_1/U and u_2/u_1), and either the rotor cascade flow angles (β_1 and β_2) or the absolute rotor flow angles (α_1 and α_2). Equations (9-7*a*) and (9-7*b*) are useful forms of the Euler equation for compressor stage design and show the dependence of the stage work on the rotor speed squared (U^2).

Velocity Diagrams

An axial-flow compressor stage consists of a rotor followed by a stator as shown in Fig. 9-12*a*. Two compressor stages (which are identical in geometry) are shown in Fig. 9-12*b* preceded by inlet guide vanes. The velocity diagrams depicted in Fig. 9-12*b* show the absolute velocities entering and leaving the guide vanes, rotor, and stator (solid vectors). In addition, for the rotors, the entering and leaving relative velocities (dashed vectors) and the rotor

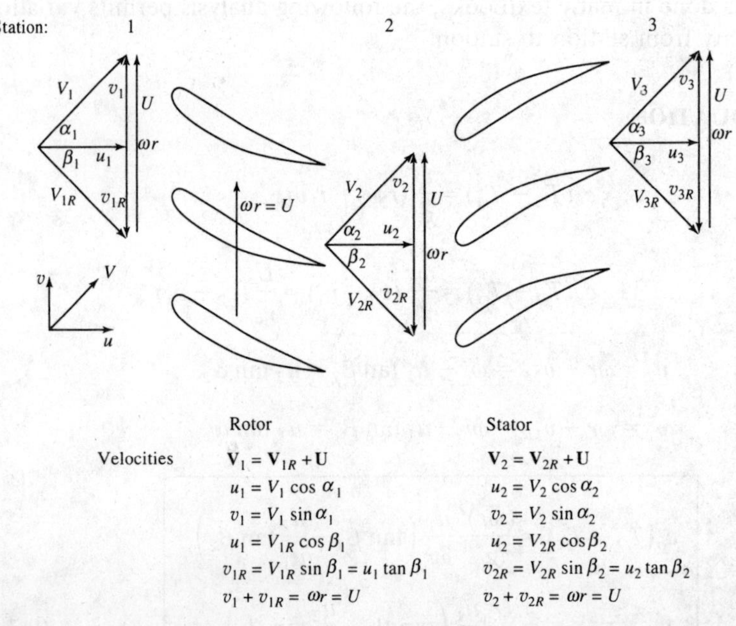

FIGURE 9-12*a*
Blade rows of a typical compressor.

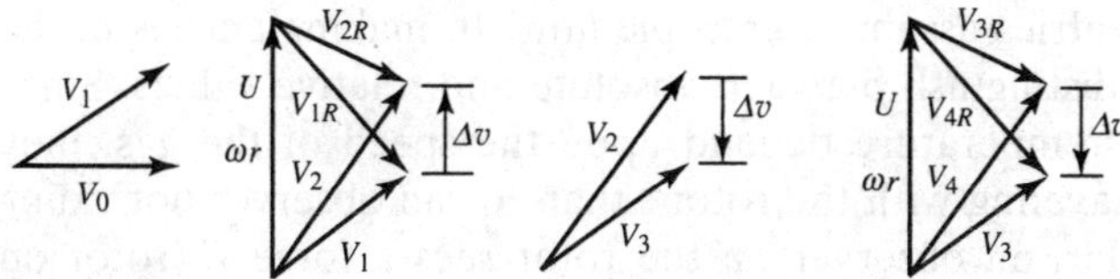

FIGURE 9-12*b*
Velocity diagrams for typical compressor.

tangential velocity are shown. We have assumed, in the diagram, that the axial velocity component is constant.

Refering to Fig. 9-12*b*, we see that the guide vanes act as nozzles through which the static pressure decreases as the air velocity increases, and the fluid is given a tangential (swirl) component in the direction of the rotor velocity. The air leaves the inlet guide vanes with velocity V_1.

The absolute velocity entering the rotor at station 1 is V_1. Subtracting the rotor speed ωr from V_1 vectorially, we obtain the relative velocity V_{1R} entering the rotor. In the rotor blade row, the blade passages act as diffusers, reducing the relative velocity from V_{1R} to V_{2R} as the static pressure is increased from P_1 to P_2. The relative velocity leaving the rotor is V_{2R}. Combining V_{2R} vectorially with ωr, we get their sum V_2—the absolute velocity leaving the rotor.

The velocity of the air leaving the rotor and entering the stator at station 2 is V_2. The stator diffuses the velocity to V_3 as the static pressure rises from P_2 to P_3. Since the velocity V_3 entering the rotor at station 3 is identical with V_1 entering the first-stage rotor, we find the velocity triangle for the second-stage rotor is a repeat of the triangle for the first stage.

The effects occurring in each compressor component are summarized in Table 9-1, where +, 0, and − mean increase, unchanged, and decrease,

TABLE 9-1
Property changes in an isentropic compressor

Property	Inlet guide vanes	Rotor	Stator
Absolute velocity	+	+	−
Relative velocity	n/a	−	n/a
Static pressure	−	+	+
Absolute total pressure	0	+	0
Relative total pressure	n/a	0	n/a
Static temperature	−	+	+
Absolute total temperature	0	+	0
Relative total temperature	n/a	0	n/a

+ = increase   − = decrease
0 = unchanged   n/a not applicable

respectively. The table entries assume isentropic flow. In making entries in the table, it is important to distinguish between absolute and relative values. Since total pressure and total temperature depend upon the speed of the gas, they have different values "traveling with the rotor" than for an observer not riding on the rotor. In particular, an observer on the rotor sees a force F (rotor on gas), but it is stationary; hence, in the rider's reference system, the force does no work on the gas. Consequently, the total temperature and total pressure do not change relative to an observer on the rotor as the gas passes through the rotor. An observer not on the rotor sees the force F (rotor on gas) moving at the rate ωr. Hence, to the stationary observer, work is done on the gas passing through the rotor, and the total temperature and total pressure increase.

Flow Annulus Area

For uniform total properties at a station i, the area of the flow annulus A_i can be obtained from the mass flow parameter (MFP) by using

$$\boxed{A_i = \frac{\dot{m}\sqrt{T_{ti}}}{P_{ti}(\cos\alpha_i)\mathrm{MFP}(M_i)}} \tag{9-8}$$

where α_i is the angle that the velocity V_i makes with the centerline of the annulus.

Example 9-1. *Mean radius stage calculation—isentropic flow.*
GIVEN: $T_{t1} = 518.7°\text{R}$, $P_{t1} = 14.70$ psia, $\omega = 1000$ rad/sec, $r = 12$ in, $\alpha_1 = \alpha_3 = 40°$, $\dot{m} = 50$ lbm/sec, $M_1 = M_3 = 0.7$, $u_2/u_1 = 1.1$, and $P_{t3}/P_{t1} = 1.3$. Gas is air.

Note: For air, $\gamma = 1.4$, $c_p = 0.24$ Btu/(lbm · °R), $Rg_c = 1716$ ft²/(sec² · °R) $c_p g_c = 6066$ ft²/(sec² · °R)

Solution.

$$T_1 = \frac{T_{t1}}{1 + [(\gamma - 1)/2]M_1^2} = \frac{518.7°\text{R}}{1 + 0.2 \times 0.7^2} = 472.4°\text{R}$$

$$a_1 = \sqrt{\gamma R g_c T_1} = \sqrt{1.4 \times 1716 \times 472.4} = 1065.3 \text{ ft/sec}$$

$$V_1 = M_1 a_1 = 0.7 \times 1065.3 \text{ ft/sec} = 745.71 \text{ ft/sec}$$

$$u_1 = V_1 \cos\alpha_1 = 745.71 \text{ ft/sec} \times 0.766 = 571.21 \text{ ft/sec}$$

$$v_1 = V_1 \sin\alpha_1 = 745.71 \text{ ft/sec} \times 0.6428 = 479.34 \text{ ft/sec}$$

$$P_1 = \frac{P_{t1}}{\{1 + [(\gamma - 1)/2]M_1^2\}^{\gamma/(\gamma-1)}} = \frac{14.70 \text{ psia}}{(1 + 0.2 + 0.7^2)^{3.5}} = 10.60 \text{ psia}$$

$$\mathrm{MFP}(M_1) = \frac{\mathrm{MFP}(M_1)\sqrt{R/g_c}}{\sqrt{R/g_c}} = \frac{0.625684}{1.28758} = 0.4859$$

$$A_1 = \frac{\dot{m}\sqrt{T_{t1}}}{P_{t1}(\cos\alpha_1)\mathrm{MFP}(M_1)} = \frac{50\sqrt{518.7}}{14.70 \times 0.7660 \times 0.4859} = 207.2 \text{ in}^2$$

$$\omega r = 1000 \times \frac{12}{12} = 1000 \text{ ft/sec}$$

$$v_{1R} = \omega r - v_1 = 1000 - 479.34 = 520.66 \text{ ft/sec}$$

$$\beta_1 = \tan^{-1}\frac{v_{1R}}{u_1} = \tan^{-1} 0.9114 = 42.35°$$

$$V_{1R} = \sqrt{u_1^2 + v_{1R}^2} = \sqrt{571.21^2 + 520.66^2} = 772.90 \text{ ft/sec}$$

$$M_{1R} = \frac{V_{1R}}{a_1} = \frac{772.90}{1065.3} = 0.7255$$

$$T_{t1R} = T_1\left(1 + \frac{\gamma - 1}{2} M_{1R}^2\right) = 472.4(1 + 0.2 \times 0.7255^2) = 552.1°\text{R}$$

$$P_{t1R} = P_1\left(\frac{T_{t1R}}{T_1}\right)^{\gamma/(\gamma-1)} = 10.60\left(\frac{522.1}{472.4}\right)^{3.5} = 15.04 \text{ psia}$$

$$P_{t2} = P_{t3} = 1.3 \times 14.70 = 19.11 \text{ psia}$$

$$T_{t3} = T_{t2} = T_{t1}\left(\frac{P_{t2}}{P_{t1}}\right)^{(\gamma-1)/\gamma} = 518.7(1.3)^{1/3.5} = 559.1°\text{R}$$

$$\tan\beta_2 = \frac{u_1}{u_2}\left[\tan\beta_1 - \frac{g_c c_p}{\omega r u_1}(T_{t2} - T_{t1})\right]$$

$$= \frac{1}{1.1}\left[\tan 42.35 - \frac{6006}{1000 \times 571.21}(559.1 - 518.7)\right] = 0.4425$$

$$\beta_2 = 23.87°$$

$$u_2 = \frac{u_2}{u_1} u_1 = 1.1 \times 571.21 = 628.33 \text{ ft/sec}$$

$$v_{2R} = u_2 \tan\beta_2 = 628.33 \times 0.4425 = 278.04 \text{ ft/sec}$$

$$V_{2R} = \sqrt{u_2^2 + v_{2R}^2} = \sqrt{628.33^2 + 278.04^2} = 687.10 \text{ ft/sec}$$

$$v_2 = \omega r - v_{2R} = 1000 - 278.04 = 721.96 \text{ ft/sec}$$

$$\alpha_2 = \tan^{-1}\frac{v_2}{u_2} = \tan^{-1}\frac{721.96}{628.33} = 48.97°$$

$$V_2 = \sqrt{u_2^2 + v_2^2} = \sqrt{628.33^2 + 721.96^2} = 957.10 \text{ ft/sec}$$

$$T_{t2R} = T_{t1R} = 552.5°\text{R}$$

$$P_{t2R} = P_{t1R} = 15.04 \text{ psia}$$

$$T_2 = T_{t2} - \frac{V_2^2}{2g_c c_p} = 559.1 - \frac{957.10^2}{2 \times 6006} = 482.8°\text{R}$$

$$P_2 = P_{t2}\left(\frac{T_2}{T_{t2}}\right)^{\gamma/(\gamma-1)} = 19.11\left(\frac{482.8}{559.1}\right)^{3.5} = 11.43 \text{ psia}$$

$$a_2 = \sqrt{\gamma R g_c T_2} = \sqrt{1.4 \times 1716 \times 482.8} = 1077.0 \text{ ft/sec}$$

$$M_2 = \frac{V_2}{a_2} = \frac{957.10}{1077.0} = 0.8887$$

$$M_{2R} = \frac{V_{2R}}{a_2} = \frac{687.10}{1077.0} = 0.6380$$

TABLE 9-2
Results for Example 9-1 axial-flow compressor stage calculation, isentropic flow

Property \ Station		1	1R	2R	2	3
T_t	°R	**518.7**	522.1	522.1	559.1	559.1
	(K)	**(288.2)**	(290.1)	(290.1)	(310.6)	(310.6)
T	°R	472.4	472.4	482.8	482.8	509.2
	(K)	(262.4)	(262.4)	(268.2)	(268.2)	(282.9)
P_t	psia	**14.70**	15.04	15.04	19.11	**19.11**
	(kPa)	**(101.3)**	(103.7)	(103.7)	(131.7)	**(131.7)**
P	psia	10.60	10.60	11.43	11.43	13.77
	(kPa)	(73.05)	(73.05)	(78.85)	(78.85)	(94.96)
M		**0.700**	0.7255	0.6380	0.8887	**0.700**
V	ft/sec	745.71	772.90	687.10	957.10	774.22
	(m/sec)	(227.30)	(235.58)	(209.43)	(291.73)	(235.99)
u	ft/sec	571.21	571.21	628.33	628.33	593.09
	(m/sec)	(174.11)	(174.11)	(191.53)	(191.52)	(180.78)
v	ft/sec	479.34	520.66	278.04	721.96	497.66
	(m/sec)	(146.10)	(158.70)	(84.75)	(220.06)	(151.69)
α	deg	**40.00**	—	—	48.97	**40.00**
β	deg	—	42.35	23.87	—	—

$$\text{MFP}(M_2) = \frac{\text{MFP}(M_2)\sqrt{R/g_c}}{\sqrt{R/g_c}} = \frac{0.677231}{1.28758} = 0.5260$$

$$A_2 = \frac{\dot{m}\sqrt{T_{t2}}}{P_{t2}(\cos\alpha_2)\text{MFP}(M_2)} = \frac{50\sqrt{559.1}}{19.11 \times 0.6566 \times 0.5260} = 179.1 \text{ in}^2$$

$$T_3 = \frac{T_{t3}}{1 + [(\gamma - 1)/2]M_3^2} = \frac{559.1°\text{R}}{1 + 0.2 \times 0.7^2} = 509.2°\text{R}$$

$$P_3 = P_{t3}\left(\frac{T_3}{T_{t3}}\right)^{\gamma/(\gamma-1)} = 19.11\left(\frac{509.2}{559.1}\right)^{3.5} = 13.77 \text{ psia}$$

$$a_3 = \sqrt{\gamma R g_c T_3} = \sqrt{1.4 \times 1716 \times 509.2} = 1106.03 \text{ ft/sec}$$

$$V_3 = M_3 a_3 = 0.7 \times 1106.03 = 774.22 \text{ ft/sec}$$

$$u_3 = V_3 \cos\alpha_3 = 593.09 \text{ ft/sec}$$

$$v_3 = V_3 \sin\alpha_3 = 497.66 \text{ ft/sec}$$

$$A_3 = \frac{\dot{m}\sqrt{T_{t3}}}{P_{t3}(\cos\alpha_3)\text{MFP}(M_3)} = \frac{50\sqrt{559.1}}{19.11 \times 0.766 \times 0.4859} = 165.3 \text{ in}^2$$

The results of this stage calculation for isentropic flow are summarized in Table 9-2, with the given data shown in bold type (SI results are shown within parentheses). Note that the flow through the rotor is adiabatic in the relative reference frame and, through the stator, is adiabatic in the absolute reference frame. Figure 9-13 is a representation of the flow properties for an isentropic stage on a T-s diagram.

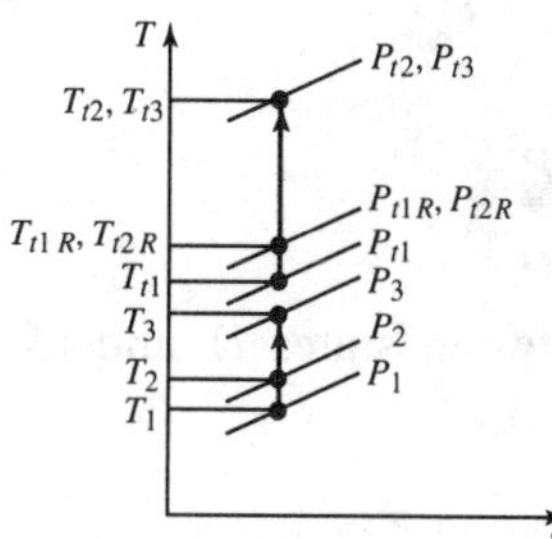

FIGURE 9-13
Property changes of an isentropic compressor stage.

Stage Parameters

EFFICIENCIES. Several efficiencies are used to compare the performance of compressor stage designs. The two efficiencies most commonly used are stage efficiency and polytropic efficiency. The *stage efficiency* of an adiabatic compressor is defined as the ratio of the ideal work per unit mass to the actual work per unit mass between the same total pressures, or

$$\boxed{\eta_s = \frac{h_{t3s} - h_{t1}}{h_{t3} - h_{t1}}} \tag{9-9}$$

For a calorically perfect gas, this simplifies to

$$\boxed{\eta_s = \frac{T_{t3s} - T_{t1}}{T_{t3} - T_{t1}} = \frac{(P_{t3}/P_{t1})^{(\gamma-1)/\gamma} - 1}{T_{t3}/T_{t1} - 1}} \tag{9-10}$$

where the states used in this equation for stage efficiency are plotted on the T-s diagram of Fig. 9-14*a*.

The *polytropic efficiency* of an adiabatic compressor is defined as the ratio of the ideal work per unit mass to the actual work per unit mass for a

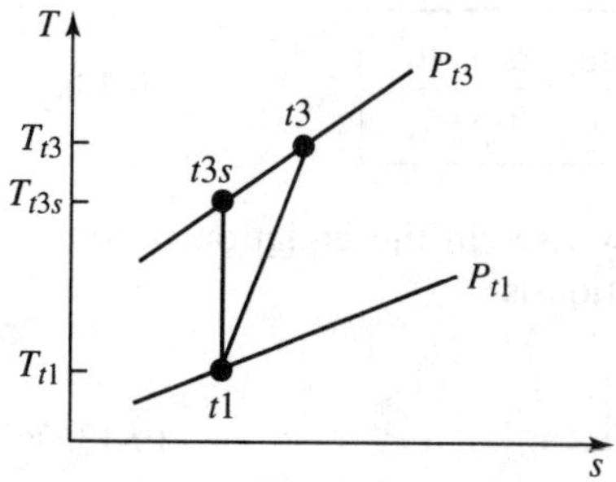

FIGURE 9-14*a*
States for definition of compressor stage efficiency.

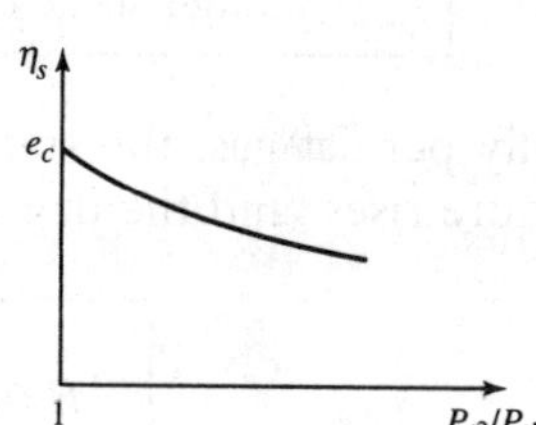

FIGURE 9-14*b*
Variation of stage efficiency with pressure ratio.

differential pressure change, or

$$e_c = \frac{dh_{ti}}{dh_t} = \frac{dT_{ti}}{dT_t} = \frac{dT_{ti}/T_t}{dT_t/T_t} = \frac{\gamma - 1}{\gamma}\frac{dP_t/P_t}{dT_t/T_t}$$

For a constant polytropic efficiency e_c, integration between states $t1$ and $t3$ gives

$$e_c = \frac{\gamma - 1}{\gamma}\frac{\ln(P_{t3}/P_{t1})}{\ln(T_{t3}/T_{t1})} \tag{9-11}$$

A useful expression for stage efficiency, in terms of the pressure ratio and polytropic efficiency, can be easily obtained by using Eqs. (9-10) and (9-11). Solving Eq. (9-11) for the temperature ratio and substituting into Eq. (9-10) give

$$\eta_s = \frac{(P_{t3}/P_{t1})^{(\gamma-1)/\gamma} - 1}{(P_{t3}/P_{t1})^{(\gamma-1)/(\gamma e_c)} - 1} \tag{9-12}$$

In the limit, as the pressure ratio approaches 1, the stage efficiency approaches the polytropic efficiency. The variation in stage efficiency with stage pressure ratio is plotted in Fig. 9-14*b* for constant polytropic efficiency.

The compressor polytropic efficiency is useful in preliminary design of compressors for gas turbine engines to predict the compressor efficiency for a given level of technology. The value of the polytropic efficiency is mainly a function of the technology level (see Table 6-2). Axial-flow compressors designed in the 1980s have a polytropic efficiency of about 0.88, whereas the compressors being designed today have a polytropic efficiency of about 0.9.

DEGREE OF REACTION. For compressible flow, the *degree of reaction* is defined as

$$°R_c = \frac{\text{rotor static enthalpy rise}}{\text{stage static enthalpy rise}} = \frac{h_2 - h_1}{h_3 - h_1} \tag{9-13a}$$

For a calorically perfect gas, the static enthalpy rises in the equation become static temperature rises, and the degree of reaction is

$$°R_c = \frac{T_2 - T_1}{T_3 - T_1} \tag{9-13b}$$

In the general case, it is desirable to have the degree of reaction in the vicinity of 0.5 because the rotor and stator rows then will "share the burden" of increasing the enthalpy of the flow. The degree of reaction for the stage data

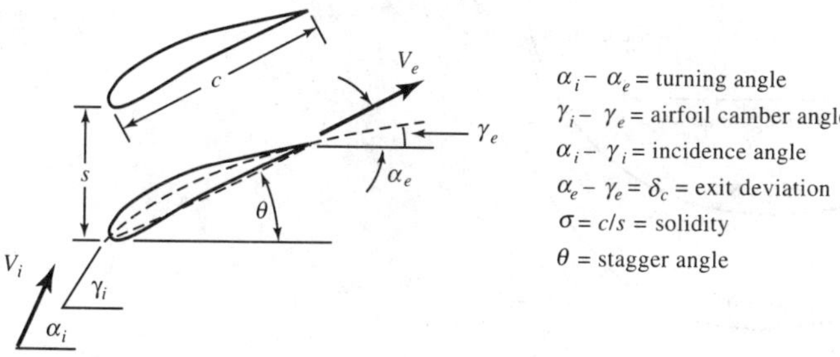

FIGURE 9-15
Cascade airfoil nomenclature.

of Example 9-1 is approximately 0.28, which means the majority of the static temperature rise occurs in the stator.

CASCADE AIRFOIL NOMENCLATURE AND LOSS COEFFICIENT. Figure 9-15 shows the cascade airfoil nomenclature and the airfoil and flow angles. Subscripts i and e are used for the inlet and exit states, respectively. The ratio of the airfoil chord c to the airfoil spacing s is called the *solidity* σ, which typically is near unity. At design, the incidence angle is nearly zero. The exit deviation can be determined by using Carter's rule:

$$\boxed{\delta_c = \frac{\gamma_i - \gamma_e}{4\sqrt{\sigma}}} \tag{9-14}$$

The airfoil angles of both the rotor and the stator can be calculated from the flow angles, given the incidence angle and solidity for each. To obtain the exit airfoil angle, Eq. (9-14) is rearranged to give

$$\gamma_e = \frac{4\alpha_e\sqrt{\sigma} - \gamma_i}{4\sqrt{\sigma} - 1}$$

For the data of Example 9-1, we obtain the following airfoil angles, assuming a solidity of 1 and a zero incidence angle for both rotor and stator:

Rotor	$\gamma_i = 42.35°$	$\gamma_e = 17.71°$
Stator	$\gamma_i = 48.97°$	$\gamma_e = 37.01°$

Losses in cascade airfoils are normally quantified in terms of the drop in total pressure divided by the dynamic pressure of the incoming flow. This ratio is called the *total pressure loss coefficient* and is defined as

$$\boxed{\phi_c \equiv \frac{P_{ti} - P_{te}}{\rho V_i^2/(2g_c)}} \tag{9-15}$$

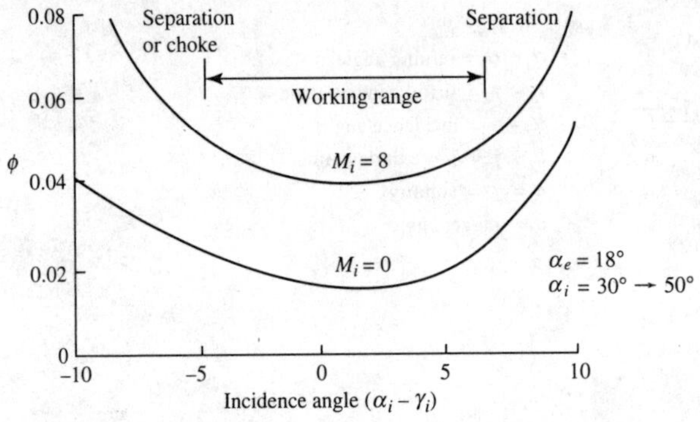

FIGURE 9-16
Compressor cascade experimental behavior.

Figure 9-16 shows the typical total pressure loss behavior of compressor airfoils obtained from cascade tests. Note that these losses increase with Mach number and incidence angle. The loss coefficients shown in Fig. 9-16 include only the two-dimensional or "profile" losses and must be increased in compressor stage design to account for end losses (e.g., tip leakage, wall boundary layer, or cavity leakage).

DIFFUSION FACTOR. The total pressure loss of a cascade depends upon many factors. The pressure and velocity distribution about a typical cascade airfoil is shown in Fig. 9-17. The upper (suction) side of the compressor blade

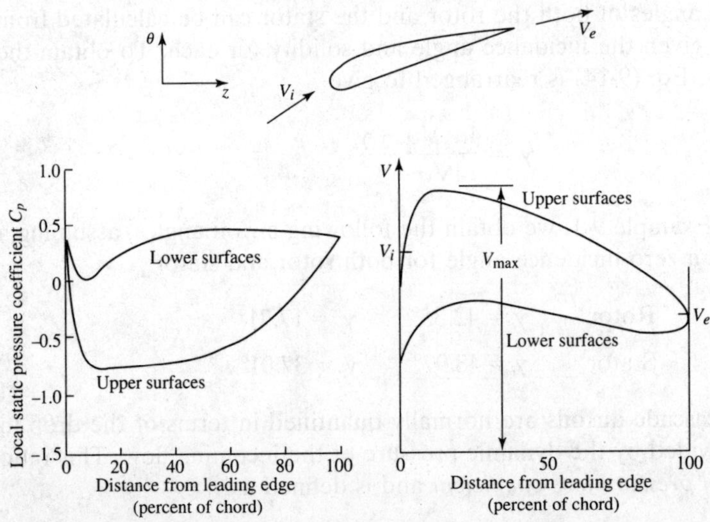

FIGURE 9-17
Compressor airfoil pressure and velocity distribution (Ref. 35).

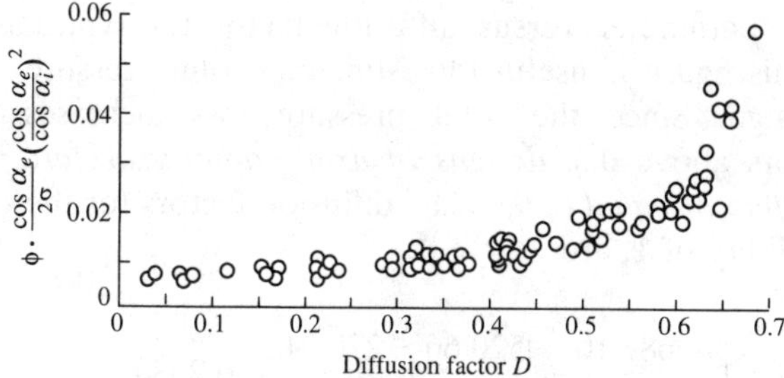

FIGURE 9-18
Total pressure loss versus diffusion factor for typical compressor airfoil (Ref. 35).

has a large static pressure rise (due to the deceleration from V_{max} to V_e) which can cause the viscous boundary layer to separate. Boundary-layer separation is not desirable because of the associated higher losses in total pressure.

Cascade test results (see Fig. 9-18) show a direct correlation between total pressure loss and the deceleration (diffusion) on the upper (suction) side of blades. The amount of diffusion is measured by the diffusion factor D. The expression for the diffusion factor is based on the fact that the diffusion of the flow on the suction surface is approximated as

$$D \approx \frac{V_{max} - V_e}{V_{av}} \approx \frac{V_{max} - V_e}{V_i}$$

where
$$V_{max} \approx V_i + f\left(\frac{\Delta v}{\sigma}\right) \approx V_i + \frac{|\Delta v|}{2\sigma}$$

Thus the *diffusion factor D* is defined by

$$\boxed{D \equiv 1 - \frac{V_e}{V_i} + \frac{|v_i - v_e|}{2\sigma V_i}} \tag{9-16}$$

where the subscripts i and e refer to the inlet and exit, respectively. Note that for a compressor stage, there is a diffusion factor for the rotor and another for the stator.

The diffusion factor for the rotor D_r is in terms of the relative velocities at stations 1 and 2, or

$$\boxed{D_r = 1 - \frac{V_{2R}}{V_{1R}} + \frac{|v_{1R} - v_{2R}|}{2\sigma V_{1R}}} \tag{9-17}$$

The diffusion factor for the stator D_s is in terms of the absolute velocities at stations 2 and 3, or

$$\boxed{D_s = 1 - \frac{V_3}{V_2} + \frac{|v_2 - v_3|}{2\sigma V_2}} \tag{9-18}$$

Figure 9-18 shows a loss parameter versus diffusion factor for typical compressor cascade airfoils. This figure is useful for estimating total pressure losses during preliminary design. Since the total pressure loss increases dramatically for diffusion factors above 0.6, *designs of axial compressors are limited to diffusion factors less than or equal to 0.6.* The diffusion factors for the data of Example 9-1, with a solidity of 1, are

$$D_r = 1 - \frac{V_{2R}}{V_{1R}} + \frac{|v_{1R} - v_{2R}|}{2\sigma V_{1R}} = 1 - \frac{687.10}{772.90} + \frac{|520.66 - 278.04|}{2 \times 1 \times 772.90} = 0.2680$$

$$D_r = 1 - \frac{V_3}{V_2} + \frac{|v_2 - v_3|}{2\sigma V_2} = 1 - \frac{774.22}{957.10} + \frac{|721.96 - 497.66|}{2 \times 1 \times 957.10} = 0.3083$$

These values of diffusion factor show that both the rotor and stator of the example problem are lightly loaded.

STAGE LOADING AND FLOW COEFFICIENTS. The ratio of the stage work to rotor speed squared is called the *stage loading coefficient* and is defined as

$$\psi \equiv \frac{g_c\, \Delta h_t}{(\omega r)^2} = \frac{g_c\, \Delta h_t}{U^2} \tag{9-19}$$

For a calorically perfect gas, the stage loading coefficient can be written as

$$\psi = \frac{g_c c_p\, \Delta T_t}{(\omega r)^2} = \frac{g_c c_p\, \Delta T_t}{U^2} \tag{9-20}$$

Modern axial-flow compressors used for aircraft gas turbine engines have stage loading coefficients in the range of 0.3 to 0.35 at the mean radius. For Example 9-1, the stage loading coefficient is 0.24, a low value.

The ratio of the axial velocity to the rotor speed is called the *flow coefficient* and is defined as

$$\Phi \equiv \frac{u_1}{\omega r} = \frac{u_1}{U} \tag{9-21}$$

The flow coefficients for modern axial-flow compressors of aircraft gas turbine engines are in the range of 0.45 to 0.55 at the mean radius. For the Example 9-1, the flow coefficient is 0.57, a high value.

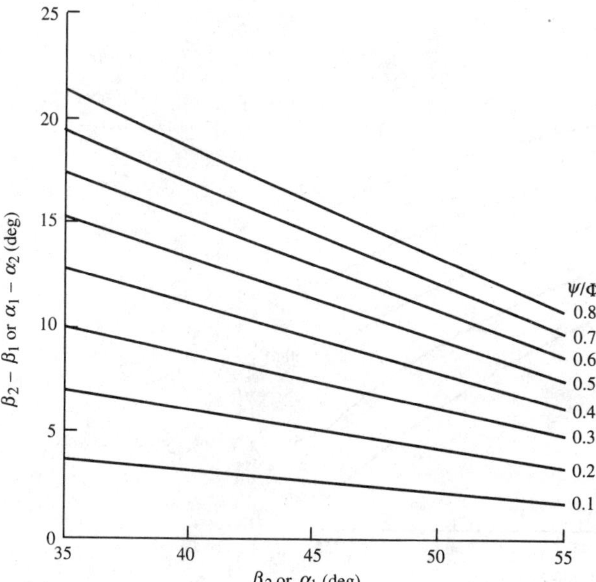

FIGURE 9-19
Stage flow angles versus Ψ/Φ for constant axial velocity.

Equations (9-20) and (9-21) can be substituted into Eqs. (9-7*a*) and (9-7*b*), respectively, to give

$$\frac{\psi}{\Phi} = \tan\beta_1 - \frac{u_2}{u_1}\tan\beta_2 \qquad \text{and} \qquad \frac{\psi}{\Phi} = \frac{u_2}{u_1}\tan\alpha_2 - \tan\alpha_1 \tag{9-22}$$

Equation (9-22) is plotted in Fig. 9-19 for the case of constant axial veloctiy ($u_1 = u_2$). This figure can be used to determine the ratio of the stage loading coefficient to the flow coefficient from stage flow angles. This figure also gives the combinations of flow angles that will give a desired value of ψ/Φ.

The flow coefficient can be expressed in terms of the flow angles (α_1 and β_1). From the velocity triangles, we have

$$U = u_1 \tan\alpha_1 + u_1 \tan\beta_1$$

Solving for the ratio u_1/U, we get

$$\Phi = \frac{1}{\tan\alpha_1 + \tan\beta_1} \tag{9-23}$$

This equation is plotted in Fig. 9-20. Given the flow angles (α_1 and β_1), one

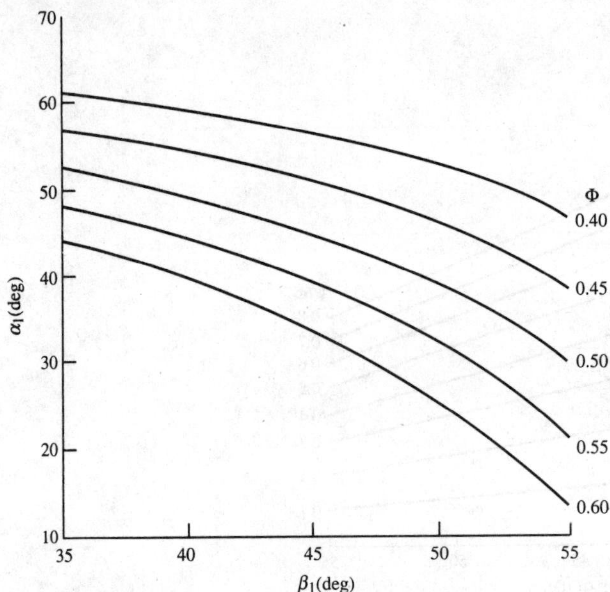

FIGURE 9-20
Flow coefficient Φ versus flow angles α_1 and β_1.

can use Eq. (9-23) or Fig. 9-20 to determine the flow coefficient. On the other hand, Fig. 9-20 can be used to find the combination of the flow angles (α_1 and β_1) that gives a desired flow coefficient.

STAGE PRESSURE RATIO. Equation (9-10) can be rewritten as

$$\frac{P_{t3}}{P_{t1}} = \left(1 + \eta_s \frac{\Delta T_t}{T_{t1}}\right)^{\gamma/(\gamma-1)} \tag{9-24}$$

Likewise, Eq. (9-11) can be rewritten as

$$\frac{P_{t3}}{P_{t1}} = \left(\frac{T_{t2}}{T_{t1}}\right)^{\gamma e_c/(\gamma-1)} = \left(1 + \frac{\Delta T_t}{T_{t1}}\right)^{\gamma e_c/(\gamma-1)} \tag{9-25}$$

The stage pressure ratio can be calculated given the stage total temperature rise and the stage efficiency or polytropic efficiency from Eq. (9-24) or (9-25), respectively. We can see from these equations and Eq. (9-20) that a high stage pressure ratio requires high work loading (change in T_t).

When the stage efficiency and polytropic efficiency are unknown, the stage pressure ratio can be determined by using loss coefficients based on cascade data and other losses. The total pressure for a compressor stage can be written in terms of loss coefficients of the rotor ϕ_{cr} and stator ϕ_{cs}. Noting that the total pressure loss of the rotor is based on the relative velocity, we write

$$\boxed{\phi_{cr} \equiv \frac{P_{t1R} - P_{t2R}}{\rho_1 V_{1R}^2/(2g_c)}} \tag{9-26}$$

Then
$$\frac{T_{t2R}}{P_{t1R}} = 1 - \phi_{cr}\frac{\rho_1 V_{1R}^2}{2g_c P_{t1R}} = 1 - \phi_{cr}\frac{\gamma P_1 M_{1R}^2}{2P_{t1R}}$$

or
$$\boxed{\frac{P_{t2R}}{P_{t1R}} = 1 - \phi_{cr}\frac{\gamma M_{1R}^2/2}{\{1 + [(\gamma - 1)/2]M_{1R}^2\}^{\gamma/(\gamma-1)}}} \tag{9-27}$$

Likewise,
$$\boxed{\phi_{cs} \equiv \frac{P_{t2} - P_{t3}}{\rho_2 V_2^2/(2g_c)}} \tag{9-28}$$

then
$$\boxed{\frac{P_{t3}}{P_{t2}} = 1 - \phi_{cs}\frac{\gamma M_2^2/2}{\{1 + [(\gamma - 1)/2]M_2^2\}^{\gamma/(\gamma-1)}}} \tag{9-29}$$

The total pressure ratio of a stage can be written in the following form:

$$\frac{P_{t3}}{P_{t1}} = \left(\frac{P_{t3}}{P_{t2}}\right)_{\phi_{cs}, M_2} \left(\frac{P_{t2}}{P_2}\right)_{M_2} \left(\frac{P_2}{P_{t2R}}\right)_{M_{2R}} \left(\frac{P_{t2R}}{P_{t1R}}\right)_{\phi_{cr}, M_{1R}} \left(\frac{P_{t1R}}{P_1}\right)_{M_{1R}} \left(\frac{P_1}{P_{t1}}\right)_{M_1} \tag{9-30}$$

where the subscripts for the ratio inside the parentheses indicate the variables of the ratio. The loss coefficient of the rotor ϕ_{cr} required in Eq. (9-27) is obtained from cascade data with allowance for other losses (tip leakage, side wall boundary layer, etc.) and can range in value from 0.05 to 0.12. Likewise, the stator's loss coefficient ϕ_{cs} required in Eq. (9-28) is also obtained from cascade data with allowance for other losses and can range in value from 0.03 to 0.06.

Figure 9-21 is a T-s diagram of a compressor stage with losses. It shows the losses in total pressure in the rotor and the stator. Comparison with the

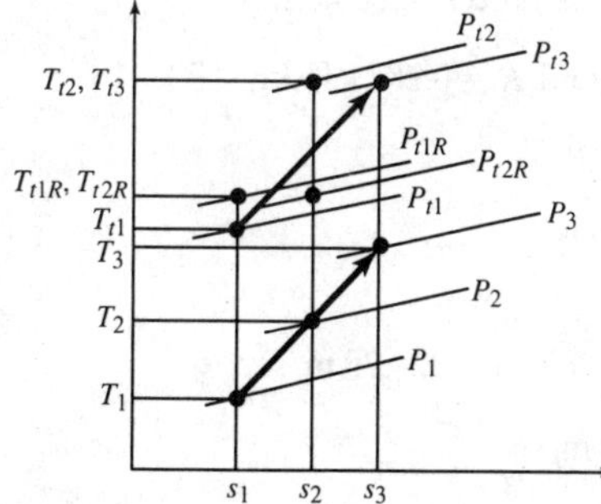

FIGURE 9-21
The T-s diagram of a typical compressor stage with losses.

T-s diagram for an ideal compressor stage (Fig. 9-13) can help you see the effects of losses on the process through a compressor stage.

BLADE MACH NUMBER M_b. Equation (9-7) can be written in terms of the flow angles (α_1 and β_2) and rearranged to give

$$\frac{\Delta T_t}{T_{t1}} = \frac{(\omega r)^2}{g_c c_p T_{t1}}\left[1 - \frac{u_2}{\omega r}\left(\tan\beta_2 + \frac{u_1}{u_2}\tan\alpha_1\right)\right]$$

or

$$\frac{\Delta T_t}{T_{t1}} = \frac{(\omega r)^2}{g_c c_p T_1}\frac{T_1}{T_{t1}}\left[1 - \frac{u_2}{\omega r}\left(\tan\beta_2 + \frac{u_1}{u_2}\tan\alpha_1\right)\right]$$

Note that

$$\frac{(\omega r)^2}{g_c c_p T_1} = \frac{\gamma R}{c_p}\frac{(\omega r)^2}{\gamma R g_c T_1} = (\gamma - 1)\frac{(\omega r)^2}{a_1^2} = (\gamma - 1)M_b^2$$

where M_b is the blade tangential Mach number based on the upstream speed of sound a_1,

$$\frac{T_1}{T_{t1}} = \frac{1}{1 + [(\gamma - 1)/2]M_1^2} \quad \text{and} \quad \frac{u_2}{\omega r} = (\cos\beta_2)\frac{M_1}{M_b}\frac{u_2}{u_1}$$

Then

$$\boxed{\frac{\Delta T_t}{T_{t1}} = \frac{(\gamma - 1)M_b^2}{1 + [(\gamma - 1)/2]M_1^2}\left[1 - (\cos\beta_2)\frac{M_1}{M_b}\left(\frac{u_2}{u_1}\tan\beta_2 + \tan\alpha_1\right)\right]} \tag{9-31}$$

If we consider that the flow angles and the velocity ratio u_2/u_1 are functions of the geometry, then the stage temperature rise is mainly a function of M_b and the ratio M_1/M_b. From Eq. (9-31), we can see that high M_b is desirable to give higher stage temperature rise. The blade Mach number for Example 9-1 is about 0.94.

Example 9-2. *Mean radius stage calculation—flow with losses.*

GIVEN: $T_{t1} = 288.16$ K, $P_{t1} = 101.3$ kPa, $\omega = 1000$ rad/sec, $r = 0.3048$ m, $\alpha_1 = \alpha_3 = 40°$, $\sigma = 1$, $\dot{m} = 22.68$ kg/sec, $M_1 = M_3 = 0.7$, $u_2/u_1 = 1.1$, $\Delta T_t = 22.43$ K, $\phi_{cr} = 0.09$, and $\phi_{cs} = 0.03$. Gas is air. The input data are the same as in Example 9-1 with the same ΔT_t specified.

Note: For air, $\gamma = 1.4$, $c_p = 1.004$ kJ/(kg · K), and $R = 0.287$ kJ/(kg · °R).

Solution.

$$T_1 = \frac{T_{t1}}{1 + [(\gamma - 1)/2]M_1^2} = \frac{288.16\text{ K}}{1 + 0.2 \times 0.7^2} = 262.44\text{ K}$$

$$a_1 = \sqrt{\gamma R g_c T_1} = \sqrt{1.4 \times 287 \times 1 \times 262.44} = 324.73\text{ m/sec}$$

$$V_1 = M_1 a_1 = 0.7 \times 324.73 = 227.31\text{ m/sec}$$

$$u_1 = V_1 \cos \alpha_1 = 227.31 \times 0.7660 = 174.13 \text{ m/sec}$$

$$v_1 = V_1 \sin \alpha_1 = 227.31 \times 0.6428 = 146.11 \text{ m/sec}$$

$$P_1 = \frac{P_{t1}}{\{1 + [(\gamma - 1)/2]M_1^2\}^{\gamma/(\gamma-1)}} = \frac{101.3 \text{ kPa}}{(1 + 0.2 \times 0.7^2)^{3.5}} = 73.03 \text{ kPa}$$

$$\text{MFP}(M_1) = \frac{\text{MFP}(M_1)\sqrt{R/g_c}}{\sqrt{R/g_c}} = \frac{0.625684}{16.9115} = 0.03700$$

$$A_1 = \frac{\dot{m}\sqrt{T_{t1}}}{P_{t1}(\cos \alpha_1)\text{MFP}(M_1)} = \frac{22.68\sqrt{288.16}}{101{,}300 \times 0.7660 \times 0.0370} = 0.134 \text{ m}^2$$

$$\omega r = 1000 \times 0.3048 = 304.8 \text{ m/sec}$$

$$v_{1R} = \omega r - v_1 = 304.80 - 146.11 = 158.69 \text{ m/sec}$$

$$\beta_1 = \tan^{-1}\frac{v_{1R}}{u_1} = \tan^{-1} 0.9113 = 42.34°$$

$$V_{1R} = \sqrt{u_1^2 + v_{1R}^2} = \sqrt{174.13^2 + 158.69^2} = 235.59 \text{ m/sec}$$

$$M_{1R} = \frac{V_{1R}}{a_1} = \frac{235.59}{324.73} = 0.7255$$

$$T_{t1R} = T_1\left(1 + \frac{\gamma - 1}{2} M_{1R}^2\right) = 262.44(1 + 0.2 \times 0.7255^2) = 290.07 \text{ K}$$

$$P_{t1R} = P_1\left(\frac{T_{t1R}}{T_1}\right)^{\gamma/(\gamma-1)} = 73.03\left(\frac{290.07}{262.44}\right)^{3.5} = 103.67 \text{ kPa}$$

$$P_{t2R} = P_{t1R}\left(\frac{P_{t2R}}{P_{t1R}}\right)_{\phi_{cr}, M_{1R}}$$

$$= P_{t1R}\left(1 - \phi_{cr}\frac{\gamma M_{1R}^2/2}{\{1 + [(\gamma - 1)/2]M_{1R}^2\}^{\gamma/(\gamma-1)}}\right)$$

$$P_{t2R} = 103.67\left[1 - \frac{0.09 \times 0.7 \times 0.7255^2}{(1 + 0.2 \times 0.7255^2)^{3.5}}\right]$$

$$= 103.67 \times 0.9766 = 101.24 \text{ kPa}$$

$$T_{t2R} = T_{t1R} = 290.07 \text{ K}$$

$$T_{t2} = T_{t1} + \Delta T_t = 288.16 + 22.43 = 310.59 \text{ K}$$

$$\tan \beta_2 = \frac{u_1}{u_2}\left[\tan \beta_1 - \frac{g_c c_p}{\omega r u_1}(T_{t2} - T_{t1})\right]$$

$$\tan \beta_2 = \frac{1}{1.1}\left[\tan 42.34 - \frac{1004}{304.8 \times 174.13}(310.59 - 288.16)\right]$$

$$= 0.4426$$

$$\beta_2 = 23.87^\circ$$

$$u_2 = \frac{u_2}{u_1} u_1 = 1.1 \times 174.13 = 191.54 \text{ m/sec}$$

$$v_{2R} = u_2 \tan \beta_2 = 191.54 \times 0.4426 = 84.78 \text{ m/sec}$$

$$V_{2R} = \sqrt{u_2^2 + v_{2R}^2} = \sqrt{191.54^2 + 84.78^2} = 209.46 \text{ m/sec}$$

$$v_2 = \omega r - v_{2R} = 304.80 - 84.78 = 220.02 \text{ m/sec}$$

$$\alpha_2 = \tan^{-1}\frac{v_2}{u_2} = \tan^{-1}\frac{220.02}{191.54} = 48.96^\circ$$

$$V_2 = \sqrt{u_2^2 + v_2^2} = \sqrt{191.54^2 + 220.02^2} = 291.71 \text{ m/sec}$$

$$T_2 = T_{t2} - \frac{V_2^2}{2g_c c_p} = 310.59 - \frac{291.71^2}{2 \times 1 \times 1004} = 268.21 \text{ K}$$

$$P_2 = P_{t2R}\left(\frac{T_2}{T_{t2R}}\right)^{\gamma/(\gamma-1)} = 101.24\left(\frac{268.21}{290.07}\right)^{3.5} = 76.96 \text{ kPa}$$

$$a_2 = \sqrt{\gamma R g_c T_2} = \sqrt{1.4 \times 287 \times 268.21} = 328.28 \text{ m/sec}$$

$$M_2 = \frac{V_2}{a_2} = \frac{291.71}{328.28} = 0.8886$$

$$M_{2R} = \frac{V_{2R}}{a_2} = \frac{209.46}{328.28} = 0.6381$$

$$P_{t2} = P_2\left(\frac{T_{t2}}{T_2}\right)^{\gamma/(\gamma-1)} = 76.96\left(\frac{310.59}{268.21}\right)^{3.5} = 128.61 \text{ kPa}$$

$$\text{MFP}(M_2) = \frac{\text{MFP}(M_2)\sqrt{R/g_c}}{\sqrt{R/g_c}} = \frac{0.677216}{16.9115} = 0.04004$$

$$A_2 = \frac{\dot{m}\sqrt{T_{t2}}}{P_{t2}(\cos\alpha_2)\text{MFP}(M_2)} = \frac{22.68\sqrt{310.59}}{128{,}610 \times 0.65659 \times 0.04004}$$

$$= 0.118 \text{ m}^2$$

$$T_{t3} = T_{t2} = T_{t1} + \Delta T_t = 310.59 \text{ K}$$

$$T_3 = \frac{T_{t3}}{1 + [(\gamma-1)/1]M_3^2} = \frac{310.59 \text{ K}}{1 + 0.2 \times 0.7^2} = 282.87 \text{ K}$$

$$P_{t3} = P_{t2}\left(\frac{P_{t3}}{P_{t2}}\right)_{\phi_{cs}, M_2}$$

$$= P_{t2}\left(1 - \phi_{cs}\frac{\gamma M_2^2/2}{\{1 + [(\gamma-1)/2]M_2^2\}^{\gamma/(\gamma-1)}}\right)$$

$$= 128.61\left[1 - \frac{0.03 \times 0.7 \times 0.8887^2}{(1 + 0.2 \times 0.8887^2)^{3.5}}\right]$$

$$= 128.61 \times 0.09900 = 127.32 \text{ kPa}$$

$$P_3 = P_{t3}\left(\frac{T_3}{T_{t3}}\right)^{\gamma/(\gamma-1)} = 127.32\left(\frac{282.87}{310.59}\right)^{3.5} = 91.79 \text{ kPa}$$

$$a_3 = \sqrt{\gamma R g_c T_3} = \sqrt{1.4 \times 287 \times 282.87} = 337.13 \text{ m/sec}$$

$$V_3 = M_3 a_3 = 0.7 \times 337.13 = 235.99 \text{ m/sec}$$

$$u_3 = V_3 \cos \alpha_3 = 180.78 \text{ m/sec}$$

$$v_3 = V_3 \sin \alpha_3 = 151.69 \text{ m/sec}$$

$$A_3 = \frac{\dot{m}\sqrt{T_{t3}}}{P_{t3}(\cos \alpha_3)\text{MFP}(M_3)} = \frac{22.68\sqrt{310.59}}{127{,}320 \times 0.7660 \times 0.0370} = 0.111 \text{ m}^2$$

$$°R_c = \frac{T_2 - T_1}{T_3 - T_1} = \frac{268.21 - 262.44}{282.87 - 262.44} = 0.2824$$

$$D_r = 1 - \frac{V_{2R}}{V_{1R}} + \frac{|v_{1R} - v_{2R}|}{2\sigma V_{1R}} = 1 - \frac{209.46}{235.59} + \frac{|158.69 - 84.78|}{2 \times 1 \times 235.59} = 0.2678$$

$$D_s = 1 - \frac{V_3}{V_2} + \frac{|v_2 - v_3|}{2\sigma V_2} = 1 - \frac{235.99}{291.71} + \frac{|220.02 - 151.69|}{2 \times 1 \times 291.71} = 0.3081$$

$$\eta_s = \frac{(P_{t3}/P_{t1})^{(\gamma-1)/\gamma} - 1}{T_{t3}/T_{t1} - 1} = \frac{(127.32/101.30)^{1/3.5} - 1}{310.59/288.16 - 1} = 0.8672$$

$$e_c = \frac{\gamma - 1}{\gamma}\frac{\ln(P_{t3}/P_{t1})}{\ln(T_{t3}/T_{t1})} = \frac{1}{3.5}\frac{\ln(127.32/101.30)}{\ln(310.59/288.16)} = 0.8714$$

$$\psi = \frac{g_c c_p \, \Delta T_t}{(\omega r)^2} = \frac{1 \times 1004 \times 22.43}{304.8^2} = 0.2424$$

$$\Phi = \frac{u_1}{\omega r} = \frac{174.13}{304.8} = 0.5713$$

The results of this example stage calculation with losses are summarized in Table 9-3, with the given data listed in boldface type (results in English units are shown within parentheses). One sees, by comparison with the isentropic flow results of Example 9-1 (see Table 9-2), that all the properties are the same except the total and static pressures at stations $2R$, 2, and 3. One might also want to compare the change in flow properties listed in Table 9-3 with those sketched in Fig. 9-21.

With losses, the resulting stage pressure ratio of Example 9-2 is 1.257. Without losses, the same amount of work per unit mass gives a pressure ratio of 1.300 for Example 9-1. Also note that the flow areas at stations 2 and 3 are larger in Example 9-2 than in Example 9-1 because of the lower total pressures resulting from losses.

Repeating-Stage, Repeating-Row, Mean-Line Design

The analysis and design of an axial-flow compressor is complex with many design choices. To simplify the design, we will consider a stage (Fig. 9-22) whose exit velocity and flow angle equal those at its inlet (repeating stage), made up of "repeating" (i.e., mirror-image) rows of airfoils. The analysis will

TABLE 9-3
Results for Example 9-2 axial-flow compressor stage calculation, flow with losses

Property		Station 1	1R	2R	2	3
T_t	K	**288.2**	290.1	290.1	310.6	**310.6**
	(°R)	(518.7)	(522.1)	(522.1)	(559.1)	(559.1)
T	K	262.4	262.4	268.2	268.2	282.9
	(°R)	(472.4)	(472.4)	(482.8)	(482.8)	(509.2)
P_t	kPa	**101.3**	103.7	101.2	128.6	127.3
	(psia)	(14.69)	(15.04)	(14.68)	(18.65)	(18.46)
P	kPa	73.03	73.03	76.96	76.96	91.79
	(psia)	(10.59)	(10.59)	(11.16)	(11.16)	(13.31)
M		**0.700**	0.7255	0.6381	0.8886	**0.700**
V	m/sec	227.31	235.59	209.46	291.71	235.99
	(ft/sec)	(745.76)	(772.92)	(687.20)	(957.04)	(774.24)
u	m/sec	174.13	174.13	191.54	191.54	180.78
	(ft/sec)	(571.29)	(571.29)	(628.40)	(628.40)	(593.10)
v	m/sec	146.11	158.69	84.78	220.02	151.69
	(ft/sec)	(479.36)	(520.63)	(278.15)	(721.84)	(497.66)
α	deg	**40.00**	—	—	48.96	**40.00**
β	deg	—	42.34	23.87	—	—

be based on the behavior of the flow at the *average radius* (halfway between the hub radius and the tip radius), known henceforth as the *mean radius.* With this introduction in mind, the development of design tools for compressors follows.

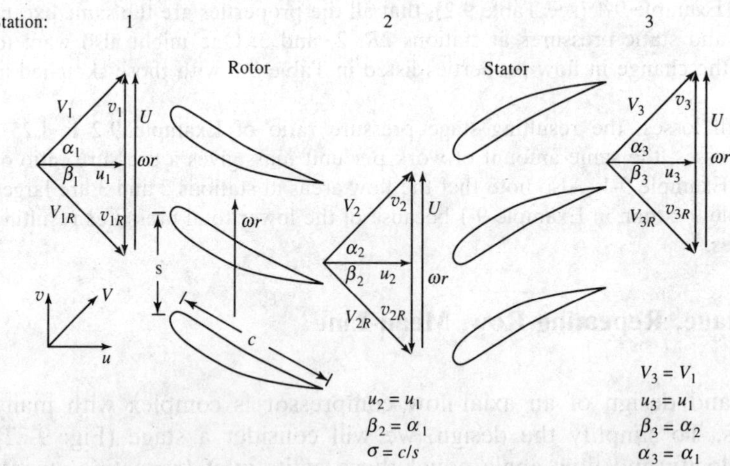

FIGURE 9-22
Repeating-row compressor stage nomenclature.

ASSUMPTIONS. We make the following assumptions for this analysis:

Repeating-row, repeating-airfoil cascade geometry ($\alpha_1 = \beta_2 = \alpha_3$, $\beta_1 = \alpha_2 = \beta_3$, $u_1 = u_2 = u_3$)

Two-dimensional flow (i.e., no variation or component of velocity normal to the page)

Polytropic efficiency e_c representing stage losses

Constant mean radius

ANALYSIS. We assume that the following data are given: D, M_1, γ, σ, e_c. The analysis of the repeating-row, repeating-stage, mean-line design follows.

Conservation of mass. Application of this law for steady one-dimensional flow gives

$$\rho_1 u_1 A_1 = \rho_2 u_2 A_2 = \rho_3 u_3 A_3$$

or

$$\rho_1 A_1 = \rho_2 A_2 = \rho_3 A_3 \tag{9-32}$$

Repeating-row constraint. Since $\beta_2 = \alpha_1$, then

$$v_{2R} = v_1 = \omega r - v_2$$

or

$$v_1 + v_2 = \omega r \tag{9-33}$$

Also, since $\beta_3 = \alpha_2$, then $v_{3R} = v_2$ and $v_3 = v_1$; thus, the stage exit conditions are indeed identical to those at the stage entrance.

Diffusion factor. Since both

$$D = 1 - \frac{V_{2R}}{V_{1R}} + \frac{v_{1R} - v_{2R}}{2\sigma V_{1R}} = 1 - \frac{V_3}{V_2} + \frac{v_2 - v_3}{2\sigma V_2}$$

and

$$D = 1 - \frac{\cos\alpha_2}{\cos\alpha_1} + \frac{\tan\alpha_2 - \tan\alpha_1}{2\sigma}\cos\alpha_2 \tag{9-34}$$

are the same for both the rotor and stator, D is evaluated only once for the stage. Rearranging Eq. (9-34) to solve for α_2, we find that

$$\boxed{\cos\alpha_2 = \frac{2\sigma(1-D)\Gamma + \sqrt{\Gamma^2 + 1 - 4\sigma^2(1-D)^2}}{\Gamma^2 + 1}} \tag{9-35}$$

where

$$\Gamma \equiv \frac{2\sigma + \sin\alpha_1}{\cos\alpha_1} \tag{9-36}$$

In words, Eq. (9-35) shows that there is *only* one value of α_2 that corresponds to the chosen values of D and σ for each α_1. Thus the entire flow field geometry is indicated by those choices.

Stage total temperature ratio. From the Euler equation, we have for constant radius

$$c_p(T_{t3} - T_{t1}) = \frac{\omega r}{g_c}(v_2 - v_1)$$

From Eq. (9-33)

$$\omega r = v_1 + v_2$$

then
$$c_p(T_{t3} - T_{t1}) = \frac{1}{g_c}(v_2 + v_1)(v_2 - v_1)$$

$$= \frac{v_2^2 - v_1^2}{g_c} = \frac{V_2^2 - V_1^2}{g_c}$$

Thus
$$\frac{T_{t3}}{T_{t1}} - 1 = \frac{V_2^2 - V_1^2}{c_p g_c T_{t1}}$$

or
$$\tau_s \equiv \frac{T_{t3}}{T_{t1}} = \frac{(\gamma - 1)M_1^2}{1 + [(\gamma - 1)/2]M_1^2}\left(\frac{\cos^2 \alpha_1}{\cos^2 \alpha_2} - 1\right) + 1 \tag{9-37}$$

Stage pressure ratio. From Eq. (9-11), we can write

$$\pi_s \equiv \frac{P_{t3}}{P_{t1}} = \left(\frac{T_{t3}}{T_{t1}}\right)^{\gamma e_c/(\gamma - 1)}$$

or
$$\pi_s = (\tau_s)^{\gamma e_c/(\gamma - 1)} \tag{9-38}$$

Degree of reaction. A special characteristic of repeating-stage, repeating-row compressor stages is that the degree of reaction must be exactly 0.5, as shown below:

$$°R_c = \frac{T_2 - T_1}{T_3 - T_1} = 1 - \frac{T_3 - T_2}{T_3 - T_1} = 1 - \frac{(V_2^2 - V_3^2)/(2g_c c_p)}{T_{t3} - T_{t1}}$$

$$= 1 - \frac{(V_2^2 - V_1^2)/(2g_c c_p)}{(V_2^2 - V_1^2)/(g_c c_p)} = \frac{1}{2}$$

Stage efficiency. From Eq. (9-10), we have

$$\eta_s = \frac{\pi_s^{(\gamma - 1)/\gamma} - 1}{\tau_s - 1} \tag{9-39}$$

Stage exit Mach number. Since

$$V_3 = V_1 \qquad \text{and} \qquad V^2 = M^2 \gamma R g_c T$$

then

$$\frac{M_3}{M_1} = \sqrt{\frac{T_1}{T_3}} = \sqrt{\frac{1}{\tau_s\{1 + [(\gamma - 1)/2]M_1^2\} - [(\gamma - 1)/2]M_1^2}} \leq 1 \tag{9-40}$$

Inlet velocity/wheel speed ratio $V_1/(\omega r)$. One of the most important trigonometric relationships for the stage is that between the total cascade inlet velocity V_1 and the mean wheel speed ωr. Since

$$V_1 = \frac{u_1}{\cos \alpha_1}$$

and

$$\omega r = v_1 + v_2 = u_1(\tan \alpha_1 + \tan \alpha_2)$$

then u_1 can be eliminated to yield

$$\frac{V_1}{\omega r} = \frac{1}{(\cos \alpha_1)(\tan \alpha_1 + \tan \alpha_2)} \tag{9-41}$$

Stage loading and flow coefficients. The stage loading coefficient ψ for the repeating-stage, repeating-row, mean-line design can be expressed in terms of the flow angles α_1 and α_2 as

$$\psi = \frac{g_c c_p \, \Delta T_t}{(\omega r)^2} = \frac{\tan \alpha_2 - \tan \alpha_1}{\tan \alpha_1 + \tan \alpha_2} \tag{9-42a}$$

Likewise, the flow coefficient can be expressed in terms of the flow angles α_1 and α_2 as

$$\Phi = \frac{u_1}{\omega r} = \frac{1}{\tan \alpha_1 + \tan \alpha_2} \tag{9-42b}$$

GENERAL SOLUTION. The behavior of all possible repeating-row compressor stages with given values of D, M_1, γ, σ, and e_c can now be computed. This is done by selecting any α_1 and using the following sequence of equations, expressed as functional relationships:

$$\alpha_2 = f(D, \sigma, \alpha_1) \tag{9-35}$$

$$\Delta\alpha = \alpha_2 - \alpha_1$$

$$\tau_s = f(M_1, \gamma, \alpha_1, \alpha_2) \tag{9-37}$$

$$\pi_s = f(\tau_s, \gamma, e_c) \tag{9-38}$$

$$\eta_s = f(\tau_s, \pi_s, \gamma, e_c) \tag{9-39}$$

$$\frac{V_1}{\omega r} = f(\alpha_1, \alpha_2) \tag{9-41}$$

In most cases, T_{t1} is also known, so that selecting M_1 fixes V_1 and ωr is known.

We can now generate plots of α_2, $\Delta\alpha$, π_s, η_s, and $V_1/(\omega r)$ versus α_1. Note that only π_s depends on M_1 and that the process may be repeated to cover the entire range of reasonable values of α_1.

These calculations have been carried out for $D = 0.6$; $M_1 = 0.45$, 0.5, 0.55, 0.6, 0.65, and 0.7; $\gamma = 1.4$; $e_c = 0.9$; and $10° < \alpha_1 < 70°$. The results are presented on Fig. 9-23. The most notable characteristics of these data are that the most direct way to increase π_s is to increase M_1 and that in order to operate at higher values of α_1, a large wheel speed is required.

The following two simple examples illustrate the use of this method and are based on the parameters of Fig. 9-23:

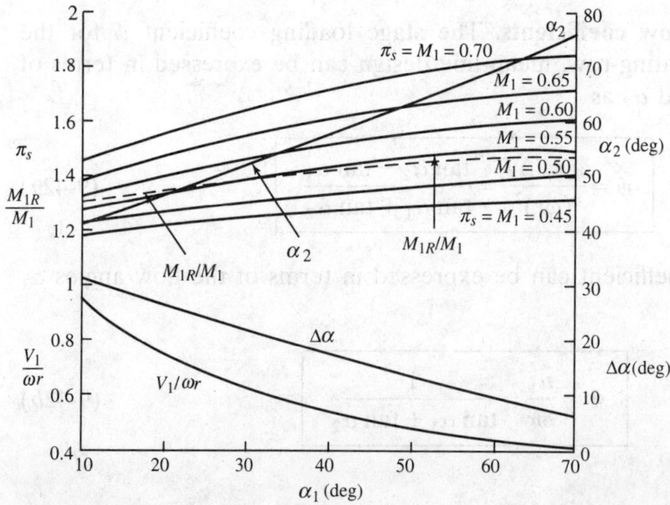

FIGURE 9-23
Repeating compressor stage ($D = 0.5$, $\sigma = 1$, and $e_c = 0.9$).

Example 9-3.

GIVEN: $M_1 = 0.6$, $a_1 = 360$ m/sec, and $\omega r = 300$ m/sec

Then
$$\frac{V_1}{\omega r} = \frac{a_1 M_1}{\omega r} = 0.72$$

$$\alpha_1 = 22^\circ \qquad \Delta\alpha = 25^\circ$$

$$\alpha_2 = 47^\circ \qquad \pi_s = 1.42$$

Example 9-4.

GIVEN: $a_1 = 320$ m/sec and $M_1/\alpha_1 = 0.5/20^\circ$ and $0.6/30^\circ$

Then

M_1	α_1	$\frac{V_1}{\omega r}$	$\frac{\omega r}{a_1}$	π_s
0.5	20°	0.75	0.67	1.28
0.6	30°	0.62	0.97	1.46

Since a_1 is unaffected by the cascade and affected only slightly by M_1, the price of higher π_s is a greatly increased ωr (that is, $0.97/0.67 = 1.45$).

Figures 9-24 and 9-25 show how the performance of repeating compressor stages changes with diffusion factor and solidity, respectively. For a given inlet flow angle α_1 and inlet velocity V_1, we can see from Fig. 9-24 that increasing the diffusion factor D will increase the exit flow angle α_2, stage pressure ratio π_s, and wheel speed ωr. Likewise, for a given inlet flow angle α_1 and inlet velocity V_1, Fig. 9-25 shows that increasing the solidity σ will increase the exit flow angle α_2, stage pressure ratio π_s, and wheel speed ωr.

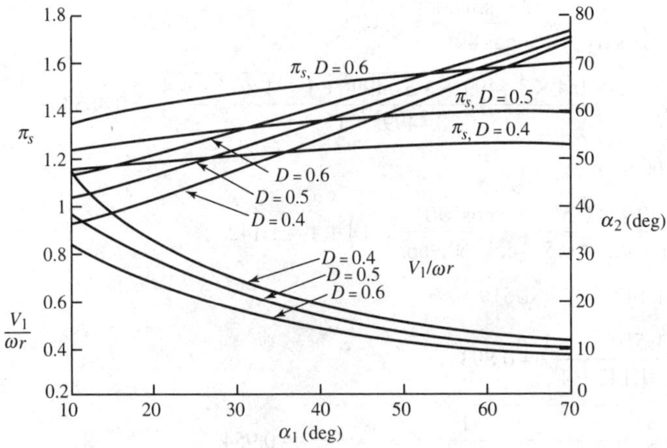

FIGURE 9-24
Repeating compressor stage—variation with D ($M_1 = 0.5$, $\sigma = 1$, and $e_c = 0.9$).

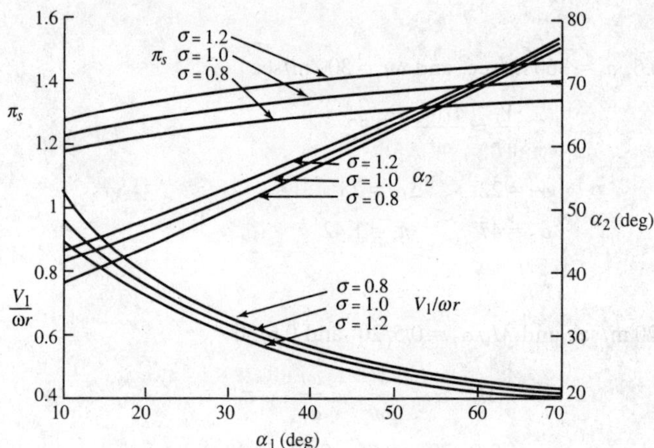

FIGURE 9-25
Repeating compressor stage—variation with σ ($M_1 = 0.5$, $D = 0.5$, and $e_c = 0.9$).

For a multistage compressor composed of numerous stages designed by using the repeating-stage, repeating-row, mean-line design, the total temperature change across each of these stages will be the same. Also the mean-line radius for each of these stages is the same. Since the ratio of M_3/M_1 is less than 1, the pressure ratio of any downstream repeating stages will be lower.

Example 9-5.

GIVEN: $\alpha_1 = 40°$, $D = 0.6$, $\sigma = 1$, $\gamma = 1.4$, $M_1 = 0.5$, $e_c = 0.9$

Solution.

$$\Gamma = \frac{2\sigma + \sin\alpha_1}{\cos\alpha_1} = \frac{2 + \sin 40°}{\cos 40°} = 3.4499$$

$$\cos\alpha_2 = \frac{2 \times 0.4 \times 3.4499 + \sqrt{3.4499^2 + 1 - 4 \times 1^2 \times 0.4^2}}{3.4499^2 + 1} = 0.4853$$

$$\alpha_2 = 60.966°$$

$$\tau_s = \frac{0.4 \times 0.5^2}{1 + 0.2 \times 0.5^2}\left(\frac{\cos^2 40°}{\cos^2 60.966°} - 1\right) + 1 = 1.142$$

$$\pi_s = 1.142^{3.5 \times 0.9} = 1.519$$

$$\eta_s = \frac{1.519^{1/3.5} - 1}{1.142 - 1} = 0.893$$

$$\frac{M_3}{M_1} = \sqrt{\frac{1}{1.142(1 + 0.2 \times 0.5^2) - 0.4 \times 0.5^2}} = 0.954$$

$$\frac{M_{1R}}{M_1} = \frac{\cos 40°}{\cos 60.966°} = 1.578$$

$$M_{1R} = 0.789$$

$$\frac{V_1}{\omega r} = \frac{1}{(\cos 40°)(\tan 40° + \tan 60.966°)} = 0.494$$

$$\psi = \frac{\tan 60.966° - \tan 40°}{\tan 40° + \tan 60.966°} = 0.364$$

$$\Phi = \frac{1}{\tan 40° + \tan 60.966°} = 0.379$$

The flow angles and Mach numbers of a repeating-stage, repeating-row, mean-line design are defined by the above calculations. The velocities and temperatures throughout this stage can now be determined by knowing either a velocity or a temperature at any station in the stage. For example, if T_{t1} = 288.16 K, then simple calculations give

$$a_1 = 332 \text{ m/sec} \quad V_1 = V_{2R} = V_3 = 166 \text{ m/sec} \quad \omega r = 336 \text{ m/sec}$$
$$V_{1R} = V_2 = 261.9 \text{ m/sec} \quad \text{and} \quad \Delta T_t = 40.9 \text{ K}$$

Flow Path Dimensions

ANNULUS AREA. The preliminary design of multistage axial-flow compressors is typically based on determining each stage's flow properties along the compressor mean line (line along compressor axis that corresponds to the mean radius). The annulus area at any station is based on the flow properties (T_t, P_t, Mach number, and flow angle) at the mean radius and the total mass flow rate. Equation (9-8) is the easiest equation to calculate the flow area at any station i:

$$\boxed{A_i = \frac{\dot{m}\sqrt{T_{ti}}}{P_{ti}(\cos \alpha_i)\text{MFP}(M_i)}} \tag{9-8}$$

The *mean radius* of a flow annulus is defined as the average of the tip radius and hub radius. Consider Fig. 9-26, which shows a typical annulus area.

In many calculations, the flow area can be calculated and the mean radius is tied to the required rotor speed at the mean radius ωr_m. The designer can select ω and calculate the required mean radius. Then the root radius and tip radius are calculated directly from the mean radius and flow area. In some calculations, the designer may want to select the ratio of the hub radius to the

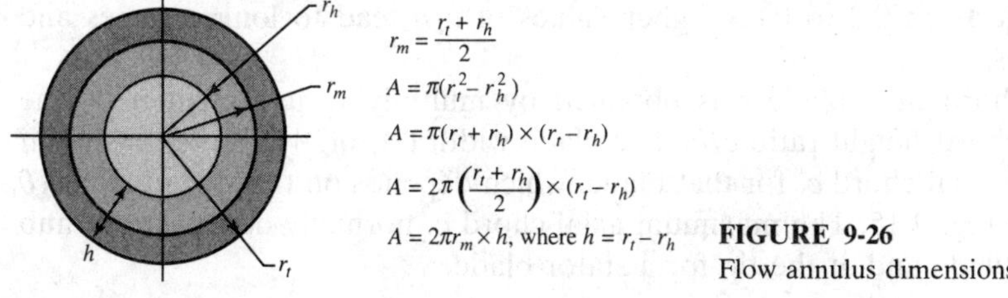

r_h
r_m
r_t
h
$r_m = \frac{r_t + r_h}{2}$
$A = \pi(r_t^2 - r_h^2)$
$A = \pi(r_t + r_h) \times (r_t - r_h)$
$A = 2\pi\left(\frac{r_t + r_h}{2}\right) \times (r_t - r_h)$
$A = 2\pi r_m \times h$, where $h = r_t - r_h$

FIGURE 9-26
Flow annulus dimensions.

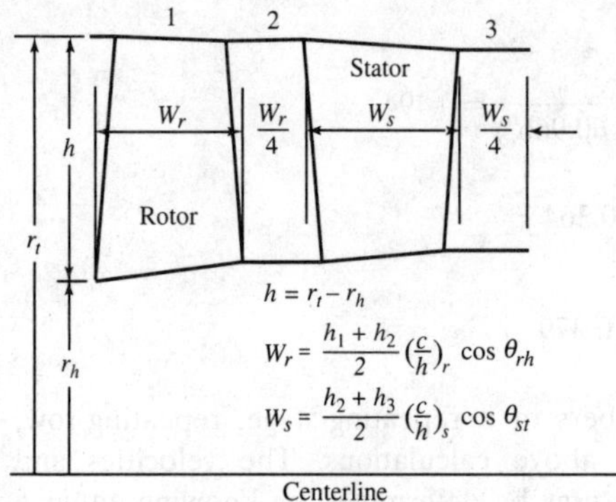

FIGURE 9-27
Typical axial dimensions of a compressor stage.

tip radius r_h/r_t. The hub/tip ratio at the inlet to a multistage compressor normally is between 0.6 and 0.75, whereas that at the compressor exit is in the range of 0.9 to 0.92. Then the tip, hub, and mean radii directly follow from the geometry:

$$A = (r_t^2 - r_h^2) = \pi r_t^2\left[1 - \left(\frac{r_h}{r_t}\right)^2\right]$$

$$r_t = \sqrt{\frac{A}{\pi[1-(r_h/r_t)^2]}} \qquad r_h = r_t\left(\frac{r_h}{r_t}\right) \qquad r_m = \frac{r_t + r_h}{2}$$

The variation of the flow area and the associated dimensions of the flow path from one station to the next can be calculated easily by using the above relationships and the results sketched. Figure 9-27 is a sketch of typical results. The calculation of the axial dimensions requires additional data.

AXIAL DIMENSIONS. The axial dimensions of a typical stage are also shown in Fig. 9-27, and these can be used to estimate the axial length of a stage. Blade axial widths (W_r and W_s) of a stage are calculated in the program COMPR along with the blade spacings ($W_r/4$ and $W_s/4$) based on user-input chord-to-height ratios c/h for the rotor and stator blades and assuming a constant chord length for each blade. A minimum width of $\frac{1}{4}$ in (0.006 m) and a minimum spacing of $\frac{1}{8}$ in (0.003 m) are used in the plot of compressor cross section and calculation of axial length.

The value of the chord/height ratio c/h selected for a blade depends on such factors as the stage loading coefficient, diffusion factor, etc. Typical values of c/h range from 0.2 to 0.8. Higher values of c/h lead to longer stages and fewer blades.

The chord of a blade c is obtained by multiplying its height h by the user-input chord/height ratio c/h. The blade width (W_r or W_s) is the maximum value of the axial chord c_x for that blade, which depends on the stagger angle θ as shown in Fig. 9-15. The maximum axial chord c_x normally occurs at the hub for a rotor blade and at the tip for a stator blade.

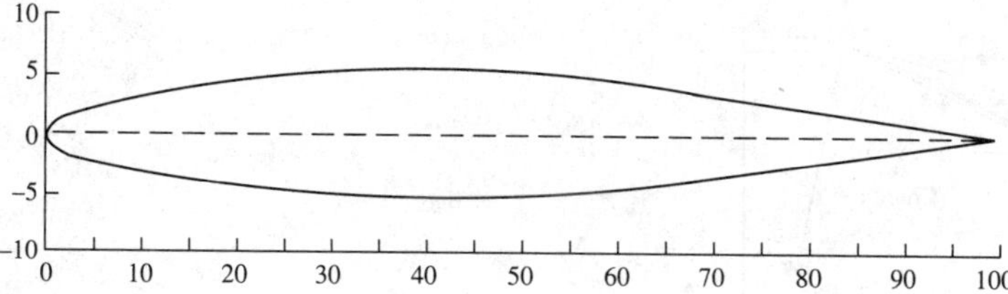

FIGURE 9-28
NACA 65A010 blade shape.

NUMBER OF BLADES. The COMPR program calculates the number of blades n_b for the rotor and stator of a stage based on the user-input values of the solidity σ along the mean line. For a rotor or stator, the blade spacing s along the mean line is equal to the blade chord c divided by its solidity ($\sigma = c/s$). The number of blades is simply the circumference of the mean line divided by the blade spacing, rounded up to the next integer.

BLADE PROFILE. The shapes of compressor rotor and stator blades are based on airfoil shapes developed specifically for compressor applications. One such airfoil shape is the symmetric NACA 65A010 compressor airfoil whose profile shape is shown in Fig. 9-28 and specified in Table 9-4. This airfoil has a thickness that is 10 percent of its chord c.

To obtain the desired change in fluid flow direction, the airfoil's chamber line is curved and the symmetric shape of the airfoil profile is distributed

TABLE 9-4
NACA 65A010 compressor airfoil

x/c (%)	y/c (%)	x/c (%)	y/c (%)
0.0	0.0	40	4.995
0.5	0.765	45	4.983
0.75	0.928	50	4.863
1.25	1.183	55	4.632
2.5	1.623	60	4.304
5	2.182	65	3.809
7.5	2.65	70	3.432
10	3.04	75	2.912
15	3.658	80	2.352
20	4.127	85	1.771
25	4.483	90	1.188
30	4.742	95	0.604
35	4.912	100	0.0

Leading-edge radius = $0.00636c$.
Trailing-edge radius = $0.00023c$.
Source: Ref. 85.

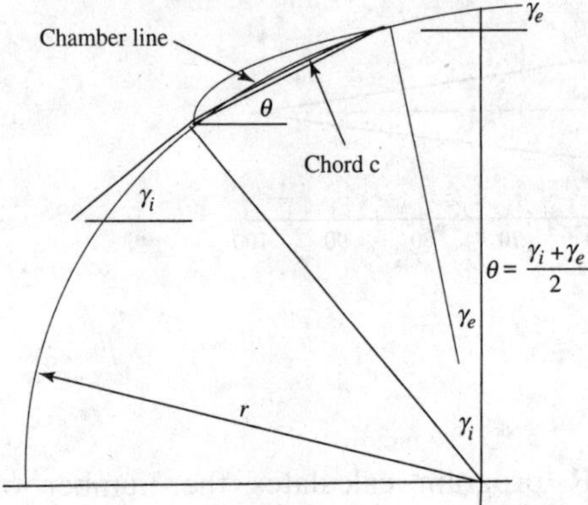

FIGURE 9-29
Circular arc chamber line.

about the chamber line. The curved chamber line of the airfoil and nomenclature used for flow through a compressor cascade are shown in Fig. 9-15. Normally, the curved chamber line is that of a circular arc or a parabola. If a circular arc is used, then the stagger angle of the airfoil θ is the average of the chamber line's inlet angle γ_i and exit angle γ_e. From Fig. 9-29 and basic trigonometry, the radius of the chamber line is given by

$$\boxed{r = \frac{c \sin \theta}{\cos \gamma_e - \cos \gamma_i}} \tag{9-43}$$

The COMPR computer program uses the NACA 65A010 compressor profile with circular arc chamber line to sketch the blade shapes for a stage. The user can change the blade thickness for the rotor or stator blades, select the desired stage, specify the number of blades to be sketched, and specify the percentage of chord for stacking blade profiles. The user can view one or more blades in the rotor and stator at a time.

If the user selects to view just one blade, the program initially sketches the blade shape at the mean radius as a solid, and the shapes at the hub and tip are drawn in dashed outline stacked over the other profile at the user-selected stacking location. Figure 9-30 is a copy of the blade profile plot screen for one blade. The user can move the slider for percentage of blade height by using the up and down arrows and replot the blade shape at a new height (radial location).

If the user selects to view more than one blade, the program initially sketches the blade shapes at the mean radius. Figure 9-31 is a copy of the blade profile plot screen for three blades. The user can move the slider for percentage of blade height by using the up and down arrows and replot the blade shape at a new height (radial location).

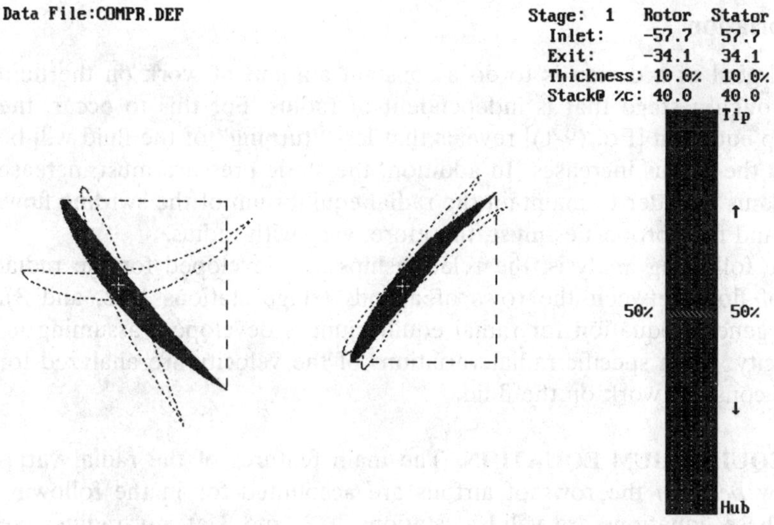

FIGURE 9-30
Single-blade profile sketch from COMPR.

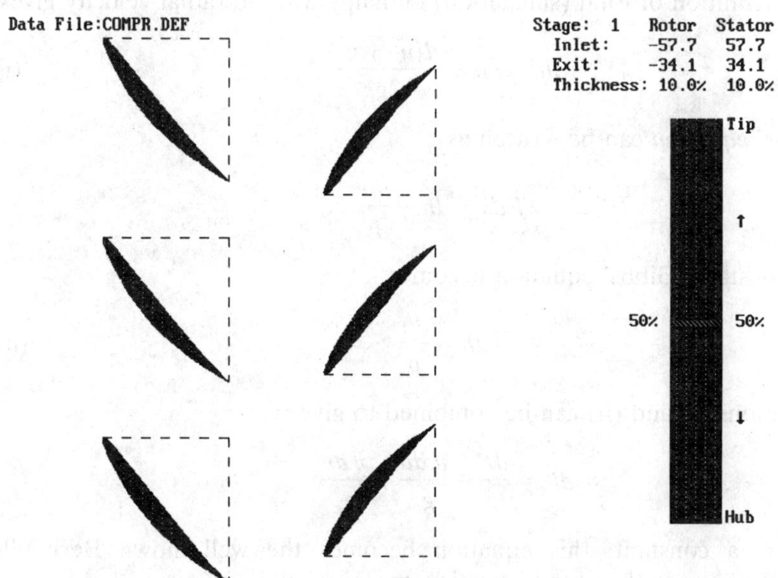

FIGURE 9-31
Three-blade profile sketch from COMPR.

Radial Variation

A practical goal of a design is to do a constant amount of work on the fluid passing through a stage that is independent of radius. For this to occur, the Euler pump equation [Eq. (9-1)] reveals that less "turning" of the fluid will be required as the radius increases. In addition, the static pressure must increase with the radius in order to maintain the radial equilibrium of the swirling flow. All airfoil and flow properties must, therefore, vary with radius.

In the following analysis, the relationships are developed for the radial variation of flow between the rows of airfoils (stage stations 1, 2, and 3). Initially, a general equation for radial equilibrium is developed, assuming no radial velocity. Then specific radial variations of the velocity are analyzed for the case of constant work on the fluid.

RADIAL EQUILIBRIUM EQUATION. The main features of the radial variation of flow *between* the rows of airfoils are accounted for in the following analysis. These equations are valid at stations 1, 2, and 3 at any radius. We assume

1. Constant losses (s = constant with respect to radius)
2. No circumferential variations
3. No radial velocity

The definition of total (stagnation) enthalpy with no radial velocity gives

$$dh_t = dh + \frac{d(u^2 + v^2)}{2g_c} \tag{i}$$

Gibbs' equation can be written as

$$T\,ds = dh - \frac{dp}{\rho}$$

With s = constant, Gibbs' equation becomes

$$dh = \frac{dh}{\rho} \tag{ii}$$

Equations (i) and (ii) can be combined to give

$$dh_t = \frac{dP}{\rho} + \frac{u\,du}{g_c} + \frac{v\,dv}{g_c}$$

When h_t is a constant, this equation becomes the well-known Bernoulli equation. We rewrite the above equation as

$$\frac{dh_t}{dr} = \frac{1}{\rho}\frac{dP}{dr} + \frac{1}{g_c}\left(u\frac{du}{dr} + v\frac{dv}{dr}\right) \tag{iii}$$

For radial equilibrium, the pressure gradient in the radial direction must balance the centrifugal acceleration, or

$$\frac{dP}{dr} = \frac{\rho v^2}{r g_c} \tag{iv}$$

Equations (iii) and (iv) may be combined to yield

$$\boxed{\frac{dh_t}{dr} = \frac{1}{g_c}\left(u\frac{du}{dr} + v\frac{dv}{dr} + \frac{v^2}{r}\right)} \tag{9-44}$$

This general form of the radial equilibrium equation prescribes the relationship between the radial variations of the three variables: h_t, u, and v. The designer can specify the radial variation of any two variables, and Eq. (9-44) specifies the radial variation of the third variable.

FREE-VORTEX VARIATION OF SWIRL. We consider the case where the axial velocity u and total enthalpy h_t do not vary with radius. For this case, Eq. (9-44) becomes

$$v\frac{dv}{dr} + \frac{v^2}{r} = 0 \qquad \text{or} \qquad \frac{dv}{v} + \frac{dr}{r} = 0$$

for which the integrated solution is

$$rv = \text{const}$$

or

$$\boxed{v = v_m \frac{r_m}{r}} \tag{9-45}$$

where the subscript m refers to values at the mean radius. Because v varies inversely with radius, this is known as *free-vortex* flow. Thus, if the flow at station 1 has $v_1 r = v_{m1} r_m$ and the rotor airfoils modify the flow to $v_2 r = v_{m2} r_m$, then the Euler equation confirms that this is a constant-work machine because

$$\begin{aligned} \omega r(v_2 - v_1) &= \omega r\left(\frac{v_{m2} r_m}{r} - \frac{v_{m1} r_m}{r}\right) \\ &= \omega r_m(v_{m2} - v_{m1}) \\ &= \text{const} \end{aligned}$$

Equation (9-45) also shows that as long as r does not vary substantially from r_m (say, ±10 percent), the airfoil and flow properties will not vary much from those of the original mean-line design.

If the compressor has constant axial velocity and repeating stages (not rows) for which $v_1 = v_3$, then the degree of reaction can be shown to be

$$^\circ R_c = 1 - \frac{v_1 + v_2}{2\omega r} \tag{9-46}$$

which, for a free-vortex machine, becomes

$$°R_c = 1 - \frac{v_{m1}r_m + v_{m2}r_m}{2\omega r^2} = 1 - \frac{\text{const}}{(r/r_m)^2} \tag{9-47}$$

For a stage whose degree of reaction is 50 percent at the mean radius (where $\omega r = v_1 + v_2$), it becomes more difficult to design rotor airfoils at $r > r_m$ and stator airfoils at $r < r_m$. In fact, since $°R_c = 0$ at $r = r_m/\sqrt{2}$, the rotor will actually experience accelerating flow for smaller radii, whereas this is never the case for the stator. Because of these problems, compressor designers have looked at other swirl distributions.

SWIRL DISTRIBUTIONS. We now consider the case where the total enthalpy does not vary with the radius and where the swirl velocity at the inlet and exit to the rotor has the following general variation with radius:

$$\boxed{v_1 = a\left(\frac{r}{r_m}\right)^n - b\frac{r_m}{r} \quad \text{and} \quad v_2 = a\left(\frac{r}{r_m}\right)^n + b\frac{r_m}{r}} \tag{9-48}$$

where a, b, and r_m are constants. From the Euler equation, the work per unit mass flow is

$$\boxed{\Delta h_t = \frac{\omega r(v_2 - v_1)}{g_c} = \frac{2b\omega r_m}{g_c}} \tag{9-49}$$

which is independent of the radius. Note from the above relationship that the constant b in Eq. (9-48) is determined by the total enthalpy rise across the rotor and the mean rotor speed. As will be shown below, constant a in Eq. (9-48) is related to the degree of reaction at the mean radius. Three cases of the swirl distribution of Eq. (9-48) are considered below: $n = -1$, $n = 0$, and $n = 1$.

For $n = -1$:

$$\boxed{v_1 = a\frac{r_m}{r} - b\frac{r_m}{r} \quad \text{and} \quad v_2 = a\frac{r_m}{r} + b\frac{r_m}{r}} \tag{9-50}$$

which is the *free-vortex* swirl distribution. For this case and constant h_t, Eq. (9-44) required that the axial velocity u not vary with the radius. Using Eq. (9-46) for a repeating stage ($v_3 = v_1$), we see that the degree of reaction is

$$\boxed{°R_c = 1 - \frac{a}{\omega r_m}\left(\frac{r_m}{r}\right)^2} \tag{9-51}$$

An equation for the constant a in Eq. (9-48) is obtained by evaluating the above equation at the mean radius. Thus

$$\boxed{a = \omega r_m(1 - {}^\circ R_{cm})} \tag{9-52}$$

For $n = 0$:

$$\boxed{v_1 = a - b\frac{r_m}{r} \qquad \text{and} \qquad v_2 = a + b\frac{r_m}{r}} \tag{9-53}$$

This is called the *exponential* swirl distribution. Before solving for the axial velocity distribution, we rewrite Eq. (9-44) for constant total enthalpy h_t in terms of the dimensionless radius r/r_m as

$$u\,du + v\,du + v^2\frac{d(r/r_m)}{r/r_m} = 0$$

Integration of the above equation from the mean radius to any radius r gives

$$\frac{1}{2}(u^2 - u_m^2) = -\frac{1}{2}(v^2 - v_m^2) - \int_1^{r/r_m} v^2\frac{d(r/r_m)}{r/r_m} \tag{9-54}$$

At the entrance to the rotor (station 1), substitution of the equation for v_1 into Eq. (9-54) and integration give the axial velocity profile

$$u_1^2 = u_{1m}^2 - 2\left(a^2 \ln\frac{r}{r_m} + \frac{ab}{r/r_m} - ab\right) \tag{9-55}$$

Likewise, at the exit from the rotor (station 2), we obtain

$$u_2^2 = u_{2m}^2 - 2\left(a^2 \ln\frac{r}{r_m} - \frac{ab}{r/r_m} + ab\right) \tag{9-56}$$

Since the axial velocity is not constant, we must start with Eq. (9-13*b*) to obtain an expression for the degree of reaction for the velocity distribution given by Eqs. (9-53), (9-55), and (9-56). We start by noting for repeating stages ($V_3 = V_1$) that

$$\begin{aligned}{}^\circ R_c &= \frac{T_2 - T_1}{T_3 - T_1} = \frac{T_{t2} - T_{t1}}{T_{t3} - T_{t1}} - \frac{V_2^2 - V_1^2}{2g_c c_p(T_{t3} - T_{t1})} \\ &= 1 - \frac{V_2^2 - V_1^2}{2g_c c_p(T_{t3} - T_{t1})} = 1 - \frac{u_2^2 - u_1^2}{2g_c c_p(T_{t3} - T_{t1})} - \frac{v_2^2 - v_1^2}{2g_c c_p(T_{t3} - T_{t1})}\end{aligned}$$

From the Euler equation, we write $g_c c_p(T_{t3} - T_{t1}) = \omega r(v_2 - v_1)$, and the above becomes

$${}^\circ R_c = 1 - \frac{u_2^2 - u_1^2}{2\omega r(v_2 - v_1)} - \frac{v_2^2 - v_1^2}{2\omega r(v_2 - v_1)}$$

$$\boxed{{}^\circ R_c = 1 + \frac{u_1^2 - u_2^2}{2\omega r(v_2 - v_1)} - \frac{v_2 + v_1}{2\omega r}} \tag{9-57}$$

For the case where $u_{1m} = u_{2m}$, Eqs. (9-55) and (9-56) give

$$u_1^2 - u_2^2 = 4ab\left(1 - \frac{r_m}{r}\right)$$

and from the swirl distribution of Eq. (9-53), we have

$$v_2 + v_1 = 2a \qquad \text{and} \qquad v_2 - v_1 = 2b\frac{r_m}{r}$$

Thus the degree of reaction for the exponential swirl distribution is given by

$$\boxed{°R_c = 1 + \frac{a}{\omega r_m} - \frac{2a}{\omega r}} \tag{9-58}$$

For $n = 1$:

$$\boxed{v_1 = a\frac{r}{r_m} - b\frac{r_m}{r} \qquad \text{and} \qquad v_2 = a\frac{r}{r_m} + b\frac{r_m}{r}} \tag{9-59}$$

This is called *first-power* swirl distribution. At the entrance to the rotor (station 1), substitution of the equation for v_1 into Eq. (9-54) and integration give the axial velocity profile

$$u_1^2 = u_{1m}^2 - 2\left[a^2\left(\frac{r}{r_m}\right)^2 + 2ab\ln\frac{r}{r_m} - a^2\right] \tag{9-60a}$$

Likewise, at the exit from the rotor (station 2), we obtain

$$u_2^2 = u_{2m}^2 - 2\left[a^2\left(\frac{r}{r_m}\right)^2 - 2ab\ln\frac{r}{r_m} - a^2\right] \tag{9-60b}$$

An equation for the degree of reaction for the case of $u_{1m} = u_{2m}$ is obtained in the same manner as above. The resulting relationship is

$$\boxed{°R_c = 1 + \frac{2a\ln(r/r_m)}{\omega r_m} - \frac{a}{\omega r_m}} \tag{9-61}$$

COMPARISON. Equations (9-51), (9-58), and (9-61) give the radial variation of the degree of reaction for the free-vortex, exponential, and first-power swirl distributions, respectively. The value of the constant a is evaluated at the mean radius and is given by Eq. (9-52) for all three cases. Consider the case where the degree of reaction at the mean radius is 0.5. Results from Eqs. (9-51),

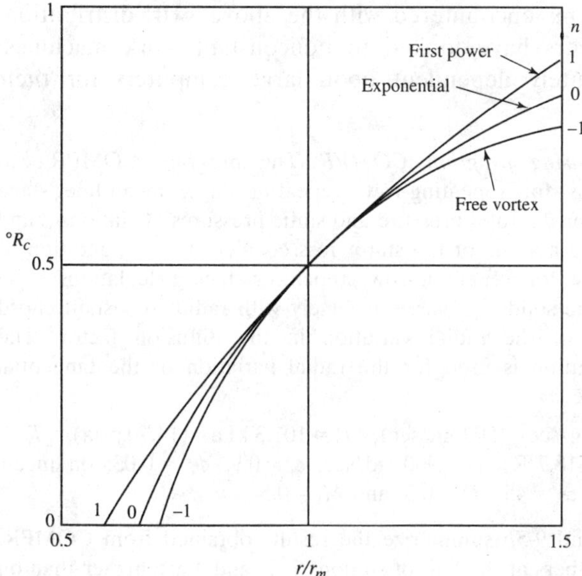

FIGURE 9-32
Radial variation of degree of reaction.

(9-58), and (9-61) are plotted in Fig. 9-32 for the range $0.5 < r/r_m < 1.5$. Note that at any radius other than the mean, the free-vortex swirl distribution results in the lowest value for the degree of reaction, and the first-power swirl distribution gives the highest value.

The low (nonzero) values for the degree of reaction can occur at the hub for stages having small hub/tip ratios r_h/r_t. The variation with the radius ratio r/r_t for the degree of reaction can be obtained from Eqs. (9-51), (9-58), and (9-61) and the following relationship between r/r_t and r/r_m:

$$\frac{r}{r_m} = \frac{r}{r_m} \frac{1 + r_h/r_t}{2} \tag{9-62}$$

For the free-vortex swirl distribution with 0.5 degree of reaction at the mean radius, the degree of reaction is 0 at $r/r_m = 0.707$, which corresponds to the hub radius for a stage having a hub/tip ratio of 0.547. It is not uncommon for the initial stages of a compressor to have a hub/tip ratio of 0.4. The degree of reaction at the hub can be increased by increasing the degree of reaction at the mean radius for stages with low hub/tip ratios. Another way to increase the degree of reaction at the hub is to change the swirl distribution.

For the first-power swirl distribution with 0.5 degree of reaction at the mean radius, the degree of reaction is 0 at $r/r_m = 0.6065$, which corresponds to the hub radius for a stage having a hub/tip ratio of 0.435. Even with this improvement over the free-vortex distribution, the degree of reaction at the mean radius will have to be greater than 0.5 to have a positive degree of reaction at the hub of a stage with a hub/tip ratio of 0.4.

Because of the problems encountered with the above swirl distribution, modern compressor designers have looked to nonconstant work machines. However, these are absolutely dependent upon large computers for their definition.

Example 9-6. *Results using program COMPR.* The program COMPR can perform the calculations for repeating-row, repeating-stage, mean-line stage design. To have values for the total pressure and static pressures at stations 2 and $2R$, the program requires a value of the stator loss coefficient ϕ_{cs} in addition to the polytropic efficiency for repeating-row, repeating-stage calculations. The program assumes that the solidity σ varies inversely with radius (constant chord length) for calculation of the radial variation in the diffusion factor. The free-vortex swirl distribution is used for the radial variation of the tangential velocity v in this example.

GIVEN: $\dot{m} = 22.68$ kg/sec (50 lbm/sec), $P_t = 101.3$ kPa (14.70 psia), $T_t = 288.16$ K (518.7°R), $\omega = 900$ rad/sec, $e_c = 0.9$, $\phi_{cs} = 0.03$; on mean line: $\sigma = 1$, $\alpha_1 = 45°$, $D = 0.5$, and $M_1 = 0.5$

Solution. Tables 9-5*a* and 9-5*b* summarize the results obtained from COMPR. Note that the Mach numbers at the hub of stations 1, 2, and 3 are higher than on the mean radius due to the swirl distribution. This affects both the static temperatures and the static pressures at the hub.

The cross section of this stage, as created by COMPR, is shown in Fig. 9-33. The stage length of 0.099 m is based on a chord/height ratio of 0.75 for both the rotor and stator blades.

The variation in tangential and axial velocities with radius across the rotor is shown in Fig. 9-34 for the free-vortex swirl distribution. To obtain the 30.5°C

TABLE 9-5*a*
Flow property results for Example 9-6

Property \ Station		$1h$	$1m$	$1t$	$1Rm$	$2Rm$	$2h$	$2m$	$2t$	$3h$	$3m$	$3t$
T_t	K	288.2	288.2	288.2	303.1	303.1	318.1	318.1	318.1	318.1	318.1	318.1
	(°R)	(518.7)	(518.7)	(518.7)	(545.6)	(545.6)	(572.6)	(572.6)	(572.6)	(572.6)	(572.6)	(572.6)
T	K	272.7	274.4	275.7	274.4	289.4	284.5	289.4	293.1	303.0	304.4	305.4
	(°R)	(490.8)	(494.0)	(496.3)	(494.0)	(520.9)	(512.1)	(520.9)	(527.6)	(545.4)	(547.9)	(549.8)
P_t	kPa	101.3	101.3	101.3	120.9	117.7	139.3	139.3	139.3	138.3	138.3	138.3
	(psia)	(14.70)	(14.70)	(14.70)	(17.55)	(17.08)	(20.21)	(20.21)	(20.21)	(20.06)	(20.06)	(20.06)
P	kPa	83.5	85.4	86.8	85.4	100.1	94.3	100.1	104.6	116.7	118.5	119.9
	(psia)	(12.11)	(12.39)	(12.59)	(12.39)	(14.52)	(13.67)	(14.52)	(15.18)	(16.93)	(17.19)	(17.40)
M		0.533	0.500	0.475	0.723	0.487	0.769	0.704	0.653	0.499	0.475	0.456
V	m/sec	176	166	158	240	166	260	240	224	174	166	160
	(ft/sec)	(578)	(545)	(519)	(788)	(545)	(853)	(788)	(735)	(571)	(545)	(524)
u	m/sec	117	117	117	117	117	117	117	117	117	117	117
	(ft/sec)	(385)	(385)	(385)	(385)	(385)	(385)	(385)	(385)	(385)	(385)	(385)
v	m/sec	132	117	106	209	117	232	209	191	128	117	108
	(ft/sec)	(432)	(385)	(348)	(687)	(385)	(761)	(687)	(626)	(421)	(385)	(355)
α	deg	48.25	45.00	42.08	—	—	63.14	60.72	58.41	47.57	45.00	42.64
β	deg	—	—	—	60.72	45.00	—	—	—	—	—	—
radii	m	0.324	0.363	0.402	0.363	0.363	0.328	0.363	0.398	0.332	0.363	0.394
	(in)	(12.76)	(14.30)	(15.83)	(14.30)	(14.30)	(12.91)	(14.30)	(15.68)	(13.07)	(14.30)	(15.52)

TABLE 9-5b
Stage results for Example 9-6

Hub	$°R_c = 0.3888$	$D_r = 0.5455$	$D_s = 0.5101$
Mean	$°R_c = 0.5000$	$D_r = 0.5000$	$D_s = 0.5000$
Tip	$°R_c = 5850$	$D_r = 0.4476$	$D_s = 0.4906$

$\Delta T_t = 29.93$ K $\eta_s = 89.55\%$ $AN^2 = 1.184 \times 10^7\ \text{m}^2 \cdot \text{rpm}^2$

$$\psi = \frac{g_c c_p \Delta T_t}{(\omega r)^2} = 0.281 \qquad \Phi = \frac{u_1}{\omega r} = 0.359$$

(54.9°F) temperature rise across the rotor, the tangential velocity is increased 92 m/sec (302 ft/sec).

Design Process

The theory and design tools presented in previous sections can now be applied to the design of a multistage axial-flow compressor. The design process requires both engineering judgment and knowledge of typical design values.

FIGURE 9-33
Cross section of a single stage from COMPR.

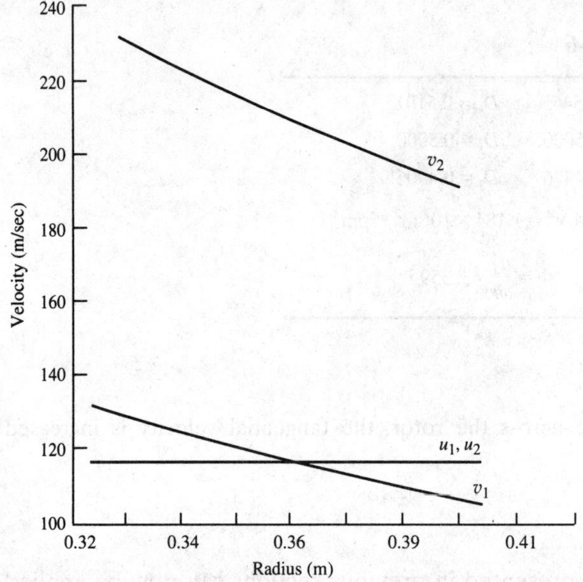

FIGURE 9-34
Axial and swirl velocity profiles at stations 1 and 2.

We will consider the design of a compressor suitable for a simple turbojet gas turbine engine. It is assumed that such a compressor will require inlet guide vanes.

From engine cycle calculations, a suitable design point for the compressor of such an engine at sea-level, standard-day conditions $[P/T = 14.70 \text{ psia}/518.7°\text{R}$ $(P/T = 101.3 \text{ kPa}/288.2 \text{ K})]$ may emerge as

Compressor pressure ratio	10.2
Air mass flow rate	150 lbm/sec (68.04 kg/sec)
Temperature entering turbine	3200°R (1778 K)

From these specified data, we will now investigate the aerodynamic design of an axial-flow compressor.

The complete design process for the compressor will include the following items:

1. Selection of rotational speed and annulus dimensions
2. Selection of the number of stages
3. Calculation of airflow angles for each stage at the mean radius
4. Calculation of airflow angle variations from the hub to tip for each stage
5. Selection of blading using experimental cascade data
6. Verification of compressor efficiency based on cascade loss data
7. Prediction of off-design performance
8. Rig testing of design

TABLE 9-6
Range of axial-flow compressor design parameters

Parameter	Design range
Fan or low-pressure compressor	
Pressure ratio for one stage	1.5–2.0
Pressure ratio for two stages	2.0–3.5
Pressure ratio for three stages	3.5–4.5
Inlet corrected mass flow rate	40–42 lbm/(sec · ft^2) [195–205 kg/(sec · m^2)]
Tip speed	1400–1500 ft/sec (427–457 m/sec)
Diffusion factor	0.50–0.55
High-pressure compressor	
Inlet corrected mass flow rate	36–38 lbm/(sec · ft^2) [175–185 kg/(sec · m^2)]
Hub/tip ratio at inlet	0.60–0.75
Hub/tip ratio at exit	0.90–0.92
Maximum rim speed at exit	1300–1500 ft/sec (396–457 m/sec)
Flow coefficient	0.45–0.55
Stage loading coefficient	0.30–0.35
Diffusion factor	0.50–0.55

Items 1 through 4 will be covered in this section. Many of the remaining steps will be discussed in following sections. The design process is inherently iterative, often requiring return to an earlier step when prior assumptions are found to be invalid. Table 9-6 lists ranges for some design parameters of axial-flow compressors and can be used as a guide.

Many technical specialities are interwoven in a design; e.g., an axial-flow air compressor involves at least thermodynamics, aerodynamics, structures, materials, manufacturing processes, and controls. Design requires the active participation and disciplined communication by many technical specialists.

SELECTION OF ROTATIONAL SPEED AND ANNULUS DIMENSIONS. Selection of the rotational speed is not a simple matter. For a simple turbojet engine, it depends on a balance of the requirements of both components on the common shaft—the compressor and the turbine. Typically, the rotational speed can be found by assuming values for the rotor blade-tip speed, the hub/tip ratio, and axial velocity of the first stage. A check of the magnitude of AN^2 (related to blade stress) is also made. For the first stage of typical compressors, the hub/tip ratio is between 0.6 and 0.75, the axial Mach number is between 0.48 and 0.6, and the rotor blade-tip speed is between 1150 and 1500 ft/sec (350 to 460 m/sec) (higher values for first-stage fans without inlet guide vanes).

Initially, we select a modest value for the axial Mach number M_0 of 0.5

entering the inlet guide vanes. Since the inlet guide vanes will accelerate and turn the flow to an angle of 30° to 45°, we will start with a compressor inlet Mach number M_1 of 0.6 and a high tip speed U_t of 1400 ft/sec (426.7 m/sec). From the definition of mass flow parameter, we can write

$$A = \frac{\dot{m}\sqrt{T_t}}{(\cos\alpha)(P_t)\mathrm{MFP}(M)}$$

For the given mass flow rate and the inlet pressure, temperature, and Mach number, we can determine the flow annulus area at the entrance to the inlet guide vanes:

$$\mathrm{MFP}(M_0) = \frac{\mathrm{MFP}(M_0)\sqrt{R/g_c}}{\sqrt{R/g_c}} = \frac{0.511053}{1.28758} = 0.3969$$

$$A_0 = \frac{\dot{m}\sqrt{T_{t0}}}{P_{t0}\,\mathrm{MFP}(M_0)} = \frac{150\sqrt{518.7}}{14.70 \times 0.3969}$$
$$= 585.7 \text{ in}^2 \ (0.3780 \text{ m}^2)$$

Likewise, the area at the face of the first-stage rotor, assuming a flow angle of 40°, is

$$\mathrm{MFP}(M_1) = \frac{\mathrm{MFP}(M_1)\sqrt{R/g_c}}{\sqrt{R/g_c}} = \frac{0.576277}{1.28758} = 0.4476$$

$$A_1 = \frac{\dot{m}\sqrt{T_t}}{(\cos\alpha_1)(P_t)\mathrm{MFP}(M)} = \frac{150\sqrt{518.7}}{0.7660 \times 14.70 \times 0.4476}$$
$$= 677.8 \text{ in}^2 \ (0.4375 \text{ m}^2)$$

The tip radius r_t and mean radius r_m are directly related to the flow area A and hub/tip ratio r_h/r_t by

$$r_t = \sqrt{\frac{A}{\pi[1-(r_h/r_t)^2]}}$$

$$r_m = r_t \frac{1 + r_h/r_t}{2}$$

The rotational speeds ω and N are related to the rotor tip speed by

$$\omega = \frac{U_t}{r_t} \qquad \text{and} \qquad N = \frac{30}{\pi}\,\omega$$

From the above relationships, we can calculate r_t, ω, N, and AN^2 over the

TABLE 9-7*a*
Variation of first-stage size and speed for a tip speed of 1400 ft/sec

$\frac{r_h}{r_t}$	r_t (in)	r_m (in)	ω (rad/sec)	N (rpm)	AN^2 ($\text{in}^2 \cdot \text{rpm}^2$)
0.60	18.36	14.69	914.8	8735.7	5.17×10^{10}
0.65	19.33	15.95	869.0	8298.2	4.67×10^{10}
0.70	20.57	17.49	816.6	7798.2	4.12×10^{10}
0.75	22.21	19.44	756.4	7222.7	3.54×10^{10}

hub/tip ratio range and obtain the data in Table 9-7*a* for a tip speed of 1400 ft/sec (426.7 m/sec).

With the information in Table 9-7*a,* it is most appropriate for the compressor designer to get together with the turbine designer to select a rotational speed. The first stages of turbines typically have tip speeds of about 1400 ft/sec (426.7 m/sec), a hub/tip ratio of 0.85 to 0.9, and Mach number entering the rotor of 1.2 at 60° to the centerline of the turbine. Assuming a fuel/air ratio of 0.04, the turbine mass flow rate is 156 lbm/sec. For $\gamma = 1.3$ and a 5 percent total pressure loss through the combustor, the annulus area at the turbine rotor is

$$\text{MFP}(M) = \frac{\text{MFP}(M)\sqrt{R/g_c}}{\sqrt{R/g_c}} = \frac{0.646508}{1.28758} = 0.5021$$

$$A = \frac{\dot{m}\sqrt{T_t}}{(\cos\alpha)(P_t)\text{MFP}(M)} = \frac{156\sqrt{3200}}{\cos 60° \times 142.40 \times 0.5021}$$
$$= 246.8 \text{ in}^2 \ (0.1593 \text{ m}^2)$$

For a hub/tip ratio of 0.9, the tip radius is 20.3 in (0.516 m). The rotor speed of 1400 ft/sec (426.7 m/sec) requires a rotational speed of 826 rad/sec. For a hub/tip ratio of 0.85, the tip radius is 16.8 in (0.427 m), and the corresponding rotational speed is 998 rad/sec. At this time, *we select a rotor speed of 800 rad/sec for the compressor* to keep the AN^2 of the compressor and turbine low. This value will be used in the preliminary design of the compressor stages. The corresponding hub, mean, and tip radii of the compressor's first stage will be 15, 18, and 21 in, respectively.

INLET GUIDE VANES. We will now consider the inlet guide vanes. The inlet guide vanes change both the direction of flow and its Mach number. For isentropic flow through the inlet guide vanes, the following relationship can be written with stations 0 and 1 corresponding to the inlet and exit, respectively:

$$\boxed{(\cos\alpha_1)(A_1)\text{MFP}(M_1) = A_0 \, \text{MFP}(M_0)} \qquad (9\text{-}63)$$

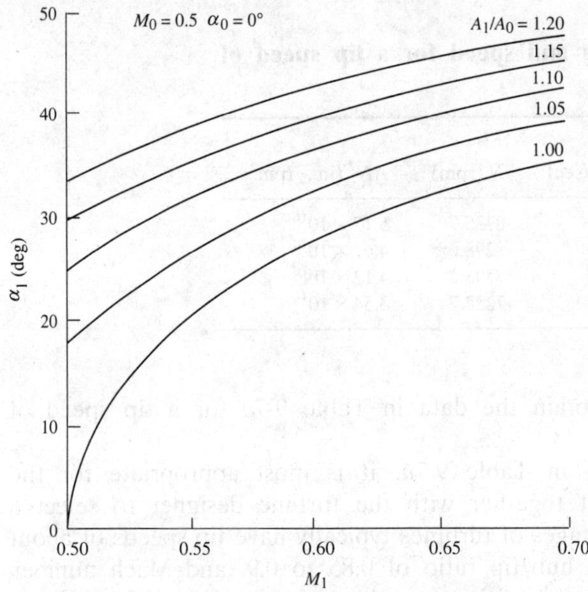

FIGURE 9-35
Mean exit conditions from inlet guide vanes.

For our case, where the entrance Mach number is 0.5, the above relationship can be used to calculate α_1 versus M_1 for different values of A_1/A_0. Results for $A_1/A_0 = 1.15$, 1.10, 1.05, and 1.0 are plotted in Fig. 9-35. Since the inlet guide vane sets up the flow for the first stage of the compressor, we will use this plot in conjunction with the repeating-stage design curves to help select the area ratio A_1/A_0 for the desired inlet Mach number M_1 and flow angle α_1.

SELECTION OF THE NUMBER OF STAGES. The number of compressor stages depends on the overall pressure ratio and the change in total temperature of each stage. Normally the changes in total temperature of the first and last stages are less than those of the other stages. In the absence of inlet guide vanes, the inlet flow to the first stage is axial, and less work can be done than in a stage whose inlet flow has swirl. The exit flow from the last stage is normally axial, which reduces the work of this stage.

The preliminary compressor design is based on repeating-row, repeating-stage design. Thus the repeating-row, repeating-stage design equations and Figs. 9-23, 9-24, and 9-25 can be used to estimate the number of compressor stages. We will base the design on a mean-line diffusion factor D of 0.5, a mean-line solidity σ of 1, and a polytropic efficiency e_c of 0.9.

Since the stage inlet Mach number decreases through the compressor, the stage pressure ratio of a repeating-row, repeating-stage design will decrease.

TABLE 9-7b
Variation in repeating-row, repeating-stage designs with inlet flow angle

α_1 (°)	α_2 (°)	τ_s	π_s	ΔT_t (°R)	$v_1/(\omega r)$	M_{1R}	ψ	Φ
30.0	51.79	1.1290	1.465	66.9	0.6250	0.840	0.375	0.541
32.0	52.94	1.1316	1.476	68.3	0.6051	0.844	0.359	0.513
34.0	54.10	1.1342	1.487	69.6	0.5867	0.848	0.344	0.486
26.0	55.28	1.1367	1.497	70.9	0.5697	0.852	0.330	0.461
38.0	56.47	1.1390	1.507	72.1	0.5541	0.856	0.318	0.437
40.0	57.67	1.1413	1.516	73.3	0.5396	0.859	0.306	0.413

However, *the change in total temperature across each stage will remain constant* for this type of design.

For $M_1 = 0.6$ and α_1 between 30° and 40°, the data in Table 9-7*b* for the first stage can be obtained from the equations for repeating-row, repeating-stage design. Thus, for the assumed value of M_1 and range of α_1, we see from Table 9-7*b* that the total temperature change for a stage will be between 66.9 and 73.3°R. The total temperature rise for the whole compressor will be approximately

$$\Delta T_t = T_{ti}[(\pi_c)^{(\gamma-1)/(\gamma e_c)} - 1] = 518.7[(10.2)^{1/(3.5\times 0.9)} - 1] = 565.5°\text{R}$$

The number of stages will then be either 9 (565.5/66.9 = 8.45) or 8 (565.5/73.3 = 7.71). *We select eight stages for this design.* Since the first stage has inlet guide vanes, we will use the same change in total temperature for this stage as for the other compressor stages. In addition, we will allow the last stage to have exit swirl (this can be removed by an additional set of stators) and will use the same change in total temperature for the last stage as for the other compressor stages. Thus each stage will have an equal temperature rise of 70.7°R (565.5/8). For the first stage, this corresponds to a temperature ratio of 1.136 which requires α_1 of about 36° and $V_1/(\omega r)$ of 0.57.

We select an inlet flow angle of 36°. The inlet air at $T_t = 518.7$°R and $M = 0.6$ has a velocity of 647 ft/sec. The resulting stage loading coefficient is 0.3302 and flow coefficient is 0.4609, both within the range of these coefficients for modern axial-flow compressors. For a rotor speed of 800 rad/sec, the mean radius is about 17 in. The inlet annulus area of the first stage will be

$$\text{MFP}(M_1) = \frac{\text{MFP}(M_1)\sqrt{R/g_c}}{\sqrt{R/g_c}} = \frac{0.56722}{1.28758} = 0.44757$$

$$A_1 = \frac{\dot{m}\sqrt{T_{t1}}}{(\cos\alpha_1)(P_{t1})\text{MFP}(M_1)} = \frac{150\sqrt{518.7}}{\cos 36° \times 14.70 \times 0.4475}$$
$$= 641.8 \text{ in}^2 \ (0.4142 \text{ m}^2)$$

This area is 1.1 times the inlet area of the guide vanes. The corresponding tip

TABLE 9-8a
Summary of eight-stage compressor design

Stage	1	2	3	4	5	6	7	8
M_1	0.600	0.560	0.528	0.500	0.476	0.456	0.438	0.422
π_s	1.497	1.430	1.379	1.338	1.306	1.279	1.256	1.237
P_{t1} (psia)	14.70	22.01	31.47	43.39	58.07	75.81	96.9	121.8
T_{t1} (°R)	518.7	589.6	660.5	731.4	802.3	873.1	944.0	1014.9
r_h (in)	14.03	14.80	15.32	15.67	15.93	16.12	16.27	16.38
r_t (in)	20.03	19.26	18.75	18.39	18.14	17.94	17.80	17.68
A_1 (in^2)	641.8	476.9	367.4	291.1	236.0	194.9	163.5	139.0

radius and hub radius at the inlet to the first stage are about 20 and 14 in, respectively, giving a first-stage hub/tip ratio of 0.7.

Example 9-7. *Preliminary design of mean line.* The COMPR program was used to perform the following analysis of a repeating-row, repeating-stage, mean-line design with a free-vortex swirl distribution. The following input data were entered:

Number of stages: 8	Mass flow rate: 150 lbm/sec
Rotor angular speed ω: 800 rad/sec	Inlet total pressure P_t: 14.70 psia
Inlet total temperature T_t: 518.7°R	Inlet flow angle α_1: 36°
Inlet Mach number M_1: 0.6	Diffusion factor D: 0.5
Solidity σ: 1.0	Polytropic efficiency e_c: 0.9
Rotor c/h: 0.6	Stator c/h: 0.6
Gas constant: 53.34 ft · lbf/(lbm · °R)	Ratio of specific heats γ: 1.4

The results from COMPR are summarized in Table 9-8*a* for the mean-line design. The mean radius is 17.032 in. and the flow angle at the entrance to the stator α_2 is 55.28°. A cross-sectional sketch of the eight stages as plotted by COMPR and captured on a laser printer is shown in Fig. 9-36*a*. The estimated

TABLE 9-8b
Number of blades with same c/h value for each row

Stage	1	2	3	4	5	6	7	8
Rotor								
c/h	0.60	0.60	0.60	0.60	0.60	0.60	0.60	0.60
Blades	56	71	87	106	128	151	177	206
Chord (in)	3.365	2.518	1.953	1.555	1.266	1.050	0.883	0.753
Stator								
c/h	0.60	0.60	0.60	0.60	0.60	0.60	0.60	0.60
Blades	48	64	81	102	124	149	176	206
Chord (in)	2.899	2.211	1.739	1.401	1.151	0.962	0.814	0.698

TABLE 9-8*c*
Number of blades with different c/h values for each row

Stage	1	2	3	4	5	6	7	8
Rotor								
c/h	0.60	0.60	0.63	0.73	0.83	0.93	1.03	1.13
Blades	56	71	83	88	92	98	104	110
Chord (in)	3.362	2.518	2.050	1.892	1.752	1.627	1.516	1.418
Stator								
c/h	0.60	0.60	0.60	0.70	0.80	0.90	1.00	1.10
Blades	48	64	81	87	93	99	106	113
Chord (in)	2.899	2.211	1.739	1.634	1.535	1.442	1.357	1.280

length of the compressor is 25.53 in. The resulting number of blades and blade chord lengths are given in Table 9-8*b* based on the input chord/height ratio of 0.6 for both the rotor and stator of all stages.

The number of blades in a rotor or stator now can be reduced by increasing its chord/height ratio. Since COMPR uses the same chord/height ratio for each

TABLE 9-8*d*
Material selection calculations for rotor blades, rims, and disks

Stage	1	2	3	4	5	6	7	8
AN^2 ($\times 10^{10}$ in$^2 \cdot$ rpm^2)	3.2530	2.4598	1.9209	1.5389	1.2587	1.0474	0.88422	0.75579
σ_c/ρ [ksi/(slug/ft^3)]*	2.7377	1.0702	1.6166	1.2951	1.0593	0.8815	0.7442	0.6361
T_{t1R} (°R)	554	625	696	767	838	909	979	1050
T_{t1R} (°F)	94	165	236	307	378	449	519	590
Blade material	←			Material 2				→
r_h (in)	14.03	14.80	15.32	15.67	15.93	16.12	16.27	16.38
ωr_h (ft/sec)	953.33	986.67	1021.3	1044.7	1062.0	1074.7	1084.7	1092.0
h_r† (in)	3.362	2.518	2.050	1.892	1.752	1.627	1.516	1.418
r_r (in)	10.668	12.282	13.270	13.778	14.178	14.493	14.754	14.962
Rim material	←			Material 2				→
σ_r/ρ [ksi/(slug/ft^3)]	4	4	4	4	4	4	4	4
$\rho(\omega r)^2/\sigma_r$	1.5188	1.6901	1.8110	1.8947	1.9581	2.0050	2.0425	2.0702
W_{dr}/W_r‡	0.4578	0.3367	0.2856	0.2735	0.2616	0.2500	0.2395	0.2299
ωr_r (ft/sec)	711.20	818.80	884.67	918.53	945.20	966.20	983.60	997.47
σ_d/ρ [ksi/(slug/ft^3)]¶	0.8781	1.1639	1.3587	1.4648	1.5510	1.6207	1.6796	1.7273
Disk material	←			Material 2				→

* Based on Eq. (J-6) and a blade taper ratio of 1.0.

† Based on h_r equal to blade chord.

‡ Based on Eq. (J-10) and $\bar{\sigma}_{\text{blades}}/\sigma_r = 0.1$.

¶ Based on Eq. (J-12).

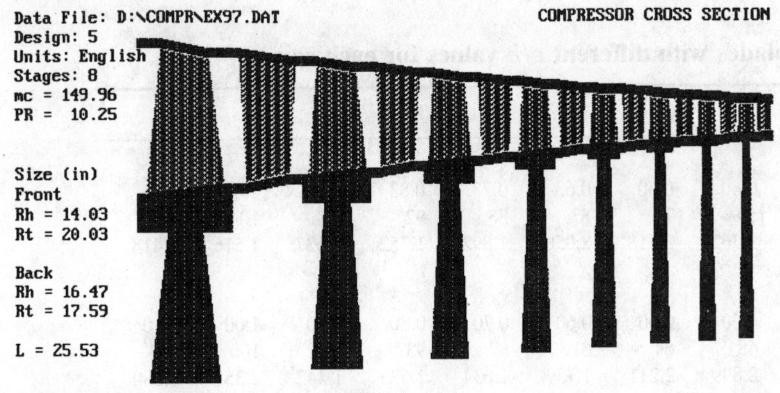

Center Line

Press <p> to print screen or <Esc> to exit screen

FIGURE 9-36*a*
Sketch of compressor cross section from COMPR with constant c/h.

Data File: D:\COMPR\EX97M.DAT
COMPRESSOR CROSS SECTION
Design: 2
Units: English
Stages: 8
mc = 149.96
PR = 10.25

Size (in)
Front
Rh = 14.03
Rt = 20.03

Back
Rh = 16.47
Rt = 17.59

L = 30.37

Center Line

Press <p> to print screen or <Esc> to exit screen

FIGURE 9-36*b*
Sketch of compressor cross section from COMPR with variable c/h.

blade row, the user must select and run the program with the constant-mean-radius design. To obtain the same stage loss coefficients, the program is first run with the repeating-row, repeating-stage design. Then the user selects the constant mean-line design, inputs the desired chord/height ratios in the stage data screen for the rotor and stator of each stage, and performs the new calculations with a mean radius of 17.032 in. This procedure was used to reduce the number of blades in a row of stages 3 through 8, and the results are shown in Table 9-8*c* and Fig. 9-36*b*. For these stages, note that the number of blades is reduced and that the chord lengths are increased (see Table 9-8*c*). In addition, the estimated length of the compressor has increased to 30.36 in (see Fig. 9-36*b*).

The AN^2 and estimated rim speed (assuming a rim height equal to the blade chord) at the inlet to each rotor are listed in Table 9-8*d* along with the relative total temperature on the mean line. These data values are related to the stresses in the turbomachinery (see App. J), and they can be used as a guide in blade and rim material selection and determining disk requirements. Based on the analytical tools and material properties of App. J, the rotor blades of stages 1 through 8 will require material 2 (a titanium alloy). The rim stress requirements can be met for these eight stages by using the same type of material as the blade. Since W_d/W_{dr} is greater than zero for each stage, each stage requires a disk.

The resulting total pressure and total temperature leaving the eight-stage compressor are 150.6 psia and 1086°R, respectively. The compressor efficiency is 86.32 percent. For axial flow at the exit with $M = 0.4$, and exit area of 98.15 in^2 (0.0633 m^2) is required for this compressor.

COMPR program calculates the variation in flow angle, diffusion factor, degree of reaction, Mach number, etc., of each stage for the selected swirl distribution. The minimum and maximum results and their location are listed in Table 9-9 for the free-vortex swirl distribution.

For this design, the inlet guide vanes have an inlet Mach number of 0.5, an exit Mach number of 0.6, and a flow angle of 36°. From Eq. (9-63), the flow area must increase from 585.7 to 639.4 in^2. For the same means radius as in the compressor stages, the entrance to the guide vanes will have a tip radius of 19.59 in and a hub radius of 14.05 in.

TABLE 9-9
Extreme values in eight-stage compressor design

Item	Value	Location
Maximum α_1 (deg)	41.41	Hub at entrance to first-stage rotor
Minimum α_1 (deg)	31.71	Tip at entrance to first-stage rotor
Maximum β_1 (deg)	62.68	Tip at entrance to first-stage rotor
Minimum β_1 (deg)	42.15	Hub at entrance to first-stage rotor
Maximum M	0.943	Hub at exit of first-stage rotor
Maximum M_R	1.053	Tip at entrance to first-stage rotor
Maximum D	0.526	Hub of first-stage stator
Minimum D	0.450	Tip of first-stage rotor
Maximum reaction	0.625	Tip of first stage
Minimum reaction	0.309	Hub of first stage

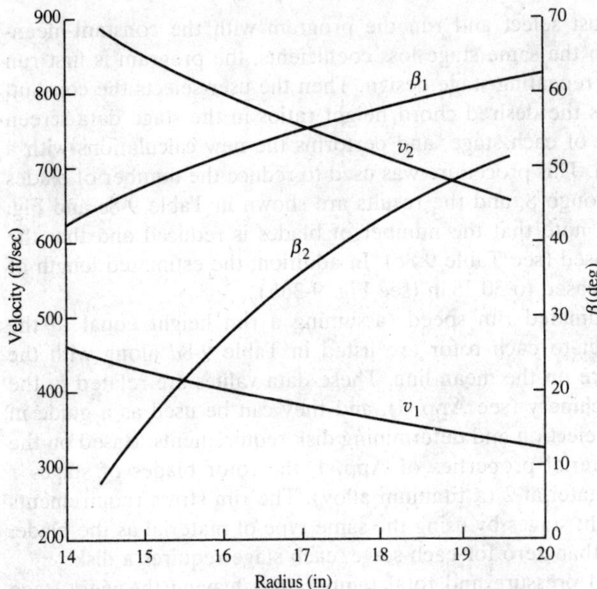

FIGURE 9-37
Swirl velocity distribution and variation of rotor flow angles.

The swirl velocity distributions v and flow angles β at the inlet and exit of the rotor are plotted in Fig. 9-37. Note the significant variation with radius of the swirl velocity and flow angles for the first stage ($14 < r < 20$) and very little for the last stage ($16.4 < r < 17.7$). In the first-stage rotor, the relative flow turns about 30° at the hub and only about 10° at the tip. The large radial variation in the rotor inlet flow angle for the first stage requires that its rotor blades have a lot of twist in them, whereas most of the relative flow in the last-stage rotor is turned about 20° and its rotor blades do not require a lot of twist.

Compressor Performance

The pumping characteristics of axial-flow compressors are best represented by a plot (based on experimental data) called the *compressor map*. The data are presented in terms of *corrected quantities* which are related to the performance of the compressor. A compressor is tested in a rig similar to the sketch of Fig. 9-38. The rotational speed is controlled by the electric motor and the mass

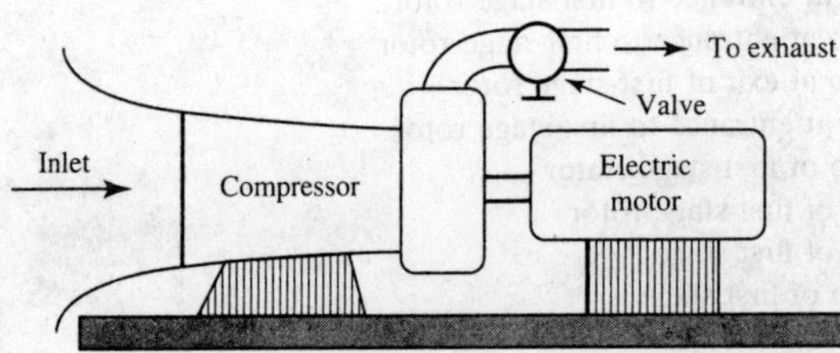

FIGURE 9-38
Sketch of compressor test rig.

flow rate by the valve. The inlet and exit conditions are measured along with the rotational speed and input power. These data are reduced to give the resulting compressor map.

CORRECTED QUANTITIES. For a compressor, the following four corrected quantities are normally used to map its performance:

Item	Symbol	Corrected
Pressure	P_{ti}	$\delta_i = \dfrac{P_{ti}}{P_{\text{ref}}}$ where $P_{\text{ref}} = 14.696$ psia
Temperature	T_{ti}	$\theta_i = \dfrac{T_{ti}}{T_{\text{ref}}}$ where $T_{\text{ref}} = 518.7°\text{R}$
Rotational speed	$N = \text{RPM}$	$\dfrac{N}{\sqrt{\theta_i}}$
Mass flow rate	$\dot{m}_i$	$\dot{m}_{ci} = \dfrac{\dot{m}_i\sqrt{\theta_i}}{\delta_i}$

The corrected rotational speed is directly proportional to the ratio of the axial to rotational velocity. The corrected mass flow rate is directly proportional to the Mach number of the entering flow. We note that

$$\dot{m}_i = \frac{P_{ti}}{\sqrt{T_{ti}}} A_i \,\text{MFP}(M_i)$$

Then $$\dot{m}_{ci} = \frac{\dot{m}_i\sqrt{T_{ti}}}{P_{ti}} \frac{P_{\text{ref}}}{\sqrt{T_{\text{ref}}}} = \frac{P_{\text{ref}}}{\sqrt{T_{\text{ref}}}} A_i \,\text{MFP}(M_i)$$

Therefore $$\dot{m}_{ci} = f(M_i)$$

At engine station 2 (entrance to compressor or fan)

$$\dot{m}_{c2} = \frac{P_{\text{ref}}}{\sqrt{T_{\text{ref}}}} A_2 \,\text{MFP}(M_2) \tag{9-64}$$

Thus the corrected mass flow rate is directly proportional to the Mach number at the entrance to the compressor.

COMPRESSOR MAP. The performance of two modern high-performance fan stages is shown in Fig. 9-39. They have no inlet guide vanes. One has a low tangential Mach number (0.96) to minimize noise. The other has supersonic tip speed and a considerably larger pressure ratio. Both have high axial Mach numbers.

Variations in the axial-flow velocity in response to changes in pressure

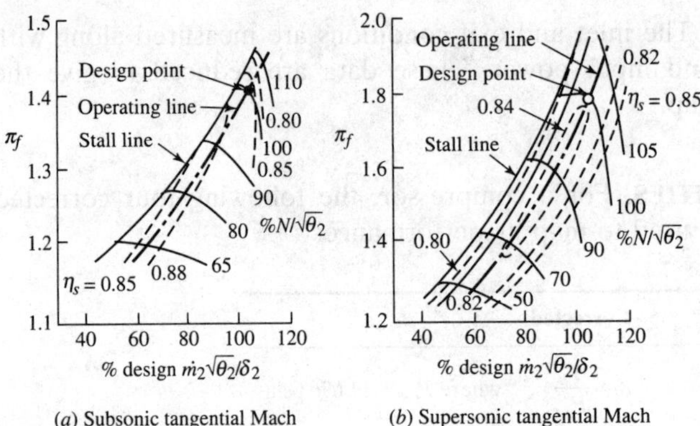

(*a*) Subsonic tangential Mach (*b*) Supersonic tangential Mach

FIGURE 9-39
Typical fan stage maps (Ref. 48).

cause the multistage compressor to have quite different mass flow versus pressure ratio characteristics from those of one of its stages. The performance map of a typical high-pressure-ratio compressor is shown in Fig. 9-40.

A limitation on fan and compressor performance of special concern is the stall or surge line. Steady operation above the line is impossible, and entering the region even momentarily is dangerous to the compressor and its application.

COMPRESSOR STARTING PROBLEMS. The cross section of a multistage compressor is shown in Fig. 9-41. Also shown (in solid lines) at three locations

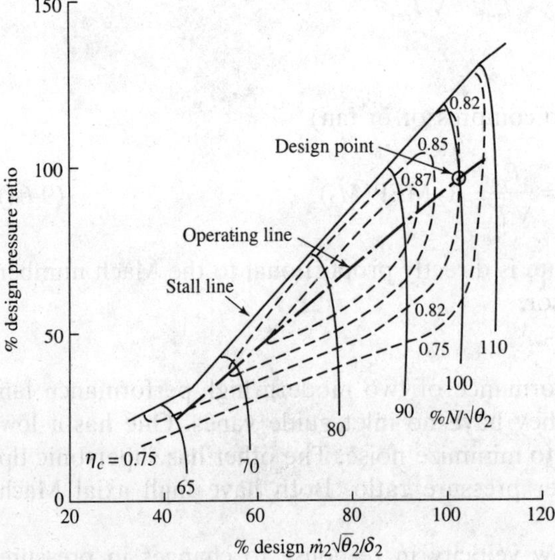

FIGURE 9-40
Typical compressor map.

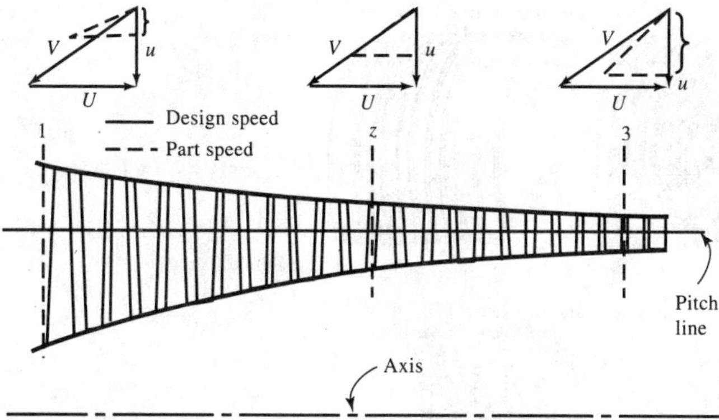

FIGURE 9-41
Cross section of a multistage compressor. Rotor-inlet velocity diagrams are shown for inlet, middle, and exit stages.

in the machine are mean-line rotor inlet velocity diagrams for on-design operation. The design shown here has a constant mean radius, a constant axial velocity, and zero swirl at the rotor-inlet stations.

Let us apply the continuity equation, which states that the mass flow rate is the same at all stations in the compressor. Then, at the inlets to the first and last stages,

$$\dot{m} = \rho_1 A_1 u_1 = \rho_3 A_3 u_3$$

or

$$\frac{u_1}{u_3} = \frac{\rho_3 A_3}{\rho_1 A_1} \tag{9-65}$$

At the design point, since $u_3 = u_1$, then $\rho_3/\rho_1 = A_1/A_3$. When the compressor is operating at a lower speed, however, it is not able to produce as high a density ratio (or pressure ratio) as at design speed; and since the area ratio remains fixed, it follows from Eq. (9-65) that the inlet/outlet axial velocity ratio must have a value less than that at design. In Fig. 9-41, the velocity diagrams shown (in dashed lines) indicate the rotor inlet conditions at partial speed. For each of the three stages represented, the blade speed is the same, but the inlet stage axial velocity is shown less than that for the outlet stage in accordance with Eq. (9-65). Because of the varying axial velocity, it is possible for only one stage near the middle of the machine (called the *pivot stage*) to operate with the same angle of attack at all speeds. At lower speeds, the blading forward of the pivot stage is pushed toward stall, and the blading aft of the pivot stage is windmilling with a tendency toward choking. At speeds higher than the design value, these trends are reversed.

Several techniques have been utilized to reduce the low-speed and starting effects:

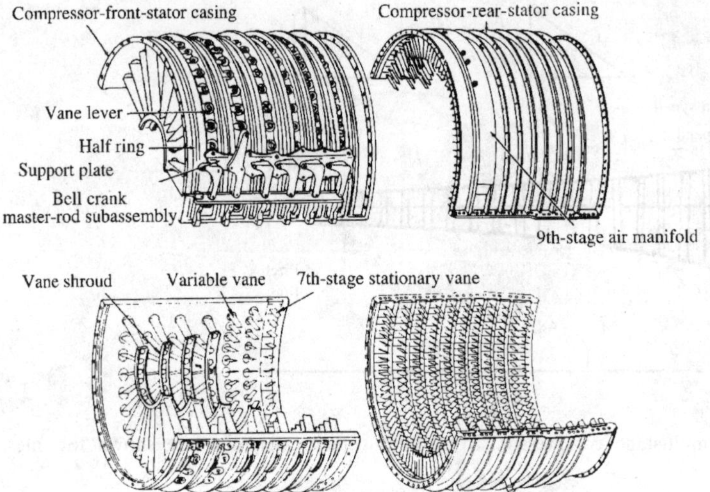

FIGURE 9-42
Compressor case for the General Electric J-79 turbojet engine (Ref. 46).

1. Bleed valves. Release air from the middle stages, reducing the tendency to windmill in later stages.
2. Multispool compressors. Run different spools at their own suitable speeds.
3. Use variable stators in the early rows.
4. Use combinations of the above.

An example of an early high-performance compressor is that used in the General Electric J-79 turbojet engine. This compressor has 17 stages on a single spool which results in a pressure ratio of 13.5. Figure 9-42 shows the compressor case of this engine with the variable stators used on the first six stages and the manifold for the bleed valves on the ninth stage. Most modern engines have compressors with multiple spools and bleed valves. The need for variable stators in the early rows is less for the multispool compressors.

9-4 CENTRIFUGAL-FLOW COMPRESSOR ANALYSIS

The centrifugal compressor has been around for many years. It was used in turbochargers before being used in the first torbojet engines of Whittle and von Ohain. Figure 9-43 shows a sketch of a centrifugal-flow compressor with radial rotor (or impeller) vanes. Flow passes through the annulus between r_{1h} and r_{1t} at station 1 and enters the inducer section of the rotor (also called *rotating guide vanes*). Flow leaves the rotor at station 2 through the cylindrical area of radius r_2 and width b. The flow then passes through the diffuser, where it is slowed and then enters the collector scroll at station 3.

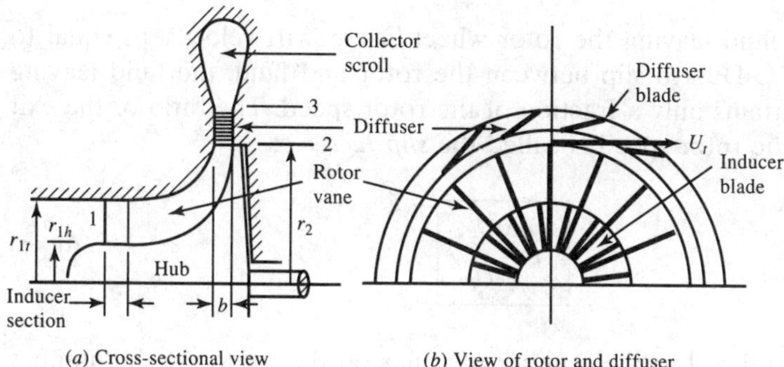

(*a*) Cross-sectional view

(*b*) View of rotor and diffuser

FIGURE 9-43
Centrifugal-flow compressor.

The velocity diagrams at the entrance and exit of the rotor (impeller) are shown in Fig. 9-44. The inlet flow is assumed to be axial of uniform velocity u_1. The relative flow angle of the flow entering the rotor increases from hub to tip and thus the twist of the inlet to the inducer section of the rotor. The flow leaves the rotor with a radial component of velocity w_2 that is approximately equal to the inlet axial velocity u_1 and a swirl (tangential) component of velocity v_2 that is about 90 percent of the rotor velocity U_t. The diffuser (which may be vaneless) slows the velocity of the flow V_3 to about 90 m/sec (300 ft/sec).

General Equations

Application of the Euler equation to flow of a calorically perfect gas through a centrifugal-flow compressor with axial flow entering gives

$$\boxed{T_{t3} - T_{t1} = \frac{v_2 U_t}{g_c c_p}} \tag{9-66}$$

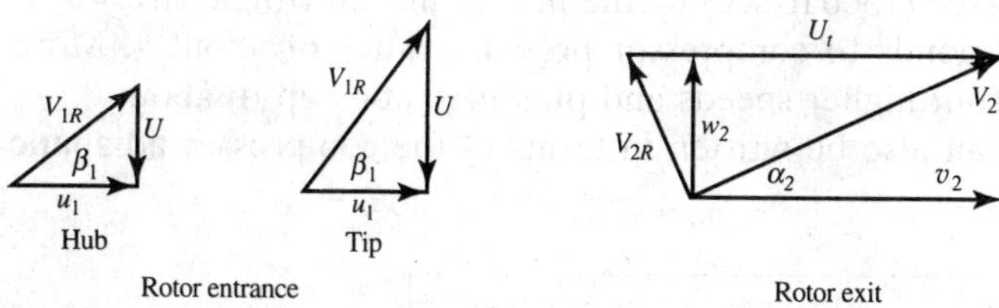

FIGURE 9-44
Velocity diagrams for radial vaned centrifugal compressor.

Ideally, the fluid leaving the rotor wheel has a swirl velocity v_2 equal to the rotor speed U_t. Due to slip between the rotor and fluid, the fluid leaving the rotor wheel attains only a fraction of the rotor speed. The ratio of the exit swirl velocity to the rotor speed is called the *slip factor* ε:

$$\boxed{\varepsilon = \frac{v_2}{U_t}} \tag{9-67}$$

The slip factor is related to the number of vanes on the rotor. As the number of vanes n is increased, the slip factor approaches 1 and the frictional losses of the rotor increase. Selection of the number of vanes is a balance between high slip factor and reasonable losses, which usually results in a slip factor of 0.9. A useful correlation between the slip factor ε and number of vanes n is

$$\varepsilon = 1 - \frac{2}{n} \tag{9-68}$$

Substitution of Eq. (9-67) into Eq. (9-66) gives a relationship for the compressor temperature rise in terms of the rotor speed U_t and slip factor ε:

$$\boxed{T_{t3} - T_{t1} = \frac{\varepsilon U_t^2}{g_c c_p}} \tag{9-69}$$

By using the polytropic compressor efficiency e_c and Eq. (9-69), the compressor pressure ratio can be expressed as

$$\boxed{\pi_c = \frac{P_{t3}}{P_{t1}} = \left(1 + \frac{\varepsilon U_t^2}{g_c c_p T_{t1}}\right)^{\gamma e_c/(\gamma - 1)}} \tag{9-70}$$

From Eq. (9-70), compressor pressure ratio π_c is plotted versus rotor speed U_t in Fig. 9-45 for air $[\gamma = 1.4,\ c_p = 1.004\ \text{kJ}/(\text{kg} \cdot \text{K})]$ at standard conditions ($T_{t1} = 288.16\ \text{K}$) with a slip factor ε of 0.9. For rotors with light alloys, U_t is limited to about 450 m/sec (1500 ft/sec) by the maximum centrifugal stresses of the rotor, which corresponds to compressor pressure ratios of about 4. More extensive materials permit higher speeds and pressure ratios up to about 8.

Equation (9-70) can also be written in terms of the compressor adiabatic efficiency η_c as

$$\boxed{\pi_c = \frac{P_{t3}}{P_{t1}} = \left(1 + \frac{\eta_c \varepsilon U_t^2}{g_c c_p T_{t1}}\right)^{\gamma/(\gamma - 1)}} \tag{9-71}$$

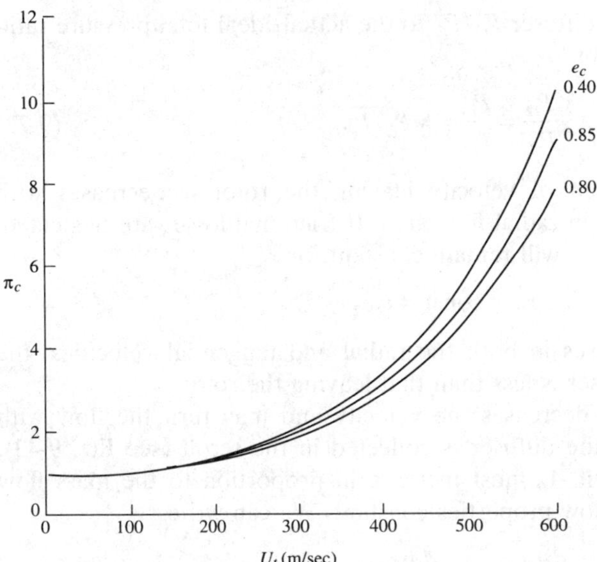

FIGURE 9-45
Compressor pressure ratio versus rotor speed.

The *T-s* diagram for the centrifugal compressor is shown in Fig. 9-46. This diagram is very useful during the analysis of centrifugal-flow compressors. Even though the rotor exit velocity V_2 may be supersonic, the flow leaving the rotor will choke only when the radial exit velocity w_2 is sonic. For determining the total pressure at station 2, an estimate must be made of the split in total pressure loss between the rotor and diffuser. As an estimate, we equate the

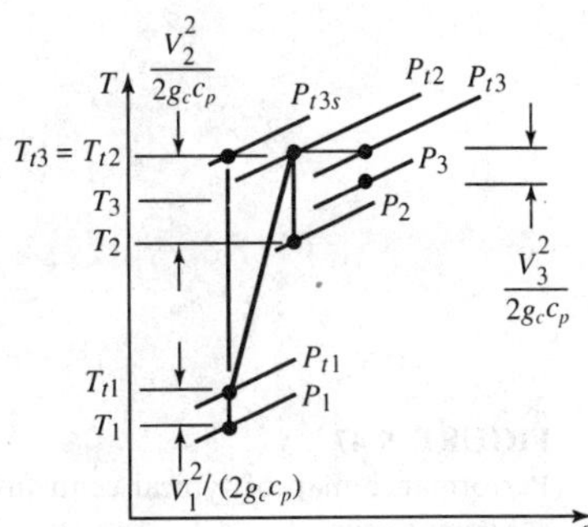

FIGURE 9-46
The *T-s* diagram for centrifugal compressor.

total pressure ratio of the diffuser P_{t3}/P_{t2} to the actual/ideal total pressure ratio leaving the rotor P_{t2}/P_{t3s}, or

$$\frac{P_{t2}}{P_{t3s}} = \frac{P_{t3}}{P_{t2}} = \sqrt{P_{t3}/P_{t3s}} \tag{9-72}$$

The radial component of velocity leaving the rotor w decreases with radius due to the increase in radial flow area. If frictional losses are neglected, the tangential momentum rv will remain constant, or

$$rv = \text{const} = r_2 v_2$$

As a result of the decreases in both the radial and tangential velocities, the velocity entering the diffuser is less than that leaving the rotor.

The diffuser further decreases the velocity and may turn the flow with blades. The flow leaving the diffuser is collected in the scroll (see Fig. 9-43). The flow area of the scroll A_θ must increase in proportion to the mass flow being added to keep the flow properties constant. We can write

$$\frac{dA_\theta}{d\theta} = \frac{1}{\rho_3 V_3} \frac{d\dot{m}}{d\theta} = r_3 b_3 \tag{9-73}$$

Centrifugal-flow compressors are used in gas turbine engines when the corrected mass flow rate is small (less than about 10 kg/sec). For small corrected mass flow rates, the rotor blades of axial-flow compressors are very short, and the losses are high. The performance of a centrifugal compressor for low flow rates can be as good as or better than that of the axial-flow compressor.

The performance of a centrifugal-flow compressor is presented as a compressor map (similar to the map of an axial-flow compressor). The map of a typical centrifugal compressor is shown in Fig. 9-47. Note that the overall pressure ratio is limited to about 4. Gas turbine engine cycles normally require a pressure ratio greater than 4 and additional stages of compression are

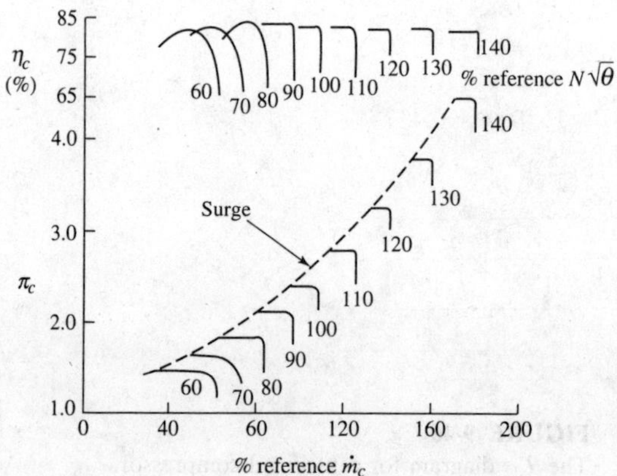

FIGURE 9-47
Performance map of typical centrifugal compressor.

needed. For engines with entering corrected mass flow rates greater than 10 kg/sec, additional compression is obtained from axial-flow stages in front of the centrifugal compressor. When the corrected mass flow is less than 10 kg/sec, higher cycle pressure ratios are obtained by using two or more centrifugal compressors in series.

Example 9-8. *Centrifugal compressor.*

GIVEN:

Mass flow rate = 8 kg/sec	$P_{t1} = 101.3$ kPa
Pressure ratio $\pi_c = 4.0$	$T_{t1} = 288.16$ K
Polytropic efficiency $e_c = 0.85$	Slip factor $\varepsilon = 0.9$
Inlet root diameter = 15 cm	Inlet tip diameter = 30 cm
Outlet diameter of impeller = 50 cm	$w_2 = u_1$
$V_3 = 90$ m/sec	

FIND:

a. Rotational speed and rpm of the rotor
b. Rotor inlet Mach number, velocity, and relative flow angles at hub and tip
c. Rotor exit velocity, Mach number, total temperature, total pressure, and direction
d. Depth of rotor exit s
e. Diffuser exit Mach number, area, total temperature, and total pressure

Solution.

$$U_t^2 = \frac{g_c c_p T_{t1}}{\varepsilon}\left(\pi_c^{(\gamma-1)/(\gamma e_c)} - 1\right)$$

$$= \frac{1004 \times 288.16}{0.9}\left(4^{1/(3.5\times 0.85)} - 1\right)$$

$$U_t = 436.8 \text{ m/sec}$$

$$N = \frac{60U_t}{\pi d_2} = \frac{60(436.8)}{\pi(0.5)} = 16{,}685 \text{ rpm}$$

$$\text{MFP}(M_1) = \frac{\dot{m}\sqrt{T_{t1}}}{P_{t1}A_1} = \frac{8\sqrt{288.16}}{101{,}300 \times \pi(0.15^2 - 0.075^2)} = 0.025287$$

$$\text{MFP}(M_1)\sqrt{\frac{R}{g_c}} = 0.025287 \times 16.9115 = 0.42764$$

$$M_1 = 0.3966$$

$$u_1 = V_1 = \sqrt{2g_c c_p T_{t1}\left\{1 - \frac{1}{1 + [(\gamma-1)/2]M_1^2}\right\}}$$

$$= \sqrt{2 \times 1004 \times 288.16\left(1 - \frac{1}{1 + 0.2 \times 0.3966^2}\right)} = 132.8 \text{ m/sec}$$

$$v_{1Rh} = \frac{d_{1h}}{d_2}U_t = \frac{15}{50}(436.8) = 131.0 \text{ m/sec}$$

$$v_{1Rt} = \frac{d_{1t}}{d_2} U_t = \frac{30}{50}(436.8) = 262.1 \text{ m/sec}$$

$$\beta_{1h} = \tan^{-1} \frac{v_{1Rh}}{u_1} = 44.6°$$

$$\beta_{1t} = \tan^{-1} \frac{v_{1Rt}}{u_1} = 63.1°$$

$$T_{t3} = T_{t2} = T_{t1} + \frac{\epsilon U_t^2}{g_c c_p} = 288.16 + \frac{0.9 \times 436.8^2}{1004} = 459.19 \text{ K}$$

$$\eta_c = \frac{(P_{t3}/P_{t1})^{\gamma/(\gamma-1)} - 1}{T_{t3}/T_{t1} - 1} = \frac{4^{1/3.5} - 1}{459.19/288.16 - 1} = 81.9\%$$

$$v_2 = \varepsilon U_t = 0.9 \times 436.8 = 393.1 \text{ m/sec}$$

$$w_2 = u_1 = 132.8 \text{ m/sec}$$

$$V_2 = \sqrt{w_2^2 + v_2^2} = \sqrt{132.8^2 + 393.1^2} = 414.9 \text{ m/sec}$$

$$\alpha_2 = \tan^{-1} \frac{w_2}{v_2} = 18.67°$$

$$M_2 = \sqrt{\frac{2}{\gamma - 1}\left[\frac{T_{t2}}{T_{t2} - V_2^2/(2g_c c_p)} - 1\right]}$$

$$= \sqrt{5\left(\frac{459.19}{459.19 - 85.73} - 1\right)} = 1.071$$

$$\frac{P_{t3s}}{P_{t1}} = \left(\frac{T_{t3}}{T_{t1}}\right)^{\gamma/(\gamma-1)} = 5.108$$

$$\frac{P_{t2}}{P_{t3s}} = \frac{P_{t3}}{P_{t2}} = \sqrt{\frac{P_{t3}/P_{t1}}{P_{t3s}/P_{t1}}} = 0.8849$$

$$P_{t2} = 0.8849 \times 5.108 \times 101.3 = 457.9 \text{ kPa}$$

$$P_{t3} = 4.0 \times 101.3 = 405.2 \text{ kPa}$$

$$\text{MFP}(M_2) = \frac{\text{MFP}(M_2)\sqrt{R/g_c}}{\sqrt{R/g_c}} = \frac{0.618966}{16.9115} = 0.040326$$

$$A_2 = \frac{\dot{m}\sqrt{T_{t2}}}{P_{t2}\,\text{MFP}(M_2)(\cos\alpha_2)} = \frac{8\sqrt{459.19}}{457{,}900 \times 0.040326 \times 0.9474} = 0.0098 \text{ m}^2$$

$$b = \frac{A_2}{\pi d_2} = \frac{0.0098}{\pi \times 0.5} = 0.624 \text{ cm}$$

$$M_3 = \sqrt{\frac{2}{\gamma - 1}\left[\frac{T_{t3}}{T_{t3} - V_3^2/(2g_c c_p)} - 1\right]}$$

$$= \sqrt{5\left(\frac{459.19}{459.19 - 4.034} - 1\right)} = 0.2105$$

TABLE 9-10
Results for Example 9-8 centrifugal compressor

Property \ Station		1	1R	2R	2	3
T_t	(K)	**288.16**	296.70/322.36 (hub/tip)	383.23	459.19	459.19
T	(K)	279.37	279.37	272.50	373.50	455.16
P_t	(kPa)	**101.3**	112.2/150.0	243.1	457.9	**405.2**
P	(kPa)	90.9	90.9	222.2	222.2	392.9
M		0.3966	0.557/0.877	0.361	1.071	0.2105
V	(m/sec)	132.8	186.54/293.82	139.8	414.9	**90**
u/w	(m/sec)	132.8	132.8	132.8	132.8	
v	(m/sec)	0	131.0/262.1	43.7	393.1	
r	(cm)		**15/30**	**50.0**	**50.0**	
α	(deg)	0	—	—	18.67	
β	(deg)	—	44.6/63.1	69.1	—	

$$\text{MFP}(M_3) = \frac{\text{MFP}(M_3)\sqrt{R/g_c}}{\sqrt{R/g_c}} = \frac{0.242559}{16.9155} = 0.014343$$

$$A_3 \cos \alpha_3 = \frac{\dot{m}\sqrt{T_{t3}}}{P_{t3}\,\text{MFP}(M_3)} = \frac{8\sqrt{459.196}}{405{,}200 \times 0.014343} = 0.0295 \text{ m}^2$$

The results of this example are summarized in Table 9-10. Note that different values of flow properties are listed for the hub and tip at station $1R$ and that M_2 is supersonic while M_{2R} is subsonic.

9-5 AXIAL-FLOW TURBINE ANALYSIS

The mass flow of a gas turbine engine, which is limited by the maximum permissible Mach number entering the compressor, is generally large enough to require an axial turbine (even for centrifugal compressors). The axial turbine is essentially the reverse of the axial compressor except for one essential difference: The turbine flow operates under a favorable pressure gradient. This permits greater angular changes, greater pressure changes, greater energy changes, and higher efficiency. However, there is more blade stress involved because of the higher work and temperatures. *It is this latter fact that generally dictates the blade shape.*

Conceptually, a turbine is a very simple device since it is fundamentally no different from a pinwheel which spins rapidly when air is blown against it. The pinwheel will turn in one direction or the other, depending on the direction of the impinging air, and a direction can be found for the air which causes no rotation at all. Thus it is important to properly direct the airstream if the desired motion and speed are to be obtained.

A modern turbine is merely an extension of these basic concepts.

Considerable care is taken to establish a directed flow of fluid of high velocity by means of stator blades, and then similar care is used in designing the blades on the rotating wheel (the vanes on the pinwheel) so that the fluid applies the required force to these rotor blades most efficiently. Conceptually, the turbine is a cousin to the pinwheel, but such an analogy gives no appreciation for the source of the tremendous power outputs which can be obtained in a modern turbine. The appreciation comes when one witnesses a static test of the stator blades which direct a gas stream to the rotor of a modern aircraft gas turbine. Such a stream exhausting into the quiescent air of a room will literally rip the paint off the wall at a point 6 ft away in line with the jet direction. When blades of the rotating element are pictured in place immediately at the exit of these directing blades, it then becomes difficult to imagine that the rotor could be constrained from turning and producing power.

Terminology can be a problem in the general field of turbomachinery. Compressor development grew out of aerodynamics and aircraft wing technology, while turbines have historically been associated with the mechanical engineers who developed the steam turbine. The symbols as well as the names used in these two fields differ, but for consistency and to minimize problems for the reader, the turbine will be presented using the nomenclature already established in the beginning of this chapter. Where a term or symbol is in such common use that to ignore it would mean an incomplete education, it will be indicated as an alternate. Thus turbine stator blades are usually called *nozzles* and rotor blades are *buckets.*

In the gas turbine, the high-pressure, high-temperature gas from the combustion chamber flows in an annular space to the stationary blades (called *stators, vanes,* or *nozzles*) and is directed tangentially against the rotating blade row (called *rotor blades* or *buckets*). A simple single-stage turbine configuration with nomenclature is shown in Fig. 9-48*a.* It is convenient to "cut" the blading on a cylindrical surface and look at the section of the stator and rotor blades in two dimensions. This leads to the construction of a vector

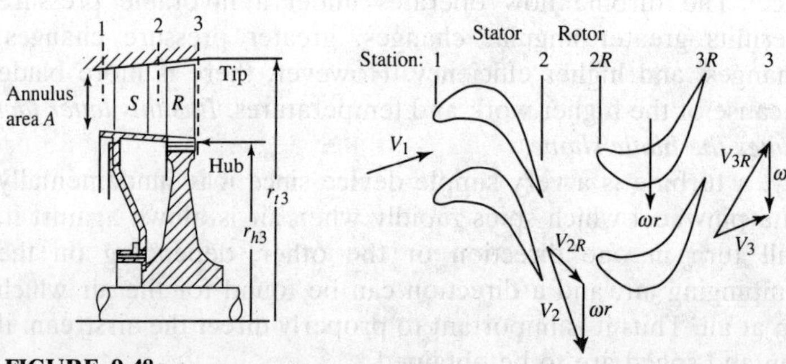

FIGURE 9-48*a*
Typical single-stage turbine and velocity diagram.

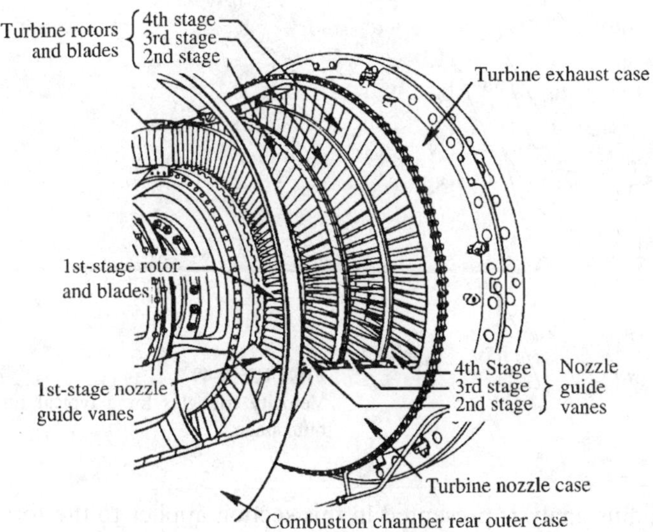

FIGURE 9-48*b*
Isometric section of multistage turbine.

or velocity diagram for the stage (see Fig. 9-48*a*) which shows the magnitude and direction of the gas velocities within the stage on the cylindrical surface.

In the stator or nozzle, the fluid is accelerated while the static pressure decreases and the tangential velocity of the fluid is increased in the direction of rotation. The *rotor* decreases the tangential velocity in the direction of rotation, tangential forces are exerted by the fluid on the rotor blades, and a resulting torque is produced on the output shaft. The absolute velocity of the fluid is reduced across the rotor. Relative to the moving blades, typically there is acceleration of the fluid with the associated decrease in static pressure and static temperature. A multistage turbine is made up of consecutive stages, each stage consisting of first a nozzle row followed by a rotor row. Figure 9-48*b* shows an isometric section of the four-stage turbine for a two-spool, low-bypass-ratio turbofan engine.

The following analysis of the axial-flow turbine stage is performed along the mean radius with radial variations being considered. In many axial-flow turbines, the hub and tip diameters vary little through a stage, and the hub/tip ratio approaches unity. There can be no large radial components of velocity between the annular walls in such stages, there is little variation in static pressure from root to tip, and the flow conditions are little different at each radius.

For these stages of high hub/tip ratio, the two-dimensional analysis is sufficiently accurate. The flow velocity triangles are drawn for the mean-radius condition, but these triangles are assumed to be valid for the other radial

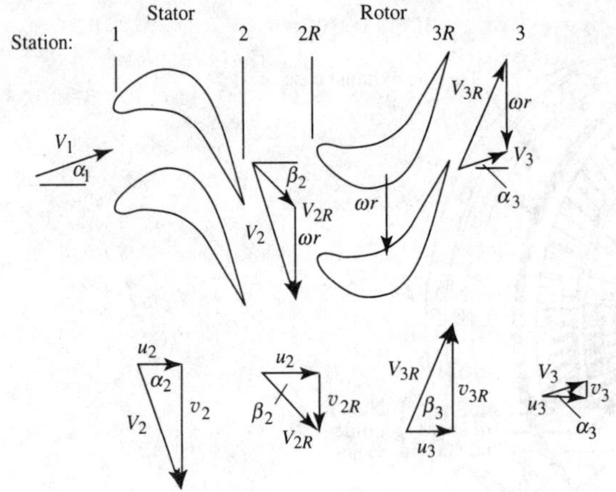

FIGURE 9-49
Velocity triangles for a typical turbine stage.

sections. The mean-radius analysis presented in this section applies to the total flow for such *two-dimensional* stages: the flow velocity, blade speed, and pressures being assumed constant along the blade length.

From the Euler turbine equation, the energy per unit mass flow exchanged between fluid and rotor for $r_2 = r_3$ is

$$h_{t2} - h_{t3} = c_p(T_{t2} - T_{t3}) = \frac{\omega r}{g_c}(v_2 + v_3) \tag{9-74}$$

Inspection of the velocity triangles (Fig. 9-49) shows that because of the large angle α_2 at the stator exit and the large turning possible in the rotor, the value of v_3 is often positive (positive α_3). As a result, the two swirl velocity terms on the right side of Eq. (9-74) add, giving large power output.

The large turning in stator and rotor is possible because, usually, the flow is accelerating through each blade row; that is, $V_2 > V_1$ and $V_{3R} > V_{2R}$. This means that the static pressure drops across both stator and rotor and, under such circumstances, a favorable pressure gradient exists for the boundary layers on the blade and wall surfaces, and separation can be avoided. Accelerating flow is an inherent feature of turbines and means that no general flow breakdown similar to compressor stall will occur.

Note that the vector diagram establishes the characteristics of a stage, and geometrically similar diagrams have the same characteristics. The angles of the vector diagram determine its shape and, therefore, become important design parameters. The velocity magnitudes are not important as performance parameters except in relation to the sonic velocity, i.e., except in terms of the Mach number. The angles may be used directly as design parameters or may be implied through the use of velocity ratios. Thus the magnitude of, say, $v_2 + v_3 = \Delta v$, although proportional to the absolute output, it not significant in defining the vector diagram, whereas the ratio $\Delta v/(\omega r)$ helps establish the vector diagram angles and, therefore, the stage charcteristics.

The stage analysis in the following sections neglects the influence of cooling air. Thus the flow through the turbine nozzle is assumed to be adiabatic ($T_{t2} = T_{t1}$), as is the flow through the rotor in the relative reference frame ($T_{t3R} = T_{t2R}$). Turbine cooling is discussed at the end of this chapter.

Example 9-9. *Mean-radius stage calculation—isentropic flow.*

GIVEN: $T_{t1} = 3200°\text{R}$, $P_{t1} = 300$ psia, $\alpha_2 = 60°$, $\alpha_3 = 0°$, $M_2 = 1.1$, $\omega r = 1400$ ft/sec, $u_3 = u_2$, $\gamma = 1.3$, and $R = 53.40$ ft · lbf/(lbm · °R)

Find the flow properties for this isentropic turbine stage.

Solution.

$$T_{t2} = T_{t1} = 3200°\text{R}$$

$$T_2 = \frac{T_{t2}}{1 + [(\gamma - 1)/2]M_2^2} = \frac{3200}{1 + 0.15 \times 1.1^2} = 2708.4°\text{R}$$

$$g_c c_p = g_c\left(\frac{\gamma}{\gamma - 1}\right)R = 32.174\left(\frac{1.3}{0.3}\right)53.40 = 7445 \text{ ft}^2/(\text{sec}^2 \cdot °\text{R})$$

$$V_2 = \sqrt{2g_c c_p(T_{t2} - T_2)} = \sqrt{2(7445)(3200 - 2708.4)} = 2705.5 \text{ ft/sec}$$

$$u_2 = V_2 \cos\alpha_2 = 2705.5 \cos 60° = 1352.8 \text{ ft/sec}$$

$$v_2 = V_2 \sin\alpha_2 = 2705.5 \sin 60° = 2343.0 \text{ ft/sec}$$

$$v_{2R} = v_2 - \omega r = 2343.0 - 1400 = 943.0 \text{ ft/sec}$$

$$V_{2R} = \sqrt{u_2^2 + v_{2R}^2} = \sqrt{1352.8^2 + 943.0^2} = 1649.0 \text{ ft/sec}$$

$$\beta_2 = \tan^{-1}\frac{v_{2R}}{u_2} = \tan^{-1}\frac{943.0}{1352.8} = 34.88°$$

$$M_{2R} = M_2\frac{V_{2R}}{V_2} = 1.1\left(\frac{1649.0}{2705.5}\right) = 0.670$$

$$T_{t2R} = T_2 + \frac{V_{2R}^2}{2g_c c_p} = 2708.4 + \frac{1649.0^2}{2(7445)} = 2891.0°\text{R}$$

$$v_3 = 0$$

$$V_3 = u_3 = u_2 = 1352.8 \text{ ft/sec}$$

$$v_{3R} = v_3 + \omega r = 0 + 1400 = 1400 \text{ ft/sec}$$

$$V_{3R} = \sqrt{u_3^2 + v_{2R}^2} = \sqrt{1352.8^2 + 1400^2} = 1946.8 \text{ ft/sec}$$

$$\beta_3 = \tan^{-1}\frac{v_{3R}}{u_3} = \tan^{-1}\frac{1400}{1352.8} = 45.98°$$

$$T_{t3} = T_{t2} - \frac{\omega r}{g_c c_p}(v_2 + v_3) = 3200 - \frac{1400}{7445}(2343.0 + 0) = 2759.4°\text{R}$$

$$T_3 = T_{t3} - \frac{V_3^2}{2g_c c_p} = 2759.4 - \frac{1352.8^2}{2(7445)} = 2636.5°\text{R}$$

$$M_3 = \sqrt{\frac{2}{\gamma - 1}\left(\frac{T_{t3}}{T_3} - 1\right)} = \sqrt{\frac{2}{0.3}\left(\frac{2759.8}{2636.5} - 1\right)} = 0.558$$

$$M_{3R} = M_3 \frac{V_{3R}}{V_3} = 0.558\left(\frac{1946.8}{1352.8}\right) = 0.803$$

$$T_{t3R} = T_{t2R} = 2891.0°\text{R}$$

$$P_{t2} = P_{t1} = 300 \text{ psia}$$

$$P_2 = P_{t2}\left(\frac{T_2}{T_{t2}}\right)^{\gamma/(\gamma-1)} = 300\left(\frac{2708.4}{3200}\right)^{1.3/0.3} = 145.6 \text{ psia}$$

$$P_{t2R} = P_2\left(\frac{T_{t2R}}{T_2}\right)^{\gamma/(\gamma-1)} = 145.6\left(\frac{2891.0}{2708.4}\right)^{1.3/0.3} = 193.2 \text{ psia}$$

$$P_{t3R} = P_{t2R} = 193.2 \text{ psia}$$

$$P_{t3} = P_{t2}\left(\frac{T_{t3}}{T_{t2}}\right)^{\gamma/(\gamma-1)} = 300\left(\frac{2759.4}{3200}\right)^{1.3/0.3} = 157.9 \text{ psia}$$

$$P_3 = P_{t3}\left(\frac{T_3}{T_{t3}}\right)^{\gamma/(\gamma-1)} = 157.9\left(\frac{2636.5}{2759.4}\right)^{1.3/0.3} = 129.6 \text{ psia}$$

Table 9-11 is a summary of the results for this axial-flow turbine stage with isentropic flow. The given data are listed in boldface type. Even though the flow leaving the nozzle (station 2) is supersonic, the relative flow entering the rotor is

TABLE 9-11
Results for Example 9-9 axial-flow turbine stage calculation, isentropic flow

Property \ Station		1	2	2R	3R	3
T_t	°R	**3200**	3200.0	2891.0	2891.0	2759.4
	(K)	(1778)	(1777.8)	(1606.1)	(1606.1)	(1533.0)
T	°R		2708.4	2708.4	2636.5	2636.5
	(K)		(1504.7)	(1504.7)	(1464.7)	(1464.7)
P_t	psia	**300**	300	193.2	193.2	157.9
	(kPa)	(2068)	(2068)	(1332)	(1332)	(1089)
P	psia		145.6	145.6	129.6	129.6
	(kPa)		(1004)	(1004)	(893.6)	(893.6)
M			**1.10**	0.670	0.803	0.558
V	ft/sec		2705.5	1649.0	1946.8	1352.8
	(m/sec)		(824.6)	(502.6)	(593.4)	(412.3)
u	ft/sec		1352.8	1352.8	1352.8	1352.8
	(m/sec)		(412.3)	(412.3)	(412.3)	(412.3)
v	ft/sec		2343.0	943.0	1400.0	0
	(m/sec)		(714.2)	(287.4)	(426.7)	(0)
α	deg		**60.0**	—	—	**0**
β	deg			34.88	45.98	—

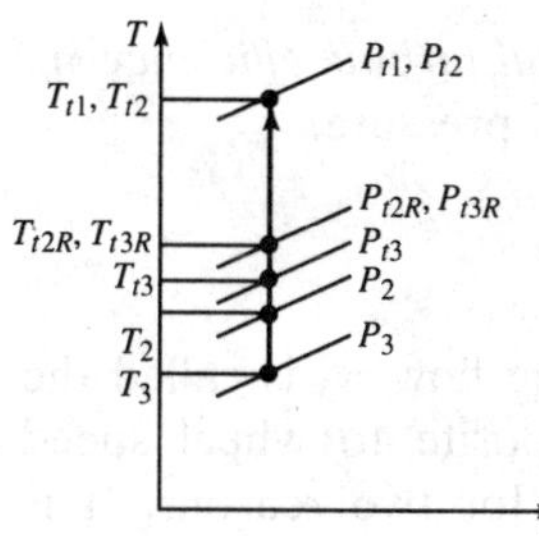

FIGURE 9-50
Property changes of an isentropic turbine stage.

subsonic. The flow through the rotor is turned 80.8°. Figure 9-50 shows the change in temperature and pressure for this isentropic turbine stage.

Stage Parameters

ADIABATIC EFFICIENCY. The adiabatic efficiency (the most common definition of efficiency for turbines) is the ratio of the actual energy output to the theoretical isentropic output (see Fig. 9-51*a*) for the same input total state and same exit total pressure:

$$\eta_t = \frac{\text{actual } \Delta h_t}{\text{ideal } \Delta h_t} = \frac{h_{t1} - h_{t3}}{h_{t1} - h_{t3s}} \tag{9-75}$$

For a calorically perfect gas, the efficiency can be written in terms of total temperatures and total pressures (see Fig. 9-51*b*) as follows:

$$\eta_t = \frac{h_{t1} - h_{t3}}{h_{t1} - h_{t3s}} = \frac{c_p(T_{t1} - T_{t3})}{c_p(T_{t1} - T_{t3s})}$$

$$\boxed{\eta_t = \frac{1 - T_{t3}/T_{t1}}{1 - (P_{t3}/P_{t1})^{(\gamma-1)/\gamma}}} \tag{9-76}$$

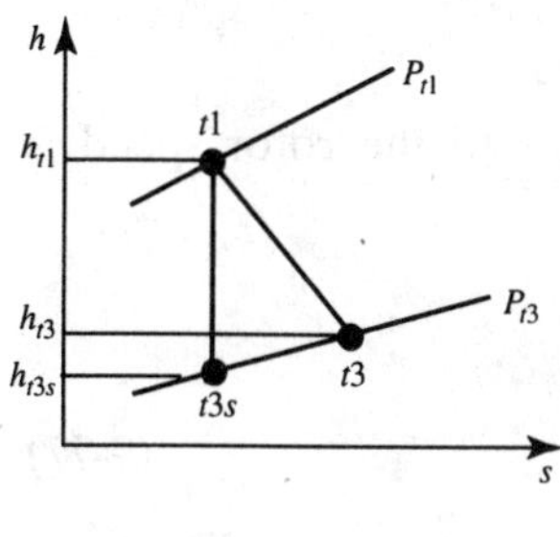

(*a*) *h-s* diagram

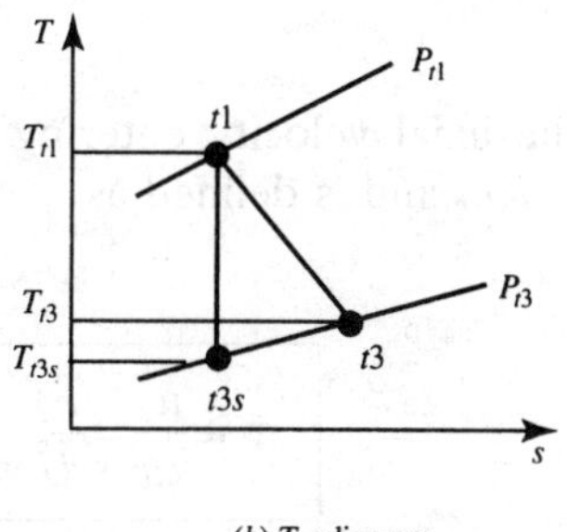

(*b*) *T-s* diagram

FIGURE 9-51
Definition of turbine adiabatic efficiency.

The above definition is sometimes called the *total-to-total turbine efficiency* η_t, since the theoretical output is based on the leaving total pressure.

EXIT SWIRL ANGLE. The absolute angle of the leaving flow α_3 is called the *swirl angle* and, by convention, is positive when opposite to wheel speed direction (*backward*-running). The angle is important for two reasons. It is difficult in any fluid dynamic situation to efficiently convert kinetic energy to pressure or potential energy, and the kinetic energy in the flow leaving a turbine stage can be minimized by having $V_3 = u_3$, that is, by having zero swirl. Conversely, we see that the higher the swirl angle (if backward-running), the higher in magnitude v_3 will be, which generally means higher output from the stage [see Eq. (9-74) and Fig. 9-49].

STAGE LOADING AND FLOW COEFFICIENTS. The *stage loading coefficient,* defined by Eq. (9-19), is the ratio of the stage work per unit mass to the rotor speed squared, or

$$\boxed{\psi \equiv \frac{g_c\,\Delta h_t}{(\omega r)^2} = \frac{g_c\,\Delta h_t}{U^2}} \tag{9-19}$$

For a calorically perfect gas, we write

$$\boxed{\psi = \frac{g_c c_p\,\Delta T_t}{(\omega r)^2} = \frac{g_c c_p\,\Delta T_t}{U^2}} \tag{9-20}$$

The ratio of the axial velocity entering the rotor to the rotor speed is called the *flow coefficient* and is defined as

$$\boxed{\Phi \equiv \frac{u_2}{\omega r} = \frac{u_2}{U}} \tag{9-77}$$

The stage loading coefficient and flow coefficient for a turbine stage have

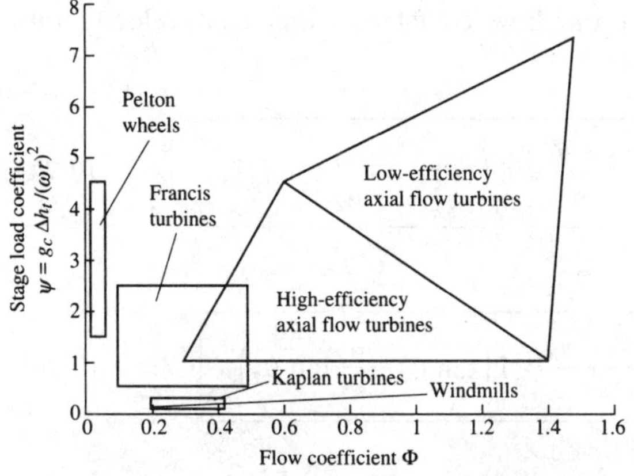

FIGURE 9-52
Stage loading versus flow coefficient for different turbine types. (*From J. H. Horlock*, Axial Flow Turbines, *Ref. 34, by courtesy of Butterworth-Heinmann Limited.*)

a range of values. Figure 9-52 shows the range of these coefficients for several types of turbines. For Example 9-9 data, the stage loading coefficient is 1.67, and the flow coefficient is 0.962, which is well within the range for high-efficiency axial-flow turbines. Both the stage loading and flow coefficients affect the turbine stage efficiency, as shown in Fig. 9-53. Modern high-pressure turbines used for aircraft gas turbine engines have stage loading coefficients in the range of 1.3 to 2.2 and flow coefficients in the range of 0.5 to 1.1.

From Fig. 9-49 and Eqs. (9-74), (9-20), and (9-77), we obtain the stage

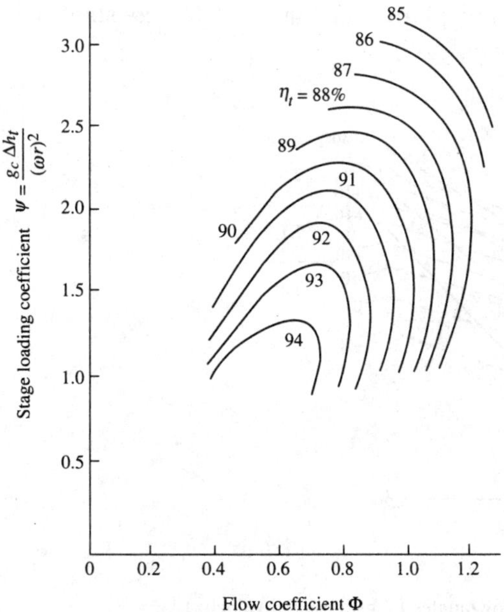

FIGURE 9-53
Stage efficiency versus stage loading and flow coefficients, corrected for zero tip leakage. (*From J. H. Horlock*, Axial Flow Turbines, *Ref. 34, by courtesy of Butterworth-Heinmann Limited.*)

loading coefficient in terms of the flow coefficient, the axial velocity ratio u_3/u_2, and flow angles as

$$\psi = \frac{g_c c_p \,\Delta T}{(\omega r)^2} = \frac{v_2 + v_3}{\omega r} = \Phi\left(\tan \alpha_2 + \frac{u_3}{u_2} \tan \alpha_3\right) \tag{9-78a}$$

or

$$\psi = \frac{g_c c_p \,\Delta T}{(\omega r)^2} = \frac{v_2 + v_3}{\omega r} = \Phi\left(\tan \beta_2 + \frac{u_3}{u_2} \tan \beta_3\right) \tag{9-78b}$$

By using Fig. 9-49, the flow coefficient can be expressed in terms of the flow angles as

$$\Phi = (\tan \alpha_2 - \tan \beta_2)^{-1} \tag{9-79}$$

We obtain the following expression for the stage loading coefficient in terms of flow angles and u_3/u_2 by combining Eqs. (9-78*a*) and (9-79):

$$\psi = \frac{\tan \alpha_2 + (u_3/u_2)(\tan \alpha_3)}{\tan \alpha_2 - \tan \beta_2} \tag{9-80}$$

Equations (9-79) and (9-80) are plotted in Fig. 9-54 for constant axial

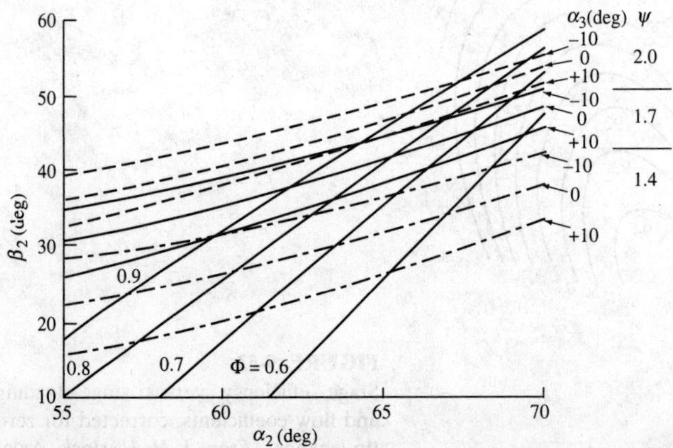

FIGURE 9-54
Stage loading and flow coefficients versus flow angles (constant axial velocity).

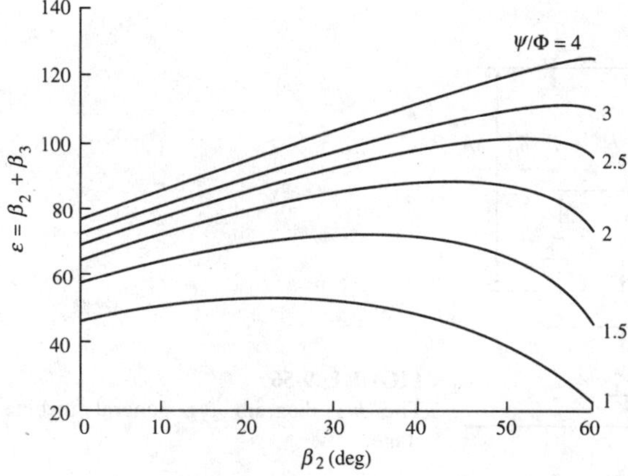

FIGURE 9-55
Rotor turning ε versus Ψ/Φ and β_2 (constant axial velocity).

velocity over a range of α_2 and β_2 and specific values of Φ, ψ, and α_3. This figure shows the effect of changing flow angles on Φ and ψ. Increasing α_3 with α_2 and β_2 held constant increases ψ and decreases Φ. Figure 9-54 also can be used to approximately determine the flow coefficient Φ from flow angles α_2 and β_2 and/or the stage loading coefficient ψ from flow angles α_2, β_2, and α_3. For example, given $\alpha_2 = 65$, $\beta_2 = 40$, and $\alpha_3 = 10$, Fig. 9-49 gives Φ of about 0.77 and ψ of about 1.8. More accurate results can be obtained by using Eqs. (9-79) and (9-80).

Figure 9-55 shows the rotor turning ($\varepsilon = \beta_2 + \beta_3$) for constant axial velocity as a function of the flow angle β_2 for different values of the ratio ψ/Φ. This figure can be used in conjunction with Fig. 9-54 to determine the rotor turning ε and the flow angle β_3.

DEGREE OF REACTION. The *degree of reaction* is defined as

$$\boxed{{}^{\circ}R_t = \frac{h_2 - h_3}{h_{t1} - h_{t3}}} \tag{9-81a}$$

For a calorically perfect gas, we can write

$$\boxed{{}^{\circ}R_t = \frac{T_2 - T_3}{T_{t1} - T_{t3}}} \tag{9-81b}$$

That is, the degree of reaction is the ratio of the static enthalpy drop in the

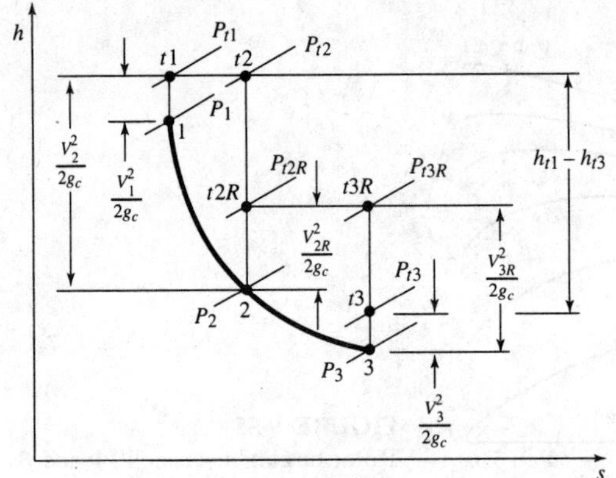

FIGURE 9-56
The *h-s* diagram for general turbine stage.

rotor to the drop in total enthalpy across both the rotor and stator. Figure 9-56 gives a complete picture for a general turbine stage. For Example 9-9, the degree of reaction is 0.166.

It can be shown that the degree of reaction may be related to the flow angles for the case of constant axial velocity ($u_3 = u_2$) by

$$°R_t = \frac{u_2}{\omega r}\frac{\tan\beta_3 - \tan\beta_2}{2} = \Phi\frac{\tan\beta_3 - \tan\beta_2}{2} \tag{9-82}$$

By using Eq. (9-82), plots of $°R_t/\Phi$ were added to Fig. 9-55, giving Fig. 9-57. One can see from this figure that zero reaction corresponds to maximum rotor turning ε for fixed value of ψ/Φ.

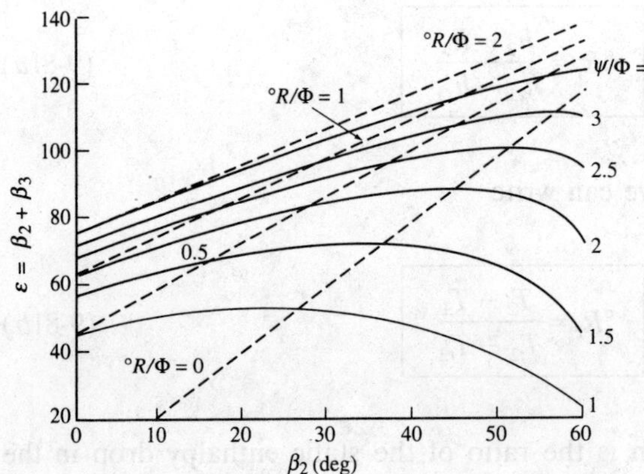

FIGURE 9-57
Degree of reaction, stage loading coefficient, and flow coefficient versus rotor flow angles.

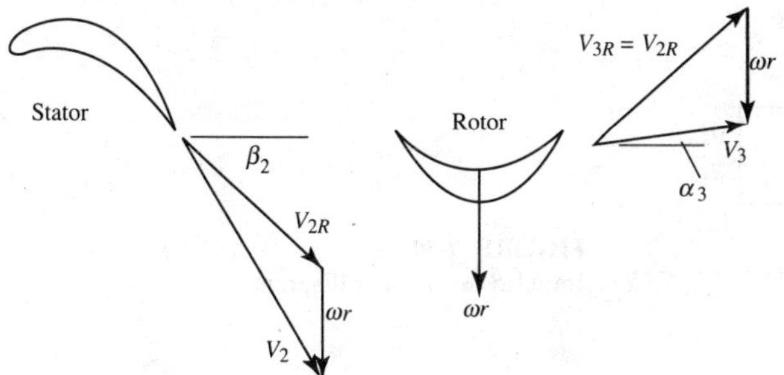

FIGURE 9-58*a*
Zero-reaction velocity diagram.

Three important basic designs of turbine are related to the choice of reaction—zero reaction, 50 percent reaction, and axial leaving velocity (variable reaction). It should be emphasized, however, that the designer is not limited to these three types and that in a three-dimensional turbine design, the reaction may vary continuously along the blades.

Zero reaction. From the definition of reaction, if the reaction is selected as zero for the case of constant axial velocity, then

$$h_3 = h_2 \qquad \text{and} \qquad \tan \beta_3 = \tan \beta_2$$

Therefore $$\beta_3 = \beta_2 \qquad V_{3R} = V_{2R}$$

Velocity triangles for this zero reaction stage are shown in Fig. 9-58*a*, and the *h-s* diagram is drawn in Fig. 9-58*b*.

If the flow is isentropic and the fluid is a perfect gas, then the condition of zero enthalpy drop ($h_3 - h_2 = 0$) implies no change in pressure across the

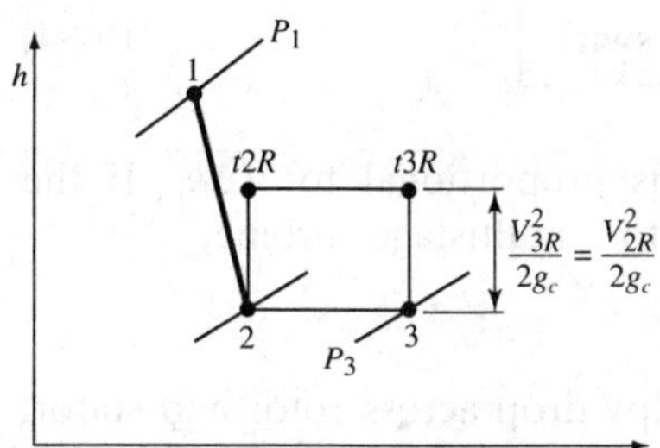

FIGURE 9-58*b*
Zero-reaction *h-s* diagram.

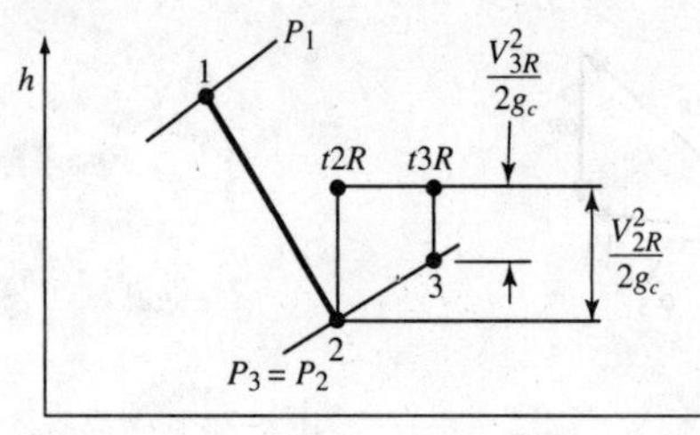

FIGURE 9-59
Impulse turbine *h-s* diagram.

rotor. The turbine is then *called* an impulse turbine, with the tangential load arising from impulsive forces only. *It is important to note that reaction is defined here not on the basis of pressure drops, but in terms of static enthalpy changes.* Note, however, that there is a pressure drop from P_2 to P_3 across the rotor, and the stage is not, therfore, truly impulse. The *h-s* diagram for an "impulse" stage of zero pressure drop is shown in Fig. 9-59. There is an enthalpy increase from h_2 to h_3 across the rotor, and the relative velocity decreases. Thus, *the impulse stage is actually one of negative reaction*!

The stage loading coefficient for the impulse stage with constant axial velocity is

$$\psi = \frac{g_c c_p \, \Delta T_t}{(\omega r)^2} = \frac{\omega r \, \Delta v}{(\omega r)^2} = \frac{\Delta v}{\omega r}$$

with
$$v_2 = u_2 \tan \alpha_2$$

$$v_3 = u_2 \tan \alpha_3 = u_2 \tan \alpha_2 - 2\omega r$$

then
$$\boxed{\psi = 2(\Phi \tan \alpha_2 - 1) = 2\Phi \tan \beta_2} \qquad (9\text{-}83)$$

We desire α_2 to be large. But this leads to large V_2 and large V_{2R}, which lead to large losses. So α_2 is generally limited to less than 70°.

Also, if (see Fig. 9-58*a*) $\alpha_3 = 0$ (no exit swirl), then $\tan \alpha_2 = 2\omega r / u_2$ and

$$\boxed{\psi = 2 \qquad \text{no exit swirl}} \qquad (9\text{-}84)$$

Thus we see that the rotor speed ωr is proportional to $\sqrt{\Delta h_t}$. If the resultant blade speed is too high, we must go to a multistage turbine.

Fifty percent reaction. If there is equal enthalpy drop across rotor and stator, then $R_t = 0.5$ and the velocity triangles are symmetrical, as shown in Fig. 9-60.

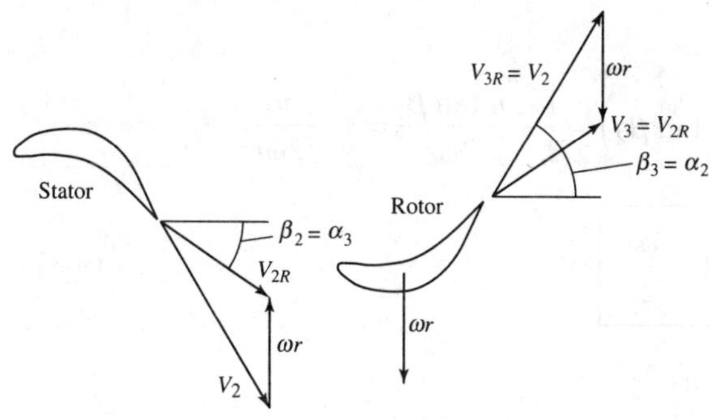

FIGURE 9-60
Diagram of 50 percent reaction turbine velocity.

Then, $\alpha_2 = \beta_3$, $\alpha_3 = \beta_2$, and

$$\tan \beta_3 - \tan \beta_2 = \tan \alpha_2 - \tan \alpha_3 = \frac{\omega r}{u_2} = \frac{1}{\Phi}$$

The stage loading coefficient for this turbine with constant axial velocity is

$$\boxed{\psi = \frac{\Delta v}{\omega r} = 2\Phi \tan \alpha_2 - 1 = 2\Phi \tan \beta_3 - 1} \tag{9-85}$$

Again, α_2 should be high but is limited to less than 70°. For *zero exit swirl*

$$\tan \beta_3 = \tan \alpha_2 = \frac{\omega r}{u} \qquad \beta_2 = 0 \qquad \boxed{\psi = 1} \tag{9-86}$$

Thus, for the same ωr and $v_3 = 0$, the work per unit mass from a zero-reaction turbine is twice that from the 50 percent reaction turbine [compare Eqs. (9-84) and (9-86)].

General zero-swirl case (constant axial velocity). If the exit swirl is to be zero (Fig. 9–61), then $\alpha_3 = 0$, $v_3 = 0$, and $\tan \beta_3 = \omega r/u$. From Eq. (9-82), the

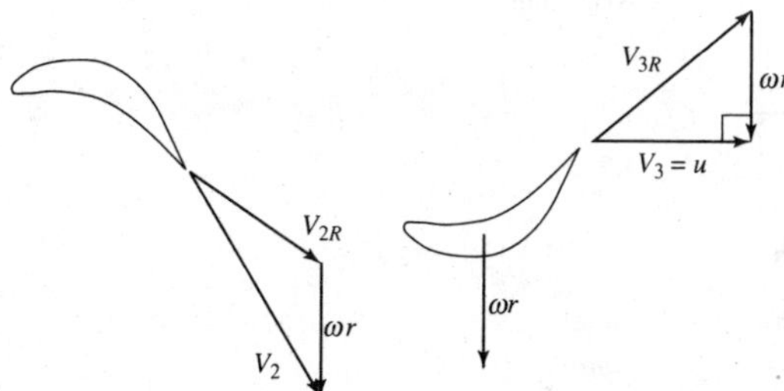

FIGURE 9-61
Zero-exis-swirl turbine.

reaction is then

$$°R_t = \frac{u}{2\omega r}\left(\frac{\omega r}{u} - \tan\beta_2\right) = \frac{1}{2} - \frac{u\tan\beta_2}{2\omega r} = 1 - \frac{v_2}{2\omega r}$$

$$\boxed{°R_t = 1 - \frac{v_2}{2\omega r} = 1 - \frac{\psi}{2}} \tag{9-87}$$

This equation can be rewritten as

$$\boxed{\psi = 2(1 - °R_t)} \tag{9-88}$$

Thus high stage loadings give a low degree of reaction. In aircraft gas turbine engines, engine weight and performance must be balanced. Weight can be reduced by increasing stage loading (reduces the number of turbine stages), but this normally leads to a loss in stage efficiency (see Fig. 9-53).

TURBINE AIRFOIL NOMENCLATURE AND DESIGN METAL ANGLES. The nomenclature for turbine airfoil cascades is presented in Fig. 9-62. The situation in unchoked turbines is similar to that in compressors except that the deviations are markedly smaller owing to the thinner boundary layers. Hence

$$\boxed{\delta_t = \frac{\gamma_i + \gamma_e}{8\sqrt{\sigma}}} \tag{9-89}$$

is a good estimate of the turbine exit deviation. More importantly, however,

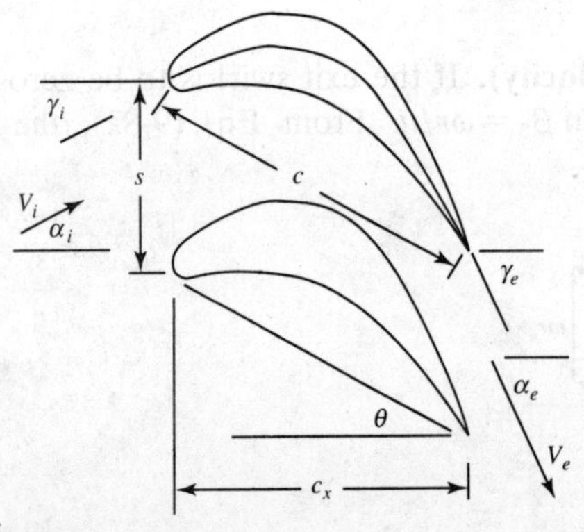

$\alpha_i - \gamma_i$ = incidence angle
$\alpha_i + \alpha_e$ = turning angle
$\gamma_e - \gamma_e = \delta_t$ = exit deviation
$\gamma_i + \gamma_e$ = blade chamber
$\sigma = c/s$ = solidity
θ = stagger angle
c_x = axial chord

FIGURE 9-62
Turbine airfoil nomenclature.

when the turbine airfoil cascade exit Mach number is near unity, the deviation is usually negligible because the cascade passage is similar to a nozzle. In fact, the suction (or convex) surface of the airfoils often has a flat stretch before the trailing edge, which evokes the name *straight-backed.* Finally, the simple concept of deviation loses all meaning at large supersonic exit Mach numbers because expansion or compression waves emanating from the trailing edge can dramatically alter the final flow direction. This is a truly fascinating field of aerodynamics, but one that requires considerable study.

STAGE TEMPERATURE RATIO τ_s**.** The stage temperature ratio ($\tau_s = T_{t1}/T_{t3}$) can be expressed as follows, by using the definition of the stage loading coefficient:

$$\boxed{\tau_s = \frac{T_{t3}}{T_{t1}} = 1 - \psi \frac{(\omega r)^2}{g_c c_p T_{t1}}} \tag{9-90}$$

Thus, for a given T_{t1} and ωr, the zero-reaction turbine stage will have the lower stage temperature ratio (greater work output per unit mass) than a 50 percent reaction turbine stage.

STAGE PRESSURE RATIO π_s**.** Once the stage temperature ratio, flow field, and airfoil characteristics are established, several avenues are open to predict the stage pressure ratio. The most simple and direct method is to employ the polytropic efficiency e_t. Recall that the polytropic efficiency is

$$e_t = \frac{dh_t}{dh_{t\,\text{ideal}}} = \frac{\gamma}{\gamma - 1} \frac{dT_t/T_t}{dP_t/P_t}$$

Integration with constant γ and e_t yields the following equation for the stage pressure ratio

$$\boxed{\pi_s = \frac{P_{t3}}{P_{t1}} = \left(\frac{T_{t3}}{T_{t1}}\right)^{\gamma/[(\gamma-1)e_t]} = \tau_s^{\gamma/[(\gamma-1)e_t]}} \tag{9-91}$$

where the stage temperature ratio can be obtained from the total temperatures or an equation like Eq. (9-90).

Another approach involves the use of experimental or empirical cascade loss correlations, such as those shown in Figs. 9-63 and 9-64, to the stator and rotor in order to determine the total pressure loss. The *total pressure loss coefficient* for turbine cascade data is defined as

$$\boxed{\phi_t \equiv \frac{P_{ti} - P_{te}}{P_{te} - P_e}} \tag{9-92}$$

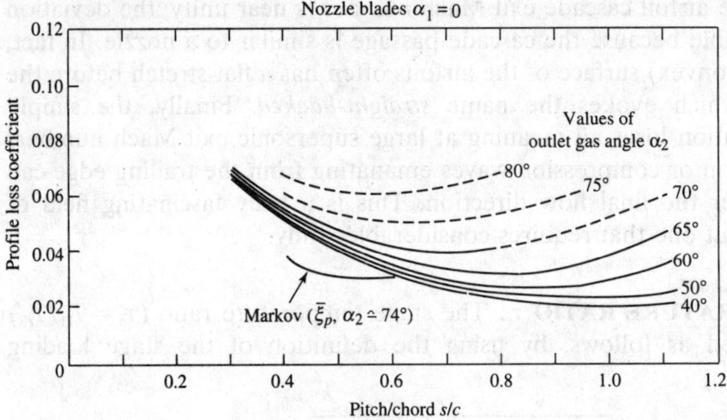

FIGURE 9-63
Turbine stator cascade loss coefficient ($\alpha_1 = 0$). (*From J. H. Horlock,* Axial Flow Turbines, *Ref. 34, by courtesy of Butterworth-Heinmann Limited.*)

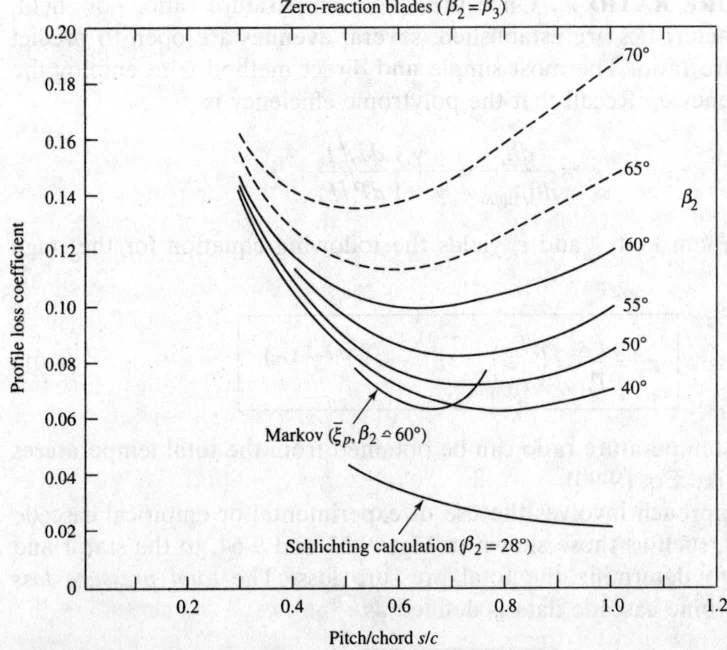

FIGURE 9-64
Turbine rotor cascade loss coefficient ($\beta_2 = \beta_3$). (*From J. H. Horlock,* Axial Flow Turbines, *Ref. 34, by courtesy of Butterworth-Heinmann Limited.*)

where subscripts i and e refer to the inlet and exit states, respectively. This equation can be rewritten for the cascade total pressure ratio as

$$\boxed{\frac{P_{te}}{P_{ti}} = \frac{1}{1+\phi_t(1-P_e/P_{te})}} \tag{9-93}$$

where P_e/P_{te} depends only upon the usually known airfoil cascade exit Mach number M_e. Note that the total pressure loss coefficient for the rotor is based on the relative total states. The stage total pressure ratio can be written as

$$\boxed{\frac{P_{t3}}{P_{t1}} = \left(\frac{P_{t2}}{P_{t1}}\right)_{\phi_t\,\text{stator},\,M_2} \frac{P_{t2R}}{P_{t2}} \left(\frac{P_{t3R}}{P_{t2R}}\right)_{\phi_t\,\text{rotor},\,M_{3R}} \frac{P_{t3}}{P_{t3R}}} \tag{9-94}$$

where $\phi_{t\,\text{stator}}$ and $\phi_{t\,\text{rotor}}$ are the loss coefficients for the stator and rotor, respectively, and the subscripted total pressure ratios are obtained from Eq. (9-93) and cascade data. Additional losses are associated with tip leakage, annulus boundary layers, and secondary flows. Then, with all the stator, rotor, and stage properties computed, the stage efficiency can be computed from Eq. (9-76).

BLADE SPACING. The momentum equation relates the tangential force of the blades on the fluid to the change in tangential momentum of the fluid. This force is equal and opposite to that which results from the difference in pressure between the pressure side and the suction side of the airfoil. Figure 9-65 shows the variation in pressure on both the suction and pressure surfaces of a typical turbine airfoil from cascade tests. On the pressure surface, the pressure is nearly equal to the inlet total pressure for 60 percent of the length before the fluid is accelerated to the exit pressure condition. However, on the suction surface, the fluid is accelerated in the first 60 percent of the length to a low pressure and then is decelerated to the exit pressure condition. The deceleration on the suction surface is limited and controlled since it can lead to boundary-layer separation.

Enough airfoils must be present in each row that the sum of the tangential force on each is equal to the change in tangential momentum of the fluid. A simple expression for the relationship of the blade spacing to the fluid flow angles is developed in this section based on an incompressible fluid. This same expression correlates to the required blade spacing in a turbine stator or rotor row.

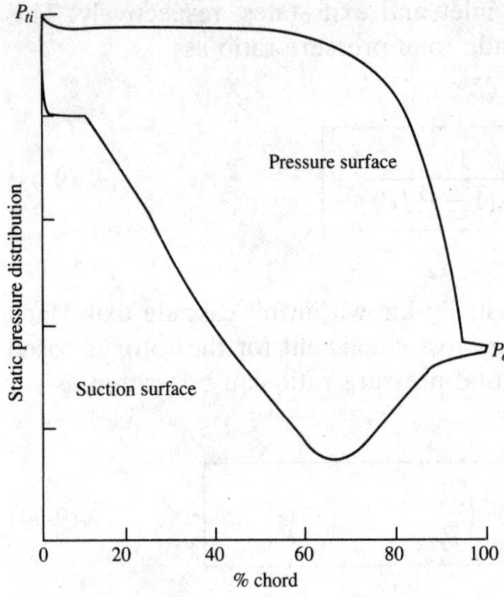

FIGURE 9-65
Pressure distribution on a turbine cascade airfoil.

Referring to the cascade nomenclature in Fig. 9-62, we see that the tangential force per unit depth of blades spaced a distance s apart is

$$F_t = \frac{\rho u_i s(v_i + v_e)}{g_c} = \frac{\rho u_i^2 s}{g_c}\left(\tan \alpha_i + \frac{u_e}{u_i}\tan \alpha_e\right) \tag{9-95}$$

Zweifel (Ref. 47) defines a tangential force coefficient that is the ratio of the force given by Eq. (9-95) to the maximum tangential force $F_{t\,\max}$ that can be achieved efficiently. And $F_{t\,\max}$ is obtained when

1. The pressure on the pressure surface is maintained at the inlet total pressure and drops to the exit static pressure at the trailing edge.
2. The pressure on the suction surface drops to the exit static pressure at the leading edge and remains at this value.

Thus the maximum tangential force is $F_{t\,\max} = (P_{ti} - P_e)c_x$, where c_x is the axial chord of the blade (see Fig. 9-62). For reversible flow of an incompressible fluid, $F_{t\,\max}$ can be written as

$$F_{t\,\max} = \frac{\rho V_e^2 c_x}{2g_c} = \frac{\rho u_e^2 c_x}{2g_c \cos^2 \alpha_e} \tag{9-96}$$

The *Zweifel tangential force coefficient* Z is defined as

$$\boxed{Z \equiv \frac{F_t}{F_{t\,\max}}} \tag{9-97}$$

From Eqs. (9-95) and (9-96), the equation of Z for a cascade airfoil becomes

$$Z = \frac{2s}{c_x}(\cos^2 \alpha_e)\left(\tan \alpha_i + \frac{u_e}{u_i}\tan \alpha_e\right)\left(\frac{u_i}{u_e}\right)^2$$

For the stator, we write

$$\boxed{Z_s = \frac{2s}{c_x}(\cos^2 \alpha_2)\left(\tan \alpha_1 + \frac{u_2}{u_1}\tan \alpha_2\right)\left(\frac{u_1}{u_2}\right)^2} \tag{9-98a}$$

Likewise for the rotor, we write

$$\boxed{Z_r = \frac{2s}{c_x}(\cos^2 \beta_3)\left(\tan \beta_2 + \frac{u_3}{u_2}\tan \beta_3\right)\left(\frac{u_2}{u_3}\right)^2} \tag{9-98b}$$

Since suction surface pressures can be less than the exit static pressure along the blade (see Fig. 9-65), *Z values near unity are attainable.* By using Eq. (9-98), lines of constant $Z_r c_x/s$ are plotted in Fig. 9-66 versus the relative rotor angles β_2 and β_3. High β_2 and zero reaction (high stage loading ψ, see Fig. 9-57) give high values of $Z_r c_x/s$ (see Fig. 9-66) and require high values of solidity $[\sigma = c/s = (c_x/s)/\cos\theta]$. High solidity at high β_2 and zero reaction can lead to high total pressure losses (see Fig. 9-64). For no exit swirl ($\alpha_3 = 0$), the

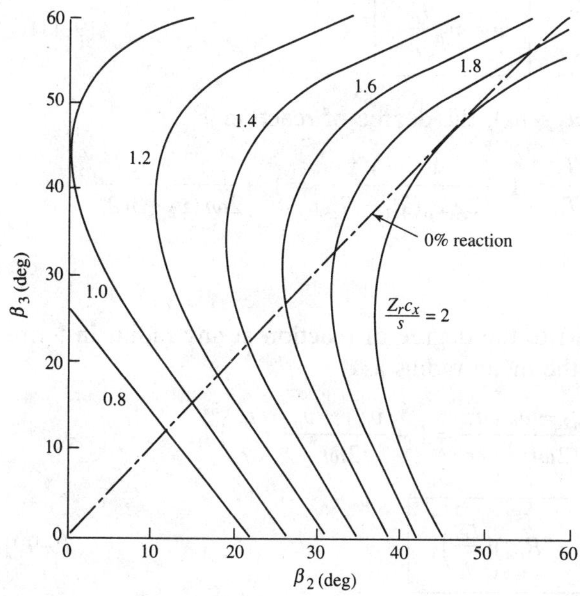

FIGURE 9-66
Zc_x/s of rotor versus β_2 and β_3.

FIGURE 9-67
Low-pressure turbine rotor blade (Ref. 46).

50 percent reaction stage ($\psi = 1$) corresponds to $\beta_2 = 0$, the required solidity is low (Fig. 9-66), and the total pressure losses are low (Fig. 9-64). Thus the turbine design for aircraft engines will be a balance between the number of stages (stage loadings) and the turbine efficiency (total pressure losses).

RADIAL VARIATIONS. Since the mass flow rate per unit area [that is, $\dot{m}/A = P_t/(\text{MFP}\sqrt{T_t})$] is higher in turbines than in compressors, turbine airfoils are correspondingly shorter. The result is little radial variation of aerodynamic properties from hub to tip except in the last few stages of the low-pressure turbine. Figure 9-67 is the rotor blade of a low-pressure turbine which shows radial variation from hub to tip. Typically, the degree of reaction varies from near zero at the hub to about 40 percent at the tip.

If the aerodynamic design of these stages began as free vortex, the swirl distribution with radius is the same as for compressors, given by

$$\boxed{v = v_m \frac{r_m}{r}} \tag{9-44}$$

For constant axial velocity ($u_2 = u_3$), the degree of reaction is

$$°R_t = \frac{T_2 - T_3}{T_{t1} - T_{t3}} = \frac{T_2 - T_3}{T_{t2} - T_{t3}} = 1 - \frac{V_2^2 - V_3^2}{2g_c c_p (T_{t1} - T_{t3})} = 1 - \frac{v_2^2 - v_3^2}{2\omega r(v_2 + v_3)}$$

$$= 1 - \frac{v_2 - v_3}{2\omega r}$$

Substituting Eq. (9-44), we write the degree of reaction at any radius in terms of the degree of reaction at the mean radius as

$$°R_t = 1 - \frac{v_{m2} - v_{m3}}{2\omega r}\frac{r_m}{r} = 1 - \frac{v_{m2} - v_{m3}}{2\omega r_m}\left(\frac{r_m}{r}\right)^2$$

$$\boxed{°R_t = 1 - (1 - °R_{tm})\left(\frac{r_m}{r}\right)^2} \tag{9-99}$$

This is the same result as for compressors [Eqs. (9-51) and (9-52)]. Consequently, the most difficult airfoil contours to design would be at the hub of the rotating airfoils and at the tips of the stationary airfoils where the degree of reaction is low. It is, therefore, possible to find portions of some airfoils near the rear of highly loaded (i.e., high work per stage), low-pressure turbines where the static pressure actually rises across the cascade and boundary-layer separation is hard to avoid. In these cases, turbine designers have used their computers to develop nonfree or controlled vortex machines without these troublesome regions in order to maintain high efficiency at high loading.

Due to radial variations, the degree of reaction is lowest at the hub. Hence the Zweifel tangential force coefficient of the rotor Z_r times c_x/s will be maximum at the hub. Although the blade spacing varies directly with radius, $Z_r c_x/s$ is greatest at the hub and decreases faster than $1/r$ with increasing radius. Thus the value of $Z_r c_x/s$ at the rotor hub determines the spacing and number of rotor blades. For the stator, $Z_s c_x/s$ will be greatest at the tip, and its value determines the spacing and number of stator blades.

VELOCITY RATIO VR. The *velocity ratio* (VR) is defined as the ratio of the rotor speed ($U = \omega r$) to the velocity equivalent of the change in stage total enthalpy, or

$$\boxed{\mathrm{VR} \equiv \frac{U}{\sqrt{2g_c\,\Delta h_t}} = \frac{\omega r}{\sqrt{2g_c\,\Delta h_t}}} \tag{9-100}$$

The velocity ratio is used by some turbine designers rather than the stage loading coefficient ψ, and one can show that

$$\boxed{\mathrm{VR} = \frac{1}{\sqrt{2\psi}}} \tag{9-101}$$

The VR at the mean radius ranges between 0.5 and 0.6 for modern aircraft gas turbine engines. This range corresponds to stage loading coefficients ψ between 1.4 and 2.

Axial-Flow Turbine Stage

ANALYSIS. Consider the flow through a single-stage turbine as shown in Fig. 9-68. For generality, we will allow the axial velocity to change from station 2 to 3. The flows through the nozzle (stator) and rotor are assumed to be adiabatic. For solution, we assume that the following data are known: M_2, T_{t1}, T_{t3}, ωr, α_3, c_p, γ, and u_3/u_2. We will develop and write the equations for a general axial-flow turbine based on these known data.

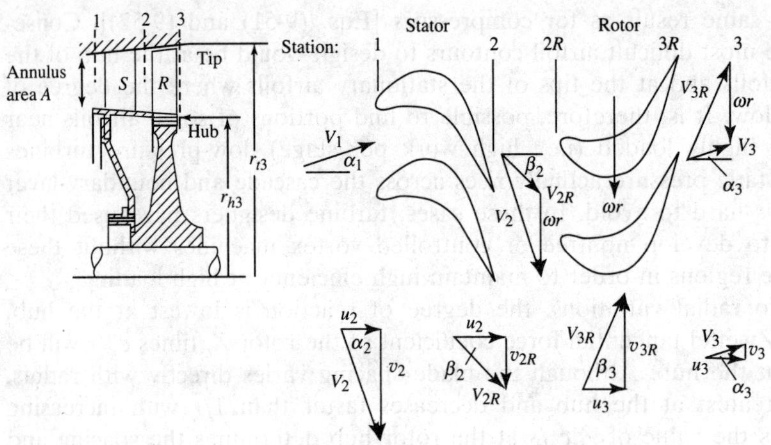

FIGURE 9-68
Axial-flow turbine stage (after Ref. 41).

To solve for the flow angle at station $2(\alpha_2)$, we first write the Euler turbine equation

$$c_p(T_{t2} - T_{t3}) = \frac{\omega r}{g_c}(v_2 + v_3) \tag{9-102}$$

Solving for v_2, we have

$$v_2 = \frac{g_c c_p \,\Delta T_t}{\omega r} - v_3$$

Then
$$\sin \alpha_2 = \frac{v_2}{V_2} = \frac{g_c c_p \,\Delta T_t}{\omega r V_2} - \frac{v_3}{V_2} \tag{i}$$

However,
$$\frac{v_3}{V_2} = \frac{u_3}{V_2} \tan \alpha_3 = \frac{u_3}{u_2}\frac{u_2}{V_2} \tan \alpha_3 = \frac{u_3}{u_2} \cos \alpha_2 \tan \alpha_3$$

Thus Eq. (i) becomes

$$\sin \alpha_2 = \frac{v_2}{V_2} = \frac{g_c c_p \,\Delta T_t}{\omega r V_2} - \frac{u_3}{u_2} \cos \alpha_2 \tan \alpha_3 \tag{ii}$$

By using the stage loading parameter ψ, Eq. (ii) can be written as

$$\sin \alpha_2 = \psi \frac{\omega r}{V_2} - \frac{u_3}{u_2} \cos \alpha_2 \tan \alpha_3 \tag{9-103}$$

The velocity at station 2 can be found from

$$V_2 = M_2 a_2 = \sqrt{\frac{2 g_c c_p T_{t2}}{1 + 2/[(\gamma - 1)M_2^2]}} \tag{9-104}$$

If $\alpha_3 = 0$, then Eq. (9-103) simplifies to

$$\boxed{\sin\alpha_2 = \psi\frac{\omega r}{V_2}} \tag{9-105}$$

If α_3 is not zero, Eq. (9-103) can be solved by substituting $\sqrt{1-\sin^2\alpha_2}$ for $\cos\alpha_2$, squaring both sides of the equation, and solving the resulting quadratic equation for $\sin\alpha_2$. The solution is

$$\boxed{\sin\alpha_2 = \frac{\left(\psi\frac{\omega r}{V_2}\right) - \left(\frac{u_3}{u_2}\tan\alpha_3\right)\sqrt{1+\left(\frac{u_3}{u_2}\tan\alpha_3\right)^2 - \left(\psi\frac{\omega r}{V_2}\right)^2}}{1+\left(\frac{u_3}{u_2}\tan\alpha_3\right)^2}} \tag{9-106}$$

The velocity at station 3 can be written in terms of that at station 2 and the two flow angles α_2 and α_3:

$$\boxed{V_3 = \frac{u_3\cos\alpha_2}{u_2\cos\alpha_3}V_2} \tag{9-107}$$

The degree of reaction can be written in terms of the given data as follows:

$$\begin{aligned}
{}^\circ R_t &= \frac{T_2 - T_3}{T_{t2} - T_{t3}} = \frac{T_{t2} - T_{t3} - (T_{t2} - T_2) + T_{t3} - T_3}{T_{t2} - T_{t3}} \\
&= 1 - \frac{V_2^2 - V_3^2}{2g_c c_p (T_{t2} - T_{t3})} = 1 - \frac{V_2^2 - V_3^2}{2\psi(\omega r)^2} \\
&= 1 - \frac{1}{2\psi(\omega r)^2}\left(\frac{u_2^2}{\cos^2\alpha_2} - \frac{u_3^2}{\cos^2\alpha_3}\right)
\end{aligned}$$

$$\boxed{{}^\circ R_t = 1 - \frac{1}{2\psi}\left(\frac{V_2}{\omega r}\right)^2\left[1 - \left(\frac{u_3\cos\alpha_2}{u_2\cos\alpha_3}\right)^2\right]} \tag{9-108}$$

The Mach number at station 3 can be found from

$$\boxed{M_3 = M_2\frac{V_3}{V_2}\sqrt{\frac{T_2}{T_3}}} \tag{9-109}$$

where

$$\boxed{\frac{T_3}{T_2} = 1 - {}^\circ R_t\frac{\Delta T_t}{T_{t2}}\left(1 + \frac{\gamma - 1}{2}M_2^2\right)} \tag{9-110}$$

An equation for the Mach number at station $2R$ can be developed as follows:

$$M_{2R} = M_2 \frac{V_{2R}}{V_2}$$

where $V_{2R} = \sqrt{u_2^2 + (v_2 - \omega r)^2} = V_2 \sqrt{\cos^2 \alpha_2 + \left(\sin \alpha_2 - \frac{\omega r}{V_2} \right)^2}$

Thus
$$M_{2R} = M_2 \sqrt{\cos^2 \alpha_2 + \left(\sin \alpha_2 - \frac{\omega r}{V_2} \right)^2} \tag{9-111}$$

Likewise, an equation for the Mach number at station $3R$ is developed as follows:

$$M_{3R} = M_3 \frac{V_{3R}}{V_3}$$

where $V_{3R} = \sqrt{u_3^2 + (v_3 + \omega r)^2} = V_3 \sqrt{\cos^2 \alpha_3 + \left(\sin \alpha_3 + \frac{\omega r}{V_3} \right)^2}$

Thus
$$M_{3R} = M_3 \sqrt{\cos^2 \alpha_3 + \left(\sin \alpha_3 + \frac{\omega r}{V_3} \right)^2} \tag{9-112}$$

An equation for the rotor relative total temperature ($T_{t2R} = T_{t3R}$) can be developed by noting that

$$T_3 = T_{t3} - \frac{V_3^2}{2g_c c_p} = T_{t3R} - \frac{V_{3R}^2}{2g_c c_p}$$

Then
$$T_{t3R} = T_{t3} + \frac{V_{3R}^2 - V_3^2}{2g_c c_p}$$

or
$$T_{t3R} = T_{t3} + \frac{V_3^2}{2g_c c_p} \left[\cos^2 \alpha_3 + \left(\sin \alpha_3 + \frac{\omega r}{V_3} \right)^2 - 1 \right] \tag{9-113}$$

Summary of Equations—Axial-Flow Turbine Stage

INPUTS: T_{t1}, T_{t3}, ωr, P_{t1}, M_1, M_2, α_1, α_3, c_p, γ, u_3/u_2, and e_t or $\phi_{t\,\text{stator}}$ and $\phi_{t\,\text{rotor}}$

OUTPUTS: α_2, V_2, u_2, v_2, T_2, P_{t2}, P_2, M_{2R}, V_3, u_3, v_3, T_3, P_{t3}, P_3, M_3, M_{3R}, ψ, VR, $°R_t$, $Z_s c_x/s$, $Z_r c_x/s$, π_s, and η_s

EQUATIONS:

$$T_1 = \frac{T_{t1}}{1 + [(\gamma - 1)/2]M_1^2}$$

$$V_1 = \sqrt{\frac{2g_c c_p T_{t1}}{1 + 2/[(\gamma - 1)M_1^2]}}$$

$$u_1 = V_1 \cos \alpha_1$$

$$T_{t2} = T_{t1}$$

$$T_2 = \frac{T_{t2}}{1 + [(\gamma - 1)/2]M_2^2}$$

$$V_2 = \sqrt{\frac{2g_c c_p T_{t2}}{1 + 2/[(\gamma - 1)M_2^2]}}$$

$$\psi = \frac{g_c c_p (T_{t1} - T_{t3})}{(\omega r)^2}$$

$$\text{VR} = \frac{1}{\sqrt{2\psi}}$$

$$\alpha_2 = \sin^{-1} \frac{\psi \dfrac{\omega r}{V_2} - \dfrac{u_3}{u_2} \tan \alpha_3 \sqrt{1 + \left(\dfrac{u_3}{u_2} \tan \alpha_3\right)^2 - \left(\psi \dfrac{\omega r}{V_2}\right)^2}}{1 + \left(\dfrac{u_3}{u_2} \tan \alpha_3\right)^2}$$

$$u_2 = V_2 \cos \alpha_2$$

$$v_2 = V_2 \sin \alpha_2$$

$$V_3 = \frac{u_3}{u_2} \frac{\cos \alpha_2}{\cos \alpha_3} V_2$$

$$u_3 = V_3 \cos \alpha_3$$

$$v_3 = V_3 \sin \alpha_3$$

$$°R_t = 1 - \frac{1}{2\psi} \left(\frac{V_2}{\omega r}\right)^2 \left[1 - \left(\frac{u_3}{u_2} \frac{\cos \alpha_2}{\cos \alpha_3}\right)^2\right]$$

$$T_3 = T_2 - °R_t (T_{t1} - T_{t3})$$

$$M_3 = M_2 \frac{V_3}{V_2} \sqrt{\frac{T_2}{T_3}}$$

$$M_{2R} = M_2 \sqrt{\cos^2 \alpha_2 + \left(\sin \alpha_2 - \frac{\omega r}{V_2}\right)^2}$$

$$M_{3R} = M_3 \sqrt{\cos^2 \alpha_3 + \left(\sin \alpha_3 + \frac{\omega r}{V_3}\right)^2}$$

$$T_{t3R} = T_{t3} + \frac{V_3^2}{2g_c c_p} \left[\cos^2 \alpha_3 + \left(\sin \alpha_3 + \frac{\omega r}{V_3}\right)^2 - 1\right]$$

$$T_{t2R} = T_{t3R}$$

$$P_2 = P_{t1}\left(\frac{T_1}{T_{t1}}\right)^{\gamma/(\gamma-1)}$$

$$\tau_s = \frac{T_{t3}}{T_{t1}}$$

$$\frac{Z_s c_x}{s} = (2\cos^2\alpha_2)\left(\tan\alpha_1 + \frac{u_2}{u_1}\tan\alpha_2\right)\left(\frac{u_1}{u_2}\right)^2$$

$$\beta_2 = \tan^{-1}\frac{v_2 - \omega r}{u_2}$$

$$\beta_3 = \tan^{-1}\frac{v_3 + \omega r}{u_3}$$

$$\frac{Z_r c_x}{s} = (2\cos^2\beta_3)\left(\tan\beta_2 + \frac{u_3}{u_2}\tan\beta_3\right)\left(\frac{u_2}{u_3}\right)^2$$

I. *$\phi_{t\,\text{stator}}$ and $\phi_{t\,\text{rotor}}$ given*:

$$P_{t2} = \frac{P_{t1}}{1 + \phi_{t\,\text{stator}}[1 - (T_2/T_{t2})^{\gamma/(\gamma-1)}]}$$

$$P_2 = P_{t2}\left(\frac{T_2}{T_{t2}}\right)^{\gamma/(\gamma-1)}$$

$$P_{t2R} = P_2\left(\frac{T_{t2R}}{T_2}\right)^{\gamma/(\gamma-1)}$$

$$P_{t3R} = \frac{P_{t2R}}{1 + \phi_{t\,\text{rotor}}[1 - (T_3/T_{t3R})^{\gamma/(\gamma-1)}]}$$

$$P_3 = P_{t3R}\left(\frac{T_3}{T_{t3R}}\right)^{\gamma/(\gamma-1)}$$

$$P_{t3} = P_3\left(\frac{T_{t3}}{T_3}\right)^{\gamma/(\gamma-1)}$$

$$\pi_s = \frac{P_{t3}}{P_{t1}}$$

$$\eta_t = \frac{1 - \tau_s}{1 - \pi_s^{(\gamma-1)/\gamma}}$$

II. *e_t given*:

$$P_{t3} = P_{t1}\left(\frac{T_{t3}}{T_{t1}}\right)^{\gamma/[(\gamma-1)e_t]}$$

$$\pi_s = \frac{P_{t3}}{P_{t1}}$$

$$\eta_s = \frac{1 - \tau_s}{1 - \pi_s^{(\gamma-1)/\gamma}}$$

$$P_3 = P_{t3}\left(\frac{T_3}{T_{t3}}\right)^{\gamma/(\gamma-1)}$$

$$P_{t3R} = P_3\left(\frac{T_{t3R}}{T_3}\right)^{\gamma/(\gamma-1)}$$

With polytropic efficiency specified, P_2, P_{t2}, and P_{t2R} cannot be calculated without an additional relationship for either P_2 or P_{t2}. For estimation of P_{t2}, the program TURBN has as the user input a value of $\phi_{t\,\text{stator}}$.

Example 9-10. *Mean-radius stage calculation—flow with losses.*

GIVEN: $T_{t1} = 1850$ K, $P_{t1} = 1700$ kPa, $M_1 = 0.4$, $\alpha_1 = 0°$, $T_{t3} = 1560$ K, $M_2 = 1.1$, $\omega r = 450$ m/sec, $\alpha_3 = 10°$, $u_3/u_2 = 0.9$, $\phi_{t\,\text{stator}} = 0.06$, $\phi_{t\,\text{rotor}} = 0.15$, $\gamma = 1.3$, and $R = 0.2873$ kJ/(kg · K) [$c_p = 1.245$ kJ/(kg · K)]

Solution.

$$T_1 = \frac{T_{t1}}{1 + [(\gamma-1)/2]M_1^2} = \frac{1850\text{ K}}{1 + 0.15 \times 0.4^2} = 1806.6\text{ K}$$

$$V_1 = \sqrt{\frac{2g_c c_p T_{t1}}{1 + 2/[(\gamma-1)M_1^2]}} = \sqrt{\frac{2 \times 1 \times 1245 \times 1850}{1 + 2/(0.3 \times 0.4^2)}} = 328.6\text{ m/sec}$$

$$u_1 = V_1 \cos\alpha_1 = 328.6\text{ m/sec}$$

$$v_1 = V_1 \sin\alpha_1 = 0$$

$$T_{t2} = T_{t1} = 1850\text{ K}$$

$$T_2 = \frac{T_{t2}}{1 + [(\gamma-1)/2]M_2^2} = \frac{1850\text{ K}}{1 + 0.15 \times 1.1^2} = 1565.8\text{ K}$$

$$V_2 = \sqrt{\frac{2g_c c_p T_{t2}}{1 + 2/[(\gamma-1)M_2^2]}}$$

$$= \sqrt{\frac{2 \times 1 \times 1245 \times 1850}{1 + 2/(0.3 \times 1.1^2)}} = 841.2\text{ m/sec}$$

$$\psi = \frac{g_c c_p (T_{t1} - T_{t3})}{(\omega r)^2} = \frac{1245(1850 - 1560)}{450^2} = 1.78296$$

$$\text{VR} = \frac{1}{\sqrt{2\psi}} = \frac{1}{\sqrt{2 \times 1.78296}} = 0.5296$$

$$\alpha_2 = \sin^{-1} \frac{\left(\psi \dfrac{\omega r}{V_2}\right) - \left(\dfrac{u_3}{u_2}\tan\alpha_3\right)\sqrt{1 + \left(\dfrac{u_3}{u_2}\tan\alpha_3\right)^2 - \left(\psi\dfrac{\omega r}{V_2}\right)^2}}{1 + \left(\dfrac{u_3}{u_2}\tan\alpha_3\right)^2}$$

$$\psi \frac{\omega r}{V_2} = 1.78296\left(\frac{450}{841.2}\right) = 0.95379$$

$$\frac{u_3}{u_2}\tan\alpha_3 = 0.9\tan 10° = 0.15869$$

$$\alpha_2 = \sin^{-1}\frac{0.95379 - 0.15869\sqrt{1 + 0.15869^2 - 0.95379^2}}{1.015869^2}$$

$$= \sin^{-1} 0.87776 = 61.37°$$

$$u_2 = V_2\cos\alpha_2 = 841.2\cos 61.37° = 403.1 \text{ m/sec}$$

$$v_2 = V_2\sin\alpha_2 = 841.2\sin 61.37° = 738.3 \text{ m/sec}$$

$$\Phi = \frac{u_2}{\omega r} = \frac{403.1}{450} = 0.8958$$

$$V_3 = \frac{u_3}{u_2}\frac{\cos\alpha_2}{\cos\alpha_3}V_2 = 0.9\left(\frac{\cos 61.37°}{\cos 10°}\right)(841.2) = 368.4 \text{ m/sec}$$

$$u_3 = V_3\cos\alpha_3 = 368.4\cos 10° = 362.8 \text{ m/sec}$$

$$v_3 = V_3\sin\alpha_3 = 368.4\sin 10° = 64.0 \text{ m/sec}$$

$$°R_t = 1 - \frac{1}{2\psi}\left(\frac{V_2}{\omega r}\right)^2\left[1 - \left(\frac{u_3}{u_2}\frac{\cos\alpha_2}{\cos\alpha_3}\right)^2\right]$$

$$= 1 - \frac{1}{2\times 1.78296}\left(\frac{841.2}{450}\right)^2\left[1 - \left(0.9\frac{\cos 61.37°}{\cos 10°}\right)^2\right] = 0.2080$$

$$T_3 = T_2 - °R_t(T_{t1} - T_{t3}) = 1565.8 - 0.2080(1850 - 1560) = 1505.5 \text{ K}$$

$$M_3 = M_2\frac{V_3}{V_2}\sqrt{\frac{T_2}{T_3}} = 1.1\left(\frac{368.4}{841.2}\right)\sqrt{\frac{1565.8}{1505.5}} = 0.4913$$

$$M_{2R} = M_2\sqrt{\cos^2\alpha_2 + \left(\sin\alpha_2 - \frac{\omega r}{V_2}\right)^2}$$

$$= 1.1\sqrt{\cos^2 61.37° + \left(\sin 61.37° - \frac{450}{841.2}\right)^2} = 0.6481$$

$$M_{3R} = M_3\sqrt{\cos^2\alpha_3 + \left(\sin\alpha_3 + \frac{\omega r}{V_3}\right)^2}$$

$$= 0.4913\sqrt{\cos^2 10° + \left(\sin 10° + \frac{450}{368.4}\right)^2} = 0.8390$$

$$T_{t3R} = T_{t3} + \frac{V_3^2}{2g_c c_p}\left[\cos^2 \alpha_3 + \left(\sin \alpha_3 + \frac{\omega r}{V_3}\right)^2 - 1\right]$$

$$= 1560 + \frac{368.4^2}{2 \times 1 \times 1245}\left[\cos^2 10° + \left(\sin 10° + \frac{450}{368.4}\right)^2 - 1\right]$$

$$= 1664.4 \text{ K}$$

$$T_{t2R} = T_{t3R} = 1664.4 \text{ K}$$

$$\tau_s = \frac{T_{t3}}{T_{t1}} = \frac{1560}{1850} = 0.8432$$

$$\frac{Z_s c_x}{s} = (2\cos^2 \alpha_2)\left(\tan \alpha_1 + \frac{u_2}{u_1}\tan \alpha_2\right)\left(\frac{u_1}{u_2}\right)^2$$

$$= (2\cos^2 61.371°)\left(\tan 0° + \frac{403.1}{328.6}\tan 61.37°\right)\left(\frac{328.6}{403.1}\right)^2 = 0.6857$$

$$\beta_2 = \tan^{-1}\frac{v_2 - \omega r}{u_2} = \tan^{-1}\frac{738.3 - 450}{403.1} = 35.57°$$

$$\beta_3 = \tan^{-1}\frac{v_3 + \omega r}{u_3} = \tan^{-1}\frac{64.0 + 450}{362.8} = 54.78°$$

$$\frac{Z_r c_x}{s} = (2\cos^2 \beta_3)\left(\tan \beta_2 + \frac{u_3}{u_2}\tan \beta_3\right)\left(\frac{u_2}{u_3}\right)^2$$

$$= (2\cos^2 54.78°)(\tan 35.573° + 0.9 \tan 54.78°)\left(\frac{1}{0.9}\right)^2$$

$$= 1.6330$$

$$P_1 = P_{t1}\left(\frac{T_1}{T_{t1}}\right)^{\gamma/(\gamma-1)} = 1700\left(\frac{1806.6}{1850}\right)^{1.3/0.3} = 1533.8 \text{ kPa}$$

$$P_{t2} = \frac{P_{t1}}{1 + \phi_{t\,\text{stator}}[1 - (T_2/T_{t2})^{\gamma/(\gamma-1)}]}$$

$$= \frac{1700}{1 + 0.06[1 - (1565.8/1850)^{1.3/0.3}]} = 1649.1 \text{ kPa}$$

$$P_2 = P_{t2}\left(\frac{T_2}{T_{t2}}\right)^{\gamma/(\gamma-1)} = 1649.1\left(\frac{1565.8}{1850}\right)^{1.3/0.3} = 800.5 \text{ kPa}$$

$$P_{t2R} = P_2\left(\frac{T_{t2R}}{T_2}\right)^{\gamma/(\gamma-1)} = 800.5\left(\frac{1664.4}{1565.8}\right)^{1.3/0.3} = 1043.0 \text{ kPa}$$

$$P_{t3R} = \frac{P_{t2R}}{1 + \phi_{t\,\text{rotor}}[1 - (T_3/T_{t3R})^{\gamma/(\gamma-1)}]}$$

$$= \frac{1043.0}{1 + 0.15[1 - (1505.5/1664.4)^{1.3/0.3}]} = 990.6 \text{ kPa}$$

$$P_3 = P_{t3R}\left(\frac{T_3}{T_{t3R}}\right)^{\gamma/(\gamma-1)} = 990.6\left(\frac{1505.5}{1664.4}\right)^{1.3/0.3} = 641.3 \text{ kPa}$$

$$P_{t3} = P_3\left(\frac{T_{t3}}{T_3}\right)^{\gamma/(\gamma-1)} = 641.3\left(\frac{1560}{1505.5}\right)^{1.3/0.3} = 748.1 \text{ kPa}$$

$$\pi_s = \frac{P_{t3}}{P_{t1}} = \frac{748.1}{1700} = 0.441$$

$$\eta_s = \frac{1-\tau_s}{1-\pi_s^{(\gamma-1)/\gamma}} = \frac{1-0.8432}{1-0.4401^{0.3/1.3}} = 90.87\%$$

Flow Path Dimensions

ANNULUS AREA. The annulus area (see Fig. 9-26) at any station of a turbine stage is based on the flow properties (T_t, P_t, Mach number, and flow angle) at the mean radius and the total mass flow rate. Equation (9-8) is the easiest equation to use to calculate the flow area at any station i:

$$A_i = \frac{\dot{m}\sqrt{T_{ti}}}{P_{ti}(\cos\alpha_i)\text{MFP}(M_i)} \tag{9-8}$$

By using the relationships of Fig. 9-26, the radii at any station i can be determined, given the flow annulus area [Eq. (9-8)] and either the mean radius r_m or the hub/tip ratio r_h/r_t.

AXIAL DIMENSIONS AND NUMBER OF BLADES. Figure 9-69 shows the cross section of a typical turbine stage which can be used to estimate its axial length. The chord/height ratio c/h of turbine blades varies from about 0.3 to 1.0. Assuming constant chord length and circular arc chamber line, the program TURBN calculates the axial blade widths W_s and W_r of a stage, the blade spacings $W_s/4$ and $W_r/4$, and the number of blades based on user inputs of the tangential force coefficient Z and chord/height ratio c/h for both the stator and rotor blades. A minimum width of $\frac{1}{4}$ in (0.6 cm) and spacing of $\frac{1}{8}$ in (0.3 cm) are used in the plot of a turbine cross section and calculation of axial length.

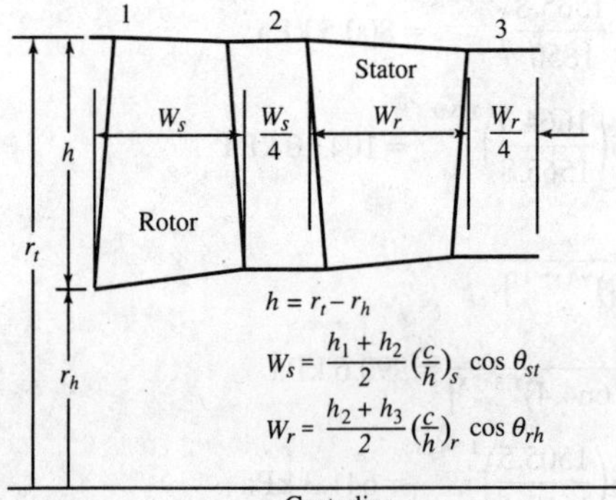

FIGURE 9-69
Typical axial dimensions of a turbine stage.

The stagger angle θ of a blade depends on the shape of the chamber line and blade angles γ_i and γ_e (see Fig. 9-62). For a circular arc chamber line, the stagger angle θ is simply given by $\theta = (\gamma_e - \gamma_i)/2$. For constant-chord blades, the axial chord (and axial blade width) is greatest where the stagger angle is closest to zero. This normally occurs at the tip of the stator and hub of the rotor blades. For estimation purposes, a turbine blade's incidence angle is normally small and can be considered to be zero. Thus $\gamma_i = \alpha_i$. The blade's exit angle γ_e can be obtained using Eq. (9-89) for the exit deviation. However, Eq. (9-89) requires that the solidity ($\sigma = c/s$) be known. For known flow conditions (α_1, α_2, u_2/u_1, α_2, α_3, and u_3/u_2) and given tangential force coefficients (Z_s and Z_r), Eqs. (9-98*a*) and (9-98*b*) will give the required axial chord/spacing ratio c_x/s for the stator and rotor, respectively. An initial guess for the blade's solidity σ is needed to obtain the stagger angle θ from c_x/s.

After the solidities are determined at the hub, mean, and tip that give the desired tangential force coefficient Z, the number of required blades follows directly from the chord/height ratio c/h, the circumference, and the blade spacing at each radius. The following example shows the calculations needed to find the axial blade width and number of blades.

Example 9-11. Here we consider the turbine stator of Example 9-10 with a mass flow rate of 60 kg/sec, a mean radius of 0.3 m, a tangential force coefficient Z_s of 0.9, and a chord/height ratio c/h of 1.0. The flow annulus areas and radii at stations 1 and 2 are as follows:

Station 1:
$$\text{MFP}(M_1) = \frac{\text{MFP}(M_1)\sqrt{R/g_c}}{\sqrt{R/g_c}} = \frac{0.416436}{\sqrt{287.3}} = 0.024569$$

$$A_1 = \frac{\dot{m}\sqrt{T_{t1}}}{P_{t1}\,\text{MFP}(M_1)(\cos\alpha_1)} = \frac{60\sqrt{1850}}{1{,}700{,}00 \times 0.024569 \times 1} = 0.0617788\ \text{m}^2$$

$$h_1 = \frac{A_1}{2\pi r_m} = \frac{0.061788}{0.6\pi} = 0.03278\ \text{m}$$

$$r_{t1} = 0.3164\ \text{m} \qquad r_{h1} = 0.2836\ \text{m}$$

$$v_{1h} = v_{1m} = v_{1t} = 0$$

Station 2:
$$\text{MFP}(M_2) = \frac{\text{MFP}(M_2)\sqrt{R/g_c}}{\sqrt{R/g_c}} = \frac{0.661762}{\sqrt{287.3}} = 0.039042$$

$$A_2 = \frac{\dot{m}\sqrt{T_{t2}}}{P_{t2}\,\text{MFP}(M_2)(\cos\alpha_2)} = \frac{60\sqrt{1850}}{1{,}649{,}100 \times 0.039042 \times \cos 61.37^\circ} = 0.083654\ \text{m}^2$$

$$h_2 = \frac{A_2}{2\pi r_m} = \frac{0.083654}{0.6\pi} = 0.04438\ \text{m} \qquad r_{t2} = 0.3222\ \text{m} \qquad r_{h2} = 0.2778\ \text{m}$$

$$v_{2h} = v_{2m}\frac{r_m}{r_{2h}} = 738.3\left(\frac{0.3}{0.2778}\right) = 797.3\ \text{m/sec}$$

$$\alpha_{2h} = \tan^{-1}\frac{v_{2h}}{u_2} = \tan^{-1}\frac{797.3}{403.1} = 63.18^\circ$$

$$v_{2t} = v_{2m}\frac{r_m}{r_{2t}} = 738.3\left(\frac{0.3}{0.3222}\right) = 687.4 \text{ m/sec}$$

$$\alpha_{2t} = \tan^{-1}\frac{v_{2t}}{u_2} = \tan^{-1}\frac{687.4}{403.1} = 59.61°$$

The chord of the stator is

$$c = \frac{c}{h}\,\frac{h_1 + h_2}{2} = 1.0\,\frac{0.03278 + 0.04438}{2} = 0.03858 \text{ m}$$

For the specified tangential force coefficient Z_s, we calculate the stagger angle, solidity, and spacing of the stator at the mean line, hub, and tip.

Mean line: $$Z_s\left(\frac{c_x}{s}\right)_m = (2\cos^2\alpha_{2m})\left(\tan\alpha_{1m} + \frac{u_2}{u_1}\tan\alpha_{2m}\right)\left(\frac{u_1}{u_2}\right)^2$$

$$= (2\cos^2 61.37°)\left(\tan 0° + \frac{403.1}{328.6}\tan 61.37°\right)\left(\frac{328.6}{403.1}\right)^2 = 0.6857$$

$$\left(\frac{c_x}{s}\right)_m = \frac{0.6857}{0.9} = 0.7619$$

$$\gamma_{1m} = \alpha_{1m} = 0$$

Initially, we assume a solidity σ of 1.0.

$$\gamma_{2m} = \frac{\gamma_{1m} + 8\sqrt{\sigma_m}\,\alpha_{2m}}{8\sqrt{\sigma_m} - 1} = \frac{0 + 8\sqrt{1}\,61.37}{8\sqrt{1} - 1} = 70.14°$$

$$\theta_m = \frac{\gamma_{2m} - \gamma_{1m}}{2} = \frac{70.14}{2} = 35.07°$$

$$\sigma_m = \frac{(c_x/s)_m}{\cos\theta_m} = \frac{0.7619}{\cos 35.07°} = 0.9309$$

After several iterations, the results are $\gamma_{2m} = 70.49°$, $\theta_m = 35.25°$, and $\sigma_m = 0.9329$. The blade spacing s is 0.04135 m, and the axial chord is 0.03150 m.

Hub: $$Z_s\left(\frac{c_x}{s}\right)_h = (2\cos^2\alpha_{2h})\left(\tan\alpha_{1h} + \frac{u_2}{u_1}\tan\alpha_{2h}\right)\left(\frac{u_1}{u_2}\right)^2$$

$$= (2\cos^2 63.18°)\left(\tan 0° + \frac{403.1}{328.6}\tan 63.18°\right)\left(\frac{328.6}{403.1}\right)^2 = 0.6565$$

$$\left(\frac{c_x}{s}\right)_h = \frac{0.6565}{0.9} = 0.7294$$

$$\gamma_{1h} = \alpha_{1h} = 0$$

Initially, we assume a solidity σ of 1.0.

$$\gamma_{2h} = \frac{\gamma_{1h} + 8\sqrt{\sigma_h}\alpha_{2h}}{8\sqrt{\sigma_h} - 1} = \frac{0 + 8\sqrt{1}63.18}{8\sqrt{1} - 1} = 72.21°$$

$$\theta_h = \frac{\gamma_{2h} - \gamma_{1h}}{2} = \frac{72.21}{2} = 36.10°$$

$$\sigma_h = \frac{(c_x/s)_h}{\cos\theta_h} = \frac{0.7294}{\cos 361.0°} = 0.9027$$

After several iterations, the results are $\gamma_{2h} = 72.73°$, $\theta_h = 36.37°$, and $\sigma_h = 0.9058$. The blade spacing s is 0.04259 m, and the axial chord is 0.03107 m.

$$\textit{Tip:} \quad Z_x\left(\frac{c_x}{s}\right)_t = (2\cos^2\alpha_{2t})\left(\tan\alpha_{1t} + \frac{u_2}{u_1}\tan\alpha_{2t}\right)\left(\frac{u_1}{u_2}\right)^2$$

$$= (2\cos^2 59.61°)\left(\tan 0° + \frac{403.1}{328.6}\tan 59.61°\right)\left(\frac{328.6}{403.1}\right)^2 = 0.7115$$

$$\left(\frac{c_x}{s}\right)_t = \frac{0.7115}{0.9} = 0.7905$$

$$\gamma_{1t} = \alpha_{1t} = 0$$

Initially, we assume a solidity σ of 1.0:

$$\gamma_{2t} = \frac{\gamma_{1t} + 8\sqrt{\sigma_t}\alpha_{2t}}{8\sqrt{\sigma_t} - 1} = \frac{0 + 8\sqrt{1}59.61}{8\sqrt{1} - 1} = 68.13°$$

$$\theta_t = \frac{\gamma_{2t} - \gamma_{1t}}{2} = \frac{68.13}{2} = 34.06°$$

$$\sigma_t = \frac{(c_x/s)_t}{\cos\theta_t} = \frac{0.7905}{\cos 34.06°} = 0.9542$$

After several iterations, the results are $\gamma_{2t} = 68.35°$, $\theta_t = 34.18°$, and $\sigma_t = 0.9555$. The blade spacing s is 0.04038 m, and the axial chord is 0.03192 m.

For this stator blade with a chord of 0.03858 m, we require:

Location	Average radius (m)	Solidity	Spacing (m)	Number of blades	Axial chord (m)
Tip	0.3193	0.9555	0.04038	49.7	0.03192
Mean	0.3000	0.9329	0.04135	45.6	0.03150
Hub	0.2807	0.9058	0.04259	41.4	0.03107

Thus the number of required stator blades is 50, which will have a mean-radius spacing s of 0.03770 m and solidity σ of 1.023 (=0.03858/0.03770) on the mean radius. The blade has an axial width W_s of 0.03192 m (see Fig. 9-69).

BLADE PROFILE. The shapes of turbine stator and rotor blades are based on airfoil shapes developed specifically for turbine applications. Two airfoil

TABLE 9-12
British C4 airfoil profile ($t/c = 0.10$)

x/c (%)	y/c (%)	x/c (%)	y/c (%)
0.0	0.0	40	4.89
1.25	1.65	50	4.57
2.5	2.27	60	4.05
5	3.08	70	3.37
7.5	3.62	80	2.54
10	4.02	90	1.60
15	4.55	95	1.06
20	4.83	100	0.0
30	5.00		

Leading-edge radius = $0.12t$.
Trailing-edge radius = $0.06t$.

shapes are included in the program TURBN to sketch the blade shapes for a stage: the C4 and T6 British profiles. The base profile of the C4 airfoil is listed in Table 9-12 and shown in Fig. 9-70 for a 10 percent thickness. Table 9-13 and Fig. 9-71 give the base profile of the T6 airfoil for a 10 percent thickness. The

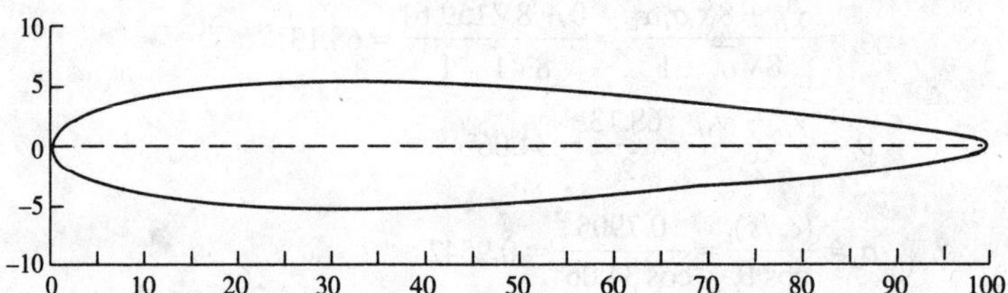

FIGURE 9-70
The C4 turbine airfoil base profile.

TABLE 9-13
British T6 airfoil profile ($t/c = 0.10$)

x/c (%)	y/c (%)	x/c (%)	y/c (%)
0.0	0.0	40	5.00
1.25	1.17	50	4.67
2.5	1.54	60	3.70
5	1.99	70	2.51
7.5	2.37	80	1.42
10	2.74	90	0.85
15	3.4	95	0.72
20	3.95	100	0.0
30	4.72		

Leading-edge radius = $0.12t$.
Trailing-edge radius = $0.06t$.

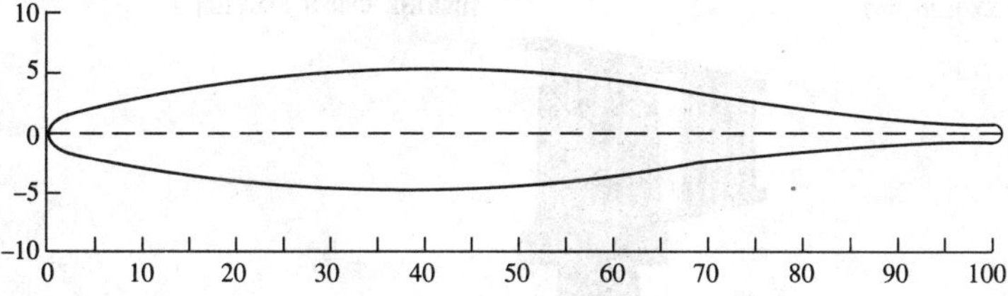

FIGURE 9-71
The T6 turbvine airfoil base profile.

program TURBN assumes a circular arc mean line for sketching the blade shapes.

Example 9-12. *Single-stage turbine using computer program TURBN.*

GIVEN: $\dot{m} = 200$ lbm/sec, $M_1 = 0.4$, $T_{t1} = 3400$°R, $T_{t3} = 2860$°R, $M_2 = 1.1$, $\omega r = 1500$ ft/sec, $r_m = 12$ in, $P_{t1} = 250$ psia, $\alpha_1 = 0°$, $\alpha_3 = 10°$, $\gamma = 1.3$, $R = 53.40$ ft · lbf/(lbm · °R), $u_3/u_2 = 0.90$, $\phi_{t\,\text{stator}} = 0.06$, and $\phi_{t\,\text{rotor}} = 0.15$

Solution. The program TURBN is run with α_2 as the unknown. The results are given in Table 9-14 with the hub and tip tangential velocities based on free-vortex swirl distribution. The cross section of the stage sketched by the computer program is shown in Fig. 9-72 for stator $c/h = 0.8$ and rotor $c/h = 0.6$. The very high AN^2 of 4.18×10^{10} in^2 · rpm^2 at a relative total temperature of

TABLE 9-14
Results for Example 9-12 axial-flow turbine stage calculation using TURBN

Property \ Station		1*h*	1*m*	1*t*	2*h*	2*m*	2*t*	2*Rm*	3*Rm*	3*h*	3*m*	3*t*
T_t	(°R)	3400	3400	3400	3400	3400	3400	3052	3052	2860	2860	2860
T	(°R)	3320	3320	3320	2767	2878	2957	2878	2768	2767	2768	2769
P_t	(psia)	250.0	250.0	250.0	242.5	242.5	242.5	151.9	144.4	109.0	109.0	109.0
P	(psia)	225.6	225.6	225.6	99.2	117.7	132.4	117.7	94.6	94.4	94.6	94.7
M		0.400	0.400	0.400	1.236	1.100	1.000	0.636	0.827	0.474	0.471	0.469
V	(ft/sec)	1089	1089	1089	3071	2789	2569	1611	2057	1178	1171	1167
u	(ft/sec)	1089	1089	1089	1282	1282	1282	1282	1153	1153	1153	1153
v	(ft/sec)	0	0	0	2791	2477	2226	977	1703	239	203	177
α	(deg)	0	0	0	65.34	62.64	60.07	—	—	11.68	10.00	8.74
β	(deg)	—	—	—	—	—	—	37.32	55.90	—	—	—
Radii	(in)	11.04	12.00	12.96	10.65	12.00	13.35	12.00	12.00	10.20	12.00	13.80

Hub: $°R_t = -0.0005$ $A_1 = 144.31$ in^2

Mean: $°R_t = 0.2034$ $A_2 = 203.72$ in^2

Tip: $°R_t = 0.3487$ $A_3 = 271.04$ in^2

$\tau_s = 0.8412$ $\pi_s = 0.4359$ RPM = 14,324 $\psi = 1.7868$ $\Phi = 0.8544$

$\eta_s = 91.08\%$ and AN^2 at 2 = 4.18×10^{10} in^2 · rpm^2

FIGURE 9-72
Sketch of cross section for turbine stage of Example 9-12.

3052°R is not possible with current materials unless the blades are cooled. Also, the high rim speed of about 1206 ft/sec would require existing materials to be cooled.

Axial-Flow Turbine Stage—α_2 Known

The above method of calculation assumed that α_2 was unknown. The program TURBN will handle the case when any one of the following four variables is unknown:

$$\alpha_2,\ T_{t3},\ \alpha_3,\ \text{or } M_2$$

When T_{t3} is unknown, Eqs. (9-20) and (9-103) are solved for T_{t3}, giving

$$T_{t3} = T_{t1} - \frac{\omega r V_2}{g_c c_p}\left(\sin\alpha_2 - \frac{u_3}{u_2}\cos\alpha_2\tan\alpha_3\right) \tag{9-114}$$

When α_3 is unknown, Eqs. (9-20) and (9-103) are solved for α_3, giving

$$\tan\alpha_3 = \frac{1}{u_3/u_2}\left(\frac{\psi}{\cos\alpha_2}\frac{\omega r}{V_2} - \tan\alpha_2\right) \tag{9-115}$$

When M_2 is unknown, the velocity at station 2 (V_2) is obtained from Eq. (9-103), giving

$$V_2 = \frac{\psi\,\omega r}{\sin\alpha_2 + (u_3/u_2)\cos\alpha_2\tan\alpha_3} \tag{9-116}$$

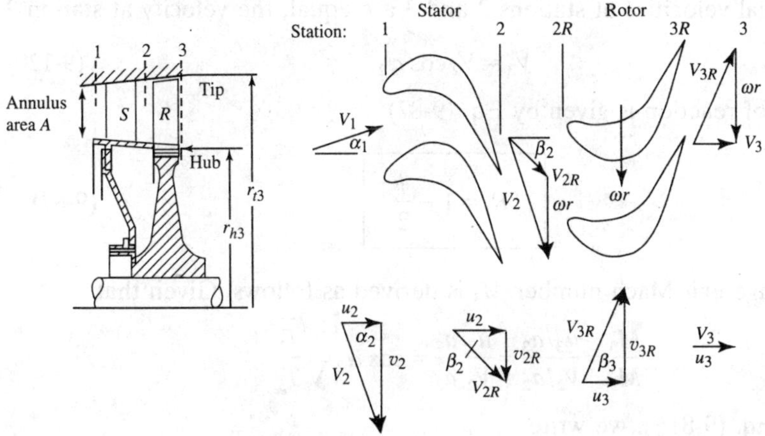

FIGURE 9-73
Generalized turbine stage, zero exit swirl.

Then M_2 is obtained from Eq. (9-104) rewritten as

$$M_2 = \frac{V_2}{\sqrt{(\gamma - 1)g_c c_p T_{t2} - [(\gamma - 1)/2]V_2^2}} \tag{9-117}$$

Axial-Flow Turbine Stage Analysis—No Exit Swirl

Consider the flow through a single-stage turbine as shown in Fig. 9-73 with zero exit swirl. We will consider the case where there is no exit swirl ($v_3 = 0$, $\alpha_3 = 0$) and the axial velocities at stations 2 to 3 are the same ($u_2 = u_3$). The flows through the nozzle (stator) and rotor are assumed to be adiabatic. For solution, we assume the following data are known:

$$M_2,\ T_{t1},\ T_{t3},\ \omega r,\ c_p, \text{ and } \gamma$$

The equations for solution of a zero exit swirl, axial-flow turbine based on these known data are developed in this section.

At station 2, V_2 is given by

$$V_2 = \sqrt{\frac{2g_c c_p T_{t2}}{1 + 2/[(\gamma - 1)M_2^2]}}$$

$$= \omega r \sqrt{\frac{2\psi/(1 - \tau_s)}{1 + 2/[(\gamma - 1)M_2^2]}} \tag{9-118}$$

and α_2 by

$$\sin \alpha_2 = \psi \frac{\omega r}{V_2} = \sqrt{(1 - \tau_s)\frac{\psi}{2}\left[1 + \frac{2}{(\gamma - 1)M_2^2}\right]} \tag{9-119}$$

Since the axial velocities at stations 2 and 3 are equal, the velocity at station 3 is given by

$$V_3 = V_2 \cos \alpha_2 \tag{9-120}$$

The degree of reaction is given by Eq. (9-87):

$$\boxed{{}^\circ R_t = 1 - \frac{\psi}{2}} \tag{9-87}$$

The stage exit Mach number M_3 is derived as follows. Given that

$$\frac{M_3}{M_2} = \frac{u_3/a_3}{V_2/a_2} = \frac{u_2}{V_2}\frac{a_2}{a_3} = \cos \alpha_2 \sqrt{\frac{T_2}{T_3}}$$

Then from Eq. (9-81*b*), we write

$${}^\circ R_t = \frac{T_2 - T_3}{T_{t1} - T_{t3}} = 1 - \frac{\psi}{2}$$

which allows the temperature ratio T_2/T_3 to be written as

$$\frac{T_2}{T_3} = \frac{1}{1 - (T_{t2}/T_2)(1 - \tau_s)(1 - \psi/2)} \tag{9-121}$$

Thus the Mach number M_3 can be written as

$$\boxed{M_3 = \frac{M_2 \cos \alpha_2}{\sqrt{1 - (1 - \tau_s)(1 - \psi/2)\{1 + (\gamma - 1)/2]M_2^2\}}}} \tag{9-122}$$

A compact equation for the rotor exit relative Mach number M_{3R} is developed as follows. Since

$$\frac{M_{3R}}{M_2} = \frac{V_{3R}}{a_3}\frac{a_2}{V_2} = \frac{V_{3R}}{V_2}\sqrt{\frac{T_2}{T_3}}$$

the velocity ratio is obtained by first writing

$$V_{3R}^2 = u^2 + (\omega r)^2 = V_2^2 - v_2^2 + (\omega r)^2$$

Thus
$$\frac{V_{3R}^2}{V_2^2} = 1 - \frac{v_2^2}{V_2^2} + \frac{(\omega r)^2}{V_2^2} = 1 - \left(\frac{\omega r}{V_2}\right)^2 \left[\left(\frac{v_2}{\omega r}\right)^2 - 1\right]$$

$$= 1 - \left(\frac{\omega r}{V_2}\right)^2 (\psi^2 - 1)$$

Since
$$\frac{M_{3R}}{M_2} = \frac{V_{3R}}{V_2}\sqrt{\frac{T_2}{T_3}}$$

then by using Eq. (9-121), the Mach number ratio is found by

$$\frac{M_{3R}}{M_2} = \sqrt{\frac{1 - (\omega r/V_2)^2(\psi^2 - 1)}{1 - (T_{t2}/T_2)(1 - \tau_s)(1 - \psi/2)}} \tag{9-123}$$

which with Eq. (9-119) becomes (and is actually used as)

$$\boxed{\frac{M_{3R}}{M_2}=\sqrt{\frac{1-(1-\tau_s)\dfrac{\psi^2-1}{2\psi}\left[1+\dfrac{2}{(\gamma-1)M_2^2}\right]}{1-(1-\tau_s)\left(1-\dfrac{\psi}{2}\right)\left(1+\dfrac{\gamma-1}{2}M_2^2\right)}}} \tag{9-124}$$

This equation contains an interesting and unexpected piece of guidance for the design of turbine stages. To ensure that stator cascade choking controls the turbine mass flow rate, M_2 should be greater than unity and M_{3R} should be less than unity. Equation (9-124) reveals, however, that when the stage loading coefficient is unity (degree of reaction is 0.5), the opposite must be true. Therefore, even though it would appear preferable to aim for a degree of reaction near 0.5 in order to balance the difficulty of designing the stator and rotor airfoils, the requirement to reduce M_{3R} translates to lower allowable values of the degree of reaction and correspondingly higher stage loadings. In actual practice, the degree of reaction is usually found in the range of 0.2 to 0.4, so that a substantial, but minority, fraction of the overall static enthalpy (and static presssure) drop still takes place across the rotor and is available to prevent the separation of the suction surface boundary layer. It is important to bear in mind that even turbine airfoil boundary layers can separate, and when they do, the effect on efficiency (and heat transfer) is usually disastrous.

The rotor relative total temperature ($T_{t2R}=T_{t3R}$), which is useful for heat transfer and structural analyses, is given by Eq. (9-113). For our case of zero exit swirl and constant axial velocity ($u_3=u_2$), this equation reduces to

$$\boxed{\frac{T_{t3R}}{T_{t2}}=\tau_s+\frac{1-\tau_s}{2\psi}} \tag{9-125}$$

Example 9-13. To illustrate the application of this method, a single-stage turbine with zero exit swirl will be designed for the following conditions:

$$M_1=0.4 \qquad M_2=1.10$$

$$\omega r=U=300\ \text{m/sec} \qquad T_{t2}=T_{t1}=1400\ \text{K}$$

$$R=0.2872\ \text{kJ/(kg}\cdot\text{K)} \qquad g_c c_p=1.158\ \text{kJ/(kg}\cdot\text{K)}$$

$$T_{t3}=1260\ \text{K} \qquad \gamma=1.33$$

$$\tau_s=\frac{T_{t3}}{T_{t1}}=0.900 \qquad \psi=1.8006\quad \text{Eq. (9-20)}$$

TABLE 9-15
Results for Example 9-13 axial-flow turbine stage calculation with zero exit swirl

Property \ Station		1	2	2*R*	3*R*	3
T_t	(K)	1400.0	1400.0	1298.9	1298.9	1260.0
T	(K)	1364.0	1167.0	1167.0	2012.7	2012.7
$\frac{P_t}{P_{t1}}$		1.0000	?	?	0.7053	0.6239
$\frac{P}{P_{t1}}$		0.9003	?	?	0.4364	0.4364
M		0.400	1.100	0.8586	0.8756	0.7498
V	(m/sec)	288.7	734.4	552.5	581.0	497.6
u	(m/sec)	288.7	497.6	497.6	497.6	497.6
v	(m/sec)	0	540.2	240.2	300.0	0
α	(deg)	0	47.35	—	—	0
β	(deg)	—	—	25.76	31.09	—

If one chooses to assume $e_t = 0.90$, the results are

$°R_t = 0.0997$	Eq. (9-87)	$M_{3R} = 0.8756$	Eq. (9-124)
$\alpha_2 = 47.35°$	Eq. (9-119)	$T_{t3R} = 1299$ K	Eq. (9-125)
$M_3 = 0.7498$	Eq. (9-122)	$\Phi = 1.6586$	Eq. (9-78*a*)
$\pi_s = 0.6239$	Eq. (9-91)	$\eta_t = 0.9053$	Eq. (9-76)

These results provide the basis for step-by-step calculations leading to the summary of flow properties given in Table 9-15.

GENERAL SOLUTION. When γ and e_t are fixed, closer examination of the turbine stage design equation set reveals that the results depend only upon the dimensionless quantities M_2, τ_s, and ψ. Under these conditions, it is therefore possible to generate graphical representations that reveal the general tendencies of such turbine stages and serve the important purpose of defining the limits of reasonable stage designs.

This has been done for typical ranges of the prevailing dimensionless parameters and γ values of 1.33 and 1.3; the results are presented in Figs. 9-74 and 9-75, respectively. These charts may be used to obtain initial ballpark-stage design estimates and also reveal some important trends. If values of M_{3R} less than 1 and stage loading coefficients ψ less than or equal to 2.0 are taken as reasonable limits, it is clear that better (i.e., lower) values of ψ are available for the same ΔT_t as τ_s decreases (lower inlet temperatures) and/or ωr increases (higher wheel speeds). By noting that ψ does not depend on M_2 [Eq. (9-87)], it is also clear that M_2 determines only M_{3R}. Larger values of M_2 are desirable because they reduce the annulus flow area A and the rotating airfoil centrifugal stresses, and ensure choking of the stator airfoil passages over a wider turbine operating range; but Figs. 9-74 and 9-75 show that increasing M_2 reduces the

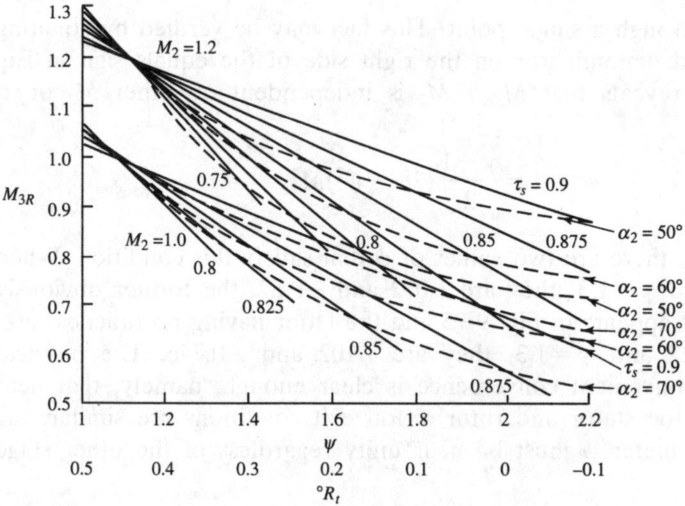

FIGURE 9-74
Generalized turbine stage behavior, zero exit swirl ($\gamma = 1.33$).

number of acceptable solutions. Finally, all other things being equal, stages having lower τ_s (i.e., more energy extraction) suffer the dual disadvantages of increased stage loading coefficient ψ and increased annulus flow area A.

Figures 9-74 and 9-75 exhibit an extremely interesting mathematical behavior in the region where all the curves for a value of M_2 appear to, and

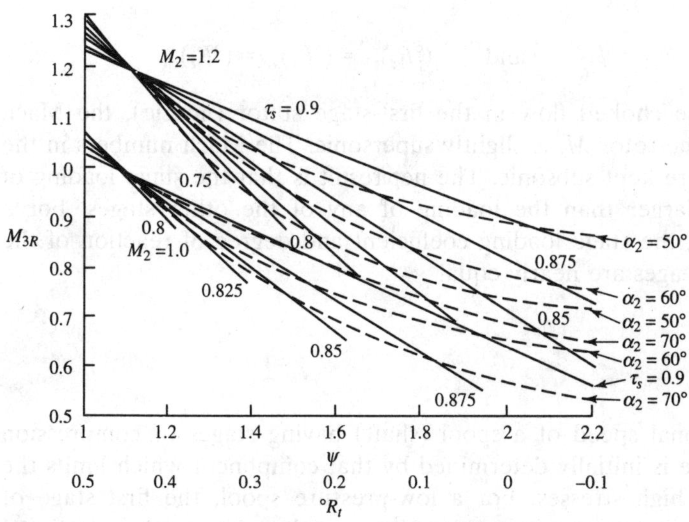

FIGURE 9-75
Generalized turbine stage behavior, zero exit swirl ($\gamma = 1.3$).

indeed do, pass through a single point. This fact may be verified by equating the numerator and denominator on the right side of the equals sign in Eq. (9-124), and this reveals that $M_{3R} = M_2$ is independent of either M_2 or τ_s provided only that

$$\psi^2 - 1 = \frac{\gamma - 1}{2}(2\psi - \psi^2)M_2^2$$

Hence, for each γ, there are two values of ψ that satisfy this condition. When $M_{3R} = M_2 = 1.0$ and $\gamma = 1.3$, they are 1.072 and -0.82, the former obviously being the one that appears in Fig. 9-75 and the latter having no practical use. For $M_{3R} = M_2 = 1.2$ and $\gamma = 1.3$, they are 1.102 and -0.746. The physical meaning of this convenient convergence is clear enough, namely, that near $M_{3R} = M_2$, where the stator and rotor airfoil exit conditions are similar, the stage loading parameter ψ must be near unity regardless of the other stage parameters.

MULTISTAGE TURBINE DESIGN. When the required stage loading coefficient ψ for a design is greater than 2.0, a single-stage design would require a hopeless negative reaction [Eq. (9-87)] and would be impossible to design with high aerodynamic efficiency. A desirable multistage design would have the total temperature difference distributed evenly among the stages:

$$(\Delta T_t)_{\text{turbine}} = (\text{number of stages}) \times (\Delta T_t)_{\text{stage}}$$

This would result in stages with the same stage loading coefficients [Eq. (9-20)] and same degree of reaction [Eq. (9-87)] for the same rotor speed U. For a three-stage design, we get

$$\psi_{s1} = \psi_{s2} = \psi_{s3} \qquad \text{and} \qquad (°R_t)_{s1} = (°R_t)_{s2} = (°R_t)_{s3}$$

To obtain the choked flow in the first-stage stator (nozzle), the Mach number entering the rotor M_2 is slightly supersonic. The Mach numbers in the remaining stages are kept subsonic. The net result is that the stage loading of the first stage is larger than the loading of any of the other stages. For a three-stage design, the stage loading coefficient and degree of reaction of the second and third stages are nearly equal.

Shaft Speed

The design rotational speed of a spool (shaft) having stages of compression driven by a turbine is initially determined by that component which limits the speed because of high stresses. For a low-pressure spool, the first stage of compression, since it has the greatest AN^2, normally dictates the rotational speed. The first stage of turbine on the high-pressure spool normally

TABLE 9-16*a*
Range of axial-flow turbine design parameters

Parameter	Design range
High-pressure turbine	
Maximum AN^2	$4\text{–}5 \times 10^{10}\ \text{in}^2 \cdot \text{rpm}^2$
Stage loading coefficient	1.4–2.0
Exit Mach number	0.40–0.50
Exit swirl angle (deg)	0–20
Low-pressure turbine	
Inlet corrected mass flow rate	40–44 lbm/(sec · ft^2)
Hub/tip ratio at inlet	0.35–0.50
Maximum stage loading at hub	2.4
Exit Mach number	0.40–0.50
Exit swirl angle (deg)	0–20

determines that spool's rotational speed because of its high AN^2 or high disk rim speed at elevated temperature.

Design Process

The design process requires both engineering judgment and knowledge of typical design values. Table 9-16a gives the range of design parameters for axial-flow turbines that can be used for guidance. The comparison of turbines

TABLE 9-16*b*
Comparison of Pratt & Whitney engines

Parameter	JT3D	JT9D
Year of introduction	1961	1970
Engine bypass ratio	1.45	4.86
Engine overall pressure ratio	13.6	24.5
Core engine flow (lb/sec)	187.7	272.0
High-pressure turbine		
Inlet temperature (°F)	1745	2500
Power output (hp)	24,100	71,700
Number of stages	1	2
Average stage loading coefficient	1.72	1.76
Coolant plus leakage flow (%)	2.5	16.1
Low-pressure turbine		
Inlet temperature (°F)	1410	1600
Power output (hp)	31,800	61,050
Number of stages	3	4
Average stage loading coefficient	1.44	2.47
Coolant plus leakage flow (%)	0.7	1.4

for Pratt & Whitney engines in Table 9-16*b* shows typical turbine design values and the leading trends in turbine technology. Note the increases over the years in inlet temperature, mass flow rate, and output power.

From Table 9-16*b*, comparison of the JT3D and JT9D high-pressure turbines shows that the stage loading coefficient did not appreciably change between the designs. However, the turbine inlet temperature increased to a value above the working temperature of available materials, requiring extensive use of cooling air. The stage loading coefficient for the low-pressure turbine increased dramatically, reducing the number of stages to four. If the stage loading coefficient of the low-pressure turbine of the JT3D were not increased significantly in the design of the JT9D, about six or seven stages of low-pressure turbine would have been required—increasing both cost and weight.

STEPS OF DESIGN. The material presented in previous sections can now be applied to the design of an axial-flow turbine. The complete design process for a turbine will include the following items:

1. Selection of rotational speed and annulus dimensions
2. Selection of the number of stages
3. Calculation of airflow angles for each stage at the mean radius
4. Calculation of airflow angle variations from the hub to tip for each stage
5. Selection of blade material
6. Selection of blading using experimental cascade data
7. Selection of turbine cooling, if needed
8. Verification of turbine efficiency based on cascade loss data
9. Prediction of off-design performance
10. Rig testing of design

Items 1 through 5 will be covered in this section. The other steps are covered in Refs. 36, 37, 41, and 42. The design process is inherently iterative, often requiring the return to an earlier step when prior assumptions are found to be invalid. Many technical specialities are interwoven in a design; e.g., an axial-flow turbine involves at least thermodynamics, aerodynamics, structures, materials, heat transfer, and manufacturing processes. Design requires the active participation and disciplined communication by many technical specialists.

Example 9-14. *Turbine design.* We will consider the design of a turbine suitable to power the eight-stage, axial-flow compressor designed earlier in this chapter for a simple turbojet gas turbine engine (see Example 9-7). From engine cycle and compressor design calculations, a suitable design point for the turbine of such an engine at sea-level, standard-day conditions ($P = 14.696$ psia and $T = 518.7°R$) may emerge as follows:

Compressor pressure ratio: 10.41	Rotor speed ω: 800 rad/sec
Compressor flow rate: 150 lbm/sec	Turbine flow rate: 156 lbm/sec
Compressor efficiency: 86.3%	T_t entering turbine: 3200°R
Compressor exit T_t: 1086°R	P_t entering turbine: 143.1 psia
Compressor γ: 1.4	Turbine γ: 1.3
Compressor R: 53.34 ft · lbf/(lbm · °R)	Turbine R: 53.40 ft · lbf/(lbm · °R)

From these specified data, we now investigate the aerodynamic design of an axial-flow turbine.

The compressor input power is

$$\dot{W}_c = \dot{m}c_p(T_{te} - T_{ti}) = (150 \times 0.240)(1086 - 518.7) = 20{,}423 \text{ Btu/sec}$$
$$= 21.55 \text{ MW}$$

Assuming that the compressor input power is 0.98 of the turbine output power (the other 2 percent of turbine power goes to shaft takeoff power and bearing losses), the required output power of the turbine is 22.0 MW (21.55 MW/0.98). The total temperature leaving the turbine is

$$T_{te} = T_{ti} - \frac{\dot{W}_t}{\dot{m}c_p} = 3200 - \frac{22{,}000/1.055}{156 \times 0.297} = 3200 - 450.1 = 2749.9°\text{R}$$

The turbine temperature ratio ($\tau_t = T_{te}/T_{ti}$) is 0.8593. If the flow entering the rotor has a Mach number of 1.2 at 60° to the centerline of the turbine and a 1 percent total pressure loss through the turbine stator (nozzle), the annulus area entering the rotor is

$$A_2 = \frac{\dot{m}\sqrt{T_{t2}}}{(\cos\alpha_2)(P_{t2})\text{MFP}(M_2)} = \frac{156\sqrt{3200}}{\cos 60° \times 143.1 \times 0.99 \times 0.502075\sqrt{53.34/53.40}}$$
$$= 248.3 \text{ in}^2$$

For a rotor angular speed ω of 800 rad/sec, AN^2 for the rotor is 1.45×10^{10} in^2 · rpm^2—this blade stress is within the capability of modern cooled turbine materials (about 2 to 3×10^{10} in^2 · rpm^2).

Calculation of the stage loading coefficient for the turbine helps in determining the number of turbine stages. For the turbine mean radius equal to that of the compressor, the stage loading coefficient on the mean line is

$$\psi = \frac{g_c c_p \, \Delta T_t}{(\omega r_m)^2} = \frac{7455 \times 450.1}{(800 \times 17.04/12)^2} = 2.600$$

Using Fig. 9-73, we see that this value of stage loading coefficient is larger than that possible for a single-stage turbine. Either the mean rotor speed ωr_m must be increased to reduce the stage loading coefficient for a single-stage turbine, or a two-stage turbine will be required. Since increasing the rotor angular speed ω will increase the blade stress AN^2 and since only a little margin exists, we will investigate the effect of increasing the mean radius on stage loading coefficient, annulus radii (r_t and r_h), and rim speed (U_r—assuming the rim radius is 1 in smaller than that of the hub). From the results given in Table 9-17, we can see that a single-stage turbine would require a mean radius of 19 to 20 in to reduce the stage loading coefficient and keep the rim speed below about 1200 ft/sec. This

TABLE 9-17
Variation of stage loading, radii, and rim speed with mean radius for Example 9-14 single-stage design

r_m (in)	ψ	r_t (in)	r_h (in)	r_h/r_t	U_r (ft/sec)
16.00	2.949	17.23	14.77	0.857	918
17.04	2.600	18.20	15.88	0.873	992
18.00	2.330	19.10	16.90	0.885	1060
19.00	2.091	20.04	17.96	0.896	1131
20.00	1.887	20.99	19.01	0.906	1201
21.00	1.712	21.94	20.06	0.914	1271

would result in a tip radius equal to or larger than the compressor's inlet radius. In addition, the tip radius of 20 to 21 in is much larger than current turbines for gas turbine engines which range between 10 and 17 in. Although a single-stage turbine is desirable because of the reduced weight, the low rotor angular speed of 800 rad/sec makes this size undesirable.

For a smaller turbine, the designer might consider increasing the rotor angular speed and redesigning the compressor. A rotor angular speed of 1000 rad/sec for a turbine with a 16-in mean radius has a stage loading coefficient for the mean radius of 1.885 and a rim speed of 1148 ft/sec which is possible for a single stage.

The designs of both a single-stage turbine and a two-stage turbine are performed in the following sections. The computer program TURBN is used to ease the calculational burden in both designs.

SINGLE-STAGE DESIGN. We consider a single-stage turbine with the following characteristics:

Rotor angular speed ω: 800 rad/sec — Turbine mass flow rate: 156 lbm/sec
T_t entering turbine: 3200°R — P_t entering turbine: 143.1 psia
T_t leaving turbine: 2749.1°R — Ratio of specific heats: 1.3
Turbine R: 53.40 ft · lbf/(lbm · °R)

To keep the degree of reaction at the hub from being too negative at a reasonable value of the stage loading coefficient ψ, we consider a nonzero exit swirl angle α_3 for a stage with a hub speed of about 1200 ft/sec (this corresponds to a rim speed of about 1130 ft/sec which will limit the disk stress). This hub speed corresponds to a hub radius of 18 in and a tip radius of about 20.1 in. The computer program TURBN was run with the exit swirl angle α_3 unknown, the data listed above, and the following additional input data:

Mean rotor speed ωr: 1270 ft/sec — ω: 800 rad/sec
M_2: 1.1 — α_2: 60°
M_1: 0.4 — α_1: 0°
u_3/u_2: 1.0 — $\phi_{t\,\text{stator}} = 0.06$ and $\phi_{t\,\text{rotor}} = 0.15$
Z_s: 0.9 — $(c/h)_s$: 1.0
Z_r: 0.9 — $(c/h)_r$: 1.0

TABLE 9-18
Results for Example 9-14 single-stage axial-flow turbine design

Property \ Station		1h	1m	1t	2h	2m	2t	2Rm	3Rm	3h	3m	3t
T_t	(°R)	3200	3200	3200	3200	3200	3200	2909	2909	2750	2750	2750
T	(°R)	3125	3125	3125	2665	2708	2745	2708	2621	2620	2621	2622
Pt	(psia)	143.1	143.1	143.1	138.8	138.8	138.8	91.8	87.0	68.3	68.3	68.3
P	(psia)	129.1	129.1	129.1	62.8	67.4	71.5	67.4	55.4	55.4	55.4	55.5
M		0.400	0.400	0.400	1.157	1.100	1.051	0.702	0.855	0.574	0.572	0.571
V	(ft/sec)	1057	1057	1057	2823	2705	2602	1727	2069	1389	1385	1381
u	(ft/sec)	1057	1057	1057	1353	1353	1353	1353	1353	1353	1353	1353
v	(ft/sec)	0	0	0	2477	2343	2222	1073	1566	316	296	278
α	(deg)	0	0	0	61.36	60.00	58.67	—	—	13.14	12.33	11.61
β	(deg)	—	—	—	—	—	—	38.42	49.17	—	—	—
Radii	(in)	18.25	19.05	19.85	18.02	19.05	20.08	19.05	19.05	17.83	19.05	20.27

Hub: $°R_t = 0.0990$ $A_1 = 190.78 \text{ in}^2$

Mean: $°R_t = 0.1939$ $A_2 = 247.52 \text{ in}^2$

Tip: $°R_t = 0.2746$ $A_3 = 291.11 \text{ in}^2$

$M_{3Rt} = 0.875$ $\tau_s = 0.8593$ $\pi_s = 0.4770$ $\psi = 2.0776$ $\Phi = 1.0652$

$\eta_s = 89.57\%$ $AN^2 \text{ at } 2 = 1.44 \times 10^{10} \text{ in}^2 \cdot \text{rpm}^2$

Computer calculations yield the single-stage turbine summarized in Table 9-18 with hub and tip tangential velocities based on free-vortex swirl distribution. This is a viable single-stage design with moderate exit swirl α_3, positive reaction, and subsonic M_{3R} at the tip.

This design gives a blade AN^2 of $1.44 \times 10^{10} \text{ in}^2 \cdot \text{rpm}^2$ and hub speed of 1201 ft/sec. This AN^2 value is well within the limits of cooled turbine materials, and the low hub speed is below the limiting speed of turbine disk materials.

A cross-sectional sketch of the single-stage turbine designed above and plotted by the computer program TURBN is shown in Fig. 9-76. Note that this sketch does not show the required exit guide vanes that will turn the flow back to axial. The estimated axial length L shown in Fig. 9-76 is based on the input values of Z and c/h for the stator and rotor blades and the scaling relationships of Fig. 9-69. For the input values of Z and c/h, the resulting solidity at the mean radius, number of blades, and chord length for the stator and rotor are as follows:

	Solidity	Number of blades	Chord (in)
Stator	0.979	64	1.831
Rotor	1.936	103	2.250

Data File: D:\TURBN\DESIGN1.DAT
Size: 3
Units: English
Stages: 1
mc = 39.79
TR = 0.8593
PR = 0.4770

Size (in)

Front
Rh = 18.25
Rt = 19.85

Back
Rh = 17.83
Rt = 20.27

Rm = 19.05
L = 4.90

TURBINE CROSS SECTION

Center Line

Press <p> to print screen or <Esc> to exit screen

FIGURE 9-76
Sketch of cross section for single-stage turbine design.

The selected axial chord and number of blades for the stator or rotor depend on many factors (e.g., flow through the blades, vibration, blade attachment). Figure 9-77 shows the computer sketch of the blades at the mean radius, using C4 base profiles.

TWO-STAGE DESIGN. In a two-stage design, the stage loading coefficients ψ are lower and the temperature ratios τ_s are higher than those for a single-stage design. This results in higher reactions, less turning of the flow, and lower loss coefficients. For good flow control of the turbine, the first-stage stator (nozzle) should be choked which requires that M_2 for this stage be supersonic. Inspection of Fig. 9-75 shows that at low ψ and high τ_s, the value of M_{3R} is a little less than M_2—thus, we will want to select a low supersonic value of M_2 (about 1.05) for the first stage. A balanced design would have about the same α_2 values for both stages with the first-stage M_{3Rt} below 0.9.

The two-stage turbine will be designed with a 17.04 in mean radius (same as multistage compressor) at an rpm of 7640 ($\omega = 800$ rad/sec), giving a mean rotor speed $U_m = \omega r_m$ of 1136 ft/sec. An initial starting point for the design of this two-stage turbine is constant axial velocity through the rotor ($u_3 = u_2$), zero exit swirl ($\alpha_3 = 0$), and a second-stage M_2 of 0.7. The stage loading

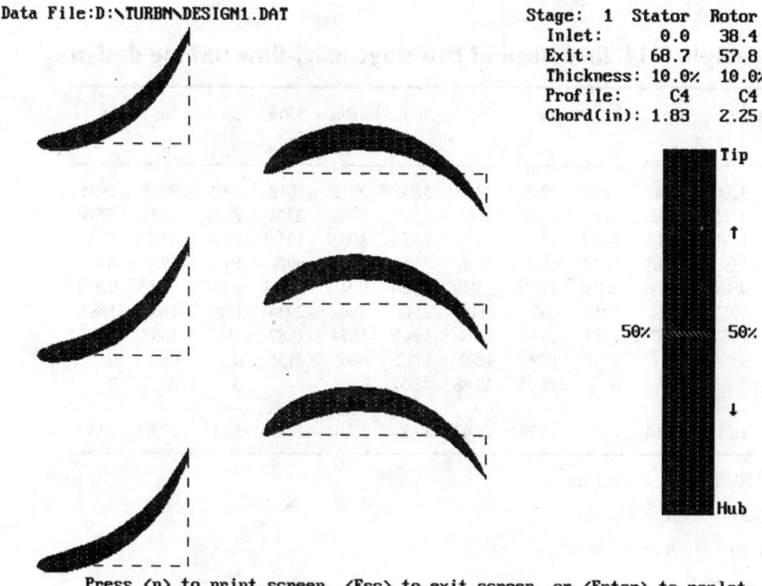

FIGURE 9-77
Sketch of blades for single-stage turbine design.

coefficients and other flow properties depend on the split in temperature drop between the stages. Calculations were performed by using the computer program TURBN with α_2 unknown at different values of the temperature leaving the first-stage turbine. The resulting α_2 and M_{3Rt} values are listed in Table 9-19. An interstage temperature of 2925°R gives a balance design for α_2 values with the first stage M_{3Rt} above 0.9. The value of M_{3Rt} can be reduced by selecting a value for the axial velocity ratio u_3/u_2 less than unity.

TABLE 9-19
Variation of stage parameters with interstage temperature for Example 9-14 two-stage design

	← Stage 1 →				← Stage 2 →		
T_{t3} (°R)	ψ	τ_s	α_2 (deg)	M_{3Rt}	ψ	τ_s	α_2 (deg)
2875	1.8750	0.8984	55.0	0.7774	1.0034	0.9565	28.61
2900	1.7307	0.9063	49.12	0.8467	0.8659	0.9482	34.90
2925	1.5865	0.9141	43.88	0.9068	1.0102	0.9401	41.65
2950	1.4423	0.9219	39.06	0.9587	1.1544	0.9322	49.13
2975	1.2981	0.9297	34.55	1.0034	1.2986	0.9243	57.90

TABLE 9-20
Results for Example 9-14, first stage of two-stage axial-flow turbine design

Property \ Station		1h	1m	1t	2h	2m	2t	2Rm	3Rm	3h	3m	3t
T_t	(R)	3200	3200	3200	3200	3200	3200	3012	3012	2925	2925	2925
T	(R)	3125	2135	3125	2724	2746	2765	2746	2734	2734	2734	2734
P_t	(psia)	143.1	143.1	143.1	139.1	139.1	139.1	106.9	105.4	92.8	92.8	92.8
P	(psia)	129.1	129.1	129.1	69.2	71.6	73.8	71.6	69.3	69.3	69.3	69.3
M		0.400	0.400	0.400	1.079	1.050	1.024	0.803	0.823	0.683	0.683	0.683
V	(ft/sec)	1057	1057	1057	2662	2600	2545	1989	2034	1687	1687	1687
u	(ft/sec)	1057	1057	1057	1874	1874	1874	1874	1687	1687	1687	1687
v	(ft/sec)	0	0	0	1891	1802	1722	666	1136	0	0	0
α	(deg)	0	0	0	45.25	43.88	42.57	—	—	0	0	0
β	(deg)	—	—	—	—	—	—	19.57	33.96	—	—	—
Radii	(in)	16.15	17.04	17.93	16.24	17.04	17.84	17.04	17.04	16.13	17.04	17.95

Hub: $^\circ R_t = -0.0359$ $A_1 = 190.78 \text{ in}^2$

Mean: $^\circ R_t = 0.0437$ $A_2 = 170.34 \text{ in}^2$

Tip: $^\circ R_t = 0.1129$ $A_3 = 194.88 \text{ in}^2$

$M_{3Rt} = 0.8370$ $\tau_s = 0.9141$ $\pi_s = 0.6488$ $\psi = 1.5865$ $\Phi = 1.650$

$\eta_s = 90.44\%$ AN^2 at $2 = 9.94 \times 10^9 \text{ in}^2 \cdot \text{rpm}^2$

A design with an interstage temperature of 2925°R and first-stage u_3/u_2 of 0.9 is selected to reduce M_{3Rt}. The losses for the first stage and second stage are estimated by using polytropic efficiencies of 0.9 and 0.92, respectively, and stator loss coefficients of 0.06 and 0.02, respectively. For all blades, a value of 0.9 is used for the tangential force coefficient Z, and a value of 1.0 is used for the chord/height ratio c/h. Results for both stages are presented in Tables 9-20 and 9-21 with hub and tip tangential velocities based on free-vortex swirl distribution.

A cross-sectional sketch of the two-stage turbine designed above and plotted by TURBN is shown in Fig. 9-78. The sketch shows the stator and rotor for both stages. Note that the turbine exit stator is not shown in the sketch. For the input values of Z and c/h, the resulting solidity at the mean radius, number of blades, and chord length for the stator and rotor blades of the two stages are as follows:

	Stage 1		Stage 2	
	Stator	Rotor	Stator	Rotor
Solidity	0.725	1.880	1.643	1.254
Blades	46	118	83	52
Chord (in)	1.686	1.706	2.120	2.581

TABLE 9-21
Results for Example 9-14 second stage of two-stage axial-flow turbine design

Property		1h	1m	1t	2h	2m	2t	2Rm	3Rm	3h	3m	3t
T_t	(R)	2925	2925	2925	2925	2925	2925	2837	2837	2750	2750	2750
T	(R)	2734	2734	2734	2711	2725	2736	2725	2638	2638	2638	2638
P_t	(psia)	92.84	92.84	92.84	92.35	92.35	92.35	80.85	79.41	69.42	69.42	69.42
P	(psia)	69.27	69.27	69.27	66.41	67.92	69.15	67.92	57.99	57.99	57.99	57.99
M		0.683	0.683	0.683	0.726	0.700	0.678	0.523	0.708	0.532	0.532	0.532
V	(ft/sec)	1687	1687	1687	1786	1727	1677	1290	1719	1290	1290	1290
u	(ft/sec)	1687	1687	1687	1290	1290	1290	1290	1290	1290	1290	1290
v	(ft/sec)	0	0	0	1235	1148	1072	12	1136	0	0	0
α	(deg)	0	0	0	43.75	41.65	39.71	—	—	0	0	0
β	(deg)	—	—	—	—	—	—	0.51	41.36	—	—	—
Radii	(in)	16.13	17.04	17.95	15.83	17.04	18.25	17.04	17.04	15.67	17.04	18.41

Hub: $°R_t = 0.4148$ $A_1 = 194.88\ \text{in}^2$

Mean: $°R_t = 0.4949$ $A_2 = 258.99\ \text{in}^2$

Tip: $°R_t = 0.5596$ $A_3 = 293.69\ \text{in}^2$

$M_{3Rt} = 0.7337$ $\tau_s = 0.9401$ $\pi_s = 0.7477$ $\psi = 1.0102$ $\Phi = 1.136$

$\eta_s = 92.24\%$ AN^2 at $2 = 1.51 \times 10^{10}\ \text{in}^2 \cdot \text{rpm}^2$

Data File: D:\TURBN\DESIGN2.DAT
Size: 2
Units: English
Stages: 2
mc = 39.79
TR = 0.8593
PR = 0.4851

Size (in)

Front
Rh = 16.15
Rt = 17.93

Back
Rh = 15.67
Rt = 18.41

Rm = 17.04
L = 9.76

TURBINE CROSS SECTION

Center Line

Press <p> to print screen or <Esc> to exit screen

FIGURE 9-78
Sketch of cross section for two-stage turbine design.

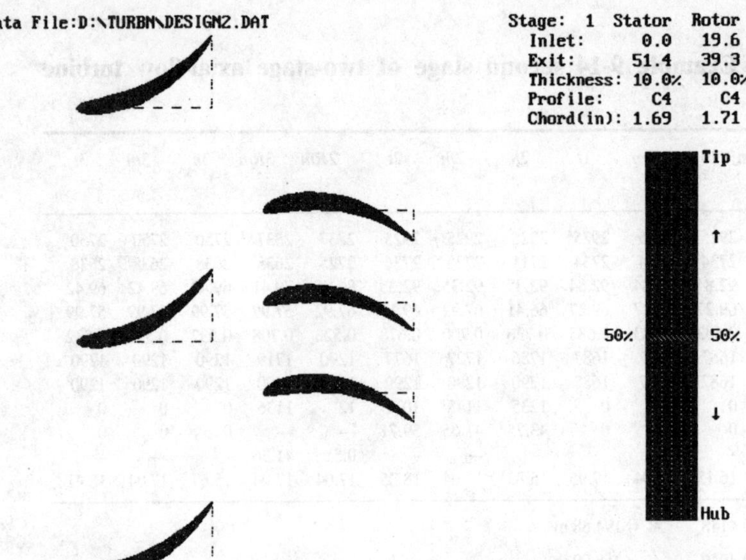

FIGURE 9-79
Sketch of blades for first stage of two-stage turbine design.

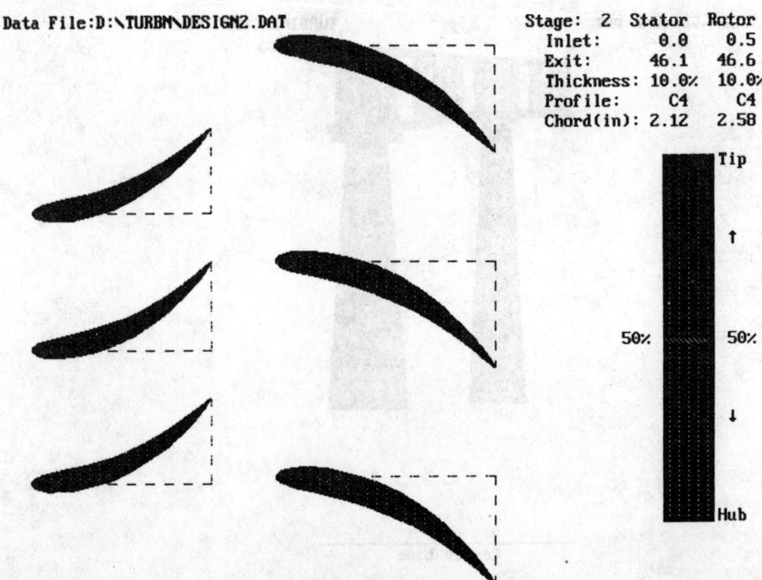

FIGURE 9-80
Sketch of blades for second stage of two-stage turbine design.

The selected axial chord and number of blades for the stator and rotor depend on many factors (e.g., flow through the blades, vibration, blade attachment). Figures 9-79 and 9-80 show the computer sketch of the blades at the mean radius, using C4 base profiles for the first and second stages, respectively.

For the first stage, this design gives a blade AN^2 of $9.94 \times 10^9\ \text{in}^2 \cdot \text{rpm}^2$ and disk speed of about 1020 ft/sec. This AN^2 is well within the limits of cooled turbine materials, and the low rim speed is below the limiting speed of turbine disk materials.

Turbine Cooling

The turbine components are subjected to much higher temperatures in the modern gas turbine engines being designed and built today than was possible 50 years ago. This is due mainly to improvements in metallurgy and cooling of turbine components. The cooling air to cool the turbine is bleed air from the compressor. A schematic of a typical turbine cooling system is shown in Fig. 9-81. The stator blades and the outer wall of the turbine flow passage use

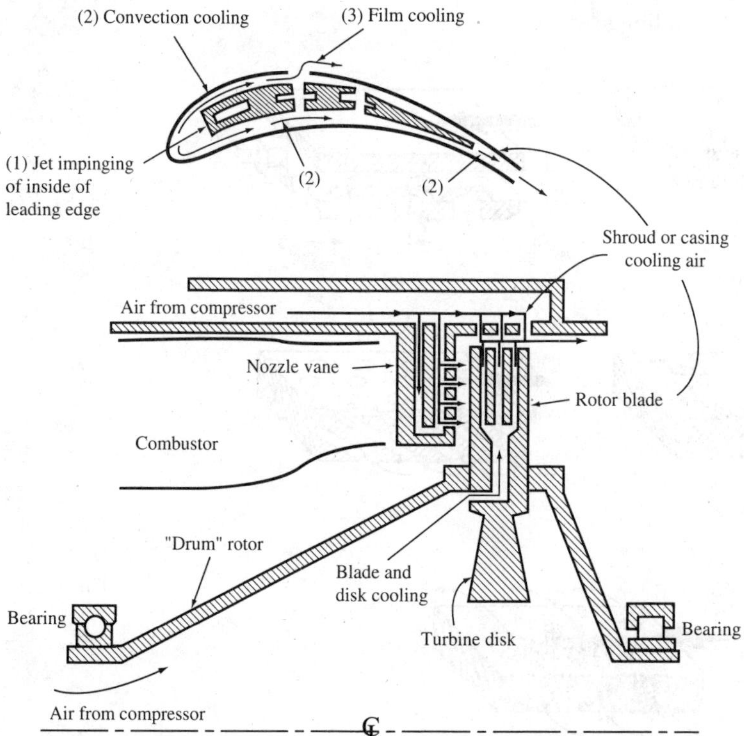

FIGURE 9-81
Schematic of air-cooled turbine. (*From J. L. Kerrebrock*, Aircraft Engines and Gas, Turbines, *Ref. 26, by courtesy of M.I.T. Press.*)

cooling air that travels from the compressor between the combustor and outer engine case. The turbine rotor blades, disks, and inner wall of the turbine flow passage use cooling air that is routed through inner passageways.

The first-stage stator blades (nozzles) are exposed to the highest turbine temperatures (including the hot spots from the combustor). The first-stage rotor blades are exposed to a somewhat lower temperature because of circumferential averaging, dilution of turbine gases with first-stage stator cooling air, and relative velocity effects. The second-stage stator blades are exposed to an even lower temperature because of additional cooling air dilution and power extraction from the turbine gases. The turbine temperature decreases in a like manner through each blade row.

The cooling methods used in the turbine are illustrated in Fig. 9-82 and can be divided into the following categories:

1. Convection cooling
2. Impingement cooling
3. Film cooling
4. Full-coverage film cooling
5. Transpiration cooling

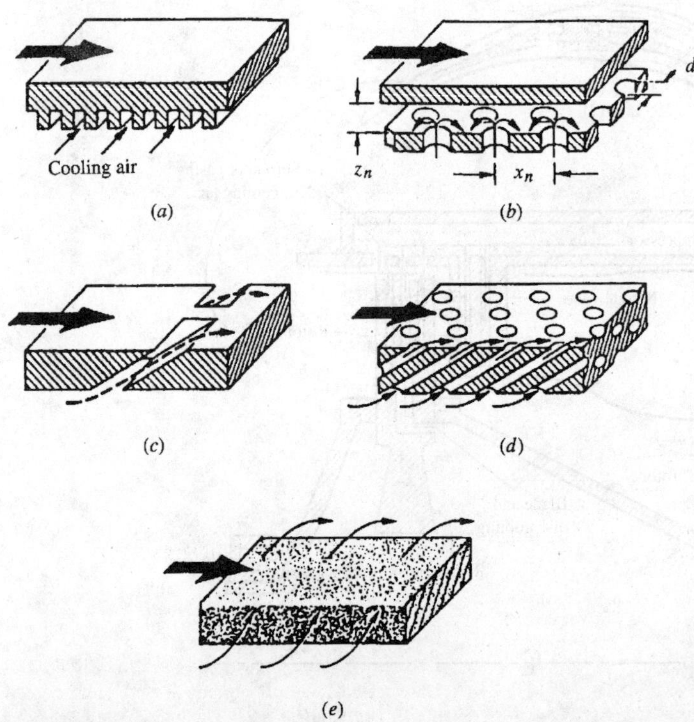

FIGURE 9-82
Methods of turbine cooling (Ref. 36). (*a*) Convection cooling. (*b*) Impingement cooling. (*c*) Film cooling. (*d*) Full-coverage film cooling. (*e*) Transpiration cooling.

Applications of these five methods of cooling to turbine blades are shown in Fig. 9-83.

Figure 9-84 shows a typical first-stage stator (nozzle) blade with cooling. This stator has cooling holes along its nose (leading edge) and pressure surface (gill holes) in addition to cooling flow exiting at its trailing edge. The cooling holes on the inside wall are also shown.

A rotor blade of the General Electric CF6-50 engine is shown in Fig. 9-85. The cross section of the blade shows the elaborate internal cooling and flow exiting the blade tip (through its cap) and along the trailing edge. The blade isometric shows flow through the gill holes on the pressure surface in addition to the tip and trailing-edge cooling flows.

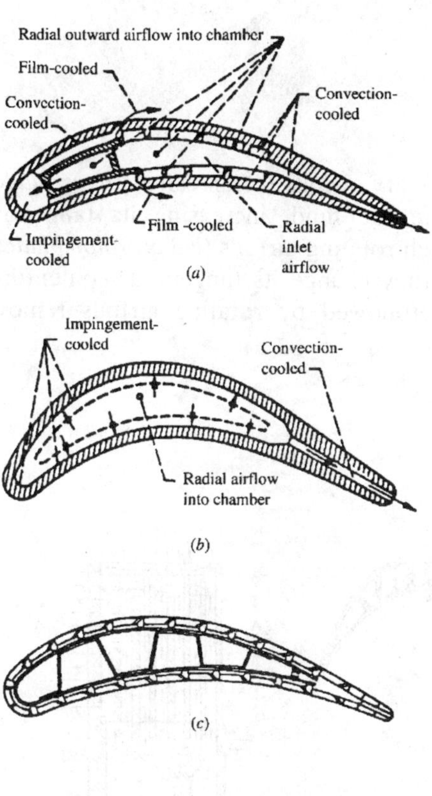

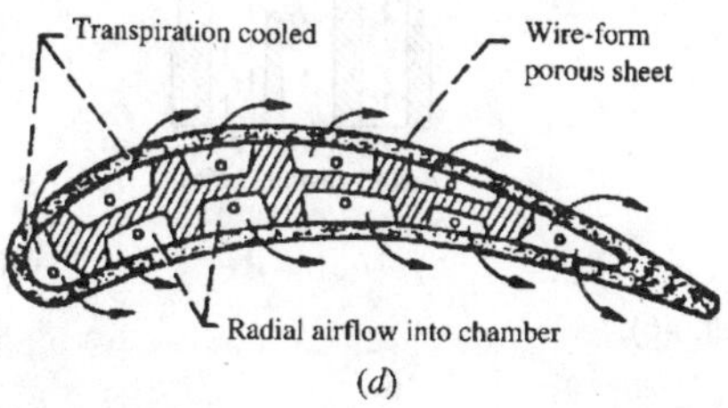

FIGURE 9-83
Turbine blade cooling (Ref. 36). (*a*) Convection-, impingement-, and film-cooled blade configuration. (*b*) Convection- and impingement-cooled blade configuration. (*c*) Full-coverage film-cooled blade configuration. (*d*) Transpiration-cooled blade configuration.

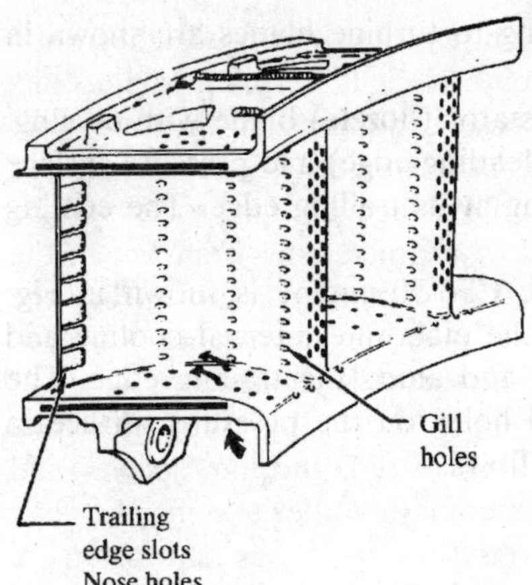

FIGURE 9-84
Typical cooled turbine nozzle (Ref. 46).

Turbine Performance

The flow enters a turbine through stationary airfoils (often called *stator blades* or *nozzles*) which turn and accelerate the fluid, increasing its tangential momentum. Then the flow passes through rotating airfoils (called *rotor blades*) that remove energy from the fluid as they change its tangential momentum. Successive pairs of stationary airfoils followed by rotating airfoils remove

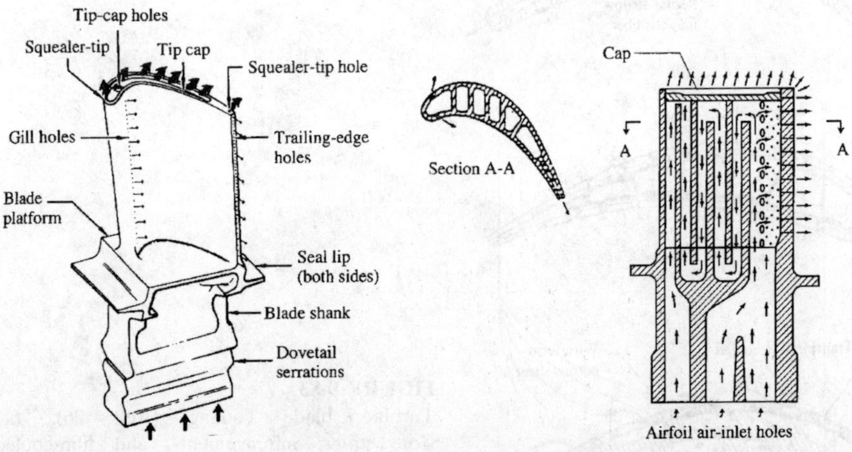

FIGURE 9-85
Construction features of air-cooled turbine blade (Ref. 46).

additional energy from the fluid. To obtain high output power to weight from a turbine, the flow entering the first-stage turbine rotor is normally supersonic, which requires the flow to pass through sonic conditions at the minimum passage area in the first-stage stators (nozzles). From Eq. (8-3), the corrected inlet mass flow rate based on this minimum passage area (throat) will be constant for fixed-inlet-area turbines. This flow characteristic is shown in the typical turbine flow map (Fig. 9-86) when the expansion ratio across the turbine (ratio of total pressure at exit to total pressure at entrance $P_{t5}/P_{t4} = 1/\pi_t$) is greater than about 2 and the flow at the throat is choked.

The performance of a turbine is normally shown by using the total pressure ratio, corrected mass flow rate, corrected turbine speed, and component efficiency. This performance is presented in either two maps or one consolidated map. One map shows the interrelationship of the total pressure ratio, corrected mass flow rate, and corrected turbine speed, like that depicted in Fig. 9-86 for a single-stage turbine. Since the corrected-speed lines collapse into one line when the turbine is choked, the turbine efficiency must be shown in a separate map (see Fig. 8-5*b*). The constant corrected speed lines of Fig. 9-86 can be spread out horizontally by multiplying the corrected mass flow rate by the percentage of corrected speed. Now the turbine efficiency lines can be superimposed without cluttering the resulting performance map. Figure 9-87 shows the consolidated turbine performance map of a multistage turbine with all four performance parameters: total pressure ratio, corrected mass flow rate, corrected turbine speed, and efficiency.

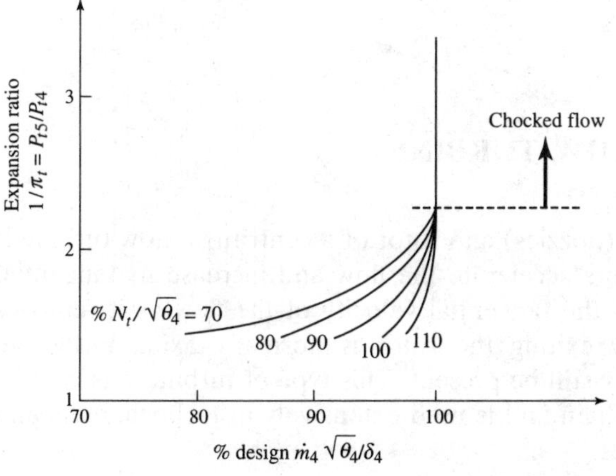

FIGURE 9-86
Typical turbine flow map.

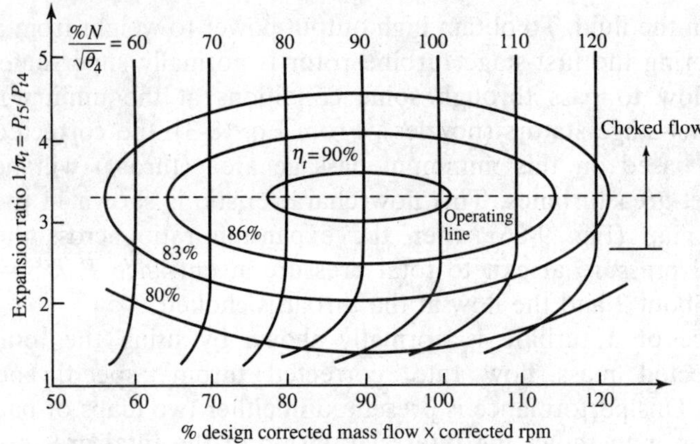

FIGURE 9-87
Typical turbine consolidated performance map.

For the majority of aircraft gas turbine engine operation, the turbine expansion ratio is constant and the turbine operating line can be drawn asa horizontal line in Fig. 9-87 (it would collapse to an operating point on the flow map of Fig. 9-86). At off-design conditions, the corrected speed and efficiency of a turbine change very little from their design values. In the analysis of gas turbine engine performance, we considered that the turbine efficiency was constant.

9-6 CENTRIFUGAL-FLOW TURBINE ANALYSIS

The flow through the stators (nozzles) and rotor of a centrifugal flow turbine is shown in Fig. 9-88. The stators accelerate the flow and increase its tangential velocity. The rotor decreases the tangential velocity of the flow as it removes energy from the flow. Flow exiting the rotor is normally axial, but some tangential (swirl) velocity may still be present. This type of turbine was used in the turbojet engine of von Ohain and is used extensively in turbochargers and very small gas turbine engines.

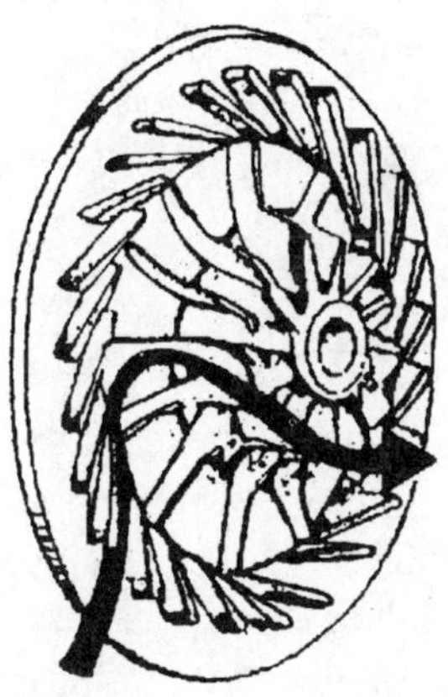

FIGURE 9-88
Flow through a centrifugal-flow turbine.

General Equations

Figure 9-89 shows the station numbering used in the analysis of the centrifugal-flow turbine. The flow enters the stators at station 1 and leaves at station 2. It then passes through the rotor and leaves at station 3. Normally the flow leaving the rotor is axial ($V_3 = u_3$). Application of the Euler turbine equation to the flow through the stator and rotor, assuming adiabatic stator, gives

$$h_{t1} - h_{t3} = \frac{U_t v_2}{g_c} \tag{9-126}$$

The relative velocity V_{2R} at the entrance to the rotor is designed to be radial ($v_{2R} = 0,\ V_{2R} = w_2$); thus, the tangential velocity at station 2 (v_2) equals the rotor speed at its tip U_t. For this case, Eq. (9-126) becomes

$$\boxed{h_{t1} - h_{t3} = \frac{U_t^2}{g_c}} \tag{9-127}$$

For a calorically perfect gas, Eq. (9-127) can be written in terms of the total temperature change, or

$$\boxed{T_{t1} - T_{t3} = \frac{U_t^2}{g_c c_p}} \tag{9-128}$$

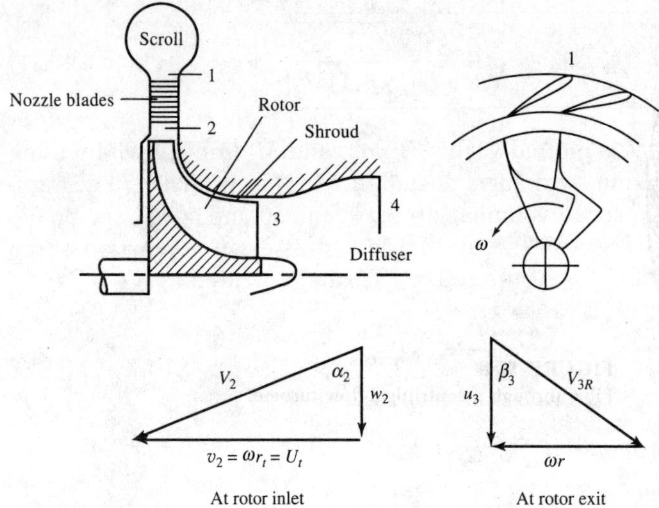

FIGURE 9-89
Station numbering for centrifugal-flow turbine. (*After Dixon, Ref. 31.*)

Note that the temperature drop through a centrifugal turbine is directly proportional to the rotor speed squared. Using the polytropic turbine efficiency e_t and Eq. (9-128), we can express the turbine pressure ratio π_t as

$$\pi_t = \frac{P_{t3}}{P_{t1}} = \left(\frac{T_{t3}}{T_{t1}}\right)^{\gamma/[(\gamma-1)e_t]} = \left(1 - \frac{U_t^2}{g_c c_p T_{t1}}\right)^{\gamma/[(\gamma-1)e_t]} \tag{9-129}$$

The tip speed U_t can be written in terms of T_{t2}, M_2, and α_2. From the velocity triangle at station 2, we can write

$$U_t = v_2 = V_2 \sin \alpha_2 \tag{9-130}$$

And V_2 can be expressed in terms of T_{t1} and M_2 as

$$V_2 = \sqrt{\frac{2g_c c_p T_{t2}}{1 + 2/[(\gamma-1)M_2^2]}}$$

$$= \sqrt{\frac{2g_c c_p T_{t1}}{1 + 2/[(\gamma-1)M_2^2]}}$$

Thus

$$U_t = \sin\alpha_2 \sqrt{\frac{2g_c c_p T_{t1}}{1 + 2/[(\gamma - 1)M_2^2]}} \qquad (9\text{-}131)$$

The rotor speed U_t is plotted versus T_{t1}, α_2, and M_2 in Fig. 9-90 by using Eq. (9-131). The maximum swirl angle at station 2 (α_2) is normally 70 degrees. The maximum rotor tip speed is limited to between 350 and 500 m/sec by the maximum centrifugal stresses of the rotor. These stresses are a function of the relative total temperature T_{t2R} of the rotor; T_{t2R} can be written as

$$T_{t2R} = T_{t2} - \frac{U_t^2}{2g_c c_p} \qquad (9\text{-}132)$$

Example 9-15. *Radial-flow turbine.*
GIVEN:

Mass flow rate = 2.5 kg/sec
$T_{t1} = 1100$ K
Polytropic efficiency $e_t = 0.85$
$\alpha_2 = 70°$
$\gamma = 1.33$
Hub/tip ratio at 3 = 0.4
$P_{t2} = 0.99 P_{t1}$

$P_{t1} = 400$ kPa
$T_{t3} = 935$ K
Rotor diameter = 0.40 m
$u_3 = w_2$
$R = 0.2872$ kJ/(kg · K)
$g_c c_p = 1.158$ kJ/(kg · K)

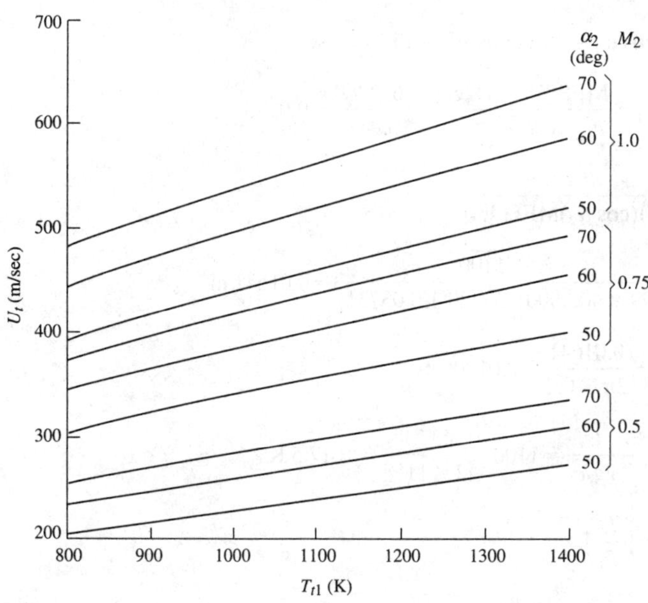

FIGURE 9-90
Rotor speed U_t versus T_{t1}, M_2, and α_2 [$\gamma = 1.33$, $c_p = 1.158$ kJ/(kg · K)].

FIND:

a. Tip speed, rotational speed, and rpm of rotor
b. Mach number, velocities, rotor depth, and T_{tR} at station 2
c. Total pressure, Mach number, and hub and tip radius at station 3
d. Values of V_{3R}, T_{t3R}, β_3, and M_{3R} at mean radius
e. Variation of M_{3R} and β_3 with radius

Solution.

$$U_t = \sqrt{g_c c_p (T_{t1} - T_{t3})} = \sqrt{1158(1100 - 935)} = 437.1 \text{ m/sec}$$

$$\omega = \frac{U_t}{r_t} = \frac{437.1}{0.20} = 2185.5 \text{ rad/sec}$$

$$\text{RPM} = \frac{30}{\pi}\omega = \frac{30}{\pi}(2185.5) = 20{,}870 \text{ rpm}$$

$$M_2 = \sqrt{\frac{2/(\gamma - 1)}{2g_c c_p T_{t1} \sin^2 \alpha_2 / U_t^2 - 1}}$$

$$= \sqrt{\frac{2/0.33}{2 \times 1158 \times 1100 \sin^2 70° / 437.1^2 - 1}}$$

$$= 0.750$$

$$V_2 = \frac{U_t}{\sin \alpha_2} = \frac{437.1}{\sin 70°} = 465.2 \text{ m/sec}$$

$$w_2 = V_2 \cos \alpha_2 = 465.2 \cos 70° = 159.1 \text{ m/sec}$$

$$\text{MFP}(M_2) = \frac{\text{MFP}(M_2)\sqrt{R/g_c}}{\sqrt{R/g_c}} = \frac{0.632280}{16.947} = 0.03731$$

$$A_2 = \frac{\dot{m}\sqrt{T_{t2}}}{(P_{t2})(\cos \alpha_2)\text{MFP}(M_2)}$$

$$= \frac{2.5\sqrt{1100}}{(0.99 \times 400{,}000)(\cos 70°)(0.03731)} = 0.01641 \text{ m}^2$$

$$b = \frac{A_2}{2\pi r_t} = \frac{0.01641}{2\pi \times 0.2} = 0.01306 \text{ m}$$

$$T_{t2R} = T_{t2} - \frac{U_t^2}{2g_c c_p} = 1100 - \frac{437.1^2}{2 \times 1158} = 1017.5 \text{ K}$$

$$\pi_t = \frac{P_{t3}}{P_{t1}} = \left(\frac{T_{t3}}{T_{t1}}\right)^{\gamma/[(\gamma-1)e_t]}$$

$$= \left(\frac{935}{1100}\right)^{1.33/(0.33 \times 0.85)} = 0.4627$$

$$P_{t3} = 0.4627P_{t1} = 0.4627 \times 400 = 185.1 \text{ kPa}$$

$$V_3 = u_3 = w_2 = 159.1 \text{ m/sec}$$

$$M_3 = \sqrt{\frac{2/(\gamma - 1)}{2g_c c_p T_{t3}/V_3^2 - 1}}$$

$$= \sqrt{\frac{2/0.33}{2 \times 1158 \times 935/159.1^2 - 2}} = 0.2677$$

$$\text{MFP}(M_3) = \frac{\text{MFP}(M_3)\sqrt{R/g_c}}{\sqrt{R/g_c}} = \frac{0.296168}{16.947} = 0.01748$$

$$A_3 = \frac{\dot{m}\sqrt{T_{t3}}}{P_{t3}\,\text{MFP}(M_3)}$$

$$= \frac{2.5\sqrt{935}}{185{,}100 \times 0.01748} = 0.02363 \text{ m}^2$$

$$r_{3t} = \sqrt{\frac{A_3}{\pi[1 - (r_h/r_t)^2]}} = \sqrt{\frac{0.02363}{\pi(1 - 0.4^2)}} = 0.09463 \text{ m}$$

$$r_{3h} = 0.4r_{3t} = 0.4 \times 0.09463 = 0.03785 \text{ m}$$

$$r_{3m} = \frac{r_{3t} + r_{3h}}{2} = 0.06624 \text{ m}$$

$$v_{3Rm} = \omega r_{3m} = 2185.5 \times 0.06624 = 144.8 \text{ m/sec}$$

$$V_{3Rm} = \sqrt{u_3^2 + v_{3Rm}^2} = \sqrt{159.1^2 + 144.8^2} = 215.1 \text{ m/sec}$$

$$T_{t3Rm} = T_3 + \frac{V_{3Rm}^2}{2g_c c_p} = T_{t3} + \frac{v_{3Rm}^2}{2g_c c_p}$$

$$= 935 + \frac{144.8^2}{2 \times 1158} = 944.1 \text{ K}$$

$$M_{3Rm} = M_3 \frac{V_{3Rm}}{V_3} = 0.2677\left(\frac{215.1}{159.1}\right) = 0.3619$$

$$\beta_{3m} = \tan^{-1}\frac{v_{3Rm}}{u_3} = \tan^{-1}\frac{144.8}{159.1} = 42.31°$$

The results of this example are summarized in Table 9-22. The radial variation of β_3 and M_{3R} are given in Fig. 9-91, using the following relationships:

$$\beta_3 = \tan^{-1}\frac{v_{3R}}{u_3} = \tan^{-1}\frac{\omega r_3}{u_3}$$

$$M_{3R} = M_3\sqrt{1 + \tan^2\beta_3}$$

TABLE 9-22
Results for Example 9-15 radial-flow turbine

Property	Station	1	2	2R	3Rm	3m
T_t	(K)	**1100.0**	1100.0	1017.5	944.1	**935.0**
T	(K)		1006.6	1006.6	924.1	924.1
P_t	(kPa)	**400.0**	396.0	289.2	192.4	185.1
P	(kPa)		276.9	276.9	176.5	176.5
M			0.7500	0.2565	0.3619	0.2677
V	(m/sec)		465.2	159.1	215.1	159.1
u/w	(m/sec)		159.1	159.1	159.1	159.1
v	(m/sec)	0	437.1	0	144.8	0
r	(m)		**0.2000**	0.2000	0.06624	
α	(deg)	0	**70.0**	—	—	0
β	(deg)		—	0	42.31	—

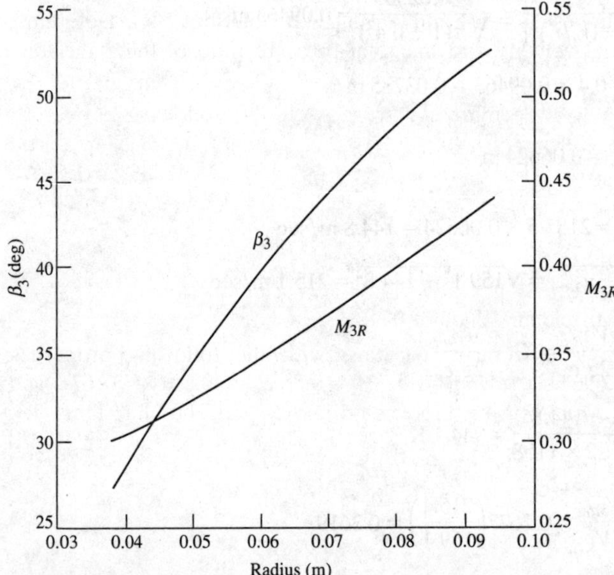

FIGURE 9-91
β_3 and M_{3R} versus radius.

PROBLEMS

9-1. Relative velocities are an important concept in the analysis of turbomachines. To help understand relative velocity, consider that a baseball is thrown at a moving train as shown in Fig. P9-1. If the baseball has a velocity of 60 mi/hr and the train is traveling at 80 mi/hr, find the magnitude and direction of the baseball velocity relative to the train.

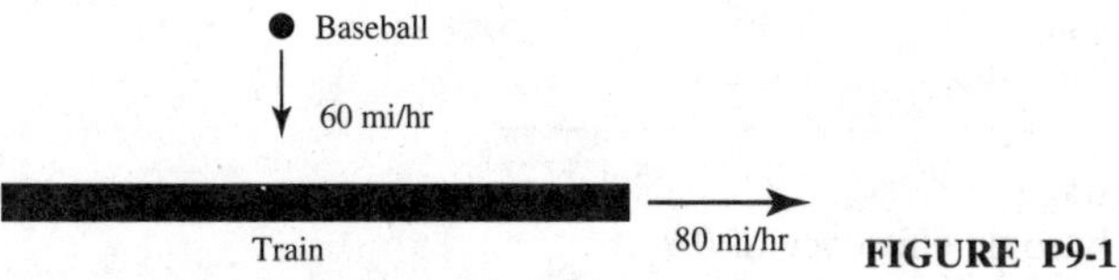

FIGURE P9-1

9-2. A small fan used to circulate air in a room is shown in Fig. P9-2. The fan blades are twisted and change their angle relative to the centerline of the fan as the radius increases. If the relative velocity of the air makes the same angle to the centerline of the fan as the blades and if the blade at a radius of 0.2 m has an angle of 60°, determine the speed of the air for fan speeds of 1725 and 3450 rpm.

9-3. Air flows through an axial compressor stage with the following properties: $T_{t1} = 300$ K, $u_2/u_1 = 1.0$, $V_1 = 120$ m/sec, $\alpha_1 = 0°$, $\beta_2 = 45°$, and $U = \omega r_m = 240$ m/sec. *Note:* For air, use $\gamma = 1.4$ and $R = 0.286$ kJ/(kg · K). Determine the change in tangential velocity and the total pressure ratio of the stage for a stage efficiency of 0.88.

9-4. Air flows through an axial compressor stage with the following properties: $T_{t1} = 540°$R, $u_2/u_1 = 1.0$, $V_1 = 400$ ft/sec, $\alpha_1 = 0°$, $\beta_2 = 45°$, and $U = \omega r_m = 800$ ft/sec. *Note:* For air, use $\gamma = 1.4$ and $R = 53.34$ ft · lbf/(lbm · °R). Determine the change in tangential velocity and the total pressure ratio of the stage for a stage efficiency of 0.9.

9-5. Air flows through an axial compressor stage with the following properties: $T_{t1} = 290$ K, $P_{t1} = 101.3$ kPa, $u_2/u_1 = 1.0$, $M_1 = 0.6$, $\alpha_1 = 40°$, $\alpha_2 = 57.67°$, and $U = \omega r_m = 360$ m/sec. *Note:* For air, use $\gamma = 1.4$ and $R = 0.286$ kJ/(kg · K). Determine the following:

a. V_1, u_1, and v_1

b. u_2, v_2, and V_2

c. ΔT_t and τ_s for the stage

d. π_s and P_{t3} for a polytropic efficiency of 0.88

9-6. Air flows through an axial compressor stage with the following properties: $T_{t1} = 518.7°$R, $P_{t1} = 14.696$ psia, $u_2/u_1 = 1.0$, $M_1 = 0.6$, $\alpha_1 = 40°$, $\alpha_2 = 57.67°$, and $U = \omega r_m = 1200$ ft/sec. *Note:* For air, use $\gamma = 1.4$ and $R = 53.34$ ft · lbf/(lbm · °R).

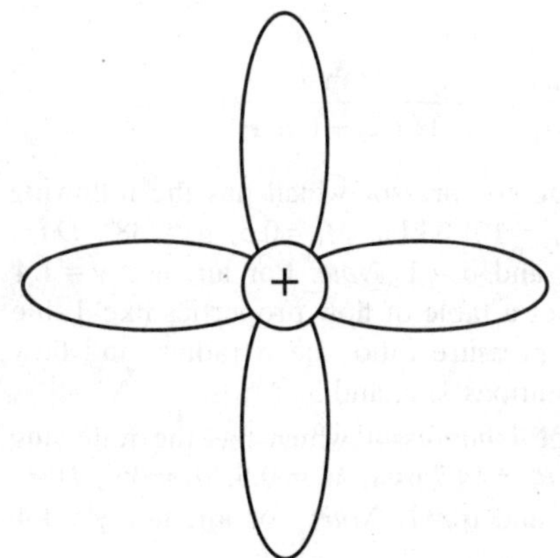

FIGURE P9-2

Determine the following:

a. V_1, u_1, and v_1

b. u_2, v_2, and V_2

c. ΔT_t and τ_s for the stage

d. π_s and P_{t3} for a polytropic efficiency of 0.9

9-7. Air enters a compressor stage which has the following properties: $\dot{m} = 50$ kg/sec, $\omega = 1200$ rad/sec, $r = 0.5$ m, $M_1 = M_3 = 0.5$, $\alpha_1 = \alpha_3 = 45°$, $T_{t1} = 290$ K, $P_{t1} = 101.3$ kPa, $u_2/u_1 = 1.0$, $T_{t3} - T_{t1} = 45$ K, $\phi_{cr} = 0.10$, $\phi_{cs} = 0.03$, and $\sigma = 1$. *Note:* For air, use $\gamma = 1.4$ and $R = 0.286$ kJ/(kg · K). Make and fill out a table of flow properties like Table 9-3, and determine the diffusion factors, degree of reaction, stage efficiency, polytropic efficiency, and flow areas and associated hub and tip radii at stations 1, 2, and 3.

9-8. Air enters a compressor stage which has the following properties: $\dot{m} = 100$ lbm/sec, $\omega = 1000$ rad/sec, $r = 12$ in, $M_1 = M_3 = 0.6$, $\alpha_1 = \alpha_3 = 45°$, $T_{t1} = 518.7°$R, $P_{t1} = 14.7$ psia, $u_2/u_1 = 1.0$, $T_{t3} - T_{t1} = 50°$R, $\phi_{cr} = 0.05$, $\phi_{cs} = 0.03$, and $\sigma = 1$. *Note:* For air, use $\gamma = 1.4$ and $R = 53.34$ ft · lbf/(lbm · °R). Make and fill out a table of flow properties like Table 9-3, and determine the diffusion factors, degree of reaction, stage efficiency, polytropic efficiency, and flow areas and associated hub and tip radii at stations 1, 2, and 3.

9-9. Some axial-flow compressors have inlet guide vanes to add tangential velocity to the axial flow and thus set up the airflow for the first-stage rotor.

a. Assuming reversible, adiabatic flow through the inlet guide vanes, use the continuity equation and the mass flow parameter to show that

$$(\cos \alpha_1)(A_1)\text{MFP}(M_1) = A_0 \,\text{MFP}(M_0)$$

where the subscripts 0 and 1 refer to the inlet and exit of the inlet guide vanes and the areas are those normal to the centerline of the axial-flow compressor.

b. For $A_0/A_1 = 1$ and 1.1, plot a curve of α_1 versus M_1 for $M_0 = 0.3$, 0.4, and 0.5 (see Fig. 9-35).

9-10. In the analysis of turbomachinery, many authors use the dimensionless stage loading coefficient ψ, defined as

$$\psi \equiv \frac{g_c c_p \,\Delta T_t}{(\omega r)^2}$$

For a repeating-stage, repeating-row compressor stage, show that the stage loading coefficient can be written as

$$\psi \equiv \frac{g_c c_p \,\Delta T_t}{(\omega r)^2} = \frac{\tan \alpha_2 - \tan \alpha_1}{\tan \alpha_2 + \tan \alpha_1} = 1 - \frac{2 \tan \alpha_1}{\tan \alpha_2 + \tan \alpha_1}$$

9-11. Air enters a repeating-row, repeating-stage compressor which has the following properties: $\dot{m} = 40$ lbm/sec, $T_{t1} = 290$ K, $P_{t1} = 101.3$ kPa, $M_1 = 0.5$, $\alpha_1 = 38°$, $D = 0.5$, $e_c = 0.9$, $\omega = 1000$ rad/sec, $\phi_{cs} = 0.03$, and $\sigma = 1$. *Note:* For air, use $\gamma = 1.4$ and $R = 0.286$ kJ/(kg · K). Make and fill out a table of flow properties like Table 9-3, and determine the temperature rise, pressure ratio, mean radius, and flow areas and associated hub and tip radii at stations 1, 2, and 3.

9-12. Air enters a repeating-row, repeating-stage compressor which has the following properties: $\dot{m} = 50$ lbm/sec, $T_{t1} = 518.7°$R, $P_{t1} = 14.7$ psia, $M_1 = 0.5$, $\alpha_1 = 35°$, $D = 0.5$, $e_c = 0.9$, $\omega = 1200$ rad/sec, $\phi_{cs} = 0.03$, and $\sigma = 1$. *Note:* For air, use $\gamma = 1.4$

and $R = 53.34 \text{ ft} \cdot \text{lbf}/(\text{lbm} \cdot {}^\circ\text{R})$. Make and fill out a table of flow properties like Table 9-3, and determine the temperature rise, pressure ratio, mean radius, and flow areas and associated hub and tip radii at stations 1, 2, and 3.

9-13. For an exponential swirl distribution and the data of Prob. 9-11, calculate and plot the variation of u_1, v_1, u_2, and v_2 versus radius from hub to tip (see Fig. 9-34).

9-14. For an exponential swirl distribution and the data of Prob. 9-12, calculate and plot the variation of u_1, v_1, u_2, and v_2 versus radius from hub to tip (see Fig. 9-34).

9-15. For the data of Prob. 9-11, determine the shape of both the rotor and the stator blades on the mean radius, using NACA 65-series airfoils with circular camber line. Assume $c/h = 0.3$ and 10% thickness.

9-16. For the data of Prob. 9-12, determine the shape of both the rotor and the stator blades on the mean radius, using NACA 65-series airfoils with circular camber line. Assume $c/h = 0.3$ and 10% thickness.

9-17. For the data of Prob. 9-11, determine AN^2 at station 1.

9-18. For the data of Prob. 9-12, determine AN^2 at station 1.

9-19. A 0.4-m-diameter rotor of a centrifugal compressor for air is needed to produce a pressure ratio of 3.8. Assuming a polytropic efficiency of 0.85, determine the angular speed ω, total temperature rise, and adiabatic efficiency. Determine the input power for a mass flow rate of 2 kg/sec at 1 atm and 288.2 K. Assume a slip factor of 0.9.

9-20. A 12-in-diameter rotor of a centrifugal compressor for air is needed to produce a pressure ratio of 4. Assuming a polytropic efficiency of 0.86, determine the angular speed ω, total temperature rise, and adiabatic efficiency. Determine the input power for a mass flow rate of 10 lbm/sec at 1 atm and 518.7°R. Assume a slip factor of 0.9.

9-21. Products of combustion flow through an axial turbine stage with the following properties: $T_{t1} = 1800$ K, $P_{t1} = 1000$ kPa, $u_3/u_2 = 1$, $M_2 = 1.1$, $U = \omega r_m = 360$ m/sec, $\alpha_2 = 45°$ and $\alpha_3 = 5°$. *Note:* For the gas, use $\gamma = 1.3$ and $R = 0.287 \text{ kJ}/(\text{kg} \cdot \text{K})$. Determine the following:

a. V_2, u_2, and v_2
b. u_3, v_3, and V_3
c. ΔT_t and τ_s for the stage
d. π_s and P_{t3} for a polytropic efficiency of 0.89

9-22. Products of combustion flow through an axial turbine stage with the following properties: $T_{t1} = 3200°$R, $P_{t1} = 200$ psia, $u_3/u_2 = 1$, $M_2 = 1.05$, $U = \omega r_m =$ 1200 ft/sec, $\alpha_2 = 40°$, and $\alpha_3 = 25°$. *Note*: For the gas, use $\gamma = 1.3$ and $R =$ $53.4 \text{ ft} \cdot \text{lbf}/(\text{lbm} \cdot {}^\circ\text{R})$. Determine the following:

a. V_2, u_2, and v_2
b. u_3, v_3, and V_3
c. ΔT_t and τ_s for the stage
d. π_s and P_{t3} for a polytropic efficiency of 0.9

9-23. In the preliminary design of turbines, many designers use the dimensionless work coefficient ψ, defined as

$$\psi \equiv \frac{g_c c_p \, \Delta T_t}{(\omega r)^2}$$

a. For a turbine stage with $\alpha_3 = 0$, show that the degree of reaction can be written as

$$^{\circ}R_t = 1 - \frac{\psi}{2}$$

b. For a turbine stage with $\alpha_3 = 0$, $\gamma = 1.3$, $R = 0.287\ \text{kJ/(kg}\cdot\text{K)}$, and $\psi = 1$ and 2, plot ΔT_t versus ωr for $250 < \omega r < 450\ \text{m/sec}$.

9-24. Products of combustion enter a turbine stage with the following properties: $\dot{m} = 40\ \text{kg/sec}$, $T_{t1} = 1780\ \text{K}$, $P_{t1} = 1.40\ \text{MPa}$, $M_1 = 0.3$, $M_2 = 1.15$, $\omega r = 400\ \text{m/sec}$, $T_{t3} = 1550\ \text{K}$ $\alpha_1 = \alpha_3 = 0$, $r_m = 0.4\ \text{m}$, $u_3/u_2 = 1.0$, $\phi_{t\,\text{stator}} = 0.04$, and $\phi_{t\,\text{rotor}} = 0.08$. *Note:* For the gas, use $\gamma = 1.3$ and $R = 0.287\ \text{kJ/(kg}\cdot\text{K)}$. Make and fill out a table of flow properties like Table 9-11 for the mean line, and determine the degree of reaction, total temperature change, stage efficiency, polytropic efficiency, and flow areas and associated hub and tip radii at stations 1, 2, and 3.

9-25. Products of combustion enter a turbine stage with the following properties: $\dot{m} = 105\ \text{lbm/sec}$, $T_{t1} = 3200°\text{R}$, $P_{t1} = 280\ \text{psia}$, $M_1 = 0.3$, $M_2 = 1.2$, $\omega r = 1400\ \text{ft/sec}$, $T_{t3} = 2700°\text{R}$, $\alpha_1 = \alpha_3 = 0$, $r_m = 14\ \text{in}$, $u_3/u_2 = 1.0$, $\phi_{t\,\text{stator}} = 0.04$, and $\phi_{t\,\text{rotor}} = 0.08$. *Note:* For the gas, use $\gamma = 1.3$ and $R = 53.34\ \text{ft}\cdot\text{lbf/(lbm}\cdot°\text{R)}$. Make and fill out a table of flow properties like Table 9-11 for the mean line, and determine the degree of reaction, total temperature change, stage efficiency, polytropic efficiency, and flow areas and associated hub and tip radii at stations 1, 2, and 3.

9-26. For the data of Prob. 9-24, determine the shape of both the nozzle and the rotor blades on the mean radius, using a C4 profile with circular camber line for the nozzle blades and T6 profile with circular camber line for the rotor blades. Assume $c/h = 1$, $Z = 0.9$, and 10 percent thickness for both nozzle and rotor blades.

9-27. For the data of Prob. 9-25, determine the shape of both the nozzle and the rotor blades on the mean radius, using a C4 profile with circular camber line for the nozzle blades and a T6 profile with circular camber line for the rotor blades. Assume $c/h = 1$, $Z = 0.9$, and 10 percent thickness for both nozzle and rotor blades.

9-28. For the data of Prob. 9-24, determine AN^2 at station 2.

9-29. For the data of Prob. 9-25, determine AN^2 at station 2.

9-30. Products of combustion [$\gamma = 1.3$, $R = 0.287\ \text{kJ/(kg}\cdot\text{K)}$] exit from a set of axial-flow turbine nozzles at a swirl angle of 60°, $M = 1.1$, $P_t = 2.0\ \text{MPa}$, and $T_t = 1670\ \text{K}$. This gas then enters the turbine rotor.

a. For a mass flow rate of 150 kg/sec, determine the area of the flow annulus upstream of the turbine rotor.

b. If the maximum centrifugal load on the turbine blade is 70 MPa, determine the maximum shaft speed (rpm, N). Assume a blade taper factor of 0.9 and material density of $8700\ \text{kg/m}^3$.

c. For the shaft speed determined in part *b*, the turbine disk designer has determined that the maximum radius of the hub is 0.6 m. Determine the tip radius, mean radius, and the total temperature drop through the turbine rotor based on the mean rotor velocity and zero exit swirl.

9-31. Products of combustion [$\gamma = 1.3$, $R = 53.34\ \text{ft}\cdot\text{lbf/(lbm}\cdot°\text{R)}$] exit from a set of axial-flow turbine nozzles at a swirl angle of 65°, $M = 1.2$, $P_t = 300\ \text{psia}$, and $T_t = 3000°\text{R}$. This gas then enters the turbine rotor.

a. For a mass flow rate of 325 lbm/sec, determine the area of the flow annulus upstream of the turbine rotor.
b. If the maximum centrifugal load on the turbine blade is 10,000 psia, determine the maximum shaft speed (rpm, N). Assume a blade taper factor of 0.9 and material density of 0.25 lb/in^3.
c. For the shaft speed determined in part *b*, the turbine disk designer has determined that the maximum radius of the hub is 15 in. Determine the tip radius, mean radius, and the total temperature drop through the turbine rotor based on the mean rotor velocity and zero exit swirl.

9-32. A centrifugal turbine has products of combustion [$\gamma = 1.33$, $R = 0.287$ kJ/(kg · K)] entering at 1200 K and 1.5 MPa and leaving at 1000 K. For a rotor diameter of 0.3 m, flow angle α_2 of 60°, and polytropic efficiency of 0.9, determine the following:
a. Rotor tip speed and angular speed ω
b. Mach number at station 2
3. Total pressure at the exit
d. Adiabatic efficiency

9-33. A centrifugal turbine has products of combustion [$\gamma = 1.33$, $R = 53.34$ ft · lbf/(lbm · °R)] entering at 2100°R and 200 psia and leaving at 1800°R. For an 8-in rotor diameter, flow angle α_2 of 55°, and polytropic efficiency of 0.85, determine the following:
a. Rotor tip speed and angular speed ω
b. Mach number at station 2
c. Total pressure at the exit
d. Adiabatic efficiency

9-34. At a total pressure of 1 atm and total temperature of 288.2 K, 2.0 kg/sec of air enters the centrifugal compressor of a turbocharger and leaves the compressor at a total pressure of 1.225 atm. This compressor is directly driven by a radial-flow turbine. Products of combustion with a mass flow rate of 2.06 kg/sec enter the turbine at a total temperature of 900 K and leave the turbine at a total pressure of 1.02 atm. Assume adiabatic flow through both compressor and turbine, no loss of power to bearings from the drive shaft that connects the compressor and turbine, $e_c = 0.80$, $e_t = 0.82$, a slip factor of 0.9 for the compressor, and the following gas properties:

For air	$\gamma = 1.40$ and $c_p = 1.004$ kJ/(kg · K)
For products of combustion	$\gamma = 1.33$ and $c_p = 1.157$ kJ/(kg · K)

Determine the following:
a. Compressor rotor tip speed U_t m/sec and exit total temperature in kelvins
b. Turbine rotor tip speed U_t m/sec and inlet total pressure in atmospheres
c. Turbine exit total temperatures in kelvins
d. Tip radius of compressor rotor and tip radius of turbine rotor for $N = 20{,}000$ rpm

9-35. At a total pressure of 14.696 psia and total temperature of 518.7°R, 2.0 lbm/sec of air enters the centrifugal compressor of a turbocharger and leaves the compressor at a total pressure of 18 psia. This compressor is directly driven by a radial-flow turbine. Products of combustion with a mass flow rate of 2.06 lbm/sec enter the turbine at a total temperature of 1600°R and leave the turbine at a total pressure of 15.0 psia. Assume adiabatic flow through both compressor and turbine, no loss of power to bearings from the drive shaft that connects the compressor and turbine, $e_c = 0.80$, $e_t = 0.82$, a slip factor of 0.9 for the compressor, and the following gas properties:

For air $\gamma = 1.40$ and $g_c c_p = 6000\ \text{ft}^2/(\text{s}^2 \cdot {}^\circ\text{R})$
For products of combustion $\gamma = 1.33$ and $g_c c_p = 6860\ \text{ft}^2/(\text{s}^2 \cdot {}^\circ\text{R})$

Determine the following:

a. Compressor rotor tip speed U_t ft/sec and exit total temperature in degrees Rankine
b. Turbine rotor tip speed U_t ft/sec and inlet total pressure in pounds per square inch absolute
c. Turbine exit total temperatures in degrees Rankine
d. Tip radius of compressor rotor and tip radius of turbine rotor for $N =$ 20,000 rpm

9-D1 AXIAL FLOW TURBOMACHINERY DESIGN PROBLEM 1

Perform the preliminary design of the turbomachinery for a turbojet engine having a thrust of 25,000 lbf at sea-level static conditions. Based on polytropic efficiencies of 0.9 for both compressor and turbine, the engineers in the engine cycle analysis group have determined the compressor and turbine inlet and exit conditions for a range of compressor pressure ratios that will give the required engine thrust. The results of their analysis are presented in Table P9-D1. Note that the mass flow rate through the

TABLE P9-D1
Compressor and turbine design data for a 25,000-lb turbojet*

π_c	T_{t3} (°R)	P_{t3} (psia)	T_{t5} (°R)	P_{t4} (psia)	P_{t5} (psia)	$\dot{m}_{\text{compr}}$ (lbm/sec)	$\dot{m}_{\text{turb}}$ (lbm/sec)	$\dot{W}_c$ (kW)	$\dot{W}_t$ (kW)
7.0	962.06	102.87	2853.21	98.76	56.85	200.28	208.66	22,298	22,523
7.5	983.36	110.22	2836.44	105.81	59.20	197.79	206.01	23,079	23,312
8.0	1003.72	117.57	2820.41	112.87	61.45	195.61	203.68	23,824	24,065
8.5	1023.22	124.92	2805.04	119.92	63.60	193.69	201.63	24,539	24,786
9.0	1041.96	132.26	2790.27	126.97	65.65	191.97	199.79	25,225	25,480
9.5	1060.00	139.61	2776.04	134.03	67.61	190.44	198.15	25,886	26,147
10.0	1077.40	146.96	2762.31	141.08	69.49	189.05	196.66	26,523	26,791
10.5	1094.22	154.31	2749.03	148.14	71.29	187.80	195.31	27,140	27,415
11.0	1110.50	161.66	2736.18	155.19	73.02	186.65	194.08	27,738	28,018
11.5	1126.28	169.00	2723.71	162.24	74.68	185.61	192.95	28,318	28,605
12.0	1141.60	176.35	2711.60	169.30	76.27	184.65	191.91	28,882	29,174
12.5	1156.49	183.70	2699.82	176.35	77.80	183.77	190.96	29,431	29,729
13.0	1170.98	191.05	2688.36	183.41	79.27	182.95	190.07	29,966	30,269

* Air entering compressor has $T_t = 518.7$°R and $P_t = 14.696$ psia. Gas enters turbine at 3200°R and P_{t4}. Polytropic efficiencies: $e_c = 0.90$ and $e_t = 0.90$.

$$\dot{W}_t = \frac{\dot{W}_c}{0.99} \qquad P_{t4} = 0.96 P_{t3}$$

compressor and turbine decreases with increasing compressor pressure ratio. To minimize on engine weight, it is desirable to have the maximum compressor pressure that can be driven by a single-stage turbine with exit guide vanes. The number of compressor stages depends on both the compressor design and the turbine design. As you can see, there are many sets of compressor/turbine designs that meet the thrust need; however, some of the designs cannot be done with one turbine stage or may be too large (high mass flow rate). Data for other compressor pressure ratios between 7 and 13 not listed in the table can be obtained by interpolation.

Assume that a turbine disk material exists that permits a rim speed of 1200 ft/sec and that the turbine rotor airfoils can withstand an AN^2 of 5×10^{10} in$^2 \cdot$ rpm^2. Use Fig. J-8 and computed AN^2 stresses to select material for each compressor stage.

For the compressor, use

$$\gamma = 1.4 \quad \text{and} \quad R = 53.34 \text{ ft} \cdot \text{lbf}/(\text{lbm} \cdot {}^\circ\text{R})$$

For the turbine, use

$$\gamma = 1.3 \quad \text{and} \quad R = 53.39 \text{ ft} \cdot \text{lbf}/(\text{lbm} \cdot {}^\circ\text{R})$$

Suggested Design Process

1. Select a set of compressor and turbine design data from Table P9-D1.
2. For the design turbine rim speed, estimate the mean turbine rotor speed ωr_m and determine the variation of turbine radii (hub, mean, and tip) and AN^2 versus RPM. Select a shaft speed (RPM).
3. Determine the turbine mean-line design, using TURBN. Make sure the turbine meets the design criteria listed below.
4. For the selected shaft speed (RPM) and compressor pressure ratio, determine the number of compressor stages and the compressor mean-line design, using the repeating-row, repeating-stage design choice in COMPR. Make sure the compressor meets the design criteria listed below.
5. Check that 99 percent of power from turbine equals the power required by the compressor.
6. Check alignment of compressor and turbine. If the mean radii are not more than 2 in apart, go back to item 2 and select a new RPM.
7. Determine the inlet and exit flow conditions for the turbine exit guide vanes (include estimate of losses).
8. Determine the inlet and exit flow conditions for the inlet guide vanes (include estimate of losses).
9. Specify compressor material for each stage based on the rotor's relative total temperature and blade AN^2.
10. Make a combined scale drawing of the compressor and turbine flow path. Allow 12 in between the compressor exit and turbine inlet for the combustor. Show the shaft centerline.

Compressor Design Criteria

1. Axial flow entering inlet guide vanes and leaving compressor
2. Reactions at all radii > 0
3. Diffusion at all radii < 0.6
4. M_{1R} at tip of first stage < 1.05

5. M_2 at hub of first stage < 1
6. Flow coefficient at mean radius between 0.45 and 0.55
7. Stage loading coefficient at mean radius between 0.3 and 0.35
8. Number of blades for rotor or stator of any stage < 85
9. Number of blades for inlet guide vanes < 85
10. AN^2 at entrance of rotor within material limits

Turbine Design Criteria

1. Axial flow entering turbine nozzle at $M = 0.3$
2. Axial flow leaving exit guide vanes of turbine
3. Reaction at all radii > −0.15
4. Number of blades for nozzle, rotor, or exit guide vanes < 85
5. $M_2 < 1.2$ at hub and >1 at tip
6. M_{3R} at tip of rotor < 0.9
7. Velocity ratio at mean radius between 0.5 and 0.6
8. AN^2 at entrance of rotor within material limits
9. Tangential force coefficient for stator or rotor < 1.0

9-D2 AXIAL-FLOW TURBOMACHINERY DESIGN PROBLEM 2

Perform the preliminary design of the turbomachinery for a turbojet engine of Prob. 9-D1 but with no inlet guide vanes for the compressor or exit guide vanes from the turbine. Thus the turbine must have zero exit swirl.

9-D3 AXIAL-FLOW TURBOMACHINERY DESIGN PROBLEM 3

Perform the preliminary design of the turbomachinery for a turbojet engine of Prob. 9-D1 scaled for a thrust of 16,000 lbf at sea-level, static conditions. Thus the mass flow rates and powers will be 64 percent of the values listed in Table P9-D1.

9-D4 AXIAL-FLOW TURBOMACHINERY DESIGN PROBLEM 4

You are to perform the preliminary design of the turbomachinery for a turbojet engine of Prob. 9-D3 but with no inlet guide vanes for the compressor or exit guide vanes from the turbine. Thus the turbine must have zero exit swirl.

CHAPTER 10

INLETS, NOZZLES, AND COMBUSTION SYSTEMS

10-1 INTRODUCTION TO INLETS AND NOZZLES

The inlet and exhaust nozzle are the two engine components that directly interface with the internal airflow and the flow about the aircraft. In fact, integration of the engine and the airframe is one of the most complex problems and has a major impact on the performance of the aircraft system. Many technical books, reports, articles, etc., are available in open literature (public domain) that concentrate on only small parts of this major technical challenge. This chapter identifies the major design considerations of inlets and exhaust nozzles and presents basic analysis tools for their preliminary sizing and design.

The results of the engine performance analysis provide a wealth of information about the required performance of both the inlet and the exhaust nozzle. For example, the required full-throttle, corrected engine airflow versus both Mach number and altitude can be obtained from the engine performance analysis program PERF (see Figs. 8-21, 8-31, 8-50, and 8-74*b*). Likewise, the engine airflow at specific partial-throttle conditions (corresponding to cruise, loiter, etc.) and the assumed inlet total pressure ratio versus Mach number can be obtained. The design information defines the requirements of the inlet in terms of total pressure ratio and mass flow rate, and preliminary design of the inlet starts with this information.

The simplest and most powerful design tool available for preliminary design of these components is one-dimensional compressible flow. Both the inlet and the exhaust nozzle can be modeled as simple one-dimensional adiabatic flows or a series of these flows. The following sections of this chapter present the basic principles of operation for each component, the major design considerations, and the basic design tools. Starting at the front of the engine, we consider the inlet first.

10-2 INLETS

The inlet interchanges the organized kinetic and random thermal energies of the gas in an essentially adiabatic process. The perfect (no-loss) inlet would thus correspond to an isentropic process. The primary purpose of the inlet is to bring the air required by the engine from free-stream conditions to the conditions required at the entrance of the fan or compressor with minimum total pressure loss. The fan or compressor works best with a uniform flow of air at a Mach number of about 0.5. Also, since the installed engine performance depends on the inlet's installation losses (additive drag, forebody or cowl drag, bypass air, boundary-layer bleed air, etc.), the design of the inlet should minimize these losses. The performance of an inlet is related to the following characteristics: high total pressure ratio π_d, controllable flow matching of requirements, good uniformity of flow, low installation drag, good starting and stability, low signatures (acoustic, radar, etc.), and minimum weight and cost while meeting life and reliability goals. An inlet's overall performance must be determined by simultaneously evaluating all these characteristics since improvement in one is often achieved at the expense of another.

The design and operation of subsonic and supersonic inlets differ considerably due to the characteristics of the flow. For the subsonic inlets, near-isentropic internal diffusion can be easily achieved, and the inlet flow rate adjusts to the demand. The internal aerodynamic performance of a supersonic inlet is a major design problem, since achieving efficient and stable supersonic diffusion over a wide range of Mach numbers is very difficult. In addition, the supersonic inlet must be able to capture its required mass flow rate, which may require variable geometry to minimize inlet loss and drag and provide stable operation. Because of these differences, in the following sections we consider the subsonic and supersonic inlets separately, beginning with the subsonic inlet.

10-3 SUBSONIC INLETS

Most subsonic aircraft have their engines placed in nacelles; thus, in this section we do not deal with the inlet alone but include the nacelle at subsonic Mach numbers. The cross section of a typical subsonic inlet and its geometric

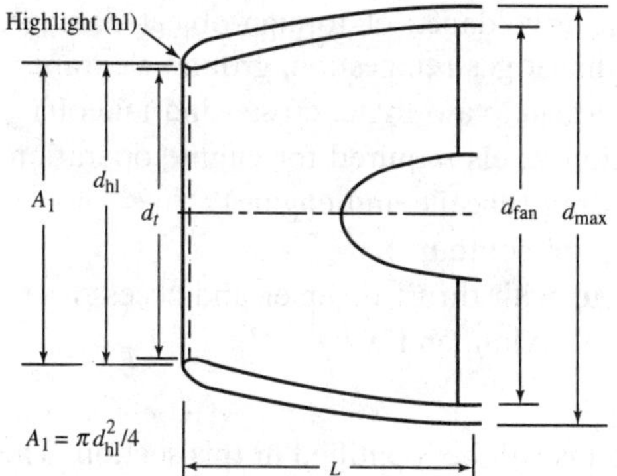

FIGURE 10-1
Subsonic inlet nomenclature.

parameters are shown in Fig. 10-1. The inlet area A_1 is based on the flow cross section at the inlet highlight. Because the subsonic inlet can draw in airflow whose free-stream area A_0 is larger than the inlet area A_1, variable inlet geometry is not required (except sometimes blow-in doors are used to reduce installation drag during takeoff). The material in this section on subsonic inlets is based on a fixed-geometry inlet.

The operating conditions of an inlet depend on the flight velocity and mass flow demanded by the engine. Figure 10-2 shows the streamline pattern for three typical subsonic conditions. Figure 10-2(a) shows acceleration of the fluid external to the inlet which will occur when the inlet operates at a velocity lower than the design value or at a mass flow higher than the design value. Figure 10-2(c) shows deceleration of the fluid external to the inlet which will occur at a velocity higher than design or a mass flow lower than design.

A list of the major design variables for the inlet and nacelle includes the following:

- Inlet total pressure ratio and drag at cruise

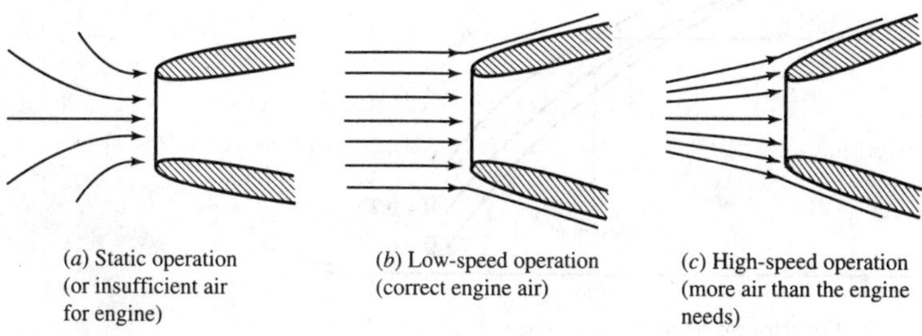

(a) Static operation (or insufficient air for engine)
(b) Low-speed operation (correct engine air)
(c) High-speed operation (more air than the engine needs)

FIGURE 10-2
Typical streamline patterns for subsonic inlet (Ref. 52).

- Engine location on wing or fuselage (avoidance of foreign-object damage, inlet flow upwash and downwash, exhaust gas reingestion, ground clearance)
- Aircraft attitude envelope (angle of attack, yaw angle, cross-wind takeoff)
- Inlet total pressure ratio and distortion levels required for engine operation
- Engine-out windmilling airflow and drag (nacelle and engine)
- Integration of diffuser and fan flow path contour
- Integration of external nacelle contour with thrust reverser and accessories
- Flow field interaction between nacelle, pylon, and wing
- Noise suppression requirements

Basic design tools for many of these items will be identified in this section. The reader is encouraged to research open literature (public domain) for a more in-depth analysis of any single item. Special attention is drawn to Ref. 49, which is a textbook on the aerodynamics of inlets.

Inlet Total Pressure Ratio π_d

In the cycle analysis used in the earlier chapters, the inlet total pressure ratio π_d was assumed to be constant for subsonic inlets and equal to $\pi_{d\,\max}$ (the total pressure ratio due to friction). Due to the complexity of the flow, we do not present a method for calculating the inlet total pressure ratio. However, Fig. 10-3 presents attainable π_d and its variation with flight Mach number and engine mass flow. The impact of the varying π_d on engine performance can be estimated by using this figure in concert with the performance analysis program and mission profile.

Inlet Sizing—Throat Diameter d_t

The diameter at the throat of the subsonic inlet is sized such that the Mach number at this location (based on one-dimensional flow) does not exceed 0.8. This will provide some margin for growth or error since the one-dimensional

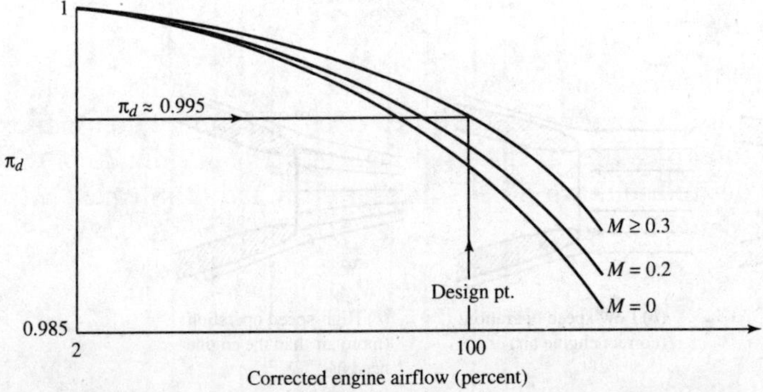

FIGURE 10-3
Typical subsonic inlet total pressure ratio (after Younghans, Ref. 53).

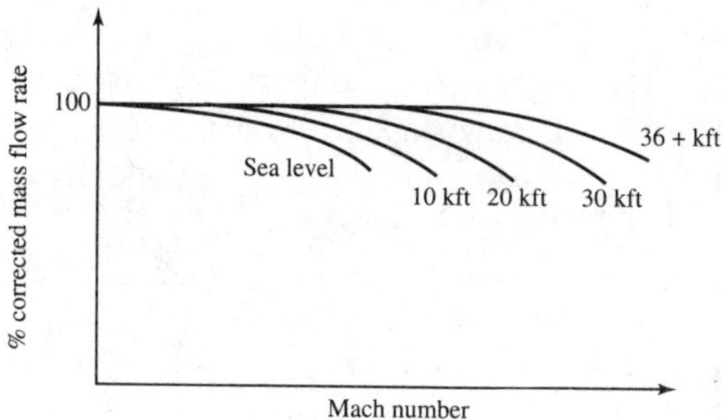

FIGURE 10-4
Typical subsonic engine airflow requirements.

Mach number at the throat corresponding to actual inlet choke is about 0.9. The maximum corrected engine mass flow that the throat must pass will then correspond to this limiting Mach number, and the diameter is easily calculated by using

$$d_t = \sqrt{\frac{4}{\pi} A_{\text{th max}}} = \sqrt{\frac{4}{\pi}\left(\frac{\dot{m}_0\sqrt{T_{t0}}}{P_{t0}}\right)_{\max} \frac{1}{\text{MFP} @ M = 0.8}}$$

which can be expressed in terms of the corrected mass flow as

$$d_t = \sqrt{\frac{4}{\pi}\frac{\sqrt{518.7}}{2116}\frac{\dot{m}_{c0\max}}{\text{MFP} @ M = 0.8}}$$

and reduces to

$$d_t = 0.1636\sqrt{\dot{m}_{c0\max}} \qquad \text{or} \qquad d_t = 1.105\sqrt{A^*_{0\max}} \tag{10-1}$$

where $\dot{m}_{c0\max}$ has units of pound-mass per second, d_t has units of feet, and $A^*_{0\max}$ has units of square feet. Figure 10-4 is a representative output from the engine performance computer program PERF of the corrected mass flow for a high-bypass-ratio turbofan engine. A figure like this can be used for selecting the point of maximum corrected mass flow that determines the throat diameter d_t.

Inlet Flow Distortion

Inlets operated with high angles of flow incidence are susceptible to flow separation from the inside contour of the inlet. This flow separation causes large regions of low total pressure, as shown in Fig. 10-5. The magnitude of this distortion from the desired uniform flow is measured by the term called *inlet distortion* and is calculated by

$$\text{Inlet distortion} = \frac{P_{t\max} - P_{t\min}}{P_{t\,\text{av}}} \tag{10-2}$$

Both the instantaneous (dynamic) and time-averaged (steady-state) distortion levels are used to measure the quality of an inlet's flow. When Eq. (10-2) is used for calculation of the dynamic inlet distortion, the average total

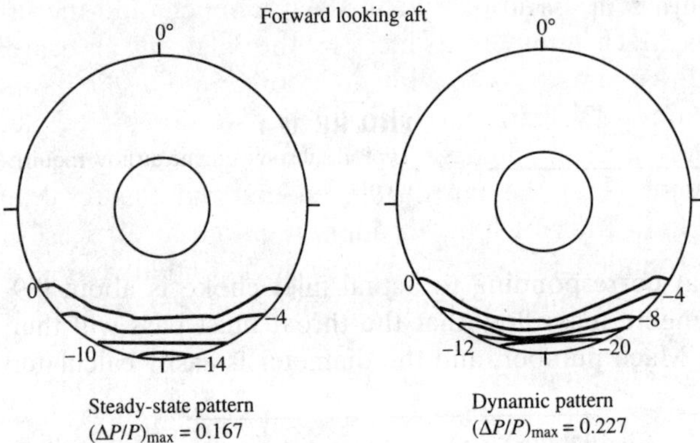

FIGURE 10-5
Typical steady-state and dynamic total pressure distortion patterns (from Younghans, Ref. 53).

pressure in the denominator is the spatial average at an instant in time, and the maximum and minimum total pressures are for that same instant in time. Determination of the steady-state inlet distortion requires time-averaging of the total pressures in the inlet. The average total pressure $P_{t\,av}$ of Eq. (10-2) is the spatial average of the time-averaged total pressures.

The magnitude of the inlet distortion is a function of the inlet's geometry, mass flow rate, flight Mach number, and flow incidence angle. The effect of high distortion is to shift the fan or compressor surge line to values of higher mass flow rate, as shown in Fig. 10–6. This shift in surge line may result in compressor surge.

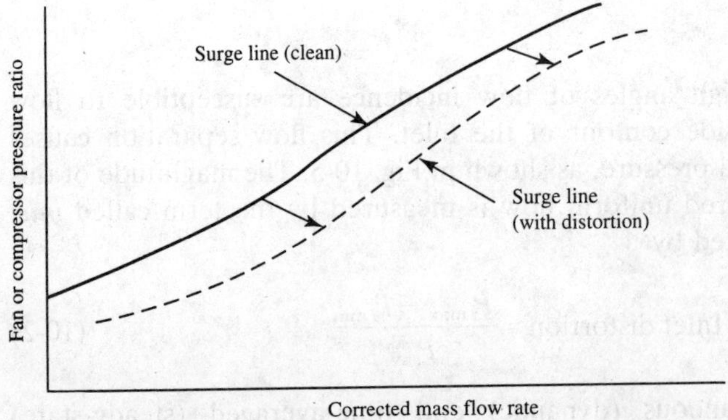

FIGURE 10-6
Effect of inlet distortion on the fan or compressor.

Inlet Drag

In Chap. 4, we looked at the additive drag that occurs when the area of the free-stream air A_0 is different from the area of the entrance to the inlet A_1. Figure 4-5 shows a subsonic inlet at various flight Mach numbers and the use of "blow-in" doors at low Mach numbers to increase the inlet entrance area and thus reduce the additive drag. These blow-in doors were used in the turbofan-powered B-707 and in the early model of the B-747. Boeing deleted the use of blow-in doors in later models of the B-747 because of the nonuniform flow they created into the fan during takeoff and the resulting unacceptable fan noise. Elimination of blow-in doors required an increase in the entrance area, a more rounded lip, and a somwehat higher additive drag at cruise conditions. Most subsonic inlets operate as shown in Fig. 10-2(*c*) at cruise conditions.

At an engine inlet, flow separation can occur on the external surface of the nacelle due to local high velocities and subsequent deceleration. Flow separation can also occur on the internal surface of the inlet due to the flow deceleration, which causes an adverse pressure gradient (static pressure increase in the direction of flow). We will discuss the flow inside the inlet subsequently.

The size of the nacelle forebody [d_{hl}/d_{max} and L/d_{max} (see Fig. 10-1)] is a design compromise between the requirement of low cruise drag and avoiding catastrophes when one or more engines are out. The nacelle forebody size that gives minimum drag at cruise may not give good engine-out drag. In Chap. 4, the additive drag given by Eq. (4-8) was used as a conservative estimate of the inlet drag for engine sizing. A portion of the additive drag can be recovered along the forebody portion of the engine nacelle if the flow does not separate. This is indicated by the suction pressures near the lip of the nacelle in Fig. 10-7. The resulting pressure force on the outside of the nacelle forebody is

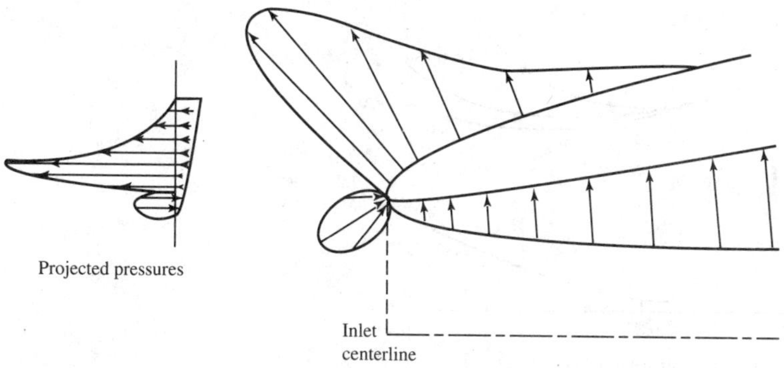

FIGURE 10-7
Pressure distribution around a subsonic inlet lip (Ref. 52).

called the *forebody drag*. The sum of the additive drag and the forebody drag is called the *inlet drag*.

Since flow around a curved surface accelerates the flow, then (at high subsonic Mach numbers) the local velocity can become supersonic adjacent to a nacelle. A shock then occurs, and a rise in static pressure across the shock reduces the negative pressure, thereby reducing the thrust component. This phenomenon is the same as that for an airfoil on which the local sonic velocity appears at the critical flight Mach number. At higher subsonic speeds, therefore, the curve of the inlet must be reduced in order to reduce the drag forces. The result is that for high subsonic Mach numbers, the inlet lip becomes very thin with little or no external curvature.

Nacelle and Interference Drag

The minimum drag for a nacelle does not necessarily occur when the inlet is designed for minimum inlet drag. The influences of the afterbody drag, interference drag, and aircraft trim drag need to be included in the integration and design of an engine nacelle. The inlet and afterbody drag of a typical nacelle is shown in Fig. 10-8 as a function of forebody diameter d_{hl}/d_{max} and flight Mach number. Note that the design value of d_{hl}/d_{max} corresponding to minimum inlet drag does not correspond to minimum inlet-plus-afterbody drag. Also note that the design value of d_{hl}/d_{max} corresponding to minimum inlet-plus-afterbody drag changes with flight Mach number. Thus the selection of d_{hl}/d_{max} for an inlet will depend on the design flight Mach number and may require the compromise of an individual component design goal to achieve the best overall system performance.

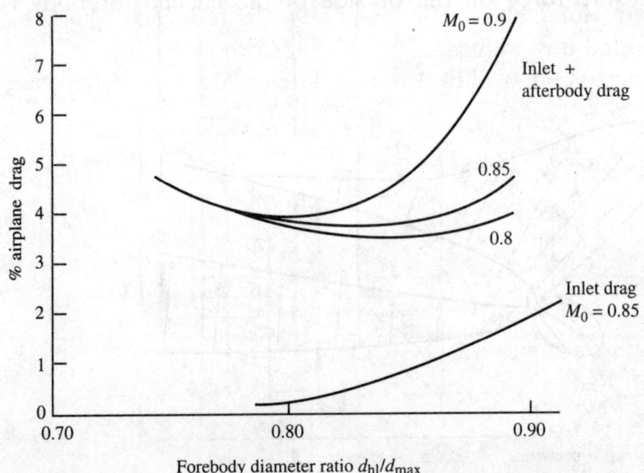

FIGURE 10-8
Typical inlet and afterbody drag (from Younghans, Ref. 53).

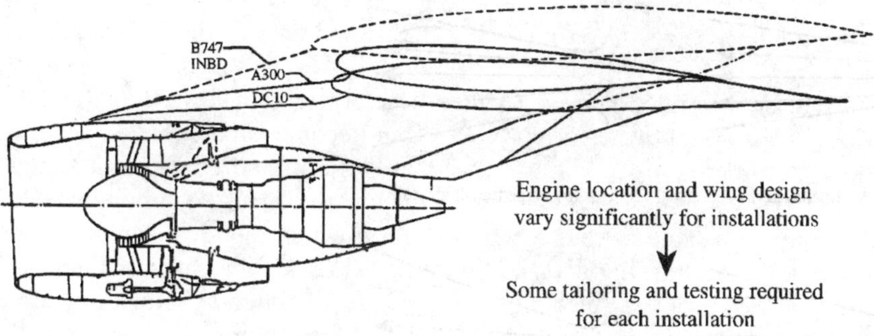

FIGURE 10-9
The CF6-50 installation on three aircraft. (*Courtesy of GE Aircraft Engines.*)

The engine location on the wing that provides the best integration of engine and airframe depends on the nacelle design, wing design, and resulting interference drag. Considerable analytical and experimental work is needed in the design of each installation. The resulting difference in best engine location on three aircraft is shown in Fig. 10-9.

Diffuser

The flow within the inlet is required to undergo diffusion in a divergent duct. This reduction in flow velocity creates an increase in static pressure that interacts with the boundary layer. If the pressure rise due to diffusion occurs more rapidly than turbulent mixing can reenergize the boundary layer, the boundary layer will assume the configurations shown in Fig. 10-10. If the flow in an inlet separates, the total and static pressures are reduced from their corresponding nonseparated flow values.

The rate of area increase in a diffuser has a direct effect on the behavior

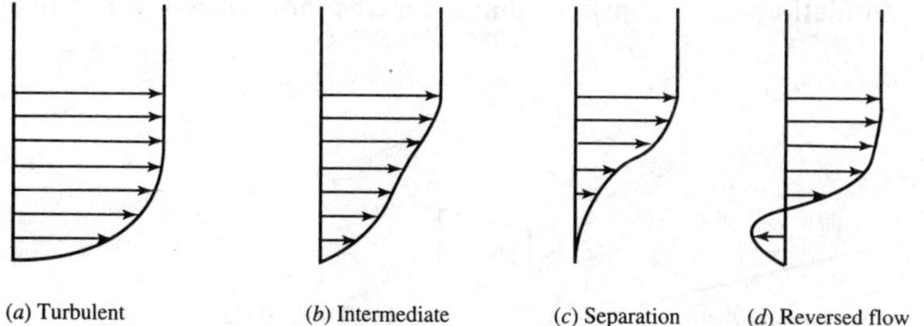

FIGURE 10-10
Boundary layer with an adverse pressure gradient (Ref. 52).

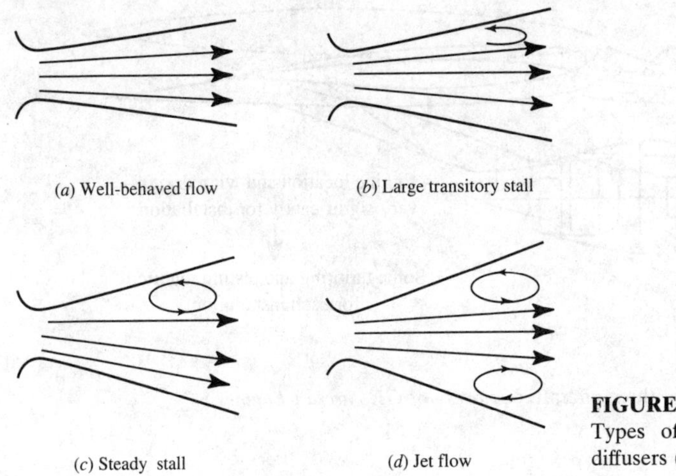

FIGURE 10-11
Types of flow in straight-walled diffusers (Ref. 35).

of flow in the diffuser, as shown in Fig. 10-11. If the rate of area increase is greater than that needed to keep the boundary layer energized and attached, the flow may be characterized by unsteady zones of stall. The turbulent mixing is no longer able to overcome the pressure forces at all points in the flow, and local separation occurs at some points. The total pressure decreases markedly due to the irreversible mixing of a fairly large portion of low-velocity fluid with the main flow. If the diffuser walls diverge rapidly, the flow will separate completely and behave much as a jet, as shown in Fig. 10–11(*d*).

The rate of area increase without stall for a diffuser depends on the characteristics of the flow at the entrance and on the length of the divergent section. Figure 10-12 shows the results for two-dimensional straight-walled diffusers as presented by S. J. Kline in Ref. 50. Kline's results are for incompressible flow, and they do not give a qualitatively valid indication of the sensitivity of any diffuser to rapid divergence of flow area.

For the design of an optimum diffuser, research has shown that the boundary-layer profile should maintain a constant shape, although the boundary-layer thickness will, of course, increase as the flow moves down the diffuser. The stipulation of a constant shape for the boundary-layer profile

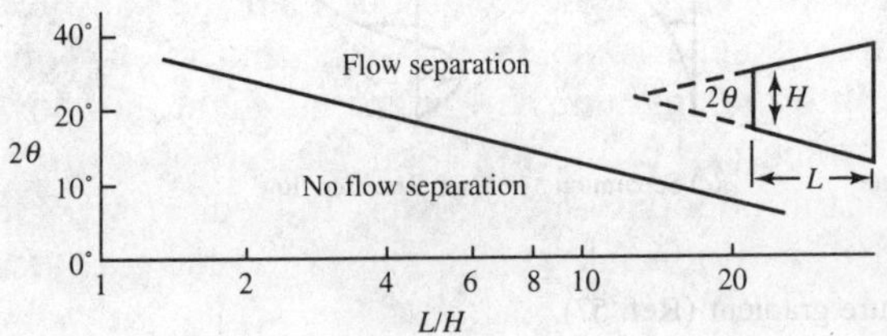

FIGURE 10-12
Flow separation limits in two-dimensional straight-walled diffusers (Ref. 50).

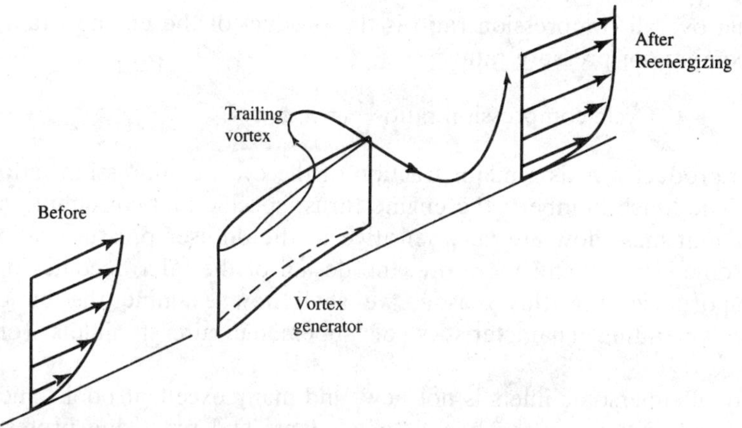

FIGURE 10-13
Vortex generators reenergize a boundary layer.

implies the assumption that mixing reenergizes the profile at the same rate as the static pressure depletes it.

In the presence of an adverse pressure gradient (static pressure increasing in the direction of flow), boundary layers tend to separate when the boundary layer is not reenergized rapidly enough by turbulent mixing. In Ref. 51, H. D. Taylor proposed the use of vortex generators as a mechanical mixing device to supplement the turbulent mixing. If vortices are generated by vortex generators in pairs, regions of inflow and outflow exist. These carry high-energy air into the boundary layer and low-energy air out. Figure 10-13 shows how vortex generators reenergize a boundary layer.

By using vortex generators together with a short, wide-angle diffuser, it may be possible to have a lower total pressure loss than with a long diffuser without vortex generators. Here, the reduced skin friction losses associated with flow separation are traded against vortex losses. The use of shorter diffusers may reduce weight and facilitate engine installation.

10-4 SUPERSONIC INLETS

The supersonic inlet is required to provide the proper quantity and uniformity of air to the engine over a wider range of flight conditions than the subsonic inlet is. In addition, the nature of supersonic flow makes this inlet more difficult to design and integrate into the airframe. In supersonic flight, the flow is decelerated by shock waves which can produce a total pressure loss much greater than, and in addition to, the boundary-layer losses. Indeed, at $M_0 = 3$, a simple pitot-type inlet preceded by a normal shock wave would have a total pressure recovery η_r of 0.32 due to the normal shock alone!

An engine overall compression ratio is the product of the engine's ram, diffuser, and compressor pressure ratios:

$$\text{Cycle compression ratio } \frac{P_{t3}}{P_0} = \pi_r \pi_d \pi_c \tag{10-3}$$

Since the product $\pi_r \pi_d$ is a major fraction of the cycle compression ratio at high supersonic Mach numbers, the engine thrust specific fuel consumption and thrust per unit mass flow are very sensitive to the diffuser pressure ratio π_d. For supersonic cruise flight, therefore, the design of the inlet becomes of paramount importance. For this reason, we shall now examine the basic principles and operating characteristics of supersonic aircraft inlets (or diffusers).

The study of supersonic inlets is not new, and many excellent books and reports have been written for the benefit of students and practicing professionals (see Refs. 49 through 60). Special attention should be paid to Ref. 49, a textbook that covers the aerodynamics of inlets.

Basics of One-Dimensional Inlet Flow

First, we review some one-dimensional perfect gas flow ideas which are basic to understanding a supersonic diffuser operation.

TOTAL AND SONIC STATE POINTS AND A/A^*. Consider the one-dimensional perfect gas flow of Fig. 10-14. The static state point of the gas at station 1 of the flow is designated as 1 in the T-s diagram of Fig. 10-14. Associated with static state point 1 at the same entropy are the total state point $t1$, where $M = 0$, and the sonic state point $*1$, where $M = 1$. The sonic and total state points can be attained by imagining a duct at station 1 decelerating the supersonic flow isentropically to a sonic throat $*1$ followed by a subsonic deceleration to zero speed $t1$ in an infinitely large storage reservoir.

Treating station 1 as any general station in the flow with no subscripts, we can write the area ratio A/A^* as

$$\boxed{\frac{A}{A^*} = \frac{1}{M}\left[\frac{2}{\gamma+1}\left(1 + \frac{\gamma-1}{2}M^2\right)\right]^{(\gamma+1)/[2(\gamma-1)]}} \tag{3-14}$$

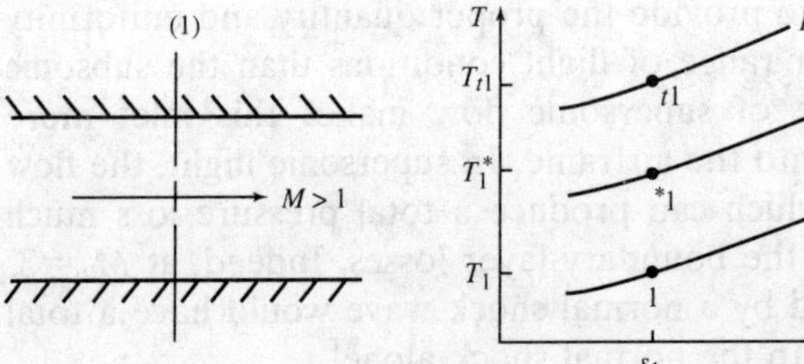

FIGURE 10-14
States for supersonic flow.

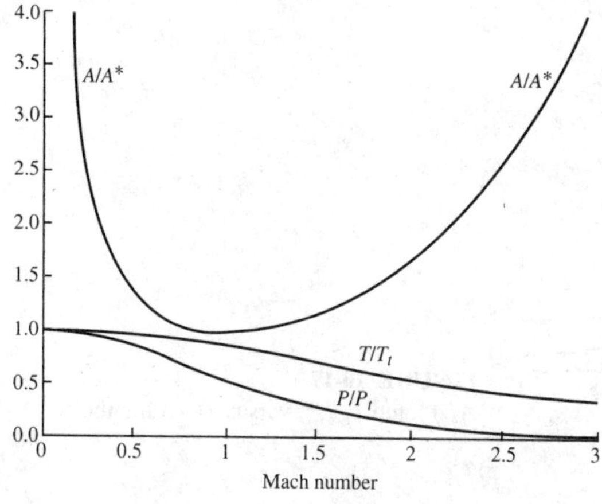

FIGURE 10-15
Compressible flow functions versus Mach number.

Since P and T in a given isentropic flow are also functions of the Mach number, this boxed equation connects A to P, T, and other flow properties in Fig. 10-15, A/A^*, P/P_t, and T/T_t are plotted versus the Mach number. Note that A/A^* varies from a minimum of 1 to 4.23 at $M=3$. This large variation tends to complicate supersonic inlet design.

NORMAL SHOCK WAVE. Consider the perfect gas flow through a normal shock wave depicted in Fig. 10-16, with subscripts x and y denoting shock upstream and downstream flow conditions, respectively. The static, sonic, and total state points of the gas entering and leaving the shock wave are shown in the T-s diagram of the figure with $s_y > s_x$ since the flow through a normal shock is irreversible and adiabatic at constant T_t. It follows that $T_x^* = T_y^*$, $P_{ty} < P_{tx}$, $V_x^* = V_y^*$, and $\rho_y^* < \rho_x^*$, as indicated in the T-s diagram.

Given the inlet conditions to a normal shock wave in a perfect gas, the exit conditions can be found since $P_y/P_x = f_1(M_x)$, $M_y = f_2(M_x)$, $P_{ty}/P_{tx} = f_3(M_x)$,

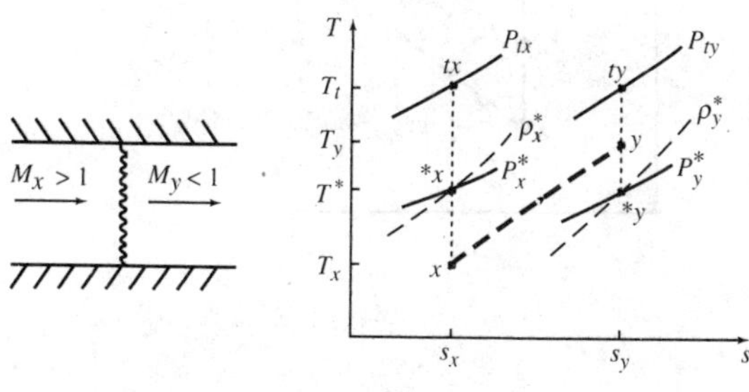

FIGURE 10-16
Normal shock wave.

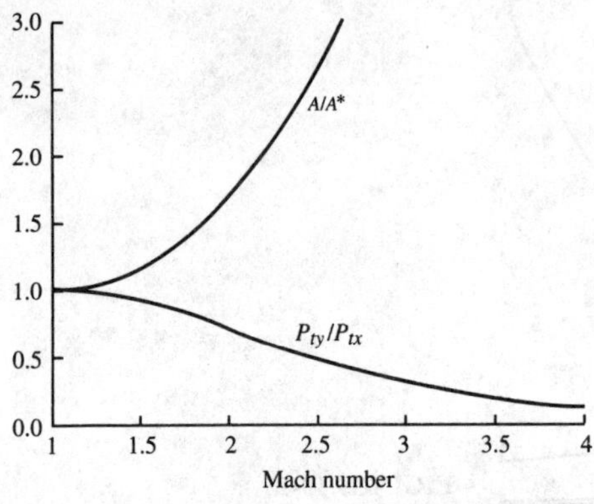

FIGURE 10-17
A/A^* and P_{ty}/P_{tx} versus Mach number.

etc. The total pressure ratio across a normal shock is of particular interest in supersonic diffuser studies and is plotted in Fig. 10-17 along with A/A^* from Fig. 10-15.

Suppose, now, that the flow of Fig. 10-16 passes through sonic throats of areas A_x^* and A_y^*, as in Fig. 10-18. What is the ratio of the area of the first throat to that of the second throat A_x^*/A_y^*? Conservation of mass and one-dimensional flow give

$$(\rho VA)_x^* = (\rho VA)_y^*$$

Since in this equation $V_x^* = V_y^*$ and $\rho_x^* > \rho_y^*$, the second throat area must be larger than the first to compensate for the lower-density gas passing through it, and

$$\frac{A_x^*}{A_y^*} = \frac{\rho_y^*}{\rho_x^*}$$

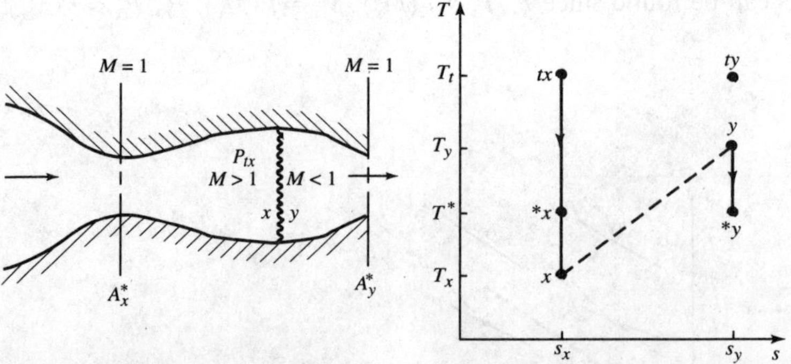

FIGURE 10-18
A/A^* and shock wave.

With $T_x^* = T_y^*$, we can write

$$\frac{\rho_y^*}{\rho_x^*} = \frac{P_y^*}{P_x^*} = \frac{P_{ty}\,(P^*/P_t)_y}{P_{tx}\,(P^*/P_t)_x} \quad (=1)$$

Therefore

$$\boxed{\frac{A_x^*}{A_y^*} = \frac{\rho_y^*}{\rho_x^*} = \frac{P_{ty}}{P_{tx}}} \tag{10-4}$$

and the plot of P_{ty}/P_{tx} in Fig. 10–17 can also be interpreted as A_x^*/A_x^* or ρ_y^*/ρ_x^* versus Mach number.

Example 10-1. Let us illustrate the preceding ideas with an example involving a supersonic inlet. The stream tube of air captured by the ideal shock-free inlet in Fig. 10-19 has an area A_0 equal to the inlet capture area A_c. Since $A_0 = A_c$, no air is spilled by the inlet. The inlet on the right is preceded by a shock wave and capture air contained in a stream tube of area $A_0 < A_c$. The free-stream airflow contained in the projected area A_c which does not enter the inlet is said to be spilled as shown. The fraction of air spilled is

$$\text{Fraction spilled} = \frac{(\rho V)_0 A_c - (\rho V)_0 A_0}{(\rho V)_0 A_c}$$

$$\boxed{\text{Fraction spilled} = \frac{A_c - A_0}{A_c} = \frac{A_c/A_t - A_0/A_t}{A_c/A_t}} \tag{10-5}$$

Consider a fixed-geometry inlet operating in a free-stream flow with $M_0 = 2$ and with a normal shock, as in Fig. 10-19. If the inlet capture/throat area ratio is $A_c/A_t = 1.34$, determine the fraction of air spilled.

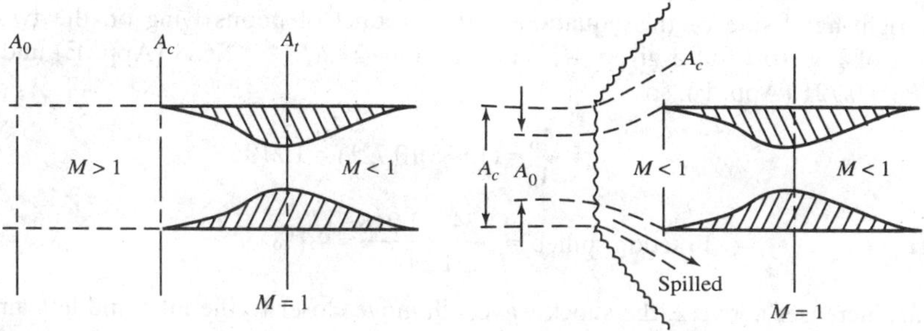

FIGURE 10-19
Inlet spillage.

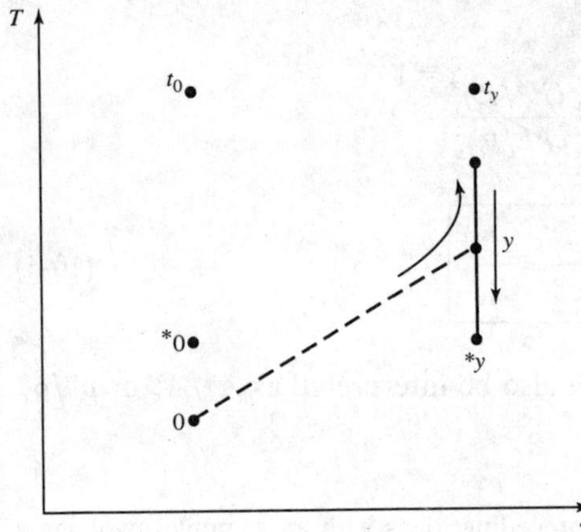

FIGURE 10-20
Stages of inlet flow across shock.

Solution. We have

$$\text{Fraction spilled} = \frac{A_c/A_t - A_0/A_t}{A_c/A_t} = \frac{1.34 - A_0/A_t}{1.34}$$

so we must find A_0/A. Using y for the exit state of the normal shock, we have the flow state points and path line shown in the T-s diagram of Fig. 10-20. By using the sonic state points *0 and *y, we can find A_0/A_t thus. Since $A_t = A_y^*$,

$$\frac{A_0}{A_t} = \left(\frac{A}{A^*}\right)_0 \frac{A_0^*}{A_y^*}$$

From Eq. (10-4),

$$\frac{A_0^*}{A_y^*} = \frac{(\rho V)_y^*}{(\rho V)_0^*} = \frac{\rho_y^*}{\rho_0^*} = \frac{P_{ty}}{P_{t0}}$$

where P_{ty}/P_{t0} is the total pressure ratio of a normal shock wave. Hence

$$\boxed{\frac{A_0}{A_t} = \left[\left(\frac{A}{A^*}\right)\frac{P_{ty}}{P_{t0}}\right]_{M_0}} \qquad (10\text{-}6)$$

The right-hand side of this equation is the product of points lying on the two curves of Fig. 10-17 at a given M_0. Thus, at $M_0 = 2$, $A/A^* = 1.688$ (App. E) and $P_{ty}/P_{t0} = 0.721$ (App. F), so

$$\frac{A_0}{A_t} = (1.688)(0.721) = 1.218$$

and

$$\text{Fraction spilled} = \frac{1.34 - 1.218}{1.34} = 9.1\%$$

As M_0 increases above 2, the shock wave will move closer to the inlet and less air is spilled. Finally, when M_0 reaches the critical value M_{0c}, the shock is at the lip of the inlet and $A_0 = A_c$. (The shock is immediately swallowed by the inlet once it gets to the inlet lips because this is an unstable condition.)

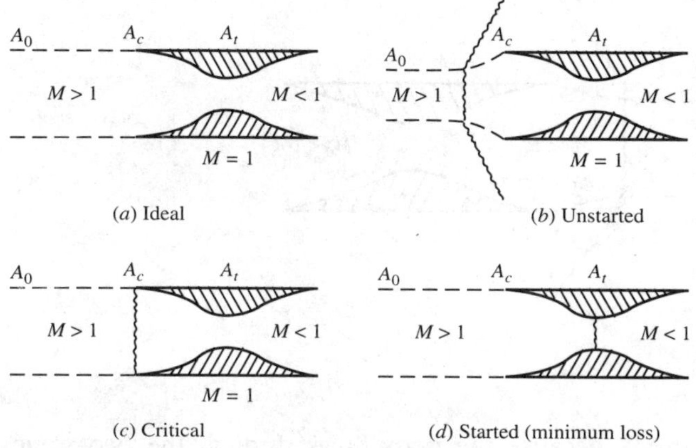

FIGURE 10-21
Operation of ideal internal compression inlet.

Ideal One-Dimensional Internal Compression Inlet

One would think initially that a supersonic inlet could operate shock-free as a simple converging-diverging nozzle in reverse. Although this is feasible in principle, a starting problem arises that prevents the attainment of this condition in a constant-geometry inlet. To fix ideas in the arguments to follow, consider a supersonic inlet with a capture/throat area ratio of $A_0/A_t = 1.34$. Assuming no viscous boundary-layer losses, as we do throughout our treatment of inlets, this inlet could, in theory, operate free at $M_0 = 1.7$, corresponding to $A_0/A^* = A_c/A_t = 1.34$ with $A_0 = A_c$ as in Fig. 10-21(*a*). This flow condition cannot be attained, however, by increasing M_0 from a lower value up to $M_0 = 1.7$ with a fixed-geometry inlet. This is the reason: $A_0/A^* < A_c/A_t$ if $M_0 < 1.7$ (Fig. 10-17), and in shock-free flow with $A_t = A_0^*$, it follows that $A_c > A_0$ so that the inlet captures more flow than the throat can pass. Consequently, air piles up in the inlet, causing, almost instantaneously, a shock to form ahead of the inlet, as in Fig. 10-21(*b*). The excess airflow spills around the inlet in the subsonic flow behind the shock wave. To find the fraction of air spilled in the unstarted condition, we must find A_0/A_t in the expression

$$\boxed{\text{Fraction spilled} = \frac{A_c - A_0}{A_c} = \frac{A_c/A_t - A_0/A_t}{A_c/A_t}}$$

This can be done by using the identity

$$\frac{A_0}{A_t} = \frac{A_0}{A_0^*}\frac{A_0^*}{A_y^*}$$

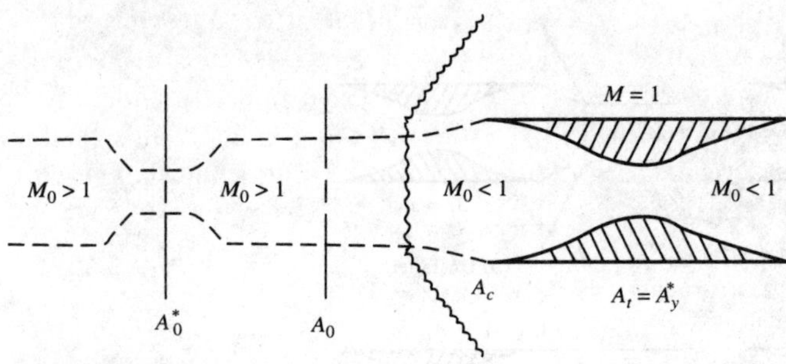

FIGURE 10-22
Area relationships.

Here, A_0^* is smaller than A_y^* because the mass flows through the two sonic throats *0 and *y (Fig. 10-22) are equal

$$(\rho AV)_0^* = (\rho AV)_y^*$$

and $V_0^* = V_y^*$, but $\rho_x^* > \rho_y^*$. In fact, by Eq. (10-4),

$$\frac{A_0^*}{A_y^*} = \frac{\rho_y^*}{\rho_0^*} = \frac{P_{ty}}{P_{t0}}$$

hence

$$\boxed{\frac{A_0}{A_t} = \left[\left(\frac{A}{A^*}\right)\frac{P_{ty}}{P_{t0}}\right]_{M_0} = f(M_0)} \tag{10-7}$$

This ratio of actual captured stream-tube area to inlet throat area is plotted versus M_0 in Fig. 10-23. The curve of A_0/A_t in Fig. 10-23 is the product of the A/A^* and P_{ty}/P_{t0} curves in accordance with Eq. (10-7). We show, in Fig. 10-23, a horizontal line representing $A_c/A_t = 1.34$. The vertical distance

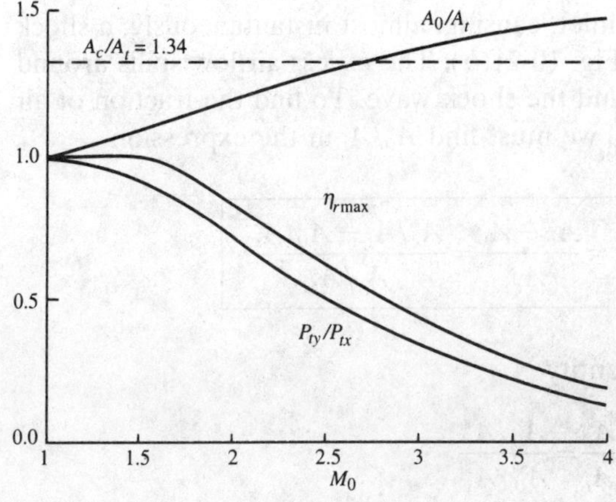

FIGURE 10-23
Performance of ideal internal compression inlet.

between this line and the A_0/A_t curve (to the left of their intersection) is proportional to the amount of air spilled by the inlet [Eq. (10-5)]. As M_0 is increased from $M_0 = 1$, this vertical distance decreases so that less and less air is spilled until at $M_{0c} = 2.66$, the shock is on the inlet lips. This is an unstable position, and the shock will move precipitously through the converging portion of the inlet if perturbed.

This can be explained as follows: The mass flow through the throat is proportional to ρ_y^* which, in turn, is proportional to P_{ty}. If the shock moves into the inlet, M_x decreases so that P_{ty} and the throat mass flow increase. Since the flow at the lips continues to be at free-stream conditions, the throat passes more air than is captured by the inlet. To make the throat mass flow equal to the flow captured, the density at the throat must decrease. This lower density is attained by the shock passing through the throat with supersonic flow at the throat as in the started condition of Fig. 10-16(*d*). Once started, the inlet backpressure can be adjusted (e.g., by closing bypass doors downstream of the throat) to place the shock at the throat for minimum M_x and least total pressure loss.

The throat Mach number of a started inlet with area ratio $A_c/A_t = A_0/A_t$ is that corresponding to the value of $(A/A^*)_t$ obtained from

$$\left(\frac{A}{A^*}\right)_{M_t} = \left(\frac{A}{A^*}\right)_{M_0}\left(\frac{A_t}{A_0}\right)_{M_0} = \left(\frac{A}{A^*}\,\frac{1}{A_0/A_t}\right)_{M_0}$$

where A_0/A_t and A/A^* on the right-hand side of this equation are each a function of M_0 as given in Figs. 10-23 and 10-17, respectively. For example, at $M_0 = 2$

$$\left(\frac{A}{A^*}\right)_{M_t} = \left(\frac{A}{A^*}\,\frac{1}{A_0/A_t}\right)_{M_0} = \frac{1.688}{1.216} = 1.388$$

and

$$M_t = 1.75$$

The value of M_t, corresponding to each flight Mach number can be found in this manner. Then, for each M_t, the corresponding normal shock total pressure loss can be determined to obtain the curve labeled $\eta_{r\,\max}$ in Fig. 10-23. For example, at $M_0 = 2$ and $M_t = 1.75$, the total pressure recovery of the inlet with a normal shock at the throat with $M_x = M_t = 1.75$ is $P_{ty}/P_{t0} = \eta_{r\,\max} = 0.835$.

Example 10-2. Design a fixed-area internal compression inlet that will start at $M_0 = 2.9$ for an aircraft that will cruise at $M_0 = 2.4$.

a. Determine the capture/throat area ratio A_c/A_t.
b. Determine both $\eta_{r\,\max}$ of the inlet after starting at $M_0 = 2.9$ and the shock located at the throat.
c. Determine $\eta_{r\,\max}$ of the inlet after starting at $M_0 = 2.4$ and the shock located at the throat.
d. Determine the Mach number at which the inlet will "unstart."

Solution.

a. Design an inlet to start at $M_0 = 2.9$. Thus $A_0 = A_c$ at $M_0 = 2.9$. Using Eq. (10-7), we have

$$\frac{A_c}{A_t} = \frac{A_0}{A_t} = \left(\frac{A}{A^*}\frac{P_{ty}}{P_{t0}}\right)_{M_0} = 3.8498 \times 0.35773 = 1.377$$

Or, using Fig. 10-23, we read $A_c/A_t = 1.38$.

b. After starting, $A_c = A_0$; thus, we want to determine the area ratio A_t/A^* to get the Mach number at the throat and $\eta_{r\,\max}$ for $M_0 = 2.9$.

$$\frac{A_t}{A^*} = \frac{A_0/A^*}{A_c/A_t} = \frac{3.8498}{1.377} = 2.796$$

From App. E, $M_t = 2.56$. Then from App. F, $P_{ty}/P_{tx} = \eta_{r\,\max} = 0.4754$. Or, using Fig. 10-23, we read $\eta_{r\,\max} = 0.48$.

c. For this inlet $A_c = A_0$

$$\frac{A_t}{A^*} = \frac{A_0/A^*}{A_c/A_t} = \frac{2.4031}{1.377} = 1.745$$

From App. E, $M_t = 2.04$. Then, from App. F, $P_{ty}/P_{tx} = \eta_{r\,\max} = 0.702$.

d. The inlet will "unstart" when $M_t = 1$. We are looking for an M_0 whose A_0/A^* is equal to the inlet's A_c/A_t. For $A_0/A^* = 1.377$, $M_0 = 1.74$ from App. E or Fig. 10-17.

Inlet Types

As discussed in Chap. 4, supersonic inlets are classified into three basic types, characterized by the location of the supersonic compression wave system: internal compression, external compression, and mixed compression.

INTERNAL COMPRESSION INLET. The internal compression inlet shown in Fig. 10-24(*a*) achieves compression through a series of internal oblique shock

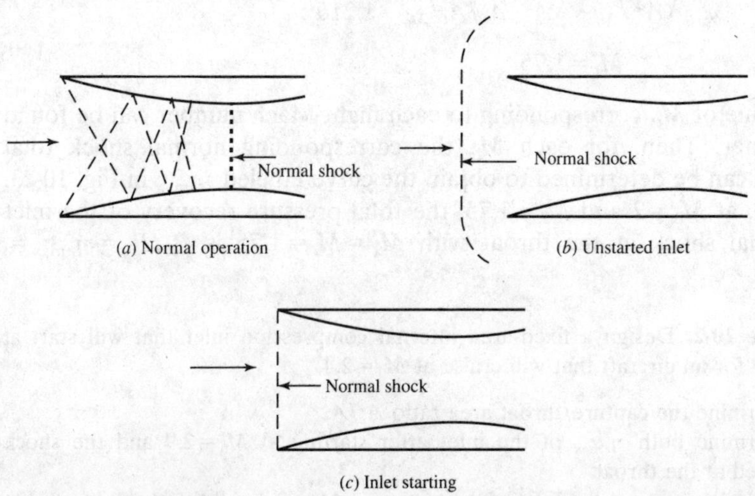

FIGURE 10-24
Internal compression inlet.

waves followed by a terminal normal shock positioned downstream of the throat (its stable location). This type of inlet requires variable throat area to allow the inlet to swallow the normal shock (during starting). Fast reaction bypass doors are also required downstream of the throat to permit proper positioning of the normal shock under varying flight and engine conditions.

Figure 10-24(a) shows an internal compression inlet with an area contraction ratio A_1/A_t of 2.56 (corresponding to $M_1 = 2.5$ and $M_t = 1.2$) operating at design. With the terminal normal shock positioned downstream of the throat for stable operation, where the Mach number is 1.3, this inlet's ideal total pressure ratio (total pressure recovery η_r) corresponds to that across a normal shock at Mach 1.3, or $\eta_r = 0.9794$ when $\gamma = 1.4$. Reduction in the flight Mach number to 2.47 or movement of the terminal shock to the throat (which is an unstable location) will cause the total internal flow pattern to be completely disrupted (inlet unstarting), followed by formation of a normal shock ahead of the inlet and its associated low total pressure ratio (about 0.52), reduced mass flow through the inlet, high spillage drag, and possible engine flameout. The unstarted inlet is shown in Fig. 10-24(b). This unstarted condition of the inlet can also be achieved by bringing the free-stream Mach number from subsonic up to 2.5 without changing the throat area sufficiently to start the inlet (swallow the normal shock).

Starting of the inlet can be achieved when the area of the throat (flow is choked at the throat) is made large enough for the normal shock to move back and touch the inlet tip (critical operation), as shown in Fig. 10-24(c). The ratio of the throat area required to start the inlet A_{ts} to the throat area required at normal operation A_{tr} (corresponding to $M_t = 1.2$) is obtained from basic one-dimensional flow, plotted in Fig. 10-25 and expressed as

$$\frac{A_{ts}}{A_{tr}} = \frac{1}{1.030(P_{ty}/P_{tx})_{M_0}} \tag{10-8}$$

where 1.030 is the value of A/A^* corresponding to $M_t = 1.2$ and $(P_{ty}/P_{tx})_{M_0}$ is the total pressure ratio across a normal shock with upstream Mach number of M_0. As can be seen in Fig. 10-25, the internal compression inlet has a large throat area variation required to start the inlet at Mach numbers greater than 2. For example, the throat area required to start an inlet at a Mach number of 2.4 is about 1.8 times the throat area required for normal operation. This large area variation, the problem of inlet upstart, the poor performance at angles of

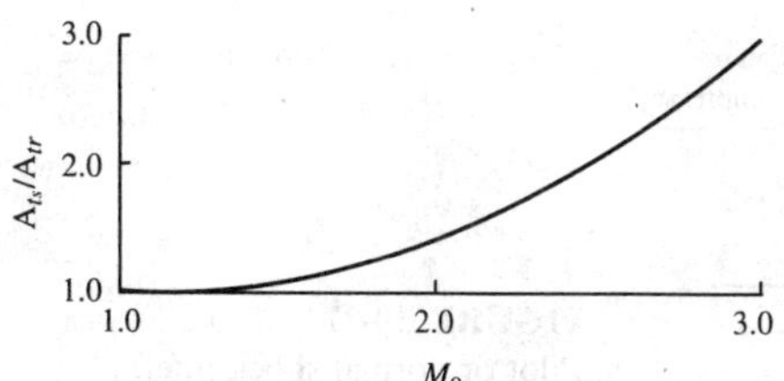

FIGURE 10-25
Throat area variation required of an internal compression inlet.

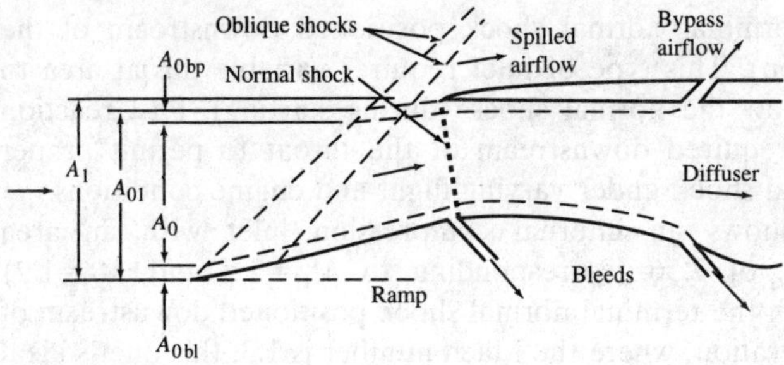

FIGURE 10-26
External compression inlet and flow areas.

attack, and many other problems have led to the demise of the internal compression inlet.

EXTERNAL COMPRESSION INLET. The compression of the external compression inlet (Fig. 10-26) is achieved through either one or a series of oblique shocks followed by a normal shock, or simply through one normal shock. As shown in Fig. 10-26, A_{0i}, A_{0e}, $A_{0\,bl}$, and $A_{0\,bp}$ are the free-stream tube areas containing the inlet, engine, boundary-layer bleed, and bypass airflows, respectively.

The external compression inlet that achieves compression through only a single normal shock is called a *pitot inlet* or *normal shock inlet* and is shown in Fig. 10-27. The pitot inlet is simple, short, lightweight, and inexpensive. The total pressure recovery η_r of this inlet corresponds to the total pressure ratio across a normal shock, shown in Fig. 10-23. The total pressure recovery of this inlet is acceptable for flight Mach numbers up to about 1.6. Above this Mach number, the total pressure recovery of the inlet is too low and another, more efficient inlet design must be used.

The external compression inlet with one or more oblique shocks (Fig. 10-26) has its inlet throat at or very near the cowl leading edge. Desired

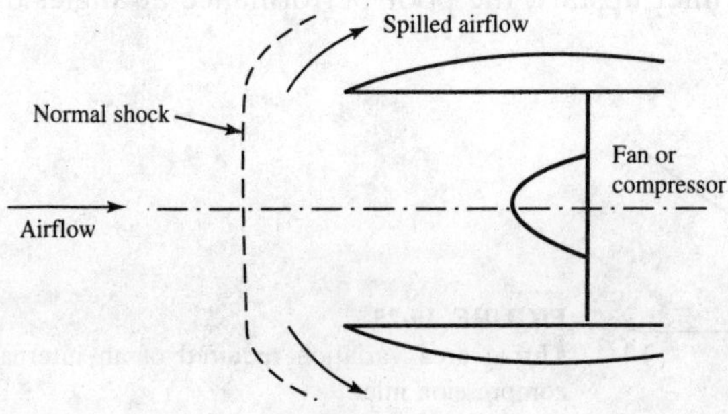

FIGURE 10-27
Pilot or normal shock inlet.

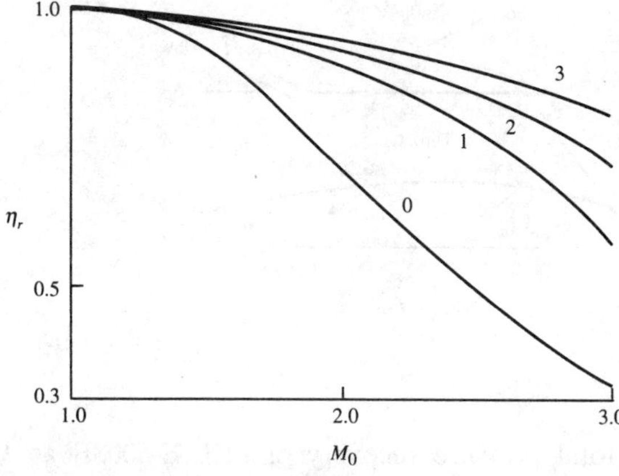

FIGURE 10-28
Total pressure recovery of oblique shocks.

operation of this inlet is with the normal shock positioned at or very near the cowl lip (critical operation).

The total pressure recovery η_r across n oblique shocks of equal strength (same total pressure ratio) followed by a normal shock is shown in Fig. 10-28. Increasing the number of oblique shocks increases η_r for any given free-stream Mach number. However, the ramp of the external compression inlet turns the flow away from the axial direction; thus, the subsonic diffuser duct must turn the flow back to the axial direction, which may add weight and length to the inlet. Figure 10-29 shows the total turning angle of an external compression

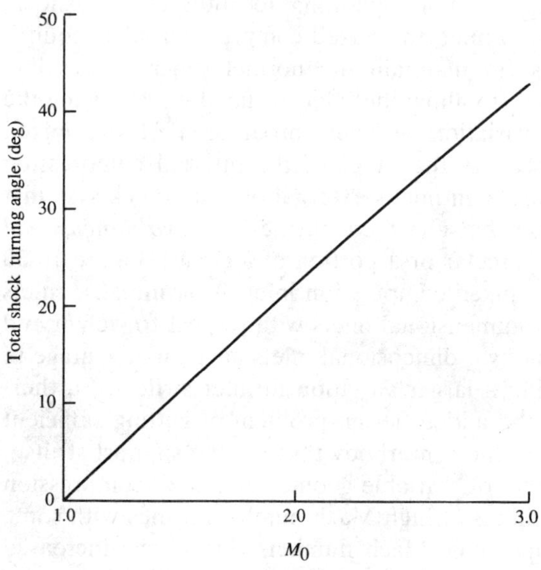

FIGURE 10-29
Turning angle of external compression shock system.

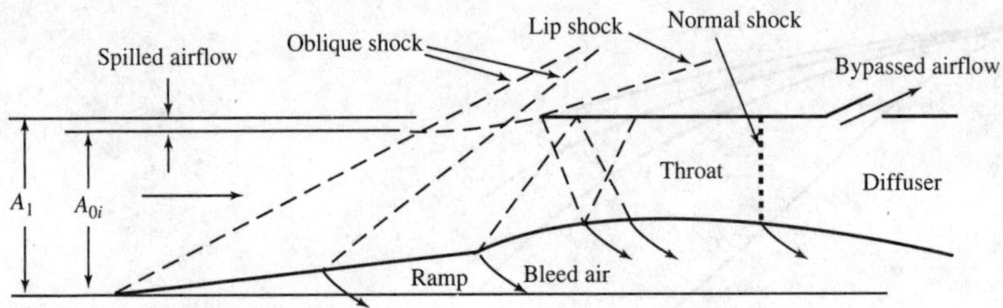

FIGURE 10-30
Two-dimensional mixed compression inlet.

shock system that attains the total pressure recovery of MIL-E-5008B as a function of free-stream Mach number. As the free-stream Mach number increases, the total shock-turning angle of the external ramp increases, resulting in increases in cowl angle and cowl drag. External compression inlets can maintain a balance between an acceptable total pressure ratio and cowl drag up to a flight Mach number of about 2.5.

MIXED COMPRESSION INLET. At flight Mach numbers above 2.5, the mixed compression inlet is used to obtain an acceptable total pressure ratio (by utilizing the required number of oblique shocks) while obtaining acceptable cowl drag. The mixed compression inlet is more complex, heavier, and costlier than the external compression inlet. The typical mixed compression inlet (Fig. 10-30) achieves compression through the external oblique shocks, the internal reflected oblique shocks, and the terminal normal shock. The ideal location of the normal shock is just downstream of the inlet throat, to minimize total pressure loss while maintaining a stable operating location of this shock. Similar to the internal compression inlet, the mixed compression inlet requires both fast-reacting bypass doors (to maintain the normal shock in a stable location) and variable throat area (to allow the inlet to start by swallowing the normal shock). However, the variation in inlet throat area of the mixed compression inlet is considerably less than that of the internal compression inlet because of the mixed compression inlet's external oblique shock system.

Supersonic inlets can also be classified further as *two-dimensional* (rectangular) and *axisymmetric* (circular or a portion of a circle). Figure 10-30 shows a typical two-dimensional mixed compression inlet. Axisymmetric inlets have a slight advantage over two-dimensional inlets with respect to weight and total pressure ratio. However, the two-dimensional inlets have an advantage in design simplicity and in providing a larger variation in inlet airflow. Furthermore, axisymmetric inlets have the added design problem of getting sufficient boundary-layer bleed air out from the centerbody through the support struts.

The improved performance of variable-geometry mixed compression inlets and external compression inlets at high Mach numbers comes with some reduced performance at low supersonic Mach numbers due to the increased

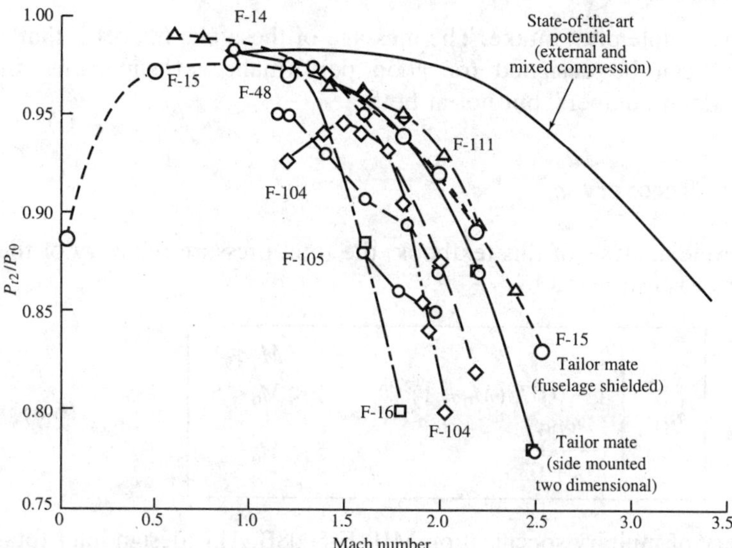

FIGURE 10-31
Total pressure ratio survey (Ref. 56).

frictional losses. Figures 10-31 and 10-32 show the total pressure recovery of past and current aircraft and the supersonic transport (SST) model. Note, in Fig. 10-32, the reduced total pressure recovery of the complex SST mixed compression inlet at subsonic and low supersonic Mach numbers when

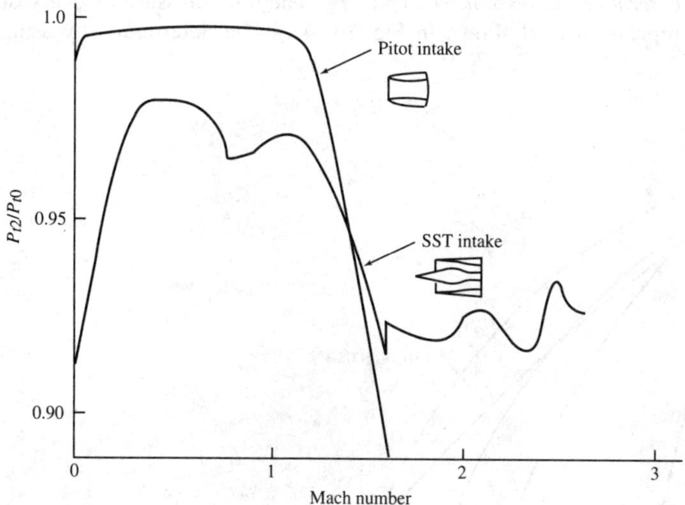

FIGURE 10-32
Total pressure ratio—SST model (Ref. 57).

compared to the simple pitot intake. The message of these two figures is that a supersonic inlet can be designed for good performance at supersonic or subsonic flight Mach numbers, but not at both.

Total Pressure Recovery η_r

In the engine cycle analysis of this textbook, the total pressure recovery of the supersonic inlet was estimated by

$$\eta_r = \begin{cases} 1 & M_0 \leq 1 \\ 1 - 0.075(M_0 - 1)^{1.35} & 1 < M_0 < 5 \\ \dfrac{800}{M_0^4 + 035} & 5 < M_0 \end{cases} \tag{6-6}$$

the ram recovery of military specification MIL-E-5008B. This design inlet total pressure recovery has been added to Fig. 10-28 to give Fig. 10-33, a very useful design tool for selection of inlet type and preliminary number of oblique shocks required. As an example, consider an inlet for flight at Mach 2.5. Equation (6-6) or Fig. 10-33 gives an allowable total pressure ratio for the shock system of 0.87. Figure 10-33 shows that more than two oblique shocks of equal strength followed by a normal shock are required. This could be obtained by an external compression inlet with three oblique shocks or a mixed compression inlet.

Example 10-3. *External compression inlet (part 1).* The total pressure recovery of the external compression inlet shown in Fig. 10-34 can be determined by using

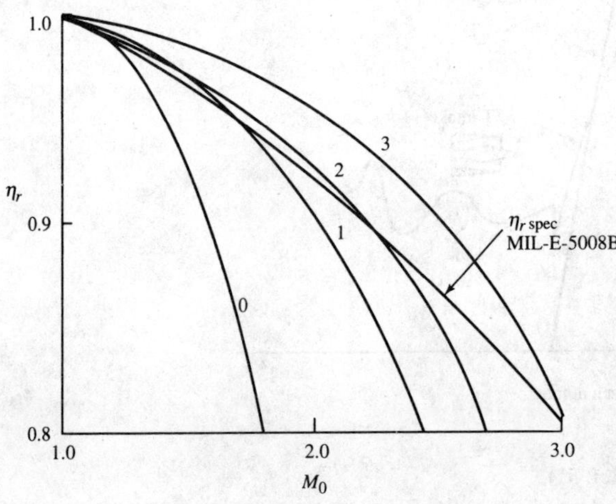

FIGURE 10-33
Total pressure recovery required.

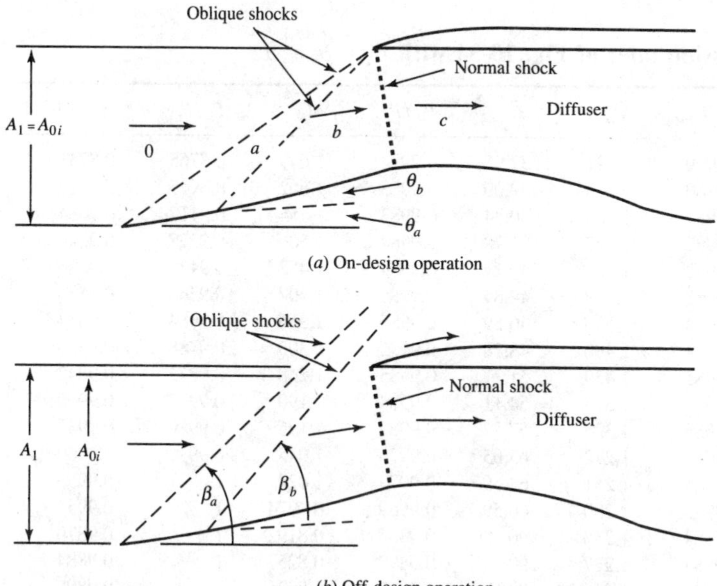

FIGURE 10-34
External compression inlet of Example 10-3.

the normal and oblique shock equations and tables of Chap. 3, App. F, and App. G. Applying the normal and oblique shock equations to this inlet with $\theta_a = \theta_b = 5°$ yields the results shown in Table 10-1 and plotted in Fig. 10-35. The total pressure recovery η_r of the inlet is the product of the total pressure ratio across each shock. This inlet exceeds the total pressure recovery required by Eq. (6-6) at Mach 1.7 (0.9654 versus 0.9537) but not at Mach 1.8 (0.9396 versus 0.9445).

Note that for M_0 between 1.42 and 1.26, the second oblique shock becomes the terminal normal shock because its ramp angle θ is larger than $\theta_{\max}$ for M_a between 1.238 and 1.023. Likewise, the first oblique shock becomes the terminal normal shock for M_0 between 1.23 and 1.0. Also note that the total pressure recovery goes through local maxima and minima as these oblique shocks become normal shocks.

Mass Flow Characteristics

The *inlet mass flow ratio* is the ratio of the actual mass flow rate of the inlet $\dot{m}_i$ to the mass flow rate that could be captured $\dot{m}_1$ by the inlet (see Fig. 10-36), and from the conservation of mass equation

$$\frac{\dot{m}_i}{\dot{m}_1} = \frac{\rho_0 V_0 A_{0i}}{\rho_0 V_0 A_1} = \frac{A_{0i}}{A_1} \tag{10-9}$$

which is the inlet area ratio. Thus the inlet mass flow ratio and the inlet area

TABLE 10-1
External compression inlet of Fig. 10-34 with $\theta_a = \theta_b = 5°$

M_0	β_a	P_{ta}/P_{t0}	M_a	β_b	P_{tb}/P_{ta}	M_b	P_{tc}/P_{tb}	η_r
2.00	34.30	0.9979	1.821	37.95	0.9982	1.649	0.8765	0.8731
1.95	35.23	0.9980	1.773	39.09	0.9983	1.602	0.8945	0.8912
1.90	36.23	0.9981	1.725	40.34	0.9983	1.554	0.9117	0.9084
1.85	37.30	0.9982	1.677	41.70	0.9984	1.506	0.9278	0.9246
1.80	38.44	0.9982	1.628	43.19	0.9984	1.457	0.9428	0.9396
1.75	39.68	0.9983	1.579	44.84	0.9985	1.407	0.9563	0.9533
1.70	41.03	0.9984	1.529	46.69	0.9985	1.356	0.9684	0.9654
1.65	42.50	0.9984	1.480	48.78	0.9985	1.303	0.9788	0.9758
1.60	44.11	0.9985	1.429	51.21	0.9985	1.248	0.9873	0.9842
1.55	45.89	0.9985	1.378	54.11	0.9984	1.190	0.9937	0.9906
1.50	47.89	0.9985	1.325	57.77	0.9982	1.125	0.9980	0.9947
1.45	50.16	0.9985	1.272	63.05	0.9976	1.045	0.9999	0.9960
1.44	50.65	0.9985	1.261	64.59	0.9973	1.024	1	0.9958
1.43	51.16	0.9985	1.250	66.59	0.9969	0.9974	1	0.9953
1.42	51.68	0.9984	1.238	90	0.9886	0.8192	1	0.9870
1.41	52.22	0.9984	1.227	90	0.9899	0.8257	1	0.9884
1.40	52.78	0.9984	1.216	90	0.9912	0.8325	1	0.9896
1.35	55.93	0.9983	1.156	90	0.9963	0.8705	1	0.9946
1.30	59.96	0.9980	1.090	90	0.9992	0.9195	1	0.9972
1.29	60.95	0.9979	1.075	90	0.9995	0.9316	1	0.9974
1.28	62.04	0.9977	1.059	90	0.9998	0.9450	1	0.9975
1.27	63.26	0.9976	1.042	90	0.9999	0.9602	1	0.9975
1.26	64.69	0.9973	1.023	90	1	0.9782	1	0.9973
1.25	66.50	0.9969	0.9986	0	1	0.9986	1	0.9969
1.24	69.90	0.9957	0.9554	0	1	0.9554	1	0.9957
1.23	90	0.9896	0.8241	0	1	0.8241	1	0.9896
1.22	90	0.9907	0.8300	0	1	0.8300	1	0.9907
1.21	90	0.9918	0.8360	0	1	0.8360	1	0.9918
1.20	90	0.9928	0.8422	0	1	0.8422	1	0.9928
1.15	90	0.9967	0.8750	0	1	0.8750	1	0.9967
1.10	90	0.9989	0.9118	0	1	0.9118	1	0.9989
1.05	90	0.9999	0.9531	0	1	0.9531	1	0.9999

ratio are used interchangeably. The difference between $\dot{m}_i$ and $\dot{m}_1$ is the air that is spilled around the inlet. The *engine mass flow ratio* is defined similarly to that of the inlet, as the ratio of the required engine mass flow rate $\dot{m}_0$ to the mass flow rate that the inlet could capture $\dot{m}_1$, or

$$\frac{\dot{m}_0}{\dot{m}_1} = \frac{\rho_0 V_0 A_0}{\rho_0 V_0 A_1} = \frac{A_0}{A_1} \tag{10-10}$$

The difference between $\dot{m}_i$ and $\dot{m}_0$ is the air that enters the inlet but is removed through boundary-layer bleed, the bypass system, or the secondary air system.

When the inlet can accept the mass flow rate of air required to position the terminal shock just inside the cowl lip (*critical* operation), the fraction of

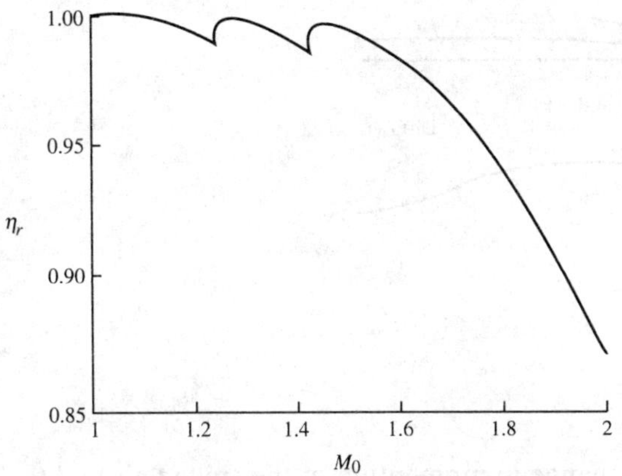

FIGURE 10-35
Total pressure recovery η_r of external compression inlet (Fig. 10-36) with $\theta_a = \theta_b = 5°$.

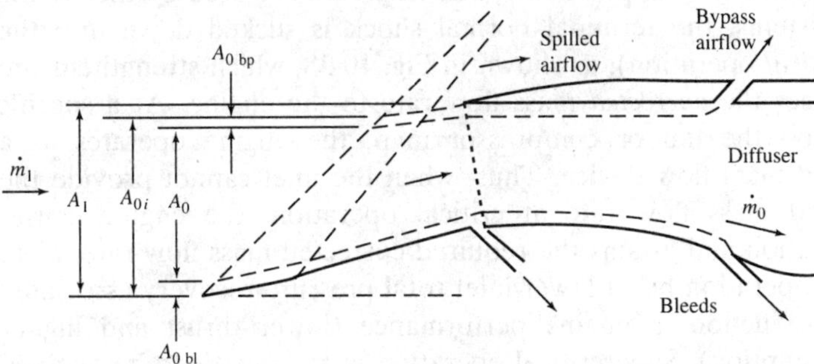

FIGURE 10-36
Critical inlet operation.

air spilled around the inlet is a minimum and the inlet is said to be *matched* to the engine. When the inlet is not matched, as shown in Fig. 10-37, the normal shock moves upstream (*subcritical* operation) and the fraction of air spilled is increased. This increase in air spillage has associated with it an increase in

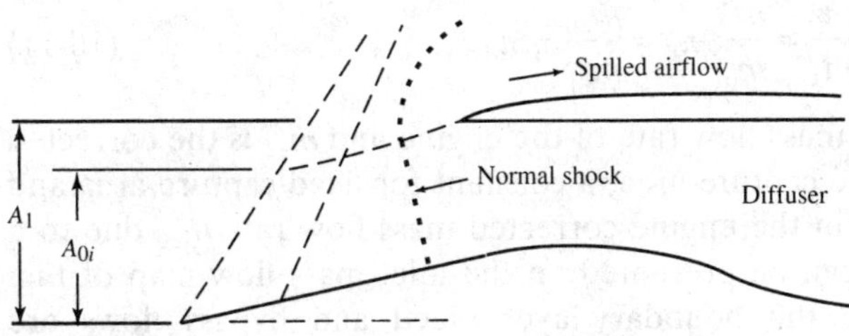

FIGURE 10-37
Subcritical inlet operation.

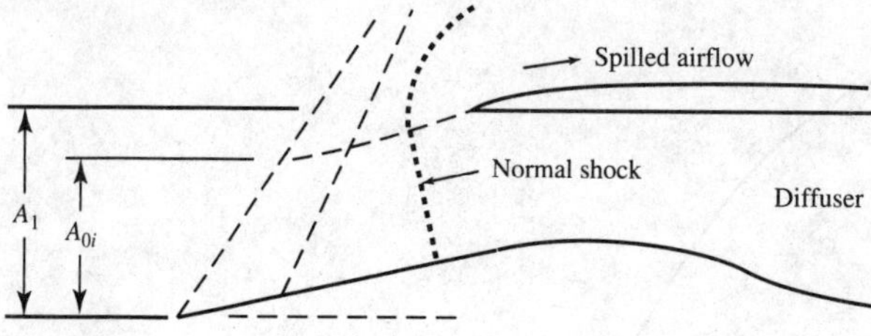

FIGURE 10-38
Supercritical inlet operation.

spillage drag, or drag due to the change in momentum of the spilled air and the pressure forces on its stream tube.

When the inlet cannot capture the mass flow rate required by the engine and the other systems, the terminal normal shock is sucked down into the diffuser (*supercritical* operation), as shown in Fig. 10-38, which strengthens the shock and increases the *corrected* mass flow rate to the engine. At a specific operating point on the fan or compressor map, the engine operates as a constant corrected mass flow device. Thus, when the inlet cannot provide the required corrected mass flow rate at critical operation, the engine causes supercritical operation and attains the required corrected mass flow rate. Note that supercritical operation has a lower inlet total pressure recovery associated with it, thus, a reduction in engine performance (lower thrust and higher specific fuel consumption). Supercritical operation of the inlet is to be avoided when possible because of poor engine performance.

A common way of presenting the mass flow rate characteristics of an inlet is through a map of the total pressure recovery versus the inlet mass flow ratio, as shown in Fig. 10-39. The performance of a typical external compression inlet is presented in Fig. 10-39 for a specific free-stream Mach number. The critical operation point and the subcritical and supercritical operating regimes are also shown on this figure.

The engine mass flow ratio $\dot{m}_0/\dot{m}_1$ can be expressed in terms of corrected mass flow rates and the inlet total pressure ratio as

$$\frac{\dot{m}_0}{\dot{m}_1} = \frac{\dot{m}_{c0}}{\dot{m}_{c1}} \pi_d = \frac{\dot{m}_{c0}}{\dot{m}_{c1}} \eta_r \pi_{d\,\max} \tag{10-11}$$

where $\dot{m}_{c0}$ is the corrected mass flow rate of the engine and $\dot{m}_{c1}$ is the corrected mass flow rate based on the capture area, a constant for fixed capture area and flight condition. Variation in the engine corrected mass flow rate $\dot{m}_{c0}$ due to a change in engine throttle can be presented on the inlet mass flow map of Fig. 10-39 for the case where the boundary-layer bleed and bypass flows are essentially constant. A line of constant $\dot{m}_{c0}$ is shown on Fig. 10-39 along with the direction of increasing $\dot{m}_{c0}$. When the engine's requirement for air

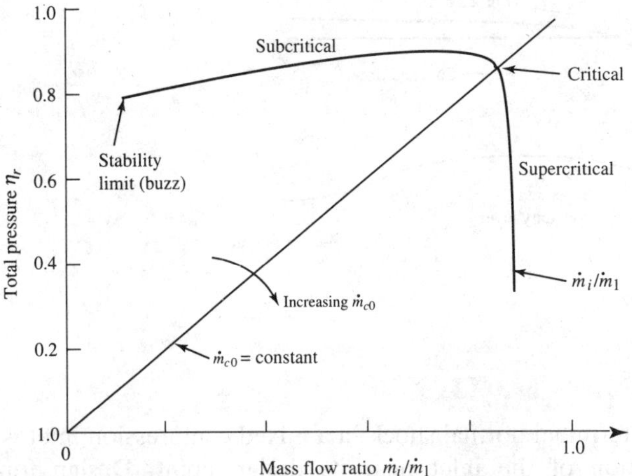

FIGURE 10-39
External compression inlet performance characteristics.

decreases below that required for critical inlet operation, the inlet operating point moves into the subcritical region as the engine mass flow rate decreases and the fraction of air spilled increases. When the engine's requirement for air increases above that required for critical operation, the inlet operating point moves into the supercritical region as the engine mass flow ratio remains constant and the total pressure recovery of the inlet decreases with the strengthening of the terminal normal shock in the diffuser.

Two supersonic flow phenomena associated with the stability of the shock structure in external and mixed compression inlets require consideration at this point. One is called inlet *buzz,* and the other is associated with the location of the terminal normal shock.

Buzz is a low-frequency, high-amplitude pressure oscillation that is linked to shock/boundary layer and/or shock/shock interaction at relatively low inlet mass flow ratio. As an example of a flow condition leading to inlet buzz, consider the external compression inlet of Fig. 10-40. When this inlet is operated in the subcritical regime, the terminal normal shock will impinge on the boundary layer formed along the wall of the ramp, causing the boundary layer to separate. If the separated boundary layer produces a large enough low-velocity flow region, the inlet will choke, reducing the inlet mass flow rate and moving the normal shock forward along the ramp. The boundary layer at this forward location is thinner; its separated mass flow region does not choke the inlet. Thus the inlet mass flow increases, moving the normal shock back up the ramp toward its original location, to be repeated again and again, creating buzz. When buzz occurs on a mixed compression inlet, the inlet will "unstart" and engine flameout is possible.

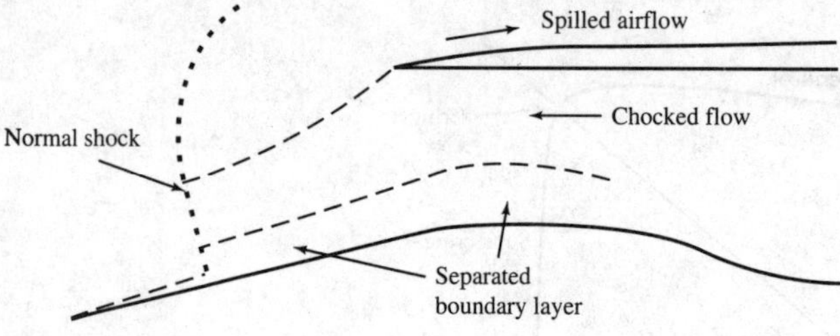

FIGURE 10-40
Condition leading to inlet "buzz."

The stability of the terminal normal shock in a mixed compression inlet is important during operation of the inlet near its design point. Design for stability of the terminal normal shock requires that the need for higher total pressure recovery be compromised, and the design throat Mach number be 1.2, with the normal shock positioned downstream where the Mach number is 1.3. Thus the mixed compression inlet is designed to operate in the supercritical regime. When the engine needs less air than provided by this inlet, the excess air must bypass the engine to maintain the terminal normal shock at its stable location and prevent the inlet from "unstarting" (expelling the normal shock). When the engine wants more air than the inlet can provide, the terminal normal shock is drawn downstream into the diffuser, strengthening the shock and increasing the corrected mass flow rate to the engine. When the normal shock is drawn downstream into the diffuser, flow separation and flow distortion become dominant design considerations. To limit this problem, the inlet needs to be designed to provide the required engine mass flow rate with the terminal normal shock positioned where the Mach number in the diffuser is 1.3.

The total pressure recovery versus mass flow ratio of a typical mixed compression inlet is shown in Fig. 10-41. Note that this inlet has a much smaller allowable variation in mass flow ratio before onset of buzz than does the external compression inlet of Fig. 10-39. This reduction in the range for the inlet mass ratio $\dot{m}_i/\dot{m}_1$ corresponds to a larger change in the amount of inlet air that is required to be bypassed $\dot{m}_{\text{bp}}$ to prevent buzz (maintain $\dot{m}_i/\dot{m}_1$ above the stability limit), with a corresponding smaller variation in the amount of air spilled.

Inlet Design and Sizing

The design and sizing for a supersonic inlet are considerably more difficult than for the subsonic inlet due mainly to differences in the nature of supersonic and subsonic flows. The supersonic inlet is designed to operate at both subsonic and supersonic flight Mach numbers. The capture and throat areas of the inlet

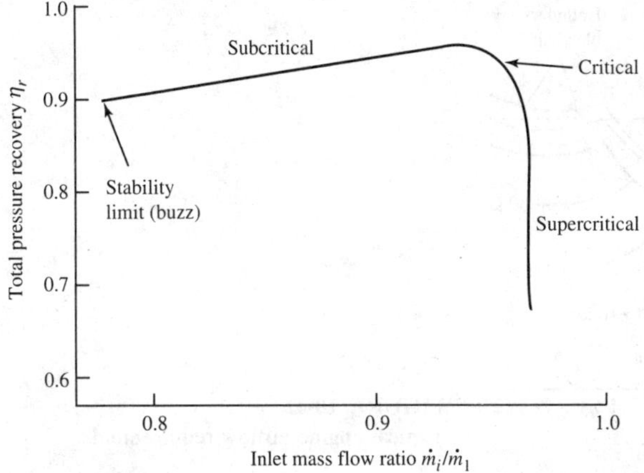

FIGURE 10-41
Mixed compression inlet performance characteristics.

must be large enough not to choke the airflow required by the engine, boundary-layer bleed system, etc. For supersonic flight conditions, the inlet's capture area A_1 is sized to capture the required airflow. Since this airflow varies with both flight Mach number and engine throttle setting, variable-geometry inlet design is sometimes needed to meet the total pressure recovery goal of military specification MIL-E-5008B and/or to keep the installation losses low (spillage drag and/or bypass air drag).

The required values of engine airflow $\dot{m}_0$ and the corresponding values of the free-stream area A_0, calculated by the engine performance analysis of Chap. 8 and/or the associated engine performance computer program PERF, are based on the total pressure recovery given by military specification MIL-E-5008B, where

$$\eta_{r\,\text{spec}} = \begin{cases} 1 & M_0 \le 1 \\ 1 - 0.075(M_0 - 1)^{1.35} & 1 < M_0 < 5 \\ \dfrac{800}{M_0^4 + 935} & 5 < M_0 \end{cases} \tag{10-12}$$

This same reference inlet total pressure recovery is used by many others.

Note: Since the total pressure recovery η_r of an inlet design may be different from $\eta_{r\,\text{spec}}$ given by Eq. (10-12), the required values of engine airflow $\dot{m}_0$ and the corresponding values of free-stream area A_0 will be different from those calculated in the engine performance analyses. Thus the values of $\dot{m}_0$ and A_0 determined by using the total pressure recovery of Eq. (10-12) will be referred to as $\dot{m}_{0\,\text{spec}}$ and $A_{0\,\text{spec}}$, respectively, from this point on.

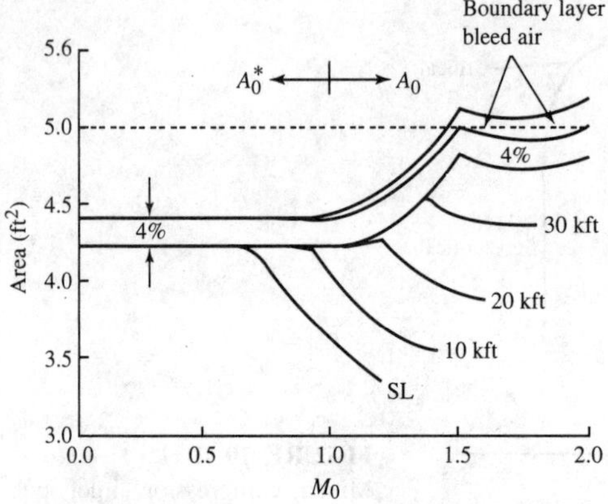

FIGURE 10-42
Typical engine airflow requirements.

Inlet design and sizing begin with an analysis of airflow requirements. Figure 10-42 shows the typical variation in inlet airflow requirements at different altitudes from engine performance analyses $A_{0\,\text{spec}}$ with flight Mach number for an advanced supersonic engine. Variable boundary-layer bleed and a safety margin of 4 percent have been added to the maximum full-throttle engine airflow to obtain the required inlet airflow $A_{0i\,\text{spec}}$.

The engine airflow requirements ($\dot{m}_0$, A_0) for a given inlet design η_r can be estimated based on the engine airflow requirements ($\dot{m}_{0\,\text{spec}}$, $A_{0\,\text{spec}}$) obtained by using a known inlet total pressure recovery $\eta_{r\,\text{spec}}$. Since the engine operates essentially as a constant corrected mass flow device ($\dot{m}_{c2} = \text{constant}$) when the throttle and flight conditions are constant, then the required engine airflow $\dot{m}_0$ for a specific inlet design η_r can be determined from required engine airflow data ($\dot{m}_{0\,\text{spec}}$, $A_{0\,\text{spec}}$) based on a reference inlet total pressure recovery $\eta_{r\,\text{spec}}$ by using

$$\frac{\dot{m}_0}{\dot{m}_{0\,\text{spec}}} = \frac{A_0}{A_{0\,\text{spec}}} = \frac{\eta_r}{\eta_{r\,\text{spec}}} \tag{10-13a}$$

Likewise, for the inlet air

$$\frac{\dot{m}_i}{\dot{m}_{i\,\text{spec}}} = \frac{A_{0i}}{A_{0i\,\text{spec}}} = \frac{\eta_r}{\eta_{r\,\text{spec}}} \tag{10-13b}$$

INLET PERFORMANCE. Consider the generalized inlet of Fig. 10-43 with capture area A_1 and area A_s at location s. The inlet mass flow ratio can be written as

$$\frac{A_{0i}}{A_1} = \frac{A_{0i}}{A_s}\frac{A_s}{A_1} \tag{10-14a}$$

where A_s/A_1 is determined by the geometry of the inlet. The shock system

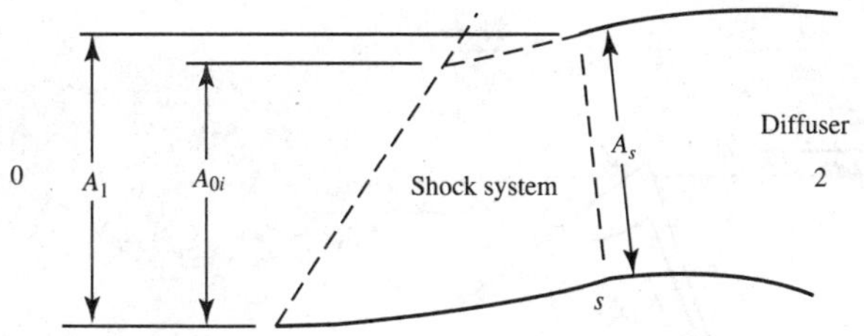

FIGURE 10-43
External compression inlet.

determines the area ratio A_{0i}/A_s as follows. Conservation of mass gives $\dot{m}_i = \dot{m}_s$ or $\rho_0 V_0 A_{0i} = \rho_s V_s A_s$; thus

$$\frac{A_{0i}}{A_s} = \frac{\dot{m}_s/A_s}{\dot{m}_i/A_{0i}} = \frac{\rho_s V_s}{\rho_0 V_0}$$

and for adiabatic flow in the inlet ($T_{ts} = T_{t0}$), the mass flow rate per unit area in the above equation can be written in terms of total pressure and mass flow parameter as

$$\frac{A_{0i}}{A_s} = \frac{P_{ts}}{P_{t0}} \frac{\text{MFP}(M_s)}{\text{MFP}(M_0)} \tag{10-14b}$$

Equations (10-14*a*) and (10-14*b*) provided the tools to estimate the inlet mass flow ratio A_{0i}/A_1 of an inlet. The area ratio A_s/A_1 is a geometric function of the inlet design, whereas the area ratio A_{0i}/A_s is a function of the flow properties at stations 0 and *s*. The previous section on total pressure recovery presented the analytical tools for determining both M_s and P_{ts}/P_{t0} of a general inlet, as shown in Example 10-3. Reference 49 contains exact solutions for one and two oblique shock inlets designed for critical operation.

INLET SIZE. The ratio of the inlet capture area A_1 to the engine's area at state 0* for the cycle reference point $A^*_{0\,\text{ref}}$ is referred to as the *inlet size* $A_1/A^*_{0\,\text{ref}}$, since this ratio is the size of the inlet relative to the engine. The required inlet size $(A_1/A^*_{0\,\text{ref}})_{\text{req}}$ at a flight condition can be calculated from the required inlet airflow $A_{0i\,\text{req}}/A^*_{0\,\text{ref}}$ and the inlet mass flow ratio $A^*_{0\,\text{ref}}/A_1$ by using

$$\left(\frac{A_1}{A^*_{0\,\text{ref}}}\right)_{\text{req}} = \frac{(A_{0i}/A^*_{0\,\text{ref}})_{\text{req}}}{A_{0i}/A_1} \tag{10-15}$$

For an inlet with fixed capture area A_1, the flight condition requiring the largest inlet size $(A_1/A^*_{0\,\text{ref}})_{\text{req}}$ is used to size the inlet capture area A_1.

Care must be taken that the inlet does not choke the flow to the engine at subsonic flight conditions. This can be ensured by having the inlet capture area A_1 larger than the maximum required one-dimensional inlet area A^*_{0i} by

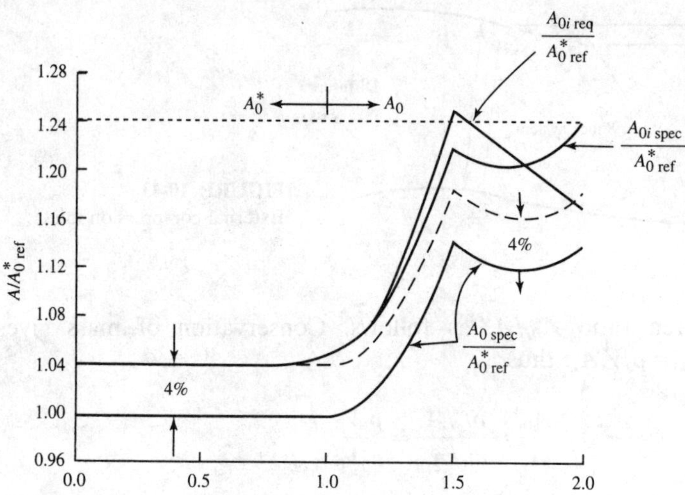

FIGURE 10-44
Airflow requirement for example inlet at altitude.

about 4 percent ($A/A^* = 1.038$ at $M = 0.8$) and/or providing additional air inlet area for very low-velocity engine airflow requirements.

Example 10-4. *External compression inlet (part 2).* We consider the double-ramp external compression inlet of Fig. 10-34 with $\theta_a = \theta_b = 5°$ to be used with the engine whose required airflow is plotted as $A_0/A^*_{0\,\text{ref}}$ in Fig. 10-44. These data are based on the airflow requirements of Fig. 10-42 at 40-kft altitude and an $A^*_{0\,\text{ref}}$ of 4.22 ft^2 at sea-level static conditions. The inlet is to be capable of operating up to Mach 2 at 40 kft with efficient operation ($\eta_r > \eta_{r\,\text{spec}}$) at Mach numbers less than 1.7. The inlet size and mass flow characteristics of the inlet and engine are considered.

Inlet performance. The total pressure recovery of this inlet η_r is tabulated in Table 10-1, is plotted in Fig. 10-35, and meets the requirement for efficient total pressure recovery ($\eta_r > \eta_{r\,\text{spec}}$) at Mach numbers less than 1.75. Analysis of the mass flow characteristics of the inlet and the engine is required before this inlet can be sized. As long as the normal shock between stations b and c touches the lip of the inlet, either station b or c of Fig. 10-34 can be equated to station s of Fig. 10-43. From Eq. (10-14b), we have

$$\frac{A_{0i}}{A_s} = \frac{P_{tb}}{P_{t0}} \frac{\text{MFP}(M_b)}{\text{MFP}(M_0)} = \frac{P_{tc}}{P_{t0}} \frac{\text{MFP}(M_c)}{\text{MFP}(M_0)} \tag{10-16a}$$

and

$$\frac{P_{tc}}{P_{t0}} = \eta_r \qquad \frac{P_{tb}}{P_{t0}} = \frac{\eta_r}{P_{tc}/P_{tb}} \tag{10-16b}$$

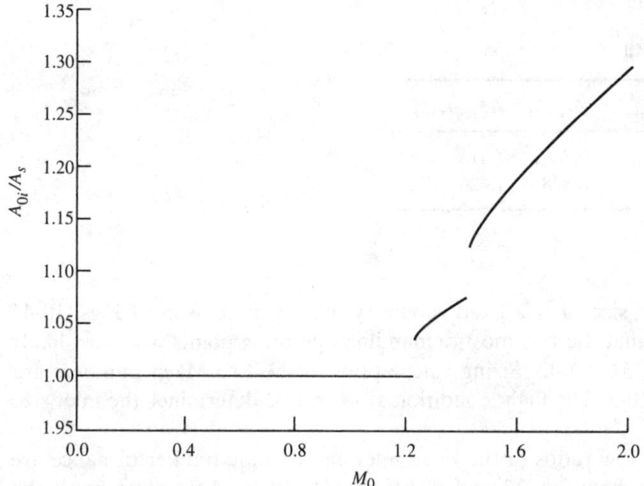

FIGURE 10-45
Area ratio of Example 10-4 inlet (Fig. 10-34).

The area ratio A_{0i}/A_s can be calculated by using the results of Table 10-1, assuming that $M_s = M_b$ at subsonic values of M_b (no local flow acceleration or deceleration). For subsonic M_0, a reasonable approximation is for choked flow at station s; thus, $A^*_{0i} = A_s$.

The results of the area ratio A_{0i}/A_s calculations for this example inlet are plotted in Fig. 10-45. Note that this plot has a minimum value of 1 at $M_0 = 1$. Also note the jumps in value of A_{0i}/A_s corresponding to the transition between normal and oblique shocks at each ramp (these also correspond to the jumps in total pressure shown in Fig. 10-35).

The selected design point of an external compression inlet sets the value of A_s/A_1. Since $A_{0i} = A_1$ at an inlet's supersonic design point, then $A_s/A_1 = 1/(A_{0i}/A_s)$ evaluated at this design point. For this example, the inlet design point is the maximum M_0 of 2.0. Thus $A_s/A_1 = 0.7681$ and the resulting values of A_{0i}/A_1, from using Eq. (10-14a), are tabulated in Table 10-2.

Inlet size. Now that the mass flow ratio of the inlet has been determined, the inlet mass flow rate requirements must be established before it can be sized. By using these data, the maximum calculated value of the inlet size $(A_1/A^*_{0\,\text{ref}})$, from

TABLE 10-2
Example 10-4 inlet performance

M_0	0.9	1.0	1.1	1.2	1.3	1.4	1.5	1.6	1.7	1.8	1.9	2.0
A_{0i}/A_1	0.7749	0.7681	0.7681	0.7681	0.8121	0.8259	0.8895	0.9151	0.9378	0.9592	0.9798	1.0

TABLE 10-3
Example 10-4 inlet sizing

M_0	$A_0/A^*_{0\,\text{ref}}$	$A_{0i\,\text{req}}/A^*_{0\,\text{ref}}$	A_{0i}/A_1	$A_{1\,\text{req}}/A^*_{0\,\text{ref}}$
1.23	1.0290	1.0854	0.7681	1.413
1.42	1.1004	1.1803	0.8283	1.425

Eq. (10-15), sets the size of this fixed-geometry inlet. Comparison of Figs. 10-44 and 10-45 indicates that the two most demanding operating points will most likely be at $M_0 = 1.23$ and $M_0 = 1.42$. Sizing calculations at the two Mach numbers are presented in Table 10-3. The flight condition at $M_0 = 1.42$ determines the inlet size as $A_1 = 1.425A^*_{0\,\text{ref}}$.

The resulting flow ratios of the sized inlet and its required performance are plotted for altitudes between 36 and 60 kft in Fig. 10-46. This plot shows the difference in flow behavior of the inlet between actual and required flows. As the flight Mach number increases above 1.5, the inlet mass flow rate A_{0i}/A_1 increases while the required inlet mass flow rate $(A_{0i}/A_1)_{\text{req}}$ decreases. The difference between these mass flow rates is airflow that is accepted by the inlet and then bypassed about the engine back to the atmosphere, or spilled about the inlet, or is a combination of bypassed and spilled. The large quantity of excess air for this inlet will correspond to a high inlet installation loss at Mach numbers above 1.5. If a better match of inlet and engine is needed, the inlet will require variable geometry.

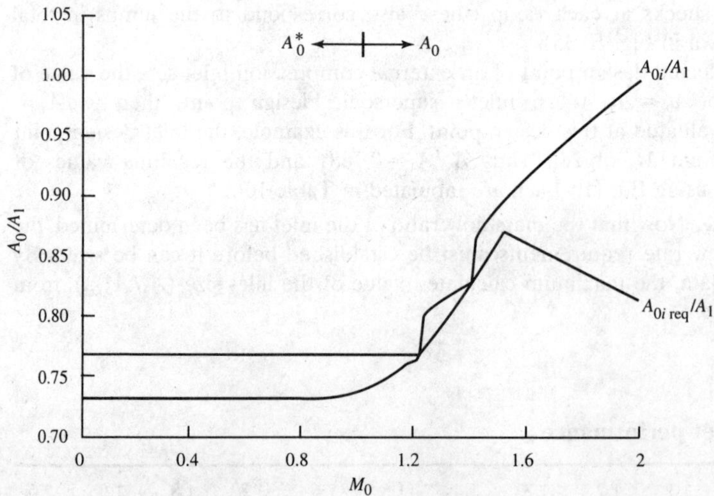

FIGURE 10-46
Mass flow performance of sized Example 10-4 inlet at altitude and full engine throttle.

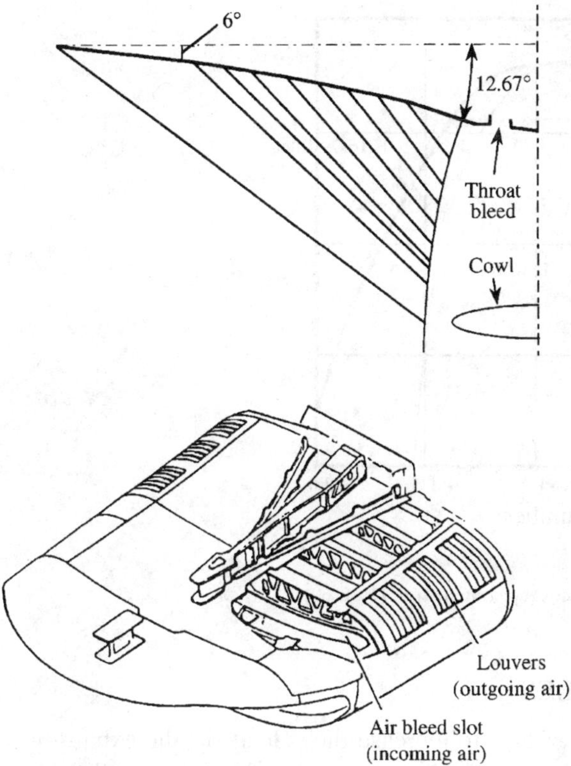

FIGURE 10-47*a*
The F-16/J-79 inlet: side and isometric views (Ref. 60).

Examples of Existing Inlet Designs

Three examples of supersonic inlet designs are shown in Figs. 10-47*a*, 10-47*b*, 10-48, and 10-49. Figure 10-47*a* shows the fixed double-ramp (6° ramp followed by a 6.67° isentropic ramp) external compression inlet with a throat slot bleed system developed in the J-79 engine installation in the F-16 aircraft. The total pressure recovery of this inlet is shown in Fig. 10-47*b*.

The variable triple-ramp external compression inlet of the F-15 aircraft is shown in Fig. 10-48. This side view of the inlet shows the ramps as they would be positioned when operating at the supersonic design point (ramp angles of 7°, 8°, and 8° for the first, second, and third ramps, respectively). The first ramp angle is fixed, and the second and third ramp angles are variable. The capture area of this inlet is variable with movement of the first ramp/top of inlet assembly from −4° to +11° (this assembly is shown at 0°).

The takeoff, transonic acceleration, and supersonic cruise modes of operation for the Concorde propulsion system are shown in Fig. 10-49. It has a complex variable-geometry inlet to satisfy the engine mass flow rate requirements at many diverse flight conditions. Note that the supersonic cruise dump control (3) is opened as an auxiliary inlet for takeoff.

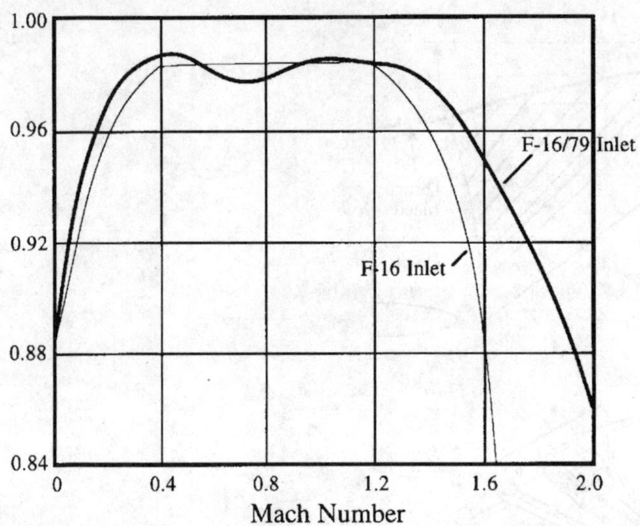

FIGURE 10-47*b*
The F-16/J-79 inlet: inlet pressure recovery comparison. (Ref. 60).

10-5 EXHAUST NOZZLES

The purpose of the exhaust nozzle is to increase the velocity of the exhaust gas before discharge from the nozzle and to collect and straighten the gas flow. For large values of specific thrust, the kinetic energy of the exhaust gas must be

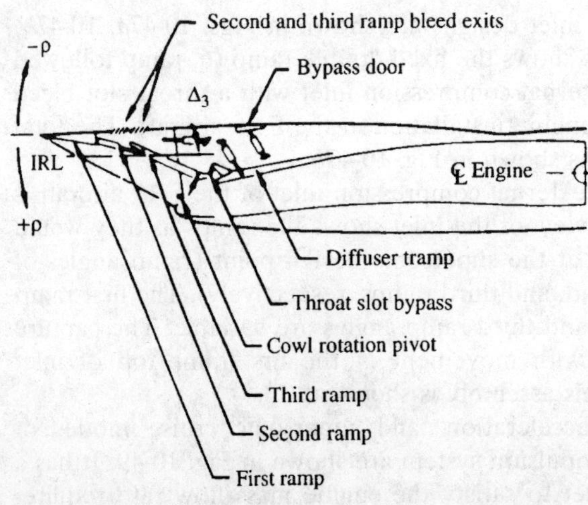

FIGURE 10-48
The F-15 inlet system (Ref. 61).

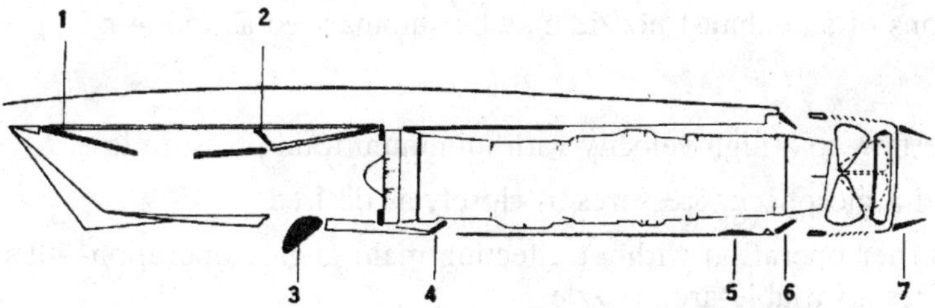

Engine variable geometry. The takeoff settings: 1-ramp sections retracted: 2-secondary control valve closed; 3-dump control open as auxiliary inlet; 4-engine bay cooling air flap open; 5-after spill flap closed; 6-tertiary doors open; 7-secondary nozzle in convergent position

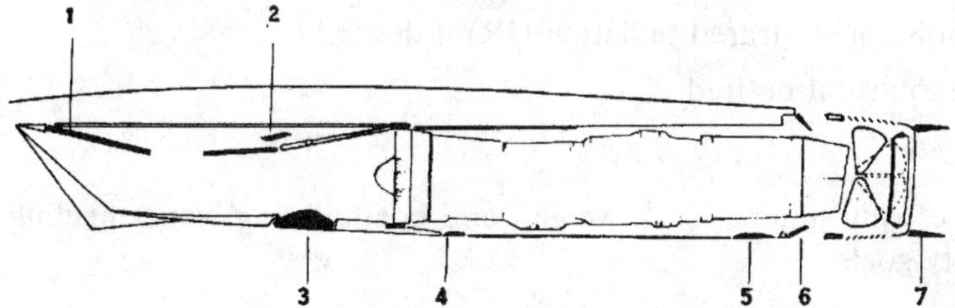

Transonic acceleration: 1-ramp section retracted; 2-secondary control valve open; 3-dump control closed; 4-cooling air flap closed; 5-spill flap closed; 6-tertiar doors open; 7-secondary nozzle trailing

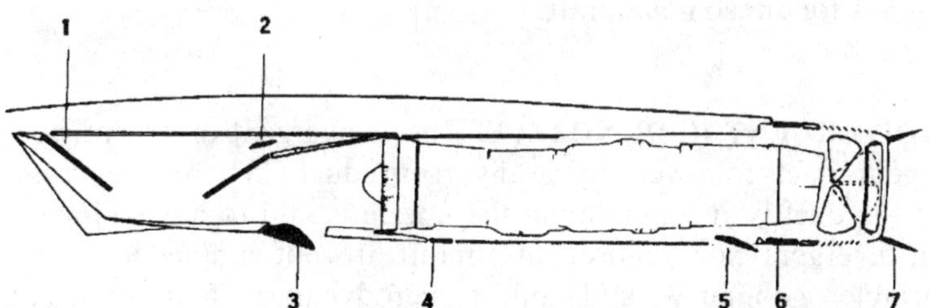

Cruise at Mach 2.2: 1-ramp sections extended; 2-secondary control valve open; 3-dump control open to dump; 4-cooling air flap closed; 5-spill flap open; 6-tertiary doors closed; 7-secondary nozzle divergent.

FIGURE 10-49
Concorde propulsion system, modes of operation.

high, which requires a high exhaust velocity. The pressure ratio across the nozzle controls the expansion process, and the maximum thrust for a given engine is obtained when the exit pressure P_e equals the ambient pressure P_0. Nozzles and their operation are discussed in many textbooks. The two basic types of nozzles used in jet engines are the *convergent* and *convergent-divergent* (C-D) nozzles.

The functions of an exhaust nozzle may be summarized as follows:

- Accelerate the flow to a high velocity with minimum total pressure loss.
- Match exit and atmospheric pressures as closely as desired.
- Permit afterburner operation without affecting main engine operation—this function requires a variable-area nozzle.
- Allow for cooling of walls if necessary.
- Mix core and bypass streams of turbofan if necessary.
- Allow for thrust reversing if desired.
- Suppress jet noise and infrared radiation (IR) if desired.
- Thrust vector control if desired.

Do all the above with minimal cost, weight, and boattail drag while meeting life and reliability goals.

CONVERGENT NOZZLE. The convergent nozzle is a simple convergent duct, as shown in Fig. 10-50. When the nozzle pressure ratio P_{te}/P_o is low (less than about 4), the convergent nozzle is used. The convergent nozzle has generally been used in engines for subsonic aircraft.

CONVERGENT-DIVERGENT (C-D) NOZZLE. The convergent-divergent nozzle is a convergent duct followed by a divergent duct. Where the cross-sectional area of the duct is at a minimum, the nozzle is said to have a *throat*. Most convergent-divergent nozzles used in aircraft are not simple ducts, but incorporate variable geometry and other aerodynamic features. The convergent-divergent nozzle is used if the nozzle pressure ratio P_{te}/P_0 is high (greater than about 6). High-performance engines in supersonic aircraft generally have some form of a convergent-divergent nozzle. If the engine incorporates an afterburner, the nozzle throat is usually scheduled to leave the operating conditions of the engine upstream of the afterburner unchanged (in other words, vary the exit nozzle area so that the engine does not know that

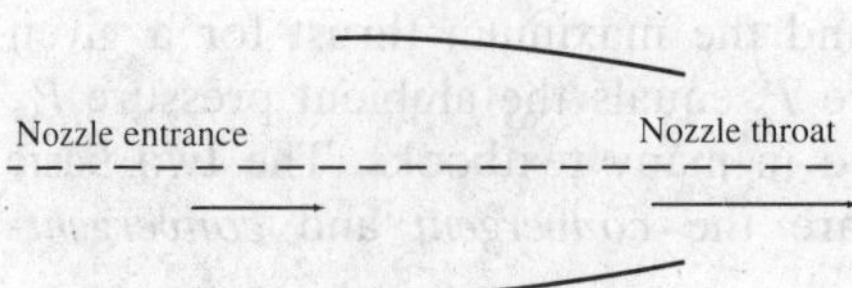

FIGURE 10-50
Convergent exhaust nozzle.

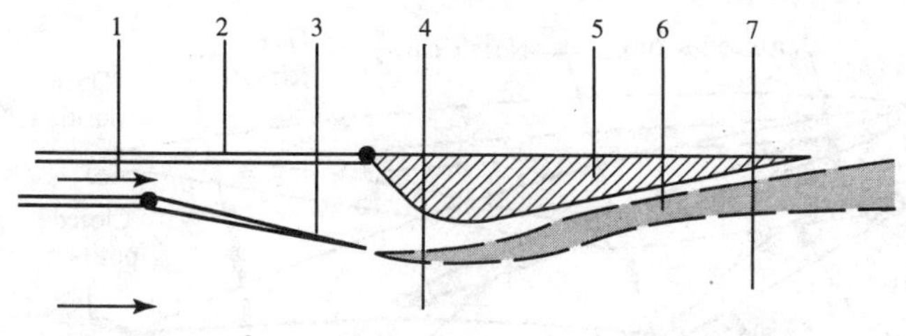

(*a*) Supersonic nozzle configuration with afterburning: (1) secondary flow; (2) outer case engine; (3) movable primary nozzle shown at maximum area; (4) primary flow, effective throat; (5) movable secondary nozzle shown at maximum exit area; (6) mixing layer between primary and secondary streams; and (7) supersonic primary flow

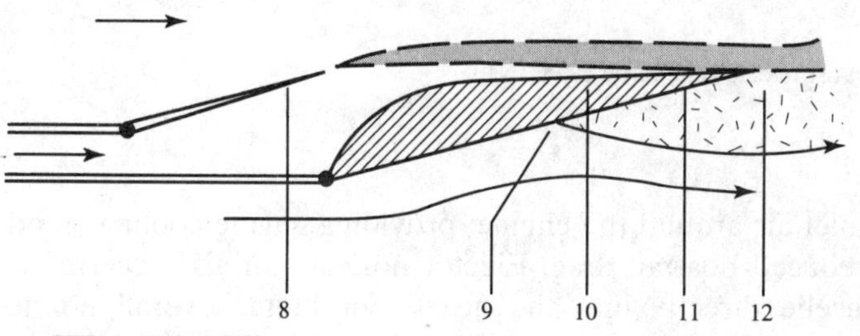

(*b*)Subsonic nozzle configuration with no afterburning: (8) primary nozzle at minimum area; (9) separation point of external flow; (10) secondary nozzle at minimum area; (11) sonic primary stream; and (12) region of separated flow in external flow

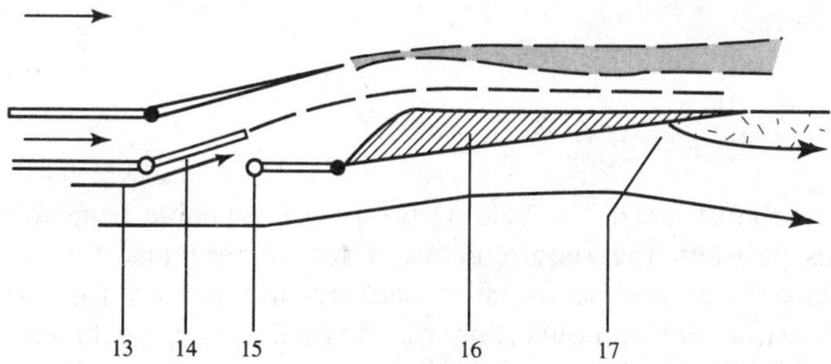

(*c*) Subsonic nozzle configuration, not afterburning, and blow-in door in use: (13) tertiary flow of ambient gas into nozzle; (14) blow-in door and inflow configuration; (15) reversible hinge/latch; (16) movable secondary nozzle; and (17) separation point of external flow.

FIGURE 10-51
Ejector nozzle configuration (Ref. 62).

the afterburner is operating). Also, the exit area must be varied to match the different flow conditions and to produce the maximum available thrust.

Earlier supersonic aircraft used ejector nozzles (Fig. 10-51) with their high-performance turbojets. Use of the ejector nozzle permitted bypassing

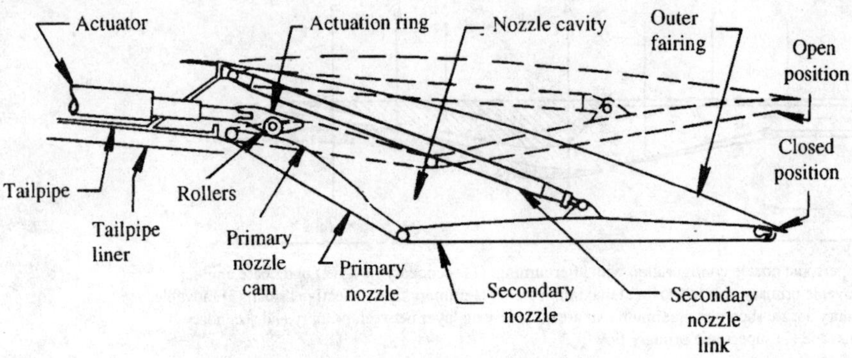

FIGURE 10-52
Convergent-divergent exhaust nozzle schematic (Ref. 62).

varying amounts of inlet air around the engine, providing engine cooling, good inlet recovery, and reduced boattail drag. Ejector nozzles can also receive air from outside the nacelle directly into the nozzle for better overall nozzle matching—these are called *two-stage ejector nozzles.* For the modern high-performance afterburning turbofan engines, simple convergent-divergent nozzles are used without secondary air, as shown in Fig. 10-52 for the F100 engine.

Nozzle Functions

One can think of the exhaust nozzle as dividing the power available from the main burner exit gas between the requirements of the turbine and the jet power (Ref. 62). Thus the nozzle serves as a backpressure control for the engine and an acceleration device converting gas thermal energy to kinetic energy. A secondary function of the nozzle is to provide required thrust reversing and/or thrust vectoring.

ENGINE BACKPRESSURE CONTROL. The throat area of the nozzle is one of the main means available to control the thrust and fuel consumption characteristics of an existing engine. In preliminary engine cycle analysis, selection of specific values for the engine design parameters and the design mass flow rate fixes the throat area of the nozzle. The engine performance methods of Chap. 8 assume that the nozzle throat area and the other internal flow areas of the engine remain constant. This assumption of constant areas establishes the off-design operating characteristics of the engine and the

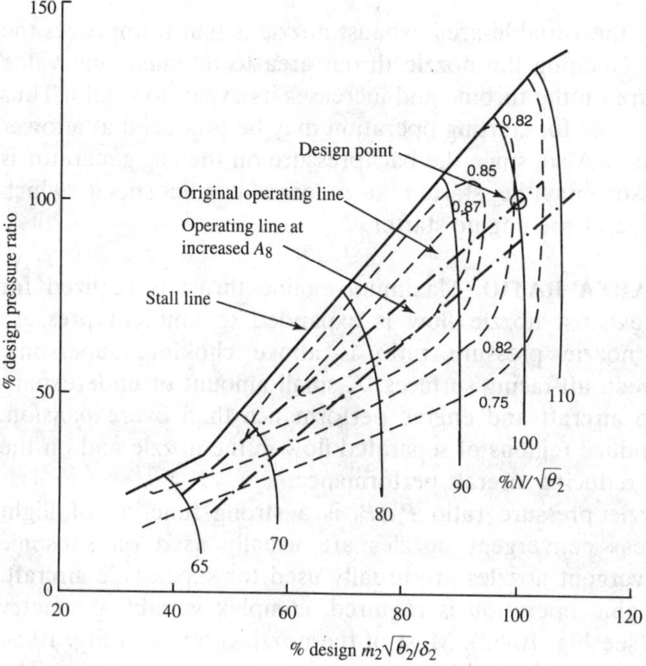

FIGURE 10-53
Compressor map with exhaust nozzle area change.

resulting operating lines for each major component. Changing the nozzle throat area from its original design value will change the engine design and the operating characteristics of the engine at both on- and off-design conditions.

At times, it is necessary to change the off-design operation of an engine in only a few operating regions, and variation of the throat area of the exhaust nozzle may provide the needed change. At reduced engine corrected mass flow rates (normally corresponding to reduced engine throttle settings), the operating line of a multistage compressor moves closer to the stall or surge line (see Fig. 10-53). Steady-state operation close to the stall or surge line is not desirable since transient operation may cause the compressor to stall or surge. The operating line can be moved away from the stall or surge line by increasing the exhaust nozzle throat area, as shown in Fig. 10-53. This increase in nozzle throat area reduces the engine backpressure and increases the corrected mass flow rate through the compressor (see Figs. 8-9 and 10-53).

Large changes in the exhaust nozzle throat area are required for afterburning engines to compensate for the large changes in total temperature leaving the afterburner. The variable-area nozzle required for an afterburning engine can also be used for back pressure control at its nonafterburning settings.

One advantage of the variable-area exhaust nozzle is that it improves the starting of the engine. Opening the nozzle throat area to its maximum value reduces the backpressure on the turbine and increases its expansion ratio. Thus the necessary turbine power for starting operation may be produced at a lower turbine inlet temperature. Also, since the backpressure on the gas generator is reduced, the compressor may be started at a lower engine speed, which reduces the required size of the engine starter.

EXHAUST NOZZLE AREA RATIO. Maximum engine thrust is realized for ideal flow when the exhaust nozzle flow is expanded to ambient pressure ($P_e = P_0$). When the nozzle pressure ratio is above choking, supersonic expansion occurs between aft-facing surfaces. A small amount of underexpansion is less harmful to aircraft and engine performance than overexpansion. Overexpansion can produce regions of separated flow in the nozzle and on the aft end of the aircraft, reducing aircraft performance.

The exhaust nozzle pressure ratio P_{te}/P_0 is a strong function of flight Mach number. Whereas convergent nozzles are usually used on subsonic aircraft, convergent-divergent nozzles are usually used for supersonic aircraft. When afterburning engine operation is required, complex variable-geometry nozzles must be used (see Fig. 10-52). Most of the nozzles shown in Fig. 10-54 are convergent-divergent nozzles with variable throat and exit areas. The

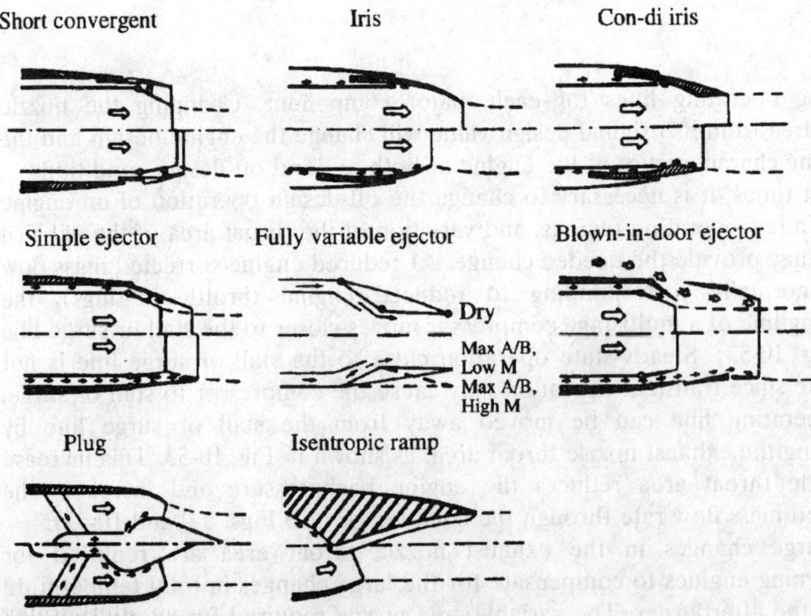

FIGURE 10-54
Typical nozzle concepts for afterburning engines (Ref. 62).

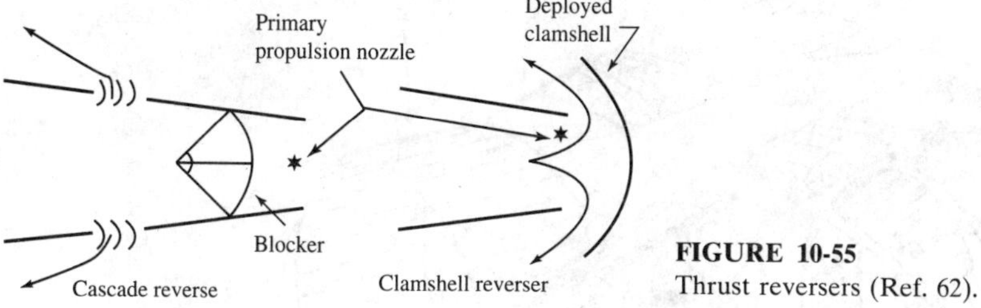

FIGURE 10-55
Thrust reversers (Ref. 62).

throat area of the nozzle is controlled to satisfy engine backpressure requirements, and the exit area is scheduled with the throat area. The sophisticated nozzles of the F-15 and B-1 aircraft have two schedules: a low-speed mode and a high-speed mode (Ref. 62).

THRUST REVERSING AND THRUST VECTORING. The need for thrust reversing and thrust vectoring is normally determined by the required aircraft and engine system performance. Thrust reversers are used on commercial transports to supplement the brakes. In-flight thrust reversal has been shown to enhance combat effectiveness of fighter aircraft (Ref. 62).

Two basic types of thrust reversers are used: the cascade-blocker type and the clamshell type (Fig. 10-55). In the cascade-blocker type, the primary nozzle exit is blocked off, and cascades are opened in the upstream portion of the nozzle duct to reverse the flow. In the clamshell type, the exhaust jet is split and reversed by the clamshell. Since both types usually provide a change in effective throat area during deployment or when deployed, most reversers are designed such that the effective nozzle throat area increases during the brief transitory period, thus preventing compressor stall.

The exhaust system for the Concorde is shown in Fig. 10-56. There are two nozzles, a primary nozzle and a secondary nozzle. The secondary nozzle is positioned as a convergent nozzle for takeoff and as a divergent nozzle for supersonic cruise. The modes of operation for this exhaust system are shown in Fig. 10-49 along with the inlet.

Development of thrust vectoring nozzles for combat aircraft has increased in the last decade. Vectoring nozzles have been used on vertical takeoff and landing (VTOL) aircraft, such as the AV-8 Harrier, and are proposed for future fighters to improve maneuvering and augment lift in combat. Thrust vectoring at augmented power settings is being developed for use in future fighters. However, cooling of the nozzle walls in contact with the hot turning or stagnating flows is very difficult and will require increased amounts of nozzle-cooling airflow. The operation of the Pratt & Whitney F119-PW-100 augmented turbofan engine's thrust vectoring nozzle is shown in Fig. 10-57. This two-dimensional nozzle was developed for use in the F-22 Advanced Tactical Fighter.

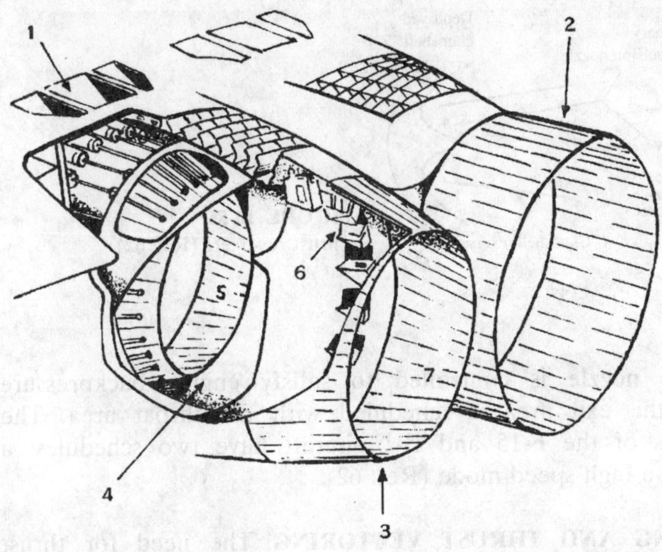

Details of the exhaust system: (1) tertiary doors; (2) nozzle in supersonic configuration; (3) subsonic configuration; (4) thrust reverse buckets; (5) primary nozzle; (6) silencer lobes; (7) secondary nozzle

FIGURE 10-56
Concorde exhaust system.

Figure 10-58 shows the schematic of a two-dimensional convergent-divergent nozzle with thrust vectoring of ±15° and thrust reversing. This is typical of the capabilities sought for use in future fighter aircraft.

Nozzle Coefficients

Nozzle performance is ordinarily evaluated by two dimensionless coefficients: the gross thrust coefficient and the discharge or flow coefficient. Figure 10-59 shows a convergent-divergent exhaust nozzle with the geometric parameters used in the following definitions of nozzle coefficients. Only total pressure losses downstream of station 8 are included in the gross thrust coefficient.

GROSS THRUST COEFFICENT. The *gross thrust coefficient* C_{fg} is the ratio of the actual gross thrust $F_{g\,\text{actual}}$ to the ideal gross thrust $F_{g\,\text{ideal}}$, or

$$C_{fg} \equiv \frac{F_{g\,\text{actual}}}{F_{g\,\text{ideal}}} \tag{10-17}$$

FIGURE 10-57
Pratt & Whitney F119-PW-100 turbofan engine with two-dimensional thrust vectoring nozzle. (*Courtesy of Pratt & Whitney.*)

Empirically derived coefficients are applied to Eq. (10-17) to account for the losses and directionality of the actual nozzle flow. Each engine organization uses somewhat different coefficients, but each of the following basic losses is accounted for:

- Thrust loss due to exhaust velocity vector angularity
- Thrust loss due to the reduction in velocity magnitude caused by friction in the boundary layers
- Thrust loss due to loss of mass flow between stations 7 and 9 from leakage through the nozzle walls
- Thrust loss due to flow nonuniformities

DISCHARGE OR FLOW COEFFICIENT. The ratio of the actual mass flow $\dot{m}_8$ to the ideal mass flow $\dot{m}_{8i}$ is called the *discharge coefficient* C_D:

$$\boxed{C_D \equiv \frac{\dot{m}_8}{\dot{m}_{8i}}} \tag{10-18}$$

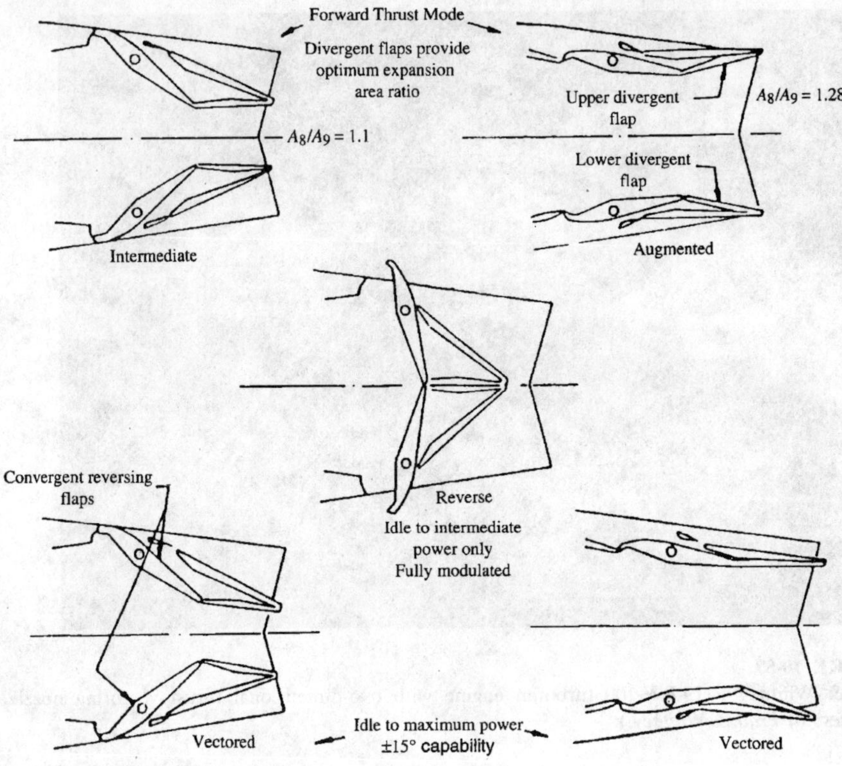

FIGURE 10-58
Typical two-dimensional thrust vectoring nozzle with thrust reversing (Ref. 61).

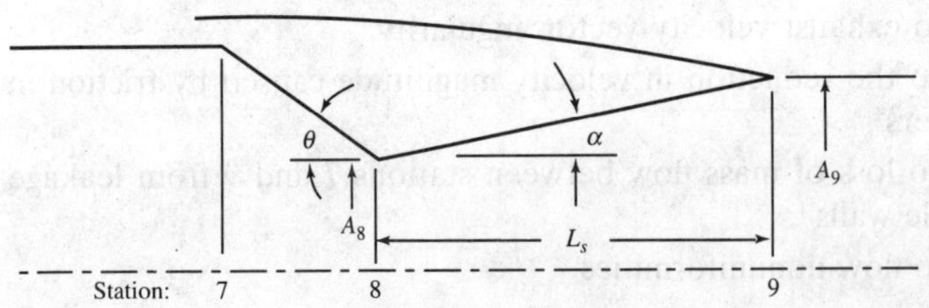

A_8 = Primary nozzle throat area
A_9 = Secondary nozzle exit area
α = Secondary nozzle half angle
θ = Primary nozzle half angle
L_s = Secondary nozzle length

FIGURE 10-59
Nozzle geometric parameters.

This coefficient can be shown to be identically equal to the ratio of the effective one-dimensional flow area required to pass the total actual nozzle flow A_{8e} to the nozzle physical throat area A_8 as follows:

$$C_D = \frac{\dot{m}_8}{\dot{m}_{8i}} = \frac{\rho_8 V_8 A_{8e}}{\rho_8 V_8 A_8} = \frac{A_{8e}}{A_8}$$

The variation of the discharge coefficient with nozzle pressure ratio is shown in Fig. 10-60*a* for a conic convergent nozzle. When the nozzle is choked, the discharge coefficient reaches a maximum value $C_{D\max}$. The value of $C_{D\max}$

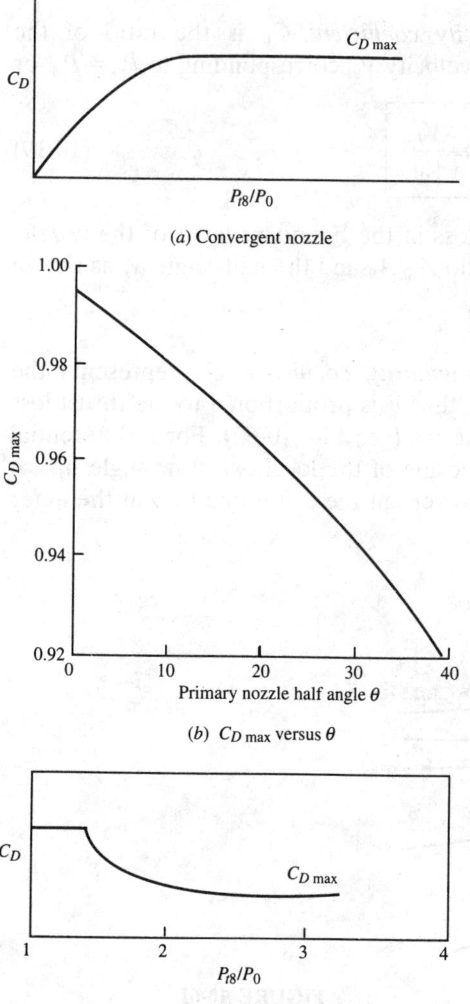

FIGURE 10-60
Nozzle discharge coefficient (Ref. 62).

is a function of the primary nozzle half-angle θ, as shown in Fig. 10-60*b*. Figure 10-60*c* shows the variation in discharge coefficient for a convergent-divergent nozzle with nozzle pressure ratio. Note the change in behavior of C_D between that of the convergent-divergent nozzle and that of the convergent nozzle as the nozzle pressure ratio drops below choking. This is due to the venturi behavior of the convergent-divergent nozzle.

The discharge coefficient is used to size the nozzle throat area to pass the desired mass flow rate. For example, consider a nozzle with $\dot{m}_8 = 200$ lbm/sec, $P_{t8} = 30$ psia, $T_{t8} = 2000°\text{R}$, $\gamma = 1.33$, $R = 53.34$ ft · lbf/(lbm · °R), and $\theta = 20°$. At $M_8 = 1$, $\text{MFP}\sqrt{R/g_c} = 0.672628$ (App. E with $\gamma = 1.33$), then MFP = 0.5224, and thus $A_{8e} = 570.7\ \text{in}^2$. Figure 10-60*b* gives $C_{D\max} = 0.96$ for $\theta = 20°$ and thus the required throat area is $594.5\ \text{in}^2$.

VELOCITY COEFFICIENT. The *velocity coefficient* C_V is the ratio of the actual exit velocity V_9 to the ideal exit velocity V_{9i} corresponding to $P_{t9} = P_{t8}$, or

$$\boxed{C_V \equiv \frac{V_9}{V_{9i}}} \tag{10-19}$$

and represents the effect of frictional loss in the boundary layer of the nozzle. It is mainly a function of the nozzle ratio A_8/A_9 and the half-angle α, as shown in Fig. 10-61.

ANGULARITY COEFFICIENT. The *angularity coefficient* C_A represents the axial friction of the nozzle momentum; thus it is proportional to the thrust loss due to the nonaxial exit of the exhaust gas (see Fig. 10-62). For a differential element of flow, this coefficient is the cosine of the local exit flow angle α_j.

The local flow angle α_j varies from zero at the centerline to α at the outer

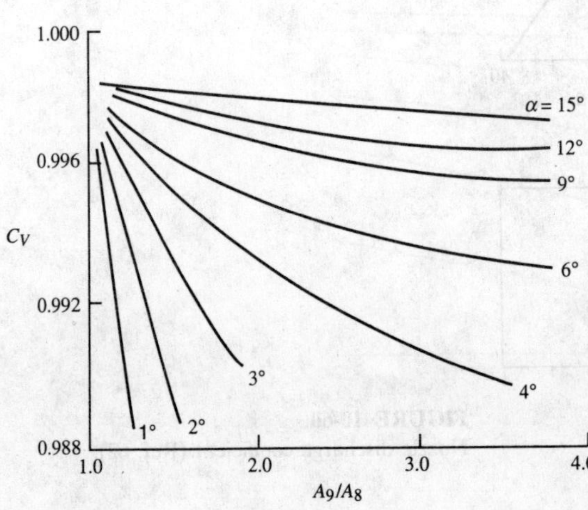

FIGURE 10-61
C-D nozzle velocity coefficient (Ref. 62).

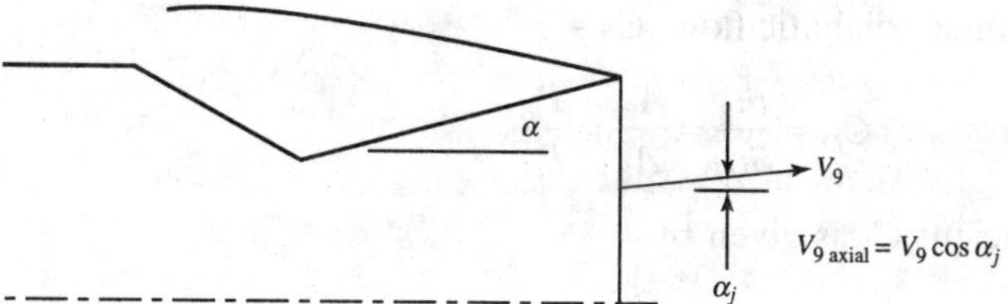

FIGURE 10-62
Local angularity coefficient.

wall; thus, the nozzle angularity coefficient is the integral of α_j across the nozzle:

$$C_A \equiv \frac{1}{\dot{m}} \int \cos \alpha_j \, d\dot{m} \tag{10-20}$$

Figure 10-63 presents the correlation of the angularity coefficient with the nozzle area ratio A_8/A_9 and half-angle α. This figure is based on analytical evaluations of the inviscid flow field in convergent-divergent nozzles for a range of practical nozzle geometries.

Nozzle Performance

Many nozzle coefficients simplify to algebraic expressions or become unity for the special case of *one-dimensional adiabatic flow*. This is a useful limit for understanding each coefficient and for preliminary analysis of nozzle performance using engine cycle performance data.

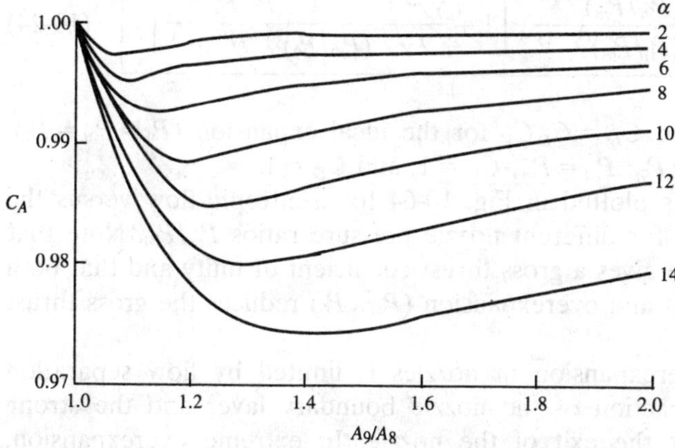

FIGURE 10-63
C-D nozzle angularity coefficient (Ref. 62).

For one-dimensional adiabatic flow, $C_A = 1$,

$$C_D = \frac{\dot{m}_8}{\dot{m}_{8i}} = \frac{A_{8e}}{A_8} = \frac{P_{t8}}{P_{t7}}$$

and the velocity coefficient C_V is given by

$$C_V \equiv \frac{V_9}{V_{9i}} \tag{10-19}$$

where V_9 is the exit velocity corresponding to T_{t8} and $(A/A^*)_9 = (P_{t9}/P_{t8})[A_9/(C_D A_8)]$ and V_{9i} is the ideal exit velocity corresponding to T_{t8} and $(A/A^*)_{9i} = A_9/(C_D A_8)$.

The gross thrust for a one-dimensional flow can be expressed as

$$F_{g\,\text{actual}} = \frac{\dot{m}_8 V_9}{g_c} + (P_9 - P_0)A_9 \tag{10-21}$$

and the ideal gross thrust (corresponds to $P_9 = P_0$) as

$$F_{g\,\text{ideal}} = \frac{\dot{m}_{8i} V_s}{g_c} \tag{10-22}$$

where V_s is the isentropic exit velocity based on P_{t8}/P_0 and T_{t8}.

For one-dimensional flow of a calorically perfect gas, Eq. (10-21) can be written as

$$F_{g\,\text{actual}} = \frac{\dot{m}_8 V_9}{g_c}\left[1 + \frac{\gamma - 1}{2\gamma}\,\frac{1 - P_0/P_9}{(P_{t9}/P_9)^{(\gamma-1)/\gamma} - 1}\right] \tag{10-23}$$

The gross thrust coefficient for one-dimensional flow of a calorically perfect gas can be obtained by substituting Eqs. (10-22) and (10-23) into Eq. (10-17), giving

$$\boxed{C_{fg} = C_D C_V \sqrt{\frac{1 - (P_{9i}/P_{t8})^{(\gamma-1)/\gamma}}{1 - (P_0/P_{t8})^{(\gamma-1)/\gamma}}}\left[1 + \frac{\gamma - 1}{2\gamma}\,\frac{1 - P_0/P_9}{(P_{t9}/P_9)^{(\gamma-1)/\gamma} - 1}\right]} \tag{10-24}$$

This equation reduces to $C_{fg} = C_D C_V$ for the ideal expansion ($P_9 = P_{9i} = P_0$). For isentropic flow, $P_9 = P_{9i}$, $P_{t9} = P_{t8}$, $C_V = 1$, and $C_D = 1$.

Equation (10-24) is plotted in Fig. 10-64 for isentropic flow versus the nozzle area ratio A_9/A_8 for different nozzle pressure ratios P_{t8}/P_{t0}. Note that ideal expansion ($P_9 = P_0$) gives a gross thrust coefficient of unity and that both underexpansion ($P_9 > P_0$) and overexpansion ($P_9 < P_0$) reduces the gross thrust coefficient below unity.

The extent of overexpansion in nozzles is limited by flow separation resulting from the interaction of the nozzle boundary layer and the strong oblique shock waves at the exit of the nozzle. In extreme overexpansion, Summerfield et al. (Ref. 67) noted that the oblique shock waves moved from

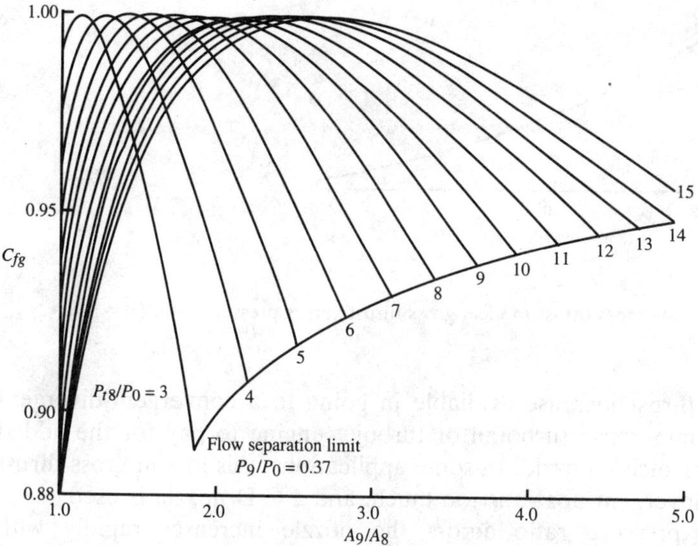

FIGURE 10-64
Thrust coefficient for one-dimensional isentropic flow ($\gamma = 1.3$).

the exit lip into the nozzle, the flow downstream of the shock waves was separated in the vicinity of the wall, and as a result, the wall static pressure downstream of the shock waves was nearly equal to the ambient pressure P_0. A simple estimate for the ratio of the pressure just preceding the shock waves P_s to the ambient pressure P_0, suggested by Summerfield (Ref. 67), is given by

$$\frac{P_s}{P_0} \approx 0.37 \tag{10-25}$$

This flow separation limit can be included in the one-dimensional gross thrust coefficient of Eq. (10-24) for isentropic flow by considering the effective exit pressure ($P_9 = P_{9i}$) to be the pressure just preceding the shock wave (P_s). Equations (10-24) and (10-25) were used to obtain the flow separation limit shown in Fig. 10-64. The design area ratio A_9/A_8 of convergent-divergent nozzles is selected such that the nozzle flow does not separate due to overexpansion for most throttle settings. This is because the increase in gross thrust coefficient associated with flow separation does not normally offset the accompanying increase in installation loss.

Nozzle pressure ratios are 3 to 5 in the subsonic cruise speed range of turbofan and turbojet engines. Typically, a subsonic engine uses a convergent exhaust nozzle. This is because, in the nozzle pressure range of 3 to 5, the convergent gross thrust (interception of lines with vertical axis, $A_9/A_8 = 1$) is 1 to 3 percent below the peak gross thrust ($P_9 = P_0$). Consequently, there may be

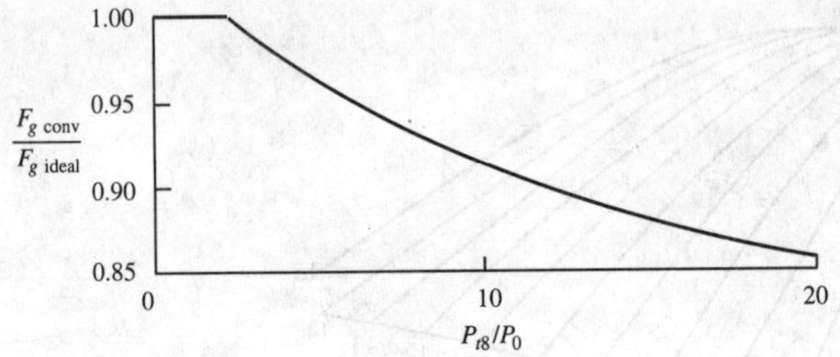

FIGURE 10-65
Ratio of convergent nozzle gross thrust to ideal gross thrust versus pressure ratio ($\gamma = 1.3$).

insufficient gross thrust increase available in going to a convergent-divergent nozzle on a subsonic cruise turbofan or turbojet engine to pay for the added drag and weight of such a nozzle. In some applications, this loss in gross thrust coefficient of a convergent nozzle is too much, and a C-D nozzle is used.

The design pressure ratio across the nozzle increases rapidly with supersonic flight Mach number. At Mach 2, a pressure ratio of about 12 is typical. At this pressure ratio, the convergent nozzle gross thrust penalty is about 9 percent, as shown in Fig. 10-65. This figure is a plot of the ratio of the gross thrust in Fig. 10-64 of a convergent nozzle ($A_9/A_8 = 1$) to the peak thrust ($P_9 = P_0$) versus P_{t8}/P_0. Substitution of convergent-divergent nozzles for convergent nozzles provides large thrust gains for supersonic aircraft.

Example 10-5. *Calculation based on one-dimensional flow*
Given:

$$\dot{m}_8 = 200 \text{ lbm/sec} \qquad P_{t8} = 30 \text{ psia} \qquad T_{t8} = 2000°\text{R}$$

$$\frac{A_9}{A_8} = 2.0 \qquad \gamma = 1.33 \qquad R = 53.34 \text{ ft} \cdot \text{lbf/(lbm} \cdot °\text{R)}$$

$$\frac{P_{t9}}{P_{t8}} = 0.98 \qquad C_D = 0.98 \qquad P_0 = 5 \text{ psia}$$

Find the dimensions of an axisymmetric nozzle and the vaues of C_{fg}, F_g, and C_V.

Solution. At $M_8 = 1$, $\text{MFP}\sqrt{R/g_c} = 0.672628$ (App. E with $\gamma = 1.33$), then MFP = 0.5224, thus

$$A_{8e} = \frac{\dot{m}_8\sqrt{T_{t8}}}{P_{t8}\,\text{MFP}(M_8 = 1)} = \frac{200\sqrt{2000}}{30 \times 0.5224} = 570.7 \text{ in}^2$$

With $C_D = 0.98$, thus $A_8 = 582.3 \text{ in}^2$ and $r_8 = 13.61$ in. Since $A_9/A_8 = 2.0$, then $A_9 = 1165 \text{ in}^2$ and $r_9 = 19.25$ in.

$$\left(\frac{A}{A^*}\right)_{9i} = \frac{A_9}{C_D A_8} = \frac{2.0}{0.98} = 2.041 \qquad \rightarrow \qquad M_{9i} = 2.168 \quad \text{and} \quad \frac{P_{9i}}{P_{t9i}} = 0.0990$$

Thus, $P_{9i} = (0.0990)(30 \text{ psia}) = 2.970$ psia,

$$V_{9i} = \sqrt{R g_c T_{t8}} \sqrt{\frac{2\gamma}{\gamma - 1}\left[1 - \left(\frac{P_{9i}}{P_{t8}}\right)^{(\gamma-1)/\gamma}\right]}$$

$$V_{9i} = \sqrt{(1716)(2000)} \sqrt{\frac{2(1.33)}{0.33}[1 - (0.0990)^{0.33/1.33}]} = 3475 \text{ ft/sec}$$

$$\left(\frac{A}{A^*}\right)_9 = \frac{P_{t9}}{P_{t8}}\frac{A_9}{C_D A_8} = \frac{0.98 \times 2.0}{0.98} = 2.0 \quad \rightarrow \quad M_9 = 2.146 \quad \text{and} \quad \frac{P_9}{P_{t9}} = 0.1025$$

Thus, $P_9 = (0.1025)(0.98)(30 \text{ psia}) = 3.014$ psia,

$$V_9 = \sqrt{(1716)(2000)} \sqrt{\frac{2(1.33)}{0.33}[1 - (0.1025)^{0.33/1.33}]} = 3456 \text{ ft/sec}$$

$$C_V = \frac{V_9}{V_{9i}} = 0.9945$$

$$C_{fg} = (0.98)(0.9945)\sqrt{\frac{1 - (2.97/30)^{0.33/1.33}}{1 - (5.0/30)^{0.33/1.33}}}\left[1 + \frac{0.33}{2 \times 1.33} \frac{1 - 5.0/3.014}{(29.4/3.014)^{0.33/1.33} - 1}\right]$$

$$= 0.9593$$

Figure 10-63*b* gives $\theta = 10°$ for $C_D = 0.98$. Likewise, Fig. 10-64 gives $\alpha = 6°$ for $C_V = 0.9945$ and $A_9/A_8 = 2$. Thus $L_s = 54$ in, and the dimensions of the exhaust nozzle are shown in Fig. 10-66. The gross thrust can be calculated in several ways: directly from Eq. (10-23)

$$F_{g\text{ actual}} = \frac{\dot{m}_8 V_9}{g_c} + (P_9 - P_0)A_9$$

$$= \frac{(200)(3456)}{32.174} + (3.014 - 5.0)(1165) = 19{,}170 \text{ lbf}$$

or from the ideal gross thrust and C_{fg} with

$$V_s = \sqrt{(1716)(2000)} \sqrt{\frac{2(1.33)}{0.33}\left[1 - \left(\frac{5}{30}\right)^{0.33/1.33}\right]} = 3151 \text{ ft/sec}$$

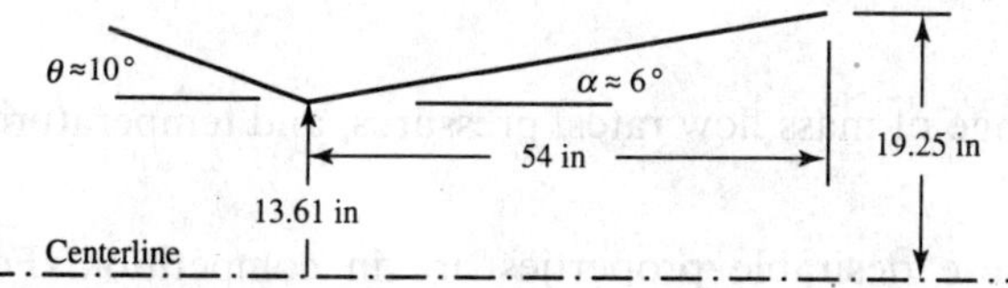

FIGURE 10-66
Dimensions of Example 10-5 exhaust nozzle.

then

$$F_{g\,\text{ideal}} = \frac{\dot{m}_{8i} V_s}{g_c} = \frac{(200/0.98)(3151)}{32.174} = 19{,}990\ \text{lbf}$$

$$F_g = C_{fg} F_{g\,\text{ideal}} = (0.9593)(19{,}990) = 19{,}170\ \text{lbf}$$

10-6 INTRODUCTION TO COMBUSTION SYSTEMS

Combustion systems of aircraft gas turbine engines largely encompass the main burners (also called *burners* or *combustors*) and afterburners (also called *augmenters* or *reheaters*). Both main burners and afterburners are covered in this section since they have many basic principles in common. The basic principles of the combustion process, combustion stability, total pressure ratio, length scaling, diffusers, and fuels are presented in the following sections and provide the means for understanding the design of the main burner and afterburner.

The thermal energy of the air/fuel mixture (reactants) flowing through an air-breathing engine is increased by the combustion process. The fuel must be vaporized and mixed with the air before this chemical reaction can occur. Once this is done, the combustion process can occur and thus increase the thermal energy of the mixture (products of combustion). All this takes time and space.

The design of the main burner and afterburner of an air-breathing engine differs in many ways from that of conventional combustion devices. Space (especially length) is at a premium in aircraft applications, and the length of the combustion chamber is reduced by hastening completion of the combustion process. The combustion intensity (rate of energy released per unit volume) is much higher for the main burner of a turbojet [40,000 Btu/(sec · ft^3) or 11,150 MW/m^3] compared to a typical steam power plant [10 Btu/(sec · ft^3) or 2.8 MW/m^3]. The following properties of the combustion chambers are desired:

- Complete combustion
- Low total pressure loss
- Stability of combustion process
- Proper temperature distribution at exit with no "hot spots"
- Short length and small cross section
- Freedom from flameout
- Relightability
- Operation over a wide range of mass flow rates, pressures, and temperatures

However, many of these desirable properties are in competition. For example, both complete combustion and low total pressure loss are contrary to small size. Hence the design of a main burner or afterburner is a compromise. We examine many of these desirable combustion properties in order to understand the design and operation of main burners and afterburners, starting with the combustion process.

Combustion Process

The combustion processes occur with the vaporized fuel and air mixed on a molecular scale. The rate of this reaction depends on both the static pressure P and temperature T in a very complex way. For many situations, the reaction rate can be approximated by a form of the Arrhenius equation (Refs. 62 and 69) written for the mass rate of reaction as

$$\text{Reaction rate} \propto P^n f(T) \exp\frac{-E}{RT} \tag{10-26}$$

where n is an exponent that depends on the number of molecules involved in a reactive collision (for example, $n = 2$ for two molecules, $n = 3$ for three molecules); $f(T)$ is a function that relates the reaction rate to the forms of energy (translation, rotation, and vibration) the molecules have; the term $\exp[-E/(RT)]$ accounts for the number of molecular collisions in which the energy of one molecule relative to another exceeds the activation energy E; and R is the universal gas constant.

For hydrocarbon-air combustion, $n = 1.8$. At low pressures, the reaction rate becomes slow and can become limiting for aircraft engines at very high altitudes. However, under most operating conditions, the rate of combustion is limited by the rate at which the fuel is vaporized and mixed with air. In most combustors, the fuel is injected as an atomized liquid-droplet spray into the hot reaction zone where it mixes with air and hot combustion gases. The atomized fuel vaporizes, and then the vapor is mixed with air. If the temperature and pressure in the reaction zone are sufficiently high, the reaction rate will be fast and the fuel vapor will react as it comes in contact with sufficient oxygen.

The stoichiometric fuel/air ratio for the typical hydrocarbon fuel can be estimated by assuming octane as a representative hydrocarbon and writing the stoichiometric chemical reaction:

$$2C_8H_{18} + 25\left(O_2 + \frac{79}{21}N_2\right) \rightarrow 16CO_2 + 18H_2O + 25\left(\frac{79}{21}\right)N_2$$

For this reason, the stoichiometric fuel/air ratio is found to be

$$f_{\text{stoich}} = \frac{2(96 + 18)}{25[32 + (79/21)28]} = 0.0664$$

The *equivalence ratio* ϕ is the actual fuel/air ratio divided by the fuel/air ratio required for complete combustion (stoichiometric fuel/air ratio), or

$$\boxed{\phi \equiv \frac{f}{f_{\text{stoich}}}} \tag{10-27}$$

The equivalence ratio ϕ is greater than 1.0 for rich fuel/air ratio and less than 1.0 for a lean fuel/air mixture. To prevent excessive temperatures at the exit of the main burner or afterburner and protect its walls, the overall fuel/air ratio must be much less than stoichiometric with $\phi < 1.0$.

As an example, an engine being flown at Mach 0.9, a 12-km altitude, and full throttle with a compressor pressure ratio of 20 and 85 percent isentropic efficiency will have a compressor pressure outlet temperature of about 653 K. If the turbine inlet temperature is limited to 1670 K, h_{PR} is 42,800 kJ/kg, and c_{pc} and c_{pt} are 1.004 and 1.235 kJ/(kg · K), then the fuel/air ratio for 100 percent efficient combustion in the main burner is, from Eq. (7-9),

$$f = \frac{1.235 \times 1670 - 1.004 \times 653}{42{,}800 - 1.235 \times 1670} = 0.0346$$

which corresponds to an overall equivalence ratio of 0.519 for a main burner using JP-4 fuel ($f_{\text{stoich}} = 0.0667$).

Figure 10-67 shows the flammability characteristics of a kerosene-type

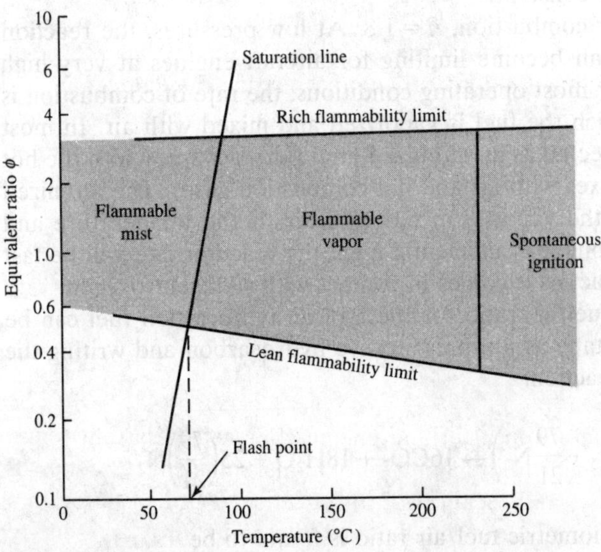

FIGURE 10-67
Flammability characteristics for a kerosene type fuel in air at atmospheric pressure (Refs. 32 and 62).

fuel. The 0.52 equivalence ratio of the above example is at the lower limit of flammability shown in Fig. 10-67. This presents a design problem at the full-throttle value of ϕ and at the engine's partial-throttle values of ϕ. The problem of lean mixtures in a burner can be overcome by mixing and burning a rich fuel/air mixture in a small region where the local equivalence ratio is near unity. By using only a portion of the total air in a region, a locally rich mixture can be efficiently burned and then the products of combustion diluted and cooled to an acceptable turbine inlet temperature by the remaining air (see Fig. 10-77).

At usual pressures and temperatures, hydrocarbon/air mixtures will react over only a rather narrow range of ϕ—from approximately 0.5 to 3 and not at all below 0.2 atm at standard temperature. Hydrogen has much wider flammability limits than do hydrocarbons—approximately $0.25 < \phi < 6$ at standard temperature and 1 atm. Some special, rather expensive fuels have flammability limits intermediate between hydrogen and hydrocarbons. These special fuels have been used at times for testing and for extending the altitude limits of engines for special applications.

A limitation is imposed by the combustion since it is necessary to maintain a stationary flame within a high-velocity airstream. Imagine the flame as propagating through the combustible mixture at the flame speed, while the mixture is carried downstream. To have a stable flame, the velocity of the mixture must be maintained within certain limits: If the velocity is too high, the flame will be "blown out" the exit; if it is too low, the flame will travel upstream and be extinguished. This problem of holding the combustion flame within the combustion system is solved by establishing regions of recirculation at the front of the main burner (see Fig. 10-77) or behind a bluff body, called a *flame holder,* at the front of an afterburner (see Fig. 10-87). These regions of recirculation create areas of local low velocity that "hold" the flame, and at the same time, the resulting turbulence gently increases the rate of energy transfer from these regions.

Provided stable combustion is attained, complete combustion in the case of lean mixtures is virtually ensured since, with excess oxygen, local fuel-rich areas are unlikely. On the other hand, combustion of a near-stoichiometric mixture requires an essentially uniform distribution of constituents to avoid wasting some fuel in local fuel-rich (oxygen-poor) regions.

Ignition

Ignition of a fuel/air mixture in a turbine engine combustion system requires inlet air and fuel conditions within flammability limits, sufficient residence time of a combustible mixture, and location of an effective ignition source in the vicinity of the combustible mixture. The flammability limits for a kerosene-type fuel are shown in Fig. 10-67. Note that the flammability region is further subdivided into two regions separated by the *spontaneous ignition temperature* (SIT). The spontaneous ignition temperature is the lowest temperature at

TABLE 10-4
Spontaneous-ignition temperatures

Fuel	SIT (K)
Propane	767
Butane	678
Pentane	558
Hexane	534
Heptane	496
Octane	491
Nonane	479
Decane	481
Hexadecane	478
Isooctane	691
Kerosene (JP-8 or jet A)	501
JP-3	511
JP-4	515
JP-5	506

which visible or audible evidence of combustion is observed. Typical values of SIT are presented in Table 10-4.

When the temperature in the combustion system is below the SIT, an ignition source is required to bring the local temperature above the spontaneous ignition temperature. The minimum amount of energy necessary to achieve ignition is shown in Fig. 10-68. Note that the minimum amount of energy is not always at a stoichiometric mixture ratio. For heavy fuels, such as C_7H_{16}, the minimum is nearer $\phi = 2$.

Once the flammability limits and SIT requirements are met, then the

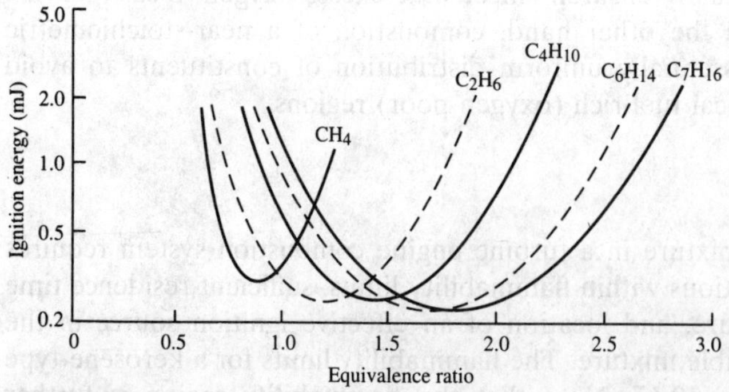

FIGURE 10-68
Minimum ignition energies at standard temperature and pressure (Refs. 62 and 63).

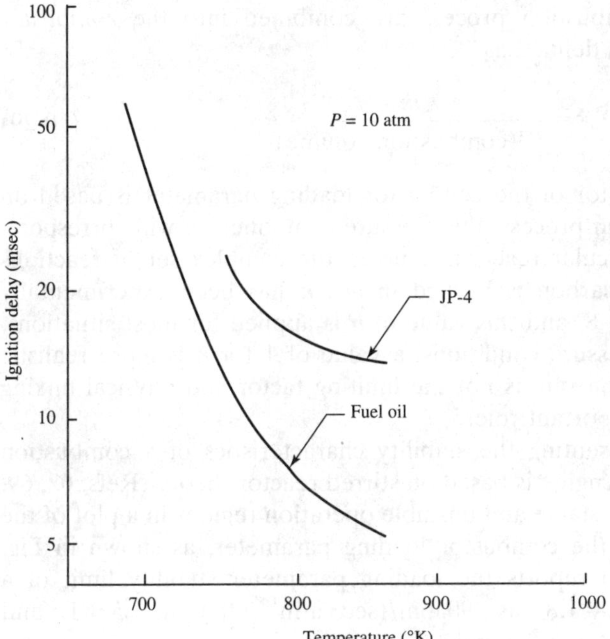

FIGURE 10-69
Ignition delay times for practical fuels (Refs. 32 and 62).

ignition delay time becomes the key combustion characteristic. The ignition delay time t_{ign} is related to the initial temperature T by

$$t_{\text{ign}} \propto \exp \frac{E}{RT} \tag{10-28}$$

The variation of ignition delay time with pressure has been experimentally observed to follow $t_{\text{ign}} \propto 1/P$. Ignition delay times for typical fuels are shown in Fig. 10-69.

Combustion Stability

The ability of the combustion process to sustain itself in a continuous manner is called *combustion stability*. Stable, efficient combustion can be upset by the fuel/air mixture becoming too lean or too rich such that the temperatures and reaction rates drop below the level necessary to effectively heat and vaporize the incoming fuel and air. Such a situation causes blowout of the combustion process. The effects of mass flow rate, combustion volume, and pressure on the stability of the combustion process are combined into the *combustor loading parameter* (CLP), defined as

$$\text{CLP} \equiv \frac{\dot{m}}{P^n(\text{combustion volume})} \tag{10-29}$$

Since the denominator of the combustor loading parameter is based on the rate of the combustion process, the pressure component n will correspond to 2 for a simple bimolecular reaction. Due to the complex set of reactions occurring when a hydrocarbon is burned in air, n has been experimentally determined to be about 1.8, and this value of n is applied for most situations. However, under high-pressure conditions, a value of 1 for n is more realistic since the chemical reaction rate is not the limiting factor and physical mixing processes play a more important role.

The method of presenting the stability characteristics of a combustion process for a gas turbine engine is based on stirred reactor theory (Refs. 62, 69, 70, and 71) and shows the stable and unstable operation regions in a plot of the equivalence ratio versus the combustor loading parameter, as shown in Fig. 10-70. Spalding (Ref. 71) reports the loading parameter stability limit of a stirred reactor with $n = 1.8$ as $90\,\text{lbm}/(\text{sec}\cdot\text{atm}^{1.8}\cdot\text{ft}^3)$ at $\phi = 1$ and $10\,\text{lbm}/(\text{sec}\cdot\text{atm}^{1.8}\cdot\text{ft}^3)$ at $\phi = 0.5$ and 1.7.

Length Scaling

An estimate of the size of the main burner and/or afterburner is required during the engine's preliminary design. The cross-sectional area can be easily determined based on one-dimensional gas dynamics, but the length requires scaling laws. The length of a main burner is primarily based on the distance required for combustion to come to near completion. Equation (10-26) gives the reaction rate in terms of pressure and temperature and will be used to develop the length-scaling equation for main burners.

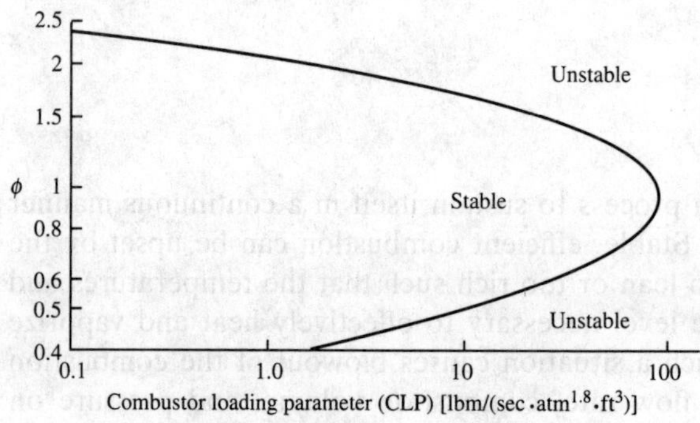

FIGURE 10-70
Combustion stability characteristics (Refs. 62 and 72).

The residence time t_{res} in the main burner is given by

$$t_{res} = \frac{L}{V_{av}} \approx \frac{L}{V_{ref}} = \frac{\rho_{t3} A_{ref} L}{\dot{m}_3} \tag{10-30}$$

where V_{ref} is based on the air mass flow rate entering the combustor; A_{ref} is the cross-sectional area normal to the airflow (case to case) of the combustion chamber; L is the length of the main burner; the density of the air entering the combustion chamber is approximated by ρ_{t3}; and the other variables have their normal meanings. Assuming an isentropic compression process, the total density at state 3 is proportional to the total pressure at this state as given by

$$\rho_{t3} \propto P_{t3}^{1/\gamma_d}$$

Substituting the above relationship into Eq. (10-30) and solving for the main burner length yield

$$L \propto \frac{\dot{m}_3}{A_{ref}} \frac{t_{res}}{P_{t3}^{1/\gamma_c}}$$

Noting that

$$\frac{\dot{m}_3}{A_{ref}} = \frac{\dot{m}_3 A_4}{A_4 A_{ref}} = \frac{P_{t4}}{\sqrt{T_{t4}}} \frac{A_4}{A_{ref}} \frac{\text{MFP}(M_4 = 1, \gamma_4)}{1+f}$$

(where station 4 is in the high-pressure turbine inlet stators and this flow is choked) and P_{t4} is approximately equal to P_{t3}, we see that the above equation for L becomes

$$L \propto \frac{P_{t3}^{(\gamma_c - 1)}}{\sqrt{T_{t4}}} \frac{A_4}{A_{ref}} t_{res} \tag{10-31}$$

The reaction time t_{rea} is inversely proportional to the reaction rate. Thus from Eq. (10-26)

$$t_{rea} \propto P_{t3}^{-n} \tag{10-32}$$

For the main burner, the residence time t_{res} is proportional to the reaction time t_{rea}. Thus t_{res} in Eq. (10-31) can be replaced by Eq. (10-32), giving

$$L \propto \frac{A_4}{A_{ref}\sqrt{T_{t4}}} P_{t3}^{-[n-(\gamma_c - 1)/\gamma_c]} \tag{10-33}$$

For the main burners of similar design, the area ratio A_4/A_{ref} is constant and

$$\boxed{L \propto P_{t3}^{-r}/\sqrt{T_{t4}}} \tag{10-34}$$

where $r = 1.51$ for $n = 1.8$ and $r = 0.714$ for $n = 1$. Thus the length of main burners having similar design varies with the pressure and temperature and is

TABLE 10-5
Contemporary main burners

Engine Type	TF39 Annular	TF41 Cannular	J79 Cannular	JT9D Annular	F100 Annular	T63 Can
Mass flow						
Air (lb/sec)	178	135	162	242	135	3.3
Fuel (lb/hr)	12,850	9965	8350	16,100	10,580	235
Size						
Length (in)	20.7	16.6	19.0	17.3	18.5	9.5
Diameter (in)	33.3	5.3/24.1*	6.5/32.0*	38.0	25.0	5.4
P_{t3} (psia)	382	314	198	316	366	92
$T_{t4\,\max}$ (°R)	2915	2620	2160	2865	3025	1840

* Can diameter/annulus diameter.

unaffected by the size of the engine. This explains both the shortening of the main burner length with increases in compressor pressure ratio and the reduction in the ratio of the main burner length to engine diameter as engine size increases.

Equation (10-34) can be used to obtain a preliminary estimate of the main burner length based on a known-reference similar design. The size and sea-level operating conditions for contemporary main burners are provided in Table 10-5, and this information may be used as a reference in estimating main burner length.

As an example of estimating main burner length, consider a design similar to the JT9D but with $P_{t3} = 350$ psia at sea level and $T_{t4} = 2900$°R. Use of Eq. (10-34) with $n = 1$ ($r = 0.714$) gives a length that is 92.4 percent of the JT9D, or 16.0 in.

Combustion System Total Pressure Ratio

An estimate of the total pressure loss resulting from increasing the gas total temperature and frictional loss of a combustion system can be obtained by modeling the combustion system as a constant-area duct (Fig. 10-71) with simple heating (increase in total temperature) and internal drag proportional to the incoming dynamic pressure (drag $= 0.5\rho_i V_i^2 C_D A$). The gas is assumed to

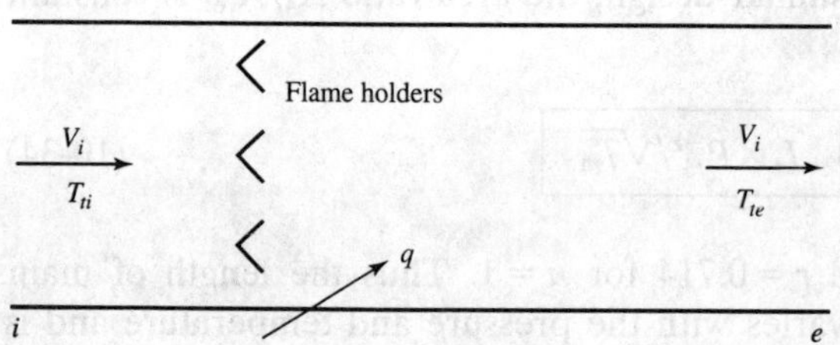

FIGURE 10-71
Model of combustion system.

be calorically perfect at inlet i and exit e, and the mass addition of fuel is neglected in comparison to the air mass flow.

The basic conservation equations are

Mass $\rho_i V_i = \rho_e V_e$

Momentum $P_i + \dfrac{\rho_i V_i^2}{g_c} = P_e + \dfrac{\rho_e V_e^2}{g_c} + C_D\left(\dfrac{1}{2}\rho_i V_i^2\right)$

Energy $q = c_{pe} T_{te} - c_{pi} T_{ti}$

Solution of these equations (Ref. 4) gives

$$\frac{T_{te}}{T_{ti}} = \frac{q + c_{pi} T_{ti}}{c_{pe} T_{ti}}$$

$$\Phi = \frac{\gamma_i}{\gamma_e} \frac{M_i^2\{1 + [(\gamma_i - 1)/2]M_i^2\}}{[1 + \gamma_i M_i^2(1 - C_D)]^2} \frac{T_{te}}{T_{ti}} \tag{10-35}$$

$$M_e^2 = \frac{2\Phi}{1 + 2\gamma_e\Phi + \sqrt{1 - 2(\gamma_e + 1)\Phi}} \tag{10-36}$$

$$\frac{P_e}{P_i} = \frac{1 + \gamma_i M_i^2(1 - C_D/2)}{1 + \gamma_e M_e^2} \tag{10-37}$$

$$\frac{P_{te}}{P_{ti}} = \frac{P_e\{1 + [(\gamma_e - 1)/2]M_3^2\}^{\gamma_e/(\gamma_e - 1)}}{P_i\{1 + [(\gamma_i - 1)/2]M_i^2\}^{\gamma_i/(\gamma_i - 1)}} < 1 \tag{10-38}$$

Example 10-6. Consider the following data for a turbojet's main burner:

$T_{t4} = 3000°\text{R}$ $\quad \gamma_t = 1.3$ $\quad C_D = 1.5$ $\quad \tau_r = 1.162\ (M_0 = 0.9)$

$T_0 = 540°\text{R}$ $\quad \gamma_c = 1.4$ $\quad \tau_c = 1.92$ $\quad (\pi_c = 7.55 \text{ and } \eta_c = 0.85)$

For convenience, the equation for the total temperature ratio can be written in terms of engine temperature ratios as

$$\frac{T_{te}}{T_{ti}} = \frac{T_{t4}}{T_{t3}} = \frac{T_{t4}/T_0}{(T_{t2}/T_0)(T_{t3}/T_{t2})} = \frac{T_{t4}/T_0}{\tau_r \tau_c} = \frac{3000/540}{1.162 \times 1.92} = 2.49$$

Thus $T_{t4}/T_{t3} = 2.49$ and calculations using Eqs. (10-35) through (10-38) yield the results of Fig. 10-72. These results show that the inlet Mach number to the combustion zone of a main burner must be kept below 0.10 to achieve a reasonable total pressure ratio ($P_{te}/P_{ti} > 0.975$) resulting from increasing gas total temperature and frictional loss.

Diffusers

Many instances arise in the design of engine components when the flow velocity must be decreased; a diffuser is used to perform this important function. One such instance is the flow entering the main burner where the flow leaving the compressor must be slowed from a high subsonic Mach

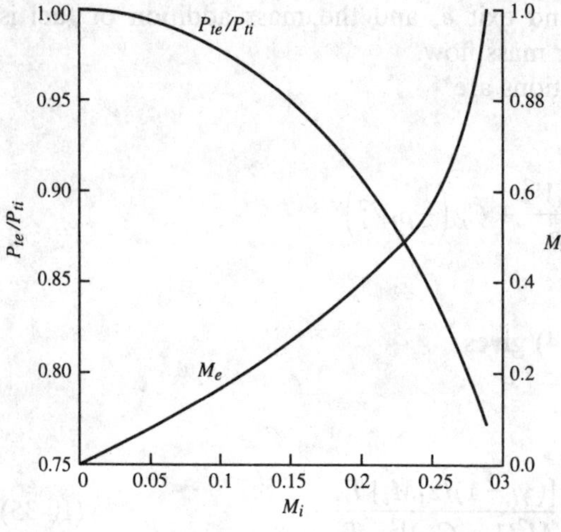

FIGURE 10-72
Main burner total pressure loss.

number to a very low Mach number (Ref. 71). Another instance is the flow entering the afterburner where the flow leaving the turbine must be slowed from a high subsonic Mach number to a Mach number of about 0.2.

Since the flow is being slowed in the diffuser, an adverse pressure exists and flow separation from the walls is possible. Figure 10-12 presents the standard diffuser flow regimes. Main burner and afterburner diffusers are designed to fall below the flow separation boundary line.

The pressure recovery coefficient C_P and the pressure recovery effectiveness η are two performance parameters used to describe diffuser performance. The *pressure recovery coefficient* C_P is a measure of the diffuser's ability to recover dynamic pressure and is defined by

$$C_P \equiv \frac{P_e - P_i}{\rho V_i^2/2} \tag{10-39}$$

where P_i and P_e are the static pressure at the inlet and exit, respectively, and $\rho V_i^2/2$ is the inlet dynamic pressure. For the ideal diffuser (incompressible flow with constant total pressure), C_P can be expressed in terms of the area ratio

$$C_{P\text{ideal}} \equiv 1 - \left(\frac{A_i}{A_e}\right)^2 \tag{10-40}$$

where A_i and A_e are the inlet and exit areas, respectively. The *pressure recovery effectiveness* η of the diffuser is the ratio of the actual pressure recovery coefficient to the ideal pressure recovery coefficient:

$$\boxed{\eta \equiv \frac{C_P}{C_{P\text{ideal}}} \equiv \frac{P_e - P_i}{(\rho V_i^2/2)[1-(A_i/A_e)^2]}} \tag{10-41}$$

The total pressure ratio of the diffuser can, therefore, be expressed in terms of the pressure recovery effectiveness η and other convenient flow

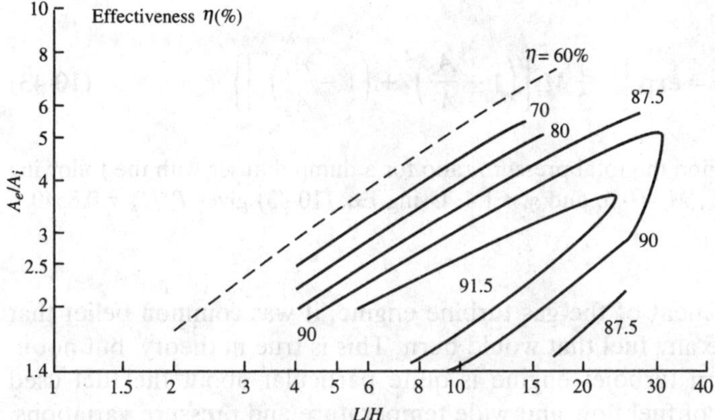

FIGURE 10-73
Diffuser performance (Ref. 62).

properties as

$$\frac{P_{te}}{P_{ti}} = 1 - \frac{\rho V_i^2}{2P_{ti}}(1-\eta)\left[1-\left(\frac{A_i}{A_e}\right)^2\right] \tag{10-42a}$$

or

$$\frac{P_{te}}{P_{ti}} = 1 - \frac{(\gamma/2)M_i^2(1-\eta)[1-(A_i/A_e)^2]}{\{1+[(\gamma-1)/2]M_i^2\}^{\gamma/(\gamma-1)}} \tag{10-42b}$$

The diffuser performance characteristics for preliminary design are presented in Fig. 10-73. This figure relates diffuser area ratio A_e/A_i and length/height ratio L/H to the pressure recovery effectiveness η.

Example 10-7. Find the total pressure ratio of a straight wall diffuser with the following data: $A_e/A_i = 4.0$, $M_i = 0.5$, $\gamma = 1.4$, and $L/H = 15$. Using Fig. 10-73 and Eq. (10-42*b*) gives $\eta = 0.9$ and $P_{te}/P_{ti} = 0.9858$.

The pressure loss for a dump diffuser, as depicted in Fig. 10-74, was investigated by Barclay (Ref. 73) and can be estimated in the range

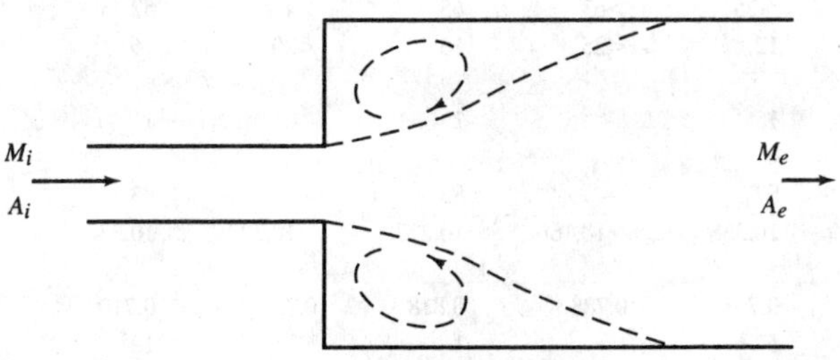

FIGURE 10-74
Model dump diffuser.

$0.2 < A_i/A_e < 1$ by

$$\frac{P_{te}}{P_{ti}} = \exp\left\{-\frac{\gamma}{2}M_i^2\left[\left(1-\frac{A_i}{A_e}\right)^2 + \left(1-\frac{A_i}{A_e}\right)^6\right]\right\} \tag{10-43}$$

Example 10-8. Find the total pressure ratio for a dump diffuser with the following data: $A_e/A_i = 5.0$, $M_i = 0.5$, and $\gamma = 1.4$. Using Eq. (10-43) gives $P_{te}/P_{ti} = 0.8540$.

Fuels

In the early development of the gas turbine engine, it was common belief that this engine could use any fuel that would burn. This is true in theory, but not in practice. The modern turbojet engine is quite particular about the fuel used due to the high rate of fuel flow and wide temperature and pressure variations.

Jet fuel is refined from crude oil petroleum. A typical pound of jet fuel might be composed of 16 percent hydrogen atoms, 84 percent carbon atoms, and a small amount of impurities, such as sulfur, nitrogen, water, and sediment. Various grades of jet fuel have evolved during the development of jet engines in an effort to ensure both satisfactory performance and adequate supply. JP-4 is the most commonly used fuel for U.S. Air Force jet engines. The U.S. Navy uses JP-5, a denser, less volatile fuel than JP-4, which allows it to be safely stored in the skin tanks of ships. The most common commercial aircraft fuels are Jet A and Jet A-1. They are alike except Jet A has a freezing point below −40°F and Jet A-1 has a freezing point below −58°F. Table 10-6

TABLE 10-6
Jet engine fuels

	JP-4		JP-5		JP-8 (Jet A-1)	
Property	**Specification requirement**	**Typical value**	**Specification requirement**	**Typical value**	**Specification requirement**	**Typical value**
Vapor pressure (atm) @ 38°C (100°F)	0.13–0.2	10.18	—	10.003	—	10.007
Initial boiling point (°C)	—	60	—	182	—	169
Endpoint (°C)	—	246	288	260	288	265
Flash point (°C)	—	−25	>63	65	>49	52
Aromatic content (% vol.)	<25	12	<25	16	<20	16
Olefinic content (% vol.)	<5	1	—	1	—	1
Saturates content (% vol.)	—	87	—	83	—	83
Net heat of combustion (cal/g)	>10,222	10,388	>10,166	10,277	>10,222	10,333
Specific gravity	0.751	0.758	0.788	0.818	0.755	0.710
U.S. yearly consumption (10^9 gal)		5		1		12

Source: Refs. 12, 15.

gives specifications for some of the most commonly used jet fuels. The heating value h_{PR} used for most jet fuels is 18,400 Btu/lbm or 42,800 kJ/kg (=10,222 cal/g).

Many aircraft engines are built to operate on any of these fuels. To do so, they must have a special switch on the fuel control to allow it to compensate for differences in specific gravity which is used in fuel metering calculations.

There are many other fuels of interest for use in aircraft gas turbine engines. High-Mach-number aircraft like the SR-71 uses JP-7, a fuel with a very high boiling point. Hydrogen is often considered a fuel because of its very high heating value (h_{PR} of approximately 49,900 Btu/lb or 116,000 kJ/kg) and its capacity to absorb the thermal loads of high-Mach-number flight.

10-7 MAIN BURNERS

Types

Turbine engine burners have undergone continuing development over the past 50 years, resulting in the evolution of a variety of basic combustor configurations. Contemporary main burner systems may be broadly classified into one of the three types, schematically illustrated in Fig. 10-75: can, cannular, or annular.

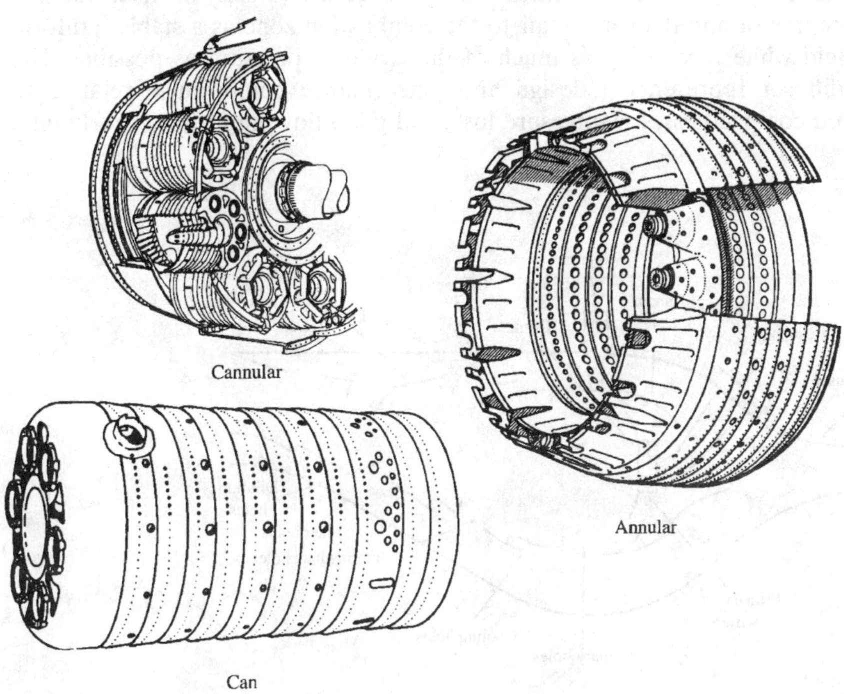

FIGURE 10-75
Main burner type (Ref. 62). (*Courtesy of Pratt & Whitney.*)

A can system consists of one or more cylindrical burners, each contained in a burner case. Because of its modular design, the can system was used during the early development of the turbojet engine. The cannular system consists of a series of cylindrical burners arranged within a common annulus—hence, the name *cannular*. This burner type was the most common in the aircraft turbine engine population, but has been replaced with the annular type in most modern engines. Most modern main burner systems employ the annular design wherein a single burner having an annular cross section supplies gas to the turbine. The improved combustion zone uniformity, design simplicity, reduced linear surface area, and shorter system length provided by the common combustion annulus have made the annular burner the leading contender for all future propulsion systems.

Main Burner Components

The turbine engine main burner system consists of three principal elements: the inlet diffuser, the dome and snout or cowl, and the liner. In addition, important subcomponents are necessary: the fuel injector, igniter, burner case, and primary swirler, if used. The term *combustion zone* is used to designate that portion of the main burner within the dome and liner. These elements are illustrated in Fig. 10-76.

The purpose of the inlet diffuser is to reduce the velocity of the air exiting the compressor and deliver the air to the combustion zone as a stable, uniform flow field while recovering as much of the dynamic pressure as possible. The inlet diffuser represents a design and performance compromise relative to required compactness, low-pressure loss, and good flow uniformity. Early inlet

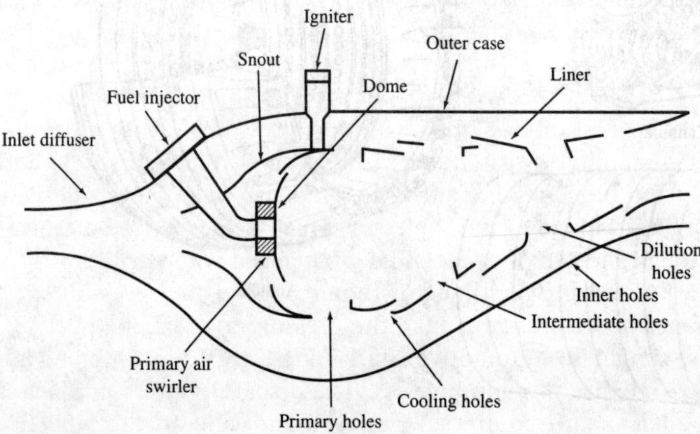

FIGURE 10-76
Main burner components (Ref. 62).

diffuser designs were of the smooth curved wall or contoured wall type. Because of the wide variations in the characteristics of the flow field exiting the compressor, however, the curved wall diffuser cannot always provide uniform, nonseparated flow at all operating conditions. This can become a critical problem in the short-length diffusers required of many current systems. Consequently, a trend toward dump, or combination curved wall and dump, diffuser designs is occurring. Although this design results in somewhat higher total pressure losses, it provides a known and constant point of flow separation at the dump plane, which prevents stalled operation at all diffuser entrance conditions.

The snout divides the incoming air into two streams: primary air and the other airflows (intermediate, dilution, and cooling air). The snout streamlines the combustor dome and permits a larger diffuser divergence angle and reduced overall diffuser length.

The combustor dome is designed to produce an area of high turbulence and flow shear in the vicinity of the fuel nozzle to finely atomize the fuel spray and promote rapid fuel/air mixing. There are two basic types of combustor domes: bluff body and swirl-stabilized. The bluff-body domes were used in early main burners, but swirl-stabilized domes are used in most modern main burners.

The combustion process is contained by the liner. The liner also allows introduction of intermediate and dilution airflow and the liner's cooling airflow. The liner must be designed to support forces resulting from pressure drop and must have high thermal resistance capable of continuous and cyclic high-temperature operation. This requires use of high-strength, high-temperature, oxidation-resistant materials (e.g., Hastalloy X) and cooling air.

Fuel injectors can be classified into four basic types according to the injection method utilized: pressure-atomizing, air blast, vaporizing, and premix/prevaporizing. The first two methods are the most common and are described below, but the reader is directed to other references (e.g., Ref. 32) for a description of the other two methods. In past main burner designs, the most common method of fuel injection was pressure atomizing, which can provide a large flow range with excellent fuel atomization when fuel system pressures are high (500 psi above main burner pressure). The pressure-atomized system is susceptible to fuel leaks (due to high fuel pressures) and plugging of orifices from fuel contaminants. Most modern main burner designs incorporate the air-blast atomizing fuel injector which achieves fuel atomization and mixing through the use of primary air momentum with strong swirling motion. The air-blast atomizing fuel injector requires lower fuel pressures (50 to 200 psi above main burner pressure) than the pressure-atomizing type.

Spark igniters, similar to automotive spark plugs, are used to ignite the cold, flowing fuel/air mixture in main burners. These spark igniters produce 4 to 12 J of ignition energy and require several thousand volts at the plug tip. Main burner starting redundancy is typically provided by use of at least two spark lighters.

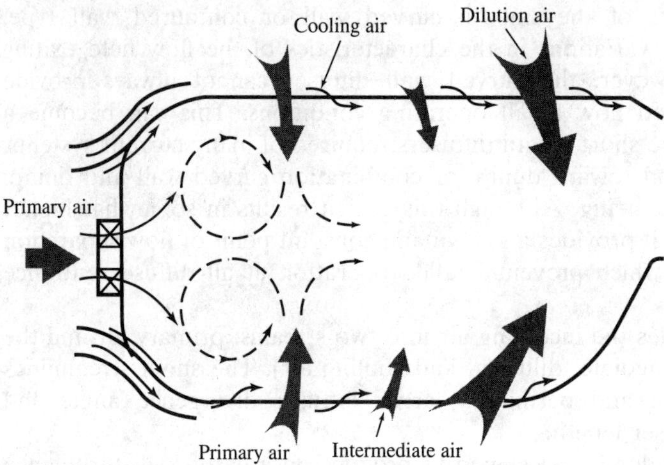

FIGURE 10-77
Main burner airflow distribution (Ref. 62).

Airflow Distribution and Cooling Air

This section identifies and briefly describes the airflow distribution terminology in, around, and through the main burner, resulting in the four basic airflow regions illustrated in Fig. 10-77. Effective control of this air distribution is vital to the attainment of complete combustion, stable operation, correct burner exit temperature profile, and acceptable liner temperatures for long life.

Primary air is the combustion air introduced through the dome or head plate of the burner and through the first row of liner airholes. This air mixes with the incoming fuel, producing the locally near-stoichiometric mixture necessary for optimum stabilization and operation. To complete the reaction process and consume the high levels of primary zone CO, H^-, and unburned fuel, intermediate air is introduced through a second row of liner holes. The reduced temperature and excess oxygen cause CO and H^- concentrations to decrease. In contemporary systems, the dilution air is introduced at the rear of the burner to reduce the high temperature of the combustion gases. The dilution air is used to carefully tailor exit temperature radial and circumferential profiles to ensure acceptable turbine durability and performance. This requires minimum temperatures at the turbine root (where stresses are highest) and at the turbine tip (to protect seal materials). However, modern and future main burner exit temperature requirements are necessitating increased combustion air in the primary and intermediate zones; thus, dilution zone airflow is necessarily reduced or eliminated to permit these increases.

Cooling air must be used to protect the burner liner and dome from the high radiative and convective heat loads produced within the burner. This air is normally introduced through the liner such that a protective blanket or film of

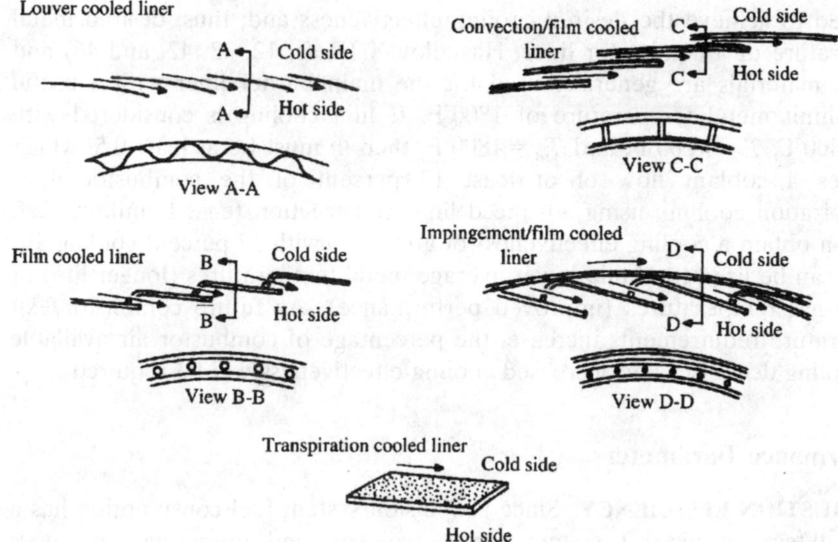

FIGURE 10-78
Liner cooling techniques (Ref. 62).

air is formed between the combustion gases and the liner hardware (see Fig. 10-78).

The effectiveness of the cooling technique is quantified by the *cooling effectiveness* Φ, defined by

$$\Phi \equiv \frac{T_g - T_m}{T_g - T_c} \tag{10-44}$$

where T_g, T_m, and T_c are the mainstream gas, average metal, and cooling air temperatures, respectively.

Figure 10-79 provides design data for the amount of coolant flow

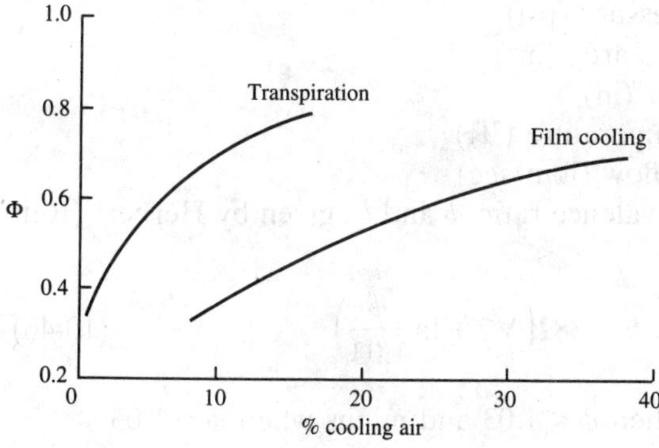

FIGURE 10-79
Liner cooling effectiveness (Refs. 74, 75, and 76).

required to achieve the desired cooling effectiveness and, thus, desired metal temperature of a combustor liner. Hastalloy X (Refs. 12, 32, 42, and 46) and similar materials are generally used for the main burner liner with a useful upper-limit metal temperature of 1800°F. If film cooling is considered with $T_g = 2400°F$, $T_c = 1200°F$, and $T_m = 1800°F$, then Φ must be at least 0.5, which requires a coolant flow of at least 17 percent of the combustor flow. Transpiration cooling, using advanced liner construction (e.g., Lamilloy, Ref. 74), can obtain a cooling effectiveness of about 0.8 with 17 percent cooling air, which can be used to obtain lower average metal temperatures (longer life) or higher gas temperatures (improved performance). As future combustor exit temperature requirements increase, the percentage of combustor air available for cooling decreases and increased cooling effectiveness will be required.

Performance Parameters

COMBUSTION EFFICIENCY. Since propulsion system fuel consumption has a direct effect on aircraft system range, payload, and operating cost, it is imperative that design-point combustion efficiency be as close to 100 percent as possible. By design, combustion efficiency at the high power/fuel consumption conditions of takeoff and cruise is near 100 percent (usually greater than 99.5 percent). However, off-design efficiency, particularly at idle, can be in the low 90's. With the advent of chemical emission controls and limitations, this parameter has particular significance during low-power operation because inefficiency and pollution are inextricably linked. For example, combustion efficiency at off-design conditions, such as idle, must now exceed 98.5 percent to satisfy regulations on exhaust carbon monoxide and unburned hydrocarbons.

One empirical model of combustion efficiency η_b is based on the reaction rate parameter θ and is plotted in Fig. 10-80. The *reaction rate parameter* θ is defined (Refs. 32 and 62) as

$$\theta = \frac{P_{t3}^{1.75} A_{\text{ref}} H \exp(T_{t3}/b)}{\dot{m}_3} \times 10^{-5} \tag{10-45}$$

where P_{t3} = main burner inlet pressure (psi)
A_{ref} = main burner reference area (in^2)
H = height of main burner (in)
T_{t3} = main burner inlet temperature (°R)
$\dot{m}_3$ = main burner inlet airflow (lbm/sec)
b = function of local equivalence ratio ϕ and b, given by Herbert (Ref. 63) as

$$b = 382\left(\sqrt{2} \pm \ln\frac{\phi}{1.03}\right) \tag{10-46}$$

where plus is used when $\phi < 1.03$ and minus when $\phi > 1.03$.

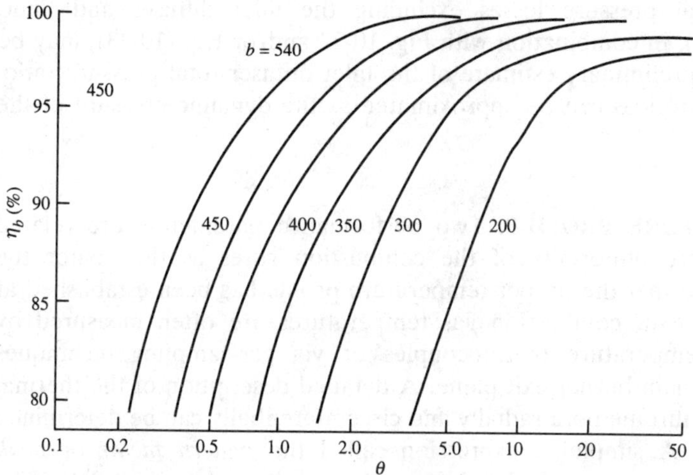

FIGURE 10-80
Combustion efficiency vs reaction rate parameter (Ref. 62).

Example 10-9. Determine the combustion efficiency of a main burner with the following data:

$$P_{t3} = 300 \text{ psia} \qquad T_{t3} = 1500°\text{R} \qquad \dot{m}_3 = 60 \text{ lbm/sec} \qquad \phi = 0.8$$
$$A_{ref} = 1.0 \text{ ft}^2 \qquad H = 2 \text{ in}$$

Equation (10-46) gives $b = 444$, Eq. (10-45) gives $\theta = 30$, and Fig. 10-80 gives $\eta_b > 0.995$. For another example, consider the following main burner data:

$$P_{t3} = 2.4 \text{ MPa} \qquad T_{t3} = 800 \text{ K} \qquad \dot{m}_3 = 200 \text{ kg/sec} \qquad \phi = 0.9$$
$$A_{ref} = 0.2 \text{ m}^2 \qquad H = 6 \text{ cm}$$

Equation (10-46) gives $b = 488$, Eq. (10-45) gives $\theta = 43.2$, and Fig. 10-80 gives $\eta_b > 0.995$.

OVERALL TOTAL PRESSURE LOSS. The overall total pressure loss of the main burner is the sum of inlet diffuser loss, burner dome and liner loss, and momentum loss resulting from main burner flow acceleration attendant with increased gas total temperature. It is normally expressed as a percentage of the compressor discharge pressure. Total pressure losses of 2 to 5 percent are typically encountered in current systems. Main burner system pressure loss is recognized as necessary to achieve certain design objectives (pattern factor, effective cooling, etc.), and it can also provide a stabilizing effect of main burner aerodynamics. However, total pressure loss also impacts engine thrust and thrust specific fuel consumption. Consequently, design goals for main burner total pressure loss represent a compromise among the above factors.

Equation (10-38) may be used to obtain a preliminary estimate of the main burner total pressure losses excluding the inlet diffuser and liner. Equation (10-42*b*), in combination with Fig. 10-73 and/or Eq. (10-43), may be used to obtain a preliminary estimate of the inlet diffuser total pressure ratio. Liner total pressure loss can be approximated as the dynamic pressure of the passage air.

EXIT TEMPERATURE PROFILE. Two performance parameters are related to the temperature uniformity of the combustion gases as they enter the turbine. To ensure that the proper temperature profile has been established at the main burner exit, combustion gas temperatures are often measured by means of high-temperature thermocouples or via gas-sampling techniques employed at the main burner exit plane. A detailed description of the thermal field entering the turbine both radially and circumferentially can be determined from these data. A simplified expression called the *pattern factor* or *peak temperature factor* may be calculated from these exit temperature data. The *pattern factor* PF is defined as

$$\mathrm{PF} \equiv \frac{T_{t\,\mathrm{max}} - T_{t\,\mathrm{av}}}{T_{t\,\mathrm{av}} - T_{t\,\mathrm{in}}} \tag{10-47}$$

where $T_{t\,\mathrm{max}}$ = maximum measured exit temperature (local)
$T_{t\,\mathrm{av}}$ = average of all temperatures at exit plane
$T_{t\,\mathrm{in}}$ = average of all temperatures at inlet plane

Contemporary main burners exhibit pattern factors ranging from 0.25 to 0.45. Pattern factor goals are based primarily on the design requirements of the turbine first-stage stationary airfoils. Thus a pattern factor of 0.0 is not required. Durability considerations require the new high-temperature-rise main burners to have exit temperature profiles corresponding to pattern factors in the range of 0.15 to 0.25.

The *profile factor* P_f characterizes the main burner average exit temperature profile and is defined by

$$P_f \equiv \frac{T_{t\,\mathrm{max\,av}} - T_{t\,\mathrm{in}}}{T_{t\,\mathrm{av}} - T_{t\,\mathrm{in}}} \tag{10-48}$$

where $T_{t\,\mathrm{max\,av}}$ is the maximum circumferential average temperature. Main burners exhibit profile factors ranging from 1.04 to 1.08, with 1.06 being the common design goal. Profile factor goals are based primarily on the design requirements of the turbine first-stage rotating airfoils, which are exposed to average gas temperatures leaving the first-stage stationary airfoils.

Pattern factor and profile factor are important main burner design parameters. They describe the possible thermal impact on the turbine and are critical factors in matching the main burner and turbine components. Failure

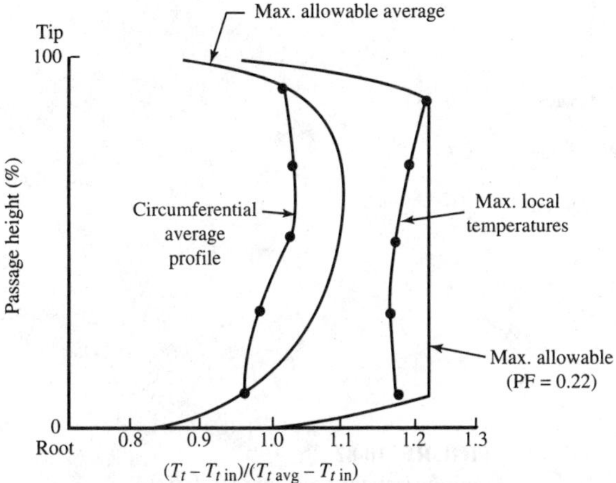

FIGURE 10-81
Radial temperature profile at main burner exit (Ref. 62).

to achieve the required pattern factor and/or profile factor will normally result in shorter turbine life and may require redesign of the main burner and/or turbine.

Although the pattern factor and profile factor define the peak and average turbine airfoil gas temperatures, the shape of the burner exit temperature radial profile is the critical factor controlling turbine airfoil life. Figure 10-81 illustrates typical radial profile characteristics and their attendant relationship with the pattern factor. By proper control of dilution air, the burner exit temperature field is tailored to give the design pattern factor and radial profile consistent with turbine requirements.

IGNITION. Reliable ignition in the main burner system is required during ground-level start-up and for relighting during altitude windmilling. The broad range of main burner inlet temperature and pressure conditions encompassed by a typical ignition/relight envelope is illustrated in Fig. 10-82. It is well known that ignition performance is improved by increases in main burner pressure, temperature, fuel/air ratio, and ignition source energy. In general, ignition is impaired by increases in reference velocity, poor fuel atomization, and low fuel volatility.

Recent development work (Ref. 77) in the application of the double-annular combustor design (Fig. 10-83) to main burners having a high temperature rise ($T_{t4} - T_{t3} = 1000$ to 1400°C or 1800 to 2500°F) has shown very good low-throttle operation when the outer annulus is designed to operate as the pilot stage with lower airflows than the inner annulus. Only the pilot stage of this double-annular combustor is fueled at starting, altitude relight, and idle conditions. This pilot-stage design attains the desired low air velocities and rich fuel/air ratios at low-temperature-rise conditions of starting, altitude relight, and idle.

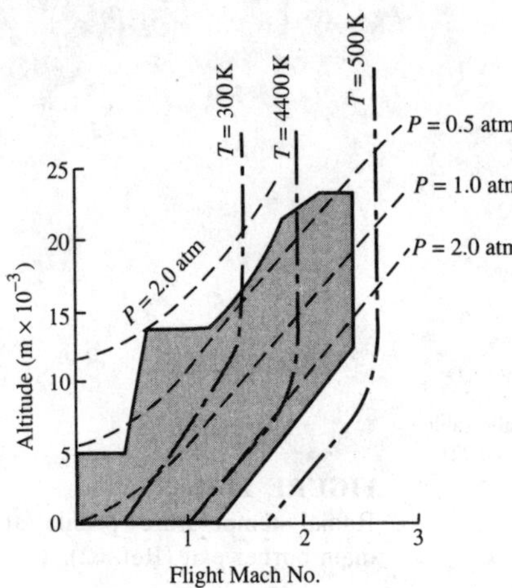

FIGURE 10-82
Ignition/relight envelope (Ref. 62).

Main Burner Design Parameters

The design of main burner systems for aircraft gas turbine engines is a complex and difficult problem that is usually solved by reaching a reasonable compromise between the conflicting requirements. Design involves a broad range

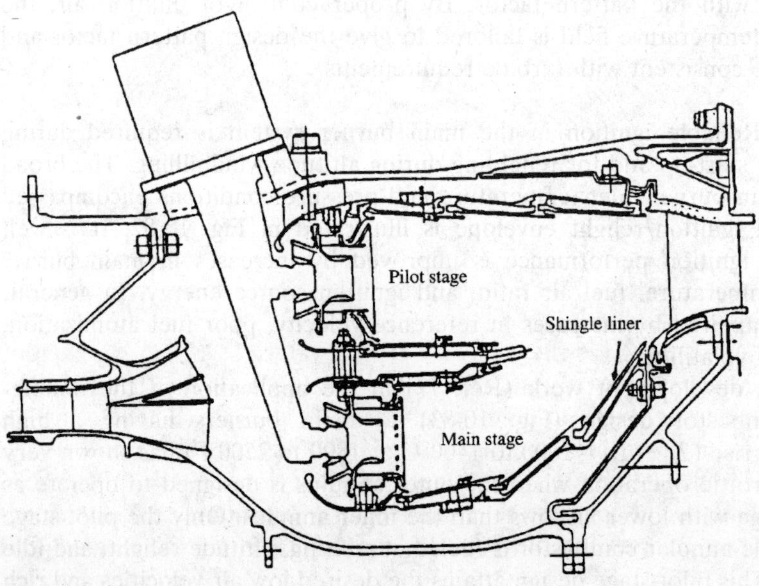

FIGURE 10-83
Double-annular main burner (Ref. 77).

of technical disciplines including combustion chemistry, fluid dynamics, heat transfer, stress analysis, and metallurgy. Although there are many design parameters for a main burner, most experts would include the following in their list of most critical design parameters:

- Equivalence ratio ϕ
- Combustor loading parameter (CLP)
- Space heat release rate SR
- Reference velocity V_{ref}
- Main burner dome height H_d
- Main burner length/dome height ratio L_{mb}/H_d
- Main burner dome velocity
- Passage velocity V_{pass}
- Number and spacing of fuel injectors
- Pattern factor correlation parameters PF
- Profile factor correlation parameter P_f

The *space heat release rate* or *space rate* (SR) is

$$\text{SR} \equiv \frac{f\dot{m}_3 h_{PR}(3600)}{P_{t3}(\text{volume})} \tag{10-49}$$

and generally is between 5×10^6 and 10×10^6 Btu/(hr · ft^3 · atm) [0.5 and 1.0 W/(m^3 · Pa)]. The reference velocity is defined as

$$V_{\text{ref}} \equiv \frac{\dot{m}_3}{\rho_{t3} A_{\text{ref}}} \tag{10-50}$$

where A_{ref} is the cross-sectional area across the whole main burner at the primary combustion zone.

Taylor (Ref. 78) gives the following typical values of design parameters: The reference velocity is typically from 60 to 100 ft/sec (18 to 30 m/sec); the ratio of main burner length to dome height L_{bm}/H_d is 2.73 to 3.5; velocities in the main burner dome are generally around 30 ft/sec (9 m/sec) and in the passages 120 to 200 ft/sec (36 to 60 m/sec); fuel injectors are typically spaced about one dome height apart in the circumferential direction; and fuel injectors require at least 25 percent of their design fuel rate to obtain good fuel atomization.

The use of selective fuel injection is a method of modulating primary zone equivalence ratio at very low engine throttle settings. Recent tests were

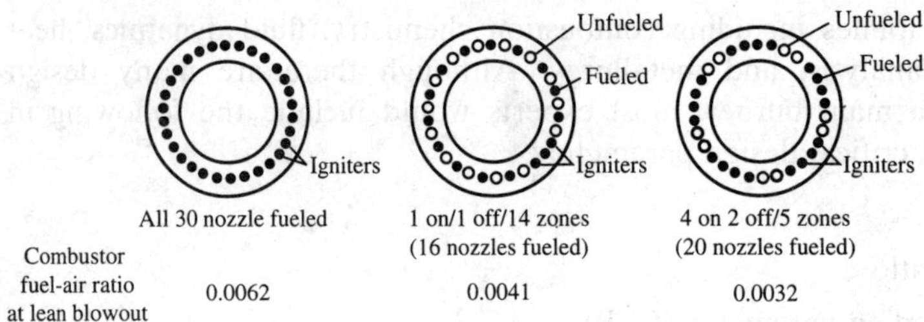

FIGURE 10-84
Lean blowout characteristics of CF6-50 main burner with selective fuel injection patterns (Ref. 77).

reported in Ref. 77 on the minimum fuel/air ratio f for the CF6-50 main burner with selective fuel injection patterns, and these results are presented in Fig. 10-84. In addition to low engine throttle operation, use of a selective fuel injection pattern can improve engine starting and relight.

10-8 AFTERBURNERS

Afterburning or reheating is one method of augmenting (increasing) the basic thrust of the turbojet engine or the turbofan engine, when required, without having to use a larger engine with its concurrent penalities of increased frontal area and weight. The afterburner increases thrust by adding thermal energy to the entering gas stream. For a turbojet engine, this gas stream corresponds to the exhaust gases of the turbine. However, for the augmented turbofan engine, this gas stream may be a mixture of the bypass air and the turbine exhaust gases. At the afterburner inlet, there is still much uncombined oxygen in the gas stream. The higher inlet temperatures and near-stoichiometric fuel/air ratio of the afterburners enable them to operate with a simpler configuration (see Figs. 10-85*a* and 10-85*b*) than the main burner can. The resultant increase in temperature raises the exhaust velocity of the exiting gases and, therefore, boosts engine thrust. Most afterburners will produce an approximate 50 percent thrust increase, but with a corresponding threefold increase in fuel flow.

Since the specific and actual fuel consumptions are considerably higher during the time the engine is in the afterburning or *hot* (also called *wet*) operation, as compared to the nonafterburning or *cold* (also called *dry*) mode of operation, afterburning is used typically for the time-limited operation of takeoff, climb, and maximum bursts of speed.

For a turbofan engine, augmentation can be used in both fan and core streams. Afterburning in a separate fan stream is normally referred to as *duct burning,* and this alone or in combination with afterburning in the core stream may be advantageous for certain flight conditions.

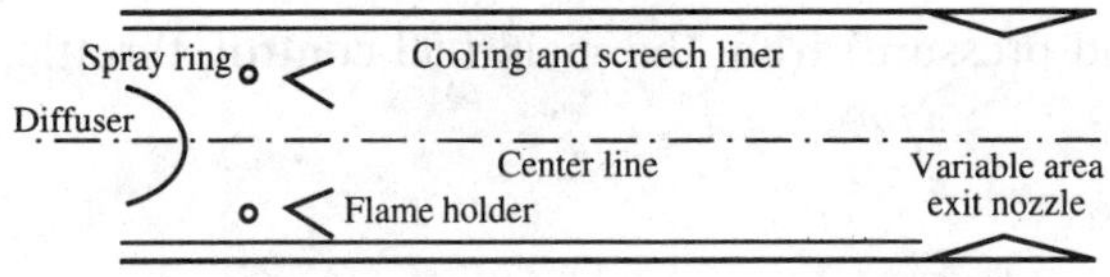

FIGURE 10-85*a*
Typical afterburner components.

The major components of an afterburner are shown in Figs. 10-85*a* and 10-85*b*. Gas leaving the turbine is deswirled and diffused, fuel is added by fuel spray bars (tubes) or rings, the combustion process is initiated by igniter or pilot burner in the wake of a number of flame-stabilizing devices (flame holders), and the thermal energy of combustion is mixed along flame surfaces spreading downstream from the stabilizing devices. Also, a liner is used in afterburners as both a cooling liner and a screech or antihowl liner (*screech* and *howl* are acoustic combustion instabilities). This liner can also serve as a passage for the cooling air required by the exhaust nozzle. All engines incorporating an afterburner must also be equipped with a variable-area throat exhaust nozzle in order to provide for proper operation under afterburning and nonafterburning conditions. In addition to these components, an afterburner will require the following components:

- Afterburner fuel pump
- Afterburner fuel control
- Pressurizing valve, if multistage operation is required

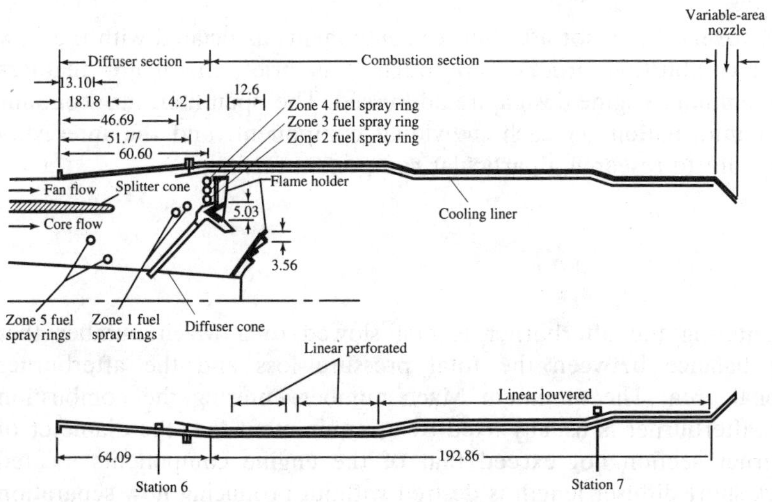

FIGURE 10-85*b*
Afterburner for TF30-P-3 augmented turbofan engine (all dimensions are in centimeters) (*From Ref. 79.*)

- Connections (mechanical and pressure) from the main fuel control, throttle, and engine

Specific design requirements for an afterburner are as follows:

- Large temperature rise. The afterburner does not have to provide for the physical and temperature limits of the turbine. The temperature rise is limited mainly by the amount of oxygen that is available for combustion and the liner and nozzle cooling air requirements.
- Low dry loss. The engine suffers a very slight penalty in thrust during cold operation due principally to the drag caused by the flame holders, fuel spray bars, and walls of the afterburner.
- Wide temperature modulation. This is necessary to obtain *degrees* (also called *zones* or *stages*) of afterburning for better control of thrust
- High combustion efficiency
- Short length; light weight
- Altitude light-off capability
- No acoustic combustion instabilities
- Long life, low cost, easy repair

Afterburner Components

This section covers the major afterburner components associated with the flow passage and combustion process. Although it is brief, the major features affecting preliminary engine design are addressed. The open literature contains a wealth of information on each individual component, and the interested reader may want to research a particular component further.

Diffuser

The flow entering the afterburner is first slowed to a Mach number that provides a balance between the total pressure loss and the afterburner cross-sectional area. The minimum Mach number entering the combustion zone of the afterburner is usually fixed by a requirement that the diameter of the afterburner section not exceed that of the engine components located upstream. A short diffuser length is desired without producing flow separation to reduce engine weight and length. In augmented turbofan engines, the diffuser may be combined with a mixer so that a mixed stream enters the combustion section.

Fuel Injection, Atomization, and Vaporization

This subject area is best summarized by Zukoski (Refs. 62 and 63) and is quoted here:

> The goal of the fuel injection stream is to produce a specified distribution of fuel vapor in the gas stream entering the afterburner. In most engines, fuel is introduced in a staged manner so that heat addition rate can be increased gradually from zero to the desired value. Because ignition, flame stabilization, and flame spreading are easiest to achieve when the fuel/air ratio is close to the stoichiometric value, staging is usually produced by adding fuel to successive annular stream tubes so that the mixture ratio in each tube is nearly stoichiometric. Each stream tube has its own set of fuel injectors and control system which can be activated independently. For example, see the two sets of injectors used in the F100 engine shown as items 6 and 7 in Fig. [10-86].
>
> The most remarkable fact concerning the fuel system for afterburners is their simplicity. In many engine systems, fuel is supplied to a circular tube which lies with its axis perpendicular to the gas stream. Fuel is injected into the gas through small diameter holes located in the sides of the tubes such that the liquid jet enters the gas stream in a direction perpendicular to the undisturbed flow direction. The liquid jet penetrates some distance into the gas stream before its momentum is dissipated. During this penetration process, the air stream tears the jet apart and produces droplets with diameters of micron size. Heat transfers from the hot gas stream then vaporizes the droplets.
>
> Given the wide range of values of mass flow of fuel required, it is remarkable that reasonably thorough mixing of the fuel with the air can be achieved with this simple injection system. In some recent engines, efforts are being made to use simple variable area injector ports which may possibly give better preparation of the fuel/air mixture.

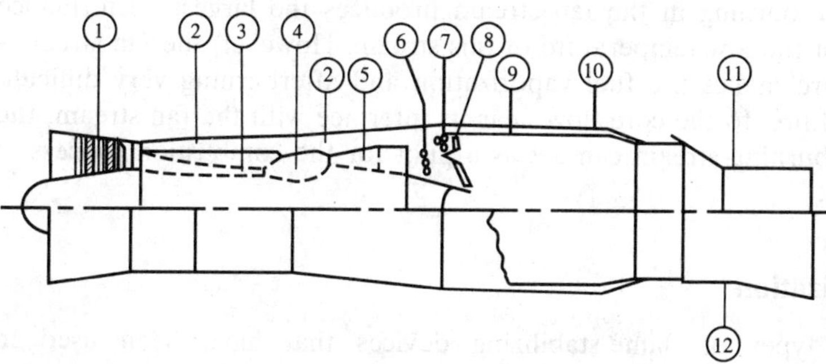

FIGURE 10-86
Pratt & Whitney F100-PW-100 augmented turbofan engine (Ref. 62): (1) three-stage fan; (2) bypass duct; (3) core engine compressor; (4) main burner; (5) turbine; (6) fuel injectors for core engine gas stream; (7) fuel injectors for bypass airstream; (8) flame stabilizer for afterburner; (9) perforated afterburner liner; (10) afterburner case; (11) nozzle closed to minimum area; and (12) nozzle opened to maximum area.

The whole area of fuel penetration, atomization, and vaporization is not well understood from first principles and one of the time-consuming parts of an afterburner development program is to determine the optimum distribution of locations for injector tubes, injector parts, and port diameters.

Ignition

Ignition of the fuel/air mixture in the afterburner is usually accomplished by using a spark or arc igniter or a pilot burner. Once initiated in the primary stream tube, combustion continues in the wake of a flame stabilizer (a bluff body) and the process will spread to the rest of the flame stabilizers if the wakes of the stabilizers overlap.

The spark or arc igniter uses a high-energy electric arc to initiate combustion of the primary stream tube. The igniter is usually placed in the wake of a sheltered flame stabilizer having its own fuel supply. A stable flame results, and combustion is initiated behind other flame stabilizers by the mechanism mentioned above.

As described earlier, ignition in an afterburner system will be easiest to achieve in gas having a local equivalence ratio near unity, in a region of the stabilization system where the residence times are longest, and where the pressures and temperatures are highest. When such a region is not available, a pilot burner can be used to locally create this region.

The pilot burner consists of a pilot zone where a small portion of the inlet air (usually 10 percent or less) is burned to stoichiometric temperatures in an enclosed protected region. The hot gases generated by the pilot burner are used as an ignition and stabilizing source for the main fuel injection system.

Afterburning for turbofan engines such as the Pratt & Whitney F100 is accomplished by adding fuel first to the core flow near the interface between the core and fan streams, then to the fan stream, and finally to the rest of the core flow. Afterburning in the fan stream produces the largest performance gain because of the low temperature of this stream. However, the fan stream's low temperature makes the fuel vaporization and afterburning very difficult. By adding fuel first to the core flow near its interface with the fan stream, the resulting afterburning stream can act as a pilot for the combustion process in the fan stream.

Flame Stabilization

Two general types of flame-stabilizing devices that have been used in afterburners are shown in Fig. 10-87: bluff-body vee-gutter flame holders and piloted burners where a small piloting heat source is used to ignite the main fuel flow. The bluff-body vee-gutter flame holders have the advantage of low flow blockage and low total pressure loss. They are simple and lightweight and have a good development history.

The wake of a flame holder, shown in Fig. 10-88, is divided into two

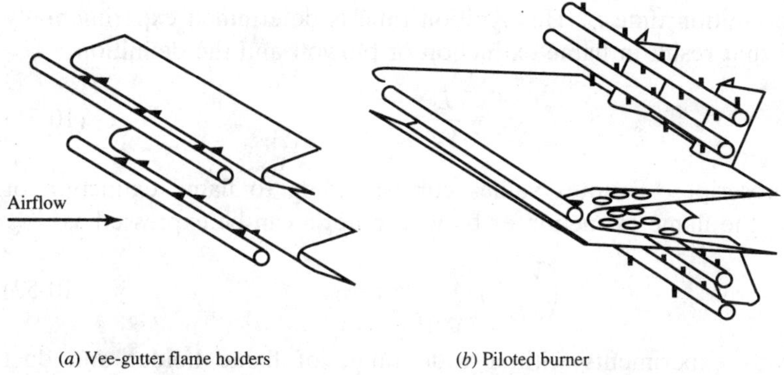

FIGURE 10-87
Common afterburner flame holders (Ref. 80).

regions: a recirculation zone and mixing zones. The recirculation zone is characterized by a strong circulating flow, very low reaction rates, and a temperature that is nearly equal to the adiabatic flame temperature corresponding to the fuel/air mixture ratio of the approaching stream. The mixing zones are characterized as turbulent regions of very strong shear, steep temperature gradients, and vigorous chemical reaction.

A stable flame is established in the mixing zones by a balance of the continuing entrainment of cool unburned gas and the heat and species transfer from the hot burned gases. The residence time of the gas in the mixing zone establishes whether a stable flame is established or the flame is blown off. Flame stabilization is characterized by the values of the velocity at the edge of the mixing zones V_2, the length of the recirculation zone L, and the

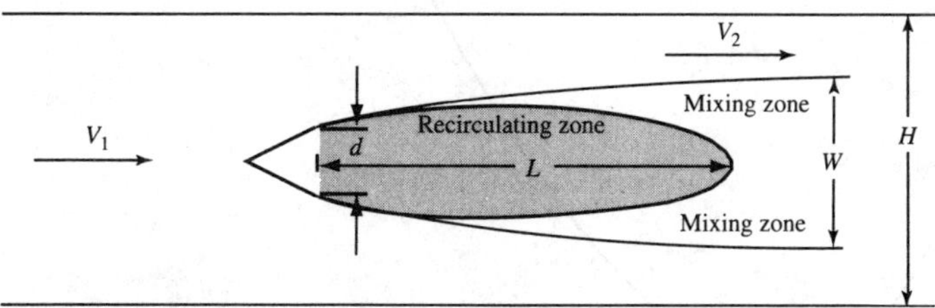

FIGURE 10-88
Typical flame holder used in analysis of stabilization:
V_1 = velocity of approaching stream
V_2 = velocity of flow at edge of mixing zone
d = width of flame holder
L = length of recirculation zone
W = width of wake
H = height of the duct

characteristic ignition time t_c. This ignition time is determined experimentally at conditions that result in flame extinction or blowoff and the definition

$$t_c \equiv \frac{L}{V_{2c}} \tag{10-51}$$

where the subscript c denotes values corresponding to flame extinction or blowoff. Thus the flame extinction or blowoff criteria can be expressed as

$$\left(\frac{V_{2c}t_c}{L}\right)_{\text{blowoff}} = 1 \tag{10-52}$$

Numerous experiments with a wide range of flame holder and duct configurations have shown that the ignition time is essentially independent of the geometry and velocity as long as the flow is turbulent. The ignition time depends on a number of chemical parameters such as fuel type, fuel/air ratio, gas temperatures and pressures, and degree of vitiation.

The variation of the characteristic ignition time t_c with equivalence ratio ϕ is shown in Fig. 10-89 for a hydrocarbon fuel with a molecular weight of about 100. Note that t_c increases very rapidly for both high and low values of ϕ. In general, t_c decreases rapidly as the static temperature of the approach stream increases and varies inversely with static pressure for hydrocarbon fuels like JP-4. This variation with temperature and pressure can be approximated by

$$t_c \propto \frac{1}{PT^{2.5}} \tag{10-53}$$

Flame holder stability calculations using Eq. (10-52) required values of t_c, V_2,

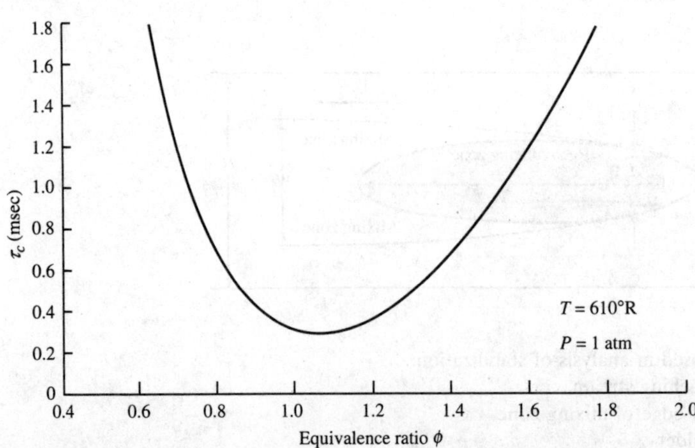

FIGURE 10-89
Variation of characteristic ignition time with equivalence ratio (Ref. 62).

and L. The characteristic ignition time can be obtained from Fig. 10-89. However, V_2 and L are not simply related to the size of the flame holder d and the velocity of the approach stream V_1. Rewriting Eq. (10-52) in a more convenient form gives

$$\left(\frac{V_{1c}t_c}{H}\right)_{\text{blowoff}} = \frac{V_1}{V_2}\frac{L}{W}\frac{W}{H} \tag{10-54}$$

To apply this criterion, values of V_1/V_2, L/W, and W/H are needed as functions of flame holder geometry, fluid dynamic parameters, and the blockage ratio B, where

$$B \equiv \frac{d}{H} \tag{10-55}$$

Calculations by Cornell (Ref. 81) yielded relationships between the blockage ratio B and values of V_2/V_1 and W/d for wedge half-angles of 15° to 90° (a flat plate) and are presented in Table 10-7. Tests of a variety of bluff-bodies show that the length/width ratio of the recirculation zone L/W depends only on the geometry of the bluff-body, and the majority of the data lie in the range of 3.6 to 4.0. For the preliminary design, this ratio can be approximated (Ref. 62) by

$$\frac{L}{W} \approx 4 \tag{10-56}$$

Now, all the parameters of Eq. (10-54) can be determined for a given flame holder shape and blockage ratio.

TABLE 10-7
Dependence of wake width W and edge velocity V_2 on blockage ratio B and wedge half-angle α

	$\alpha = 15$		$\alpha = 90°$	
$B = dH$	W/d	V_2/V_1	W/d	V_2/V_1
0.05	1.6	1.15	4.0	1.25
0.10	1.9	1.23	3.0	1.43
0.20	1.5	1.42	2.2	1.75
0.30	1.3	1.62	1.7	2.09
0.40	1.2	1.90	1.6	2.50
0.50	1.2	2.30	1.4	3.16

Source: Ref. 12

Example 10-10. *Flame holder stability calculation.*
Given: $T = 100°R$, $P = 0.2$ atm, $M_1 = 0.25$, $\gamma = 1.3$, $\phi = 0.8$, $H = 1$ ft, $B = 0.2$, and a 15° half-angle flame holder. Table 10-7 gives $W/d = 1.5$ and $V_2/V_1 = 1.42$. Then $W/H = (W/d)(d/H) = (1.5)(0.2) = 0.3$. Thus, with $L/W = 4$, Eq. (10-54) gives

$$\left(\frac{V_{1c}t_c}{H}\right)_{\text{blowoff}} = \left(\frac{1}{1.42}\right)(4)(0.3) = 0.845$$

Figure 10-89 gives $t_c = 0.7$ msec at 610°R, $\phi = 0.8$, and 1 atm. Thus, at 1000°R, $\phi = 0.8$, and 0.2 atm, Eq. (10-53) gives $t_c = 1.3$ msec. Using this value of t_c and $H = 1$ ft, we get $V_{1c} = H/t_c = 770$ ft/sec. For $T = 1000°R$, $M_1 = 0.25$, and $\gamma = 1.3$, then $V_1 = 373$ ft/sec and $V_2 = 530$ ft/sec. Since $V_1 < V_{1c}$, flame stabilization will occur at the given conditions.

Multiple-Flame-Holder Arrays

The material presented above on flame holder stabilization was restricted to a single flame holder located on the centerline of a constant-area duct. When multiple flame holders are positioned in a single plane perpendicular to the approaching flow and spaced so that each lies on the centerline of equivalent ducts of equal height, then the above analysis can be used directly to estimate the stability characteristics. When flame holders are spaced irregularly, the analysis presented above does not directly apply. However, this analysis is useful in a qualitative manner.

Flame Spread

To achieve maximum combustion efficiency, the afterburner length needs to be longer than the burning length. The complex flame holder shape and interactions do not permit determination of afterburner length from the burning length measurements of basic flame holder experiments. However, most modern afterburners use 17° total angle for estimating spread.

Afterburner Liner

The afterburner liner is used as a cooling liner and to improve combustion stability. As a cooling liner, it isolates the very high temperatures from the outer casing (similar to the liner of the main burner). A film of cooler air is distributed along the length of the cooling liner, which reduces the metal temperature of this liner and subjects the outer casing of the afterburner to the afterburner pressure and temperature of the cooling flow.

The liner is also used as a screech or antihowl liner to prevent extreme high frequency and amplitude pressure fluctuations resulting from combustion instability or the unsteady state of thermal energy. This function is accomplished by use of multiple holes along the initial length of the liner. Selective frequencies can be dampened by the selection of the proper size hole.

Total Pressure Loss

The total pressure loss of the afterburner is mainly composed of that due to the diffuser, to the drag of the flame holders, and to the combustion process. The total pressure ratio of the diffuser can be estimated by the methods presented earlier. The total pressure ratio due to the friction of the flame holders and combustion process can be estimated, by using Eqs. (10-35) through (10-38), provided that C_D of the flame holders, based on the duct area and upstream velocity V_1, is known. The drag coefficient of a bluff-body is about 1.0 (Ref. 82) based on the frontal area and the edge velocity (V_2 of Fig. 10-87). This drag coefficient can be expressed in terms of a C_D based on the duct area and upstream velocity V_1 by

$$C_D \approx B\left(\frac{V_2}{V_1}\right)^2 \tag{10-57}$$

where B is the blockage ratio [see Eq. (10-55)].

Afterburner Design Parameters

The design of the afterburner system for aircraft gas turbine engines is a difficult problem and involves compromise similar to the complexity of the main burner system. The major design parameters for the afterburner include

- Equivalence ratio ϕ
- Reference Mach number M_{ref}
- Flame holder blockage B
- Flame holder width d
- Flame holder edge Mach number
- Afterburner burning length
- Spray bar spacing
- Space heat release rate (SR)

The reference Mach number is at the entrance to the afterburner and ranges from 0.20 to 0.25. Flame holder blockage is normally 25 to 30 percent with an edge Mach number of about 0.30. The burning length is 35 to 50-in (0.9 to 1.3 m), and the spray bar spacing is about 3 in (8 cm) at the outer flame holder position (Ref. 78). A space heat release rate [Eq. (10-49)] near 8×10^6 Btu/(hr · ft^3 · atm) [0.8 W/(m^3 · Pa)] is desired (Ref. 80).

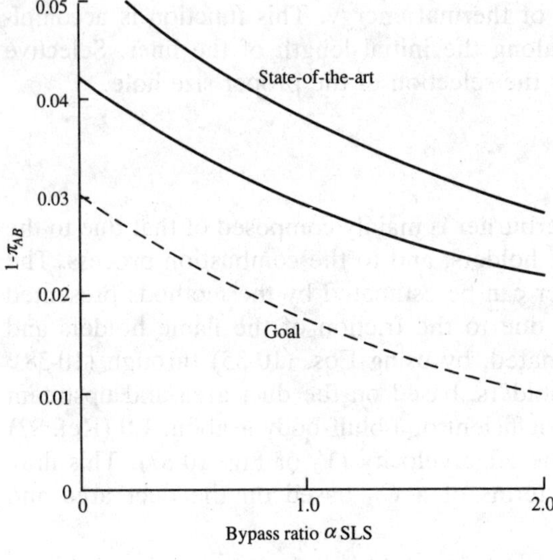

FIGURE 10-90
Afterburner total pressure loss (Ref. 83).

The performance and size of the afterburner of an augmented turbofan engine depend on the bypass ratio (Ref. 83), as shown in Figs. 10-90, 10-91, and 10-92. Both the current state-of-the-art and the goal of future afterburner development are shown.

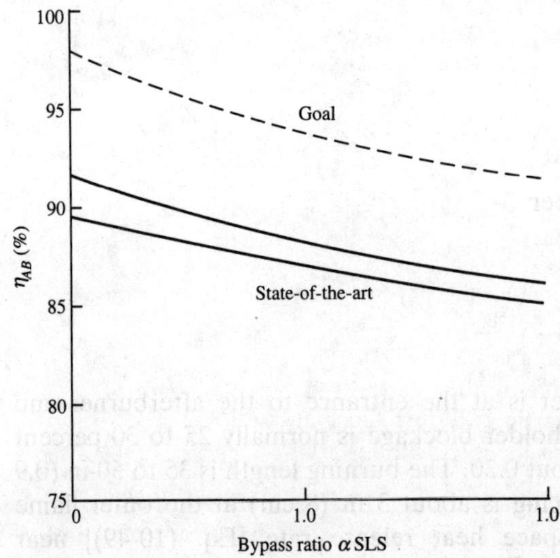

FIGURE 10-91
Afterburner combustion efficiency (Ref. 83).

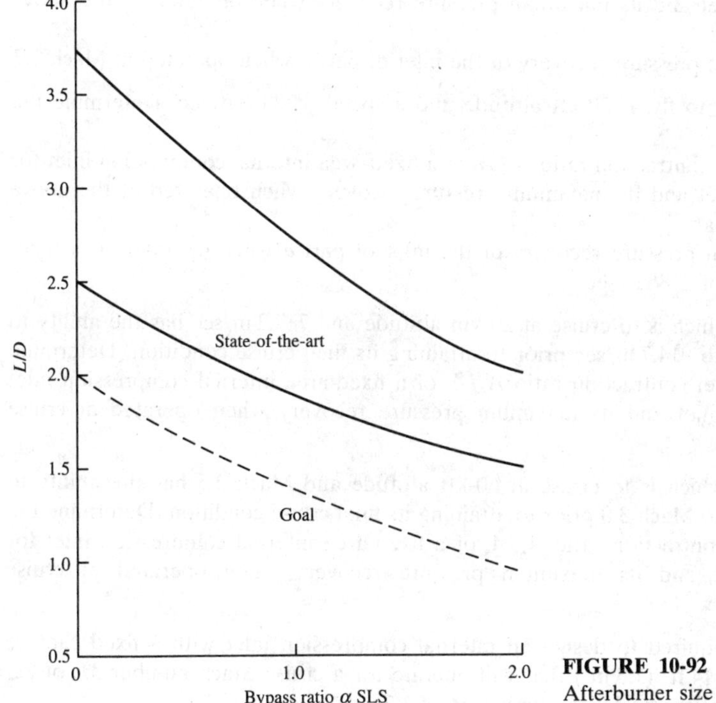

FIGURE 10-92
Afterburner size (Ref. 83).

PROBLEMS

10-1. Develop Eq. (10-1) in SI units.

10-2. Determine the throat diameter of an inlet for the turbojet engine of Example 8-4 for subsonic operation ($M_0 < 0.8$).

10-3. Determine the throat diameter of an inlet for the turbofan engine of Example 8-9 for subsonic operation ($M_0 < 0.8$).

10-4. Determine the throat diameter of an inlet for the turboprop engine of Example 8-11 for subsonic operation ($M_0 < 0.8$).

10-5. A fixed-area internal compression inlet has a capture/throat area ratio A_c/A_t of 1.2. Determine the following:
a. The Mach number at which the inlet will start
b. The Mach number at the throat after starting
c. The π_d of the inlet after starting with the shock at the throat
d. The Mach number at which the inlet will unstart

10-6. A ramjet is to fly at 9-km altitude and Mach 2.3. Determine the following:
a. The inlet contraction ratio A_c/A_t of a fixed-area internal compression inlet for

this ramjet and its maximum pressure recovery when operated at the above conditions

b. Maximum pressure recovery of the inlet of part *a* when operated at Mach 2.7

10-7. A ramjet is to fly at 30-kft altitude and a speed of 2388 ft/sec. Determine the following:

a. The inlet contraction ratio A_c/A_t of a fixed-area internal compression inlet for this ramjet and its maximum pressure recovery when operated at the above conditions

b. Maximum pressure recovery of the inlet of part *a* when operated at a flight velocity of 2786 ft/sec

10-8. A ramjet which is to cruise at 20-km altitude and 767.2 m/sec has the ability to overspeed to 914.7 m/sec prior to attaining its final cruise condition. Determine the best inlet contraction ratio A_c/A_t of a fixed-area internal compression inlet for this ramjet and its maximum pressure recovery when operated at cruise conditions.

10-9. A ramjet which is to cruise at 60-kft altitude and Mach 2.5 has the ability to overspeed to Mach 3.0 prior to attaining its final cruise condition. Determine the best inlet contraction ratio A_c/A_t of a fixed-area internal compression inlet for this ramjet and its maximum pressure recovery when operated at cruise conditions.

10-10. You are required to design an internal compression inlet with a fixed capture area A_c of 14 ft^2 (1.3 m^2) that will operate for a cruise Mach number M_0 of 2.5 with an inlet throat Mach number M_t of 1.2.

a. Determine A_t and A_c/A_t for cruise.

b. If the throat area is held constant, can this inlet be started for M_0 of 4.0 or less?

c. If it is desired to start the inlet at $M_0 = 2.0$, find the required values of A_c/A_t and A_t.

10-11. An aircraft with a turbojet engine uses a fixed contraction ratio, internal compression inlet designed for $M_0 = 3.0$. The aircraft is flying at $M_0 = 2.0$ with the inlet started, and the shock is optimally positioned when the inlet suddenly unstarts, popping the shock.

a. Find the maximum pressure recovery for the started and unstarted conditions

b. Find the ratio of the unstarted inlet mass flow rate to the started inlet mass flow rate

10-12. For supersonic flight conditions, a conservative estimate of the inlet drag is the momentum loss of the bleed and bypass air. Variable A_1 is the capture area of an inlet, and A_0 is the free-stream area for the engine mass flow rate (see Fig. 10-36).

a. Show that the inlet drag coefficient can be written as

$$\phi_{\text{inlet}} = \frac{\rho_0 V_0 (A_1 - A_0)(V_0 - V_e)}{F g_c}$$

where V_e is the axial velocity with which the bypass and bleed flows leave the inlet *b.* For adiabatic flow with $M_e = 1$, show that the above equation becomes

$$\phi_{\text{inlet}} = \frac{(A_1/A_0 - 1)\{M_0 - \sqrt{2/(\gamma+1) + [(\gamma-1)/(\gamma+1)]M_0^2}\}}{Fg_c/(\dot{m}_0 a_0)}$$

c. Using the A_{0i}/A_1 results of Fig. 10-46, calculate and plot ϕ_{inlet} for $Fg_c/(\dot{m}_0 a_0) = 3.0$.

10-13. Determine the total pressure recovery η_r and area ratio A_{0i}/A_s of a pitot inlet with a normal shock over the range of Mach numbers from 1 to 2. Compare this inlet's performance to that of Examples 10-3 and 10-4.

10-14. Determine the total pressure recovery η_r and area ratio A_{0i}/A_s of an external compression inlet with a single 10° ramp over the range of Mach numbers from 1 to 2. Compare this inlet's performance to that of Examples 10-3 and 10-4.

10-15. Determine the total pressure recovery η_r and area ratio A_{0i}/A_s of an external compression inlet with a single 8° ramp over the range of Mach numbers from 1 to 2. Compare this inlet's performance to that of Examples 10-3 and 10-4.

10-16. Calculate the dimensions and values of C_{fg}, F_g, and C_V for an axisymmetric exhaust nozzle with a mass flow rate of 150 lbm/sec and the following data: $P_{t8} = 25$ psia, $T_{t8} = 3600$°R, $A_9/A_8 = 1.8$, $\gamma = 1.3$, $R = 53.4$ ft · lbf/(lbm · °R), $P_{t9}/P_{t8} = 0.98$, $C_d = 0.98$, and $P_0 = 3$ psia.

10-17. Calculate the dimensions and values of C_{fg}, F_g, and C_V for an axisymmetric exhaust nozzle with a mass flow rate of 75 kg/sec and the following data: $P_{t8} = 350$ kPa, $T_{t8} = 1600$ K, $A_9/A_8 = 1.8$, $\gamma = 1.33$, $R = 0.287$ kJ/(kg · K), $P_{t9}/P_{t8} = 0.98$, $C_D = 0.98$, and $P_0 = 40$ kPa.

10-18. Determine the fuel/air ratios of the main burners listed in Table 10-5.

10-19. Estimate the length of a main burner similar to the JT9D but with $P_{t3} = 2.5$ MPa at sea level and $T_{t4} = 1500$ K.

10-20. Estimate the length of a main burner similar to the F100 but with $P_{t3} = 300$ psia at sea level and $T_{t4} = 3200$°R.

10-21. Estimate the total pressure ratio P_{te}/P_{ti} and exit Mach number M_e of a main burner with $T_{te}/T_{ti} = 3$, $M_i = 0.05$, $C_D = 2$, $\gamma_i = 1.38$, and $\gamma_e = 1.3$.

10-22. Estimate the total pressure ratio P_{te}/P_{ti} and exit Mach number M_e of an afterburner with $T_{te}/T_{ti} = 2$, $M_i = 0.3$, $C_D = 1.5$, $\gamma_i = 1.33$, and $\gamma_e = 1.3$.

10-23. Estimate the total pressure ratio P_{te}/P_{ti} and exit Mach number M_e of a straight wall diffuser with an area ratio $A_e/A_i = 4$ and $L/H = 10$ for a gas with $\gamma = 1.38$ at $M_i = 0.1$.

10-24. Estimate the total pressure ratio P_{te}/P_{ti} and exit Mach number M_e of a dump diffuser with an area ratio $A_e/A_i = 4$ for a gas with $\gamma = 1.38$ at $M_i = 0.1$, 0.2, and 0.3.

10-25. Find the shortest L/H of a straight wall diffuser that gives a total pressure ratio P_{te}/P_{ti} of 0.999 with an area ratio $A_e/A_i = 4$ for a gas with $\gamma = 1.38$ at $M_i = 0.1$.

10-26. Determine the combustion efficiency of a main burner with the following data:

$$P_{t3} = 200 \text{ psia} \qquad T_{t3} = 1000\text{°R} \qquad \dot{m}_3 = 100 \text{ lbm/sec} \qquad \phi = 0.6$$

$$A_{\text{ref}} = 1.5 \text{ ft}^2 \qquad H = 2 \text{ in}$$

10-27. Determine the combustion efficiency of a main burner with the following data:

$$P_{t3} = 1.8 \text{ MPa} \qquad T_{t3} = 600 \text{ K} \qquad \dot{m}_3 = 100 \text{ kg/sec} \qquad \phi = 1.3$$
$$A_{\text{ref}} = 0.1 \text{ m}^2 \qquad H = 6 \text{ cm}$$

10-28. Estimate the volume of the F100 main burner (see data in Table 10-5) if its space rate SR is in the range 5×10^6 to 10×10^6 Btu/(hr · ft^3 · atm).

10-29. Determine the characteristic ignition time t_c, the blowoff velocity V_{1c}, and the flame holder stability for the following data: $T = 800°\text{R}$, $M_1 = 0.5$, $\gamma = 1.33$, $\phi = 1.4$, $H = 10$ in, $B = 0.3$, a 15° half-angle flame holder, and pressures P of 0.4 and 0.1 atm.

APPENDIXES

APPENDIX A

U.S. STANDARD ATMOSPHERE, 1976

English units				
Geometric altitude (kft)	Pressure ratio $\delta = P/P_{ref}$	Temperature ratio $\theta = T/T_{ref}$	Density ratio $\sigma = \rho/\rho_{ref}$	Speed of sound ratio a/a_{ref}
0	1.0000	1.0000	1.0000	1.0000
2	0.9298	0.9863	0.9428	0.9931
4	0.8637	0.9725	0.8881	0.9862
6	0.8014	0.9588	0.8359	0.9792
8	0.7429	0.9450	0.7861	0.9721
10	0.6878	0.9313	0.7386	0.9650
12	0.6362	0.9175	0.6933	0.9579
14	0.5877	0.9038	0.6502	0.9507
16	0.5422	0.8901	0.6092	0.9434
18	0.4997	0.8763	0.5702	0.9361
20	0.4599	0.8626	0.5332	0.9288
22	0.4227	0.8489	0.4980	0.9214
24	0.3880	0.8352	0.4646	0.9139
26	0.3557	0.8215	0.4330	0.9063
28	0.3256	0.8077	0.4031	0.8987
30	0.2975	0.7940	0.3747	0.8911
32	0.2715	0.7803	0.3480	0.8834
34	0.2474	0.7666	0.3227	0.8756
36	0.2250	0.7529	0.2988	0.8677
38	0.2044	0.7519	0.2719	0.8671
40	0.1858	0.7519	0.2471	0.8671
42	0.1688	0.7519	0.2245	0.8671
44	0.1534	0.7519	0.2040	0.8671
46	0.1394	0.7519	0.1854	0.8671
48	0.1267	0.7519	0.1685	0.8671
50	0.1151	0.7519	0.1531	0.8671
52	0.1046	0.7519	0.1391	0.8671
54	0.09507	0.7519	0.1265	0.8671
56	0.08640	0.7519	0.1149	0.8671
58	0.07852	0.7519	0.1044	0.8671
60	0.07137	0.7519	0.09492	0.8671
62	0.06486	0.7519	0.08627	0.8671
64	0.05895	0.7519	0.07841	0.8671
66	0.05358	0.7520	0.07125	0.8672
68	0.04871	0.7542	0.06459	0.8684
70	0.04429	0.7563	0.05857	0.8696
72	0.04028	0.7584	0.05312	0.8708
74	0.03665	0.7605	0.04820	0.8720
76	0.03336	0.7626	0.04374	0.8732
78	0.03036	0.7647	0.03971	0.8744
80	0.02765	0.7668	0.03606	0.8756
82	0.02518	0.7689	0.03276	0.8768
84	0.02294	0.7710	0.02976	0.8780
86	0.02091	0.7731	0.02705	0.8792
88	0.01906	0.7752	0.02459	0.8804
90	0.01738	0.7772	0.02236	0.8816

English units				
Geometric altitude (kft)	**Pressure ratio** $\delta = P/P_{ref}$	**Temperature ratio** $\theta = T/T_{ref}$	**Density ratio** $\sigma = \rho/\rho_{ref}$	**Speed of sound ratio** a/a_{ref}
92	0.01585	0.7793	0.02034	0.8828
94	0.01446	0.7814	0.01851	0.8840
96	0.01320	0.7835	0.01684	0.8852
98	0.01204	0.7856	0.01533	0.8864
100	0.01100	0.7877	0.01396	0.8875
105	0.008769	0.7930	0.01106	0.8905
110	0.007011	0.8066	0.008692	0.8981
115	0.005629	0.8213	0.006854	0.9063
120	0.004537	0.8359	0.005428	0.9143
125	0.003671	0.8506	0.004316	0.9223
130	0.002982	0.8652	0.003446	0.9302
135	0.002430	0.8798	0.002762	0.9380
140	0.001988	0.8944	0.002222	0.9458
145	0.001631	0.9091	0.001794	0.9534
150	0.001343	0.9237	0.001454	0.9611
155	0.001109	0.9383	0.001182	0.9686
160	0.0009176	0.9393	0.0009770	0.9692
165	0.0007593	0.9393	0.0008084	0.9692
170	0.0006283	0.9354	0.0006717	0.9672
175	0.0005188	0.9208	0.0005634	0.9596
180	0.0004271	0.9063	0.0004713	0.9520
185	0.0003505	0.8917	0.0003931	0.9443
190	0.0002868	0.8772	0.0003270	0.9366
195	0.0002339	0.8626	0.0002711	0.9288
200	0.0001901	0.8481	0.0002242	0.9209
205	0.0001540	0.8336	0.0001847	0.9130
210	0.0001243	0.8191	0.0001517	0.9050
215	0.00009992	0.8046	0.0001242	0.8970
220	0.00008003	0.7901	0.0001013	0.8888
225	0.00006384	0.7756	0.00008232	0.8800
230	0.00005072	0.7611	0.00006664	0.8724
235	0.00004012	0.7466	0.00005374	0.8640
240	0.00003161	0.7358	0.00004296	0.8578
245	0.00002482	0.7254	0.00003422	0.8517
250	0.00001943	0.7151	0.00002717	0.8456

Reference values: $P_{ref} = 2116\ \text{lbf/ft}^2$ $\rho_{ref} = 0.07647\ \text{lbm/ft}^3$

$T_{ref} = 518.7°\text{R}$ $a_{ref} = 1116\ \text{ft/sec}$

Metric units				
Geometric altitude (km)	**Pressure ratio** $\delta = P/P_{\text{ref}}$	**Temperature ratio** $\theta = T/T_{\text{ref}}$	**Density ratio** $\sigma = \rho/\rho_{\text{ref}}$	**Speed of sound ratio** a/a_{ref}
0	1.0000	1.0000	1.0000	1.0000
1	0.8870	0.9774	0.9075	0.9887
2	0.7846	0.9549	0.8217	0.9772
3	0.6920	0.9324	0.7423	0.9656
4	0.6085	0.9098	0.6689	0.9538
5	0.5334	0.8873	0.6012	0.9420
6	0.4660	0.8648	0.5389	0.9299
7	0.4057	0.8423	0.4817	0.9178
8	0.3519	0.8198	0.4292	0.9054
9	0.3040	0.7973	0.3813	0.8929
10	0.2615	0.7748	0.3376	0.8802
11	0.2240	0.7523	0.2978	0.8673
12	0.1915	0.7519	0.2546	0.8671
13	0.1636	0.7519	0.2176	0.8671
14	0.1399	0.7519	0.1860	0.8671
15	0.1195	0.7519	0.1590	0.8671
16	0.1022	0.7519	0.1359	0.8671
17	0.08734	0.7519	0.1162	0.8671
18	0.07466	0.7519	0.09930	0.8671
19	0.06383	0.7519	0.08489	0.8671
20	0.05457	0.7519	0.07258	0.8671
21	0.04667	0.7551	0.06181	0.8690
22	0.03995	0.7585	0.05266	0.8709
23	0.03422	0.7620	0.04490	0.8729
24	0.02933	0.7654	0.03832	0.8749
25	0.02516	0.7689	0.03272	0.8769
26	0.02160	0.7723	0.02797	0.8788
27	0.01855	0.7758	0.02392	0.8808
28	0.01595	0.7792	0.02047	0.8827
29	0.01372	0.7826	0.01753	0.8847
30	0.01181	0.7861	0.01503	0.8866
31	0.01018	0.7895	0.01289	0.8885
32	0.008774	0.7930	0.01107	0.8905
33	0.007573	0.8016	0.009447	0.8953
34	0.006547	0.8112	0.008071	0.9007
35	0.005671	0.8208	0.006909	0.9060
36	0.004920	0.8304	0.005925	0.9113
37	0.004276	0.8400	0.005090	0.9165
38	0.003722	0.8496	0.004381	0.9217
39	0.003245	0.8591	0.003777	0.9269
40	0.002834	0.8688	0.003262	0.9321

Metric units				
Geometric altitude (km)	**Pressure ratio** $\delta = P/P_{\text{ref}}$	**Temperature ratio** $\theta = T/T_{\text{ref}}$	**Density ratio** $\sigma = \rho/\rho_{\text{ref}}$	**Speed of sound ratio** a/a_{ref}
41	0.002478	0.8784	0.002822	0.9372
42	0.002171	0.8880	0.002445	0.9423
43	0.001904	0.8976	0.002122	0.9474
44	0.001673	0.9072	0.001844	0.9525
45	0.001472	0.9168	0.001605	0.9575
46	0.001296	0.9263	0.001399	0.9625
47	0.001143	0.9359	0.001222	0.9674
48	0.001010	0.9393	0.001075	0.9692
49	0.0008916	0.9393	0.0009492	0.9692
50	0.0007874	0.9393	0.0008383	0.9692
55	0.0004197	0.9050	0.0004638	0.9513
60	0.0002167	0.8573	0.0002528	0.9259
65	0.0001079	0.8096	0.0001332	0.8998
70	0.00005153	0.7621	0.00006762	0.8730
75	0.00002357	0.7232	0.00003259	0.8504
80	0.00001039	0.6894	0.00001507	0.8303

Reference values: $P_{\text{ref}} = 1.013 \times 10^5\ \text{N/m}^2$ $\rho_{\text{ref}} = 1.225\ \text{kg/m}^3$
$T_{\text{ref}} = 288.2\ \text{K}$ $a_{\text{ref}} = 340.3\ \text{m/sec}$

APPENDIX B

GAS TURBINE ENGINE DATA

TABLE B-1
Data for some military gas turbine engines

Model no.	Type	Max. thrust or power @ SLS	SFC at max.	Airflow (lb/sec)	OPR π_c (stages)	Maximum D (in)	Maximum L (in)	Weight (lb)	TIT (°F)	Remarks
J57-P-23	TJ	16,000 lb	2.10	165	11.5 (16)	40	246	5,169	1,600	AB, F-102A, F-100D
J57-P-43WB	TJ	11,200 lb	0.775	180	12 (16)	39	167.3	3,870	1,600	Water-injected, KC-135
J58-P	TJ	*32,500 lb	—	*450	*6 (9)	—	—	—	—	AB, YF-12A, SR-71
J60-P-3	TJ	3,000 lb	0.96	50	7 (9)	23.4	79.5	460	1,600	T-39A, C-140A
J69-T-25	TJ	1,025 lb	1.14	20.5	3.9 (1)	22.3	43.3	364	1,525	T-37B
J75-P-17	TJ	24,500 lb	2.15	252	12.0 (15)	43	237.6	5,875	1,610	AB, F-106A/B
J79-GE-17	TJ	17,820 lb	1.965	170	13.5 (17)	39.1	208.7	3,855	1,210	AB, F-4E/G
J85-GE-5H	TJ	3,850 lb	2.20	44	7 (8)	20.4	109.1	584	1,640	AB, T-38A/B
J85-GE-17	TJ	2,850 lb	0.99	44	7 (8)	17.7	40.4	395	1,640	A-37B
J85-GE-21	TJ	5,000 lb	2.13	51.9	8 (8)	20	116	667	1,790	AB, F-5E/F
PT6A-42	TP	850 eshp	0.601	8.0	8 (3, 1)	19	67	391	—	C-12E
PT6A-45R	TP	1,197 eshp	0.553	8.6	8.7 (3, 1)	19	72	434	—	C-23A
T400-CP-400	TS	1,800 shp	0.606	6.51	7 (3, 1)	43.5	66.3	716	1,920	Bell UH-1N
T406-AD-400	TS	6,150 shp	0.424	—	(14)	24.5	77.9	975	1,422	CV-22
T53-L-13	TS	1,400 shp	0.58	12.2	7 (5, 1)	23	47.6	549	1,720	Bell UH-1H, AH-1G
T55-L-11	TS	3,750 shp	0.52	—	8 (6, 1)	24.3	44	670	—	Boeing CH-47C
T56-A-7	TP	3,775 eshp	0.528	32.5	9.45 (14)	40.9	146	1,833	1,780	C-130B/E/F
T56-A-15	TP	4,591 eshp	0.54	32.5	9.55 (14)	44.6	146.3	1,848	1,970	C-130H/N/P
T58-GE-100	TS	1,500 shp	0.606	14	8.4 (10)	21.5	58.6	335	1,372	Sikorsky CH-3E, HH-3E, F
T64-GE-100	TS	4,330 shp	0.487	29.3	14 (14)	20.2	77.1	720	1,520	MH-53T
T700-GE-700	TS	1,622 shp	0.46	—	15 (5, 1)	25	47	423	1,563	UH-60A
T76-G-10	TS	715 shp	0.60	6.16	8.6 (2)	27.1	44.5	348	1,818	OV-10A

TJ = turbojet TP = turboprop OPR = overall pressure ratio TIT = turbine inlet temperature TS = turboshaft (Stages) = (axial, centrifugal) compressor stages SFC = specific fuel consumption.

* J-58 Reference: Lockheed SR-71 by Jay Miller, Aerofax Minigraph 1, Aerofax, Inc., Arlington, TX, 1985.

Source: Reference 86 and manufacturers' literature.

TABLE B-2
Data for some military turbofan engines

	Max./mil. power @ SLS				Maximum						
Model no.	**Thrust (lb)**	**TSFC [(lbm/hr)/lbf]**	**Airflow (lb/sec)**	**OPR** π_c	D **(in)**	L **(in)**	**Weight (lb)**	**TIT (°F)**	**FPR** π_f	**BR** α	**Remarks**
F100-PW-229	29,000/17,800	2.05/0.74	248	23.0	47	191	3,036	2,700	3.8	0.4	F-15, F16
F101-GE-102	30,780/17,390	2.460/0.562	356	26.8	55.2	180.7	4,448	2,550	2.31	1.91	B-1B
F103-GE-101	51,711	0.399	1,476	30.2	86.4	173	8,768	2,490	—	4.31	KC-10A
F107-WR-101	635	0.685	13.6	13.8	12	48.5	141	—	2.1	1.0	Air Launch Cruise Missile
F108-CF-100	21,634	0.363	785	23.7	72	115.4	4,610	2,228	1.5	6.0	KC-135R
F110-GE-100	28,620/18,330	2.08/1.47	254	30.4	46.5	182	3,895	—	2.98	0.80	F-16
F117-PW-100	41,700	0.33	—	31.8	84.5	146.8	7,100	—	—	5.8	(PW2040) C-17A
F118-GE-100	19,000	—	—	—	—	—	—	—	—	—	B-2
F404-GE-FID	10,000	—	—	25	34.5	87	1,730	—	—	—	F-117A
F404-GE-400	16,000	—	—	25	35	159	—	—	—	0.34	F-18, F-5G
JT3D-3B	18,000	0.535	458	13.6	53	136.4	4,300	1,600	1.74	1.37	(TF33-102) EC/RC-135
JT8D-7B	14,500	0.585	318	16.9	45	123.7	3.252	1,076	—	1.03	C-22, C-9, T-43A
TF30-P-111	25,100/14,560	2.450/0.686	260	21.8	49	241.7	3,999	2,055	2.43	0.73	F-111F
TF33-P-3	17,000	0.52	450	13.0	53	136	3,900	1,600	1.7	1.55	B-52H
TF33-P-7	21,000	0.56	498	16.0	54	142	4,650	1,750	1.9	1.21	C-141
TF34-GE-100	9,065	0.37	333	20.0	50	100	1,421	2,234	1.5	6.42	A-10
TF39-GE-1	40,805	0.315	1,549	26.0	100	203	7,186	2,350	1.56	8.0	C-5A
TF41-A-1B	14,500	0.647	260	20.0	40	114.5	3,511	2.165	2.45	0.76	A-7D, K
TFE731-2	3,500	0.504	113	17.7	40	50	625	—	1.54	2.67	C-21A

OPR = overall pressure ratio FPR = fan pressure ratio TSFC = thrust specific-fuel consumption TIT = turbine inlet temperature BR = bypass ratio.

Sources: Reference 86 and manufacturers' literature.

TABLE B-3
Data for some civil gas turbine engines

		Takeoff				Cruise				
Model no.	Manufacturer	Thrust (lb)	BR	OPR π_c	Airflow (lb/sec)	Alt. (kft)	M_0	Thrust (lb)	TSFC [(lbm/hr)/lbf]	Aircraft application
CF6-50C2	General Electric	52,500	4.31	30.4	1,476	35	0.80	11,555	0.630	DC10-10, A300B, 747-200
CF6-80C2	General Electric	52,500	5.31	27.4	1.650	35	0.80	12,000	0.576	767-200, −300, −200ER
GE90-B4	General Electric	87,400	8.40	39.3	3.037	35	0.80	17,500	—	777
JT8D-15A	Pratt & Whitney	15,500	1.04	16.6	327	30	0.80	4,920	0.779	727, 737, DC9
JT9D-59A	Pratt & Whitney	53,000	4.90	24.5	1.639	35	0.85	11,950	0.646	DC10-40, A300B, 747-200
PW2037	Pratt & Whitney	38,250	6.00	27.6	1.210	35	0.85	6,500	0.582	757-200
PW4052	Pratt & Whitney	52,000	5.00	27.5	1,700					767, A310-300
PW4084	Pratt & Whitney	87,900	6.41	34.4	2,550	35	0.83		—	777
CFM56-3	CFM International	23,500	5.00	22.6	655	35	0.85	4,890	0.667	737-300, −400, −500
CFM56-5C	CFM International	31,200	6.60	31.5	1.027	35	0.80	6,600	0.545	A340
RB211-524B	Rolls Royce	50,000	4.50	28.4	1.513	35	0.85	11,000	0.643	L1011-200, 747-200
RB211-535E	Rolls Royce	40,100	4.30	25.8	1.151	35	0.80	8,495	0.607	757-200
RB211-882	Rolls Royce	84,700	6.01	39.0	2.640	35	0.83	16,200	0.557	777
V2528-D5	International Aero Engines	28,000	4.70	30.5	825	35	0.80	5,773	0.574	MD-90
ALF502R-5	Textron Lycoming	6,970	5.70	12.2		25	0.70	2,250	0.720	BAe 146-100, −200
TFE731-5	Garrett	4,500	3.34	14.4	140	40	0.80	986	0.771	BAe 125-800
PW300	Pratt & Whitney Canada	4,750	4.50	23.0	180	40	0.80	1,113	0.675	BAe 1000
FJ44	Williams Rolls	1,900	3.28	12.8	63.3	30	0.70	600	0.750	
Olympus 593	Rolls Royce/SNECMA	38,000	0	*11.3	410	53	2.00	10,030	1.190	Concorde

OPR = overall pressure ratio TSFC = thrust specific fuel consumption BR = bypass ratio.

* At cruise.

Sources: Reference 87 and manufacturers' literature.

TABLE B-4
Temperature/pressure data for some engines

Engine: Type: Exhaust:	Pegasus Turbofan Separate	J57 Turbojet	JT3D Turbofan Separate	JT8D Turbofan Mixed	JT9D Turbofan Separate	F100-PW-100 Turbofan Mixed w/AB
P_{t2} (psia)	14.7	14.7	14.7	14.7	14.7	13.1
T_{t2} (°F)	59	59	59	59	59	59
$P_{t2.5}$ (psia)	36.1	54	63	60	32.1	
$T_{t2.5}$ (°F)	242	330	360	355	210	
P_{t13} (psia)	36.5		26	28	22.6	39.3
T_{t13} (°F)	257		170	190	130	297
P_{t3} (psia)	216.9	167	200	233	316	316
T_{t3} (°F)	708	660	715	800	880	1,014
P_{t4} (psia)		158	190	220	302	304
T_{t4} (°F)	1,028	1,570	1,600	1,720	1,970	2,566
P_{t5} or P_{t6} (psia)	29.3	36			20.9	38.0
T_{t5} or T_{t6} (°F)	510	1,013			850	1,368
P_{t16} (psia)						36.8
T_{t16} (°F)						303
P_{t6A} (psia)				29		37.5
T_{t6A} (°F)				890		960
P_{t7} (psia)		31.9	28	29	20.9	33.8
T_{t7} (°F)		2,540	890	890	850	3,204
P_{t17} (psia)	36.5		26		22.4	
T_{t17} (°F)	257		170		130	
Bypass ratio α	1.4	n/a	1.36	1.1	5.0	0.69
Thrust (lb)	21,500	16,000	18,000	14,000	43,500	23,700
Airflow (lb/sec)	444	167	460	315	1,495	224

Sources: Reference 88 and manufacturers' literature.

APPENDIX C

DATA FOR SOME LIQUID PROPELLANT ROCKET ENGINES

TABLE C-1
Data for some liquid-propellant rocket engines

Engine	Thrust (lbf) in vacuum	Expansion ratio ($\varepsilon = A_e/A_t$)	Design alt. (ft) ($P_e = P_a$)	I_{sp} (sec) Vacuum	SL	Application
LR-87-BC-13	16,000	45:1	60,000	293	—	Agena
LR-87-AJ-9	474,000	8:1	20,000	283	257	Titan 2—1st stage Titan 3—2d stage Titan Gemini—1st stage
LR-87-AJ-11	548,000	15:1	—	301		Titan 4—1st stage
LR-91-AJ-7	100,570	49:1	100,000	309	—	Titan 2—2d stage Titan 3A—Gemini Titan 3C—3d stage
LR-91-AJ-11	105,000	49.2:1	—	316	—	Titan 4—2d stage
LR-105*	83,700	24.9:1	100,000	304	212	Std. launch vehicle
F-1*	1,726,000	24.9:1	80,000	305	265	Saturn V—1st stage
H-1*	219,000	8:1	80,000	287	255	Saturn 1B
J-2*	200,000	25.5:1	100,000	426	380	Saturn V—2nd and 3d stages
RS-27*	231,700	8:1	—	—	263	Delta launch vehicle
SSME*	470,000	77:1	44,600	455	364	Space shuttle main engine
STME*	650,000	45:1		428	364	Space transportation main engine
RL10A-4‡	20,800	—	—	449	—	Atlas IIA upper stage

Manufacturers: BC = Bell Aerosystems Co. AJ = Aerojet * = Rocketdyne † = Pratt & Whitney

APPENDIX D

AIR AND $(CH_2)_n$ PROPERTIES AT LOW PRESSURE

Metric units

T K	T °C	f = 0 h (kJ/kg)	f = 0 P_r	f = 0.0169 h (kJ/kg)	f = 0.0169 P_r	f = 0.0338 h (kJ/kg)	f = 0.0338 P_r	f = 0.0507 h (kJ/kg)	f = 0.0507 P_r	f = 0.0676 h (kJ/kg)	f = 0.0676 P_r
170	-103	169.80	0.1903	170.82	0.1870	171.81	0.1840	172.76	0.1810	173.69	0.1783
180	-93	179.85	0.2324	180.95	0.2288	182.01	0.2254	183.04	0.2221	184.03	0.2190
190	-83	189.90	0.2809	191.08	0.2769	192.22	0.2731	193.33	0.2695	194.40	0.2661
200	-73	199.93	0.3361	201.21	0.3318	202.44	0.3278	203.63	0.3239	204.79	0.3202
210	-63	209.96	0.3985	211.34	0.3941	212.66	0.3899	213.95	0.3859	215.19	0.3821
220	-53	219.99	0.4688	221.47	0.4644	222.89	0.4602	224.28	0.4561	225.62	0.4522
230	-43	230.01	0.5475	231.60	0.5433	233.13	0.5392	234.62	0.5352	236.06	0.5315
240	-33	240.02	0.6352	241.73	0.6313	243.38	0.6276	244.98	0.6240	246.53	0.6205
250	-23	250.04	0.7325	251.87	0.7292	253.64	0.7260	255.36	0.7230	257.02	0.7201
260	-13	260.05	0.8399	262.01	0.8376	263.91	0.8353	265.75	0.8331	267.53	0.8310
270	-3	270.07	0.9581	272.17	0.9571	274.19	0.9561	276.16	0.9551	278.06	0.9542
280	7	280.08	1.0878	282.32	1.0885	284.49	1.0891	286.58	1.0898	288.61	1.0904
290	17	290.10	1.2296	292.49	1.2325	294.79	1.2352	297.03	1.2379	299.19	1.2406
300	27	300.13	1.3841	302.66	1.3897	305.11	1.3952	307.49	1.4005	309.79	1.4056
310	37	310.15	1.5521	312.85	1.5611	315.45	1.5699	317.97	1.5783	320.41	1.5865
320	47	320.19	1.7344	323.04	1.7474	325.80	1.7601	328.47	1.7724	331.05	1.7844
330	57	330.23	1.9315	333.25	1.9494	336.16	1.9667	338.99	1.9836	341.72	2.00
340	67	340.28	2.14	343.47	2.17	346.55	2.19	349.53	2.21	352.42	2.23
350	77	350.34	2.37	353.70	2.40	356.95	2.43	360.09	2.46	363.13	2.49
360	87	360.41	2.62	363.94	2.66	367.36	2.69	370.67	2.73	373.88	2.77
370	97	370.49	2.88	374.20	2.93	377.80	2.98	381.27	3.02	384.64	3.06
380	107	380.58	3.17	384.48	3.22	388.25	3.28	391.90	3.33	395.44	3.39
390	117	390.68	3.47	394.77	3.54	398.72	3.61	402.55	3.67	406.26	3.74
400	127	400.80	3.80	405.08	3.88	409.22	3.95	413.22	4.03	417.10	4.11
410	137	410.93	4.14	415.40	4.24	419.73	4.33	423.92	4.42	427.98	4.51
420	147	421.07	4.51	425.74	4.62	430.26	4.73	434.64	4.84	438.88	4.94
430	157	431.23	4.90	436.10	5.03	440.82	5.16	445.38	5.28	449.80	5.40
440	167	441.41	5.32	446.49	5.47	451.40	5.61	456.15	5.76	460.76	5.90
450	177	451.60	5.76	456.89	5.93	462.00	6.10	466.95	6.26	471.74	6.43
460	187	461.81	6.23	467.31	6.42	472.62	6.61	477.77	6.80	482.75	6.99
470	197	472.04	6.72	477.75	6.94	483.27	7.16	488.62	7.38	493.79	7.59
480	207	482.28	7.25	488.21	7.50	493.94	7.74	499.49	7.99	504.86	8.23
490	217	492.55	7.80	498.69	8.08	504.63	8.36	510.39	8.64	515.96	8.92
500	227	502.83	8.39	509.20	8.70	515.35	9.02	521.31	9.33	527.09	9.64
510	237	513.13	9.01	519.72	9.36	526.10	9.71	532.27	10.06	538.24	10.41
520	247	523.46	9.66	530.27	10.05	536.87	10.44	543.25	10.83	549.43	11.23
530	257	533.80	10.35	540.85	10.78	547.66	11.22	554.26	11.65	560.65	12.09
540	267	544.17	11.07	551.44	11.55	558.48	12.03	565.30	12.52	571.89	13.01
550	277	554.55	11.83	562.06	12.36	569.33	12.90	576.36	13.44	583.17	13.98
560	287	564.96	12.63	572.71	13.21	580.20	13.81	587.46	14.41	594.48	15.01
570	297	575.39	13.47	583.38	14.11	591.10	14.77	598.58	15.43	605.82	16.09
580	307	585.84	14.35	594.07	15.06	602.03	15.78	609.73	16.50	617.19	17.24
590	317	596.32	15.27	604.79	16.05	612.98	16.84	620.91	17.64	628.59	18.45
600	327	606.81	16.24	615.53	17.09	623.96	17.96	632.12	18.83	640.02	19.72

Metric units

T		f = 0		f = 0.0169		f = 0.0338		f = 0.0507		f = 0.0676	
K	°C	h (kJ/kg)	P_r	h (kJ/kg)	P_r	h (kJ/kg)	P_r	h (kJ/kg)	P_r	h (kJ/kg)	P_r
600	327	606.81	16.24	615.53	17.09	623.96	17.96	632.12	18.83	640.02	19.72
610	337	617.33	17.25	626.30	18.18	634.97	19.13	643.36	20.09	651.49	21.06
620	347	627.88	18.32	637.09	19.33	646.00	20.36	654.63	21.41	662.98	22.48
630	357	638.44	19.43	647.91	20.53	657.07	21.66	665.93	22.80	674.51	23.97
640	367	649.03	20.59	658.75	21.79	668.16	23.01	677.25	24.26	686.07	25.53
650	377	659.65	21.80	669.62	23.11	679.27	24.44	688.61	25.79	697.65	27.18
660	387	670.29	23.07	680.52	24.48	690.42	25.93	700.00	27.40	709.28	28.91
670	397	680.95	24.40	691.44	25.93	701.59	27.49	711.42	29.09	720.93	30.72
680	407	691.63	25.78	702.39	27.43	712.79	29.12	722.86	30.86	732.61	32.63
690	417	702.34	27.23	713.36	29.01	724.02	30.83	734.34	32.71	744.33	34.63
700	427	713.07	28.73	724.36	30.65	735.28	32.62	745.84	34.65	756.08	36.72
710	437	723.83	30.30	735.38	32.36	746.56	34.49	757.38	36.68	767.85	38.92
720	447	734.61	31.93	746.43	34.15	757.87	36.44	768.94	38.80	779.67	41.22
730	457	745.41	33.64	757.51	36.02	769.21	38.48	780.54	41.02	791.51	43.63
740	467	756.24	35.41	768.61	37.97	780.58	40.61	792.16	43.34	803.38	46.15
750	477	767.09	37.25	779.74	39.99	791.98	42.83	803.82	45.76	815.29	48.79
760	487	777.97	39.17	790.90	42.10	803.40	45.15	815.50	48.29	827.22	51.54
770	497	788.87	41.16	802.08	44.30	814.85	47.56	827.22	50.94	839.19	54.42
780	507	799.79	43.23	813.28	46.59	826.33	50.08	838.96	53.69	851.19	57.43
790	517	810.74	45.39	824.51	48.97	837.83	52.70	850.73	56.57	863.21	60.58
800	527	821.71	47.62	835.77	51.45	849.37	55.43	862.53	59.57	875.27	63.86
810	537	832.70	49.94	847.05	54.02	860.93	58.27	874.36	62.69	887.36	67.28
820	547	843.72	52.35	858.35	56.69	872.51	61.22	886.22	65.94	899.48	70.85
830	557	854.76	54.85	869.69	59.47	884.13	64.30	898.10	69.33	911.64	74.57
840	567	865.82	57.44	881.04	62.36	895.77	67.50	910.02	72.86	923.82	78.45
850	577	876.90	60.13	892.42	65.35	907.43	70.82	921.96	76.53	936.03	82.49
860	587	888.01	62.91	903.83	68.46	919.12	74.27	933.93	80.35	948.27	86.70
870	597	899.14	65.80	915.26	71.68	930.84	77.86	945.93	84.33	960.54	91.09
880	607	910.29	68.79	926.71	75.02	942.59	81.58	957.96	88.46	972.84	95.65
890	617	921.47	71.88	938.19	78.49	954.36	85.44	970.01	92.75	985.17	100.40
900	627	932.66	75.08	949.69	82.08	966.15	89.46	982.09	97.21	997.52	105.33
910	637	943.88	78.40	961.21	85.80	977.97	93.62	994.20	101.84	1009.91	110.46
920	647	955.12	81.82	972.76	89.66	989.82	97.93	1006.33	106.64	1022.32	115.80
930	657	966.38	85.37	984.33	93.65	1001.69	102.40	1018.49	111.64	1034.77	121.34
940	667	977.66	89.03	995.92	97.78	1013.58	107.04	1030.68	116.81	1047.24	127.10
950	677	988.96	92.82	1007.54	102.06	1025.50	111.84	1042.89	122.19	1059.73	133.09
960	687	1000.28	96.74	1019.17	106.48	1037.45	116.82	1055.13	127.76	1072.26	139.29
970	697	1011.62	100.78	1030.83	111.06	1049.41	121.97	1067.40	133.53	1084.81	145.74
980	707	1022.99	104.96	1042.51	115.79	1061.41	127.31	1079.69	139.52	1097.39	152.43
990	717	1034.37	109.27	1054.22	120.68	1073.42	132.83	1092.00	145.72	1110.00	159.36
1000	727	1045.77	113.72	1065.94	125.74	1085.46	138.54	1104.34	152.14	1122.63	166.55

Metric units

T		f = 0		f = 0.0169		f = 0.0338		f = 0.0507		f = 0.0676	
K	°C	h (kJ/kg)	P_r	h (kJ/kg)	P_r	h (kJ/kg)	P_r	h (kJ/kg)	P_r	h (kJ/kg)	P_r
1000	727	1045.77	113.72	1065.94	125.74	1085.46	138.54	1104.34	152.14	1122.63	166.55
1010	737	1057.19	118.31	1077.69	130.96	1097.52	144.45	1116.71	158.79	1135.29	174.01
1020	747	1068.63	123.05	1089.45	136.36	1109.60	150.56	1129.09	165.68	1147.97	181.74
1030	757	1080.09	127.94	1101.24	141.93	1121.70	156.88	1141.51	172.81	1160.68	189.74
1040	767	1091.56	132.98	1113.05	147.68	1133.83	163.41	1153.94	180.19	1173.42	198.03
1050	777	1103.06	138.18	1124.87	153.62	1145.98	170.15	1166.40	187.82	1186.18	206.6
1060	787	1114.57	143.53	1136.72	159.74	1158.15	177.13	1178.89	195.71	1198.97	215.5
1070	797	1126.10	149.05	1148.59	166.06	1170.34	184.32	1191.39	203.9	1211.78	224.7
1080	807	1137.65	154.73	1160.47	172.58	1182.55	191.76	1203.92	212.3	1224.61	234.2
1090	817	1149.22	160.59	1172.38	179.30	1194.78	199.43	1216.47	221.0	1237.47	244.1
1100	827	1160.80	166.62	1184.30	186.23	1207.04	207.4	1229.04	230.0	1250.35	254.3
1110	837	1172.40	172.83	1196.24	193.38	1219.31	215.5	1241.64	239.3	1263.26	264.8
1120	847	1184.01	179.22	1208.21	200.7	1231.61	224.0	1254.25	248.9	1276.18	275.7
1130	857	1195.65	185.79	1220.18	208.3	1243.92	232.7	1266.89	258.9	1289.13	287.0
1140	867	1207.29	192.55	1232.18	216.1	1256.25	241.6	1279.55	269.1	1302.11	298.6
1150	877	1218.96	199.51	1244.19	224.2	1268.60	250.9	1292.23	279.7	1315.10	310.6
1160	887	1230.64	206.7	1256.22	232.4	1280.97	260.4	1304.93	290.6	1328.12	323.0
1170	897	1242.33	214.0	1268.27	241.0	1293.36	270.2	1317.65	301.8	1341.16	335.9
1180	907	1254.05	221.6	1280.34	249.8	1305.77	280.3	1330.39	313.4	1354.22	349.1
1190	917	1265.77	229.4	1292.42	258.8	1318.20	290.8	1343.15	325.4	1367.30	362.8
1200	927	1277.51	237.4	1304.52	268.1	1330.64	301.5	1355.92	337.7	1380.41	376.8
1210	937	1289.27	245.6	1316.63	277.6	1343.10	312.5	1368.72	350.4	1393.53	391.4
1220	947	1301.03	254.0	1328.76	287.4	1355.58	323.9	1381.54	363.5	1406.68	406.4
1230	957	1312.82	262.6	1340.91	297.5	1368.08	335.6	1394.38	377.0	1419.84	421.9
1240	967	1324.61	271.5	1353.07	307.9	1380.59	347.7	1407.23	390.9	1433.02	437.8
1250	977	1336.43	280.6	1365.24	318.6	1393.12	360.1	1420.10	405.2	1446.23	454.3
1260	987	1348.25	290.0	1377.44	329.6	1405.67	372.8	1432.99	420.0	1459.45	471.2
1270	997	1360.09	299.6	1389.64	340.8	1418.23	385.9	1445.90	435.2	1472.69	488.7
1280	1007	1371.94	309.5	1401.86	352.4	1430.81	399.4	1458.83	450.8	1485.96	506.7
1290	1017	1383.80	319.6	1414.10	364.3	1443.41	413.3	1471.77	466.8	1499.24	525.2
1300	1027	1395.68	330.0	1426.35	376.5	1456.02	427.5	1484.73	483.4	1512.54	544.3
1310	1037	1407.57	340.6	1438.61	389.0	1468.64	442.2	1497.71	500.4	1525.85	564.0
1320	1047	1419.47	351.6	1450.89	401.8	1481.29	457.2	1510.70	517.9	1539.19	584.2
1330	1057	1431.38	362.7	1463.18	415.0	1493.94	472.6	1523.71	535.9	1552.54	605.0
1340	1067	1443.31	374.2	1475.49	428.6	1506.61	488.5	1536.74	554.4	1565.91	626.5
1350	1077	1455.25	386.0	1487.81	442.5	1519.30	504.8	1549.78	573.4	1579.30	648.5
1360	1087	1467.20	398.0	1500.14	456.7	1532.00	521.6	1562.84	593.0	1592.70	671.2
1370	1097	1479.16	410.3	1512.48	471.3	1544.72	538.8	1575.92	613.1	1606.13	694.6
1380	1107	1491.13	423.0	1524.84	486.3	1557.45	556.4	1589.01	633.7	1619.57	718.6
1390	1117	1503.11	435.9	1537.21	501.7	1570.19	574.5	1602.11	654.9	1633.02	743.3
1400	1127	1515.11	449.2	1549.59	517.4	1582.95	593.1	1615.23	676.7	1646.49	768.6

Metric units

T		f = 0		f = 0.0169		f = 0.0338		f = 0.0507		f = 0.0676	
K	°C	h (kJ/kg)	P_r	h (kJ/kg)	P_r	h (kJ/kg)	P_r	h (kJ/kg)	P_r	h (kJ/kg)	P_r
1400	1127	1515.11	449.2	1549.59	517.4	1582.95	593.1	1615.23	676.7	1646.49	768.6
1410	1137	1527.11	462.8	1561.99	533.6	1595.72	612.2	1628.37	699.1	1659.98	794.7
1420	1147	1539.13	476.7	1574.39	550.1	1608.51	631.7	1641.52	722.0	1673.49	821.5
1430	1157	1551.16	490.9	1586.81	567.1	1621.30	651.8	1654.68	745.6	1687.01	849.1
1440	1167	1563.20	505.4	1599.25	584.4	1634.12	672.4	1667.86	769.8	1700.54	877.4
1450	1177	1575.25	520.4	1611.69	602.2	1646.94	693.4	1681.06	794.6	1714.09	906.5
1460	1187	1587.31	535.6	1624.14	620.4	1659.78	715.1	1694.27	820.2	1727.66	936.4
1470	1197	1599.38	551.2	1636.61	639.1	1672.63	737.2	1707.49	846.3	1741.24	967.0
1480	1207	1611.46	567.2	1649.09	658.2	1685.49	760.0	1720.72	873.1	1754.84	998.5
1490	1217	1623.55	583.5	1661.58	677.8	1698.37	783.2	1733.97	900.7	1768.45	1030.8
1500	1227	1635.65	600.2	1674.08	697.8	1711.26	807.1	1747.24	928.9	1782.08	1064.0
1510	1237	1647.76	617.2	1686.59	718.3	1724.16	831.5	1760.51	957.8	1795.72	1098.1
1520	1247	1659.88	634.7	1699.11	739.3	1737.07	856.6	1773.80	987.5	1809.38	1133.1
1530	1257	1672.01	652.5	1711.65	760.7	1749.99	882.2	1787.11	1018.0	1823.05	1168.9
1540	1267	1684.15	670.7	1724.19	782.7	1762.93	908.5	1800.42	1049.1	1836.73	1205.7
1550	1277	1696.29	689.4	1736.75	805.2	1775.88	935.4	1813.75	1081.1	1850.43	1243.5
1560	1287	1708.45	708.4	1749.31	828.2	1788.84	962.9	1827.10	1113.9	1864.14	1282.2
1570	1297	1720.62	727.9	1761.89	851.6	1801.81	991.1	1840.45	1147.4	1877.86	1321.9
1580	1307	1732.80	747.7	1774.48	875.7	1814.80	1019.9	1853.82	1181.8	1891.60	1362.6
1590	1317	1744.98	768.0	1787.08	900.3	1827.79	1049.5	1867.20	1217.0	1905.36	1404.3
1600	1327	1757.18	788.8	1799.68	925.4	1840.80	1079.7	1880.59	1253.1	1919.12	1447.1
1610	1337	1769.38	810.0	1812.30	951.1	1853.81	1110.6	1893.99	1290.0	1932.90	1490.9
1620	1347	1781.59	831.6	1824.93	977.3	1866.84	1142.2	1907.41	1327.8	1946.69	1535.9
1630	1357	1793.82	853.7	1837.56	1004.2	1879.88	1174.6	1920.84	1366.6	1960.50	1581.9
1640	1367	1806.05	876.2	1850.21	1031.6	1892.93	1207.6	1934.28	1406.2	1974.31	1629.1
1650	1377	1818.29	899.2	1862.87	1059.6	1905.99	1241.5	1947.73	1446.8	1988.15	1677.4
1660	1387	1830.54	922.7	1875.54	1088.2	1919.06	1276.1	1961.19	1488.3	2001.99	1726.9
1670	1397	1842.79	946.7	1888.21	1117.4	1932.15	1311.5	1974.67	1530.8	2015.84	1777.6
1680	1407	1855.06	971.2	1900.90	1147.3	1945.24	1347.6	1988.15	1574.3	2029.71	1829.5
1690	1417	1867.33	996.1	1913.59	1177.8	1958.34	1384.6	2001.65	1618.8	2043.59	1882.6
1700	1427	1879.61	1021.6	1926.30	1209.0	1971.45	1422.4	2015.16	1664.3	2057.48	1937.0
1710	1437	1891.90	1047.6	1939.01	1240.8	1984.58	1461.0	2028.68	1710.8	2071.38	1992.8
1720	1447	1904.20	1074.1	1951.73	1273.2	1997.71	1500.5	2042.21	1758.4	2085.30	2049.8
1730	1457	1916.51	1101.1	1964.46	1306.4	2010.85	1540.8	2055.75	1807.1	2099.23	2108.1
1740	1467	1928.82	1128.7	1977.20	1340.2	2024.01	1582.0	2069.30	1856.9	2113.16	2167.8
1750	1477	1941.14	1156.8	1989.95	1374.8	2037.17	1624.1	2082.86	1907.8	2127.11	2229
1760	1487	1953.47	1185.5	2002.71	1410.0	2050.34	1667.1	2096.44	1959.8	2141.07	2291
1770	1497	1965.81	1214.7	2015.48	1446.0	2063.52	1711.0	2110.02	2013.0	2155.05	2355
1780	1507	1978.16	1244.5	2028.25	1482.7	2076.71	1755.8	2123.61	2067.3	2169.03	2421
1790	1517	1990.51	1274.9	2041.04	1520.1	2089.91	1801.6	2137.22	2122.8	2183.02	2488
1800	1527	2002.87	1305.8	2053.83	1558.3	2103.12	1848.3	2150.83	2179.6	2197.03	2556

Metric units

T		f = 0		f = 0.0169		f = 0.0338		f = 0.0507		f = 0.0676	
K	°C	h (kJ/kg)	P_r	h (kJ/kg)	P_r	h (kJ/kg)	P_r	h (kJ/kg)	P_r	h (kJ/kg)	P_r
1800	1527	2002.87	1305.8	2053.83	1558.3	2103.12	1848.3	2150.83	2180	2197.03	2556
1810	1537	2015.24	1337.4	2066.63	1597.3	2116.34	1896.0	2164.45	2238	2211.04	2626
1820	1547	2027.61	1369.5	2079.44	1637.0	2129.57	1944.8	2178.08	2297	2225.07	2697
1830	1557	2040.00	1402.3	2092.25	1677.6	2142.80	1994.5	2191.73	2357	2239.10	2771
1840	1567	2052.39	1435.7	2105.08	1718.9	2156.05	2045.2	2205.38	2419	2253.15	2845
1850	1577	2064.78	1469.7	2117.91	1761.0	2169.30	2097	2219.04	2482	2267.20	2922
1860	1587	2077.19	1504.3	2130.75	1804.0	2182.56	2150	2232.71	2547	2281.27	3000
1870	1597	2089.60	1539.6	2143.60	1847.8	2195.83	2204	2246.39	2613	2295.34	3080
1880	1607	2102.02	1575.6	2156.45	1892.4	2209.11	2259	2260.08	2680	2309.43	3161
1890	1617	2114.44	1612.2	2169.32	1938.0	2222.40	2315	2273.77	2748	2323.52	3244
1900	1627	2126.87	1649.4	2182.19	1984.3	2235.69	2372	2287.48	2818	2337.63	3329
1910	1637	2139.31	1687.4	2195.06	2031.6	2249.00	2430	2301.19	2890	2351.74	3416
1920	1647	2151.75	1726.0	2207.95	2079.8	2262.31	2490	2314.92	2963	2365.86	3505
1930	1657	2164.20	1765.4	2220.84	2128.8	2275.62	2551	2328.65	3037	2379.99	3595
1940	1667	2176.66	1805.4	2233.74	2178.8	2288.95	2612	2342.39	3113	2394.13	3688
1950	1677	2189.12	1846.2	2246.64	2230	2302.28	2676	2356.13	3191	2408.28	3782
1960	1687	2201.59	1887.7	2259.55	2282	2315.62	2740	2369.89	3270	2422.43	3879
1970	1697	2214.06	1929.9	2272.47	2334	2328.97	2805	2383.65	3350	2436.60	3977
1980	1707	2226.54	1972.8	2285.40	2388	2342.32	2872	2397.42	3433	2450.77	4078
1990	1717	2239.03	2016.6	2298.33	2443	2355.68	2940	2411.20	3516	2464.95	4180
2000	1727	2251.52	2061	2311.26	2499	2369.05	3010	2424.98	3602	2479.14	4285
2010	1737	2264.02	2106	2324.21	2556	2382.43	3080	2438.77	3689	2493.34	4392
2020	1747	2276.52	2152	2337.16	2614	2395.81	3152	2452.57	3778	2507.54	4501
2030	1757	2289.03	2199	2350.11	2672	2409.20	3226	2466.38	3869	2521.75	4612
2040	1767	2301.55	2247	2363.07	2732	2422.59	3301	2480.19	3961	2535.97	4725
2050	1777	2314.07	2295	2376.04	2793	2435.99	3377	2494.01	4055	2550.20	4841
2060	1787	2326.59	2345	2389.01	2855	2449.40	3454	2507.84	4152	2564.43	4959
2070	1797	2339.12	2395	2401.99	2919	2462.81	3533	2521.67	4249	2578.67	5079
2080	1807	2351.65	2446	2414.98	2983	2476.23	3614	2535.52	4349	2592.92	5202
2090	1817	2364.19	2497	2427.97	3048	2489.66	3696	2549.36	4451	2607.18	5327
2100	1827	2376.74	2550	2440.96	3115	2503.09	3779	2563.22	4554	2621.44	5455
2110	1837	2389.29	2604	2453.97	3183	2516.53	3864	2577.07	4660	2635.71	5585
2120	1847	2401.85	2658	2466.97	3252	2529.97	3950	2590.94	4767	2649.98	5717
2130	1857	2414.41	2713	2479.98	3322	2543.42	4038	2604.81	4877	2664.26	5853
2140	1867	2426.97	2769	2493.00	3393	2556.88	4128	2618.69	4988	2678.55	5990
2150	1877	2439.54	2827	2506.03	3465	2570.34	4219	2632.58	5102	2692.85	6131
2160	1887	2452.12	2885	2519.06	3539	2583.80	4312	2646.47	5218	2707.15	6274
2170	1897	2464.70	2944	2532.09	3614	2597.28	4406	2660.37	5336	2721.46	6420
2180	1907	2477.29	3004	2545.13	3690	2610.76	4502	2674.27	5456	2735.77	6568
2190	1917	2489.88	3065	2558.18	3768	2624.24	4600	2688.18	5578	2750.10	6720
2200	1927	2502.48	3126	2571.23	3847	2637.73	4699	2702.10	5702	2764.43	6874
2210	1937	2515.08	3189	2584.29	3927	2651.23	4801	2716.02	5829	2778.76	7031
2220	1947	2527.69	3253	2597.35	4008	2664.74	4904	2729.95	5958	2793.11	7191

English units

T		*f* = 0		*f* = 0.0169		*f* = 0.0338		*f* = 0.0507		*f* = 0.0676	
°R	°F	*h* (Btu/lbm)	P_r	*h* (Btu/lbm)	P_r	*h* (Btu/lbm)	P_r	*h* (Btu/lbm)	P_r	*h* (Btu/lbm)	P_r
300	-160	71.55	0.1775	71.98	0.1744	72.40	0.1715	72.80	0.1687	73.19	0.1660
320	-140	76.36	0.2225	76.82	0.2190	77.27	0.2156	77.71	0.2124	78.13	0.2094
340	-120	81.16	0.2752	81.66	0.2712	82.15	0.2675	82.62	0.2639	83.08	0.2605
360	-100	85.95	0.3361	86.50	0.3318	87.03	0.3278	87.54	0.3239	88.04	0.3202
380	-80	90.74	0.4059	91.34	0.4015	91.91	0.3973	92.47	0.3933	93.01	0.3894
400	-60	95.53	0.4856	96.18	0.4812	96.80	0.4769	97.40	0.4729	97.99	0.4690
420	-40	100.32	0.5757	101.02	0.5716	101.69	0.5675	102.35	0.5637	102.98	0.5600
440	-20	105.10	0.6772	105.86	0.6736	106.59	0.6700	107.30	0.6667	107.99	0.6634
460	0	109.88	0.7909	110.70	0.7881	111.49	0.7854	112.26	0.7828	113.00	0.7803
480	20	114.67	0.9175	115.55	0.9160	116.40	0.9145	117.23	0.9131	118.03	0.9117
500	40	119.45	1.0580	120.40	1.0582	121.32	1.0585	122.21	1.0587	123.07	1.0589
520	60	124.24	1.213	125.25	1.216	126.24	1.218	127.19	1.221	128.12	1.223
540	80	129.02	1.384	130.11	1.390	131.17	1.395	132.19	1.400	133.18	1.406
560	100	133.81	1.572	134.98	1.581	136.11	1.590	137.20	1.599	138.25	1.608
580	120	138.61	1.777	139.85	1.791	141.05	1.805	142.21	1.818	143.34	1.831
600	140	143.41	2.00	144.73	2.02	146.00	2.04	147.24	2.06	148.44	2.08
620	160	148.21	2.24	149.61	2.27	150.97	2.30	152.28	2.32	153.55	2.35
640	180	153.01	2.51	154.50	2.54	155.94	2.58	157.33	2.61	158.68	2.64
660	200	157.83	2.79	159.40	2.84	160.92	2.88	162.39	2.92	163.81	2.96
680	220	162.65	3.10	164.30	3.16	165.91	3.21	167.46	3.26	168.97	3.31
700	240	167.47	3.44	169.22	3.50	170.91	3.57	172.55	3.63	174.13	3.70
720	260	172.30	3.80	174.14	3.88	175.92	3.95	177.64	4.03	179.31	4.11
740	280	177.14	4.18	179.07	4.28	180.94	4.37	182.75	4.47	184.51	4.56
760	300	181.99	4.59	184.02	4.71	185.98	4.82	187.88	4.93	189.72	5.04
780	320	186.84	5.04	188.97	5.17	191.02	5.30	193.01	5.44	194.94	5.57
800	340	191.71	5.51	193.93	5.67	196.08	5.82	198.16	5.98	200.18	6.13
820	360	196.58	6.02	198.90	6.20	201.15	6.38	203.32	6.56	205.43	6.74
840	380	201.46	6.56	203.89	6.77	206.23	6.97	208.50	7.18	210.70	7.39
860	400	206.35	7.13	208.88	7.37	211.32	7.61	213.69	7.85	215.98	8.09
880	420	211.25	7.74	213.89	8.02	216.43	8.29	218.89	8.57	221.28	8.84
900	440	216.17	8.39	218.90	8.70	221.55	9.02	224.11	9.33	226.59	9.64
920	460	221.09	9.08	223.93	9.43	226.68	9.79	229.35	10.14	231.92	10.50
940	480	226.02	9.81	228.97	10.21	231.83	10.61	234.59	11.01	237.27	11.42
960	500	230.96	10.58	234.03	11.03	236.99	11.48	239.86	11.94	242.63	12.39
980	520	235.92	11.40	239.09	11.91	242.16	12.41	245.13	12.92	248.01	13.44
1000	540	240.89	12.27	244.17	12.83	247.35	13.40	250.43	13.97	253.40	14.54
1020	560	245.86	13.18	249.26	13.81	252.55	14.44	255.73	15.08	258.82	15.72
1040	580	250.85	14.15	254.37	14.84	257.77	15.55	261.06	16.26	264.24	16.98
1060	600	255.86	15.17	259.49	15.94	263.00	16.72	266.39	17.51	269.69	18.31
1080	620	260.87	16.24	264.62	17.09	268.24	17.96	271.75	18.83	275.15	19.72
1100	640	265.89	17.37	269.76	18.31	273.50	19.26	277.12	20.23	280.62	21.22

English units

T °R	T °F	f = 0 h (Btu/lbm)	f = 0 P_r	f = 0.0169 h (Btu/lbm)	f = 0.0169 P_r	f = 0.0338 h (Btu/lbm)	f = 0.0338 P_r	f = 0.0507 h (Btu/lbm)	f = 0.0507 P_r	f = 0.0676 h (Btu/lbm)	f = 0.0676 P_r
1100	640	265.89	17.37	269.76	18.31	273.50	19.26	277.12	20.23	280.62	21.22
1120	660	270.93	18.56	274.92	19.59	278.77	20.64	282.50	21.72	286.12	22.80
1140	680	275.98	19.81	280.09	20.94	284.06	22.10	287.90	23.28	291.63	24.48
1160	700	281.05	21.12	285.27	22.37	289.36	23.64	293.32	24.93	297.15	26.25
1180	720	286.12	22.50	290.47	23.86	294.68	25.26	298.75	26.68	302.70	28.13
1200	740	291.21	23.95	295.68	25.44	300.01	26.96	304.20	28.52	308.26	30.11
1220	760	296.31	25.47	300.91	27.09	305.36	28.75	309.66	30.46	313.83	32.20
1240	780	301.42	27.06	306.15	28.83	310.72	30.64	315.14	32.50	319.43	34.40
1260	800	306.55	28.73	311.40	30.65	316.10	32.62	320.64	34.65	325.04	36.72
1280	820	311.69	30.48	316.67	32.56	321.49	34.70	326.15	36.91	330.66	39.17
1300	840	316.84	32.31	321.95	34.56	326.89	36.89	331.68	39.28	336.31	41.75
1320	860	322.00	34.22	327.24	36.66	332.31	39.18	337.22	41.78	341.97	44.46
1340	880	327.18	36.22	332.55	38.86	337.75	41.59	342.78	44.40	347.65	47.31
1360	900	332.37	38.28	337.87	41.16	343.20	44.11	348.35	47.16	353.34	50.30
1380	920	337.57	40.49	343.21	43.64	348.66	46.95	353.94	50.39	359.05	53.95
1400	940	342.79	42.77	348.56	46.07	354.14	49.51	359.54	53.07	364.78	56.75
1420	960	348.01	45.14	353.92	48.70	359.63	52.40	365.17	56.24	370.52	60.22
1440	980	353.25	47.62	359.30	51.45	365.14	55.43	370.80	59.57	376.28	63.86
1460	1000	358.50	50.21	364.69	54.31	370.67	58.59	376.45	63.04	382.06	67.67
1480	1020	363.77	52.90	370.09	57.30	376.20	61.90	382.12	66.69	387.85	71.66
1500	1040	369.04	55.70	375.50	60.42	381.75	65.35	387.80	70.49	393.66	75.85
1520	1060	374.33	58.62	380.93	63.67	387.32	68.96	393.50	74.48	399.48	80.23
1540	1080	379.63	61.66	386.37	67.06	392.90	72.72	399.21	78.64	405.32	84.81
1560	1100	384.95	64.83	391.83	70.59	398.49	76.65	404.93	82.98	411.18	89.61
1580	1120	390.27	68.11	397.30	74.27	404.10	80.74	410.68	87.52	417.05	94.62
1600	1140	395.60	71.53	402.78	78.10	409.72	85.01	416.43	92.26	422.93	99.86
1620	1160	400.95	75.08	408.27	82.08	415.35	89.46	422.20	97.21	428.83	105.33
1640	1180	406.31	78.77	413.78	86.22	421.00	94.09	427.98	102.36	434.75	111.05
1660	1200	411.68	82.60	419.29	90.53	426.66	98.91	433.78	107.74	440.68	117.01
1680	1220	417.06	86.58	424.82	95.01	432.33	103.93	439.60	113.34	446.63	123.24
1700	1240	422.45	90.70	430.36	99.66	438.02	109.15	445.42	119.18	452.59	129.73
1720	1260	427.86	94.98	435.92	104.50	443.72	114.59	451.26	125.26	458.57	136.51
1740	1280	433.27	99.42	441.48	109.52	449.43	120.23	457.12	131.58	464.56	143.56
1760	1300	438.70	104.02	447.06	114.73	455.15	126.11	462.98	138.17	470.57	150.92
1780	1320	444.13	108.78	452.65	120.13	460.89	132.21	468.86	145.02	476.59	158.58
1800	1340	449.58	113.72	458.25	125.74	466.64	138.54	474.76	152.14	482.62	166.55
1820	1360	455.03	118.83	463.86	131.55	472.40	145.12	480.66	159.55	488.67	174.85
1840	1380	460.50	124.13	469.48	137.58	478.17	151.95	486.58	167.24	494.73	183.49
1860	1400	465.97	129.60	475.11	143.82	483.96	159.03	492.51	175.24	500.80	192.47
1880	1420	471.46	135.27	480.76	150.29	489.75	166.38	498.46	183.55	506.89	201.8
1900	1440	476.95	141.13	486.41	157.00	495.56	174.00	504.42	192.17	512.99	211.5

English units

T °R	T °F	f = 0 h (Btu/lbm)	f = 0 P_r	f = 0.0169 h (Btu/lbm)	f = 0.0169 P_r	f = 0.0338 h (Btu/lbm)	f = 0.0338 P_r	f = 0.0507 h (Btu/lbm)	f = 0.0507 P_r	f = 0.0676 h (Btu/lbm)	f = 0.0676 P_r
1900	1440	476.95	141.13	486.41	157.00	495.56	174.00	504.42	192.17	512.99	211.5
1920	1460	482.46	147.19	492.08	163.93	501.38	181.90	510.39	201.1	519.11	221.6
1940	1480	487.97	153.46	497.75	171.11	507.21	191.09	516.37	210.4	525.23	232.1
1960	1500	493.50	159.93	503.44	178.55	513.05	198.57	522.36	220.0	531.37	243.0
1980	1520	499.03	166.62	509.13	186.23	518.91	207.4	528.37	230.0	537.53	254.3
2000	1540	504.57	173.53	514.84	194.2	524.77	216.4	534.38	240.4	543.69	266.0
2020	1560	510.12	180.66	520.55	202.4	530.64	225.9	540.41	251.1	549.87	278.2
2040	1580	515.68	188.02	526.28	210.9	536.53	235.6	546.45	262.2	556.06	290.8
2060	1600	521.24	195.62	532.01	219.7	542.42	245.7	552.50	273.8	562.26	303.9
2080	1620	526.82	203.5	537.75	228.7	548.33	256.1	558.56	285.7	568.47	317.5
2100	1640	532.40	211.6	543.50	238.1	554.24	266.9	564.63	298.0	574.70	331.5
2120	1660	537.99	219.9	549.26	247.8	560.16	278.1	570.72	310.8	580.93	346.1
2140	1680	543.59	228.5	555.03	257.8	566.10	289.6	576.81	324.0	587.18	361.2
2160	1700	549.20	237.4	560.81	268.1	572.04	301.5	582.91	337.7	593.44	376.8
2180	1720	554.82	246.5	566.60	278.7	578.00	313.8	589.03	351.9	599.71	393.0
2200	1740	560.44	255.9	572.39	289.7	583.96	326.5	595.15	366.5	605.99	409.8
2220	1760	566.07	265.6	578.20	301.0	589.93	339.6	601.28	381.6	612.28	427.1
2240	1780	571.71	275.6	584.01	312.6	595.91	353.1	607.43	397.2	618.58	445.1
2260	1800	577.35	285.8	589.83	324.6	601.90	367.1	613.58	413.4	624.89	463.6
2280	1820	583.00	296.4	595.66	337.0	607.90	381.5	619.74	430.0	631.21	482.8
2300	1840	588.66	307.3	601.49	349.8	613.90	396.4	625.91	447.3	637.54	502.6
2320	1860	594.33	318.5	607.34	362.9	619.92	411.7	632.10	465.0	643.89	523.1
2340	1880	600.00	330.0	613.19	376.5	625.94	427.5	638.29	483.4	650.24	544.3
2360	1900	605.68	341.8	619.05	390.4	631.97	443.8	644.49	502.3	656.60	566.2
2380	1920	611.37	354.0	624.91	404.7	638.01	460.6	650.69	521.8	662.97	588.8
2400	1940	617.06	366.5	630.78	419.5	644.06	477.9	656.91	542.0	669.35	612.1
2420	1960	622.76	379.4	636.66	434.7	650.12	495.7	663.14	562.8	675.74	636.2
2440	1980	628.46	392.6	642.55	450.3	656.18	514.1	669.37	584.2	682.14	661.1
2460	2000	634.17	406.2	648.45	466.4	662.25	533.0	675.61	606.3	688.55	686.7
2480	2020	639.89	420.2	654.35	482.9	668.33	552.4	681.86	629.1	694.97	713.2
2500	2040	645.62	434.5	660.26	499.9	674.42	572.5	688.12	652.5	701.39	740.5
2520	2060	651.34	449.2	666.17	517.4	680.51	593.1	694.39	676.7	707.83	768.6
2540	2080	657.08	464.3	672.09	535.4	686.61	614.3	700.66	711.6	714.27	797.7
2560	2100	662.82	479.8	678.02	553.8	692.72	636.1	706.95	727.2	720.72	827.6
2580	2120	668.57	495.7	683.95	572.8	698.83	658.6	713.24	753.6	727.18	858.4
2600	2140	674.32	512.0	689.89	592.3	704.96	681.7	719.53	780.8	733.65	890.2
2620	2160	680.08	528.8	695.84	612.3	711.09	705.4	725.84	808.7	740.13	923.0
2640	2180	685.84	546.0	701.79	632.8	717.22	729.8	732.15	837.5	746.61	956.7
2660	2200	691.61	563.6	707.75	653.9	723.36	754.9	738.47	867.1	753.11	991.4
2680	2220	697.38	581.6	713.72	675.6	729.51	780.6	744.80	897.6	759.61	1027.2
2700	2240	703.16	600.2	719.69	697.8	735.67	807.1	751.14	928.9	766.12	1064.0

English units

T		f = 0		f = 0.0169		f = 0.0338		f = 0.0507		f = 0.0676	
°R	°F	h (Btu/lbm)	P_r	h (Btu/lbm)	P_r	h (Btu/lbm)	P_r	h (Btu/lbm)	P_r	h (Btu/lbm)	P_r
2700	2240	703.16	600.2	719.69	697.8	735.67	807.1	751.14	928.9	766.12	1064.0
2720	2260	708.95	619.2	725.66	720.6	741.83	834.3	757.48	961.1	772.63	1101.9
2740	2280	714.74	638.6	731.65	744.0	748.00	862.2	763.83	994.2	779.16	1141.0
2760	2300	720.53	658.6	737.63	768.0	754.18	890.9	770.19	1028.3	785.69	1181.1
2780	2320	726.33	679.0	743.63	792.6	760.36	920.4	776.55	1063.3	792.23	1222.4
2800	2340	732.14	699.9	749.63	817.9	766.55	950.6	782.92	1099.2	798.77	1264.9
2820	2360	737.95	721.3	755.63	843.8	772.74	981.6	789.30	1136.1	805.33	1308.5
2840	2380	743.77	743.3	761.65	870.3	778.94	1013.5	795.68	1174.1	811.89	1353.4
2860	2400	749.59	765.8	767.66	897.5	785.15	1046.2	802.07	1213.1	818.46	1399.6
2880	2420	755.41	788.8	773.68	925.4	791.36	1079.7	808.47	1253.1	825.03	1447.1
2900	2440	761.24	812.3	779.71	954.0	797.58	1114.1	814.87	1294.2	831.61	1495.9
2920	2460	767.08	836.4	785.74	983.2	803.80	1149.3	821.28	1336.4	838.20	1546.0
2940	2480	772.91	861.1	791.78	1013.2	810.03	1185.5	827.69	1379.7	844.80	1597.5
2960	2500	778.76	886.4	797.82	1044.0	816.27	1222.6	834.12	1424.1	851.40	1650.4
2980	2520	784.61	912.2	803.87	1075.4	822.51	1260.6	840.54	1469.7	858.01	1704.7
3000	2540	790.46	938.6	809.93	1107.6	828.75	1299.6	846.98	1516.5	864.63	1760.5
3020	2560	796.32	965.7	815.98	1140.6	835.01	1339.5	853.42	1564.5	871.25	1817.9
3040	2580	802.18	993.3	822.05	1174.4	841.27	1380.5	859.87	1613.8	877.88	1876.7
3060	2600	808.05	1021.6	828.12	1209.0	847.53	1422.4	866.32	1664.3	884.51	1937.0
3080	2620	813.92	1050.5	834.19	1244.3	853.80	1465.4	872.78	1716.1	891.15	1999.0
3100	2640	819.79	1080.0	840.27	1280.6	860.07	1509.4	879.24	1769.2	897.80	2063
3120	2660	825.67	1110.2	846.35	1317.6	866.35	1554.4	885.71	1823.6	904.45	2128
3140	2680	831.55	1141.1	852.44	1355.5	872.63	1600.6	892.18	1879.4	911.11	2195
3160	2700	837.44	1172.6	858.53	1394.3	878.92	1647.8	898.66	1936.5	917.78	2263
3180	2720	843.33	1204.9	864.62	1433.9	885.22	1696.2	905.15	1995.1	924.45	2334
3200	2740	849.23	1237.8	870.73	1474.5	891.52	1745.8	911.64	2055	931.13	2406
3220	2760	855.13	1271.5	876.83	1515.9	897.82	1796.4	918.14	2117	937.81	2480
3240	2780	861.03	1305.8	882.94	1558.3	904.13	1848.3	924.64	2180	944.50	2556
3260	2800	866.94	1340.9	889.06	1601.7	910.45	1901.4	931.15	2244	951.20	2634
3280	2820	872.85	1376.8	895.17	1646.0	916.77	1955.7	937.66	2310	957.90	2714
3300	2840	878.77	1413.4	901.30	1691.2	923.09	2011	944.18	2378	964.60	2795
3320	2860	884.69	1450.7	907.43	1737.5	929.42	2068	950.70	2447	971.31	2879
3340	2880	890.61	1488.8	913.56	1784.8	935.75	2126	957.23	2518	978.03	2965
3360	2900	896.54	1527.8	919.69	1833.1	942.09	2186	963.76	2590	984.75	3053
3380	2920	902.47	1567.5	925.83	1882.4	948.43	2246	970.30	2665	991.48	3143
3400	2940	908.40	1608.1	931.98	1932.8	954.78	2309	976.84	2741	998.21	3235
3420	2960	914.34	1649.4	938.12	1984.3	961.13	2372	983.39	2818	1004.95	3329
3440	2980	920.28	1691.6	944.27	2037	967.48	2437	989.94	2898	1011.69	3426
3460	3000	926.23	1734.7	950.43	2091	973.84	2503	996.49	2979	1018.43	3524
3480	3020	932.18	1778.6	956.59	2145	980.20	2571	1003.05	3062	1025.18	3626
3500	3040	938.13	1823.4	962.75	2201	986.57	2640	1009.62	3147	1031.94	3730

English units

T		f = 0		f = 0.0169		f = 0.0338		f = 0.0507		f = 0.0676	
°R	°F	h (Btu/lbm)	P_r	h (Btu/lbm)	P_r	h (Btu/lbm)	P_r	h (Btu/lbm)	P_r	h (Btu/lbm)	P_r
3500	3040	938.13	1823.4	962.75	2201	986.57	2640	1009.62	3147	1031.94	3730
3520	3060	944.08	1869.1	968.92	2258	992.94	2711	1016.19	3234	1038.70	3836
3540	3080	950.04	1915.7	975.08	2317	999.31	2783	1022.76	3323	1045.46	3944
3560	3100	956.00	1963.2	981.26	2376	1005.69	2857	1029.34	3414	1052.23	4055
3580	3120	961.96	2012	987.43	2437	1012.07	2933	1035.92	3507	1059.01	4169
3600	3140	967.93	2062	993.61	2499	1018.46	3010	1042.50	3602	1065.78	4285
3620	3160	973.90	2111	999.80	2562	1024.85	3088	1049.09	3699	1072.57	4404
3640	3180	979.87	2163	1005.98	2627	1031.24	3169	1055.68	3798	1079.35	4525
3660	3200	985.85	2215	1012.17	2692	1037.63	3251	1062.28	3899	1086.14	4649
3680	3220	991.83	2268	1018.36	2759	1044.03	3334	1068.88	4003	1092.93	4776
3700	3240	997.81	2322	1024.56	2828	1050.44	3420	1075.48	4109	1099.73	4906
3720	3260	1003.79	2378	1030.76	2897	1056.84	3507	1082.09	4217	1106.53	5039
3740	3280	1009.78	2434	1036.96	2969	1063.25	3596	1088.70	4327	1113.34	5174
3760	3300	1015.77	2492	1043.16	3041	1069.66	3686	1095.31	4439	1120.15	5313
3780	3320	1021.76	2550	1049.37	3115	1076.08	3779	1101.93	4554	1126.96	5455
3800	3340	1027.76	2610	1055.58	3190	1082.50	3873	1108.55	4672	1133.77	5599
3820	3360	1033.75	2670	1061.80	3267	1088.92	3970	1115.17	4792	1140.59	5747
3840	3380	1039.75	2732	1068.01	3345	1095.34	4068	1121.80	4914	1147.41	5898
3860	3400	1045.76	2795	1074.23	3425	1101.77	4168	1128.43	5039	1154.24	6052
3880	3420	1051.76	2859	1080.45	3506	1108.21	4270	1135.06	5166	1161.07	6210
3900	3440	1057.77	2924	1086.68	3589	1114.64	4374	1141.70	5296	1167.91	6371
3920	3460	1063.78	2990	1092.91	3673	1121.08	4481	1148.34	5429	1174.74	6535
3940	3480	1069.80	3058	1099.14	3759	1127.52	4589	1154.99	5564	1181.58	6703
3960	3500	1075.81	3126	1105.37	3847	1133.96	4699	1161.63	5702	1188.43	6874
3980	3520	1081.83	3196	1111.61	3936	1140.41	4812	1168.29	5843	1195.28	7049
4000	3540	1087.86	3268	1117.85	4027	1146.86	4927	1174.94	5987	1202.13	7227

APPENDIX E

COMPRESSIBLE FLOW FUNCTIONS

$$\frac{T}{T_t} = \left(1 + \frac{\gamma - 1}{2} M^2\right)^{-1}$$

$$\frac{P}{P_t} = \left(1 + \frac{\gamma - 1}{2} M^2\right)^{-\gamma/(\gamma-1)}$$

$$\frac{\rho}{\rho_t} = \left(1 + \frac{\gamma - 1}{2} M^2\right)^{-1/(\gamma-1)}$$

$$\frac{A}{A^*} = \frac{1}{M}\left[\frac{2}{\gamma + 1}\left(1 + \frac{\gamma - 1}{2} M^2\right)\right]^{(\gamma+1)/[2(\gamma-1)]}$$

$$\text{MFP}(M)\sqrt{\frac{R}{g_c}} = \frac{\dot{m}\sqrt{T_t}}{P_t A}\sqrt{\frac{R}{g_c}} = \frac{M\sqrt{\gamma}}{\{1 + [(\gamma - 1)/2]M^2\}^{(\gamma+1)/[2(\gamma-1)]}}$$

For air,

$$\sqrt{\frac{R}{g_c}} = 1.28758 \text{ lbf} \cdot \text{sec}/(\text{lbm} \cdot \sqrt{°\text{R}}) \qquad \text{or} \qquad \sqrt{\frac{R}{g_c}} = 16.9115 \text{ N} \cdot \text{sec}/(\text{kg} \cdot \sqrt{\text{K}})$$

Compressible flow functions ($\gamma = 1.4$)

M	T/T_t	P/P_t	ρ/ρ_t	A/A^*	$\mathbf{MFP}\sqrt{R/g_c}$	M
0	1	1	1	Indef	0	0
0.01	0.999980	0.999930	0.999950	57.8738	0.011831	0.01
0.02	0.999920	0.999720	0.999800	28.9421	0.023659	0.02
0.03	0.999820	0.999370	0.999550	19.3005	0.035477	0.03
0.04	0.999680	0.998881	0.999200	14.4815	0.047283	0.04
0.05	0.999500	0.998252	0.998751	11.5914	0.059072	0.05
0.06	0.999281	0.997484	0.998202	9.66591	0.070840	0.06
0.07	0.999021	0.996578	0.997554	8.29153	0.082582	0.07
0.08	0.998722	0.995533	0.996807	7.26161	0.094295	0.08
0.09	0.998383	0.994351	0.995961	6.46134	0.105974	0.09
0.10	0.998004	0.993031	0.995017	5.82183	0.117614	0.10
0.11	0.997586	0.991576	0.993976	5.29923	0.129213	0.11
0.12	0.997128	0.989985	0.992836	4.86432	0.140766	0.12
0.13	0.996631	0.988259	0.991600	4.49686	0.152269	0.13
0.14	0.996095	0.986400	0.990267	4.18240	0.163717	0.14
0.15	0.995520	0.984408	0.988838	3.91034	0.175108	0.15
0.16	0.994906	0.982285	0.987314	3.67274	0.186436	0.16
0.17	0.994253	0.980030	0.985695	3.46351	0.197699	0.17
0.18	0.993562	0.977647	0.983982	3.27793	0.208892	0.18
0.19	0.992832	0.975135	0.982176	3.11226	0.220011	0.19
0.20	0.992063	0.972497	0.980277	2.96352	0.231053	0.20
0.21	0.991257	0.969733	0.978286	2.82929	0.242015	0.21
0.22	0.990413	0.966845	0.976204	2.70760	0.252892	0.22
0.23	0.989531	0.963835	0.974032	2.59681	0.263682	0.23
0.24	0.988611	0.960703	0.971771	2.49556	0.274380	0.24
0.25	0.987654	0.957453	0.969421	2.40271	0.284983	0.25
0.26	0.986660	0.954085	0.966984	2.31729	0.295488	0.26
0.27	0.985630	0.950600	0.964460	2.23847	0.305893	0.27
0.28	0.984562	0.947002	0.961851	2.16555	0.316192	0.28
0.29	0.983458	0.943291	0.959157	2.09793	0.326385	0.29
0.30	0.982318	0.939470	0.956380	2.03507	0.336467	0.30
0.31	0.981142	0.935540	0.953521	1.97651	0.346435	0.31
0.32	0.979931	0.931503	0.950580	1.92185	0.356287	0.32
0.33	0.978684	0.927362	0.947560	1.87074	0.366021	0.33
0.34	0.977402	0.923118	0.944460	1.82288	0.375633	0.34
0.35	0.976086	0.918773	0.941283	1.77797	0.385120	0.35
0.36	0.974735	0.914330	0.938029	1.73578	0.394481	0.36
0.37	0.973350	0.909790	0.934700	1.69609	0.403713	0.37
0.38	0.971931	0.905156	0.931297	1.65870	0.412813	0.38
0.39	0.970478	0.900430	0.927821	1.62343	0.421780	0.39
0.40	0.968992	0.895614	0.924274	1.59014	0.430611	0.40
0.41	0.967474	0.890711	0.920657	1.55867	0.439304	0.41
0.42	0.965922	0.885722	0.916971	1.52890	0.447857	0.42
0.43	0.964339	0.880651	0.913217	1.50072	0.456269	0.43
0.44	0.962723	0.875498	0.909398	1.47401	0.464538	0.44
0.45	0.961076	0.870267	0.905513	1.44867	0.472662	0.45
0.46	0.959398	0.864960	0.901566	1.42463	0.480639	0.46
0.47	0.957689	0.859580	0.897556	1.40180	0.488468	0.47
0.48	0.955950	0.854128	0.893486	1.38010	0.496147	0.48
0.49	0.954180	0.848607	0.889357	1.35947	0.503676	0.49
0.50	0.952381	0.843019	0.885170	1.33984	0.511053	0.50

Compressible flow functions ($\gamma = 1.4$)

M	T/T_t	P/P_t	ρ/ρ_t	A/A^*	$\text{MFP}\sqrt{R/g_c}$	M
0.50	0.952381	0.843019	0.885170	1.33984	0.511053	0.50
0.51	0.950552	0.837367	0.880927	1.32117	0.518277	0.51
0.52	0.948695	0.831654	0.876629	1.30339	0.525347	0.52
0.53	0.946808	0.825881	0.872278	1.28645	0.532263	0.53
0.54	0.944894	0.820050	0.867876	1.27032	0.539022	0.54
0.55	0.942951	0.814165	0.863422	1.25495	0.545626	0.55
0.56	0.940982	0.808228	0.858920	1.24029	0.552072	0.56
0.57	0.938985	0.802241	0.854371	1.22633	0.558360	0.57
0.58	0.936961	0.796206	0.849775	1.21301	0.564491	0.58
0.59	0.934911	0.790127	0.845135	1.20031	0.570463	0.59
0.60	0.932836	0.784004	0.840452	1.18820	0.576277	0.60
0.61	0.930735	0.777841	0.835728	1.17665	0.581931	0.61
0.62	0.928609	0.771639	0.830963	1.16565	0.587427	0.62
0.63	0.926458	0.765402	0.826160	1.15515	0.592764	0.63
0.64	0.924283	0.759131	0.821319	1.14515	0.597941	0.64
0.65	0.922084	0.752829	0.816443	1.13562	0.602960	0.65
0.66	0.919862	0.746498	0.811533	1.12654	0.607821	0.66
0.67	0.917616	0.740140	0.806590	1.11789	0.612523	0.67
0.68	0.915349	0.733758	0.801616	1.10965	0.617067	0.68
0.69	0.913059	0.727353	0.796612	1.10182	0.621454	0.69
0.70	0.910747	0.720928	0.791579	1.09437	0.625684	0.70
0.71	0.908414	0.714485	0.786519	1.08729	0.629758	0.71
0.72	0.906060	0.708025	0.781434	1.08057	0.633676	0.72
0.73	0.903685	0.701552	0.776324	1.07419	0.637439	0.73
0.74	0.901291	0.695068	0.771191	1.06814	0.641048	0.74
0.75	0.898876	0.688573	0.766037	1.06242	0.644503	0.75
0.76	0.896443	0.682070	0.760863	1.05700	0.647807	0.76
0.77	0.893991	0.675562	0.755670	1.05188	0.650959	0.77
0.78	0.891520	0.669050	0.750460	1.04705	0.653961	0.78
0.79	0.889031	0.662536	0.745234	1.04251	0.656813	0.79
0.80	0.886525	0.656022	0.739992	1.03823	0.659518	0.80
0.81	0.884001	0.649509	0.734738	1.03422	0.662076	0.81
0.82	0.881461	0.643000	0.729471	1.03046	0.664488	0.82
0.83	0.878905	0.636496	0.724193	1.02696	0.666756	0.83
0.84	0.876332	0.630000	0.718905	1.02370	0.668882	0.84
0.85	0.873744	0.623512	0.713609	1.02067	0.670866	0.85
0.86	0.871141	0.617034	0.708306	1.01787	0.672710	0.86
0.87	0.868523	0.610569	0.702997	1.01530	0.674415	0.87
0.88	0.865891	0.604117	0.697683	1.01294	0.675984	0.88
0.89	0.863245	0.597680	0.692365	1.01080	0.677417	0.89
0.90	0.860585	0.591260	0.687044	1.008863	0.678716	0.90
0.91	0.857913	0.584858	0.681722	1.007131	0.679883	0.91
0.92	0.855227	0.578476	0.676400	1.005597	0.680920	0.92
0.93	0.852529	0.572114	0.671079	1.004258	0.681828	0.93
0.94	0.849820	0.565775	0.665759	1.003108	0.682610	0.94
0.95	0.847099	0.559460	0.660443	1.0021452	0.683266	0.95
0.96	0.844366	0.553170	0.655130	1.0013646	0.683798	0.96
0.97	0.841623	0.546905	0.649822	1.0007630	0.684209	0.97
0.98	0.838870	0.540669	0.644520	1.0003371	0.684501	0.98
0.99	0.836106	0.534460	0.639225	1.0000838	0.684674	0.99
1.00	0.833333	0.528282	0.633938	1.0000000	0.684731	1.00

Compressible flow functions ($\gamma = 1.4$)

M	T/T_t	P/P_t	ρ/ρ_t	A/A^*	MFP$\sqrt{R/g_c}$	M
1.00	0.833333	0.528282	0.633938	1.0000000	0.684731	1.00
1.01	0.830551	0.522134	0.628660	1.0000829	0.684675	1.01
1.02	0.827760	0.516018	0.623391	1.0003297	0.684506	1.02
1.03	0.824960	0.509935	0.618133	1.0007380	0.684227	1.03
1.04	0.822152	0.503886	0.612887	1.0013052	0.683839	1.04
1.05	0.819336	0.497872	0.607653	1.0020291	0.683345	1.05
1.06	0.816513	0.491894	0.602432	1.002907	0.682746	1.06
1.07	0.813683	0.485952	0.597225	1.003938	0.682046	1.07
1.08	0.810846	0.480047	0.592033	1.005119	0.681244	1.08
1.09	0.808002	0.474181	0.586856	1.006449	0.680344	1.09
1.10	0.805153	0.468354	0.581696	1.007925	0.679347	1.10
1.11	0.802298	0.462567	0.576553	1.009547	0.678256	1.11
1.12	0.799437	0.456820	0.571427	1.01131	0.677072	1.12
1.13	0.796572	0.451114	0.566320	1.01322	0.675798	1.13
1.14	0.793701	0.445451	0.561232	1.01527	0.674435	1.14
1.15	0.790826	0.439829	0.556164	1.01745	0.672985	1.15
1.16	0.787948	0.434251	0.551116	1.01978	0.671450	1.16
1.17	0.785065	0.428716	0.546090	1.02224	0.669833	1.17
1.18	0.782179	0.423225	0.541085	1.02484	0.668135	1.18
1.19	0.779290	0.417778	0.536102	1.02757	0.666358	1.19
1.20	0.776398	0.412377	0.531142	1.03044	0.664504	1.20
1.21	0.773503	0.407021	0.526205	1.03344	0.662575	1.21
1.22	0.770606	0.401711	0.521292	1.03657	0.660573	1.22
1.23	0.767707	0.396446	0.516403	1.03983	0.658500	1.23
1.24	0.764807	0.391229	0.511539	1.04323	0.656358	1.24
1.25	0.761905	0.386058	0.506701	1.04675	0.654148	1.25
1.26	0.759002	0.380934	0.501888	1.05041	0.651873	1.26
1.27	0.756098	0.375857	0.497102	1.05419	0.649534	1.27
1.28	0.753194	0.370828	0.492342	1.05810	0.647133	1.28
1.29	0.750289	0.365847	0.487608	1.06214	0.644673	1.29
1.30	0.747384	0.360914	0.482903	1.06630	0.642154	1.30
1.31	0.744480	0.356029	0.478225	1.07060	0.639579	1.31
1.32	0.741576	0.351192	0.473575	1.07502	0.636949	1.32
1.33	0.738672	0.346403	0.468953	1.07957	0.634266	1.33
1.34	0.735770	0.341663	0.464361	1.08424	0.631532	1.34
1.35	0.732869	0.336971	0.459797	1.08904	0.628749	1.35
1.36	0.729970	0.332328	0.455263	1.09396	0.625918	1.36
1.37	0.727072	0.327733	0.450758	1.09902	0.623041	1.37
1.38	0.724176	0.323187	0.446283	1.10419	0.620119	1.38
1.39	0.721282	0.318690	0.441838	1.10950	0.617155	1.39
1.40	0.718391	0.314241	0.437423	1.11493	0.614150	1.40
1.41	0.715502	0.309840	0.433039	1.12048	0.611105	1.41
1.42	0.712616	0.305488	0.428686	1.12616	0.608022	1.42
1.43	0.709733	0.301185	0.424363	1.13197	0.604903	1.43
1.44	0.706854	0.296929	0.420072	1.13790	0.601749	1.44
1.45	0.703977	0.292722	0.415812	1.14396	0.598561	1.45
1.46	0.701105	0.288563	0.411583	1.15015	0.595341	1.46
1.47	0.698236	0.284452	0.407386	1.15646	0.592091	1.47
1.48	0.695372	0.280388	0.403220	1.16290	0.588812	1.48
1.49	0.692511	0.276372	0.399086	1.16947	0.585505	1.49
1.50	0.689655	0.272403	0.394984	1.17617	0.582172	1.50

Compressible flow functions ($\gamma = 1.4$)

M	T/T_t	P/P_t	ρ/ρ_t	A/A^*	MFP$\sqrt{R/g_c}$	M
1.50	0.689655	0.272403	0.394984	1.17617	0.582172	1.50
1.51	0.686804	0.268481	0.390914	1.18299	0.578814	1.51
1.52	0.683957	0.264607	0.386876	1.18994	0.575432	1.52
1.53	0.681115	0.260779	0.382870	1.19702	0.572028	1.53
1.54	0.678279	0.256997	0.378897	1.20423	0.568603	1.54
1.55	0.675447	0.253262	0.374955	1.21157	0.565159	1.55
1.56	0.672622	0.249573	0.371045	1.21904	0.561696	1.56
1.57	0.669801	0.245930	0.367168	1.22664	0.558215	1.57
1.58	0.666987	0.242332	0.363323	1.23438	0.554719	1.58
1.59	0.664178	0.238779	0.359510	1.24224	0.551207	1.59
1.60	0.661376	0.235271	0.355730	1.25023	0.547682	1.60
1.61	0.658579	0.231808	0.351982	1.25836	0.544144	1.61
1.62	0.655789	0.228389	0.348266	1.26663	0.540595	1.62
1.63	0.653006	0.225014	0.344582	1.27502	0.537035	1.63
1.64	0.650229	0.221683	0.340930	1.28355	0.533466	1.64
1.65	0.647459	0.218395	0.337311	1.29222	0.529888	1.65
1.66	0.644695	0.215150	0.333723	1.30102	0.526303	1.66
1.67	0.641939	0.211948	0.330168	1.30996	0.522712	1.67
1.68	0.639190	0.208788	0.326644	1.31904	0.519115	1.68
1.69	0.636448	0.205670	0.323152	1.32825	0.515513	1.69
1.70	0.633714	0.202593	0.319693	1.33761	0.511908	1.70
1.71	0.630986	0.199558	0.316264	1.34710	0.508300	1.71
1.72	0.628267	0.196564	0.312868	1.35674	0.504691	1.72
1.73	0.625555	0.193611	0.309502	1.36651	0.501080	1.73
1.74	0.622851	0.190697	0.306169	1.37643	0.497469	1.74
1.75	0.620155	0.187824	0.302866	1.38649	0.493859	1.75
1.76	0.617467	0.184990	0.299595	1.39670	0.490250	1.76
1.77	0.614787	0.182195	0.296354	1.40705	0.486644	1.77
1.78	0.612115	0.179438	0.293145	1.41755	0.483040	1.78
1.79	0.609451	0.176720	0.289966	1.42819	0.479440	1.79
1.80	0.606796	0.174040	0.286818	1.43898	0.475844	1.80
1.81	0.604149	0.171398	0.283701	1.44992	0.472254	1.81
1.82	0.601511	0.168792	0.280614	1.46101	0.468669	1.82
1.83	0.598881	0.166224	0.277557	1.47225	0.465090	1.83
1.84	0.596260	0.163691	0.274530	1.48365	0.461519	1.84
1.85	0.593648	0.161195	0.271533	1.49519	0.457955	1.85
1.86	0.591044	0.158734	0.268566	1.50689	0.454399	1.86
1.87	0.588450	0.156309	0.265628	1.51875	0.450852	1.87
1.88	0.585864	0.153918	0.262720	1.53076	0.447314	1.88
1.89	0.583288	0.151562	0.259841	1.54293	0.443787	1.89
1.90	0.580720	0.149240	0.256991	1.55526	0.440269	1.90
1.91	0.578162	0.146951	0.254169	1.56774	0.436762	1.91
1.92	0.575612	0.144696	0.251377	1.58039	0.433267	1.92
1.93	0.573072	0.142473	0.248613	1.59320	0.429784	1.93
1.94	0.570542	0.140283	0.245877	1.60617	0.426313	1.94
1.95	0.568020	0.138126	0.243170	1.61931	0.422854	1.95
1.96	0.565509	0.135999	0.240490	1.63261	0.419409	1.96
1.97	0.563006	0.133905	0.237839	1.64608	0.415977	1.97
1.98	0.560513	0.131841	0.235215	1.65972	0.412559	1.98
1.99	0.558029	0.129808	0.232618	1.67352	0.409156	1.99
2.00	0.555556	0.127805	0.230048	1.68750	0.405767	2.00

Compressible flow functions ($\gamma = 1.4$)

M	T/T_t	P/P_t	ρ/ρ_t	A/A^*	**MFP**$\sqrt{R/g_c}$	M
2.00	0.555556	0.127805	0.230048	1.68750	0.405767	2.00
2.02	0.550637	0.123888	0.224990	1.71597	0.399035	2.02
2.04	0.545756	0.120087	0.220037	1.74514	0.392365	2.04
2.06	0.540915	0.116399	0.215190	1.77502	0.385761	2.06
2.08	0.536113	0.112823	0.210446	1.80561	0.379224	2.08
2.10	0.531350	0.109353	0.205803	1.83694	0.372756	2.10
2.12	0.526626	0.105988	0.201259	1.86902	0.366359	2.12
2.14	0.521942	0.102726	0.196814	1.90184	0.360036	2.14
2.16	0.517298	0.0995621	0.192466	1.93544	0.353787	2.16
2.18	0.512694	0.0964950	0.188212	1.96981	0.347613	2.18
2.20	0.508130	0.0935217	0.184051	2.00497	0.341516	2.20
2.22	0.503606	0.0906395	0.179981	2.04094	0.335497	2.22
2.24	0.499122	0.0878460	0.176001	2.07773	0.329557	2.24
2.26	0.494677	0.0851387	0.172110	2.11535	0.323697	2.26
2.28	0.490273	0.0825150	0.168304	2.15381	0.317916	2.28
2.30	0.485909	0.0799726	0.164584	2.19313	0.312216	2.30
2.32	0.481584	0.0775091	0.160946	2.23332	0.306598	2.32
2.34	0.477300	0.0751223	0.157390	2.27440	0.301060	2.34
2.36	0.473055	0.0728098	0.153914	2.31638	0.295604	2.36
2.38	0.468850	0.0705696	0.150516	2.35928	0.290230	2.38
2.40	0.464684	0.0683994	0.147195	2.40310	0.284937	2.40
2.42	0.460558	0.0662971	0.143950	2.44787	0.279725	2.42
2.44	0.456471	0.0642608	0.140777	2.49360	0.274595	2.44
2.46	0.452423	0.0622884	0.137677	2.54031	0.269546	2.46
2.48	0.448414	0.0603780	0.134648	2.58801	0.264578	2.48
2.50	0.444444	0.0585277	0.131687	2.63672	0.259691	2.50
2.52	0.440513	0.0567356	0.128794	2.68645	0.254883	2.52
2.54	0.436620	0.0550001	0.125968	2.73723	0.250155	2.54
2.56	0.432766	0.0533193	0.123206	2.78906	0.245506	2.56
2.58	0.428949	0.0516915	0.120507	2.84197	0.240935	2.58
2.60	0.425170	0.0501152	0.117871	2.89598	0.236442	2.60
2.62	0.421429	0.0485886	0.115295	2.95109	0.232027	2.62
2.64	0.417725	0.0471103	0.112778	3.00733	0.227687	2.64
2.66	0.414058	0.0456788	0.110320	3.06472	0.223424	2.66
2.68	0.410428	0.0442925	0.107918	3.12327	0.219235	2.68
2.70	0.406835	0.0429500	0.105571	3.18301	0.215121	2.70
2.72	0.403278	0.0416500	0.103279	3.24395	0.211079	2.72
2.74	0.399757	0.0403911	0.101039	3.30611	0.207111	2.74
2.76	0.396272	0.0391721	0.098851	3.36952	0.203214	2.76
2.78	0.392822	0.0379915	0.096714	3.43418	0.199387	2.78
2.80	0.389408	0.0368483	0.094626	3.50012	0.195631	2.80
2.82	0.386029	0.0357412	0.092587	3.56737	0.191943	2.82
2.84	0.382684	0.0346691	0.090594	3.63593	0.188323	2.84
2.86	0.379374	0.0336308	0.088648	3.70584	0.184771	2.86
2.88	0.376098	0.0326253	0.086747	3.77711	0.181284	2.88
2.90	0.372856	0.0316515	0.084889	3.84977	0.177863	2.90
2.92	0.369648	0.0307084	0.083075	3.92383	0.174506	2.92
2.94	0.366472	0.0297950	0.081302	3.99932	0.171212	2.94
2.96	0.363330	0.0289104	0.079571	4.07625	0.167981	2.96
2.98	0.360220	0.0280536	0.077879	4.15466	0.164810	2.98
3.00	0.357143	0.0272237	0.076226	4.23457	0.161700	3.00

Compressible flow functions ($\gamma = 1.4$)

M	T/T_t	P/P_t	ρ/ρ_t	A/A^*	$\text{MFP}\sqrt{R/g_c}$	M
3.00	0.357143	0.0272237	0.076226	4.23457	0.1617004	3.00
3.02	0.354098	0.0264199	0.074612	4.31599	0.1586500	3.02
3.04	0.351084	0.0256413	0.073034	4.39895	0.1556579	3.04
3.06	0.348102	0.0248871	0.071494	4.48347	0.1527234	3.06
3.08	0.345151	0.0241565	0.069988	4.56959	0.1498454	3.08
3.10	0.342231	0.0234487	0.068517	4.65731	0.1470229	3.10
3.12	0.339342	0.0227631	0.067080	4.74667	0.1442551	3.12
3.14	0.336483	0.0220989	0.065676	4.83769	0.1415410	3.14
3.16	0.333654	0.0214553	0.064304	4.93039	0.1388797	3.16
3.18	0.330854	0.0208319	0.062964	5.02481	0.1362702	3.18
3.20	0.328084	0.0202278	0.061654	5.12096	0.1337116	3.20
3.22	0.325343	0.0196424	0.060374	5.21887	0.1312031	3.22
3.24	0.322631	0.0190752	0.059124	5.31857	0.1287436	3.24
3.26	0.319947	0.0185256	0.057902	5.42008	0.1263324	3.26
3.28	0.317291	0.0179930	0.056708	5.52343	0.1239685	3.28
3.30	0.314663	0.0174768	0.055541	5.62865	0.1216512	3.30
3.32	0.312063	0.0169765	0.054401	5.73576	0.1193794	3.32
3.34	0.309490	0.0164917	0.053287	5.84479	0.1171524	3.34
3.36	0.306944	0.0160217	0.052197	5.95577	0.1149693	3.36
3.38	0.304425	0.0155662	0.051133	6.06873	0.1128294	3.38
3.40	0.301932	0.0151246	0.050093	6.18370	0.1107317	3.40
3.42	0.299466	0.0146965	0.049076	6.30070	0.1086755	3.42
3.44	0.297025	0.0142816	0.048082	6.41976	0.1066600	3.44
3.46	0.294610	0.0138792	0.047111	6.54092	0.1046844	3.46
3.48	0.292220	0.0134891	0.046161	6.66419	0.1027479	3.48
3.50	0.289855	0.0131109	0.045233	6.78962	0.1008497	3.50
3.52	0.287515	0.0127442	0.044325	6.91723	0.0989892	3.52
3.54	0.285199	0.0123885	0.043438	7.04705	0.0971656	3.54
3.56	0.282908	0.0120436	0.042571	7.17912	0.0953782	3.56
3.58	0.280640	0.0117091	0.041723	7.31346	0.0936262	3.58
3.60	0.278396	0.0113847	0.040894	7.45011	0.0919089	3.60
3.62	0.276176	0.0110701	0.040083	7.58910	0.0902257	3.62
3.64	0.273979	0.0107649	0.039291	7.73045	0.0885759	3.64
3.66	0.271804	0.0104688	0.038516	7.87421	0.0869587	3.66
3.68	0.269652	0.0101816	0.037758	8.02040	0.0853737	3.68
3.70	0.267523	0.0099029	0.037017	8.16907	0.0838200	3.70
3.72	0.265415	0.0096325	0.036292	8.32023	0.0822972	3.72
3.74	0.263330	0.0093702	0.035584	8.47393	0.0808045	3.74
3.76	0.261266	0.0091157	0.034890	8.63020	0.0793413	3.76
3.78	0.259223	0.0088687	0.034212	8.78907	0.0779071	3.78
3.80	0.257202	0.0086290	0.033549	8.95059	0.0765013	3.80
3.82	0.255201	0.0083963	0.032901	9.11477	0.0751233	3.82
3.84	0.253221	0.0081705	0.032266	9.28167	0.0737725	3.84
3.86	0.251261	0.0079513	0.031646	9.45131	0.0724483	3.86
3.88	0.249322	0.0077386	0.031039	9.62373	0.0711503	3.88
3.90	0.247402	0.0075320	0.030445	9.79897	0.0698779	3.90
3.92	0.245502	0.0073315	0.029863	9.97707	0.0686305	3.92
3.94	0.243622	0.0071369	0.029295	10.1581	0.0674077	3.94
3.96	0.241761	0.0069479	0.028739	10.3420	0.0662090	3.96
3.98	0.239919	0.0067643	0.028194	10.5289	0.0650338	3.98
4.00	0.238095	0.0065861	0.027662	10.7188	0.0638817	4.00

Compressible flow functions ($\gamma = 1.33$)

M	T/T_t	P/P_t	ρ/ρ_t	A/A^*	MFP$\sqrt{R/g_c}$	M
0	1	1	1	Indef	0	0
0.01	0.999984	0.999934	0.999950	58.3277	0.011532	0.01
0.02	0.999934	0.999734	0.999800	29.1689	0.023060	0.02
0.03	0.999852	0.999402	0.999550	19.4516	0.034580	0.03
0.04	0.999736	0.998937	0.999200	14.5947	0.046087	0.04
0.05	0.999588	0.998339	0.998751	11.6819	0.057579	0.05
0.06	0.999406	0.997610	0.998202	9.74111	0.069050	0.06
0.07	0.999192	0.996748	0.997554	8.35585	0.080498	0.07
0.08	0.998945	0.995755	0.996807	7.31775	0.091917	0.08
0.09	0.998665	0.994632	0.995961	6.51110	0.103305	0.09
0.10	0.998353	0.993378	0.995017	5.86647	0.114656	0.10
0.11	0.998007	0.991994	0.993974	5.33967	0.125968	0.11
0.12	0.997630	0.990481	0.992834	4.90125	0.137236	0.12
0.13	0.997219	0.988840	0.991597	4.53081	0.148457	0.13
0.14	0.996776	0.987071	0.990264	4.21378	0.159626	0.14
0.15	0.996301	0.985176	0.988834	3.93949	0.170740	0.15
0.16	0.995794	0.983155	0.987308	3.69992	0.181796	0.16
0.17	0.995254	0.981010	0.985688	3.48894	0.192788	0.17
0.18	0.994682	0.978741	0.983973	3.30181	0.203715	0.18
0.19	0.994079	0.976349	0.982165	3.13474	0.214572	0.19
0.20	0.993443	0.973836	0.980263	2.98473	0.225356	0.20
0.21	0.992776	0.971202	0.978269	2.84935	0.236064	0.21
0.22	0.992077	0.968450	0.976184	2.72660	0.246691	0.22
0.23	0.991347	0.965580	0.974009	2.61484	0.257235	0.23
0.24	0.990585	0.962594	0.971743	2.51270	0.267691	0.24
0.25	0.989793	0.959494	0.969388	2.41902	0.278058	0.25
0.26	0.988969	0.956279	0.966946	2.33283	0.288332	0.26
0.27	0.988114	0.952953	0.964416	2.25329	0.298509	0.27
0.28	0.987229	0.949517	0.961800	2.17970	0.308587	0.28
0.29	0.986313	0.945972	0.959099	2.11145	0.318563	0.29
0.30	0.985367	0.942320	0.956314	2.04799	0.328433	0.30
0.31	0.984391	0.938563	0.953445	1.98888	0.338195	0.31
0.32	0.983385	0.934702	0.950495	1.93369	0.347846	0.32
0.33	0.982349	0.930740	0.947464	1.88209	0.357384	0.33
0.34	0.981283	0.926677	0.944353	1.83375	0.366806	0.34
0.35	0.980188	0.922516	0.941163	1.78839	0.376109	0.35
0.36	0.979064	0.918259	0.937895	1.74577	0.385290	0.36
0.37	0.977910	0.913908	0.934552	1.70567	0.394349	0.37
0.38	0.976728	0.909464	0.931133	1.66789	0.403281	0.38
0.39	0.975518	0.904930	0.927640	1.63225	0.412086	0.39
0.40	0.974279	0.900307	0.924075	1.59860	0.420760	0.40
0.41	0.973012	0.895597	0.920438	1.56679	0.429302	0.41
0.42	0.971717	0.890804	0.916731	1.53670	0.437711	0.42
0.43	0.970395	0.885928	0.912956	1.50819	0.445983	0.43
0.44	0.969045	0.880971	0.909113	1.48118	0.454117	0.44
0.45	0.967668	0.875936	0.905204	1.45555	0.462113	0.45
0.46	0.966264	0.870826	0.901230	1.43123	0.469967	0.46
0.47	0.964833	0.865641	0.897193	1.40812	0.477678	0.47
0.48	0.963376	0.860385	0.893093	1.38616	0.485246	0.48
0.49	0.961893	0.855059	0.888933	1.36528	0.492668	0.49
0.50	0.960384	0.849665	0.884714	1.34541	0.499944	0.50

Compressible flow functions ($\gamma = 1.33$)

M	T/T_t	P/P_t	ρ/ρ_t	A/A^*	$\text{MFP}\sqrt{R/g_c}$	M
0.50	0.960384	0.849665	0.884714	1.34541	0.499944	0.50
0.51	0.958850	0.844207	0.880437	1.32649	0.507072	0.51
0.52	0.957290	0.838685	0.876104	1.30849	0.514051	0.52
0.53	0.955705	0.833102	0.871715	1.29133	0.520881	0.53
0.54	0.954095	0.827461	0.867273	1.27498	0.527559	0.54
0.55	0.952460	0.821763	0.862779	1.25940	0.534087	0.55
0.56	0.950802	0.816011	0.858234	1.24454	0.540461	0.56
0.57	0.949119	0.810206	0.853640	1.23038	0.546684	0.57
0.58	0.947413	0.804352	0.848999	1.21687	0.552752	0.58
0.59	0.945683	0.798450	0.844310	1.20399	0.558667	0.59
0.60	0.943931	0.792503	0.839577	1.19170	0.564427	0.60
0.61	0.942155	0.786512	0.834801	1.17998	0.570033	0.61
0.62	0.940357	0.780480	0.829982	1.16881	0.575483	0.62
0.63	0.938537	0.774409	0.825123	1.15815	0.580779	0.63
0.64	0.936694	0.768300	0.820225	1.14799	0.585919	0.64
0.65	0.934831	0.762158	0.815290	1.13830	0.590905	0.65
0.66	0.932945	0.755982	0.810318	1.12907	0.595735	0.66
0.67	0.931039	0.749776	0.805311	1.12028	0.600411	0.67
0.68	0.929112	0.743542	0.800271	1.11191	0.604931	0.68
0.69	0.927165	0.737281	0.795199	1.10394	0.609298	0.69
0.70	0.925198	0.730996	0.790097	1.09636	0.613510	0.70
0.71	0.923211	0.724689	0.784966	1.08916	0.617569	0.71
0.72	0.921204	0.718361	0.779807	1.08231	0.621475	0.72
0.73	0.919178	0.712016	0.774622	1.07581	0.625228	0.73
0.74	0.917133	0.705654	0.769412	1.06965	0.628829	0.74
0.75	0.915070	0.699277	0.764179	1.06381	0.632280	0.75
0.76	0.912989	0.692888	0.758923	1.05829	0.635580	0.76
0.77	0.910889	0.686489	0.753647	1.05307	0.638730	0.77
0.78	0.908772	0.680081	0.748352	1.04815	0.641732	0.78
0.79	0.906638	0.673667	0.743039	1.04350	0.644586	0.79
0.80	0.904486	0.667247	0.737708	1.03914	0.647294	0.80
0.81	0.902318	0.660824	0.732363	1.03504	0.649856	0.81
0.82	0.900134	0.654400	0.727004	1.03121	0.652273	0.82
0.83	0.897933	0.647977	0.721631	1.02762	0.654548	0.83
0.84	0.895717	0.641555	0.716248	1.02429	0.656680	0.84
0.85	0.893485	0.635137	0.710854	1.02119	0.658671	0.85
0.86	0.891239	0.628725	0.705451	1.01833	0.660523	0.86
0.87	0.888977	0.622319	0.700040	1.01569	0.662237	0.87
0.88	0.886701	0.615923	0.694623	1.01328	0.663813	0.88
0.89	0.884411	0.609536	0.689200	1.01108	0.665255	0.89
0.90	0.882106	0.603161	0.683773	1.009100	0.666563	0.90
0.91	0.879789	0.596799	0.678344	1.007324	0.667738	0.91
0.92	0.877458	0.590452	0.672912	1.005750	0.668783	0.92
0.93	0.875114	0.584121	0.667480	1.004376	0.669698	0.93
0.94	0.872757	0.577807	0.662048	1.003195	0.670486	0.94
0.95	0.870388	0.571512	0.656617	1.0022060	0.671148	0.95
0.96	0.868007	0.565237	0.651189	1.0014037	0.671686	0.96
0.97	0.865615	0.558984	0.645765	1.0007851	0.672101	0.97
0.98	0.863210	0.552753	0.640345	1.0003470	0.672395	0.98
0.99	0.860795	0.546546	0.634931	1.0000863	0.672570	0.99
1.00	0.858369	0.540364	0.629524	1.0000000	0.672628	1.00

Compressible flow functions ($\gamma = 1.33$)

M	T/T_t	P/P_t	ρ/ρ_t	A/A^*	$\mathbf{MFP}\sqrt{R/g_c}$	M
1.00	0.858369	0.540364	0.629524	1.0000000	0.672628	1.00
1.01	0.855932	0.534208	0.624124	1.0000854	0.672571	1.01
1.02	0.853486	0.528080	0.618733	1.0003399	0.672400	1.02
1.03	0.851029	0.521980	0.613352	1.0007609	0.672117	1.03
1.04	0.848562	0.515910	0.607981	1.0013462	0.671724	1.04
1.05	0.846086	0.509870	0.602621	1.0020936	0.671223	1.05
1.06	0.843601	0.503861	0.597274	1.003001	0.670616	1.06
1.07	0.841108	0.497885	0.591940	1.004066	0.669904	1.07
1.08	0.838605	0.491942	0.586619	1.005288	0.669091	1.08
1.09	0.836095	0.486034	0.581314	1.006663	0.668176	1.09
1.10	0.833576	0.480160	0.576024	1.008192	0.667163	1.10
1.11	0.831050	0.474323	0.570751	1.009872	0.666053	1.11
1.12	0.828517	0.468522	0.565494	1.01170	0.664849	1.12
1.13	0.825976	0.462758	0.560256	1.01368	0.663552	1.13
1.14	0.823429	0.457033	0.555036	1.01580	0.662163	1.14
1.15	0.820875	0.451347	0.549836	1.01808	0.660686	1.15
1.16	0.818315	0.445700	0.544656	1.02049	0.659122	1.16
1.17	0.815748	0.440093	0.539496	1.02305	0.657473	1.17
1.18	0.813176	0.434527	0.534358	1.02575	0.655741	1.18
1.19	0.810598	0.429002	0.529241	1.02860	0.653927	1.19
1.20	0.808016	0.423519	0.524148	1.03158	0.652034	1.20
1.21	0.805428	0.418079	0.519077	1.03471	0.650064	1.21
1.22	0.802835	0.412682	0.514030	1.03798	0.648019	1.22
1.23	0.800238	0.407327	0.509008	1.04138	0.645900	1.23
1.24	0.797636	0.402017	0.504010	1.04493	0.643709	1.24
1.25	0.795031	0.396751	0.499038	1.04861	0.641448	1.25
1.26	0.792422	0.391529	0.494092	1.05243	0.639120	1.26
1.27	0.789809	0.386352	0.489172	1.05639	0.636725	1.27
1.28	0.787193	0.381221	0.484278	1.06048	0.634266	1.28
1.29	0.784574	0.376135	0.479413	1.06471	0.631745	1.29
1.30	0.781953	0.371095	0.474574	1.06908	0.629164	1.30
1.31	0.779328	0.366100	0.469764	1.07359	0.626523	1.31
1.32	0.776701	0.361153	0.464983	1.07823	0.623826	1.32
1.33	0.774073	0.356251	0.460230	1.08301	0.621074	1.33
1.34	0.771442	0.351397	0.455506	1.08792	0.618268	1.34
1.35	0.768809	0.346589	0.450813	1.09298	0.615411	1.35
1.36	0.766175	0.341828	0.446149	1.09816	0.612503	1.36
1.37	0.763540	0.337114	0.441515	1.10349	0.609548	1.37
1.38	0.760904	0.332448	0.436912	1.10895	0.606546	1.38
1.39	0.758267	0.327829	0.432339	1.11455	0.603499	1.39
1.40	0.755629	0.323257	0.427798	1.12028	0.600409	1.40
1.41	0.752991	0.318732	0.423288	1.12616	0.597278	1.41
1.42	0.750353	0.314255	0.418810	1.13217	0.594106	1.42
1.43	0.747715	0.309826	0.414364	1.13832	0.590896	1.43
1.44	0.745077	0.305443	0.409949	1.14461	0.587650	1.44
1.45	0.742439	0.301109	0.405567	1.15104	0.584368	1.45
1.46	0.739801	0.296821	0.401217	1.15760	0.581053	1.46
1.47	0.737165	0.292581	0.396900	1.16431	0.577705	1.47
1.48	0.734529	0.288387	0.392615	1.17116	0.574327	1.48
1.49	0.731895	0.284241	0.388364	1.17815	0.570920	1.49
1.50	0.729262	0.280142	0.384145	1.18528	0.567484	1.50

Compressible flow functions ($\gamma = 1.33$)

M	T/T_t	P/P_t	ρ/ρ_t	A/A^*	$\mathrm{MFP}\sqrt{R/g_c}$	M
1.50	0.729262	0.280142	0.384145	1.18528	0.567484	1.50
1.51	0.726630	0.276090	0.379959	1.19256	0.564023	1.51
1.52	0.724000	0.272084	0.375807	1.19997	0.560536	1.52
1.53	0.721371	0.268125	0.371688	1.20754	0.557026	1.53
1.54	0.718745	0.264212	0.367602	1.21524	0.553493	1.54
1.55	0.716121	0.260346	0.363550	1.22309	0.549940	1.55
1.56	0.713499	0.256525	0.359532	1.23109	0.546367	1.56
1.57	0.710879	0.252751	0.355547	1.23924	0.542775	1.57
1.58	0.708262	0.249022	0.351595	1.24753	0.539167	1.58
1.59	0.705648	0.245338	0.347678	1.25598	0.535542	1.59
1.60	0.703037	0.241700	0.343794	1.26457	0.531903	1.60
1.61	0.700429	0.238106	0.339943	1.27331	0.528251	1.61
1.62	0.697824	0.234557	0.336127	1.28221	0.524586	1.62
1.63	0.695222	0.231053	0.332344	1.29126	0.520910	1.63
1.64	0.692624	0.227592	0.328594	1.30046	0.517224	1.64
1.65	0.690030	0.224176	0.324879	1.30982	0.513529	1.65
1.66	0.687439	0.220803	0.321196	1.31933	0.509826	1.66
1.67	0.684852	0.217473	0.317548	1.32900	0.506116	1.67
1.68	0.682270	0.214187	0.313933	1.33883	0.502400	1.68
1.69	0.679691	0.210943	0.310351	1.34882	0.498680	1.69
1.70	0.677117	0.207741	0.306803	1.35897	0.494955	1.70
1.71	0.674547	0.204582	0.303288	1.36928	0.491228	1.71
1.72	0.671982	0.201464	0.299806	1.37975	0.487499	1.72
1.73	0.669421	0.198388	0.296358	1.39039	0.483768	1.73
1.74	0.666865	0.195353	0.292942	1.40120	0.480038	1.74
1.75	0.664314	0.192358	0.289559	1.41217	0.476308	1.75
1.76	0.661768	0.189404	0.286209	1.42331	0.472580	1.76
1.77	0.659227	0.186490	0.282892	1.43462	0.468854	1.77
1.78	0.656691	0.183616	0.279608	1.44611	0.465131	1.78
1.79	0.654161	0.180781	0.276355	1.45776	0.461412	1.79
1.80	0.651636	0.177985	0.273136	1.46959	0.457698	1.80
1.81	0.649116	0.175228	0.269948	1.48160	0.453989	1.81
1.82	0.646602	0.172508	0.266792	1.49378	0.450287	1.82
1.83	0.644094	0.169827	0.263669	1.50614	0.446591	1.83
1.84	0.641592	0.167184	0.260577	1.51868	0.442903	1.84
1.85	0.639095	0.164577	0.257516	1.53141	0.439223	1.85
1.86	0.636605	0.162008	0.254487	1.54431	0.435551	1.86
1.87	0.634120	0.159474	0.251489	1.55741	0.431890	1.87
1.88	0.631642	0.156977	0.248523	1.57069	0.428238	1.88
1.89	0.629170	0.154516	0.245587	1.58416	0.424597	1.89
1.90	0.626704	0.152090	0.242682	1.59782	0.420967	1.90
1.91	0.624244	0.149698	0.239807	1.61167	0.417349	1.91
1.92	0.621792	0.147342	0.236963	1.62572	0.413743	1.92
1.93	0.619345	0.145019	0.234149	1.63996	0.410150	1.93
1.94	0.616905	0.142731	0.231366	1.65440	0.406570	1.94
1.95	0.614472	0.140475	0.228611	1.66904	0.403004	1.95
1.96	0.612046	0.138253	0.225887	1.68388	0.399452	1.96
1.97	0.609627	0.136064	0.223192	1.69892	0.395915	1.97
1.98	0.607214	0.133906	0.220526	1.71417	0.392393	1.98
1.99	0.604808	0.131781	0.217889	1.72962	0.388887	1.99
2.00	0.602410	0.129687	0.215281	1.74529	0.385396	2.00

Compressible flow functions ($\gamma = 1.33$)

M	T/T_t	P/P_t	ρ/ρ_t	A/A^*	$\text{MFP}\sqrt{R/g_c}$	M
2.00	0.602410	0.129687	0.215281	1.74529	0.385396	2.00
2.02	0.597634	0.125593	0.210150	1.77726	0.378464	2.02
2.04	0.592886	0.121620	0.205133	1.81008	0.371601	2.04
2.06	0.588168	0.117766	0.200226	1.84379	0.364807	2.06
2.08	0.583480	0.114028	0.195428	1.87839	0.358087	2.08
2.10	0.578821	0.110403	0.190738	1.91391	0.351443	2.10
2.12	0.574193	0.106888	0.186154	1.95035	0.344875	2.12
2.14	0.569595	0.103480	0.181673	1.98775	0.338387	2.14
2.16	0.565028	0.1001767	0.177295	2.02611	0.331979	2.16
2.18	0.560492	0.0969749	0.173017	2.06547	0.325654	2.18
2.20	0.555988	0.0938721	0.168838	2.10583	0.319413	2.20
2.22	0.551515	0.0908655	0.164756	2.14722	0.313256	2.22
2.24	0.547075	0.0879526	0.160769	2.18966	0.307184	2.24
2.26	0.542666	0.0851307	0.156875	2.23317	0.301199	2.26
2.28	0.538290	0.0823973	0.153072	2.27777	0.295301	2.28
2.30	0.533946	0.0797499	0.149360	2.32348	0.289491	2.30
2.32	0.529634	0.0771861	0.145735	2.37034	0.283769	2.32
2.34	0.525355	0.0747035	0.142196	2.41835	0.278135	2.34
2.36	0.521109	0.0722997	0.138742	2.46754	0.272590	2.36
2.38	0.516896	0.0699725	0.135371	2.51795	0.267134	2.38
2.40	0.512715	0.0677195	0.132080	2.56958	0.261766	2.40
2.42	0.508568	0.0655386	0.128869	2.62248	0.256486	2.42
2.44	0.504453	0.0634276	0.125735	2.67665	0.251295	2.44
2.46	0.500372	0.0613845	0.122678	2.73213	0.246192	2.46
2.48	0.496323	0.0594072	0.119695	2.78895	0.241176	2.48
2.50	0.492308	0.0574937	0.116784	2.84713	0.236248	2.50
2.52	0.488325	0.0556421	0.113945	2.90670	0.231406	2.52
2.54	0.484375	0.0538504	0.111175	2.96769	0.226651	2.54
2.56	0.480459	0.0521168	0.108473	3.03012	0.221981	2.56
2.58	0.476575	0.0504395	0.105838	3.09403	0.217396	2.58
2.60	0.472724	0.0488168	0.103267	3.15944	0.212895	2.60
2.62	0.468905	0.0472470	0.100760	3.22639	0.208477	2.62
2.64	0.465120	0.0457283	0.098315	3.29490	0.204142	2.64
2.66	0.461367	0.0442592	0.095931	3.36501	0.199889	2.66
2.68	0.457646	0.0428382	0.093606	3.43675	0.195716	2.68
2.70	0.453957	0.0414636	0.091338	3.51016	0.191624	2.70
2.72	0.450301	0.0401340	0.089127	3.58525	0.187610	2.72
2.74	0.446677	0.0388480	0.086971	3.66208	0.183674	2.74
2.76	0.443085	0.0376041	0.084869	3.74066	0.179815	2.76
2.78	0.439525	0.0364010	0.082819	3.82105	0.176032	2.78
2.80	0.435996	0.0352375	0.080821	3.90326	0.172325	2.80
2.82	0.432499	0.0341121	0.078872	3.98735	0.168691	2.82
2.84	0.429033	0.0330237	0.076972	4.07334	0.165129	2.84
2.86	0.425598	0.0319710	0.075120	4.16128	0.161640	2.86
2.88	0.422195	0.0309530	0.073315	4.25119	0.158221	2.88
2.90	0.418822	0.0299684	0.071554	4.34313	0.154872	2.90
2.92	0.415480	0.0290162	0.069838	4.43712	0.151591	2.92
2.94	0.412168	0.0280953	0.068165	4.53321	0.148378	2.94
2.96	0.408887	0.0272047	0.066533	4.63144	0.145231	2.96
2.98	0.405636	0.0263433	0.064943	4.73185	0.142149	2.98
3.00	0.402414	0.0255103	0.063393	4.83448	0.139131	3.00

Compressible flow functions ($\gamma = 1.33$)

M	T/T_t	P/P_t	ρ/ρ_t	A/A^*	MFP$\sqrt{R/g_c}$	M
3.00	0.402414	0.0255103	0.063393	4.83448	0.1391314	3.00
3.02	0.399223	0.0247046	0.061882	4.93938	0.1361766	3.02
3.04	0.396061	0.0239254	0.060408	5.04659	0.1332838	3.04
3.06	0.392928	0.0231718	0.058972	5.15615	0.1304518	3.06
3.08	0.389825	0.0224429	0.057572	5.26810	0.1276795	3.08
3.10	0.386750	0.0217380	0.056207	5.38250	0.1249658	3.10
3.12	0.383704	0.0210561	0.054876	5.49938	0.1223098	3.12
3.14	0.380686	0.0203967	0.053579	5.61881	0.1197102	3.14
3.16	0.377697	0.0197588	0.052314	5.74081	0.1171661	3.16
3.18	0.374736	0.0191418	0.051081	5.86545	0.1146764	3.18
3.20	0.371802	0.0185451	0.049879	5.99276	0.1122401	3.20
3.22	0.368897	0.0179678	0.048707	6.12281	0.1098561	3.22
3.24	0.366018	0.0174094	0.047564	6.25564	0.1075235	3.24
3.26	0.363167	0.0168692	0.046450	6.39130	0.1052412	3.26
3.28	0.360343	0.0163467	0.045364	6.52985	0.1030082	3.28
3.30	0.357545	0.0158412	0.044305	6.67134	0.1008236	3.30
3.32	0.354774	0.0153522	0.043273	6.81582	0.0986864	3.32
3.34	0.352029	0.0148790	0.042266	6.96334	0.0965956	3.34
3.36	0.349310	0.0144213	0.041285	7.11397	0.0945503	3.36
3.38	0.346617	0.0139784	0.040328	7.26776	0.0925496	3.38
3.40	0.343950	0.0135499	0.039395	7.42477	0.0905925	3.40
3.42	0.341308	0.0131352	0.038485	7.58505	0.0886782	3.42
3.44	0.338691	0.0127340	0.037598	7.74866	0.0868058	3.44
3.46	0.336099	0.0123458	0.036733	7.91567	0.0849743	3.46
3.48	0.333532	0.0119701	0.035889	8.08613	0.0831830	3.48
3.50	0.330989	0.0116065	0.035066	8.26011	0.0814309	3.50
3.52	0.328470	0.0112547	0.034264	8.43767	0.0797174	3.52
3.54	0.325976	0.0109141	0.033481	8.61887	0.0780414	3.54
3.56	0.323505	0.0105845	0.032718	8.80377	0.0764023	3.56
3.58	0.321058	0.0102655	0.031974	8.99245	0.0747992	3.58
3.60	0.318634	0.0099567	0.031248	9.1850	0.0732314	3.60
3.62	0.316233	0.0096578	0.030540	9.3814	0.0716981	3.62
3.64	0.313855	0.0093684	0.029849	9.5818	0.0701986	3.64
3.66	0.311500	0.0090883	0.029176	9.7862	0.0687321	3.66
3.68	0.309167	0.0088171	0.028519	9.9948	0.0672979	3.68
3.70	0.306857	0.0085545	0.027878	10.2075	0.0658954	3.70
3.72	0.304568	0.0083003	0.027253	10.4245	0.0645237	3.72
3.74	0.302302	0.0080541	0.026643	10.6458	0.0631822	3.74
3.76	0.300057	0.0078158	0.026048	10.8716	0.0618704	3.76
3.78	0.297833	0.0075849	0.025467	11.1018	0.0605874	3.78
3.80	0.295631	0.0073614	0.024901	11.3366	0.0593327	3.80
3.82	0.293449	0.0071449	0.024348	11.5760	0.0581057	3.82
3.84	0.291288	0.0069352	0.023809	11.8201	0.0569057	3.84
3.86	0.289148	0.0067321	0.023283	12.0690	0.0557321	3.86
3.88	0.287028	0.0065354	0.022769	12.3227	0.0545843	3.88
3.90	0.284929	0.0063449	0.022268	12.5815	0.0534618	3.90
3.92	0.282849	0.0061603	0.021779	12.8452	0.0523641	3.92
3.94	0.280789	0.0059814	0.021302	13.1141	0.0512904	3.94
3.96	0.278748	0.0058082	0.020837	13.3882	0.0502404	3.96
3.98	0.276727	0.0056403	0.020382	13.6676	0.0492134	3.98
4.00	0.274725	0.0054776	0.019939	13.9523	0.0482090	4.00

Compressible flow functions ($\gamma = 1.3$)

M	T/T_t	P/P_t	ρ/ρ_t	A/A^*	MFP$\sqrt{R/g_c}$	M
0	1	1	1	Indef	0	0
0.01	0.999985	0.999935	0.999950	58.5261	0.011401	0.01
0.02	0.999940	0.999740	0.999800	29.2681	0.022798	0.02
0.03	0.999865	0.999415	0.999550	19.5177	0.034188	0.03
0.04	0.999760	0.998961	0.999200	14.6442	0.045565	0.04
0.05	0.999625	0.998377	0.998751	11.7214	0.056927	0.05
0.06	0.999460	0.997663	0.998202	9.77400	0.068269	0.06
0.07	0.999266	0.996821	0.997554	8.38398	0.079588	0.07
0.08	0.999041	0.995851	0.996807	7.34230	0.090879	0.08
0.09	0.998786	0.994752	0.995961	6.53287	0.102139	0.09
0.10	0.998502	0.993526	0.995016	5.88600	0.113364	0.10
0.11	0.998188	0.992173	0.993974	5.35736	0.124551	0.11
0.12	0.997845	0.990694	0.992834	4.91740	0.135694	0.12
0.13	0.997471	0.989089	0.991596	4.54566	0.146791	0.13
0.14	0.997069	0.987359	0.990262	4.22751	0.157838	0.14
0.15	0.996636	0.985506	0.988832	3.95224	0.168832	0.15
0.16	0.996175	0.983529	0.987306	3.71181	0.179767	0.16
0.17	0.995684	0.981430	0.985685	3.50007	0.190642	0.17
0.18	0.995164	0.979210	0.983969	3.31225	0.201453	0.18
0.19	0.994614	0.976870	0.982160	3.14457	0.212195	0.19
0.20	0.994036	0.974411	0.980257	2.99401	0.222865	0.20
0.21	0.993428	0.971834	0.978262	2.85813	0.233461	0.21
0.22	0.992792	0.969140	0.976176	2.73492	0.243979	0.22
0.23	0.992127	0.966331	0.973998	2.62274	0.254414	0.23
0.24	0.991434	0.963407	0.971731	2.52020	0.264765	0.24
0.25	0.990712	0.960371	0.969374	2.42616	0.275028	0.25
0.26	0.989962	0.957223	0.966929	2.33963	0.285200	0.26
0.27	0.989183	0.953965	0.964397	2.25978	0.295277	0.27
0.28	0.988377	0.950599	0.961778	2.18590	0.305257	0.28
0.29	0.987542	0.947126	0.959074	2.11737	0.315137	0.29
0.30	0.986680	0.943547	0.956285	2.05366	0.324914	0.30
0.31	0.985790	0.939865	0.953413	1.99430	0.334585	0.31
0.32	0.984872	0.936080	0.950459	1.93888	0.344148	0.32
0.33	0.983928	0.932195	0.947423	1.88706	0.353599	0.33
0.34	0.982956	0.928211	0.944306	1.83851	0.362936	0.34
0.35	0.981957	0.924130	0.941111	1.79296	0.372157	0.35
0.36	0.980931	0.919954	0.937838	1.75015	0.381260	0.36
0.37	0.979878	0.915684	0.934488	1.70987	0.390241	0.37
0.38	0.978799	0.911323	0.931062	1.67192	0.399099	0.38
0.39	0.977694	0.906872	0.927562	1.63612	0.407832	0.39
0.40	0.976563	0.902333	0.923989	1.60232	0.416436	0.40
0.41	0.975405	0.897708	0.920344	1.57036	0.424911	0.41
0.42	0.974222	0.892999	0.916628	1.54012	0.433255	0.42
0.43	0.973013	0.888209	0.912843	1.51147	0.441464	0.43
0.44	0.971780	0.883338	0.908990	1.48433	0.449539	0.44
0.45	0.970520	0.878389	0.905070	1.45857	0.457477	0.45
0.46	0.969236	0.873364	0.901085	1.43412	0.465275	0.46
0.47	0.967928	0.868266	0.897036	1.41090	0.472934	0.47
0.48	0.966594	0.863095	0.892924	1.38882	0.480451	0.48
0.49	0.965237	0.857855	0.888750	1.36783	0.487826	0.49
0.50	0.963855	0.852547	0.884517	1.34785	0.495056	0.50

Compressible flow functions ($\gamma = 1.3$)

M	T/T_t	P/P_t	ρ/ρ_t	A/A^*	$\text{MFP}\sqrt{R/g_c}$	M
0.50	0.963855	0.852547	0.884517	1.34785	0.495056	0.50
0.51	0.962450	0.847173	0.880225	1.32884	0.502140	0.51
0.52	0.961021	0.841736	0.875877	1.31073	0.509078	0.52
0.53	0.959569	0.836237	0.871472	1.29347	0.515868	0.53
0.54	0.958093	0.830679	0.867013	1.27703	0.522510	0.54
0.55	0.956595	0.825064	0.862501	1.26136	0.529003	0.55
0.56	0.955073	0.819393	0.857938	1.24642	0.535345	0.56
0.57	0.953530	0.813670	0.853324	1.23216	0.541537	0.57
0.58	0.951964	0.807896	0.848662	1.21857	0.547577	0.58
0.59	0.950376	0.802073	0.843953	1.20561	0.553465	0.59
0.60	0.948767	0.796203	0.839198	1.19324	0.559200	0.60
0.61	0.947136	0.790289	0.834399	1.18145	0.564783	0.61
0.62	0.945483	0.784333	0.829557	1.17020	0.570212	0.62
0.63	0.943810	0.778336	0.824674	1.15947	0.575489	0.63
0.64	0.942116	0.772301	0.819751	1.14924	0.580612	0.64
0.65	0.940402	0.766229	0.814789	1.13949	0.585581	0.65
0.66	0.938667	0.760124	0.809790	1.13019	0.590397	0.66
0.67	0.936913	0.753986	0.804756	1.12134	0.595059	0.67
0.68	0.935139	0.747819	0.799687	1.11290	0.599569	0.68
0.69	0.933345	0.741623	0.794586	1.10488	0.603925	0.69
0.70	0.931532	0.735401	0.789453	1.09724	0.608128	0.70
0.71	0.929701	0.729156	0.784291	1.08998	0.612179	0.71
0.72	0.927850	0.722888	0.779100	1.08308	0.616079	0.72
0.73	0.925982	0.716600	0.773882	1.07653	0.619827	0.73
0.74	0.924095	0.710294	0.768638	1.07032	0.623424	0.74
0.75	0.922190	0.703972	0.763370	1.06443	0.626871	0.75
0.76	0.920268	0.697636	0.758079	1.05886	0.630169	0.76
0.77	0.918328	0.691287	0.752766	1.05360	0.633318	0.77
0.78	0.916372	0.684927	0.747433	1.04863	0.636319	0.78
0.79	0.914399	0.678559	0.742082	1.04395	0.639173	0.79
0.80	0.912409	0.672183	0.736713	1.03954	0.641881	0.80
0.81	0.910403	0.665802	0.731327	1.03541	0.644444	0.81
0.82	0.908381	0.659418	0.725927	1.03154	0.646863	0.82
0.83	0.906343	0.653032	0.720513	1.02792	0.649140	0.83
0.84	0.904290	0.646646	0.715087	1.02455	0.651274	0.84
0.85	0.902222	0.640262	0.709650	1.02142	0.653268	0.85
0.86	0.900139	0.633880	0.704203	1.01853	0.655123	0.86
0.87	0.898041	0.627504	0.698748	1.01587	0.656840	0.87
0.88	0.895929	0.621134	0.693285	1.01343	0.658420	0.88
0.89	0.893803	0.614772	0.687816	1.01121	0.659865	0.89
0.90	0.891663	0.608420	0.682342	1.009206	0.661176	0.90
0.91	0.889510	0.602078	0.676865	1.007410	0.662354	0.91
0.92	0.887343	0.595749	0.671385	1.005819	0.663402	0.92
0.93	0.885163	0.589433	0.665904	1.004428	0.664321	0.93
0.94	0.882971	0.583133	0.660422	1.003234	0.665111	0.94
0.95	0.880766	0.576850	0.654941	1.0022331	0.665776	0.95
0.96	0.878549	0.570585	0.649462	1.0014212	0.666315	0.96
0.97	0.876321	0.564338	0.643986	1.0007950	0.666732	0.97
0.98	0.874080	0.558113	0.638514	1.0003515	0.667028	0.98
0.99	0.871828	0.551909	0.633048	1.0000874	0.667204	0.99
1.00	0.869565	0.545728	0.627587	1.0000000	0.667262	1.00

Compressible flow functions ($\gamma = 1.3$)

M	T/T_t	P/P_t	ρ/ρ_t	A/A^*	$\mathbf{MFP}\sqrt{R/g_c}$	M
1.00	0.869565	0.545728	0.627587	1.0000000	0.667262	1.00
1.01	0.867291	0.539571	0.622133	1.0000865	0.667205	1.01
1.02	0.865007	0.533439	0.616688	1.0003444	0.667033	1.02
1.03	0.862712	0.527334	0.611251	1.0007712	0.666748	1.03
1.04	0.860407	0.521256	0.605825	1.0013646	0.666353	1.04
1.05	0.858093	0.515207	0.600410	1.0021225	0.665849	1.05
1.06	0.855769	0.509188	0.595006	1.003043	0.665238	1.06
1.07	0.853435	0.503198	0.589615	1.004124	0.664522	1.07
1.08	0.851093	0.497241	0.584238	1.005363	0.663703	1.08
1.09	0.848742	0.491315	0.578875	1.006760	0.662782	1.09
1.10	0.846382	0.485423	0.573528	1.008312	0.661762	1.10
1.11	0.844014	0.479565	0.568196	1.010018	0.660644	1.11
1.12	0.841637	0.473742	0.562881	1.01188	0.659431	1.12
1.13	0.839254	0.467955	0.557584	1.01389	0.658123	1.13
1.14	0.836862	0.462204	0.552306	1.01605	0.656724	1.14
1.15	0.834463	0.456490	0.547046	1.01836	0.655235	1.15
1.16	0.832058	0.450814	0.541807	1.02081	0.653658	1.16
1.17	0.829645	0.445177	0.536588	1.02342	0.651995	1.17
1.18	0.827226	0.439579	0.531390	1.02617	0.650248	1.18
1.19	0.824800	0.434021	0.526214	1.02906	0.648418	1.19
1.20	0.822368	0.428504	0.521060	1.03210	0.646508	1.20
1.21	0.819931	0.423027	0.515930	1.03529	0.644520	1.21
1.22	0.817488	0.417592	0.510823	1.03861	0.642455	1.22
1.23	0.815039	0.412199	0.505741	1.04208	0.640316	1.23
1.24	0.812585	0.406848	0.500683	1.04570	0.638103	1.24
1.25	0.810127	0.401540	0.495651	1.04945	0.635820	1.25
1.26	0.807663	0.396276	0.490645	1.05335	0.633468	1.26
1.27	0.805195	0.391055	0.485665	1.05739	0.631049	1.27
1.28	0.802723	0.385879	0.480712	1.06157	0.628564	1.28
1.29	0.800246	0.380747	0.475787	1.06589	0.626017	1.29
1.30	0.797766	0.375660	0.470889	1.07035	0.623407	1.30
1.31	0.795282	0.370617	0.466020	1.07495	0.620738	1.31
1.32	0.792795	0.365621	0.461179	1.07969	0.618011	1.32
1.33	0.790305	0.360669	0.456368	1.08458	0.615227	1.33
1.34	0.787811	0.355764	0.451586	1.08960	0.612389	1.34
1.35	0.785315	0.350905	0.446833	1.09477	0.609499	1.35
1.36	0.782816	0.346092	0.442111	1.10008	0.606557	1.36
1.37	0.780314	0.341325	0.437420	1.10553	0.603567	1.37
1.38	0.777811	0.336605	0.432759	1.11112	0.600529	1.38
1.39	0.775305	0.331931	0.428130	1.11686	0.597445	1.39
1.40	0.772798	0.327304	0.423532	1.12274	0.594317	1.40
1.41	0.770288	0.322724	0.418965	1.12876	0.591147	1.41
1.42	0.767778	0.318191	0.414431	1.13492	0.587936	1.42
1.43	0.765266	0.313704	0.409929	1.14123	0.584685	1.43
1.44	0.762753	0.309265	0.405459	1.14769	0.581397	1.44
1.45	0.760239	0.304873	0.401022	1.15429	0.578073	1.45
1.46	0.757725	0.300527	0.396618	1.16103	0.574715	1.46
1.47	0.755210	0.296229	0.392247	1.16792	0.571323	1.47
1.48	0.752695	0.291977	0.387909	1.17496	0.567900	1.48
1.49	0.750179	0.287772	0.383604	1.18215	0.564448	1.49
1.50	0.747664	0.283614	0.379333	1.18949	0.560966	1.50

Compressible flow functions ($\gamma = 1.3$)

M	T/T_t	P/P_t	ρ/ρ_t	A/A^*	$\mathbf{MFP}\sqrt{R/g_c}$	M
1.50	0.747664	0.283614	0.379333	1.18949	0.560966	1.50
1.51	0.745148	0.279502	0.375096	1.19697	0.557458	1.51
1.52	0.742633	0.275437	0.370892	1.20461	0.553924	1.52
1.53	0.740118	0.271418	0.366722	1.21240	0.550366	1.53
1.54	0.737605	0.267446	0.362587	1.22034	0.546784	1.54
1.55	0.735091	0.263519	0.358485	1.22843	0.543182	1.55
1.56	0.732579	0.259639	0.354418	1.23668	0.539559	1.56
1.57	0.730068	0.255805	0.350384	1.24508	0.535917	1.57
1.58	0.727558	0.252016	0.346385	1.25364	0.532258	1.58
1.59	0.725050	0.248272	0.342421	1.26236	0.528583	1.59
1.60	0.722543	0.244574	0.338490	1.27124	0.524892	1.60
1.61	0.720038	0.240921	0.334594	1.28027	0.521188	1.61
1.62	0.717535	0.237312	0.330733	1.28947	0.517470	1.62
1.63	0.715034	0.233749	0.326905	1.29883	0.513742	1.63
1.64	0.712535	0.230229	0.323113	1.30835	0.510003	1.64
1.65	0.710038	0.226754	0.319354	1.31804	0.506254	1.65
1.66	0.707544	0.223322	0.315630	1.32789	0.502498	1.66
1.67	0.705052	0.219934	0.311940	1.33791	0.498734	1.67
1.68	0.702563	0.216589	0.308284	1.34810	0.494965	1.68
1.69	0.700077	0.213287	0.304662	1.35846	0.491190	1.69
1.70	0.697593	0.210028	0.301075	1.36899	0.487412	1.70
1.71	0.695113	0.206811	0.297521	1.37969	0.483630	1.71
1.72	0.692636	0.203636	0.294002	1.39057	0.479847	1.72
1.73	0.690162	0.200503	0.290516	1.40163	0.476062	1.73
1.74	0.687692	0.197412	0.287064	1.41286	0.472277	1.74
1.75	0.685225	0.194361	0.283646	1.42427	0.468493	1.75
1.76	0.682762	0.191352	0.280262	1.43587	0.464711	1.76
1.77	0.680302	0.188383	0.276911	1.44764	0.460930	1.77
1.78	0.677847	0.185454	0.273593	1.45960	0.457154	1.78
1.79	0.675395	0.182565	0.270308	1.47175	0.453381	1.79
1.80	0.672948	0.179715	0.267057	1.48408	0.449613	1.80
1.81	0.670504	0.176905	0.263839	1.49661	0.445851	1.81
1.82	0.668065	0.174133	0.260653	1.50932	0.442095	1.82
1.83	0.665631	0.171400	0.257500	1.52223	0.438346	1.83
1.84	0.663200	0.168705	0.254380	1.53533	0.434605	1.84
1.85	0.660775	0.166047	0.251292	1.54863	0.430872	1.85
1.86	0.658354	0.163427	0.248236	1.56213	0.427149	1.86
1.87	0.655938	0.160844	0.245212	1.57583	0.423435	1.87
1.88	0.653526	0.158297	0.242220	1.58974	0.419732	1.88
1.89	0.651120	0.155787	0.239260	1.60384	0.416039	1.89
1.90	0.648719	0.153313	0.236331	1.61816	0.412359	1.90
1.91	0.646323	0.150874	0.233434	1.63269	0.408690	1.91
1.92	0.643932	0.148470	0.230568	1.64742	0.405034	1.92
1.93	0.641546	0.146101	0.227733	1.66237	0.401392	1.93
1.94	0.639166	0.143767	0.224928	1.67754	0.397763	1.94
1.95	0.636791	0.141466	0.222155	1.69292	0.394149	1.95
1.96	0.634421	0.139199	0.219411	1.70852	0.390549	1.96
1.97	0.632057	0.136966	0.216698	1.72435	0.386964	1.97
1.98	0.629699	0.134765	0.214015	1.74040	0.383396	1.98
1.99	0.627347	0.132597	0.211361	1.75668	0.379843	1.99
2.00	0.625000	0.130461	0.208737	1.77319	0.376307	2.00

Compressible flow functions ($\gamma = 1.3$)

M	T/T_t	P/P_t	ρ/ρ_t	A/A^*	$\mathbf{MFP}\sqrt{R/g_c}$	M
2.00	0.625000	0.130461	0.208737	1.77319	0.376307	2.00
2.02	0.620324	0.126284	0.203577	1.80690	0.369285	2.02
2.04	0.615673	0.122231	0.198533	1.84157	0.362334	2.04
2.06	0.611045	0.118300	0.193603	1.87720	0.355457	2.06
2.08	0.606443	0.114487	0.188784	1.91382	0.348655	2.08
2.10	0.601866	0.110789	0.184077	1.95145	0.341932	2.10
2.12	0.597314	0.107205	0.179478	1.99011	0.335289	2.12
2.14	0.592789	0.103729	0.174985	2.02983	0.328728	2.14
2.16	0.588291	0.1003610	0.170598	2.07063	0.322251	2.16
2.18	0.583819	0.0970969	0.166313	2.11253	0.315860	2.18
2.20	0.579374	0.0939341	0.162130	2.15555	0.309555	2.20
2.22	0.574957	0.0908700	0.158047	2.19973	0.303338	2.22
2.24	0.570568	0.0879019	0.154060	2.24508	0.297211	2.24
2.26	0.566207	0.0850272	0.150170	2.29164	0.291173	2.26
2.28	0.561874	0.0822433	0.146373	2.33942	0.285225	2.28
2.30	0.557569	0.0795476	0.142669	2.38847	0.279369	2.30
2.32	0.553293	0.0769378	0.139054	2.43879	0.273604	2.32
2.34	0.549046	0.0744113	0.135528	2.49043	0.267930	2.34
2.36	0.544828	0.0719657	0.132089	2.54341	0.262349	2.36
2.38	0.540640	0.0695988	0.128734	2.59777	0.256860	2.38
2.40	0.536481	0.0673082	0.125462	2.65352	0.251463	2.40
2.42	0.532351	0.0650916	0.122272	2.71071	0.246157	2.42
2.44	0.528251	0.0629469	0.119161	2.76937	0.240944	2.44
2.46	0.524180	0.0608719	0.116128	2.82952	0.235821	2.46
2.48	0.520140	0.0588645	0.113171	2.89121	0.230790	2.48
2.50	0.516129	0.0569228	0.110288	2.95446	0.225849	2.50
2.52	0.512148	0.0550445	0.107478	3.01931	0.220998	2.52
2.54	0.508197	0.0532280	0.104739	3.08580	0.216237	2.54
2.56	0.504276	0.0514711	0.102069	3.15396	0.211564	2.56
2.58	0.500385	0.0497721	0.099468	3.22382	0.206979	2.58
2.60	0.496524	0.0481292	0.096932	3.29544	0.202481	2.60
2.62	0.492693	0.0465406	0.094462	3.36883	0.198069	2.62
2.64	0.488892	0.0450047	0.092054	3.44406	0.193743	2.64
2.66	0.485121	0.0435196	0.089709	3.52114	0.189502	2.66
2.68	0.481380	0.0420839	0.087423	3.60013	0.185344	2.68
2.70	0.477669	0.0406959	0.085197	3.68107	0.181269	2.70
2.72	0.473988	0.0393541	0.083028	3.76400	0.177275	2.72
2.74	0.470336	0.0380571	0.080915	3.84896	0.173362	2.74
2.76	0.466714	0.0368033	0.078856	3.93599	0.169528	2.76
2.78	0.463122	0.0355914	0.076851	4.02515	0.165773	2.78
2.80	0.459559	0.0344200	0.074898	4.11648	0.162095	2.80
2.82	0.456025	0.0332879	0.072996	4.21002	0.158494	2.82
2.84	0.452521	0.0321936	0.071143	4.30583	0.154967	2.84
2.86	0.449047	0.0311360	0.069338	4.40394	0.151515	2.86
2.88	0.445601	0.0301139	0.067580	4.50442	0.148135	2.88
2.90	0.442184	0.0291260	0.065869	4.60731	0.144827	2.90
2.92	0.438797	0.0281713	0.064201	4.71266	0.141589	2.92
2.94	0.435438	0.0272487	0.062578	4.82053	0.138421	2.94
2.96	0.432107	0.0263571	0.060997	4.93097	0.135321	2.96
2.98	0.428805	0.0254954	0.059457	5.04403	0.132288	2.98
3.00	0.425532	0.0246626	0.057957	5.15977	0.129320	3.00

Compressible flow functions ($\gamma = 1.3$)

M	T/T_t	P/P_t	ρ/ρ_t	A/A^*	MFP$\sqrt{R/g_c}$	M
3.00	0.425532	0.0246626	0.057957	5.15977	0.1293201	3.00
3.02	0.422287	0.0238579	0.056497	5.27825	0.1264173	3.02
3.04	0.419069	0.0230802	0.055075	5.39952	0.1235780	3.04
3.06	0.415880	0.0223286	0.053690	5.52365	0.1208010	3.06
3.08	0.412718	0.0216023	0.052341	5.65069	0.1180851	3.08
3.10	0.409584	0.0209004	0.051028	5.78070	0.1154293	3.10
3.12	0.406478	0.0202221	0.049750	5.91375	0.1128323	3.12
3.14	0.403398	0.0195665	0.048504	6.04990	0.1102931	3.14
3.16	0.400346	0.0189330	0.047292	6.18921	0.1078105	3.16
3.18	0.397320	0.0183208	0.046111	6.33176	0.1053834	3.18
3.20	0.394322	0.0177291	0.044961	6.47759	0.1030108	3.20
3.22	0.391350	0.0171573	0.043841	6.62680	0.1006915	3.22
3.24	0.388404	0.0166046	0.042751	6.77943	0.0984245	3.24
3.26	0.385484	0.0160705	0.041689	6.93557	0.0962087	3.26
3.28	0.382591	0.0155542	0.040655	7.09528	0.0940431	3.28
3.30	0.379723	0.0150553	0.039648	7.25864	0.0919266	3.30
3.32	0.376881	0.0145730	0.038667	7.42573	0.0898582	3.32
3.34	0.374064	0.0141069	0.037713	7.59661	0.0878369	3.34
3.36	0.371272	0.0136564	0.036783	7.77136	0.0858617	3.36
3.38	0.368506	0.0132209	0.035877	7.95007	0.0839317	3.38
3.40	0.365764	0.0127999	0.034995	8.13280	0.0820458	3.40
3.42	0.363048	0.0123930	0.034136	8.31965	0.0802031	3.42
3.44	0.360355	0.0119996	0.033299	8.51070	0.0784028	3.44
3.46	0.357687	0.0116193	0.032485	8.70602	0.0766438	3.46
3.48	0.355043	0.0112517	0.031691	8.90571	0.0749252	3.48
3.50	0.352423	0.0108963	0.030918	9.10985	0.0732463	3.50
3.52	0.349826	0.0105527	0.030165	9.31852	0.0716060	3.52
3.54	0.347254	0.0102204	0.029432	9.53182	0.0700037	3.54
3.56	0.344704	0.0098992	0.028718	9.74984	0.0684383	3.56
3.58	0.342177	0.0095886	0.028022	9.97267	0.0669091	3.58
3.60	0.339674	0.0092883	0.027345	10.2004	0.0654153	3.60
3.62	0.337193	0.0089979	0.026685	10.4331	0.0639561	3.62
3.64	0.334735	0.0087171	0.026042	10.6710	0.0625306	3.64
3.66	0.332299	0.0084455	0.025415	10.9140	0.0611382	3.66
3.68	0.329885	0.0081828	0.024805	11.1623	0.0597781	3.68
3.70	0.327493	0.0079288	0.024211	11.4160	0.0584496	3.70
3.72	0.325123	0.0076832	0.023632	11.6753	0.0571518	3.72
3.74	0.322774	0.0074455	0.023067	11.9401	0.0558842	3.74
3.76	0.320447	0.0072157	0.022518	12.2106	0.0546461	3.76
3.78	0.318141	0.0069934	0.021982	12.4870	0.0534366	3.78
3.80	0.315856	0.0067783	0.021460	12.7693	0.0522553	3.80
3.82	0.313592	0.0065702	0.020952	13.0576	0.0511014	3.82
3.84	0.311348	0.0063689	0.020456	13.3521	0.0499742	3.84
3.86	0.309125	0.0061742	0.019973	13.6529	0.0488733	3.86
3.88	0.306922	0.0059858	0.019503	13.9601	0.0477979	3.88
3.90	0.304739	0.0058034	0.019044	14.2737	0.0467475	3.90
3.92	0.302576	0.0056270	0.018597	14.5941	0.0457215	3.92
3.94	0.300432	0.0054563	0.018162	14.9211	0.0447193	3.94
3.96	0.298308	0.0052911	0.017737	15.2551	0.0437404	3.96
3.98	0.296203	0.0051312	0.017323	15.5960	0.0427841	3.98
4.00	0.294118	0.0049765	0.016920	15.9441	0.0418500	4.00

APPENDIX F

NORMAL SHOCK FUNCTIONS ($\gamma = 1.4$)

For a one-dimensional normal shock as shown in Fig. F-1, the following relationships are tabulated as functions of the upstream Mach number M_x for $\gamma = 1.4$.

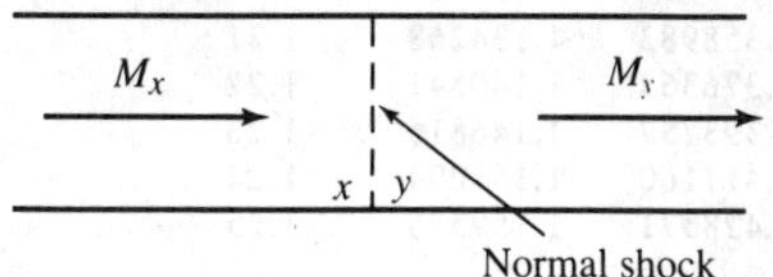

FIGURE F-1
Normal shock wave.

$$M_y = \sqrt{\frac{M_x^2 + \dfrac{2}{\gamma - 1}}{\dfrac{2\gamma}{\gamma - 1} M_x^2 - 1}}$$

$$\frac{P_{ty}}{P_{tx}} = \left(\frac{\dfrac{\gamma + 1}{2} M_x^2}{1 + \dfrac{\gamma - 1}{2} M_x^2} \right)^{\gamma/(\gamma - 1)} \left(\frac{2\gamma}{\gamma + 1} M_x^2 - \frac{\gamma - 1}{\gamma + 1} \right)^{-1/(\gamma - 1)}$$

$$\frac{P_y}{P_x} = \frac{2\gamma}{\gamma + 1} M_x^2 - \frac{\gamma - 1}{\gamma + 1} \qquad \frac{\rho_y}{\rho_x} = \frac{P_y / P_x}{T_y / T_x}$$

$$\frac{T_y}{T_x} = \frac{\left(1 + \dfrac{\gamma - 1}{2} M_x^2\right)\left(\dfrac{2\gamma}{\gamma - 1} M_x^2 - 1\right)}{\dfrac{(\gamma + 1)^2}{2(\gamma - 1)} M_x^2}$$

M_x	M_y	P_{ty}/P_{tx}	P_y/P_x	ρ_y/ρ_x	T_y/T_x	M_x
1.00	1.000000	1.000000	1.000000	1.000000	1.000000	1.00
1.01	0.990132	0.999999	1.023450	1.016694	1.006645	1.01
1.02	0.980519	0.999990	1.047133	1.033441	1.013249	1.02
1.03	0.971154	0.999967	1.071050	1.050240	1.019814	1.03
1.04	0.962025	0.999923	1.095200	1.067088	1.026345	1.04
1.05	0.953125	0.999853	1.119583	1.083982	1.032843	1.05
1.06	0.944445	0.999751	1.144200	1.100921	1.039312	1.06
1.07	0.935977	0.999611	1.169050	1.117903	1.045753	1.07
1.08	0.927713	0.999431	1.194133	1.134925	1.052170	1.08
1.09	0.919647	0.999204	1.219450	1.151985	1.058564	1.09
1.10	0.911770	0.998928	1.245000	1.169082	1.064938	1.10
1.11	0.904078	0.998599	1.270783	1.186213	1.071294	1.11
1.12	0.896563	0.998213	1.296800	1.203377	1.077634	1.12
1.13	0.889219	0.997768	1.323050	1.220571	1.083960	1.13
1.14	0.882042	0.997261	1.349533	1.237793	1.090274	1.14
1.15	0.875024	0.996690	1.376250	1.255042	1.096577	1.15
1.16	0.868162	0.996052	1.403200	1.272315	1.102872	1.16
1.17	0.861451	0.995345	1.430383	1.289610	1.109159	1.17
1.18	0.854884	0.994569	1.457800	1.306927	1.115441	1.18
1.19	0.848459	0.993720	1.485450	1.324262	1.121719	1.19
1.20	0.842170	0.992798	1.513333	1.341615	1.127994	1.20
1.21	0.836014	0.991802	1.541450	1.358983	1.134268	1.21
1.22	0.829986	0.990731	1.569800	1.376364	1.140541	1.22
1.23	0.824083	0.989583	1.598383	1.393757	1.146816	1.23
1.24	0.818301	0.988359	1.627200	1.411160	1.153094	1.24
1.25	0.812636	0.987057	1.656250	1.428571	1.159375	1.25
1.26	0.807085	0.985677	1.685533	1.445989	1.165661	1.26
1.27	0.801645	0.984219	1.715050	1.463412	1.171953	1.27
1.28	0.796312	0.982682	1.744800	1.480839	1.178251	1.28
1.29	0.791084	0.981067	1.774783	1.498267	1.184558	1.29
1.30	0.785957	0.979374	1.805000	1.515695	1.190873	1.30
1.31	0.780929	0.977602	1.835450	1.533122	1.197198	1.31
1.32	0.775997	0.975752	1.866133	1.550546	1.203533	1.32
1.33	0.771159	0.973824	1.897050	1.567965	1.209880	1.33
1.34	0.766412	0.971819	1.928200	1.585379	1.216239	1.34
1.35	0.761753	0.969737	1.959583	1.602785	1.222612	1.35
1.36	0.757181	0.967579	1.991200	1.620182	1.228998	1.36
1.37	0.752692	0.965344	2.023050	1.637569	1.235398	1.37
1.38	0.748286	0.963035	2.055133	1.654945	1.241814	1.38
1.39	0.743959	0.960652	2.087450	1.672307	1.248246	1.39
1.40	0.739709	0.958194	2.120000	1.689655	1.254694	1.40
1.41	0.735536	0.955665	2.152783	1.706988	1.261159	1.41
1.42	0.731436	0.953063	2.185800	1.724303	1.267643	1.42
1.43	0.727408	0.950390	2.219050	1.741600	1.274144	1.43
1.44	0.723451	0.947648	2.252533	1.758878	1.280665	1.44
1.45	0.719562	0.944837	2.286250	1.776135	1.287205	1.45
1.46	0.715740	0.941958	2.320200	1.793370	1.293765	1.46
1.47	0.711983	0.939012	2.354383	1.810582	1.300346	1.47
1.48	0.708290	0.936001	2.388800	1.827770	1.306948	1.48
1.49	0.704659	0.932925	2.423450	1.844933	1.313571	1.49
1.50	0.701089	0.929787	2.458333	1.862069	1.320216	1.50

M_x	M_y	P_{ty}/P_{tx}	P_y/P_x	ρ_y/ρ_x	T_y/T_x	M_x
1.50	0.701089	0.929787	2.458333	1.862069	1.320216	1.50
1.51	0.697578	0.926586	2.493450	1.879177	1.326884	1.51
1.52	0.694125	0.923324	2.528800	1.896257	1.333574	1.52
1.53	0.690729	0.920003	2.564383	1.913308	1.340288	1.53
1.54	0.687388	0.916624	2.600200	1.930327	1.347026	1.54
1.55	0.684101	0.913188	2.636250	1.947315	1.353787	1.55
1.56	0.680867	0.909697	2.672533	1.964270	1.360573	1.56
1.57	0.677685	0.906151	2.709050	1.981192	1.367384	1.57
1.58	0.674553	0.902552	2.745800	1.998079	1.374220	1.58
1.59	0.671471	0.898901	2.782783	2.014931	1.381081	1.59
1.60	0.668437	0.895200	2.820000	2.031746	1.387969	1.60
1.61	0.665451	0.891450	2.857450	2.048524	1.394882	1.61
1.62	0.662511	0.887653	2.895133	2.065264	1.401822	1.62
1.63	0.659616	0.883809	2.933050	2.081965	1.408789	1.63
1.64	0.656765	0.879921	2.971200	2.098627	1.415783	1.64
1.65	0.653958	0.875988	3.009583	2.115248	1.422804	1.65
1.66	0.651194	0.872014	3.048200	2.131827	1.429853	1.66
1.67	0.648471	0.867999	3.087050	2.148365	1.436930	1.67
1.68	0.645789	0.863944	3.126133	2.164860	1.444035	1.68
1.69	0.643147	0.859851	3.165450	2.181311	1.451168	1.69
1.70	0.640544	0.855721	3.205000	2.197719	1.458330	1.70
1.71	0.637979	0.851556	3.244783	2.214081	1.465521	1.71
1.72	0.635452	0.847356	3.284800	2.230398	1.472742	1.72
1.73	0.632962	0.843124	3.325050	2.246669	1.479991	1.73
1.74	0.630508	0.838860	3.365533	2.262893	1.487270	1.74
1.75	0.628089	0.834565	3.406250	2.279070	1.494579	1.75
1.76	0.625705	0.830242	3.447200	2.295199	1.501918	1.76
1.77	0.623354	0.825891	3.488383	2.311279	1.509287	1.77
1.78	0.621037	0.821513	3.529800	2.327310	1.516687	1.78
1.79	0.618753	0.817111	3.571450	2.343292	1.524117	1.79
1.80	0.616501	0.812684	3.613333	2.359223	1.531578	1.80
1.81	0.614281	0.808234	3.655450	2.375104	1.539069	1.81
1.82	0.612091	0.803763	3.697800	2.390934	1.546592	1.82
1.83	0.609931	0.799271	3.740383	2.406712	1.554146	1.83
1.84	0.607802	0.794761	3.783200	2.422438	1.561732	1.84
1.85	0.605701	0.790232	3.826250	2.438112	1.569349	1.85
1.86	0.603629	0.785686	3.869533	2.453733	1.576999	1.86
1.87	0.601585	0.781125	3.913050	2.469301	1.584680	1.87
1.88	0.599569	0.776549	3.956800	2.484814	1.592393	1.88
1.89	0.597579	0.771959	4.000783	2.500274	1.600138	1.89
1.90	0.595616	0.767357	4.045000	2.515679	1.607916	1.90
1.91	0.593680	0.762743	4.089450	2.531030	1.615726	1.91
1.92	0.591769	0.758119	4.134133	2.546325	1.623568	1.92
1.93	0.589883	0.753486	4.179050	2.561565	1.631444	1.93
1.94	0.588022	0.748844	4.224200	2.576749	1.639352	1.94
1.95	0.586185	0.744195	4.269583	2.591877	1.647294	1.95
1.96	0.584372	0.739540	4.315200	2.606949	1.655268	1.96
1.97	0.582582	0.734879	4.361050	2.621964	1.663276	1.97
1.98	0.580816	0.730214	4.407133	2.636922	1.671317	1.98
1.99	0.579072	0.725545	4.453450	2.651823	1.679392	1.99
2.00	0.577350	0.720874	4.500000	2.666667	1.687500	2.00

M_x	M_y	P_{ty}/P_{tx}	P_y/P_x	ρ_y/ρ_x	T_y/T_x	M_x
2.00	0.577350	0.720874	4.500000	2.666667	1.687500	2.00
2.02	0.573972	0.711527	4.593800	2.696181	1.703817	2.02
2.04	0.570679	0.702180	4.688533	2.725463	1.720271	2.04
2.06	0.567467	0.692839	4.784200	2.754511	1.736860	2.06
2.08	0.564334	0.683512	4.880800	2.783325	1.753586	2.08
2.10	0.561277	0.674203	4.978333	2.811902	1.770450	2.10
2.12	0.558294	0.664919	5.076800	2.840243	1.787453	2.12
2.14	0.555383	0.655666	5.176200	2.868345	1.804594	2.14
2.16	0.552541	0.646447	5.276533	2.896209	1.821876	2.16
2.18	0.549766	0.637269	5.377800	2.923834	1.839297	2.18
2.20	0.547056	0.628136	5.480000	2.951220	1.856860	2.20
2.22	0.544409	0.619053	5.583133	2.978365	1.874563	2.22
2.24	0.541822	0.610023	5.687200	3.005271	1.892409	2.24
2.26	0.539295	0.601051	5.792200	3.031936	1.910396	2.26
2.28	0.536825	0.592140	5.898133	3.058362	1.928527	2.28
2.30	0.534411	0.583295	6.005000	3.084548	1.946801	2.30
2.32	0.532051	0.574517	6.112800	3.110495	1.965218	2.32
2.34	0.529743	0.565810	6.221533	3.136202	1.983779	2.34
2.36	0.527486	0.557177	6.331200	3.161671	2.002485	2.36
2.38	0.525278	0.548621	6.441800	3.186902	2.021336	2.38
2.40	0.523118	0.540144	6.553333	3.211896	2.040332	2.40
2.42	0.521004	0.531748	6.665800	3.236653	2.059473	2.42
2.44	0.518936	0.523435	6.779200	3.261174	2.078760	2.44
2.46	0.516911	0.515208	6.893533	3.285461	2.098194	2.46
2.48	0.514929	0.507067	7.008800	3.309514	2.117773	2.48
2.50	0.512989	0.499015	7.125000	3.333333	2.137500	2.50
2.52	0.511089	0.491052	7.242133	3.356921	2.157374	2.52
2.54	0.509228	0.483181	7.360200	3.380279	2.177394	2.54
2.56	0.507406	0.475402	7.479200	3.403407	2.197563	2.56
2.58	0.505620	0.467715	7.599133	3.426307	2.217879	2.58
2.60	0.503871	0.460123	7.720000	3.448980	2.238343	2.60
2.62	0.502157	0.452625	7.841800	3.471427	2.258956	2.62
2.64	0.500477	0.445223	7.964533	3.493651	2.279717	2.64
2.66	0.498830	0.437916	8.088200	3.515651	2.300626	2.66
2.68	0.497216	0.430705	8.212800	3.537431	2.321685	2.68
2.70	0.495634	0.423590	8.338333	3.558991	2.342892	2.70
2.72	0.494082	0.416572	8.464800	3.580333	2.364249	2.72
2.74	0.492560	0.409650	8.592200	3.601458	2.385756	2.74
2.76	0.491068	0.402825	8.720533	3.622369	2.407412	2.76
2.78	0.489604	0.396096	8.849800	3.643066	2.429218	2.78
2.80	0.488167	0.389464	8.980000	3.663551	2.451173	2.80
2.82	0.486758	0.382927	9.111133	3.683827	2.473279	2.82
2.84	0.485376	0.376486	9.243200	3.703894	2.495536	2.84
2.86	0.484019	0.370141	9.376200	3.723755	2.517942	2.86
2.88	0.482687	0.363890	9.510133	3.743411	2.540500	2.88
2.90	0.481380	0.357733	9.645000	3.762864	2.563207	2.90
2.92	0.480096	0.351670	9.780800	3.782115	2.586066	2.92
2.94	0.478836	0.345701	9.917533	3.801167	2.609076	2.94
2.96	0.477599	0.339823	10.05520	3.820021	2.632237	2.96
2.98	0.476384	0.334038	10.19380	3.838679	2.655549	2.98
3.00	0.475191	0.328344	10.33333	3.857143	2.679012	3.00

M_x	M_y	P_{ty}/P_{tx}	P_y/P_x	ρ_y/ρ_x	T_y/T_x	M_x
3.00	0.475191	0.328344	10.33333	3.857143	2.679012	3.00
3.02	0.474019	0.322740	10.47380	3.875414	2.702627	3.02
3.04	0.472868	0.317226	10.61520	3.893495	2.726394	3.04
3.06	0.471737	0.311800	10.75753	3.911387	2.750312	3.06
3.08	0.470625	0.306462	10.90080	3.929092	2.774381	3.08
3.10	0.469534	0.301211	11.04500	3.946612	2.798603	3.10
3.12	0.468460	0.296046	11.19013	3.963948	2.822977	3.12
3.14	0.467406	0.290967	11.33620	3.981103	2.847502	3.14
3.16	0.466369	0.285971	11.48320	3.998078	2.872180	3.16
3.18	0.465350	0.281059	11.63113	4.014875	2.897010	3.18
3.20	0.464349	0.276229	11.78000	4.031496	2.921992	3.20
3.22	0.463364	0.271480	11.92980	4.047943	2.947127	3.22
3.24	0.462395	0.266811	12.08053	4.064216	2.972414	3.24
3.26	0.461443	0.262221	12.23220	4.080319	2.997854	3.26
3.28	0.460507	0.257710	12.38480	4.096253	3.023446	3.28
3.30	0.459586	0.253276	12.53833	4.112020	3.049191	3.30
3.32	0.458680	0.248918	12.69280	4.127621	3.075088	3.32
3.34	0.457788	0.244635	12.84820	4.143059	3.101139	3.34
3.36	0.456912	0.240426	13.00453	4.158334	3.127342	3.36
3.38	0.456049	0.236290	13.16180	4.173449	3.153698	3.38
3.40	0.455200	0.232226	13.32000	4.188406	3.180208	3.40
3.42	0.454365	0.228232	13.47913	4.203205	3.206870	3.42
3.44	0.453543	0.224309	13.63920	4.217850	3.233685	3.44
3.46	0.452734	0.220454	13.80020	4.232341	3.260654	3.46
3.48	0.451938	0.216668	13.96213	4.246680	3.287776	3.48
3.50	0.451154	0.212948	14.12500	4.260870	3.315051	3.50
3.52	0.450382	0.209293	14.28880	4.274910	3.342479	3.52
3.54	0.449623	0.205704	14.45353	4.288804	3.370061	3.54
3.56	0.448875	0.202177	14.61920	4.302553	3.397797	3.56
3.58	0.448138	0.198714	14.78580	4.316158	3.425685	3.58
3.60	0.447413	0.195312	14.95333	4.329621	3.453728	3.60
3.62	0.446699	0.191971	15.12180	4.342944	3.481924	3.62
3.64	0.445995	0.188690	15.29120	4.356128	3.510273	3.64
3.66	0.445302	0.185467	15.46153	4.369175	3.538776	3.66
3.68	0.444620	0.182302	15.63280	4.382086	3.567433	3.68
3.70	0.443948	0.179194	15.80500	4.394864	3.596244	3.70
3.72	0.443285	0.176141	15.97813	4.407508	3.625208	3.72
3.74	0.442633	0.173143	16.15220	4.420021	3.654326	3.74
3.76	0.441990	0.170200	16.32720	4.432405	3.683598	3.76
3.78	0.441356	0.167309	16.50313	4.444661	3.713024	3.78
3.80	0.440732	0.164470	16.68000	4.456790	3.742604	3.80
3.82	0.440117	0.161683	16.85780	4.468794	3.772338	3.82
3.84	0.439510	0.158946	17.03653	4.480674	3.802225	3.84
3.86	0.438912	0.156258	17.21620	4.492432	3.832267	3.86
3.88	0.438323	0.153619	17.39680	4.504069	3.862463	3.88
3.90	0.437742	0.151027	17.57833	4.515586	3.892813	3.90
3.92	0.437170	0.148483	17.76080	4.526986	3.923317	3.92
3.94	0.436605	0.145984	17.94420	4.538268	3.953975	3.94
3.96	0.436049	0.143531	18.12853	4.549435	3.984788	3.96
3.98	0.435500	0.141122	18.31380	4.560488	4.015754	3.98
4.00	0.434959	0.138756	18.50000	4.571429	4.046875	4.00

APPENDIX G

TWO-DIMENSIONAL OBLIQUE SHOCK FUNCTIONS

For a two-dimensional oblique shock as shown in Fig. G-1, the following property ratios apply across the shock.

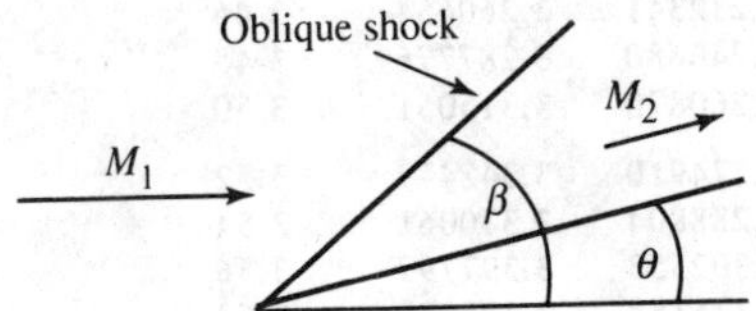

FIGURE G-1
Oblique shock nomenclature.

Because a two-dimensional oblique shock acts as a normal shock perpendicular to the flow, the normal shock relations can be applied to oblique shocks. The normal shock relations of App. F apply, with M_x replaced by $M_1 \sin\beta$ and M_y replaced by $M_2 \sin(\beta - \theta)$. Thus, we can write

$$\frac{P_2}{P_1} = f_1(M_1 \sin\beta) = \frac{2\gamma}{\gamma+1}(M_1 \sin\beta)^2 - \frac{\gamma-1}{\gamma+1} \tag{G-1}$$

$$\frac{\rho_2}{\rho_1} = f_2(M_1 \sin\beta) = \frac{\dfrac{(\gamma+1)^2}{2(\gamma-1)}(M_1 \sin\beta)^2\left[\dfrac{2\gamma}{\gamma+1}(M_1 \sin\beta)^2 - \dfrac{\gamma-1}{\gamma+1}\right]}{\left[1 + \dfrac{\gamma-1}{2}(M_1 \sin\beta)^2\right]\left[\dfrac{2\gamma}{\gamma+1}(M_1 \sin\beta)^2 - 1\right]} \tag{G-2}$$

$$\frac{T_2}{T_1} = f_3(M_1 \sin\beta) = \frac{\left[1 + \dfrac{\gamma-1}{2}(M_1 \sin\beta)^2\right]\left[\dfrac{2\gamma}{\gamma+1}(M_1 \sin\beta)^2 - 1\right]}{\dfrac{(\gamma+1)^2}{2(\gamma-1)}(M_1 \sin\beta)^2} \tag{G-3}$$

$$\frac{P_{t2}}{P_{t1}} = f_4(M_1 \sin\beta)$$

$$\frac{P_{t2}}{P_{t1}} = \left[\frac{\frac{\gamma+1}{2}(M_1 \sin\beta)^2}{1+\frac{\gamma-1}{2}(M_1 \sin\beta)^2}\right]^{\gamma/(\gamma-1)} \left[\frac{2\gamma}{\gamma+1}(M_1 \sin\beta)^2 - \frac{\gamma-1}{\gamma+1}\right]^{-1/(\gamma-1)} \tag{G-4}$$

$$M_2 \sin(\beta-\theta) = f_5(M_1 \sin\beta) = \sqrt{\frac{(M_1 \sin\beta)^2 + \frac{2}{\gamma-1}}{\frac{2\gamma}{\gamma-1}(M_1 \sin\beta)^2 - 1}} \tag{G-5}$$

The relationships for the static pressure ratio, static density ratio, total pressure ratio, and downstream Mach number M_2 are plotted, for $\gamma = 1.4$, versus upstream Mach number M_1 and flow deflection angle θ in Figs. 3-28, 3-29, 3-30, and 3-31, respectively.

The relationship between the upstream Mach number M_1, shock angle β, and flow deflection angle θ for an oblique shock is

$$\tan(\beta-\theta) = \frac{2+(\gamma-1)M_1^2 \sin^2\beta}{(\gamma+1)M_1^2 \sin\beta \cos\beta} \tag{G-6}$$

which is given in chart form in Fig. 3-27. This relationship is also given as a table in the following pages. The maximum flow deflection angle θ_{max} and the corresponding shock angle β are also listed in this table for many upstream Mach numbers M_1.

TABLE G-1
Wave angle β for oblique shock waves ($\gamma = 1.4$)

	Flow turning angle θ, deg													
M_1	0.0	2.0	4.0	6.0	8.10	10.0	12.0	14.0	16.0	18.0	20.0	22.0	β	θ_{max}
1.00														
1.01	81.93												85.36	0.05
1.02	78.64												83.49	0.14
1.03	76.14												82.08	0.26
1.04	74.06												80.93	0.40
1.05	72.25												79.94	0.56
1.06	70.63												79.06	0.73
1.07	69.16												78.27	0.91
1.08	67.81												77.56	1.10
1.09	66.55												76.90	1.30
1.10	65.38												76.30	1.52
1.11	64.28												75.73	1.73
1.12	63.23												75.21	1.96
1.13	62.25	70.93											74.72	2.19
1.14	61.31	68.71											74.26	2.43
1.15	60.41	67.00											73.82	2.67
1.16	59.55	65.56											73.41	2.92
1.17	58.73	64.28											73.02	3.17
1.18	57.94	63.11											72.66	3.42
1.19	57.18	62.05											72.31	3.68
1.20	56.44	61.05											71.98	3.94
1.21	55.74	60.12	68.09										71.66	4.21
1.22	55.05	59.24	66.03										71.36	4.47
1.23	54.39	58.40	64.47										71.07	4.74
1.24	53.75	57.60	63.15										70.80	5.01
1.25	53.13	56.84	61.99										70.54	5.29
1.26	52.53	56.12	60.93										70.29	5.56
1.27	51.94	55.42	59.97										70.05	5.83
1.28	51.38	54.75	59.06	67.38									69.82	6.11
1.29	50.82	54.10	58.22	65.05									69.60	6.39
1.30	50.28	53.47	57.42	63.46									69.40	6.66
1.31	49.76	52.87	56.67	62.16									69.19	6.94
1.32	49.25	52.28	55.95	61.03									69.00	7.22
1.33	48.75	51.72	55.26	60.02									68.82	7.49
1.34	48.27	51.17	54.60	59.09									68.64	7.77
1.35	47.79	50.63	53.97	58.23	66.91								68.47	8.05
1.36	47.33	50.11	53.36	57.43	64.29								68.31	8.33
1.37	46.88	49.61	52.77	56.68	62.70								68.15	8.60
1.38	46.44	49.12	52.20	55.96	61.43								68.00	8.88
1.39	46.01	48.64	51.65	55.28	60.34								67.85	9.15
1.40	45.58	48.17	51.12	54.63	59.37								67.72	9.43
1.41	45.17	47.72	50.60	54.01	58.48								67.58	9.70
1.42	44.77	47.27	50.10	53.42	57.67								67.45	9.97
1.43	44.37	46.84	49.61	52.84	56.91	63.95							67.33	10.25
1.44	43.98	46.42	49.14	52.29	56.19	62.31							67.21	10.52
1.45	43.60	46.00	48.68	51.76	55.52	61.05							67.10	10.79
1.46	43.23	45.60	48.23	51.24	54.87	59.98							66.99	11.05
1.47	42.86	45.20	47.79	50.74	54.26	59.04							66.88	11.32
1.48	42.51	44.82	47.37	50.25	53.68	58.19							66.78	11.59
1.49	42.16	44.44	46.95	49.78	53.11	57.41							66.68	11.85
1.50	41.81	44.06	46.54	49.33	52.57	56.68	64.36						66.59	12.11
M_1	0.0	2.0	4.0	6.0	8.0	10.0	12.0	14.0	16.0	18.0	20.0	22.0	β	θ_{max}
	Flow turning angle θ, deg													

M_1	0.0	2.0	4.0	6.0	8.10	10.0	12.0	14.0	16.0	18.0	20.0	22.0	β	θ_{max}
					Flow turning angle θ, deg									
1.50	41.81	44.06	46.54	49.33	52.57	56.68	64.36						66.59	12.11
1.51	41.47	43.70	46.15	48.88	52.05	56.00	62.42						66.50	12.37
1.52	41.14	43.34	45.76	48.45	51.55	55.35	61.10						66.41	12.63
1.53	40.81	42.99	45.38	48.03	51.06	54.74	60.02						66.33	12.89
1.54	40.49	42.65	45.01	47.62	50.59	54.16	59.08						66.25	13.15
1.55	40.18	42.32	44.64	47.21	50.13	53.60	58.24						66.17	13.40
1.56	39.87	41.99	44.29	46.82	49.69	53.06	57.47						66.10	13.66
1.57	39.56	41.66	43.94	46.44	49.26	52.55	56.77						66.03	13.91
1.58	39.27	41.34	43.59	46.07	48.84	52.06	56.10	63.38					65.96	14.16
1.59	38.97	41.03	43.26	45.70	48.43	51.58	55.48	61.73					65.89	14.41
1.60	38.68	40.72	42.93	45.34	48.03	51.12	54.89	60.54					65.83	14.65
1.61	38.40	40.42	42.61	44.99	47.64	50.67	54.33	59.55					65.77	14.90
1.62	38.12	40.13	42.29	44.65	47.26	50.23	53.79	58.69					65.71	15.14
1.63	37.84	39.84	41.98	44.32	46.89	49.81	53.28	57.91					65.65	15.38
1.64	37.57	39.55	41.68	43.99	46.53	49.41	52.79	57.20					65.60	15.62
1.65	37.31	39.27	41.38	43.67	46.18	49.01	52.31	56.54					65.55	15.86
1.66	37.04	38.99	41.08	43.35	45.84	48.62	51.85	55.93	63.58				65.50	16.09
1.67	36.78	38.72	40.79	43.04	45.50	48.24	51.41	55.34	61.80				65.45	16.32
1.68	36.53	38.45	40.51	42.74	45.17	47.88	50.98	54.79	60.60				65.40	16.55
1.69	36.28	38.19	40.23	42.44	44.85	47.52	50.57	54.27	59.63				65.36	16.78
1.70	36.03	37.93	39.96	42.14	44.53	47.17	50.17	53.77	58.79				65.32	17.01
1.71	35.79	37.67	39.69	41.86	44.22	46.82	49.78	53.29	58.05				65.28	17.24
1.72	35.55	37.42	39.42	41.57	43.91	46.49	49.40	52.83	57.36				65.24	17.46
1.73	35.31	37.17	39.16	41.30	43.61	46.16	49.03	52.39	56.73				65.20	17.68
1.74	35.08	36.93	38.90	41.02	43.32	45.84	48.67	51.96	56.14				65.17	17.90
1.75	34.85	36.69	38.65	40.76	43.03	45.53	48.32	51.55	55.59	62.94			65.13	18.12
1.76	34.62	36.45	38.40	40.49	42.75	45.22	47.98	51.15	55.06	61.42			65.10	18.34
1.77	34.40	36.22	38.16	40.23	42.48	44.92	47.64	50.76	54.57	60.34			65.07	18.55
1.78	34.18	35.99	37.91	39.98	42.20	44.63	47.32	50.38	54.09	59.46			65.04	18.76
1.79	33.96	35.76	37.68	39.73	41.94	44.34	47.00	50.02	53.63	58.69			65.01	18.97
1.80	33.75	35.54	37.44	39.48	41.67	44.06	46.69	49.66	53.20	57.99			64.99	19.18
1.81	33.54	35.32	37.21	39.24	41.42	43.78	46.38	49.31	52.78	57.36			64.96	19.39
1.82	33.33	35.10	36.99	39.00	41.16	43.51	46.08	48.98	52.37	56.78			64.94	19.59
1.83	33.12	34.89	36.76	38.76	40.91	43.24	45.79	48.65	51.98	56.23			64.91	19.80
1.84	32.92	34.68	36.54	38.53	40.67	42.98	45.50	48.33	51.60	55.71			64.89	20.00
1.85	32.72	34.47	36.32	38.30	40.42	42.72	45.22	48.01	51.23	55.23	62.10		64.87	20.20
1.86	32.52	34.26	36.11	38.08	40.19	42.46	44.95	47.71	50.88	54.76	60.91		64.85	20.40
1.87	32.33	34.06	35.90	37.86	39.95	42.21	44.68	47.41	50.53	54.32	59.99		64.83	20.59
1.88	32.13	33.86	35.69	37.64	39.72	41.97	44.41	47.12	50.19	53.90	59.21		64.82	20.79
1.89	31.94	33.66	35.48	37.42	39.50	41.73	44.15	46.83	49.86	53.49	58.52		64.80	20.98
1.90	31.76	33.47	35.28	37.21	39.27	41.49	43.90	46.55	49.54	53.10	57.90		64.78	21.17
1.91	31.57	33.27	35.08	37.00	39.05	41.26	43.65	46.28	49.23	52.72	57.33		64.77	21.36
1.92	31.39	33.08	34.88	36.79	38.84	41.03	43.40	46.01	48.93	52.35	56.80		64.75	21.54
1.93	31.21	32.90	34.69	36.59	38.62	40.80	43.16	45.74	48.63	52.00	56.30		64.74	21.73
1.94	31.03	32.71	34.49	36.39	38.41	40.58	42.92	45.48	48.34	51.65	55.83		64.73	21.91
1.95	30.85	32.53	34.30	36.19	38.20	40.36	42.69	45.23	48.06	51.32	55.38	62.86	64.72	22.09
1.96	30.68	32.35	34.12	36.00	38.00	40.14	42.46	44.98	47.78	51.00	54.96	61.49	64.71	22.27
1.97	30.51	32.17	33.93	35.80	37.80	39.93	42.23	44.74	47.51	50.68	54.55	60.53	64.70	22.45
1.98	30.33	31.99	33.75	35.61	37.60	39.72	42.01	44.50	47.25	50.38	54.16	59.74	64.69	22.63
1.99	30.17	31.82	33.57	35.43	37.40	39.52	41.79	44.26	46.99	50.08	53.78	59.06	64.68	22.80
2.00	30.00	31.65	33.39	35.24	37.21	39.31	41.58	44.03	46.73	49.79	53.42	58.46	64.67	22.97
M_1	0.0	2.0	4.0	6.0	8.0	10.0	12.0	14.0	16.0	18.0	20.0	22.0	β	θ_{max}
					Flow turning angle θ, deg									

M_1	Flow turning angle θ, deg 0.0	2.0	4.0	6.0	8.0	10.0	12.0	14.0	16.0	18.0	20.0	22.0	24.0	26.0	28.0	30.0	32.0	34.0	36.0	β	θ_{max}
2.00	30.00	31.65	33.39	35.24	37.21	39.31	41.58	44.03	46.73	49.79	53.42	58.46								64.67	22.97
2.02	29.67	31.31	33.04	34.88	36.83	38.92	41.15	43.58	46.24	49.22	52.74	57.39								64.65	23.31
2.04	29.35	30.98	32.70	34.52	36.46	38.53	40.75	43.14	45.76	48.69	52.09	56.46								64.64	23.65
2.06	29.04	30.66	32.37	34.18	36.10	38.15	40.35	42.72	45.30	48.17	51.49	55.63								64.63	23.98
2.08	28.74	30.34	32.04	33.84	35.75	37.79	39.97	42.31	44.86	47.68	50.91	54.87	61.28							64.63	24.30
2.10	28.44	30.03	31.72	33.51	35.41	37.43	39.59	41.91	44.43	47.21	50.36	54.17	59.77							64.62	24.61
2.12	28.14	29.73	31.41	33.19	35.08	37.09	39.23	41.53	44.02	46.75	49.84	53.52	58.62							64.62	24.92
2.14	27.86	29.44	31.11	32.88	34.76	36.75	38.87	41.15	43.62	46.32	49.35	52.91	57.65							64.62	25.23
2.16	27.58	29.15	30.81	32.57	34.44	36.42	38.53	40.79	43.23	45.89	48.87	52.34	56.81							64.62	25.52
2.18	27.30	28.87	30.52	32.27	34.13	36.10	38.20	40.44	42.85	45.49	48.41	51.79	56.05							64.62	25.82
2.20	27.04	28.59	30.24	31.98	33.83	35.79	37.87	40.09	42.49	45.09	47.98	51.28	55.36	62.70						64.62	26.10
2.22	26.77	28.32	29.96	31.69	33.53	35.48	37.55	39.76	42.14	44.71	47.55	50.79	54.72	60.85						64.62	26.38
2.24	26.51	28.06	29.69	31.42	33.24	35.18	37.24	39.44	41.79	44.34	47.15	50.32	54.12	59.63						64.63	26.66
2.26	26.26	27.80	29.42	31.14	32.96	34.89	36.94	39.12	41.46	43.98	46.75	49.87	53.56	58.65						64.64	26.93
2.28	26.01	27.54	29.16	30.87	32.69	34.60	36.64	38.81	41.13	43.64	46.37	49.44	53.03	57.82						64.64	27.19
2.30	25.77	27.29	28.91	30.61	32.42	34.33	36.35	38.51	40.82	43.30	46.01	49.03	52.54	57.08						64.65	27.45
2.32	25.53	27.05	28.66	30.35	32.15	34.05	36.07	38.22	40.51	42.97	45.65	48.63	52.06	56.41						64.66	27.71
2.34	25.30	26.81	28.41	30.10	31.89	33.79	35.80	37.93	40.21	42.65	45.31	48.25	51.61	55.79						64.67	27.96
2.36	25.07	26.58	28.17	29.86	31.64	33.53	35.53	37.65	39.91	42.34	44.97	47.88	51.18	55.22	61.97					64.68	28.20
2.38	24.85	26.35	27.93	29.61	31.39	33.27	35.26	37.38	39.63	42.04	44.65	47.52	50.77	54.69	60.65					64.70	28.45
2.40	24.62	26.12	27.70	29.38	31.15	33.02	35.01	37.11	39.35	41.75	44.34	47.17	50.37	54.18	59.66					64.71	28.68
2.42	24.41	25.90	27.48	29.14	30.91	32.78	34.76	36.85	39.08	41.46	44.03	46.84	49.99	53.71	58.83					64.72	28.91
2.44	24.19	25.68	27.25	28.92	30.68	32.54	34.51	36.60	38.82	41.18	43.73	46.52	49.62	53.26	58.11					64.74	29.14
2.46	23.99	25.47	27.03	28.69	30.45	32.31	34.27	36.35	38.56	40.91	43.45	46.20	49.27	52.83	57.47					64.75	29.36
2.48	23.78	25.26	26.82	28.47	30.23	32.08	34.03	36.10	38.30	40.65	43.16	45.90	48.93	52.43	56.88					64.77	29.58
2.50	23.58	25.05	26.61	28.26	30.01	31.85	33.80	35.87	38.06	40.39	42.89	45.60	48.60	52.04	56.33					64.78	29.80
2.52	23.38	24.85	26.40	28.05	29.79	31.63	33.58	35.63	37.82	40.14	42.62	45.31	48.28	51.66	55.83	64.27				64.80	30.01
2.54	23.18	24.65	26.20	27.84	29.58	31.41	33.35	35.41	37.58	39.89	42.36	45.04	47.97	51.30	55.36	62.05				64.81	30.22
2.56	22.99	24.45	26.00	27.64	29.37	31.20	33.14	35.18	37.35	39.65	42.11	44.76	47.67	50.96	54.91	60.94				64.83	30.42
2.58	22.81	24.26	25.80	27.44	29.17	30.99	32.92	34.96	37.12	39.41	41.86	44.50	47.38	50.63	54.49	60.08				64.85	30.62
2.60	22.62	24.07	25.61	27.24	28.97	30.79	32.71	34.75	36.90	39.19	41.62	44.24	47.10	50.31	54.09	59.35				64.87	30.81
2.62	22.44	23.89	25.42	27.05	28.77	30.59	32.51	34.54	36.68	38.96	41.39	43.99	46.83	50.00	53.71	58.72				64.88	31.01
2.64	22.26	23.70	25.24	26.86	28.58	30.39	32.31	34.33	36.47	38.74	41.16	43.75	46.56	49.70	53.34	58.14				64.90	31.19

M_1	0.0	2.0	4.0	6.0	8.0	10.0	12.0	14.0	16.0	18.0	20.0	22.0	24.0	26.0	28.0	30.0	32.0	34.0	36.0	β	θ_{max}
2.66	22.08	23.52	25.05	26.67	28.39	30.20	32.11	34.13	36.26	38.53	40.93	43.51	46.31	49.41	52.99	57.62				64.92	31.38
2.68	21.91	23.35	24.87	26.49	28.20	30.01	31.92	33.93	36.06	38.32	40.71	43.28	46.05	49.12	52.66	57.14				64.94	31.56
2.70	21.74	23.17	24.70	26.31	28.02	29.82	31.73	33.74	35.86	38.11	40.50	43.05	45.81	48.85	52.33	56.69				64.96	31.74
2.72	21.57	23.00	24.52	26.13	27.84	29.64	31.54	33.55	35.67	37.91	40.29	42.83	45.57	48.59	52.02	56.26				64.97	31.92
2.74	21.41	22.83	24.35	25.96	27.66	29.46	31.36	33.36	35.48	37.71	40.08	42.61	45.34	48.33	51.72	55.87	63.25			64.99	32.09
2.76	21.24	22.67	24.18	25.79	27.49	29.28	31.18	33.18	35.29	37.52	39.88	42.40	45.11	48.08	51.44	55.49	62.00			65.01	32.26
2.78	21.08	22.50	24.02	25.62	27.32	29.11	31.00	33.00	35.10	37.33	39.68	42.19	44.89	47.84	51.16	55.13	61.14			65.03	32.42
2.80	20.92	22.34	23.85	25.45	27.15	28.94	30.83	32.82	34.92	37.14	39.49	41.99	44.68	47.60	50.89	54.79	60.43			65.05	32.59
2.82	20.77	22.19	23.69	25.29	26.98	28.77	30.66	32.65	34.75	36.96	39.30	41.79	44.47	47.38	50.62	54.46	59.83			65.07	32.75
2.84	20.62	22.03	23.54	25.13	26.82	28.61	30.49	32.48	34.57	36.78	39.12	41.60	44.26	47.15	50.37	54.14	59.29			65.09	32.91
2.86	20.47	21.88	23.38	24.97	26.66	28.45	30.33	32.31	34.40	36.60	38.94	41.41	44.06	46.93	50.13	53.84	58.80			65.11	33.06
2.88	20.32	21.73	23.23	24.82	26.50	28.29	30.17	32.15	34.23	36.43	38.76	41.23	43.86	46.72	49.89	53.55	58.35			65.13	33.21
2.90	20.17	21.58	23.08	24.67	26.35	28.13	30.01	31.99	34.07	36.26	38.58	41.04	43.67	46.51	49.65	53.27	57.93			65.15	33.36
2.92	20.03	21.43	22.93	24.52	26.20	27.98	29.85	31.83	33.91	36.10	38.41	40.87	43.48	46.31	49.43	53.00	57.54			65.16	33.51
2.94	19.89	21.29	22.78	24.37	26.05	27.82	29.70	31.67	33.75	35.94	38.25	40.69	43.30	46.12	49.21	52.74	57.17			65.18	33.65
2.96	19.75	21.15	22.64	24.22	25.90	27.67	29.55	31.52	33.59	35.78	38.08	40.52	43.12	45.92	49.00	52.49	56.83			65.20	33.80
2.98	19.61	21.00	22.49	24.08	25.75	27.53	29.40	31.37	33.44	35.62	37.92	40.36	42.95	45.73	48.79	52.25	56.50			65.22	33.94
3.00	19.47	20.87	22.35	23.94	25.61	27.38	29.25	31.22	33.29	35.47	37.76	40.19	42.78	45.55	48.59	52.01	56.18	63.67		65.24	34.07
3.05	19.14	20.53	22.01	23.59	25.26	27.03	28.90	30.86	32.92	35.10	37.38	39.80	42.36	45.11	48.10	51.45	55.46	61.50		65.29	34.41
3.10	18.82	20.20	21.68	23.26	24.93	26.69	28.55	30.51	32.57	34.74	37.02	39.42	41.97	44.69	47.65	50.93	54.80	60.21		65.34	34.73
3.15	18.51	19.89	21.37	22.94	24.60	26.37	28.23	30.18	32.24	34.40	36.67	39.06	41.59	44.30	47.22	50.45	54.20	59.20		65.38	35.03
3.20	18.21	19.59	21.06	22.63	24.29	26.05	27.91	29.86	31.92	34.07	36.34	38.72	41.24	43.92	46.81	49.99	53.65	58.35		65.43	35.33
3.25	17.92	19.29	20.76	22.33	23.99	25.75	27.60	29.56	31.61	33.76	36.02	38.39	40.90	43.56	46.43	49.57	53.14	57.62		65.47	35.61
3.30	17.64	19.01	20.48	22.04	23.70	25.46	27.31	29.26	31.31	33.46	35.71	38.08	40.57	43.22	46.06	49.16	52.67	56.96		65.52	35.88
3.35	17.37	18.73	20.20	21.76	23.42	25.17	27.03	28.98	31.02	33.17	35.42	37.78	40.26	42.90	45.72	48.78	52.22	56.37	63.38	65.56	36.14
3.40	17.10	18.47	19.93	21.49	23.15	24.90	26.75	28.70	30.75	32.89	35.13	37.49	39.97	42.59	45.39	48.42	51.81	55.84	61.91	65.60	36.39
3.45	16.85	18.21	19.67	21.23	22.88	24.64	26.49	28.44	30.48	32.62	34.86	37.21	39.68	42.29	45.07	48.08	51.42	55.34	60.90	65.65	36.63
3.50	16.60	17.96	19.42	20.97	22.63	24.38	26.24	28.18	30.22	32.36	34.60	36.95	39.41	42.01	44.77	47.76	51.05	54.89	60.09	65.69	36.87
3.55	16.36	17.71	19.17	20.73	22.38	24.14	25.99	27.94	29.98	32.12	34.35	36.69	39.15	41.74	44.49	47.45	50.70	54.46	59.40	65.73	37.09
3.60	16.13	17.48	18.93	20.49	22.14	23.90	25.75	27.70	29.74	31.88	34.11	36.45	38.90	41.48	44.21	47.15	50.38	54.07	58.79	65.77	37.31
3.65	15.90	17.25	18.70	20.26	21.91	23.67	25.52	27.47	29.51	31.65	33.88	36.21	38.66	41.23	43.95	46.87	50.06	53.69	58.25	65.81	37.51
3.70	15.68	17.03	18.48	20.03	21.69	23.44	25.30	27.25	29.29	31.42	33.65	35.99	38.43	40.99	43.70	46.61	49.77	53.34	57.76	65.85	37.71
3.75	15.47	16.81	18.26	19.81	21.47	23.23	25.08	27.03	29.07	31.21	33.44	35.77	38.20	40.76	43.46	46.35	49.49	53.01	57.31	65.88	37.91

Flow turning angle θ, deg

M_1	Flow turning angle θ, deg																				
	0.0	2.0	4.0	6.0	8.0	10.0	12.0	14.0	16.0	18.0	20.0	22.0	24.0	26.0	28.0	30.0	32.0	34.0	36.0	38.0	40.0
3.80	15.26	16.60	18.05	19.60	21.26	23.02	24.87	26.82	28.86	31.00	33.23	35.56	37.99	40.54	43.23	46.10	49.22	52.70	56.89	64.19	
3.85	15.05	16.39	17.84	19.40	21.05	22.81	24.67	26.62	28.66	30.80	33.03	35.35	37.78	40.33	43.01	45.87	48.96	52.41	56.51	62.94	
3.90	14.86	16.20	17.64	19.20	20.85	22.61	24.47	26.42	28.47	30.61	32.83	35.16	37.58	40.13	42.80	45.65	48.72	52.13	56.15	62.09	
3.95	14.66	16.00	17.45	19.00	20.66	22.42	24.28	26.23	28.28	30.42	32.65	34.97	37.39	39.93	42.60	45.43	48.48	51.86	55.81	61.41	
4.00	14.48	15.81	17.26	18.81	20.47	22.23	24.09	26.05	28.10	30.24	32.46	34.79	37.21	39.74	42.40	45.22	48.26	51.61	55.50	60.83	
4.05	14.29	15.63	17.07	18.63	20.29	22.05	23.91	25.87	27.92	30.06	32.29	34.61	37.03	39.56	42.21	45.03	48.04	51.36	55.20	60.32	
4.10	14.12	15.45	16.89	18.45	20.11	21.88	23.74	25.70	27.75	29.89	32.12	34.44	36.86	39.38	42.03	44.83	47.84	51.13	54.92	59.86	
4.15	13.94	15.27	16.72	18.27	19.94	21.70	23.57	25.53	27.58	29.72	31.95	34.27	36.69	39.21	41.86	44.65	47.64	50.91	54.65	59.45	
4.20	13.77	15.10	16.55	18.10	19.77	21.54	23.41	25.37	27.42	29.56	31.79	34.11	36.53	39.05	41.69	44.47	47.45	50.70	54.39	59.07	
4.25	13.61	14.94	16.38	17.94	19.60	21.37	23.24	25.21	27.27	29.41	31.64	33.96	36.37	38.89	41.52	44.30	47.27	50.50	54.15	58.73	
4.30	13.45	14.77	16.22	17.78	19.44	21.22	23.09	25.06	27.11	29.26	31.49	33.81	36.22	38.74	41.37	44.14	47.09	50.30	53.92	58.40	
4.35	13.29	14.62	16.06	17.62	19.29	21.06	22.94	24.91	26.97	29.11	31.35	33.67	36.08	38.59	41.22	43.98	46.92	50.12	53.71	58.10	
4.40	13.14	14.46	15.90	17.46	19.13	20.91	22.79	24.76	26.82	28.97	31.20	33.53	35.94	38.45	41.07	43.83	46.76	49.94	53.50	57.81	
4.45	12.99	14.31	15.75	17.31	18.99	20.77	22.65	24.62	26.68	28.83	31.07	33.39	35.80	38.31	40.93	43.68	46.60	49.77	53.30	57.54	65.77
4.50	12.84	14.16	15.61	17.17	18.84	20.62	22.50	24.48	26.55	28.70	30.94	33.26	35.67	38.17	40.79	43.54	46.45	49.60	53.10	57.29	64.34
4.55	12.70	14.02	15.46	17.02	18.70	20.48	22.37	24.35	26.42	28.57	30.81	33.13	35.54	38.04	40.66	43.40	46.31	49.44	52.92	57.05	63.58
4.60	12.56	13.88	15.32	16.88	18.56	20.35	22.24	24.22	26.29	28.44	30.68	33.00	35.41	37.92	40.53	43.27	46.17	49.29	52.75	56.83	63.00
4.65	12.42	13.74	15.18	16.75	18.43	20.22	22.11	24.09	26.16	28.32	30.56	32.88	35.29	37.80	40.40	43.14	46.03	49.14	52.58	56.61	62.51
4.70	12.28	13.60	15.05	16.61	18.30	20.09	21.98	23.97	26.04	28.20	30.44	32.77	35.18	37.68	40.28	43.01	45.90	49.00	52.41	56.40	62.09
4.75	12.15	13.47	14.92	16.48	18.17	19.96	21.86	23.85	25.92	28.09	30.33	32.65	35.06	37.56	40.17	42.89	45.77	48.86	52.26	56.21	61.71
4.80	12.02	13.34	14.79	16.36	18.04	19.84	21.74	23.73	25.81	27.97	30.22	32.54	34.95	37.45	40.05	42.78	45.65	48.73	52.11	56.02	61.37
4.85	11.90	13.22	14.66	16.23	17.92	19.72	21.62	23.61	25.70	27.86	30.11	32.44	34.85	37.34	39.94	42.66	45.53	48.60	51.96	55.84	61.06
4.90	11.78	13.09	14.54	16.11	17.80	19.60	21.50	23.50	25.59	27.76	30.00	32.33	34.74	37.24	39.84	42.55	45.42	48.47	51.82	55.67	60.78
4.95	11.66	12.97	14.42	15.99	17.68	19.49	21.39	23.39	25.48	27.65	29.90	32.23	34.64	37.14	39.73	42.45	45.30	48.35	51.69	55.51	60.51
5.00	11.54	12.85	14.30	15.88	17.57	19.38	21.28	23.29	25.38	27.55	29.80	32.13	34.54	37.04	39.63	42.34	45.20	48.24	51.56	55.35	60.26
5.25	10.98	12.29	13.75	15.33	17.03	18.85	20.78	22.79	24.90	27.08	29.34	31.68	34.09	36.59	39.17	41.87	44.70	47.71	50.97	54.65	59.21
5.50	10.48	11.79	13.24	14.84	16.55	18.39	20.32	22.35	24.47	26.66	28.93	31.28	33.69	36.19	38.77	41.46	44.28	47.26	50.47	54.06	58.40
5.75	10.02	11.33	12.79	14.39	16.12	17.97	19.92	21.96	24.09	26.30	28.57	30.92	33.34	35.84	38.42	41.11	43.91	46.87	50.04	53.56	57.74
6.00	9.59	10.91	12.37	13.98	15.73	17.59	19.55	21.61	23.75	25.97	28.26	30.61	33.04	35.54	38.12	40.79	43.58	46.52	49.67	53.14	57.19
6.25	9.21	10.52	11.99	13.61	15.37	17.24	19.22	21.29	23.45	25.67	27.97	30.33	32.76	35.26	37.84	40.52	43.30	46.22	49.35	52.77	56.72

M_1	0.0	2.0	4.0	6.0	8.0	10.0	12.0	14.0	16.0	18.0	20.0	22.0	24.0	26.0	28.0	30.0	32.0	34.0	36.0	38.0	40.0
6.50	8.85	10.16	11.64	13.27	15.04	16.93	18.92	21.01	23.17	25.41	27.71	30.08	32.52	35.02	37.60	40.27	43.05	45.96	49.06	52.44	56.32
6.75	8.52	9.83	11.32	12.96	14.74	16.64	18.65	20.75	22.93	25.17	27.48	29.86	32.30	34.80	37.38	40.05	42.82	45.72	48.81	52.16	55.98
7.00	8.21	9.53	11.02	12.67	14.46	16.38	18.40	20.51	22.70	24.96	27.28	29.66	32.10	34.61	37.19	39.85	42.62	45.51	48.58	51.91	55.67
7.25	7.93	9.24	10.74	12.40	14.21	16.14	18.18	20.30	22.50	24.76	27.09	29.48	31.92	34.43	37.01	39.68	42.44	45.33	48.38	51.69	55.41
7.50	7.66	8.98	10.48	12.16	13.98	15.92	17.97	20.10	22.31	24.58	26.92	29.31	31.76	34.27	36.86	39.52	42.28	45.16	48.20	51.49	55.17
7.75	7.41	8.73	10.24	11.93	13.76	15.72	17.78	19.92	22.14	24.42	26.76	29.16	31.61	34.13	36.71	39.37	42.13	45.00	48.04	51.31	54.96
8.00	7.18	8.50	10.02	11.71	13.56	15.53	17.60	19.76	21.98	24.27	26.62	29.02	31.48	34.00	36.58	39.24	41.99	44.86	47.89	51.15	54.77
8.25	6.96	8.28	9.81	11.51	13.37	15.35	17.44	19.60	21.84	24.14	26.49	28.90	31.36	33.88	36.46	39.12	41.87	44.74	47.76	51.00	54.60
8.50	6.76	8.08	9.61	11.33	13.20	15.19	17.29	19.46	21.71	24.01	26.37	28.78	31.24	33.77	36.35	39.01	41.76	44.62	47.64	50.87	54.44
8.75	6.56	7.89	9.43	11.15	13.04	15.04	17.15	19.33	21.58	23.89	26.26	28.67	31.14	33.67	36.25	38.91	41.66	44.52	47.52	50.74	54.30
9.00	6.38	7.71	9.25	10.99	12.88	14.90	17.02	19.21	21.47	23.79	26.16	28.58	31.05	33.57	36.16	38.82	41.57	44.42	47.42	50.63	54.17
9.25	6.21	7.54	9.09	10.84	12.74	14.77	16.90	19.10	21.36	23.69	26.06	28.48	30.96	33.49	36.08	38.74	41.48	44.33	47.33	50.53	54.06
9.50	6.04	7.38	8.94	10.69	12.61	14.65	16.78	18.99	21.27	23.60	25.97	28.40	30.88	33.41	36.00	38.66	41.40	44.25	47.24	50.44	53.95
9.75	5.89	7.22	8.79	10.56	12.48	14.53	16.68	18.90	21.18	23.51	25.89	28.32	30.80	33.33	35.93	38.58	41.33	44.17	47.16	50.35	53.85
10.00	5.74	7.08	8.65	10.43	12.37	14.43	16.58	18.81	21.09	23.43	25.82	28.25	30.73	33.27	35.86	38.52	41.26	44.10	47.09	50.27	53.76
11.00	5.22	6.56	8.17	9.99	11.96	14.06	16.24	18.50	20.81	23.16	25.56	28.01	30.50	33.04	35.63	38.29	41.03	43.87	46.84	50.01	53.46
12.00	4.78	6.14	7.77	9.63	11.64	13.77	15.98	18.26	20.58	22.96	25.37	27.82	30.32	32.86	35.46	38.12	40.86	43.69	46.66	49.80	53.23
13.00	4.41	5.78	7.44	9.33	11.38	13.54	15.77	18.07	20.41	22.79	25.22	27.68	30.18	32.73	35.33	37.99	40.72	43.56	46.51	49.65	53.06
14.00	4.10	5.48	7.17	9.09	11.16	13.35	15.60	17.91	20.27	22.66	25.09	27.56	30.07	32.62	35.22	37.88	40.62	43.45	46.40	49.53	52.92
15.00	3.82	5.21	6.93	8.88	10.99	13.19	15.46	17.79	20.15	22.56	24.99	27.47	29.98	32.53	35.13	37.80	40.53	43.36	46.31	49.43	52.81
16.00	3.58	4.98	6.73	8.71	10.84	13.06	15.35	17.68	20.06	22.47	24.91	27.39	29.90	32.46	35.06	37.73	40.46	43.29	46.23	49.35	52.72
17.00	3.37	4.78	6.55	8.56	10.71	12.95	15.25	17.60	19.98	22.40	24.84	27.32	29.84	32.40	35.00	37.67	40.40	43.23	46.17	49.28	52.64
18.00	3.18	4.61	6.40	8.43	10.60	12.86	15.17	17.52	19.91	22.33	24.79	27.27	29.79	32.35	34.95	37.62	40.35	43.18	46.12	49.22	52.58
19.00	3.02	4.45	6.27	8.32	10.51	12.78	15.10	17.46	19.86	22.28	24.74	27.22	29.74	32.31	34.91	37.58	40.31	43.13	46.07	49.18	52.53
20.00	2.87	4.31	6.15	8.22	10.43	12.71	15.04	17.41	19.81	22.24	24.70	27.18	29.71	32.27	34.88	37.54	40.28	43.10	46.04	49.14	52.48
21.00	2.73	4.19	6.04	8.14	10.36	12.65	14.99	17.36	19.77	22.20	24.66	27.15	29.67	32.24	34.85	37.51	40.24	43.07	46.00	49.10	52.44
22.00	2.61	4.07	5.95	8.06	10.29	12.60	14.94	17.32	19.73	22.17	24.63	27.12	29.65	32.21	34.82	37.48	40.22	43.04	45.98	49.07	52.41
23.00	2.49	3.97	5.87	8.00	10.24	12.55	14.90	17.29	19.70	22.14	24.60	27.09	29.62	32.19	34.80	37.46	40.20	43.02	45.95	49.05	52.38
24.00	2.39	3.88	5.79	7.94	10.19	12.51	14.87	17.26	19.67	22.11	24.58	27.07	29.60	32.17	34.78	37.44	40.17	42.99	45.93	49.02	52.36
25.00	2.29	3.79	5.73	7.88	10.15	12.47	14.84	17.23	19.65	22.09	24.56	27.05	29.58	32.15	34.76	37.42	40.16	42.98	45.91	49.00	52.33

Flow turning angle θ, deg

APPENDIX H

RAYLEIGH LINE FLOW FUNCTIONS ($\gamma = 1.4$)

$$\phi(M^2) = \frac{M^2\left(1 + \frac{\gamma - 1}{2} M^2\right)}{(1 + \gamma M^2)^2}$$

$$\frac{T_t}{T_t^*} = \frac{2(\gamma + 1)M^2}{(1 + \gamma N^2)^2}\left(1 + \frac{\gamma - 1}{2} M^2\right)$$

$$\frac{P_t}{P_t^*} = \frac{\gamma + 1}{1 + \gamma M^2}\left[\left(\frac{2}{\gamma + 1}\right)\left(1 + \frac{\gamma - 1}{2} M^2\right)\right]^{\gamma/(\gamma - 1)}$$

$$\frac{T}{T^*} = \frac{(\gamma + 1)^2 M^2}{(1 + \gamma M^2)^2}$$

$$\frac{P}{P^*} = \frac{\gamma + 1}{1 + \gamma M^2}$$

M	$\phi(M^2)$	T_t/T_t^*	T/T^*	P_t/P_t^*	P/P^*	M
0	0	0	0	1.267876	2.400000	0
0.01	0.000100	0.000480	0.000576	1.267788	2.399664	0.01
0.02	0.000400	0.001918	0.002301	1.267522	2.398657	0.02
0.03	0.000898	0.004310	0.005171	1.267079	2.396980	0.03
0.04	0.001593	0.007648	0.009175	1.266460	2.394636	0.04
0.05	0.002484	0.011922	0.014300	1.265667	2.391629	0.05
0.06	0.003567	0.017119	0.020529	1.264700	2.387965	0.06
0.07	0.004838	0.023223	0.027841	1.263562	2.383648	0.07
0.08	0.006295	0.030215	0.036212	1.262256	2.378687	0.08
0.09	0.007932	0.038075	0.045616	1.260782	2.373089	0.09
0.10	0.009745	0.046777	0.056020	1.259146	2.366864	0.10
0.11	0.011729	0.056297	0.067393	1.257348	2.360021	0.11
0.12	0.013876	0.066606	0.079698	1.255394	2.352572	0.12
0.13	0.016182	0.077675	0.092896	1.253286	2.344528	0.13
0.14	0.018640	0.089471	0.106946	1.251029	2.335903	0.14
0.15	0.021242	0.101961	0.121805	1.248626	2.326709	0.15
0.16	0.023981	0.115110	0.137429	1.246083	2.316960	0.16
0.17	0.026850	0.128882	0.153769	1.243403	2.306672	0.17
0.18	0.029841	0.143238	0.170779	1.240592	2.295860	0.18
0.19	0.032946	0.158142	0.188410	1.237655	2.284539	0.19
0.20	0.036157	0.173554	0.206612	1.234596	2.272727	0.20
0.21	0.039465	0.189434	0.225333	1.231421	2.260440	0.21
0.22	0.042863	0.205742	0.244523	1.228136	2.247696	0.22
0.23	0.046341	0.222439	0.264132	1.224745	2.234512	0.23
0.24	0.049892	0.239484	0.284108	1.221255	2.220906	0.24
0.25	0.053508	0.256837	0.304400	1.217672	2.206897	0.25
0.26	0.057179	0.274459	0.324957	1.214000	2.192502	0.26
0.27	0.060898	0.292311	0.345732	1.210246	2.177740	0.27
0.28	0.064657	0.310353	0.366674	1.206416	2.162630	0.28
0.29	0.068448	0.328549	0.387737	1.202515	2.147190	0.29
0.30	0.072263	0.346860	0.408873	1.198549	2.131439	0.30
0.31	0.076094	0.365252	0.430037	1.194524	2.115395	0.31
0.32	0.079935	0.383689	0.451187	1.190446	2.099076	0.32
0.33	0.083779	0.402138	0.472279	1.186320	2.082502	0.33
0.34	0.087618	0.420565	0.493273	1.182153	2.065689	0.34
0.35	0.091446	0.438940	0.514131	1.177949	2.048656	0.35
0.36	0.095257	0.457232	0.534816	1.173714	2.031419	0.36
0.37	0.099044	0.475413	0.555292	1.169455	2.013997	0.37
0.38	0.102803	0.493456	0.575526	1.165175	1.996406	0.38
0.39	0.106528	0.511336	0.595488	1.160881	1.978663	0.39
0.40	0.110214	0.529027	0.615148	1.156577	1.960784	0.40
0.41	0.113856	0.546508	0.634479	1.152268	1.942785	0.41
0.42	0.117450	0.563758	0.653456	1.147960	1.924681	0.42
0.43	0.120991	0.580756	0.672055	1.143657	1.906487	0.43
0.44	0.124476	0.597485	0.690255	1.139364	1.888218	0.44
0.45	0.127901	0.613927	0.708037	1.135085	1.869887	0.45
0.46	0.131264	0.630068	0.725383	1.130825	1.851509	0.46
0.47	0.134561	0.645893	0.742278	1.126587	1.833097	0.47
0.48	0.137790	0.661390	0.758707	1.122377	1.814662	0.48
0.49	0.140948	0.676549	0.774659	1.118197	1.796219	0.49
0.50	0.144033	0.691358	0.790123	1.114053	1.777778	0.50

M	$\phi(M^2)$	T_t/T_t^*	T/T^*	P_t/P_t^*	P/P^*	M
0.50	0.144033	0.691358	0.790123	1.114053	1.777778	0.50
0.51	0.147044	0.705810	0.805091	1.109946	1.759350	0.51
0.52	0.149978	0.719897	0.819554	1.105882	1.740947	0.52
0.53	0.152836	0.733612	0.833508	1.101863	1.722579	0.53
0.54	0.155615	0.746952	0.846948	1.097892	1.704255	0.54
0.55	0.158315	0.759910	0.859870	1.093973	1.685985	0.55
0.56	0.160935	0.772486	0.872274	1.090109	1.667779	0.56
0.57	0.163474	0.784675	0.884158	1.086302	1.649643	0.57
0.58	0.165933	0.796478	0.895523	1.082556	1.631588	0.58
0.59	0.168311	0.807894	0.906371	1.078872	1.613619	0.59
0.60	0.170609	0.818923	0.916704	1.075253	1.595745	0.60
0.61	0.172826	0.829566	0.926527	1.071702	1.577972	0.61
0.62	0.174964	0.839825	0.935843	1.068221	1.560306	0.62
0.63	0.177022	0.849703	0.944657	1.064811	1.542754	0.63
0.64	0.179001	0.859203	0.952976	1.061475	1.525320	0.64
0.65	0.180902	0.868329	0.960806	1.058214	1.508011	0.65
0.66	0.182726	0.877084	0.968155	1.055031	1.490831	0.66
0.67	0.184474	0.885473	0.975030	1.051927	1.473785	0.67
0.68	0.186146	0.893502	0.981439	1.048904	1.456876	0.68
0.69	0.187745	0.901175	0.987391	1.045962	1.440109	0.69
0.70	0.189271	0.908499	0.992895	1.043104	1.423488	0.70
0.71	0.190725	0.915479	0.997961	1.040330	1.407014	0.71
0.72	0.192109	0.922122	1.002598	1.037642	1.390692	0.72
0.73	0.193424	0.928435	1.006815	1.035041	1.374523	0.73
0.74	0.194672	0.934423	1.010624	1.032528	1.358511	0.74
0.75	0.195853	0.940095	1.014035	1.030104	1.342657	0.75
0.76	0.196970	0.945456	1.017057	1.027769	1.326964	0.76
0.77	0.198024	0.950515	1.019702	1.025525	1.311432	0.77
0.78	0.199016	0.955279	1.021980	1.023372	1.296064	0.78
0.79	0.199949	0.959754	1.023901	1.021311	1.280861	0.79
0.80	0.200823	0.963948	1.025477	1.019343	1.265823	0.80
0.81	0.201639	0.967869	1.026717	1.017468	1.250951	0.81
0.82	0.202401	0.971524	1.027633	1.015687	1.236247	0.82
0.83	0.203109	0.974921	1.028235	1.013999	1.221710	0.83
0.84	0.203764	0.978066	1.028533	1.012407	1.207341	0.84
0.85	0.204368	0.980968	1.028538	1.010909	1.193139	0.85
0.86	0.204924	0.983633	1.028260	1.009507	1.179106	0.86
0.87	0.205431	0.986069	1.027708	1.008200	1.165241	0.87
0.88	0.205892	0.988283	1.026894	1.006989	1.151543	0.88
0.89	0.206309	0.990282	1.025827	1.005875	1.138012	0.89
0.90	0.206682	0.992073	1.024516	1.004856	1.124649	0.90
0.91	0.207013	0.993663	1.022971	1.003934	1.111451	0.91
0.92	0.207304	0.995058	1.021201	1.003109	1.098418	0.92
0.93	0.207555	0.996266	1.019215	1.002381	1.085550	0.93
0.94	0.207769	0.997293	1.017023	1.001749	1.072846	0.94
0.95	0.207947	0.998145	1.014632	1.001215	1.060305	0.95
0.96	0.208089	0.998828	1.012052	1.000778	1.047925	0.96
0.97	0.208198	0.999350	1.009291	1.000437	1.035706	0.97
0.98	0.208274	0.999715	1.006357	1.000194	1.023646	0.98
0.99	0.208319	0.999930	1.003257	1.000049	1.011745	0.99
1.00	0.208333	1.000000	1.000000	1.000000	1.000000	1.00

M	$\phi(M^2)$	T_t/T_t^*	T/T^*	P_t/P_t^*	P/P^*	M
1.00	0.208333	1.000000	1.000000	1.000000	1.000000	1.00
1.01	0.208319	0.999931	0.996593	1.000049	0.988411	1.01
1.02	0.208277	0.999730	0.993043	1.000194	0.976976	1.02
1.03	0.208208	0.999400	0.989358	1.000437	0.965694	1.03
1.04	0.208114	0.998947	0.985543	1.000778	0.954563	1.04
1.05	0.207995	0.998376	0.981607	1.001215	0.943582	1.05
1.06	0.207853	0.997692	0.977555	1.001750	0.932749	1.06
1.07	0.207688	0.996901	0.973393	1.002381	0.922063	1.07
1.08	0.207501	0.996006	0.969129	1.003110	0.911522	1.08
1.09	0.207294	0.995012	0.964767	1.003936	0.901124	1.09
1.10	0.207067	0.993924	0.960313	1.004858	0.890869	1.10
1.11	0.206822	0.992745	0.955773	1.005878	0.880753	1.11
1.12	0.206558	0.991480	0.951151	1.006995	0.870777	1.12
1.13	0.206278	0.990133	0.946455	1.008208	0.860937	1.13
1.14	0.205981	0.988708	0.941687	1.009519	0.851233	1.14
1.15	0.205668	0.987209	0.936853	1.010926	0.841662	1.15
1.16	0.205341	0.985638	0.931958	1.012430	0.832224	1.16
1.17	0.205000	0.984001	0.927005	1.014031	0.822915	1.17
1.18	0.204646	0.982299	0.922000	1.015729	0.813736	1.18
1.19	0.204278	0.980536	0.916946	1.017524	0.804683	1.19
1.20	0.203899	0.978717	0.911848	1.019415	0.795756	1.20
1.21	0.203509	0.976842	0.906708	1.021403	0.786952	1.21
1.22	0.203108	0.974916	0.901532	1.023488	0.778271	1.22
1.23	0.202696	0.972942	0.896321	1.025670	0.769709	1.23
1.24	0.202275	0.970922	0.891081	1.027949	0.761267	1.24
1.25	0.201845	0.968858	0.885813	1.030325	0.752941	1.25
1.26	0.201407	0.966754	0.880522	1.032798	0.744731	1.26
1.27	0.200961	0.964612	0.875209	1.035368	0.736635	1.27
1.28	0.200507	0.962433	0.869878	1.038035	0.728651	1.28
1.29	0.200046	0.960222	0.864532	1.040799	0.720777	1.29
1.30	0.199579	0.957979	0.859174	1.043660	0.713012	1.30
1.31	0.199106	0.955706	0.853805	1.046619	0.705355	1.31
1.32	0.198626	0.953407	0.848428	1.049675	0.697804	1.32
1.33	0.198142	0.951082	0.843046	1.052829	0.690357	1.33
1.34	0.197653	0.948734	0.837661	1.056081	0.683013	1.34
1.35	0.197159	0.946365	0.832274	1.059430	0.675771	1.35
1.36	0.196662	0.943976	0.826888	1.062878	0.668628	1.36
1.37	0.196160	0.941569	0.821505	1.066424	0.661584	1.37
1.38	0.195655	0.939145	0.816127	1.070068	0.654636	1.38
1.39	0.195147	0.936706	0.810755	1.073810	0.647784	1.39
1.40	0.194636	0.934254	0.805391	1.077652	0.641026	1.40
1.41	0.194123	0.931790	0.800037	1.081592	0.634360	1.41
1.42	0.193607	0.929315	0.794694	1.085631	0.627786	1.42
1.43	0.193090	0.926830	0.789363	1.089770	0.621301	1.43
1.44	0.192570	0.924338	0.784046	1.094008	0.614905	1.44
1.45	0.192050	0.921838	0.778744	1.098346	0.608596	1.45
1.46	0.191528	0.919333	0.773459	1.102785	0.602373	1.46
1.47	0.191005	0.916823	0.768191	1.107324	0.596235	1.47
1.48	0.190481	0.914310	0.762942	1.111963	0.590179	1.48
1.49	0.189957	0.911794	0.757713	1.116703	0.584206	1.49
1.50	0.189432	0.909276	0.752504	1.121545	0.578313	1.50

M	$\phi(M^2)$	T_t/T_t^*	T/T^*	P_t/P_t^*	P/P^*	M
1.50	0.189432	0.909276	0.752504	1.121545	0.578313	1.50
1.51	0.188908	0.906757	0.747317	1.126489	0.572500	1.51
1.52	0.188383	0.904238	0.742152	1.131534	0.566765	1.52
1.53	0.187859	0.901721	0.737011	1.136682	0.561107	1.53
1.54	0.187334	0.899205	0.731894	1.141932	0.555525	1.54
1.55	0.186811	0.896692	0.726802	1.147285	0.550017	1.55
1.56	0.186288	0.894181	0.721735	1.152742	0.544583	1.56
1.57	0.185766	0.891675	0.716694	1.158302	0.539222	1.57
1.58	0.185244	0.889173	0.711680	1.163967	0.533931	1.58
1.59	0.184724	0.886677	0.706694	1.169736	0.528711	1.59
1.60	0.184205	0.884186	0.701735	1.175611	0.523560	1.60
1.61	0.183688	0.881702	0.696805	1.181591	0.518477	1.61
1.62	0.183172	0.879225	0.691903	1.187676	0.513461	1.62
1.63	0.182657	0.876754	0.687031	1.193869	0.508511	1.63
1.64	0.182144	0.874292	0.682188	1.200168	0.503626	1.64
1.65	0.181633	0.871839	0.677375	1.206574	0.498805	1.65
1.66	0.181124	0.869394	0.672593	1.213089	0.494047	1.66
1.67	0.180616	0.866958	0.667841	1.219711	0.489351	1.67
1.68	0.180111	0.864531	0.663120	1.226443	0.484715	1.68
1.69	0.179607	0.862115	0.658430	1.233284	0.480140	1.69
1.70	0.179106	0.859709	0.653771	1.240235	0.475624	1.70
1.71	0.178607	0.857314	0.649144	1.247297	0.471167	1.71
1.72	0.178110	0.854929	0.644549	1.254470	0.466766	1.72
1.73	0.177616	0.852556	0.639985	1.261754	0.462422	1.73
1.74	0.177124	0.850195	0.635454	1.269151	0.458134	1.74
1.75	0.176634	0.847845	0.630954	1.276661	0.453901	1.75
1.76	0.176147	0.845507	0.626487	1.284284	0.449721	1.76
1.77	0.175663	0.843181	0.622052	1.292021	0.445595	1.77
1.78	0.175181	0.840868	0.617649	1.299873	0.441521	1.78
1.79	0.174701	0.838567	0.613279	1.307841	0.437498	1.79
1.80	0.174225	0.836279	0.608941	1.315925	0.433526	1.80
1.81	0.173751	0.834004	0.604636	1.324125	0.429604	1.81
1.82	0.173280	0.831743	0.600363	1.332443	0.425731	1.82
1.83	0.172811	0.829494	0.596122	1.340879	0.421907	1.83
1.84	0.172346	0.827259	0.591914	1.349434	0.418130	1.84
1.85	0.171883	0.825037	0.587738	1.358108	0.414400	1.85
1.86	0.171423	0.822829	0.583595	1.366903	0.410717	1.86
1.87	0.170966	0.820635	0.579483	1.375819	0.407079	1.87
1.88	0.170511	0.818455	0.575404	1.384856	0.403486	1.88
1.89	0.170060	0.816288	0.571357	1.394016	0.399937	1.89
1.90	0.169612	0.814136	0.567342	1.403300	0.396432	1.90
1.91	0.169166	0.811997	0.563359	1.412707	0.392970	1.91
1.92	0.168723	0.809873	0.559407	1.422240	0.389550	1.92
1.93	0.168284	0.807762	0.555488	1.431898	0.386171	1.93
1.94	0.167847	0.805666	0.551599	1.441683	0.382834	1.94
1.95	0.167413	0.803584	0.547743	1.451595	0.379537	1.95
1.96	0.166983	0.801517	0.543917	1.461635	0.376279	1.96
1.97	0.166555	0.799463	0.540123	1.471805	0.373061	1.97
1.98	0.166130	0.797424	0.536360	1.482104	0.369882	1.98
1.99	0.165708	0.795399	0.532627	1.492534	0.366740	1.99
2.00	0.165289	0.793388	0.528926	1.503096	0.363636	2.00

M	$\phi(M^2)$	T_t/T_t^*	T/T^*	P_t/P_t^*	P/P^*	M
2.00	0.165289	0.793388	0.528926	1.503096	0.363636	2.00
2.02	0.164460	0.789410	0.521614	1.524618	0.357539	2.02
2.04	0.163643	0.785488	0.514422	1.546678	0.351584	2.04
2.06	0.162838	0.781624	0.507350	1.569283	0.345770	2.06
2.08	0.162045	0.777816	0.500396	1.592441	0.340090	2.08
2.10	0.161263	0.774064	0.493558	1.616159	0.334541	2.10
2.12	0.160493	0.770368	0.486835	1.640446	0.329121	2.12
2.14	0.159735	0.766727	0.480225	1.665310	0.323824	2.14
2.16	0.158988	0.763142	0.473727	1.690759	0.318647	2.16
2.18	0.158252	0.759611	0.467338	1.716801	0.313588	2.18
2.20	0.157528	0.756135	0.461058	1.743446	0.308642	2.20
2.22	0.156815	0.752712	0.454884	1.770702	0.303807	2.22
2.24	0.156113	0.749342	0.448815	1.798578	0.299079	2.24
2.26	0.155422	0.746024	0.442849	1.827083	0.294455	2.26
2.28	0.154741	0.742758	0.436985	1.856227	0.289934	2.28
2.30	0.154071	0.739543	0.431220	1.886020	0.285510	2.30
2.32	0.153412	0.736379	0.425554	1.916471	0.281183	2.32
2.34	0.152763	0.733264	0.419984	1.947589	0.276949	2.34
2.36	0.152125	0.730199	0.414509	1.979386	0.272807	2.36
2.38	0.151496	0.727182	0.409127	2.011871	0.268752	2.38
2.40	0.150878	0.724213	0.403836	2.045055	0.264784	2.40
2.42	0.150269	0.721291	0.398635	2.078948	0.260899	2.42
2.44	0.149670	0.718415	0.393523	2.113561	0.257096	2.44
2.46	0.149080	0.715585	0.388497	2.148905	0.253372	2.46
2.48	0.148500	0.712800	0.383556	2.184991	0.249725	2.48
2.50	0.147929	0.710059	0.378698	2.221831	0.246154	2.50
2.52	0.147367	0.707362	0.373923	2.259436	0.242656	2.52
2.54	0.146814	0.704708	0.369228	2.297818	0.239229	2.54
2.56	0.146270	0.702096	0.364611	2.336987	0.235871	2.56
2.58	0.145734	0.699525	0.360073	2.376958	0.232582	2.58
2.60	0.145207	0.696995	0.355610	2.417741	0.229358	2.60
2.62	0.144689	0.694506	0.351222	2.459349	0.226198	2.62
2.64	0.144178	0.692055	0.346907	2.501795	0.223101	2.64
2.66	0.143676	0.689644	0.342663	2.545091	0.220066	2.66
2.68	0.143181	0.687271	0.338490	2.589250	0.217089	2.68
2.70	0.142695	0.684935	0.334387	2.634285	0.214171	2.70
2.72	0.142216	0.682636	0.330350	2.680211	0.211309	2.72
2.74	0.141744	0.680374	0.326381	2.727039	0.208503	2.74
2.76	0.141281	0.678146	0.322476	2.774784	0.205750	2.76
2.78	0.140824	0.675954	0.318636	2.823459	0.203050	2.78
2.80	0.140374	0.673796	0.314858	2.873080	0.200401	2.80
2.82	0.139932	0.671672	0.311142	2.923659	0.197802	2.82
2.84	0.139496	0.669582	0.307486	2.975211	0.195251	2.84
2.86	0.139067	0.667523	0.303889	3.027751	0.192749	2.86
2.88	0.138645	0.665497	0.300351	3.081293	0.190293	2.88
2.90	0.138230	0.663502	0.296869	3.135853	0.187882	2.90
2.92	0.137820	0.661538	0.293443	3.191445	0.185515	2.92
2.94	0.137418	0.659604	0.290072	3.248086	0.183192	2.94
2.96	0.137021	0.657700	0.286754	3.305790	0.180910	2.96
2.98	0.136630	0.655825	0.283490	3.364573	0.178670	2.98
3.00	0.136246	0.653979	0.280277	3.424452	0.176471	3.00

M	$\phi(M^2)$	T_t/T_t^*	T/T^*	P_t/P_t^*	P/P^*	M
3.00	0.136246	0.653979	0.280277	3.424452	0.176471	3.00
3.02	0.135867	0.652161	0.277115	3.485442	0.174310	3.02
3.04	0.135494	0.650371	0.274002	3.547559	0.172188	3.04
3.06	0.135127	0.648608	0.270938	3.610821	0.170104	3.06
3.08	0.134765	0.646872	0.267922	3.675243	0.168056	3.08
3.10	0.134409	0.645162	0.264954	3.740844	0.166044	3.10
3.12	0.134058	0.643478	0.262031	3.807639	0.164067	3.12
3.14	0.133712	0.641819	0.259153	3.875646	0.162124	3.14
3.16	0.133372	0.640185	0.256320	3.944883	0.160215	3.16
3.18	0.133036	0.638575	0.253530	4.015368	0.158339	3.18
3.20	0.132706	0.636989	0.250783	4.087118	0.156495	3.20
3.22	0.132381	0.635427	0.248078	4.160151	0.154681	3.22
3.24	0.132060	0.633888	0.245414	4.234486	0.152899	3.24
3.26	0.131744	0.632371	0.242790	4.310142	0.151146	3.26
3.28	0.131433	0.630877	0.240206	4.387137	0.149423	3.28
3.30	0.131126	0.629405	0.237661	4.465489	0.147729	3.30
3.32	0.130824	0.627954	0.235154	4.545219	0.146062	3.32
3.34	0.130526	0.626525	0.232684	4.626346	0.144423	3.34
3.36	0.130232	0.625116	0.230251	4.708889	0.142811	3.36
3.38	0.129943	0.623727	0.227854	4.792868	0.141225	3.38
3.40	0.129658	0.622359	0.225492	4.878303	0.139665	3.40
3.42	0.129377	0.621010	0.223166	4.965214	0.138130	3.42
3.44	0.129100	0.619681	0.220873	5.053622	0.136619	3.44
3.46	0.128827	0.618370	0.218614	5.143548	0.135133	3.46
3.48	0.128558	0.617078	0.216387	5.235012	0.133671	3.48
3.50	0.128293	0.615805	0.214193	5.328035	0.132231	3.50
3.52	0.128031	0.614549	0.212031	5.422639	0.130815	3.52
3.54	0.127773	0.613312	0.209899	5.518846	0.129420	3.54
3.56	0.127519	0.612091	0.207799	5.616676	0.128048	3.56
3.58	0.127268	0.610888	0.205728	5.716153	0.126696	3.58
3.60	0.127021	0.609701	0.203686	5.817298	0.125366	3.60
3.62	0.126777	0.608531	0.201674	5.920134	0.124056	3.62
3.64	0.126537	0.607378	0.199690	6.024684	0.122766	3.64
3.66	0.126300	0.606240	0.197734	6.130970	0.121495	3.66
3.68	0.126066	0.605117	0.195806	6.239015	0.120244	3.68
3.70	0.125836	0.604010	0.193904	6.348844	0.119012	3.70
3.72	0.125608	0.602919	0.192029	6.460479	0.117799	3.72
3.74	0.125384	0.601842	0.190179	6.573945	0.116603	3.74
3.76	0.125162	0.600780	0.188356	6.689265	0.115425	3.76
3.78	0.124944	0.599732	0.186557	6.806464	0.114265	3.78
3.80	0.124729	0.598698	0.184783	6.925566	0.113122	3.80
3.82	0.124516	0.597678	0.183034	7.046596	0.111996	3.82
3.84	0.124307	0.596672	0.181308	7.169580	0.110886	3.84
3.86	0.124100	0.595679	0.179605	7.294542	0.109792	3.86
3.88	0.123896	0.594699	0.177926	7.421508	0.108715	3.88
3.90	0.123694	0.593732	0.176269	7.550504	0.107652	3.90
3.92	0.123496	0.592778	0.174634	7.681556	0.106605	3.92
3.94	0.123299	0.591837	0.173021	7.814690	0.105573	3.94
3.96	0.123106	0.590908	0.171430	7.949932	0.104556	3.96
3.98	0.122915	0.589991	0.169860	8.087310	0.103553	3.98
4.00	0.122726	0.589086	0.168310	8.226849	0.102564	4.00

APPENDIX I

FANNO LINE FLOW FUNCTIONS ($\gamma = 1.4$)

$$\frac{4c_f L^*}{D} = \frac{1 - M^2}{\gamma M^2} + \frac{\gamma + 1}{2\gamma} \ln \frac{M^2}{\left(\frac{2}{\gamma + 1}\right)\left(1 + \frac{\gamma - 1}{2} M^2\right)}$$

$$\frac{I}{I^*} = \frac{1 + \gamma M^2}{M\sqrt{2(\gamma + 1)\left(1 + \frac{\gamma - 1}{2} M^2\right)}}$$

where $I = PA + \dot{m}V = PA(1 + \gamma M^2)$

$$\frac{T}{T^*} = \left[\left(\frac{2}{\gamma + 1}\right)\left(1 + \frac{\gamma - 1}{2} M^2\right)\right]^{-1}$$

$$\frac{P_t}{P_t^*} = \frac{1}{M}\left[\frac{2}{\gamma + 1}\left(1 + \frac{\gamma - 1}{2} M^2\right)\right]^{\{(\gamma + 1)/[2(\gamma - 1)]\}}$$

$$\frac{P}{P^*} = \frac{1}{M\sqrt{\left(\frac{2}{\gamma + 1}\right)\left(1 + \frac{\gamma - 1}{2} M^2\right)}}$$

M	$4c_fL^*/D$	I/I^*	T/T^*	P_t/P_t^*	P/P^*	M
0	Indef	Indef	1.200000	Indef	Indef	0
0.01	7134.405	45.64948	1.199976	57.87384	109.5434	0.01
0.02	1778.450	22.83364	1.199904	28.94213	54.77006	0.02
0.03	787.0814	15.23231	1.199784	19.30054	36.51155	0.03
0.04	440.3522	11.43462	1.199616	14.48149	27.38175	0.04
0.05	280.0203	9.158370	1.199400	11.59144	21.90343	0.05
0.06	193.0311	7.642847	1.199137	9.665910	18.25085	0.06
0.07	140.6550	6.562023	1.198825	8.291525	15.64155	0.07
0.08	106.7182	5.752883	1.198466	7.261610	13.68431	0.08
0.09	83.49612	5.124867	1.198059	6.461342	12.16177	0.09
0.10	66.92156	4.623634	1.197605	5.821829	10.94351	0.10
0.11	54.68790	4.214608	1.197103	5.299230	9.946564	0.11
0.12	45.40796	3.874734	1.196554	4.864318	9.115592	0.12
0.13	38.20700	3.588055	1.195958	4.496859	8.412296	0.13
0.14	32.51131	3.343168	1.195314	4.182400	7.809317	0.14
0.15	27.93197	3.131716	1.194624	3.910343	7.286591	0.15
0.16	24.19783	2.947427	1.193887	3.672739	6.829072	0.16
0.17	21.11518	2.785508	1.193104	3.463509	6.425253	0.17
0.18	18.54265	2.642227	1.192274	3.277926	6.066183	0.18
0.19	16.37516	2.514642	1.191398	3.112259	5.744799	0.19
0.20	14.53327	2.400397	1.190476	2.963520	5.455447	0.20
0.21	12.95602	2.297584	1.189509	2.829294	5.193552	0.21
0.22	11.59605	2.204644	1.188495	2.707602	4.955370	0.22
0.23	10.41609	2.120287	1.187437	2.596812	4.737808	0.23
0.24	9.386481	2.043440	1.186333	2.495562	4.538289	0.24
0.25	8.483409	1.973200	1.185185	2.402710	4.354648	0.25
0.26	7.687567	1.908803	1.183992	2.317287	4.185054	0.26
0.27	6.983170	1.849600	1.182755	2.238471	4.027947	0.27
0.28	6.357214	1.795031	1.181474	2.165554	3.881988	0.28
0.29	5.798913	1.744617	1.180150	2.097928	3.746024	0.29
0.30	5.299253	1.697941	1.178782	2.035065	3.619057	0.30
0.31	4.850663	1.654640	1.177371	1.976507	3.500217	0.31
0.32	4.446743	1.614396	1.175917	1.921851	3.388741	0.32
0.33	4.082055	1.576931	1.174421	1.870745	3.283961	0.33
0.34	3.751953	1.541997	1.172883	1.822876	3.185286	0.34
0.35	3.452452	1.509377	1.171303	1.777969	3.092193	0.35
0.36	3.180118	1.478876	1.169682	1.735778	3.004218	0.36
0.37	2.931977	1.450322	1.168020	1.696086	2.920945	0.37
0.38	2.705448	1.423560	1.166317	1.658696	2.842004	0.38
0.39	2.498277	1.398450	1.164574	1.623433	2.767062	0.39
0.40	2.308493	1.374868	1.162791	1.590140	2.695819	0.40
0.41	2.134364	1.352700	1.160968	1.558673	2.628006	0.41
0.42	1.974366	1.331845	1.159107	1.528905	2.563377	0.42
0.43	1.827151	1.312209	1.157207	1.500718	2.501710	0.43
0.44	1.691525	1.293709	1.155268	1.474005	2.442804	0.44
0.45	1.566427	1.276267	1.153292	1.448672	2.386476	0.45
0.46	1.450911	1.259814	1.151278	1.424629	2.332557	0.46
0.47	1.344135	1.244285	1.149227	1.401795	2.280894	0.47
0.48	1.245341	1.229620	1.147140	1.380097	2.231346	0.48
0.49	1.153853	1.215767	1.145016	1.359468	2.183784	0.49
0.50	1.069060	1.202676	1.142857	1.339844	2.138090	0.50

M	$4c_fL^*/D$	I/I^*	T/T^*	P_t/P_t^*	P/P^*	M
0.50	1.069060	1.202676	1.142857	1.339844	2.138090	0.50
0.51	0.990414	1.190299	1.140663	1.321168	2.094153	0.51
0.52	0.917418	1.178596	1.138434	1.303388	2.051873	0.52
0.53	0.849624	1.167526	1.136170	1.286454	2.011156	0.53
0.54	0.786625	1.157054	1.133873	1.270321	1.971916	0.54
0.55	0.728053	1.147146	1.131542	1.254948	1.934072	0.55
0.56	0.673571	1.137771	1.129178	1.240294	1.897550	0.56
0.57	0.622874	1.128899	1.126782	1.226326	1.862280	0.57
0.58	0.575683	1.120503	1.124353	1.213007	1.828199	0.58
0.59	0.531743	1.112559	1.121894	1.200308	1.795246	0.59
0.60	0.490822	1.105041	1.119403	1.188200	1.763364	0.60
0.61	0.452705	1.097930	1.116882	1.176654	1.732502	0.61
0.62	0.417197	1.091203	1.114330	1.165646	1.702610	0.62
0.63	0.384116	1.084842	1.111749	1.155151	1.673643	0.63
0.64	0.353299	1.078828	1.109139	1.145148	1.645558	0.64
0.65	0.324591	1.073144	1.106501	1.135616	1.618313	0.65
0.66	0.297853	1.067774	1.103834	1.126535	1.591871	0.66
0.67	0.272955	1.062704	1.101140	1.117887	1.566197	0.67
0.68	0.249775	1.057919	1.098418	1.109655	1.541257	0.68
0.69	0.228204	1.053405	1.095670	1.101822	1.517018	0.69
0.70	0.208139	1.049150	1.092896	1.094373	1.493452	0.70
0.71	0.189483	1.045143	1.090096	1.087294	1.470531	0.71
0.72	0.172149	1.041372	1.087272	1.080571	1.448227	0.72
0.73	0.156054	1.037825	1.084422	1.074192	1.426515	0.73
0.74	0.141122	1.034494	1.081549	1.068144	1.405372	0.74
0.75	0.127282	1.031369	1.078652	1.062417	1.384775	0.75
0.76	0.114468	1.028441	1.075731	1.056999	1.364704	0.76
0.77	0.102617	1.025700	1.072789	1.051881	1.345137	0.77
0.78	0.091672	1.023140	1.069824	1.047053	1.326055	0.78
0.79	0.081580	1.020752	1.066837	1.042505	1.307441	0.79
0.80	0.072290	1.018528	1.063830	1.038230	1.289277	0.80
0.81	0.063755	1.016463	1.060802	1.034219	1.271546	0.81
0.82	0.055932	1.014549	1.057753	1.030464	1.254233	0.82
0.83	0.048778	1.012781	1.054685	1.026959	1.237324	0.83
0.84	0.042256	1.011151	1.051598	1.023696	1.220803	0.84
0.85	0.036330	1.009654	1.048493	1.020669	1.204658	0.85
0.86	0.030965	1.008285	1.045369	1.017871	1.188875	0.86
0.87	0.026130	1.007039	1.042228	1.015297	1.173443	0.87
0.88	0.021795	1.005910	1.039069	1.012941	1.158349	0.88
0.89	0.017931	1.004895	1.035894	1.010798	1.143583	0.89
0.90	0.014512	1.003987	1.032702	1.008863	1.129133	0.90
0.91	0.011514	1.003184	1.029495	1.007131	1.114989	0.91
0.92	0.008913	1.002480	1.026273	1.005597	1.101143	0.92
0.93	0.006687	1.001872	1.023035	1.004258	1.087583	0.93
0.94	0.004815	1.001356	1.019784	1.003108	1.074302	0.94
0.95	0.003278	1.000929	1.016518	1.002145	1.061290	0.95
0.96	0.002057	1.000586	1.013240	1.001365	1.048540	0.96
0.97	0.001135	1.000325	1.009948	1.000763	1.036043	0.97
0.98	0.000495	1.000143	1.006644	1.000337	1.023792	0.98
0.99	0.000121	1.000035	1.003328	1.000084	1.011780	0.99
1.00	0.000000	1.000000	1.000000	1.000000	1.000000	1.00

M	$4c_fL^*/D$	I/I^*	T/T^*	P_t/P_t^*	P/P^*	M
1.00	0.000000	1.000000	1.000000	1.000000	1.000000	1.00
1.01	0.000117	1.000034	0.996661	1.000083	0.988445	1.01
1.02	0.000459	1.000135	0.993312	1.000330	0.977108	1.02
1.03	0.001013	1.000300	0.989952	1.000738	0.965984	1.03
1.04	0.001769	1.000527	0.986582	1.001305	0.955066	1.04
1.05	0.002714	1.000813	0.983204	1.002029	0.944349	1.05
1.06	0.003838	1.001156	0.979816	1.002907	0.933827	1.06
1.07	0.005131	1.001553	0.976419	1.003938	0.923495	1.07
1.08	0.006585	1.002003	0.973015	1.005119	0.913347	1.08
1.09	0.008189	1.002503	0.969603	1.006449	0.903380	1.09
1.10	0.009935	1.003052	0.966184	1.007925	0.893588	1.10
1.11	0.011816	1.003647	0.962757	1.009547	0.883966	1.11
1.12	0.013823	1.004287	0.959325	1.011312	0.874510	1.12
1.13	0.015949	1.004970	0.955886	1.013219	0.865216	1.13
1.14	0.018188	1.005694	0.952441	1.015267	0.856080	1.14
1.15	0.020533	1.006458	0.948992	1.017454	0.847097	1.15
1.16	0.022977	1.007259	0.945537	1.019780	0.838265	1.16
1.17	0.025516	1.008097	0.942078	1.022242	0.829579	1.17
1.18	0.028142	1.008970	0.938615	1.024840	0.821035	1.18
1.19	0.030851	1.009876	0.935148	1.027573	0.812630	1.19
1.20	0.033638	1.010815	0.931677	1.030440	0.804362	1.20
1.21	0.036498	1.011784	0.928203	1.033440	0.796226	1.21
1.22	0.039426	1.012783	0.924727	1.036572	0.788219	1.22
1.23	0.042418	1.013810	0.921249	1.039835	0.780339	1.23
1.24	0.045471	1.014864	0.917768	1.043229	0.772582	1.24
1.25	0.048579	1.015944	0.914286	1.046753	0.764946	1.25
1.26	0.051739	1.017049	0.910802	1.050406	0.757428	1.26
1.27	0.054947	1.018178	0.907318	1.054189	0.750025	1.27
1.28	0.058201	1.019330	0.903832	1.058100	0.742735	1.28
1.29	0.061497	1.020503	0.900347	1.062138	0.735555	1.29
1.30	0.064832	1.021697	0.896861	1.066305	0.728483	1.30
1.31	0.068203	1.022911	0.893376	1.070598	0.721516	1.31
1.32	0.071607	1.024144	0.889891	1.075018	0.714652	1.32
1.33	0.075041	1.025394	0.886407	1.079565	0.707889	1.33
1.34	0.078504	1.026662	0.882924	1.084239	0.701224	1.34
1.35	0.081991	1.027947	0.879443	1.089038	0.694656	1.35
1.36	0.085503	1.029247	0.875964	1.093964	0.688183	1.36
1.37	0.089035	1.030562	0.872486	1.099015	0.681803	1.37
1.38	0.092586	1.031891	0.869011	1.104193	0.675513	1.38
1.39	0.096155	1.033233	0.865539	1.109496	0.669312	1.39
1.40	0.099738	1.034588	0.862069	1.114926	0.663198	1.40
1.41	0.103335	1.035955	0.858602	1.120481	0.657169	1.41
1.42	0.106943	1.037334	0.855139	1.126162	0.651224	1.42
1.43	0.110562	1.038723	0.851680	1.131969	0.645360	1.43
1.44	0.114189	1.040123	0.848224	1.137903	0.639577	1.44
1.45	0.117823	1.041532	0.844773	1.143963	0.633873	1.45
1.46	0.121462	1.042950	0.841326	1.150150	0.628245	1.46
1.47	0.125106	1.044377	0.837884	1.156463	0.622694	1.47
1.48	0.128753	1.045811	0.834446	1.162904	0.617216	1.48
1.49	0.132401	1.047253	0.831013	1.169471	0.611812	1.49
1.50	0.136050	1.048702	0.827586	1.176167	0.606478	1.50

M	$4c_fL^*/D$	I/I^*	T/T^*	P_t/P_t^*	P/P^*	M
1.50	0.136050	1.048702	0.827586	1.176167	0.606478	1.50
1.51	0.139699	1.050158	0.824165	1.182991	0.601215	1.51
1.52	0.143346	1.051619	0.820749	1.189943	0.596021	1.52
1.53	0.146990	1.053086	0.817338	1.197024	0.590894	1.53
1.54	0.150631	1.054558	0.813935	1.204234	0.585833	1.54
1.55	0.154268	1.056035	0.810537	1.211574	0.580838	1.55
1.56	0.157899	1.057517	0.807146	1.219044	0.575906	1.56
1.57	0.161525	1.059002	0.803762	1.226644	0.571037	1.57
1.58	0.165143	1.060490	0.800384	1.234376	0.566229	1.58
1.59	0.168754	1.061982	0.797014	1.242239	0.561482	1.59
1.60	0.172357	1.063477	0.793651	1.250235	0.556794	1.60
1.61	0.175951	1.064974	0.790295	1.258364	0.552165	1.61
1.62	0.179535	1.066474	0.786947	1.266626	0.547593	1.62
1.63	0.183109	1.067975	0.783607	1.275022	0.543077	1.63
1.64	0.186673	1.069478	0.780275	1.283553	0.538617	1.64
1.65	0.190226	1.070982	0.776950	1.292219	0.534211	1.65
1.66	0.193766	1.072486	0.773635	1.301021	0.529858	1.66
1.67	0.197295	1.073992	0.770327	1.309960	0.525559	1.67
1.68	0.200811	1.075498	0.767028	1.319037	0.521310	1.68
1.69	0.204314	1.077004	0.763738	1.328252	0.517113	1.69
1.70	0.207803	1.078510	0.760456	1.337606	0.512966	1.70
1.71	0.211279	1.080016	0.757184	1.347100	0.508867	1.71
1.72	0.214740	1.081521	0.753920	1.356735	0.504817	1.72
1.73	0.218187	1.083025	0.750666	1.366511	0.500815	1.73
1.74	0.221620	1.084528	0.747421	1.376430	0.496859	1.74
1.75	0.225037	1.086030	0.744186	1.386492	0.492950	1.75
1.76	0.228438	1.087531	0.740960	1.396698	0.489086	1.76
1.77	0.231824	1.089029	0.737744	1.407049	0.485266	1.77
1.78	0.235195	1.090526	0.734538	1.417546	0.481490	1.78
1.79	0.238549	1.092021	0.731342	1.428190	0.477757	1.79
1.80	0.241886	1.093514	0.728155	1.438982	0.474067	1.80
1.81	0.245208	1.095004	0.724979	1.449923	0.470418	1.81
1.82	0.248512	1.096492	0.721813	1.461013	0.466811	1.82
1.83	0.251800	1.097977	0.718658	1.472255	0.463244	1.83
1.84	0.255070	1.099460	0.715512	1.483648	0.459717	1.84
1.85	0.258324	1.100939	0.712378	1.495194	0.456230	1.85
1.86	0.261560	1.102415	0.709253	1.506894	0.452781	1.86
1.87	0.264778	1.103888	0.706140	1.518750	0.449370	1.87
1.88	0.267979	1.105357	0.703037	1.530761	0.445996	1.88
1.89	0.271163	1.106823	0.699945	1.542930	0.442660	1.89
1.90	0.274328	1.108285	0.696864	1.555257	0.439360	1.90
1.91	0.277476	1.109744	0.693794	1.567743	0.436096	1.91
1.92	0.280606	1.111198	0.690735	1.580391	0.432867	1.92
1.93	0.283718	1.112649	0.687687	1.593200	0.429673	1.93
1.94	0.286812	1.114096	0.684650	1.606172	0.426513	1.94
1.95	0.289888	1.115538	0.681625	1.619309	0.423387	1.95
1.96	0.292946	1.116976	0.678610	1.632611	0.420295	1.96
1.97	0.295986	1.118409	0.675607	1.646080	0.417235	1.97
1.98	0.299008	1.119838	0.672616	1.659717	0.414208	1.98
1.99	0.302011	1.121263	0.669635	1.673523	0.411212	1.99
2.00	0.304997	1.122683	0.666667	1.687500	0.408248	2.00

M	$4c_fL^*/D$	I/I^*	T/T^*	P_t/P_t^*	P/P^*	M
2.00	0.304997	1.122683	0.666667	1.687500	0.408248	2.00
2.02	0.310913	1.125508	0.660764	1.715971	0.402413	2.02
2.04	0.316756	1.128314	0.654907	1.745139	0.396698	2.04
2.06	0.322526	1.131100	0.649098	1.775017	0.391100	2.06
2.08	0.328225	1.133866	0.643335	1.805614	0.385616	2.08
2.10	0.333851	1.136610	0.637620	1.836944	0.380243	2.10
2.12	0.339405	1.139334	0.631951	1.869016	0.374978	2.12
2.14	0.344887	1.142035	0.626331	1.901843	0.369818	2.14
2.16	0.350299	1.144715	0.620758	1.935437	0.364760	2.16
2.18	0.355639	1.147372	0.615233	1.969810	0.359802	2.18
2.20	0.360910	1.150007	0.609756	2.004975	0.354940	2.20
2.22	0.366111	1.152619	0.604327	2.040944	0.350173	2.22
2.24	0.371243	1.155208	0.598946	2.077731	0.345498	2.24
2.26	0.376306	1.157774	0.593613	2.115349	0.340913	2.26
2.28	0.381302	1.160316	0.588328	2.153811	0.336415	2.28
2.30	0.386230	1.162835	0.583090	2.193131	0.332002	2.30
2.32	0.391092	1.165331	0.577901	2.233323	0.327672	2.32
2.34	0.395888	1.167803	0.572760	2.274401	0.323423	2.34
2.36	0.400619	1.170252	0.567666	2.316381	0.319253	2.36
2.38	0.405286	1.172677	0.562620	2.359275	0.315160	2.38
2.40	0.409889	1.175079	0.557621	2.403100	0.311142	2.40
2.42	0.414429	1.177456	0.552669	2.447870	0.307197	2.42
2.44	0.418907	1.179811	0.547765	2.493602	0.303324	2.44
2.46	0.423324	1.182141	0.542908	2.540309	0.299521	2.46
2.48	0.427680	1.184448	0.538097	2.588010	0.295787	2.48
2.50	0.431977	1.186732	0.533333	2.636719	0.292119	2.50
2.52	0.436214	1.188993	0.528616	2.686453	0.288516	2.52
2.54	0.440393	1.191230	0.523944	2.737228	0.284976	2.54
2.56	0.444514	1.193444	0.519319	2.789063	0.281499	2.56
2.58	0.448579	1.195634	0.514739	2.841972	0.278083	2.58
2.60	0.452588	1.197802	0.510204	2.895975	0.274725	2.60
2.62	0.456541	1.199947	0.505715	2.951089	0.271426	2.62
2.64	0.460441	1.202069	0.501270	3.007331	0.268183	2.64
2.66	0.464286	1.204169	0.496870	3.064720	0.264996	2.66
2.68	0.468079	1.206246	0.492514	3.123274	0.261863	2.68
2.70	0.471819	1.208301	0.488202	3.183011	0.258783	2.70
2.72	0.475508	1.210334	0.483933	3.243951	0.255755	2.72
2.74	0.479146	1.212345	0.479708	3.306113	0.252777	2.74
2.76	0.482735	1.214334	0.475526	3.369515	0.249849	2.76
2.78	0.486274	1.216302	0.471387	3.434179	0.246970	2.78
2.80	0.489765	1.218248	0.467290	3.500123	0.244138	2.80
2.82	0.493208	1.220173	0.463235	3.567368	0.241352	2.82
2.84	0.496604	1.222076	0.459221	3.635934	0.238612	2.84
2.86	0.499953	1.223959	0.455249	3.705842	0.235917	2.86
2.88	0.503257	1.225821	0.451318	3.777113	0.233265	2.88
2.90	0.506516	1.227662	0.447427	3.849768	0.230655	2.90
2.92	0.509731	1.229483	0.443577	3.923829	0.228088	2.92
2.94	0.512902	1.231284	0.439767	3.999317	0.225561	2.94
2.96	0.516030	1.233065	0.435996	4.076255	0.223074	2.96
2.98	0.519115	1.234826	0.432264	4.154664	0.220627	2.98
3.00	0.522159	1.236568	0.428571	4.234568	0.218218	3.00

M	$4c_f L^*/D$	I/I^*	T/T^*	P_t/P_t^*	P/P^*	M
3.00	0.522159	1.236568	0.428571	4.234568	0.218218	3.00
3.02	0.525162	1.238290	0.424917	4.315989	0.215847	3.02
3.04	0.528125	1.239993	0.421301	4.398950	0.213512	3.04
3.06	0.531048	1.241677	0.417723	4.483475	0.211214	3.06
3.08	0.533932	1.243343	0.414182	4.569587	0.208951	3.08
3.10	0.536777	1.244989	0.410678	4.657311	0.206723	3.10
3.12	0.539584	1.246618	0.407210	4.746670	0.204529	3.12
3.14	0.542353	1.248228	0.403779	4.837689	0.202368	3.14
3.16	0.545086	1.249820	0.400384	4.930393	0.200240	3.16
3.18	0.547783	1.251394	0.397025	5.024808	0.198144	3.18
3.20	0.550444	1.252951	0.393701	5.120957	0.196080	3.20
3.22	0.553070	1.254490	0.390411	5.218868	0.194046	3.22
3.24	0.555661	1.256012	0.387157	5.318566	0.192043	3.24
3.26	0.558218	1.257517	0.383936	5.420078	0.190069	3.26
3.28	0.560741	1.259005	0.380749	5.523429	0.188125	3.28
3.30	0.563232	1.260477	0.377596	5.628647	0.186209	3.30
3.32	0.565690	1.261932	0.374476	5.735759	0.184321	3.32
3.34	0.568116	1.263371	0.371388	5.844792	0.182460	3.34
3.36	0.570510	1.264794	0.368333	5.955774	0.180626	3.36
3.38	0.572874	1.266201	0.365310	6.068734	0.178819	3.38
3.40	0.575207	1.267592	0.362319	6.183699	0.177038	3.40
3.42	0.577510	1.268968	0.359359	6.300698	0.175282	3.42
3.44	0.579783	1.270328	0.356430	6.419760	0.173552	3.44
3.46	0.582027	1.271674	0.353532	6.540915	0.171845	3.46
3.48	0.584242	1.273004	0.350664	6.664192	0.170163	3.48
3.50	0.586429	1.274320	0.347826	6.789621	0.168505	3.50
3.52	0.588588	1.275621	0.345018	6.917231	0.166870	3.52
3.54	0.590720	1.276907	0.342239	7.047055	0.165258	3.54
3.56	0.592825	1.278180	0.339489	7.179122	0.163668	3.56
3.58	0.594903	1.279438	0.336768	7.313463	0.162100	3.58
3.60	0.596955	1.280682	0.334076	7.450111	0.160554	3.60
3.62	0.598981	1.281913	0.331411	7.589097	0.159029	3.62
3.64	0.600982	1.283130	0.328774	7.730452	0.157524	3.64
3.66	0.602957	1.284334	0.326165	7.874211	0.156041	3.66
3.68	0.604909	1.285524	0.323583	8.020404	0.154577	3.68
3.70	0.606836	1.286701	0.321027	8.169066	0.153133	3.70
3.72	0.608739	1.287866	0.318498	8.320230	0.151709	3.72
3.74	0.610618	1.289018	0.315996	8.473930	0.150303	3.74
3.76	0.612474	1.290157	0.313519	8.630199	0.148917	3.76
3.78	0.614308	1.291283	0.311068	8.789073	0.147549	3.78
3.80	0.616119	1.292398	0.308642	8.950585	0.146199	3.80
3.82	0.617908	1.293500	0.306241	9.114772	0.144867	3.82
3.84	0.619675	1.294590	0.303865	9.281668	0.143552	3.84
3.86	0.621421	1.295669	0.301514	9.451309	0.142255	3.86
3.88	0.623145	1.296735	0.299186	9.623732	0.140974	3.88
3.90	0.624849	1.297791	0.296883	9.798973	0.139710	3.90
3.92	0.626532	1.298834	0.294603	9.977069	0.138463	3.92
3.94	0.628195	1.299867	0.292346	10.15806	0.137231	3.94
3.96	0.629838	1.300888	0.290113	10.34197	0.136015	3.96
3.98	0.631461	1.301899	0.287902	10.52886	0.134815	3.98
4.00	0.633065	1.302899	0.285714	10.71875	0.133631	4.00

APPENDIX J

TURBOMACHINERY STRESSES AND MATERIALS

J-1 INTRODUCTION

Even though the focus of this textbook is the aerothermodynamics of the gas turbine engine, the importance of the engine structure is also very significant. Because of its importance, this appendix addresses the major stresses of the rotating components and the properties of materials used in these components. The rotating components of the compressor and turbine have very high momentum, and failure of one part can be catastrophic, with a resulting destruction of the engine and, in the extreme, the aircraft. This is especially true of the "critical" parts of the turbomachinery such as the long first-stage fan blades and the heavy airfoils and disks of the cooled high-pressure turbine.

Over their lives, the rotating parts must endure in a very harsh environment where the loads are very dependent on the engine use. For example, an engine developed for a commercial aircraft will not be subjected to as many throttle excursions as one developed for a fighter aircraft. As a result, the "hot section" [combustor and turbine(s)] of the fighter engine will be subjected to many more thermal cycles per hour of operation than that of the commercial aircraft.

The main focus of the analytical tools developed in this appendix is on the fundamental source of stresses in rotating components—the centrifugal force. To get some idea of the brutal climate in which these components must live, the centrifugal force experienced by an element of material rotating at 10,000 rpm with a radius of 1 ft (0.3 m) is equivalent to more than 34,000 g. Yet, there are many other forces at work that can consume the life of (or destroy) rotating parts, all of which must be considered in the design process. Some of the most important include:

- Stresses due to bending moments like those due to the lift on the airfoils or pressure differences across disks.
- Buffeting or vibratory stresses that occur as the airfoils pass through nonuniform incident flows such as the wakes of upstream blades. This can be most devastating when the *blade passing* frequency coincides with one of the lower natural frequencies of the airfoils.
- Airfoil or disk flutter, an aeroelastic phenomenon in which a natural frequency is spontaneously excited, the driving energy being extracted from the flowing gas. This is most often found in fan and compressor rows, and once it has begun, the life of the engine is measured in minutes.
- Torsional stresses that result from the transfer of power from the turbine to the compressor.
- Temperature gradients that can give rise to very high stresses. These can be very extreme during throttle transients when the engine is moving from one power setting to another. These cyclic thermal stresses extract life from components, especially in the hot section of fighter engines. This is commonly called *thermal* or *low-cycle* fatigue.

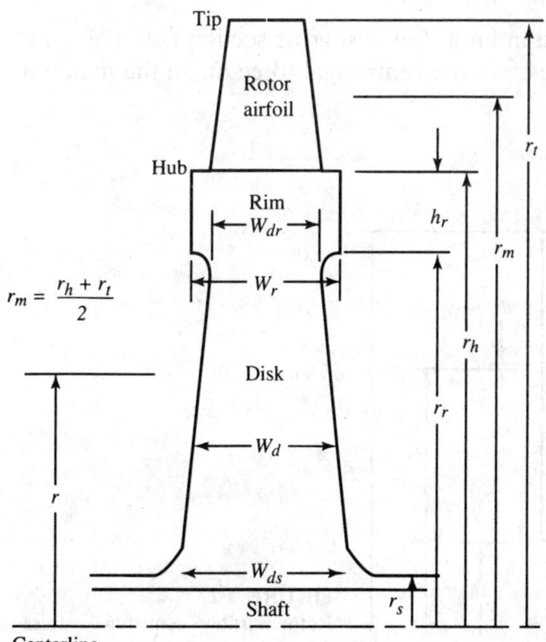

FIGURE J-1
Turbomachinery rotor nomenclature.

- Local stress concentrations which result from holes, slots, corners, and cracks—the most feared of all.
- Foreign object damage (FOD) and domestic object damage (DOD) that result from external and internal objects, respectively. The need to withstand FOD or DOD can dramatically impact the design. The use of lightweight, nonmetallic materials for large fan blades has been prevented for several decades due to requirement that they withstand bird strikes.

Each of the above areas and many others are included in the design of engine components and material selection. After these are accounted for, an *allowable working stress* is developed and commonly used for the principal tensile stresses alone.

The next section analyzes dominant stresses in the rotating components. Figure J-1 depicts a turbine rotor with its airfoils, rim, and disk. A compressor or fan rotor is constructed similarly. However, the portion of the airfoil stresses carried by the compressor or fan's rim is much greater than that of a turbine rotor; hence, its disk is either much smaller or nonexistent. We consider the principal stresses of each part, starting with the airfoils.

J-2 TURBOMACHINERY STRESSES

Rotor Airfoil Centrifugal Stress σ_c

We start by considering the force in an airfoil at a cross section (see Fig. J-2). At any radius r, the force must restrain the centrifugal force on all the material

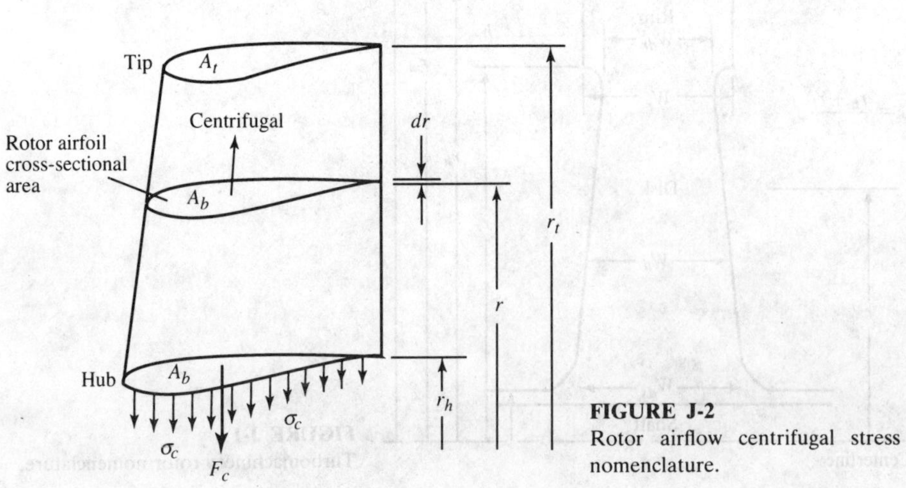

FIGURE J-2
Rotor airflow centrifugal stress nomenclature.

beyond it. Thus the hub or base of the airfoil must experience the greatest force. The total centrifugal force acting on A_h is

$$F_c = \int_{r_h}^{r_t} \rho\omega^2 A_b r\, dr \tag{J-1}$$

so that the principal tensile stress is

$$\sigma_c = \frac{F_c}{A_h} = \rho\omega^2 \int_{r_h}^{r_t} \frac{A_b}{A_h} r\, dr \tag{J-2}$$

The airfoil cross-sectional area usually tapers down or reduces with increasing radius, which, according to Eq. (J-2), has the effect of reducing σ_c. If the taper is *linear*, we can write

$$\frac{A_b}{A_h} = 1 - \left(1 - \frac{A_t}{A_h}\right)\left(\frac{r - r_h}{r_t - r_h}\right) \tag{J-3}$$

and Eq. (J-2) becomes

$$\sigma_c = \rho\omega^2 \left[\frac{A}{2\pi} - \left(1 - \frac{A_t}{A_h}\right) \int_{r_h}^{r_t} \left(\frac{r - r_h}{r_t - r_h}\right) r\, dr\right] \tag{J-4}$$

where A is the flow path annulus area $\pi(r_t^2 - r_h^2)$. Integration of Eq. (J-4) gives

$$\sigma_c = \frac{\rho\omega^2 A}{4\pi}\left[2 - \frac{2}{3}\left(1 - \frac{A_t}{A_h}\right)\left(1 + \frac{1}{1 + r_h/r_t}\right)\right] \tag{J-5}$$

Equation (J-5) has an upper limit (corresponding to $r_h/r_t = 1$) of

$$\boxed{\sigma_c = \frac{\rho\omega^2 A}{4\pi}\left(1 + \frac{A_t}{A_h}\right)} \tag{J-6}$$

This equation reveals the basic characteristic that σ_c is proportional to $\rho\omega^2 A$. It also shows that tapering can, at most, reduce the stress of a *straight* airfoil (i.e., $A_t = A_h$) by half (i.e., $A_t = 0$).

Common practice in the industry is to refer to $\omega^2 A$ as the term AN^2 because it is easy to calculate and use. The COMPR computer program calculates and outputs AN^2 for each stage for proper material selection. The TURBN computer program permits the turbine to be sized based on a user input value of AN^2. When another sizing criterion is used in TURBN, the value of AN^2 is calculated and output for each stage.

We note that

$$AN^2 = A\omega^2\left(\frac{30}{\pi}\right)^2 \tag{J-7}$$

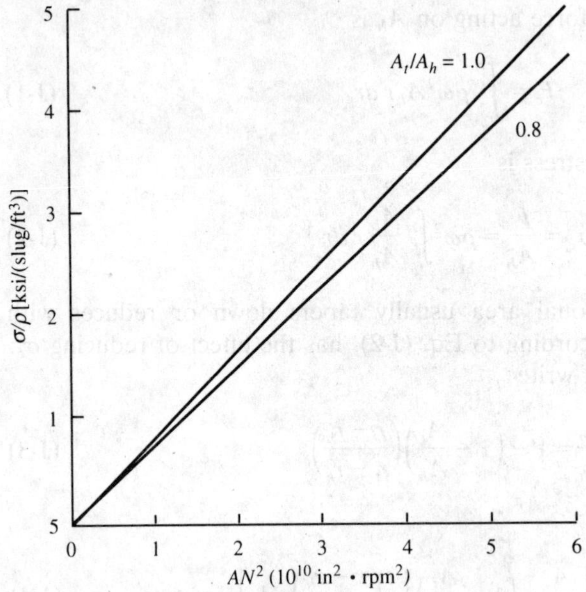

FIGURE J-3
Variation of centrifugal stress-to-density ratio with AN^2.

By using Eq. (J-7), we obtain for Eq. (J-6)

$$\boxed{\frac{\sigma_c}{\rho} = AN^2 \frac{\pi}{3600}\left(1 + \frac{A_t}{A_h}\right)} \tag{J-8}$$

For a fixed value of AN^2, Eq. (J-8) shows the obvious reduction in centrifugal stress by using more lightweight materials [e.g., titanium with a density of about 9 slug/ft^3 (about 4600 kg/m^3)] rather than the heavier materials [densities of about 16 slug/ft^3 (about 8200 kg/m^3)]. This equation is given in graphical form in Fig. J-3 for several different airfoil taper ratios A_t/A_h for AN^2 values from 0 to 6×10^{10} in$^2 \cdot$ rpm^2 (3.87×10^7 m$^2 \cdot$ rpm^2).

Example J-1. In this example, we determine the centrifugal stresses at 10,000 rpm in typical airfoil materials of a compressor ($\rho = 9.0$ slug/ft^3) and turbine ($\rho =$ 15.0 slug/ft^3) with flow annulus areas of 2.0 and 1.0 ft^2, respectively. Table J-1 summarizes the results, using Eq. (J-8) for an airfoil taper A_t/A_h of 0.8. For the compressor, $\sigma_c = (\pi/3.6)(9/1.44^2)(2.88)(1.8) = 19.63$ ksi. Even though the compressor centrifugal stress is higher than that in the turbine airfoil, the turbine airfoils are subjected to higher temperatures and will, most likely, have a lower *allowable working stress.*

TABLE J-1
Centrifugal stress results for Example J-1

	Compressor	Turbine
ρ (slug/ft^3)	9.0	15.0
(kg/m^3)	4611	7686
N (rpm)	10,000	10,000
A (ft^2)	2.0	1.0
(m^2)	0.186	0.0929
AN^2 (in$^2 \cdot$ rpm^2)	2.88×10^{10}	1.44×10^{10}
(m$^2 \cdot$ rpm^2)	1.86×10^7	9.29×10^6
A_t/A_h	0.8	0.8
σ_c (psi)	19,630	16,360
(MPa)	135.3	112.8

Rim Web Thickness W_{dr}

The rotating airfoils are inserted into slots in an otherwise solid annulus of material known as the *rim* (see Fig. J-1), which maintains their circular motion. The airfoil hub tensile stress σ_c is treated as though "smeared out" over the outer rim surface, so that

$$\bar{\sigma}_{\text{blades}} = \frac{\sigma_c n_b A_h}{2\pi r W_r} \tag{J-9}$$

where n_b is the number of blades on the *wheel.*

Assuming uniform stress within the rim σ_r, we can use the force diagram of Fig. J-4 to determine the dimension W_{dr} (see Fig. J-1) necessary to balance the blade and rim centrifugal forces. Please note that W_r and h_r are simply sensible initial choices, where W_r approximates the axial chord of the airfoil and h_r is similar in magnitude to W_r. It is important to realize that it will always be possible to design a rim large enough to "carry" the airfoils. The real question is whether the size of the rim is practical from the standpoint of space required, weight, and manufacturing cost. Thus, there is no absolute solution, and the final choice must be based on experience and a sense of proportion.

A radial force balance of the differential rim element shown in Fig. J-4 gives

$$\bar{\sigma}_{\text{blades}} r_h W_r \, d\theta + \rho\omega^2 h_r W_r (r_h + h_r/2)^2 \, d\theta = \sigma_r r_r W_{dr} \, d\theta + 2\left(\sigma_r h_r W_r \frac{d\theta}{2}\right)$$

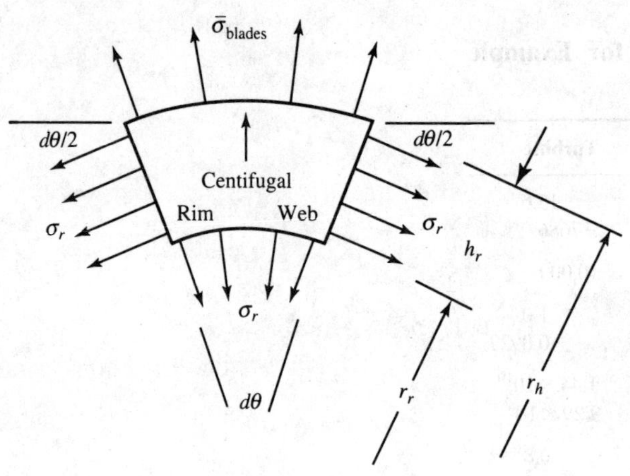

FIGURE J-4
Rim segment radial equilibrium nomenclature.

TABLE J-2
Typical data for Example J-2

	Compressor	Turbine
$\bar{\sigma}_{\text{blades}}/\sigma_r$	0.10	0.20
h_r/r_r	0.05	0.10
$\rho(\omega r_h)^2/\sigma_r$	6.0	4.0

which, for any infinitesimal $d\theta$, becomes

$$\boxed{\frac{W_{dr}}{W_r} = \left[\frac{\bar{\sigma}_{\text{blades}}}{\sigma_r}\left(1+\frac{r_r}{h_r}\right) + \frac{\rho(\omega r_h)^2}{\sigma_r}\left(1+\frac{h_r}{2r_r}\right)^2 - 1\right]\frac{h_r}{r_r}} \tag{J-10}$$

If σ_r is sufficiently large, this equation clearly shows that W_{dr} can be zero or less, which means that the rim is *self-supporting*. Nevertheless, a token disk may still be required in order to transfer torque to the shaft and, of course, to keep the rim and airfoils in the right axial and radial position.

Example J-2. Using typical values of the terms in Eq. (J-10) for the compressor and turbine based on disk materials given in Table J-2, Eq. (J-10) yields $W_{dr}/W_r = 0.37$ for the compressor and $W_{dr}/W_r = 0.56$ for the turbine.

Disk of Uniform Stress

The disk supports and positions the rim while connecting it to the shaft. Its thickness begins with a value of W_{dr} at the inside edge of the rim and must grow as the radius decreases because of the accumulating centrifugal force that must be resisted. Just as was found for the rim, a disk can always be found which will perform the required job, but the size, weight, and/or cost may be excessive. Thus the final choice usually involves trial and error and judgment.

It is impossible to overemphasize the importance of ensuring the structural integrity of the disks, particularly the large ones found in cooled high-pressure turbines. Because they are very difficult to inspect and because massive fragments that fly loose when they disintegrate cannot be contained, they must not be allowed to fail.

The most efficient way to use available disk materials is to design the disk for constant radial and circumferential stress. Since the rim and disk are one continuous piece of material, the design stress would be the same throughout ($\sigma_r = \sigma_d$).

Applying locally radial equilibrium to the infinitesimal element of the disk of Fig. J-5 leads to the equation

$$\rho(\omega r_r)^2 W_d \, dr \, d\theta = \sigma_d\left[\left(r - \frac{dr}{2}\right)\left(W_d - \frac{dW_d}{2}\right) d\theta - \left(r + \frac{dr}{2}\right)\left(W_d + \frac{dW_d}{2}\right) d\theta + 2\left(W_d \, dr \frac{d\theta}{2}\right)\right]$$

which becomes in the limit

$$\frac{dW_d}{W_d} + \frac{\rho\omega^2}{\sigma_d} d\left(\frac{r^2}{2}\right) = 0$$

This equation may be integrated, by starting from $r = r_r$ and $W_d = W_{dr}$, to yield

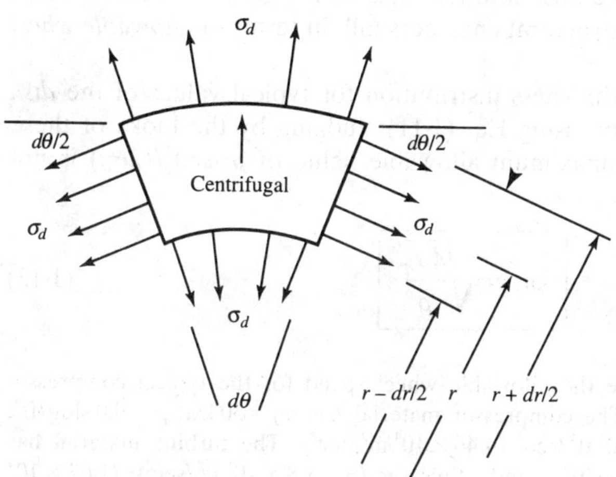

FIGURE J-5
Disk element radial equilibrium nomenclature.

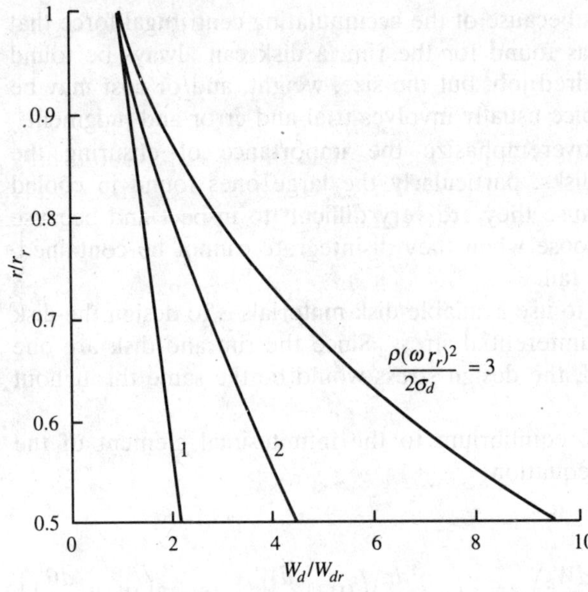

FIGURE J-6
Disk thickness distributions.

the desired result

$$\boxed{\frac{W_d}{W_{dr}} = \exp\left\{\frac{\rho(\omega r_r)^2}{2\sigma_d}\left[1-\left(\frac{r}{r_r}\right)^2\right]\right\}} \tag{J-11}$$

The fundamental feature of Eq. (J-11) is that the disk thickness W_d grows exponentially in proportion to $(\omega r_r)^2$, which is the square of the maximum or rim velocity of the disk. Since this parameter has such a great influence on disk design, it is normal to hear structural engineers talk in terms of *allowable wheel speed.*

Figure J-6 shows the thickness distribution for typical values of the *disk shape factor* $\rho(\omega r_r)^2/(2\sigma_d)$ by using Eq. (J-11). Judging by the looks of these thickness distributions, the maximum allowable value of $\rho(\omega r_r)^2/(2\sigma_d)$ is not much more than 2, so that

$$\boxed{\omega r_r \approx \sqrt{\frac{4\sigma_d}{\rho}}} \tag{J-12}$$

Example J-3. Determine the allowable wheel speed for the typical compressor and turbine materials. The compressor material has $\sigma_d = 30$ ksi, $\rho = 9.0$ slug/ft^3, and thus $\sigma_d/\rho = 4.8 \times 10^5$ ft^2/sec^2 (4.46×10^4 m^2/sec^2). The turbine material has $\sigma_d = 20$ ksi, $\rho = 16.0$ slug/ft^3, and thus $\sigma_d/\rho = 1.8 \times 10^5$ ft^2/sec^2 (1.67×10^4

m^2/sec^2). Using Eq. (J-12), we see that the allowable wheel speed for the compressor is about 1400 ft/sec (420 m/sec) and that for the turbine is about 850 ft/sec (260 m/sec). This indicates that the allowable wheel speed is more likely to limit the design of a turbine than the design of a compressor.

Note: At this point it should be apparent that, on the low-pressure spool where the annulus flow area A is largest, the rotational speed (ω or N) is most likely to be limited by the allowable blade centrifugal stress [Eq. (J-6) or Eq. (J-8)]. Conversely, on the high-pressure spool, where the annulus flow area is considerably less, the rotational speed will probably be limited by the allowable wheel speed [Eq. (J-12)].

Disk Torsional Stress τ_d

The tangential disk shear stress required to transfer the shaft horsepower to the airfoils is easily calculated, since

$$\text{HP} = \text{shear stress} \times \text{area} \times \text{velocity}$$

Thus

$$\boxed{\tau_d = \frac{\text{HP}}{2\pi r^2 W_d \omega}} \tag{J-13}$$

Example J-4. Determine the disk torsional stress for the following typical values:

$$\text{HP} = 10{,}000 \text{ hp (7457 kW)}$$
$$r = 0.30 \text{ ft (0.0914 m)}$$
$$W_d = 0.10 \text{ ft (0.0305 m)}$$
$$\omega = 1000 \text{ rad/sec}$$

Equation (J-13) gives $\tau_d = 675$ psi (4.65 MPa), which makes a relatively small contribution to the overall stress.

Disk Thermal Stress σ_{tr} and $\sigma_{t\theta}$

For a disk of constant thickness with no center hole and a temperature distribution that depends only on radius [$T = T(r)$], it can be shown (Ref. 38) that the radial tensile stress is

$$\sigma_{tr} = \alpha E \left[\frac{1}{r_h^2} \int_0^{r_h} T(r)\, dr - \frac{1}{r^2} \int_0^{r} T(r)\, dr \right] \tag{J-14}$$

where α is the coefficient of linear thermal expansion and E is the modulus of elasticity, and the tangential tensile stress is

$$\sigma_{t\theta} = \alpha E\left[\frac{1}{r_h^2}\int_0^{r_h} T(r)\,dr + \frac{1}{r^2}\int_0^{r} T(r)\,dr - T\right] \tag{J-15}$$

both of which are zero if the temperature is constant. An interesting illustrative case is that of the linear temperature distribution $T = T_0 + \Delta T\,(r/r_h)$, for which Eq. (J-14) becomes

$$\boxed{\sigma_{tr} = \frac{\alpha E\,\Delta T}{3}\left(1 - \frac{r}{r_h}\right)} \tag{J-16}$$

and Eq. (J-15) becomes

$$\boxed{\sigma_{t\theta} = \frac{\alpha E\,\Delta T}{3}\left(1 - 2\frac{r}{r_h}\right)} \tag{J-17}$$

both of which have a maximum magnitude of $\alpha E\,\Delta T/3$ at $r = 0$.

Example J-5. For typical values of $\alpha = 1 \times 10^{-5}(°\text{F})^{-1}$ $[1.8 \times 10^{-5}\,1(°\text{C})^{-1}]$, $E = 10 \times 10^6$ psi (6.9×10^4 MPa), and $\Delta T = 100°\text{F}$ (55.6°C), the maximum magnitude of σ_{tr} and $\sigma_{t\theta}$ is 6700 psi (46 MPa)! This simple case demonstrates forcefully that thermal stresses can be very large and, therefore, must be carefully accounted for and reduced as much as possible. This is especially true during transient operation.

With this perspective, it is possible to imagine that truly enormous stresses could be generated in the thin outer wall of the cooled turbine airfoils, if they are not very carefully designed. Because such stresses will be proportional to the temperature difference between the mainstream and the cooling air, there is also a limit to how cold a coolant may be used before it no longer truly *protects* the material.

J-3 ENGINE MATERIALS

The harsh environment of the gas turbine engine requires special materials. Many of these materials are developed exclusively for this application by material experts—most of these experts work for either an engine company or a materials company. Therefore, the properties of many materials used for critical components in gas turbine engines are corporate secrets, and published data are limited. However, some materials have been and continue to be developed in the public sector, and their properties can be found in references such as the *Aerospace Structural Metals Handbook* (Ref. 89) and *The Superalloys* (Ref. 90), textbooks (Refs. 91 and 92), and journals (Ref. 93).

To provide examples and general guidance, the data for several materials commonly found in critical parts of gas turbine engines are given in Table J-3

TABLE J-3
Material types

Material no.	Type	Density (slug/ft^3)	Density (kg/m^3)
1	Aluminium alloy	5.3	2716
2	Titanium alloy	9.1	4663
3	Wrought nickel alloy	16.0	8200
4	High-strength nickel alloy	17.0	8710
5	Single-crystal superalloy	17.0	8710

and Figs. J-7 and J-8. Figure J-7 gives the 1 percent creep curves of typical materials for 1000 hr at temperatures between 0 and 2000°F. Dividing the material's creep strength by its density gives the material's strength/weight ratio. The variations of strength/weight ratio with temperature are given in Fig. J-8.

Compressor and Fan Materials

Normal practice for compressor and fan blades is to base designs on creep and creep-rupture data. Common practice is to allow less than 1 percent creep

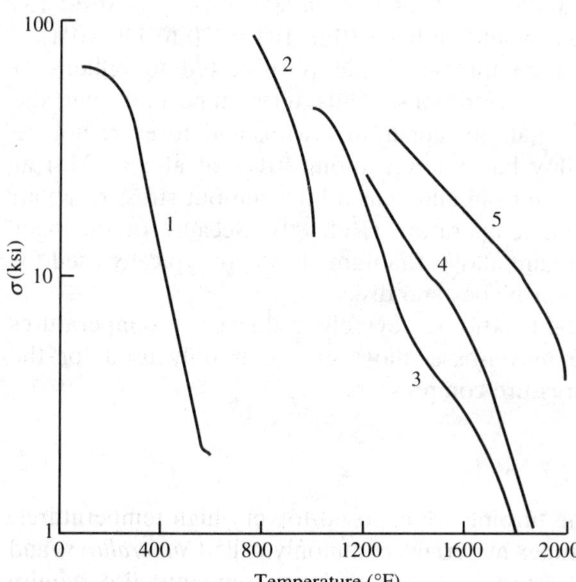

FIGURE J-7
Strength at 1% creep for 1000 hours.

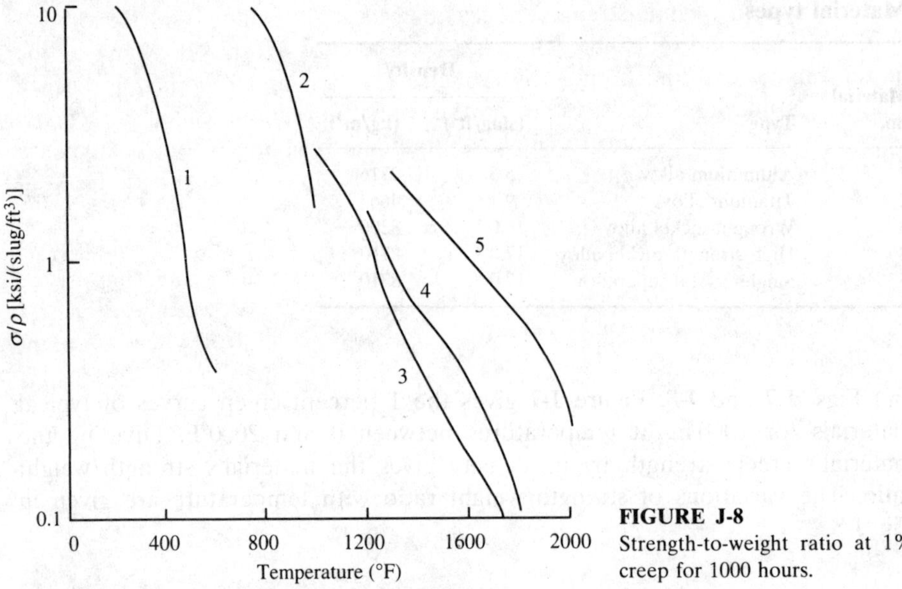

FIGURE J-8
Strength-to-weight ratio at 1% creep for 1000 hours.

during the life of the part. A reasonable estimate of the *allowable working stress* is 30 to 50 percent of the value obtained from Fig. J-7 for 1000 hr. For example, Fig. J-7 gives a 1 percent creep stress for material 1 of about 32 ksi at 300°F (220 MPa at 150°C) and 1000 hr. Thus the *allowable working stress* for this material at these conditions would be from 10 to 16 ksi (70 to 110 MPa).

During its life, a fan or compressor blade is subjected to billions of *high-cycle fatigue* cycles due to vibrations. Thus it is important that the *run-out* stress, which the material can apparently withstand forever, not be exceeded. Aluminum 2124 alloy has a low run-out stress of about 12 ksi at room temperature while titanium 6246 alloy has a high run-out stress of about 140 ksi (about 1 MPa) at room temperature (Ref. 89). Because of the poor fatigue characteristics of aluminum alloys, titanium alloys are typically used for fan and low-pressure compressor blades and disks.

Titanium's strength/weight ratio is severely reduced at temperatures above 900°F (480°C). Hence nickel-base alloys are commonly used for the critical components of high-pressure compressors.

Turbine Materials

The critical components of the turbine are exposed to very high temperatures. Many of these parts require super materials, commonly called *superalloys*, and compressor air for cooling. Certain materials and environments also require protective coatings. Typical examples of these materials are Mar-M 509, a high-chromium, carbide-strengthened, cobalt-base superalloy, and René 80, a cast, precipitation-hardenable, nickel-base superalloy (Ref. 89). Many of the newer superalloys for turbine rotor blades are cast and solidified in such a manner as to align the crystals in the radial direction, called *directional solidification,* or to produce a single crystal. The resulting turbine blades are capable of operating at temperatures 100 to 200°F (55 to 110°C) above those of conventionally cast blades.

In high-pressure turbines, the blades are typically made of superalloys while high-strength, nickel-base alloys are used for the disks and rims. Since the temperatures are much lower in the low-pressure turbine, the critical components are not cooled and are frequently made from high-strength, nickel-base alloys.

APPENDIX K

ABOUT THE SOFTWARE

A comprehensive set of software is included with the text to assist you in solving some of the problems in the text and your design problems. The AFPROP program defines the properties of air with hydrocarbon fuels and uses simple menus. The other four software programs use pull-down menus and edit fields that support a mouse to make them very user-friendly.

PARA and PERF are a set of user friendly computer programs written for the preliminary analyses of common air-breathing aircraft engine cycles. COMPR and TURBN are a set of computer programs that perform the preliminary analyses of axial-flow compressors and turbines, respectively. These programs allow you to solve a single problem, a number of "what if" solutions, or a design problem.

The current version of PARA, PERF, COMPR, and TURBN are written in Microsoft Professional BASIC 7.1 with pull-down menu and data entry procedures from MicroHelp. The help pull-down menu contains guidance on data entry, plots, optimum solutions, etc. Each program tries to use the highest resolution for your computer monitor. The user can select the graphics resolution and color by using the output pull-down menu.

K-1 GETTING STARTED

To get started, you need an IBM PC, or compatible personal computer, MS-DOS operating system version 3.3 or later, 640K random access memory (RAM), and graphics capability with a CGA, EGA, or VGA graphics card and color monitor. The software is supplied on a 3.5-in, 1.44-Mbyte diskette.

If you have a hard disk, copy all the files into a directory named EGTP and place the diskette in a safe place. To do this, at the computer prompt "C>", type the command "MD EGTP" and press the ⟨enter⟩ key. Now enter the command "CD EGTP" to make the EGTP directory your current directory. Now insert the diskette into drive A (or B), type "COPY A:*.*" (or "COPY B:*.*"), and press the ⟨enter⟩ key. Now put that diskette away in a safe place just in case you need to reinstall the software at a later date. You may now start any program by just typing its name. For example, to start the parametric engine analysis program, type the word "PARA" and press the ⟨enter⟩ key.

If you do not have a hard disk, then you first need to make a copy of all the files on the diskette onto another formatted diskette (you can use the DISKCOPY command or COPY command) and then place the original diskette away in a safe place. Once you have a working copy of these programs, you can start any program by inserting the diskette into drive A (or B), typing the name of the program, and pressing the ⟨enter⟩ key.

Capturing graphics screens is aided by a built-in print feature of the PARA, PERF, COMPR, and TURBN programs that works for Epson-like dot-matrix printers and Laser Jet-like printers. You can also load the GRAPHICS.COM program (supplied with most versions of MS-DOS) into memory before running a program so that you get a copy of the current graphics screen by simply pressing the ⟨Prt Sc⟩ key.

K-2 THE SOFTWARE

AFPROP.EXE (and AFPROP.BAS)

This program calculates the thermodynamic properties of air and fuel as a function of temperature and fuel/air ratio by using the equations in Chap. 2. Written in QuickBASIC, this program is supplied in both executable form (AFPROP.EXE) and source code (AFPROP.BAS). The source code can be used to write your own analysis programs with variable specific heats as discussed in Chaps. 7 and 8.

After selecting the unit system (English or SI), the user enters the fuel/air ratio and the temperature, or the enthalpy, or the reduced pressure. Input temperatures are limited to the range of 300°R (167 K) to 4000°R (2222 K), and the fuel/air ratio has a maximum value of 0.0676. The program will calculate the other properties in addition to the gas constant, specific heat at constant pressure, ratio of specified heats, and speed of sound.

PARA.EXE

The PARA computer program determines the variation in gas tubine engine performance with cycle design variables such as the compressor pressure ratio. The program is based on the engine models contained in Chaps. 5 through 7 of this book and is intended to be used with this textbook. Through pull-down menus, the user can select the type of analysis model (ideal or real), the engine cycle (one of the nine engine cycles listed below), the iteration variable (one of the nine variables listed below) along with its applicable range and increment, the unit system (SI or English), and the output device(s). Data are entered and/or changed on a data screen through edit fields. Results can be plotted on the screen by using defined ranges of plot data. In addition, the temperature versus entropy of the defined engine cycle data can be plotted on the screen. Screen-plotted results can be printed on some dot-matrix or laser printers.

Engine cycles	Variables
Ramjet	Single-point calculation
Turbojet	Mach number
Turbojet with afterburner	Combustor exit temperature
Turbofan	Compressor pressure ratio
Turbofan with afterburner and duct burner	Fan pressure ratio
Mixed-flow turbofan	Bypass ratio
Mixed turbofan with afterburner	Afterburner exit temperature
Turboprop	Turbine temperature ratio
Turboshaft with regeneration	Exit temperature ratio

This program is very useful for examining the trends of a selected engine cycle's specific performance (specific thrust and thrust specific fuel consumption) with changes in applicable design variables. Up to 15 sets of results can be plotted at a time. When one variable is used for calculations, results can be plotted versus the iteration variable. If more than one variable is used for calculations, only the specific performance (thrust specific fuel consumption versus specific thrust) of the cycle can be plotted. Results from a single iteration run can be saved in a file for input into a spread-sheet program.

The PARA program must have the default data file (PARA.DEF) on the same directory as the program, or else the program will not start. The escape key ⟨Esc⟩ is used to leave the data and plot screens. The user accepts values in the data entry screens by pressing the escape key ⟨Esc⟩. A copy of a plot screen is sent to the defined graphics printer by pressing ⟨P⟩ or ⟨p⟩ when the plot screen is shown. Remember to define the type of graphics printer by using the plot pull-down menu before you try to capture a copy.

PERF.EXE

The PERF computer program determines the performance of a specific engine and its variation with flight condition and throttle. The program is based on the engine models contained in Chap. 8 of this book and is intended to be used with this textbook. Through pull-down menus, the user can select the specific engine cycle (one of the 10 engine cycles listed below) and its design, the iteration variable (one of the 11 variables listed below) along with its applicable range and increment, the control system limits (e.g., temperature leaving compressor), the unit system (SI or English), and the output device(s). Data are entered and/or changed on a data screen through edit fields. Results can be plotted on the screen by using defined ranges of plot data. Screen-plotted results can be printed on some dot-matrix or laser printers.

Engine cycles	**Variables**
Ramjet	Single point @ throttle
Turbojet, one spool	Single point @ thrust
Turbojet, two spools	Mach number
Turbojet with afterburner	Ambient temperature
Turbofan	Ambient pressure
Turbofan with afterburner and duct burner	Altitude
Mixed-flow turbofan	T_{t4}—total temperature leaving combustor
Mixed turbofan with afterburner	T_{t7}—total temperature leaving afterburner
Turboprop	T_{t17}—total temperature leaving duct burner
Turboshaft with regeneration	Exit nozzle pressure ratio
	Exit nozzle area ratio

PERF is very useful for examining the variation of an engine's performance with changes in flight condition, throttle, and control system limits. Up to ten sets of results can be plotted at a time. When one variable is used for calculations, results can be plotted versus the iteration variable. If more than one variable is used for calculations, only the thrust specific fuel consumption versus thrust of the engine(s) can be plotted. Results from a single iteration run can be saved in a file for input into a spread-sheet program.

The PERF program must have the default data file (PERF.DEF) on the same directory as the program, or else the program will not start. The escape key ⟨Esc⟩ is used to leave the data and plot screens. The user accepts values in the data entry screens by pressing the escape key ⟨Esc⟩. A copy of a plot screen is sent to the defined graphics printer by pressing ⟨P⟩ or ⟨p⟩ when the plot screen is shown. Remember to define the type of graphics printer by using the plot pull-down menu before you try to capture a copy.

COMPR.EXE

The COMPR program calculates the change in properties along the mean line of a multistage, axial-flow compressor based on user input data. The program is based on the methods contained in Chap. 9 of this book and is intended to be used with this textbook. The user can select the type of design (one of the five types of design listed below), type of swirl distribution (one of the three swirl distributions listed below), unit system (SI or English), and output device(s). Data are entered and/or changed on a data screen through edit fields. The results are given for the hub, mean, and tip radius for both rotor and stator blades of each stage and include flow angles, diffusion factors, degree of reactions, pressures, Mach numbers, temperatures, velocities, number of blades, and blade centrifugal stress.

Type of design	Swirl distribution
Constant tip radius	Free vortex
Constant mean radius	Exponential
Constant hub radius	First power
User-specified tip radius	
Repeating row/stage	

After stage calculations are completed, the user can have the computer sketch a cross-sectional drawing on the graphics screen (e.g., see Figs. 9-33, 9-36*a*, and 9-36*b*). The user can also have the computer sketch the relative position and angle of rotor and stator blades, using the NACA 65A010 profile for a specified stage and number of blades. One can also look at the change in spacing and blade angles with changes in radius (e.g., see Figs. 9-30 and 9-31).

The COMPR program must have the default data file (COMPR.DEF) on the same directory as the program, or else the program will not start. The escape key ⟨Esc⟩ is used to leave the data and plot screens. The user accepts values in the data entry screens by pressing the escape key ⟨Esc⟩. A copy of a plot screen is sent to the defined graphics printer by pressing ⟨P⟩ or ⟨p⟩ when the plot screen is shown. Remember to define the type of graphics printer, using the plot pull-down menu before trying to capture a copy.

TURBN.EXE

The TURBN program calculates the change in properties along the mean line of a multistage, axial-flow turbine based on user input data. The program is based on the methods contained in Chap. 9 of this book and is intended to be used with this textbook. The user can select the unknown (one of the four unknowns listed below), the design limit (one of the three limits listed below), the unit system (SI or English), and the output device(s). Data are entered and/or changed on a data screen through edit fields. The results are given for the hub, mean, and tip radius for both stator and rotor blades of each stage and include flow angles, degree of reactions, pressures, Mach numbers, temperatures, velocities, number of blades, and solidities.

Unknown	Design limit
Flow angle entering rotor	Centrifugal stress (AN^2)
Flow angle leaving rotor	Mean radius
Mach number entering rotor	Angular speed
Total temperature leaving rotor	

After stage calculations are completed, the user can have the computer sketch a cross-sectional drawing of the turbine on the graphics screen (e.g., see Figs. 9-72, 9-76, and 9-78). The user can also have the computer sketch the relative position and angle of rotor and stator blades, using the British C4 or T6 profile for a specified stage and number of blades. One can also look at the change in spacing and blade angles with changes in radius (e.g., see Figs. 9-77, 9-79, and 9-80).

The TURBN program must have the default data file (TURBN.DEF) on the same directory as the program, or else the program will not start. The escape key ⟨Esc⟩ is used to leave the data and plot screens. The user accepts values in the data entry screens by pressing the escape key ⟨Esc⟩. A copy of a plot screen is sent to the defined graphics printer by pressing ⟨P⟩ or ⟨p⟩ when the plot screen is shown. Remember to define the type of graphics printer, using the plot pull-down menu before trying to capture a copy.

REFERENCES

1. *The Random House College Dictionary,* Revised Edition, Random House Inc., New York, 1975.
2. NOAA, NASA, and USAF, "U.S. Standard Atmosphere, 1976," U.S. Government Printing Office, Washington, October 1976.
3. "1989 AIAA/General Dynamics Corporation, Team Aircraft Design Competition, Engine Data Package," Director of Student Programs, AIAA, Washington, 1988.
4. Oates, G. C., *Aerothermodynamics of Gas Turbine and Rocket Propulsion,* revised and enlarged, AIAA Education Series, AIAA, Washington, 1988.
5. "2000 Is (Nearly) Now," *Air Force Magazine,* February 1987, pp. 52–63.
6. "Squeezing More Power from Turbine Engines," *Machine Design,* March 10, 1988, pp. 44–60.
7. Mattingly, J. D., "Improved Methodology for Teaching Aircraft Gas Turbine Engine Analysis and Performance," *1992 ASEE Annual Conference Proceedings,* vol. 1, ASEE, Washington, 1992, pp. 240–247.
8. Nicolai, L. M., *Fundamentals of Aircraft Designs,* METS, Inc., San Jose, CA, 1975.
9. Raymer, D. P., *Aircraft Design: A Conceptual Approach,* 2d ed., AIAA Education Series, AIAA, Washington, 1993.
10. Hale, F. J., *Introduction to Aircraft Performance, Selection and Design,* John Wiley & Sons, Inc., New York, 1984.
11. Anderson, J. D., *Introduction to Flight,* 3d ed., McGraw-Hill, Inc., New York, 1989.
12. Mattingly, J. D., Heiser, W. H., and Daley, D. H., *Aircraft Engine Design,* AIAA Education Series, AIAA, Washington, 1987.
13. Penner, S. S., *Chemistry Problems in Jet Propulsion,* Pergamon Press, London, 1957.
14. Prandtl, L., and Tiejens, O. G., *Fundamentals of Hydro- and AeroMechanics,* Dover Publications, Inc., New York, 1957.
15. Keenan, J. H., and Kaye, J., *Gas Tables,* John Wiley & Sons, New York, 1948.
16. McKinney, John S. (Captain, USAF), "Simulation of Turbofan Engine (SMOTE)," AFAPL-TR-67-125, Air Force Aero Propulsion Laboratory, Wright-Patterson AFB, OH, November 1967.
17. von Karman, T. H., "Supersonic Aerodynamics—Principles and Applications," *Journal of the Aeronautical Sciences,* vol. 14, no. 7, July 1947, p. 373.

18. von Karman, T. H., *Aerodynamics—Selected Topics in the Light of Their Historical Development,* Cornell University Press, Ithaca, NY, 1954, p. 116.
19. Dailey, C. L., and Wood, F. C., *Computational Curves for Compressible Fluid Problems,* John Wiley & Sons, Inc., New York, 1949.
20. "Equations, Tables and Charts for Compressible Flow," NACA Report 1135, U.S. Government Printing Office, Washington, 1953.
21. Zucrow, M. J., and Hoffman, J. D., *Gas Dynamics,* vol. 1, John Wiley & Sons, Inc., New York, 1976.
22. Ferri, A., and Naucci, L. M., "Preliminary Investigation of a New Type of Supersonic Inlet," NACA Report 1104, U.S. Government Printing Office, Washington, 1953.
23. Wyatt, D. D., "Aerodynamic Forces Associated with Inlets of Turbojet Installations," *Aero Engr. Review.,* October 1951.
24. Sibulkin, M., "Theoretical and Experimental Investigation of Additive Drag," *NACA Report* 1187, U.S. Government Printing Office, Washington, 1954.
25. "Definition of the Thrust of a Jet Engine and Internal Drag . . . ," *Journal of the Royal Society,* August 1955, pp. 517–526.
26. Kerrebrock, J. L., *Aircraft Engines and Gas Turbines,* M.I.T. Press, Cambridge, MA, 1972.
27. "Gas Turbine Engine Performance Station Identification and Nomenclature," Aerospace Recommended Practice (ARP) 755A, Society of Automotive Engineers, Warrendale, PA, 1974.
28. *Model Specification for Engines, Aircraft, Turbojet,* Military Specification MIL-E-5008B, Department of Defense, January 1959.
29. Oates, G. C., "Performance Estimation for Turbofans with and without Mixers," *Journal of Propulsion and Power,* vol. 1, May–June 1985, pp. 252–256.
30. Sobey, A. J., and Suggs, A. M., *Control of Aircraft and Missile Powerplants,* John Wiley & Sons, Inc., New York, 1963.
31. Dixon, S. L., *Thermodynamics of Turbomachinery,* 3d ed., Pergamon Press, Inc., Elmsford, NY, 1978.
32. Oates, G. C. (ed.), *Aerothermodynamics of Aircraft Engine Components,* AIAA Education Series, AIAA, Washington, 1985.
33. Horlock, J. H., *Axial Flow Compressors,* Robert E. Krieger Publishing Co., Melbourne, FL, 1973.
34. Horlock, J. H., *Axial Flow Turbines,* Robert E. Krieger Publishing Co., Melbourne, FL, 1973.
35. Johnsen, I. A., and Bullock, R. O. (eds.), *Aerodynamic Design of Axial-Flow Compressors,* NASA SP-36, U.S. Government Printing Office, Washington, 1965.
36. Glassman, A. J. (ed.), *Turbine Design and Application,* vols. 1 to 3, NASA SP-290, U.S. Government Printing Office, Washington, 1972.
37. Wilson, D. G., *The Design of High-Efficiency Turbomachinery and Gas Turbines,* M.I.T. Press, Cambridge, MA, 1984.
38. Sorensen, H. A., *Gas Turbines,* The Ronald Press Co., New York, 1951.
39. Hess, W. J., and Mumford, N. V., *Jet Propulsion for Aerospace Applications,* 2d ed., Pitman Publishing Corporation, New York, 1964.
40. Bathie, W. W., *Fundamentals of Gas Turbines,* John Wiley & Sons, Inc., New York, 1972.
41. Cohen, H., Rogers, G. F. C., and Saravanamuttoo, H. I. H., *Gas Turbine Theory,* John Wiley & Sons, Inc., New York, 1972.
42. Hill, P. G., and Peterson, C. R., *Mechanics and Thermodynamics of Propulsion,* 2d ed., Addison-Wesley Publishing Company, Inc., Reading, MA, 1992.
43. Glauert, H., *The Elements of Aerofoil and Airscrew Theory,* 3d ed., Cambridge University Press, Cambridge, UK, 1959.
44. Theodorsen, T., *Theory of Propellers,* McGraw-Hill, Inc., New York, 1948.
45. Theodorsen, T., "Theory of Static Propellers and Helicopter Rotors," Paper 326, presented at 25th Annual Forum, American Helicopter Society, Alexandria, VA, May 1969.
46. Treager, I. E., *Aircraft Gas Turbine Engine Technology,* 2d ed., McGraw-Hill, Inc., New York, 1979.

47. Zweifel, O., "The Spacing of Turbomachinery Blading, Especially with Large Angular Deflection," *Brown Boveri Review,* vol. 32, 1945, p. 12.
48. Nikkanen, J. P., and Brooky, J. D., "Single Stage Evaluation of Highly Loaded High Mach Number Compressor Stages V," NASA CR 120887 (PWA-4312), U.S. Government Printing Office, Washington, March 1972.
49. Seddon, J., and Goldsmith, E. L., *Intake Aerodynamics,* AIAA Education Series, AIAA, New York, 1985.
50. Kline, S. J., "On the Nature of Stall," *Journal of Basic Engineering,* vol. 81, series D, no. 3, September 1959, pp. 305–320.
51. Taylor, H. D., "Application of Vortex Generator Mixing Principle to Diffusers, Concluding Report," Air Force Contract W33-038 AC-21825, United Aircraft Corp. Report R-15064-5, United Aircraft Corp. Research Dept, East Hartford, CT, December 31, 1948.
52. McCloy, R. W., *The Fundamentals of Supersonic Propulsion,* Publication D6A-10380-1, The Boeing Company, Supersonic Propulsion Test Group, Seattle, WA, May 1968.
53. Younghans, J., "*Engine Inlet Systems and Integration with Airframe,*" lecture notes for aero propulsion short course, University of Tennessee Space Institute, Tullahoma, TN, 1980.
54. Covert, E. E. (ed.), *Thrust and Drag: its Prediction and Verification,* vol. 98, Progress in Astronautics and Aeronautics, AIAA, Washington, 1985.
55. Fabri, J. (ed.), *Air Intake Problems in Supersonic Propulsion,* 11th AGARD Combustion and Propulsion Panel Meeting, Paris, December 1956, Pergamon Press, Inc., Elmsford, NY, 1958.
56. Sedlock, D., and Bowers, D., "Inlet/Nozzle Airframe Integration," lecture notes for aircraft design and propulsion design courses, U.S. Air Force Academy, Colorado Springs, CO, 1984.
57. Swan, W., "Performance Problems Related to Installation of Future Engines in Both Subsonic and Supersonic Transport Aircraft," Paper presented at the 2d International Symposium on Air-Breathing Engines, Sheffield, UK, March 1974.
58. Surber, L., "Trends in Airframe/Propulsion Integration," lecture notes for aircraft design and propulsion design courses, Dept. of Aeronautics, U.S. Air Force Academy, Colorado Springs, CO, 1984.
59. Kitchen, R., and Sedlock, D., "Subsonic Diffuser Development for Advanced Tactical Aircraft," AIAA Paper 83-1168, AIAA, Washington, 1983.
60. Hunter, L., and Cawthon, J., "Improved Supersonic Performance Design for the F-16 Inlet Modified for the J-79 Engine," AIAA Paper 84-1271, AIAA, Washington, 1984.
61. Stevens, C., Spong, E., and Oliphant, R., "Evaluation of a Statistical Method for Determining Peak Inlet Flow Distortion Using F-15 and F-18 Data," AIAA Paper 80-1109, AIAA, Washington, 1980.
62. Oates, G. C. (ed.), *The Aerothermodynamics of Aircraft Gas Turbine Engines,* AFAPL-TR-78-52, Air Force Aero Propulsion Laboratory, Wright-Patterson AFB, OH, July 1978. (*Note:* This extensive reference is no longer available. However, the contents have been updated and are published in three textbooks; see Refs. 4, 32, and 63.)
63. Oates, G. C. (ed.), *Aircraft Propulsion Systems Technology and Design,* AIAA Education Series, AIAA, Washington, 1989.
64. Stevens, H. L., "F-15/Nonaxisymmetric Nozzle System Integration Study Support Program," NASA CR-135252, U.S. Government Printing Office, Washington, 1978.
65. Tindell, R., "Inlet Drag and Stability Considerations for $M_0 = 2.00$ Design," AIAA Paper 80-1105, AIAA, Washington, 1980.
66. Murthy, S. N., and Curran, E. T. (eds.), *High-Speed Flight Propulsion Systems,* vol. 137, Progress in Astronautics and Aeronautics, AIAA, Washington, 1991.
67. Summerfield, M., Foster, C. R., and Swan, W. C., "Flow Separation in Overexpanded Supersonic Exhaust Nozzles," *Jet Propulsion,* vol. 24, September–October 1954, pp. 319–321.
68. Swavely, C. E., and Soileau, J. F., "Aircraft Aftbody/Propulsion System Integration for Low Drag," AIAA Paper 72-1101, AIAA, Washington, 1972.
69. Lefebvre, A. H., *Gas Turbine Combustion,* Hemisphere Publishing Corp., New York, 1983.
70. Williams, F. A., *Combustion Theory,* Addison-Wesley Publishing Co., Reading, MA, 1965.
71. Spalding, D. B., *Combustion and Mass Transfer,* Pergamon Press, Inc., Elmsford, NY, 1979.

72. Grobman, J., Jones, R. E., and Marek, C. J., "Combustion," *Aircraft Propulsion,* NASA SP-259, U.S. Government Printing Office, Washington, 1970.
73. Barclay, L. P., "Pressure Losses in Dump Combustors," AFAPL-TR-72-57, Air Force Aero Propulsion Laboratory, Wright-Patterson AFB, OH, 1972.
74. Nealy, D. A., and Reider, S. B., "Evaluation of Laminated Porous Wall Materials for Combustor Liner Cooling," ASME Paper 79-GT-100, American Society of Mechanical Engineers, March 1979.
75. Hopkins, K. N., "Turbopropulsion Combustion—Trends and Challenges," AIAA Paper 80-1199, AIAA, Washington, 1980.
76. Norgren, C. T., and Riddlebaugh, S. M., "Advanced Liner-Cooling Techniques for Gas Turbine Combustors," AIAA Paper 85-1290, AIAA, Washington, 1985.
77. Bahr, D. W., "Technology for the Design of High Temperature Rise Combustors," AIAA Paper 85-1292, AIAA, Washington, 1985.
78. Taylor, J. R., "Combustion System Design," lecture notes for aero propulsion short course, University of Tennessee Space Institute, Tullahoma, TN, 1978.
79. McAuley, J. E., and Abdelwahab, M., "Experimental Evaluation of a TF30-P-3 Turbofan Engine in an Altitute Facility: Afterburner Performance and Engine-Afterburner Operating Limits," NASA TN D-6839, U.S. Government Printing Office, Washington, July 1972.
80. Marshall, R. L., Canuel, G. E., and Sullivan, D. J., "Augmentation Systems for Turbofan Engines," *Combustion in Advanced Gas Turbine Systems,* Cranfield International Symposium Series, vol. 10, Pergamon Press, Inc., Elmsford, NY, 1967.
81. Cornell, W. G., "The Flow in a Vee-Gutter Cascade," *Transactions, American Society of Mechanical Engineers,* vol. 78, 1956, p. 573.
82. VonMises, R., *Theory of Flight,* Dover Publications, New York, 1958.
83. Cifone, A. J., and Krueger, E. L., "Combustion Technology: A Navy Perspective," AIAA Paper 85-1400, AIAA, Washington, 1985.
84. Shapiro, A. H., *The Dynamics and Thermodynamics of Compressible Fluid Flow,* vol. 1, The Ronald Press Company, New York, 1953.
85. Abbott, I. H., and Von Doenhoff, A. E., *Theory of Wing Sections,* Dover Publications, Inc., New York, 1959.
86. *The Engine Handbook,* Directorate of Propulsion, Headquarters Air Force Logistics Command, Wright-Patterson AFB, OH, 1991.
87. *Aero Data,* Rolls Royce PLC, Derby, England, November 1991.
88. *The Aircraft Gas Turbine Engine and Its Operation,* PWA OI 200, East Hartford, CT, May 1974.
89. *Aerospace Structural Metals Handbook,* Batelle Memorial Institute, Columbus Laboratories, Columbus, OH, 1984.
90. Sims, C. T., and Hagel, W. C., *The Superalloys,* John Wiley & Sons, Inc. New York, 1972.
91. Smith, W. F., *Structure and Properties of Engineering Alloys,* 2d ed., McGraw-Hill, Inc., New York, 1993.
92. Brick, R. M., Pense, A. W., and Gordon, R. B., *Structure and Properties of Engineering Materials,* 4th ed., McGraw-Hill, Inc., New York, 1977.
93. Imarigeon, J. P., "The Super Alloys: Materials for Gas Turbine Hot Section Components," *Canadian Aeronautics and Space Institute Journal,* vol. 27, 1981.
94. Cumpsty, N. A., *Compressor Aerodynamics,* Longman Scientific and Technical, London, 1989.

INDEX